Neuroendocrinology

VOLUME II

Contributors to Volume II

CHARLES A. BARRACLOUGH
MILDRED ELWERS BAR-SELA
M. T. CLEGG
VAUGHN CRITCHLOW
L. L. DOYLE
WILLIAM ETKIN
DONALD S. FARNER
WILLIAM F. GANONG
ERNEST M. GOLD
ROBERT W. GOY
IRVINE R. HAGADORN
C. BARKER JØRGENSEN
JULIAN I. KITAY
LIS OLESEN LARSEN
ROBERT D. LISK
LEOLA LORENZEN
RONALD R. NOVALES
ANDREAS OKSCHE
JACK H. OPPENHEIMER
CHARLES H. PHOENIX
ANTONIA VERNADAKIS
U. S. von EULER
FRED E. WILSON
DIXON M. WOODBURY
RICHARD J. WURTMAN
WILLIAM C. YOUNG

NEUROENDOCRINOLOGY

EDITED BY

LUCIANO MARTINI
ISTITUTO DI FARMACOLOGIA E DI TERAPIA
UNIVERSITÀ DEGLI STUDI
MILAN, ITALY

AND

WILLIAM F. GANONG
DEPARTMENT OF PHYSIOLOGY
UNIVERSITY OF CALIFORNIA SCHOOL OF MEDICINE
SAN FRANCISCO MEDICAL CENTER
SAN FRANCISCO, CALIFORNIA

VOLUME II

ACADEMIC PRESS New York and London 1967

ACADEMIC PRESS INC.
111 Fifth Avenue, New York, New York 10003

United Kingdom Edition published by
ACADEMIC PRESS INC. (LONDON) LTD.
Berkeley Square House, London W.1

LIBRARY OF CONGRESS CATALOG CARD NUMBER: 66–26256

PRINTED IN THE UNITED STATES OF AMERICA

List of Contributors

Numbers in parentheses indicate the pages on which the authors' contributions begin.

CHARLES A. BARRACLOUGH, Department of Physiology, School of Medicine, University of Maryland, Baltimore, Maryland (61)

MILDRED ELWERS BAR-SELA, Department of Anatomy, College of Medicine, Baylor University, Texas Medical Center, Houston, Texas (101)

M. T. CLEGG, Department of Animal Husbandry, University of California, Davis, California (1)

VAUGHN CRITCHLOW, Department of Anatomy, College of Medicine, Baylor University, Texas Medical Center, Houston, Texas (101)

L. L. DOYLE, Department of Obstetrics and Gynecology, University of California, San Francisco, California (1)

WILLIAM ETKIN, Department of Anatomy, Albert Einstein College of Medicine, Yeshiva University, and The City College of New York, New York, New York (261)

DONALD S. FARNER, Department of Zoology, University of Washington, Seattle, Washington (529)

WILLIAM F. GANONG, Department of Physiology, School of Medicine, University of California Medical Center, San Francisco, California (377, 583)

ERNEST M. GOLD, Department of Medicine, University of California Center for the Health Sciences and Veterans Administration, Los Angeles, California (377)

ROBERT W. GOY, Oregon Regional Primate Research Center, Beaverton, Oregon, and University of Oregon Medical School, Portland, Oregon (163)

IRVINE R. HAGADORN, Department of Zoology, The University of North Carolina, Chapel Hill, North Carolina (439)

C. BARKER JØRGENSEN, Zoophysiological Laboratory A, University of Copenhagen, Copenhagen, Denmark (485)

JULIAN I. KITAY, Departments of Medicine and Physiology, School of Medicine, University of Virginia, Charlottesville, Virginia (641)

LIS OLESEN LARSEN, Zoophysiological Laboratory A, University of Copenhagen, Copenhagen, Denmark (485)

ROBERT D. LISK, Department of Biology, Princeton University, Princeton, New Jersey (197)

LEOLA LORENZEN, Department of Physiology, School of Medicine, University of California Medical Center, San Francisco, California (583)

RONALD R. NOVALES, Department of Biological Sciences, Northwestern University, Evanston, Illinois (241)

ANDREAS OKSCHE, Anatomisches Institut der Universität, Giessen, Germany (529)

JACK H. OPPENHEIMER, Endocrine Research Laboratory, Medical Division, Montefiore Hospital and Medical Center, New York, New York (665)

CHARLES H. PHOENIX, Oregon Regional Primate Research Center, Beaverton, Oregon, and University of Oregon Medical School, Portland, Oregon (163)

ANTONIA VERNADAKIS, Department of Pharmacology, University of Utah College of Medicine, Salt Lake City, Utah (335)[1]

U. S. VON EULER, Fysiologiska Instituitionen, Karolinska Institut, Stockholm, Sweden (283)

FRED E. WILSON, Department of Zoology, Washington State University, Pullman, Washington (529)[2]

DIXON M. WOODBURY, Department of Pharmacology, University of Utah College of Medicine, Salt Lake City, Utah (335)

RICHARD J. WURTMAN, Unit of Experimental Medicine, Department of Nutrition and Food Science, Massachusetts Institute of Technology, Cambridge, Massachusetts, and Section on Pharmacology, Laboratory of Clinical Science, National Institutes of Mental Health, Bethesda, Maryland (19)

WILLIAM C. YOUNG, Oregon Regional Primate Research Center, Beaverton, Oregon, and University of Oregon Medical School, Portland, Oregon (163)[3]

[1] Present address: Department of Physiology, University of California, Berkeley, California.

[2] Present address: Department of Zoology, Kansas State University, Manhattan, Kansas.

[3] Deceased.

Preface

The two volumes of this treatise are designed to provide a survey of all aspects of the rapidly expanding science of neuroendocrinology. Only in recent years have the relations between the nervous system and the endocrine system come under intensive scrutiny, but their interactions have already been shown to be multiple and diverse. This diversity is reflected in the range of subjects covered; there are chapters on: neural control of endocrine function; the effects of hormones on the brain; brain-endocrine interrelations during various phases of development; and the comparative aspects of neuroendocrine integration. The relation of brain chemistry to endocrine function, the effect of drugs on neuroendocrine mechanisms, and the new discipline of clinical neuroendocrinology have also been considered. Consequently, not only neurophysiologists and endocrinologists, but pharmacologists, zoologists, biochemists, psychologists, and those in clinical medicine will find the treatise of interest. Parts of neuroendocrinology have been discussed in other works, but this is the first treatise of which we are aware in which an attempt has been made to cover all ramifications of neuroendocrinology. We believe it can be used both as a text for advanced students and as a reference source.

The individual chapters have been written by experts in their fields. Each author was instructed to make his chapter a survey of the present status of the subject he covered, without attempting to review it in an exhaustive or encyclopedic fashion. Those concerned with research methods and procedures will be interested in Chapter 4 in which the techniques of stereotaxis and making lesions are described and in the appendix to this chapter in which references to the stereotaxic atlases available for various animal species are provided.

Authors were encouraged to present their own opinions on controversial subjects, and many of them have done so. Consequently, there is not complete agreement on all subjects from chapter to chapter. However, the individual authors have done a good job of supporting their points of view with relevant data and references, so the reader may explore the controversies in depth and draw his own conclusions.

The preparation of this treatise was marred by the untimely death of three outstanding neuroendocrinologists who were working on contributions to it. This treatise is dedicated to these three individuals—John D. Green, Giuseppe Mangili, and William C. Young.

July, 1967

LUCIANO MARTINI
WILLIAM F. GANONG

Contents

Chapter 23. Melanocyte-Stimulating Hormone and the Intermediate Lobe of the Pituitary: Chemistry, Effects, and Mode of Action

RONALD R. NOVALES

Chapter 24. Relation of the Pars Intermedia to the Hypothalamus

WILLIAM ETKIN

Chapter 25. Adrenal Medullary Secretion and Its Neural Control

U. S. VON EULER

Chapter 26. Influence of Hormones on Brain Activity

DIXON M. WOODBURY and ANTONIA VERNADAKIS

Contents of Volume I

Erratum

NEUROENDOCRINOLOGY, VOLUME I

(L. Martini and W. F. Ganong, *eds.*)

The last 9 lines on p. 146 should read:

of the teleost *Carassius auratus* (goldfish). Single-unit extracellular records have also been acquired from the hypothalamus of several mammalian species. None of the mammalian studies has revealed action potentials of unusual duration; however, it was not possible to say that any individual cell recorded was definitely neurosecretory.

Bennett and Fox (1962) have commented on the possible significance not only of the long action potentials but also of the very slow conduction velocities recorded by them from the terminations of the caudal neurons. It is possible that these features are related to the need for

Neuroendocrinology

VOLUME II

CHAPTER 17

Role in Reproductive Physiology of Afferent Impulses from the Genitalia and Other Regions

M. T. CLEGG and L. L. DOYLE

I. Introduction

The involvement of neuroendocrine reflex mechanisms in a variety of reproductive functions is implied by a number of observations. In reflex ovulators such as the rabbit, cat, and ferret, stimuli applied to the external genitalia result in pituitary gonadotropin release and ovulation, whereas in some spontaneous ovulators such as the rat and mouse, this same stimulus causes pseudopregnancy. Olfactory stimuli supplied by strange male mice block pregnancy. A seasonal change in length of daylight appears to be the important factor regulating or monitoring annual cycles of gonadal activity in many species. The influence of psychic stimuli on reproductive function has been clearly demonstrated. For example, when rams are placed with ewes shortly before the breeding season, the females display estrous activity; breeding and conception occur much earlier than normal. Indeed, examples drawn from the animal kingdom can be used to illustrate the influence of many different sensory stimuli on reproductive functions. In spite of these well-recognized phenomena, the afferent neural limb of the neuroendocrine reflex arc has not been adequately described, although the importance of the hypothalamus in regulating pituitary gonadotropic activity seems clearly established. The degree of dependence of reproductive activity upon external stimuli, however, shows considerable species variation.

In this summary of the role of afferent impulses, references are made for the most part to review articles; specific references to original data can be found in these reviews.

II. Innervation of the Reproductive Tract

The innervation of the reproductive tract has been the subject of countless papers, but few of these well-devised anatomical investigations can be related to physiological events. Most of the nerves that have been identified are efferent, and very little information exists on afferent pathways. The neuroanatomical features appear much the same for all classes of mammals and are illustrated in the diagram in Fig. 1. Craniosacral fibers of the autonomic nervous system in the sacral region have their origin in the second, third, and fourth sacral segments. The fibers from this area make up the pelvic nerve (nervus erigens), pass through and are scattered in the pelvic plexus and terminate in ganglia of the pelvic viscera. In the male most fibers pass from there directly to the prostate, seminal vesicles, and external genitalia. They also pass to the blood vessels of these parts where they are vasodilator in function. In the female, sacral autonomic fibers reach the walls of the uterus and vagina through the uterovaginal plexus which contains several ganglia, the largest of which, the cervical ganglion, is located at the level of the cervix uteri. Numerous small ganglia from which postganglionic inhibitory fibers reach the smooth muscle of the uterus and vagina are found in the upper and middle wall of the vagina. The oviduct and ovary receive similar fibers. Other fibers, vasodilator in function, reach the blood vessels of these organs as well as those of the clitoris and labia minora. Visceral afferent nerves from the uterus reach the spinal cord by way of the hypogastric plexus and the eleventh and twelfth thoracic nerves. Afferent fibers from the clitoris pass through the dorsal nerve of the clitoris which is a branch of the pudendal nerve. Similar fibers from the labia minora pass through the ilioinguinal, pudendal, and perineal branch of the posterior cutaneous nerve of the thigh. Visceral afferents in the male reach the spinal cord through the spermatic plexus and hypogastric plexus. Fibers from the testes enter the spinal cord through the tenth thoracic nerve, and those from the epididymis through the eleventh and twelfth thoracic, and first lumbar nerves. The glans and skin of the penis are supplied by the dorsal nerve of the penis which is a branch of the pudendal nerve. Afferent fibers of the pudendal nerve to the penis and clitoris are somatic, but the pudendal nerve includes autonomic fibers to these organs. A detailed description of the neuroanatomical features

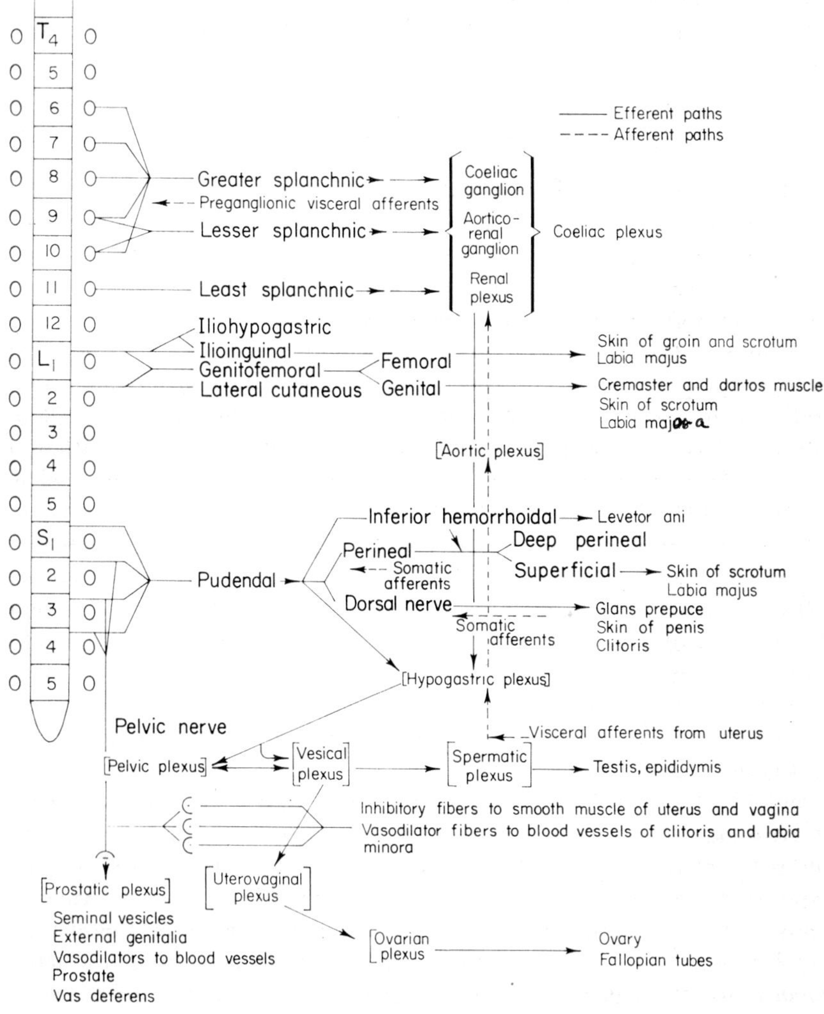

FIG. 1. Innervation of the reproductive organs in mammals. Major nervous pathways to and from the genitalia are shown.

of the reproductive system is beyond the scope of this chapter. Excellent reviews, particularly those of Kranz (1958, 1959) and Albert (1961), have been published, and the reader may refer to them for further information.

III. The Role of Peripheral Nerves in Reproductive Processes in the Male

It is generally known that erection and ejaculation can be elicited as spinal reflexes from an animal in which the spinal cord has been transected in the lower thoracic or upper lumbar region (Bard, 1939; Sherrington, 1900). An intact sympathetic nerve supply appears necessary for ejaculation in the rodent and in the cat. Although a role of the parasympathetic system has been implicated in the process of erection, studies by Root and Bard (1947) showed that male cats deprived of the spinal origin of the nervi erigenti regularly developed full erections when they seized and attempted to mount estrous females. They proposed a suprasacral vasodilator outflow which originated chiefly from the second, third, and fourth lumbar segments of the spinal cord. The pathway runs through the lumbar portion of the sympathetic chains and in most cases reaches the pelvis by way of the inferior mesenteric ganglia and hypogastric nerves. Contraction of the seminal vesicle, cauda epididymidis, and vas deferens can be effected by hypothalamic stimulation, a response involving the sympathetic system since it can be prevented by section of the hypogastric nerves.

The integrity of the spinal cord appears unnecessary for spermatogenesis in the mouse (Josimivich, 1958), although histological studies of testicular tissue in human paraplegics show varying stages of degeneration (Albert, 1961). There is considerable evidence to indicate that disruption of sympathetic pathways alters normal spermatogenesis in cats (Weidenmann, 1952), guinea pigs (Coujard, 1952), and possibly man (Bandmann, 1949). The effect of sympathectomy is apparently related to the ability of the gonads to respond to gonadotropic hormones (Coujard, 1951). Evidence of the essentiality of an intact nerve supply based upon testicular transplant experiments is difficult to interpret. Experiments of this kind must also account for a temperature effect upon spermatogenic function. Where successful homotesticular transplants were made in the anterior chamber of the eye of rats, normal interstitial cell function continued as indicated by maintenance of secretory activity in the seminal vesicles, prostates, and bulbourethral glands (Turner, 1938). Spermatogenesis has been reported to continue up to the spermatocyte stage in the presence of intraperitoneal, subcutaneous, and intramuscular testicular grafts, and normal seminiferous tubules have been observed in scrotal grafts (C. R. Moore, 1926). Most evidence suggests that an intact sympathetic nerve supply plays an important role in normal testicular function, but there is little evidence that a neuroendocrine reflex mechanism is involved. A recent paper by Endröczi and Lissák (1963) is worthy of mention. They measured the effect of copulation or housing with the female without copulation on the secretion rate of androstenedione and testosterone in spermatic vein blood of male rabbits. If the males were allowed to mate or were sham-mated, the output of these steroids was significantly increased over that of isolated control animals. To explain this effect, they postulated that afferent impulses from spinal sex centers as well as exteroceptive factors were capable of activating the pituitary to release gonadotropins essential in testosterone production. Other interpretations should be considered. They observed a considerable increase in rate of blood flow under conditions of mating or sham-mating. This in itself could help to account for the increased secretory rate of the testicular steroids and might not necessarily involve pituitary activation but only an effect upon the sympathetic nervous system influencing vascular responses.

A functional relationship between afferent impulses from the male genitalia and the endocrine system regulating testicular function has not been established. Studies directed toward this problem may provide additional decisive information.

IV. The Role of Peripheral Nerves in Reproductive Processes in the Female

In contrast to the male, there is abundant evidence indicating an important role of afferent stimuli on reproductive processes in the female of many species (see Ganong, 1959). For example, ovulation in the rabbit is induced by the act of coitus or vaginal stimulation with a glass rod. This stimulus causes a release of pituitary "ovulating hormone" into the blood stream. Ovulation in response to coitus, however, appears not to be dependent solely upon genital receptors, since local anesthesia of the vulva and vagina does not affect the response. Indeed, after coital stimulation, ovulation can be demonstrated following denervation of the genital region, abdominal sympathectomy, hysterectomy, and extirpation of the proximal half of the vagina. Copulatory-induced ovulation can also be demonstrated after removal of the olfactory bulbs, blinding, or extirpation of the vestibular apparatus and cochlea. In the cat, another species which ovulates only after coitus, abdominal sympathectomy, removal of the uterus and proximal vagina, or a combination of these procedures does not alter the response.

It seems likely that a variety of receptors and afferent pathways capable of activating the release of a pituitary ovulating hormone exist, none of which by itself is critical to the process. These kinds of experiments, however, do not discount an important role of afferent stimuli from the genitalia in the normal ovarian function of reflex ovulators.

Another example of a role of genital stimulation on ovarian function is the phenomenon of pseudopregnancy, particularly well studied in the rat and mouse (Bradbury *et al.*, 1950). In these species, pseudopregnancy can be induced by mechanical or electrical stimulation of the cervix or by sterile mating. A variety of other procedures not necessarily involving neural elements can also be used, such as stimulation of the nipples and the injection of estrogens, androgens, or a variety of drugs (Everett, 1964). Although superficially resembling the process by which ovulation is brought about in reflex ovulators, the mechanism is probably more complex. The response appears to be associated with a convergence of afferent impulses on the hypothalamus, causing the release of a pituitary luteotropic substance, presumably prolactin (see Chapter 16) which activates the corpora lutea to secrete progesterone. The length of the pseudopregnant period is determined by the functional life of the corpora lutea and is approximately 12–13 days or about one-half the length of the normal gestation period. This period can be prolonged by hysterectomy or by the induction of deciduomata. The degree of prolongation appears to be related to the amount of decidual tissue present. The extent of prolongation, however, cannot be made to exceed the normal gestation period.

A number of hypotheses have been advanced to explain the mechanisms bringing about regressive changes in the luteal function after this prescribed time, and these, together with other factors influencing the life span of the corpus luteum, are discussed in the next section.

Rats are capable of normal mating and gestation following either abdominal sympathectomy or cervical ganglionectomy. Although sterile mating induces pseudopregnancy in these animals, mechanical or electrical stimulation of the cervix does not. This finding clearly demonstrates the existence of alternate receptors and afferent pathways capable of bringing about pituitary activation and further suggests the involvement of visceral afferent tracts conducting impulses from the genitalia. An excellent discussion of pseudopregnancy by Everett (1961) appears in the latest edition of "Sex and Internal Secretions."

V. Modification of Gonadal Function by Manipulation of the Genital Tract

The existence of an important relationship between ovarian activity and the uterus, first demonstrated by Loeb (1923), has been amply confirmed and expanded. The subject has been reviewed a number of times (Anderson *et al.*, 1963; Everett, 1964; Short, 1964; Anderson and Melampy, 1965; Spies, 1965). The evidence for this relationship has been provided mostly by experiments involving different types of uterine manipulation. Uterine distention is capable of altering the estrous cycle; hysterectomy inhibits the estrous cycle and prolongs the life of the corpus luteum in a variety of species.

A. Effects of Uterine Distention

Uterine distention is accompanied by an alteration of the estrous cycle length in some species. This effect has been attributed to a neurogenic stimulus from the distended horn acting by way of the hypothalamo-pituitary pathway to influence the release of hormones controlling the persistence or regression of corpora lutea.

W. W. Moore and Nalbandov (1953) reported that in sheep the insertion of a plastic bead 8 mm in diameter *in utero* during the early luteal phase shortened the cycle by several days; successive cycles in the same animal tended to be unusually short. A similar effect of uterine distention on the modification of estrous cycle length has been reported for the cow (Hansel and Wagner, 1960) and guinea pig (Donovan, 1961), but could not be demonstrated in pigs (Anderson *et al.*, 1963). Somewhat related to this phenomenon is the finding that the presence of a mechanical irritant in the magnum portion of the oviduct of laying hens suppresses ovulation (see Nalbandov, 1961).

The time during the cycle when the beads are inserted as well as the size has an important influence upon the observed response. For example, in sheep and guinea pigs if beads are inserted late in the cycle there is some extension of the cycle length and, in sheep, when inserted during the follicular phase there is no modification. The insertion of small plastic beads (2 mm in diameter) at any time did not alter the mean cycle length in sheep.

These effects appear to be mediated by way of afferent impulses from uterine receptors, since denervation of the segment containing the bead results in essentially normal cycles. The exact nature of the afferent neural pathways involved in the response is unknown. Section of the uterine hypogastric nerve in the cycling ewe does not affect the normal cycle length but does appear to influence conception. The recovery of fertilized and cleaved ova from these treated animals suggests that implantation is adversely affected (Nalbandov and St. Clair, 1958).

Studies directly related to alterations in the secretion of anterior pituitary gonadotropic hormones by uterine distention have not been reported, but the secretion of posterior pituitary hormones (oxytocin) following genital stimulation is well documented, particularly in ruminants (Hays and VanDemark, 1953). Debackere *et al.* (1961), using cross circulation techniques, were able to demonstrate an increase in pressure in the mammary gland of the ewe following vaginal distention. Similar results have been reported in cattle. One of the earliest accounts directly relating to this phenomenon describes the interesting Hottentot custom of blowing air into the vagina of a calfless cow to cause milk ejection. Studies of a somewhat more recent vintage have shown increased mammary pressure in cows following massage of the vulva or cervix at any time during the estrous cycle; in addition, only blood taken from these animals following massage caused contractions of perfused uterine strips (Hays and VanDemark, 1953).

A possible role of oxytocin in luteal function in the bovine is supported by a series of investigations (Armstrong and Hansel, 1959). It has been demonstrated that the injection of oxytocin early in the estrous cycle inhibits the development of the corpus luteum and produces a precocious estrus. On the other hand, when a similar treatment was given to hysterectomized animals, the induction of estrus did not occur. It is tempting to speculate that stimulation of the uterus by injections of oxytocin or distention results either in an inhibition of a pituitary luteotropic factor by way of neural pathways or alternatively by the production of a uterine luteolytic factor.

B. Intrauterine Foreign Bodies

Although the idea was first introduced by Grafenberg in 1920, only recently has considerable attention been given to the use of nonreactive plastic devices inserted *in utero* for contraceptive purposes in humans. These devices do not appear to cause uterine distention and do not influence the length of the estrous or menstrual cycle. The principal effect of this procedure is to prevent pregnancy, but the mechanism by which this is accomplished is not understood. Most of the available evidence, however, argues against an involvement of a neuroendocrine mechanism. In humans, the endometrium is not grossly altered histologically and shows the typical changes found during a normal cycle (Sujan-Tejuja *et al.*, 1965).

Studies on the effect of loosely placed sutures in the uterine horn of laboratory rodents have produced interesting results (Doyle and Margolis, 1965). In the rat, implantation fails to occur in the operated horn and deciduomata following uterine trauma of the horn containing the suture cannot be produced in either the pregnant or pseudopregnant animal. The fact that deciduomata can be produced in the unoperated horn, however, indicates that progesterone secretion is not affected.

The apparent differences among species in the response to intrauterine foreign bodies has clouded interpretations based upon comparative studies, and at the present time no reliable explanation of their mechanism of action is known.

C. Effects of Removal of Uterus

Loeb as early as 1923 demonstrated that removal of the uterus causes a significant prolongation of the life span of corpora lutea in the guinea pig. Subsequent studies have demonstrated that such a response is also characteristic of the pig, cow, and sheep as well as the pseudopregnant rat, mouse, and rabbit. On the other hand, this operation appears not to influence ovarian function in the ferret, opossum, monkey, or human (Anderson *et al.*, 1963).

In most species in which this manipulation is effective, the prolongation of luteal function approaches that of the normal gestation period. There is, however, some evidence that the length of the pseudopregnant period may be related, to a degree, to the amount of uterine tissue removed.

A number of hypotheses have been suggested to account for this phenomenon. The first of these suggests that the endometrium is a source of some type of luteolytic substance and is based upon several experimental observations. The existence of a blood-borne luteolytic factor from the uterus is suggested by the results of parabiotic experiments. Vaginal cycles of normal intact cycling female rats were not affected when these rats were paired with hysterectomized pseudopregnant partners (Spies, 1965), but other observations suggest that the length of pseudopregnancy in the hysterectomized partner is significantly reduced (Anderson and Melampy, 1965). When hysterectomized pseudopregnant rats were united with ovariectomized animals, the life of the corpus luteum was not shortened (Spies, 1965). Thus, a relationship between the uterine action and stage of the ovarian cycle is implied.

Other evidence supporting the existence of a uterine factor has been introduced. Endometrial filtrates alter the rate of progesterone secretion by luteal tissue of gilt ovaries *in vitro* (Duncan *et al.*, 1961). An increased secretion resulted when the filtrates were from the luteal phase while follicular phase filtrates tended to decrease the rate. Evidence for a local ovarian-uterine vascular relationship initiating luteolysis of the sow ovary is provided by observations showing that the presence of a nongravid portion of the uterus in partially hysterectomized animals or those with fetuses in only one uterine horn results in luteal regression only on the nonpregnant side (Anderson and Melampy, 1965).

In spite of the general failure of injections of endometrial or uterine suspensions to influence the length of pseudopregnancy in hysterectomized animals (Malven and Hansel, 1965; Spies, 1965), viable uterine or endometrial autotransplants are capable of doing so (Anderson and Melampy, 1965). The results of the latter experiment argue against a role of neural mechanisms involved in the control of the corpus luteum. On the other hand, the nervous system must be a contributing factor in the initial formation of corpora lutea in some reflex ovulators such as the rabbit and in the production of pseudopregnancy in the rat. In the latter species, bilateral pelvic neurectomy prevents pregnancy or pseudopregnancy in response to mating, although normal fertile ova may be recovered from the tubes. The implantation failure would appear to be due to the absence of functional corpora lutea since exogenously administered progesterone results in implantations (Kollar, 1953). Implantations also occur if the animals are given reserpine 24 hours after mating. When reserpine is given at estrus in the absence of mating, pseudopregnancy of normal length occurs. Results of this nature support the theory that afferent impulses from the genitalia impinging on centers in the central nervous system may be of prime importance in establishing functional corpora lutea in the rat and present convincing evidence for an important role of a hypothalamic luteotropic hormone (LTH) inhibiting factor (see Chapter 16).

The concept of luteal control involving uterine metabolites of ovarian hormones is an attractive alternative. The fact that only viable uterine transplants are capable of shortening the functional life of the corpus luteum, whereas the injections of endometrial or uterine suspensions are ineffective *in vivo*, argues for the presence of a functioning enzyme system. A number of observations have demonstrated that estrogen is effective in prolonging luteal activity (Everett, 1964). Presumably this effect is associated with a role of this hormone on hypothalamic neurons influencing the secretion of a luteotropic hormone (see Chapter 16). In the absence of a uterine mechanism capable of metabolizing estrogen, pseudopregnancy would be prolonged. This concept may require some modification in the light of other work (Gans *et al.*, 1964). The rat uterus appears not to utilize measurable amounts of estrogen and, if anything, urinary estrone levels are lower in hysterectomized gilts than in normal cycling or pregnant ones. It has been proposed that increased levels of progesterone may prolong the life of corpora lutea in the rat by maintaining the secretion of pituitary luteotropic factors and, rather than estrogen, this steroid may be the important factor accounting for the effects of hysterectomy in this species. On the other hand, data from other experiments indicate that progesterone apparently has a luteolytic effect in the pregnant sow when injected into this animal on days 12–16 of pregnancy (Nalbandov, 1961).

At the moment any attempt to place these many observations into a logical perspective is difficult. One clear fact emerges and that is that the uterus is important in many species in regulating the life of the corpus luteum. There does appear to be some basis for concluding, at least in the guinea pig, that the maintenance of corpora lutea as a result of hysterectomy is dependent on the pituitary.

VI. Exteroceptive Stimuli Influencing Reproductive Processes

A. Olfactory Stimuli

The effects of olfactory stimuli on reproduction have recently been reviewed by Bruce (1966). When male domestic animals are exposed to a receptive female, most display a somewhat stereotyped behavioral pattern. This includes smelling and licking the vulva, tasting the urine, and an occasional lifting of the head, curling the lip, and expanding the nares (Flehman response). This sort of deportment has led many to suspect an important role of olfactory stimuli in the arousal of sexual behavior of the male animal, but tactile, gustatory, or visual cues cannot be overlooked.

A number of experimental investigations have been devised to determine the role of olfactory stimuli in mating behavior and some importance has been attached to the odor emanating from the urine or vaginal secretions of the female in estrus. It has been claimed that the smell of the estrous mare causes stimulation of the stallion. Wiping swabs from the vaginal or perineal region of estrous ewes onto the vulva of nonestrous ones increased mounting attempts by the ram (Kelley, 1937). Dogs are attracted to estrous bitches over long distances, an effect which has been attributed to an odor derived from the urine of the bitch (Beach and Gilmour, 1949). Rendering rams anosmic either by topical anesthesia or ablation of the olfactory bulbs does not affect courtship behavior but does appear to interfere with their ability to detect ewes in heat (Lindsay, 1965). Pigs in estrus show an "immobilization reflex" in response to manual pressure on the back 50% of the time, whereas, if the study is carried out in a pen which is redolent of a boar, 81% respond.

These observations imply the existence of a "sex attractant" substance in the urine of some mammals, but the nature of this substance has not been identified. The situation is reminiscent of the sex attractant pheromones of insects (Gilbert, 1963).

In most laboratory rodents, olfaction does not appear to be important for copulation as long as other sensory capacities remain active. Anosmic male mice show no alteration of spermatogenesis but usually will not mate. Rabbits and rats, in contrast, show no alteration in sexual behavior after removal of the olfactory bulbs as long as the neocortex is intact.

The role of olfactory stimuli on reproductive processes other than sexual behavior has received considerable attention. The female reacts to olfactory stimuli perhaps more profoundly than the male. Female mice caged in groups have aberrant cycles characterized by prolonged periods of diestrus. This pattern can be returned to normal if the females are exposed to a male, or even if they are placed in a cage previously soiled by a male. In a random group of normal female mice with 4-day cycles, approximately one-fourth of the group is in estrus each night; however, if these females are placed with males, the highest percentage of mating occurs on the third night. Although probably not mediated by olfactory stimuli, this same sort of synchronization of estrus due to the presence of a male is demonstrable in sheep. Ewes, seasonally breeding animals, that have begun to cycle show no alteration in the established length of cycle in response to the presence of the ram. If, however, the male is introduced during the latter part of the anestrous period, a twofold effect occurs; the estrous season begins earlier and the first estrus is synchronized (Schinckel, 1954).

Very little is known concerning the mechanism of action or the possible endocrinological mediation of the olfactory stimuli mentioned above. In contrast to these, the "strange-male-pregnancy-block" in some rodents is well defined (Bruce, 1966). When males other than the stud male are placed with a female 1–2 days after mating, implantation fails to occur in a large percentage of the females. When females are simply placed into cages recently occupied by strange males, a similar block to pregnancy is observed. These results imply the involvement of olfactory stimuli since total darkness does not alter the response. The implantation block is more pronounced if the male is of a different strain from the female, and, in cases of interspecies stimuli, a strange female is almost as effective as a male. Removal of the olfactory bulb abolishes the response.

Since the effect of the male can be counteracted by established lactation or the administration of 10 IU of prolactin on the first or second day after coitus, it would appear that the effect is related to some interference with the release of pituitary LTH. Such an explanation is supported by other observations. Treating the nasal mucosa with nupercaine or silver nitrate or removal of the sphenopalatine ganglion, thereby interrupting the nonolfactory nerve supply to the mucosa, causes female rats to become pseudopregnant.

An interference with the discharge of pituitary gonadotropins by removal of olfactory stimuli is indicated by other experiments. Female mice made anosmic at 6–7 weeks of age have smaller than normal uteri. Ovaries are also smaller and contain, if present, only atrophic corpora lutea. These mice will not mate. Although they demonstrate no signs of stress, the presence of large fat deposits could suggest an alteration in steroid hormone secretion normally controlled by pituitary gonadotropins. Similarly, complete ablation of the olfactory bulbs of sexually mature sows causes a permanent anestrus, a reduction in uterine weight, ovarian atrophy, and an accumulation of secretory material in the beta and gamma cells of the hypophysis.

B. Visual Stimuli

It is difficult to separate responses due strictly to visual stimuli from those due to other sensory stimuli. Effects of light on mammals have been reviewed by Thibault *et al.* (1966). Bulls show an increased interest in the nonestrous heifer if first an estrous cow has been led past the stanchion. An increased uterine motility can be demonstrated in heifers at the sight of a bull. On the other hand, the proximity of the male has not been shown to have a direct effect upon the initiation or induction of estrous behavior in cows. In young female pigs the presence of a male apparently triggers a release of pituitary gonadotropins which precipitates first estrus. Visual stimuli have marked effects on reproduction in birds (Ganong, 1959). One clear example of a purely visual stimulus affecting reproductive processes is the observation that the pigeon will ovulate when she sees another pigeon or an image of herself in a mirror. Many birds display definite courtship performances such as a type of dance. It has been proposed that these sexual displays and the presence of other animals serve to cause afferent stimulation of the hypothalamus and in turn activation of the pituitary. Whether these responses are associated only with a visual component cannot be decided.

C. Auditory Stimuli

The ringing of an alarm clock engenders a complex of responses both physical and emotional in man; the rat also responds dramatically (Zondek and Tamari, 1960, 1964). If an alarm bell is rung 1 out of every 10 minutes persistently, after 1 week females develop prolonged and more or less persistent estrus. At autopsy 60 days later, both the uterine and ovarian weight of these animals are increased over that of controls. The ovaries are mainly comprised of corpora lutea that are large and well vascularized. This response apparently depends on established pituitary gonadotropin secretion since 3-week-old rats show no response, but 5-week-old females have slightly enlarged ovaries. Mature rats also have enlarged adrenal cortices and show an increase in the production of corticosteroids when repeatedly exposed to auditory stimuli. Rabbits react to auditory stimuli by forming large hemorrhagic ovarian follicles similar to those found in a positive pregnancy test. These same audiogenic stimuli, on the other hand, cause no observable changes in the testes of either the immature or mature male rat, and, although the mature male will mate, the mating is sterile. Female rats also are sterile, and, even if the auditory stimulus is not begun until after mating, pregnancy still does not occur (Zondek and Tamari, 1960, 1964). Other observations also suggest that stress may exert an effect on reproductive processes in domestic animals.

Transporting animals from one location to another often causes an earlier appearance of estrus and a tendency for synchronization. Studies of estrous sows discussed earlier in connection with olfactory stimuli also demonstrate a role of auditory stimuli in sexual responses. In trials where estrous sows were exposed to combined auditory and olfactory stimuli from a boar, 90% responded to manual pressure on the back with an immobilization reflex in contrast to 50% in the absence of these stimuli and 81% of those exposed to olfactory stimuli alone (Signoret and du Mesnil du Buisson, 1961). This same reflex could also be elicited by playing a record of the sounds of a boar at mating. Apparently the rhythm of the sounds is the significant factor since by mimicking this rhythm the reflex can also be triggered. Dairy bulls who have refused to mount a cow for a long time have been induced to mount it again when stimulated by specific calls of cows emitted by a magnetophone.

The importance of tactile stimuli influencing reproduction is well documented in reflex ovulators and has been discussed in detail above. Another example of this type, however, is the intriguing observation that most birds lay a characteristic number of eggs (see Ganong, 1959). When this number is reached, further ovulation is prevented. Excellent reviews concerning the influence of a variety of exteroceptive factors affecting reproductive performance appear in the proceedings of a recent symposium (Bruce, 1966; Thibault *et al.*, 1966).

VII. Summary and Conclusions

Evidence for the role of a variety of exteroceptive stimuli in reproductive processes seems irrefutable. These range from genital manipulations to social contact. It is difficult to prove that one sensory modality or one afferent pathway is of primary importance over another; rather, it would seem that all the senses are involved and to some degree interrelated, no one sense being absolutely essential. The impulses apparently impinge upon neurons of the hypothalamus and thereby affect pituitary gonadotropin secretion.

References

Albert, A. (1961). The mammalian testis. *In* "Sex and Internal Secretions" (W. C. Young, ed.), 3rd ed., Vol. 1, pp. 305–365. Williams & Wilkins, Baltimore, Maryland.

Anderson, L., and Melampy, R. M. (1965). Mechanisms controlling the formation and persistence of the corpus luteum and discussion. (Proc. Conf. on Estrous Cycle Control in Domestic Animals). *U.S. Dept. Agr. Misc. Publ.* **1005,** 64–77.

Anderson, L., Bowerman, A. M., and Melampy, R. M. (1963). Neuro-utero-ovarian relationships. *In* "Advances in Neuroendocrinology" (A. V. Nalbandov, ed.), pp. 345–373. Univ. of Illinois Press, Urbana, Illinois.

Armstrong, D. T., and Hansel, W. (1959). Alteration of bovine estrous cycle with oxytocin. *J. Dairy Sci.* **42,** 533–542.

Bandmann, F. (1949). Über die Beeinflussung der Hodenfunktion durch Resektion des lumbalen Grenzstranges. *Chirurg* **20,** 132–136.

Bard, P. (1939). Central nervous mechanisms for emotional behavior patterns in animals. *Proc. Assoc. Res. Nervous Mental Disease* **19,** 190–218.

Beach, F. A., and Gilmour, R. W. (1949). Response of male dogs to urine from females in heat. *J. Mammal.* **30,** 391–392.

Bradbury, J. T., Brown, W. E., and Gray, L. A. (1950). Maintenance of the corpus luteum and physiologic actions of progesterone. *Recent Progr. Hormone Res.* **5,** 151–194.

Bruce, H. (1966). Smell as an exteroceptive factor. *Proc. 7th Biennial Symp. Animal Reprod., Michigan State Univ., 1965—J. Animal Sci. Suppl.* **25,** 83–87.

Coujard, R. (1951). Inhibition de l'action gonadotrope de l'hypophyse par déstruction du ganglion sympathique prostatovesiculo-déférentiel. *Compt. Rend. Soc. Biol.* **145,** 1469–1470.

Coujard, R. (1952). Effects sur le testicule et l'épididyme de la phénolisation de fibres nerveuses. *Compt. Rend. Soc. Biol.* **146,** 704–706.

Debackere, M., Peelers, G., and Tuyttens, N. (1961). Reflex release of an oxytocic hormone by stimulation of genital organs in male and female sheep studies by a cross circulation technique. *J. Endocrinol.* **22,** 321–334.

Donovan, B. T. (1961). The role of the uterus in regulation of the estrous cycle. *J. Reprod. Fertility* **2,** 508–510.

Doyle, L. L., and Margolis, A. J. (1965). Intrauterine foreign body studies in rodents. *Excerpta Medica Found., Intern. Congr. Ser.* **86,** 185–188.

Duncan, G. W., Bowerman, A. M., Anderson, L., Hearn, W., and Melampy, R. M. (1961). Factors influencing *in vitro* synthesis of progesterone. *Endocrinology* **68,** 199–207.

Endröczi, E., and Lissák, K. (1963). Role of reflexogenic factors in testicular hormone secretion. Effect of copulation on the testicular hormone production of the rabbit. *Acta Physiol. Acad. Sci. Hung.* **21,** 203–206.

Everett, J. W. (1961). The mammalian female reproductive cycle and its controlling mechanisms. *In* "Sex and Internal Secretions" (W. C. Young, ed.), 3rd ed., Vol. 1, pp. 497–555. Williams & Wilkins, Baltimore, Maryland.

Everett, J. W. (1964). Central neural control of reproductive functions of the adenohypophysis. *Physiol. Rev.* **44,** 373–431.

Ganong, W. F. (1959). Role of the nervous system in reproductive processes. *In* "Reproduction in Domestic Animals" (H. H. Cole and P. T. Cupps, eds.), pp. 185–221. Academic Press, New York.

Gans, E., de Jongh, S. E., van Rees, G. P., Van der Werff ten Bosch, J. J., and Wolthuis, O. L. (1964). Cyclic variations in the hypophyseal FSH content in the female rat. *Acta Endocrinol.* **45,** 335–339.

Gilbert, L. I. (1963). Hormones controlling reproduction and molting in invertebrates. *In* "Comparative Endocrinology" (U. S. von Euler and H. Heller, eds.), pp. 1–46. Academic Press, New York.

Grafenberg, E. (1920). An intrauterine contraceptive method. *In* "Practice of Contraception" (M. Sanger and H. M. Stone, eds.), pp. 33–47. Williams & Wilkins, Baltimore, Maryland.

Hansel, W., and Wagner, W. C. (1960). Luteal inhibition in the bovine as a result of oxytocin injections, uterine dilatation, and intrauterine infusions of seminal and preputial fluids. *J. Dairy Sci.* **43,** 796–805.

Hays, R. L., and VanDemark, N. L. (1953). Effect of stimulation of the reproductive organs of the cow on the release of an oxytocic-like substance. *Endocrinology* **52,** 634–637.

Josimivich, J. B. (1958). Effects of destruction of the thoracic spinal cord on spermatogenesis in the mouse. *Endocrinology* **63,** 254–256.

Kelley, R. B. (1937). Studies in fertility of sheep. *Bull. Council Sci. Ind. Res. Australia* **112.**

Kollar, E. J. (1953). Reproduction in the female rat after pelvic nerve neurectomy. *Anat. Record* **115,** 641–658.

Krantz, K. (1958). Innervation of the human vulva and vagina. *Obstet. Gynecol.* **12,** 382–396.

Krantz, K. (1959). Innervation of the human uterus. *Ann. N.Y. Acad. Sci.* **75,** 770–784.

Lindsay, D. R. (1965). The importance of olfactory stimuli in the mating behaviour of the ram. *Animal Behaviour* **13,** 75–78.

Loeb, L. (1923). The effect of extirpation of the uterus on the life and function of the corpus luteum in the guinea pig. *Proc. Soc. Exptl. Biol. Med.* **20,** 441–443.

Malven, P. V., and Hansel, W. (1965). Effect of bovine endometrial extracts, vasopressin, and oxytocin on the duration of pseudopregnancy in hysterectomized and intact rats. *J. Reprod. Fertility* **9,** 207–215.

Moore, C. R. (1926). The biology of the mammalian testis and scrotum. *Quart. Rev. Biol.* **1,** 4–50.

Moore, W. W., and Nalbandov, A. V. (1953). Neurogenic effects of uterine distention on the estrous cycle of the ewe. *Endocrinology* **53,** 1–11.

Nalbandov, A. V. (1961). Comparative physiology and endocrinology of domestic animals. *Recent Progr. Hormone Res.* **17,** 119–139.

Nalbandov, A. V., and St. Clair, L. E. (1958). Relation of the nervous system to implantation. *Proc. 3rd Symp. Reproduction Infertility, Colorado State Univ., 1957* pp. 83–87. Pergamon Press, Oxford.

Root, W. S., and Bard, P. (1947). The mediation of feline erection through sympathetic pathways with some remarks on sexual behavior after deafferentiation of the genitalia. *Am. J. Physiol.* **151,** 80–90.

Schinckel, P. G. (1954). The effect of the ram on the incidence and occurrence of oestrus in ewes. *Australian Vet. J.* **30,** 189–195.

Sherrington, C. S. (1900). *In* "Textbook of Physiology" (E. A. Schafer, ed.), pp. 783–883. Pentland, Edinburgh and London.

Short, R. V. (1964). Ovarian steroid synthesis and secretion *in vivo*. *Recent Progr. Hormone Res.* **20,** 303–333.

Signoret, J. P., and du Mesnil du Buisson, F. (1961). Étude du Comportement de la truie en oestrus. *Proc. 4th Intern. Congr. Animal Reprod., The Hague, 1961* pp. 171–175.

Spies, H. G. (1965). Factors influencing the regression of the corpora lutea in the ewe, rabbit, and rat. (Proc. Conf. on Estrous Cycle Control in Domestic Animals). *U.S. Dept. Agr. Misc. Publ.* **1005,** 83–85.

Sujan-Tejuja, S., Virick, R. K., and Malkani, P. K. (1965). Uterine histopathology in the presence of intrauterine devices. *Excerpta Med., Intern. Congr. Ser.* **86,** 172–177.

Thibault, C., Courot, M., Martinet, L., Mauleon, P., du Mesnil du Buisson, F., Ortavant, R., Pelletier, J., Signoret, J. (1966). Regulation of mammalian breeding seasons and estrous cycles by light and external stimuli. *Proc. 7th Biennial Symp. Animal Reprod., Michigan State Univ., 1965—J. Animal Sci. Suppl.* **25,** 119–139.

Turner, C. D. (1938). Intra-ocular homotransplantation of prepuberal testes in the rat. *Am. J. Anat.* **63,** 101–159.

Weidenmann, W. (1952). Auswirkungen der lumbalen Sympathektomie auf dem Gesamtorganismus, besonders auf Hoden und Nebennieren. *Zentr. Chir.* **77,** 1–9.

Zondek, B., and Tamari, I. (1960). Effect of audiogenic stimulation on genital function and reproduction. *Am. J. Obstet. Gynecol.* **80,** 1041–1048.

Zondek, B., and Tamari, I. (1964). Effect of audiogenic stimulation on genital function and reproduction. III. Infertility induced by auditory stimuli prior to mating. *Acta Endocrinol.* Suppl. 90, 227–234.

CHAPTER 18

Effects of Light and Visual Stimuli on Endocrine Function

RICHARD J. WURTMAN[1]

[1] Part of this chapter was written while the author was a Fellow in Endocrinology at the Massachusetts General Hospital and Harvard Medical School, Boston, Massachusetts.

I. Introduction

A. Control of the Annual Gonad Cycle in Birds and Mammals by Changing Day Length

Four decades ago, Rowan (1925) first drew the attention of biologists to the relation between changes in environmental lighting and gonad function in animals. He demonstrated that the annual period of testicular growth in the junco (*Junco hyemalis*) could be made to occur prematurely, in the middle of the Canadian winter, by gradually increasing the amount of time each day that the birds were exposed to light. Control birds, which lived in natural lighting in "Riviera-like California," did not develop sexually until springtime. Several years later, Bissonette (1932) showed that extra light could also induce a state of premature estrus in a monoestrous mammal, the ferret (*Mustela*), and Baker and Ranson (1932) demonstrated that this effect of light on the field mouse (*Microtus agrestis*) was unrelated to changes in ambient temperature or humidity, or to food intake.

The ability of light to modify gonad function had been recognized for some time (see Rowan, 1938): Dutch and Japanese farmers traditionally exposed song birds to extra illumination in the fall in order to induce singing—a behavioral consequence of testicular activation—in the winter. However, the unequivocal demonstration that light, an environmental variable, could generate specific changes in the gonads was of revolutionary impact to endocrinology. It proved that the pituitary and the target glands were not related *solely* as a closed feedback system, but were also profoundly influenced by the external milieu. It now became necessary to characterize the biological machinery through which information about light was received by the body and translated into an endocrine message. After four decades, this task is by no means complete, but it is generally agreed that light must activate photoreceptors which are connected to neural elements, and that special neuroendocrine organs must then transduce the resulting nervous stimuli into endocrine information.

B. Variation in Responsiveness to Light among Related Species

In 1934, Hill and Parkes, and F. H. A. Marshall and Bowden showed that although extra light could hasten the onset of estrus in the ferret, light was not a prerequisite for normal sexual maturation, since animals kept in constant darkness came into estrus at approximately the same time as those in natural lighting. Subsequently, it was shown (Thomson,

1954) that blinded ferrets (which do not respond to extra lighting) also became estrous at the normal time of the year. Unlike the ferret, the white-crowned sparrow (*Zonotrichia leucophrys*) may have an absolute light requirement for seasonal gonad growth (Farner, 1961); however, sexual development in the prairie dog (*Cynomys ludouicianus*), another annual breeder, appears to be entirely unaffected by environmental lighting (Foreman, 1962). Continuous lighting rapidly alters the vaginal estrous cycle of the C3H mouse (Chu, 1965), but has no effect on this function in the hamster (*Cricetus auratus*), another polyestrous mammal (Greenwald, 1963; Chu, 1965). These observations indicate that there is wide variation among closely related species in the extent to which cyclic gonadal function is regulated by, or can be perturbed by, environmental lighting.

C. Diurnal Endocrine Rhythms and Their Relation to the Day-Night Light Cycle

Since Pincus (1943) first described the nocturnal decrease in urinary ketosteroid excretion in young men, a large body of information has been accumulated concerning diurnal rhythms in endocrine gland activity and in consequent metabolic events. Most of these rhythms can be modified experimentally by varying lighting schedules. For example, the concentration of eosinophiles in the blood of the mouse fluctuates with a diurnal cycle; animals kept in light during the day and in darkness at night show a peak eosinophile level at noon, just before the level of adrenal secretion starts to increase (Halberg and Visscher, 1950). If the start of the daily light period is moved forward by 12 hours, the time of peak eosinophilia is shifted by an equal number of hours after 9 days of exposure to the new lighting conditions (Halberg, 1953). If mice are placed in constant darkness, the eosinophile cycle remains about 24 hours in length, and the times of the peaks and valleys persist unchanged. When the animals are exposed to continuous lighting for 9 days, however, the eosinophile cycle disappears, but can be renewed if the mice are returned to cyclic illumination (Halberg, 1953). These data suggest several characteristics of the diurnal blood eosinophile rhythm of mice (and the underlying adrenal secretory rhythm): (1) it does not have an absolute requirement for cyclic light changes, and hence may represent an "endogenous" rhythm; (2) it is normally synchronized by the day-night light cycle; and (3) it is subject to marked perturbation, even extinction, by certain experimental lighting conditions. The data also illustrate a cardinal tenet of photoneuroendocrinology: the demonstration that an endocrine event can be modified by experimental lighting does not constitute proof that light normally regulates the event.

D. Light, Sexual Maturation, and Endocrine Rhythms

It seems well established that light does play a physiological role in at least two endocrine mechanisms, and the remainder of this chapter will be concerned largely with these: (1) Environmental light participates in setting the pace of sexual development in several species, such as the ferret and junco, mentioned above, and also in polyestrous mammals like the rat (Fiske, 1941) and the human (Zacharias and Wurtman, 1964). (2) Seasonal and diurnal changes in lighting can synchronize, or even generate, rhythmic changes in endocrine function, (such as the gonadal and adrenal cycles).

There are many advantages to the animal of gearing control of its internal milieu to an external "biological clock" such as light (Aschoff, 1960; Farner, 1961). Such a mechanism (1) enables the individual to synchronize several "independent" internal cycles (such as diurnal rhythms in adrenal cortical and adrenal medullary secretion); (2) enables two or more individuals of the same species to synchronize their behavioral and endocrine rhythms; and (3) enables the individual's endocrine systems to anticipate regular changes in the environment. For example, gonad growth in spring-breeding monoestrous mammals may be initiated in winter, several months in advance of need, by changes in the length of the day; the birth of the young at the appropriate time of the year is thereby ensured.

The data to be considered here will be limited largely to studies on mammals and birds (see also Chapter 30). The reader is referred to reviews by Bünning (1964), Scharrer and Scharrer (1963), and Farner (1961), and to the Symposia of the American Association for the Advancement of Science (Withrow, 1959) and the New York Academy of Sciences (Hague, 1964) for information on the effects of light on endocrine function in other phyla.

II. Physical and Temporal Characteristics of Natural Light, and Their Endocrine Significance

A. Physical Properties: Spectrum and Intensity

1. *Spectrum*

Environmental lighting may be characterized physically by its wavelengths and its intensity; both may influence its effects on neuroendocrine systems. Visible light (i.e., light which activates retinal photoreceptors) includes the spectrum of wavelengths from blue (3800–5000 Å) through green (5300 Å), yellow (5800 Å), and red (6000–7600 Å). Yellow light is the most efficient stimulus to mammalian visual pigment. The entire spectrum from 3000 Å to 20,000 Å is present in sunlight, with waves of peak energy between 4500 Å and 7000 Å. Most incandescent light bulbs provide wavelengths of 3500 Å–25,000 Å, with peak energy at 10,000 Å. It is apparent that much of the energy emitted by this light source is wasted as nonvisible heat rays. "Cool white" fluorescent bulbs emit waves of 3800 Å–7500 Å, peaking at 6000 Å; this range provides a close approximation of the visual spectrum. The sun and both incandescent and fluorescent bulbs thus emit essentially all the light waves which can activate mammalian retinal photoreceptors.

To determine whether the photoreceptors involved in the "photosexual reflex" of ducks differed from those utilized for vision, Benoit and colleagues studied the efficacy of different monochromatic light sources in stimulating testicular growth. They found that the longer waves were most potent (Benoit *et al.*, 1950), whereas the shortest produced essentially no gonadal stimulation (Benoit and Assenmacher, 1959). Hollwich and Tilgner confirmed these findings in ducks (1961), but showed (1963) that the rapid, adrenal-dependent, eosinopenic response of the mouse to light could be brought on equally well by monochromatic lights of 4360 Å, 5460 Å, 6320 Å, or 7070 Å. F. H. A. Marshall and Bowden (1934) found that ultraviolet light (i.e., 3650 Å) was particularly effective in inducing premature estrus in ferrets; infrared light (7500 Å) was ineffective (1936). So far, however, there has been little supporting evidence presented to show that the endocrine responses of mammals to visible light are related to particular wavelengths within its spectrum.

2. *Intensity*

Light intensity is measured in foot-candle and lux units; the former represents the amount of light projected by a standard candle on a square foot of surface 1 ft from the light source, and the latter is the projection of a candle on a square meter of surface 1 meter from the light source. One foot-candle of light is thus equivalent to 10.76 lux. In direct sunlight, the earth's surface receives about 10,000 ft-c of light; this is reduced 20-fold in the shade. The intensity of full moonlight is about 0.02 ft-c. Most commercially lit offices and laboratories provide 50–150 ft-c of light at eye level. The human visual apparatus can perceive 10^{-5} to 10^{-6} ft-c.

F. H. A. Marshall (1940) claimed that the onset of estrus could be hastened in ferrets by increasing the intensity of the illumination provided for a fixed number of hours. In the experiments described, the light projecting onto each animal was not measured; ferrets of different ages and periods of domestication were kept 1–22 feet distant from a single 1000-watt lamp. The animals closest to the lamp came into estrus soonest. The data are of questionable significance, since (1) the animals near to the lamp almost certainly were subjected to a large and unmeasured amount of radiant heat, (2) there was considerable variation in the time of onset of estrus among animals treated the same way, and (3) it has been shown (Van der Werff ten Bosch, 1963) that the domestication of ferrets, per se, influences the onset of subsequent estrous periods; hence animals with very different periods of captivity are not comparable. Other workers (see Farner, 1961) have found that, whereas ferrets will not show a gonadal response to extra lighting below an intensity of 100 lux, intensities thirteen times greater are no more effective in inducing premature estrus than this threshold level. Browman (1937) observed that "persistent estrus" was not induced in rats by direct summer sunlight, but could be produced in littermates by continuous exposure to an artificial light source providing 30 ft-c.

Rowan (1938) claimed that light intensity was not a determinant of gonadal development in birds, once a low threshold was reached. Bartholomew (1949) studied the relation between light intensity and testicular growth in sparrows exposed to light for 16 hours per day. When the intensity was increased from 0.04 to 10.3 ft-c, there was an increase in the rate of gonad growth; however, intensities of 50 or 250 ft-c were no more effective than 10 ft-c. Wilson *et al.* (1956) found that it was possible to *make* light intensity the limiting factor in the rate of sexual development in Leghorn chickens by restricting the hours and frequency of light exposure. Under these conditions, animals reared in 0–0.4 ft-c matured less rapidly than those kept in 0.4–6.6 ft-c of light; chickens in 0.5–30.0 ft-c exposures matured most rapidly. As little as 1 ft-c of light is adequate for optimal egg production by chickens (Dobie, 1946), and for the activation of the "photosexual reflex" of ducks (Benoit, 1961). Although relatively little information is available relating the intensity of light exposure to its efficacy as a neuroendocrine stimulus, it seems likely that the range in which intensity may be rate-limiting in birds and mammals is well below that provided by sunlight, or by the systems of artificial illumination generally used.

B. Cyclic Variations in Natural Lighting

There are two major cycles governing the amount of time for which a particular geographic locus is exposed to sunlight: an on-off, 24-hour cycle of day and night, whose components are usually of unequal length but each average 12 hours per day in the course of a year, and a continuous, annual cycle of change in the length of the daily light period. These cycles are accompanied by parallel cycles in the intensity of the sunlight. In the popular jargon of the computer era, the 24-hour cycle provides digital information, and the annual cycle analog information. The former cycle is universal; the latter is absent near the equator, where all days are 12 hours long, and may be represented by a sine wave, with a period of a year, an amplitude which depends upon geographic location (i.e., zero at the equator, and 24 hours at the poles), and maxima and minima at the first days of summer and winter, respectively. Isomorphic with, and frequently dependent upon, these two physical cycles are two major endocrine phenomena: diurnal and annual rhythms. A third endocrine rhythm, cyclic ovulation in polyestrous mammals, may also be synchronized to the 24-hour light cycle.

1. *24-Hour Endocrine Rhythms*

Many endocrine functions in birds and mammals demonstrate 24-hour periodicity. These include: (1) the secretion of corticosteroids from the adrenal in mice (Halberg *et al.*, 1959), rats (Guillemin *et al.*, 1959), monkeys (Migeon *et al.*, 1955), and humans (Bliss *et al.*, 1953); (2) the level of ascorbic acid in the ovary of the pseudopregnant rat (Stevens *et al.*, 1964), the release of an ovulation-inducing hormone in chickens (Fraps, 1954), and the time of day that the guinea pig, a polyestrous mammal, comes into estrus (Dempsey *et al.*, 1934); (3) the prolactin content of the rat pituitary (Clark and Baker, 1964); (4) the level of calcium in the serum of humans with hyperparathyroidism (but not in normals) (McIntosh, 1966); (5) the activity of renin in the plasma of normal humans (Gordon *et al.*, 1966); (6) the level of thyroid-stimulating hormone in the blood (Schindler *et al.*, 1965) and pituitary (Bakke and Lawrence, 1965) of the rat, and the rate of decline of the I^{131} content of the cat thyroid (Woods *et al.*, 1966) [there is apparently no diurnal rhythm in the level of protein-bound iodine in human serum (Schatz and Volpe, 1959)]; and (7) a variety of metabolic events presumed or demonstrated to depend upon endocrine factors. This last group includes rectal temperature, liver phospholipid content, adrenal parenchymal mitoses, susceptibility to the toxic effects of certain drugs and to *Escherichia coli* endotoxin, and liver glycogen content in mice (Halberg, 1959a,b); the renal excretion of water and electrolytes in the human (Stanbury and Thompson, 1951); the content of deoxyribonucleic acid (DNA) and ribonucleic acid (RNA) (Barnum *et al.*, 1958) and the mitochondrial oxidative activity (Glick and Cohen, 1964) of the rat liver, and the incidence of mitotic figures in mouse epiphyseal cartilage (Simmons, 1962). Many of the above metabolic phenomena appear to be related to diurnal periodicity in adrenal function.

Photic Control of 24-Hour Endocrine Rhythms. In all cases where these diurnal endocrine rhythms have been studied, they have been found to be naturally synchronized to the ambient lighting schedule. The adrenal-dependent rhythms tend to respond to experimental lighting regimens in a manner similar to that described for the mouse eosinophile cycle (Section I,C); they rapidly resynchronize to new lighting schedules, and persist when animals are kept in constant darkness, but not constant light, for short periods. Synchrony to ambient lighting could be the consequence of either of two mechanisms. An endogenous, or intrinsic, rhythm of about 24 hours' periodicity could be cued by light (i.e., light could operate as a "Zeitgeber") (Aschoff, 1960). Alternately, lighting shifts might operate to *produce* the rhythm. A truly *exogenous* 24-hour rhythm would rapidly become extinct in animals deprived of photoreceptors, or kept in continuous light or darkness. The daily activity cycle of the pineal enzyme which synthesizes melatonin and other methoxyindoles (Section V,D) may represent such a rhythm. Several endogenous rhythms have been shown to be *circadian* (see Halberg, 1959b). When the animal is deprived of an external synchronizer, the rhythm persists, but its period becomes somewhat shorter or longer than 24 hours. It can not be assumed without experimental proof that *all* endogenous rhythms are circadian. Some characteristics of endogenous and exogenous 24-hour rhythms are described in Table I.

2. *Annual and Photoperiodic Endocrine Rhythms*

The annual (or seasonal) endocrine rhythms that have been best studied are those which involve sexual development, and consequent function and behavior (courtship, migration, and molting; see Hammond, 1954, and Farner, 1961) in monoestrous birds and mammals. The highly specialized endocrine cycles of hibernating animals [for example, gonad growth in the ground squirrel, *Tamias* sp. (Wells, 1959)] have not been shown to be related to light, and will not be

TABLE I

24-HOUR RHYTHMS IN THE RAT ADRENAL AND PINEAL, AND THEIR RELATION TO LIGHT[a]

	Adrenal corticosterone	Pineal serotonin	Pineal HIOMT activity
Maximum level	End of light period	Middle of light period	Middle of dark period
Minimum level	End of dark period	Middle of dark period	End of light period
Effect on rhythm:			
Blinding	Persists	Persists	Extinguished
Superior cervical ganglionectomy	—	Extinguished	Extinguished
Constant dark	Persists	Persists	Extinguished
Constant light	Extinguished	Extinguished	Extinguished

[a] Rats were exposed to light for 12–14 hours daily, except as indicated. HIOMT = hydroxyindole-*O*-methyl transferase. The effect of superior cervical ganglionectomy on the adrenal corticosterone cycle was not tested. The pineal HIOMT rhythm is exogenous. The adrenal corticosterone cycle is endogenous, and probably circadian. The pineal serotonin rhythm is endogenous; it has not yet been determined whether it is also circadian.

TABLE II

SEASON OF GONADAL GROWTH AND ESTRUS IN SOME MONOESTROUS BIRDS AND MAMMALS, AND EFFECT OF ADDED LIGHTING

Species	Season	Effect of added lighting	References
Ferret (*Mustela* sp.)	Winter–spring	Stimulatory	Bissonette (1932)
Raccoon (*Procyon lotor*)	Late winter	Stimulatory	Bissonette and Csech (1937)
Hedgehog (*Exinaceus* sp.)	Winter–spring	Stimulatory	Allanson and Deanesley (1934)
Cat	Winter–spring	Stimulatory	Scott and Lloyd-Jacob (1959)
Field mouse (*Microtus agrestis*)	Winter–spring	Stimulatory	Baker and Ranson (1932)
Hare	Winter–spring	Stimulatory	Quoted in Farner (1961)
Bat	Spring	Stimulatory	Skreb (1954)
Junco (*Junco hyemalis*)	Winter–spring	Stimulatory	Rowan (1925)
White-crowned sparrow (*Zonotrichia leucophrys*)	Spring	Stimulatory	Farner (1962)
Sheep[a]	Fall–winter	Not tested	Hendricks (1956)
Goat	Fall–winter	Not tested	Quoted in Farner (1961)
Deer	Late summer–fall	Not tested	Wislocki *et al.* (1947)
Prairie dog (*Cynomys ludouicianus*)	Winter	No effect	Foreman (1962)
Rhesus monkey	Late summer–fall	Not tested	Sade (1964)

[a] Short days increase sperm production (Ortavant, 1958).

considered here. At a fixed time of the year, the gonads of essentially all the males and females of a given monoestrous species begin to grow and to produce mature gametes and characteristic hormones. The rate of growth can be surprisingly rapid. The weight of the testis of the European starling (*Sturnus vulgaris vulgaris*) increases 6-fold under natural lighting conditions between March 15 and April 1 (Bissonette and Chapnick, 1930). Several months later, the females come into full estrus. Most monoestrous animals show gonadal recrudesence in the winter, coincident with increasing day length or photoperiod, and come into estrus in the spring; a smaller number are "short-day breeders," i.e., they come into estrus in late summer or fall (Table II). After the single estrous period, the gonads regress until the cycle begins anew the following year.

Photic Control of Annual Endocrine Rhythms. The onset of the yearly estrous period can be hastened in most species (Table II) by altering the ambient lighting. The annual estrous cycle has been termed "photoperiodic" in these animals, on the assumption that in nature it also occurs in synchrony with the yearly rhythm of changing day length. While this assumption seems safe, it should be recognized that there is little evidence that any species (except perhaps among the passeriform birds) is absolutely dependent upon cyclic light changes in order to undergo cyclic gonadal maturation, but there is much to indicate the necessity for other control mechanisms. First, it has never been possible to delay maturation consistently in the ferret by changing light exposure or by blinding. Second, yearly cycles of gonadal growth and migration are observed in birds living in an essentially constant day length near the equator. Last, the gonads of all birds, and possibly some mammals (Hammond, 1951), eventually become refractory to continued stimulation by light.

There are a variety of ways in which a cycle generated by two alternating elements (day and night) whose sum is constant (24 hours) but whose ratio (length of day to length of night) varies regularly, could transmit information to a neuroendocrine control mechanism. For example, the mechanism could respond to changing day length, to day length greater than a certain number of hours, or to the number of day-night cycles, independent of their length. Experimental models of these three information systems have all been utilized to stimulate gonadal growth.

(*i*) *Single light period of gradually increasing length.* This system, which simulates the natural change in lighting that follows the winter solstice, produces premature estrus in the junco (Rowan, 1925) and accelerates maturation in domestic fowl (Morris and Fox, 1958).

(*ii*) *Single light period of constant length.* This system substitutes a "square wave" for the natural "sine wave" of changing day-night ratios. Animals that respond to "long days" (i.e., light periods of greater than 12 hours) with premature gonadal maturation are indicated in Table II. Farner (1959) found that the rate of testicular growth in the white-crowned sparrow was a linear function of the length of the daily light period, between 9.5 and 18 hours daily. Below 9.5 hours, gonad growth was negligible; beyond 18 hours, the rate of growth continued to increase with increasing day length, but not proportionately. Several workers have noted a different effect of very long photoperiods on sexual maturation in the ferret. This animal shows an optimal estrous response to 14–16 hours of light daily. As the daily light period is extended beyond this range, the speed with which premature estrus is attained actually decreases (Hart, 1951; Hammond, 1954), but estrus still comes earlier than in animals kept in natural lighting. This suggests that an interval of darkness may increase the effect of light.

(*iii*) *Multiple light and dark periods of constant total length.* Multiple light periods during a given amount of time can be more effective as a stimulus to gonadal maturation than a single, longer photoperiod. Hart (1951) observed that exposing ferrets to a single extra hour of light at midnight in the winter effectively induced premature estrus. Hammond (1954) found that a schedule of 2 hours' light, 10 dark, 2 light, 10 dark (2L : 10D : 2L : 10D) was more effective in stimulating gonad growth in ferrets than 24 hours of light, and almost as effective as 14 hours of light. Such a lighting regimen would, of course, never be found in nature. W. O. Wilson (personal communication, 1964) studied the effect of various lighting regimens on testis growth in young Japanese quail. He found that 4L : 20D, 8L :16D, and 12L : 12D were nonstimulatory; 14L : 10D, 16L : 8D, and 24L all caused growth, in order of increasing efficacy. When 12 hours of light were administered daily in several short periods (i.e., 6L : 6D, 6L : 6D, 4L : 4D . . . , 3L : 3D . . .), the rate of testis growth increased as a function of the number of light periods.

3. *Polyestrous and Menstrual Rhythms*

These rhythms constitute a third kind of endocrine cycle in mammals that ovulate spontaneously; they are analogous to the daily egg-laying cycle of domestic fowl. It is generally believed that a periodic neuroendocrine stimulus causes the pituitary to release a burst of luteinizing hormone (LH). This acts on a "prepared" ovary to induce ovulation, which is approximately concurrent with estrous behavior and vaginal cytology in the rat, and which leads after a fortnight to menstruation in the human. Unlike the diurnal adrenal or annual breeding cycles described above, the period of the ovulatory cycle in most mammals (i.e., 4 or 5 days in the rat, 28 days in the human) does not resemble any known light cycle. Yet the age at which ovulation first appears can be profoundly influenced by experimental variations in lighting, as can its periodicity in the adult animal (see Section V,C,2). The mechanism by which the 24-hour light rhythm "drives" a 4-, 5-, or 28-day ovulatory cycle is not yet understood.

a. The "Critical Period" and Ovulation. In 1949, Everett, and co-workers presented evidence for a timed neuroendocrine event that was thought to be a prerequisite to ovulation in the rat. They showed that ovulation, which ordinarily occurred near 2 A.M. on the morning after proestrus, could be blocked by treating animals with certain drugs [Dibenzyline and atropine (Everett *et al.*, 1949), pentobarbital and other barbiturates (Everett and Sawyer, 1950)] provided that those agents were administered at about 2 P.M. on the day of proestrus. If the drugs were given after 4 P.M., ovulation occurred at the expected time; thus 2–4 P.M. was a "critical period" in the neuroendocrine control of ovulation in the rat. These drugs were all believed to exert their effect on ovulation through an action on the central nervous system. Since hypophysectomy of the proestrous rat during this 2-hour period, but not after 4 P.M., also interfered with ovulation (Everett, 1956), and since electrical stimulation of the median eminence overcame the effect of pentobarbital (Critchlow, 1958), it was suggested that the critical period represented diurnal activation of hypothalamic centers which control the release of LH, and that it was this activation which was blocked by the drugs.

When LH release was blocked pharmacologically on the day of proestrus, the critical period was found to occur again 24 hours later (Everett and Sawyer, 1950). The LH release could be brought on prematurely in rats with 5-day estrous cycles by administering progesterone on the morning of the fourth day (Everett and Sawyer, 1949); this effect was also blocked by pentobarbital administered during the critical period. These observations have been taken as evidence that activation of the hypothalamic LH-releasing mechanism takes place daily, and not only on the day of proestrus; hence it is a true 24-hour rhythm. However, there is other evidence which suggests that this "diurnal" event may in fact be limited to only certain days of the estrous cycle. Critchlow and Sawyer (1955) found that on the day of proestrus there was a marked increase in the electrical activity of the preoptic area and the anterior hypothalamus for about 20 minutes between 2 and 4 P.M. This heightened electrical activity was *not* present on the days of diestrus or estrus. It has not been possible to demonstrate diurnal variations in the LH content of the pituitary (Schwartz and Bartosik, 1962) or the blood (Ramirez and McCann, 1964), except on the day of proestrus. It must be concluded that it has not yet been proved that a true diurnal rhythm, present each day of the estrous cycle, exists in the neural LH-release mechanism. Also, it has not been proved that the pharmacological blockade of ovulation by barbiturates and antiadrenergic or anticholinergic drugs operates solely at the level of the central nervous system.

b. Photic Control of the Critical Period. If such a diurnal rhythm exists, or even if this "neural clock" functions only on the day of proestrus, it provides one mechanism whereby the 24-hour light cycle could influence ovulatory rhythms. Hemmingsen and Krarup (1937) showed that estrus, a nocturnal event in the rat, could be made to occur in the daytime by shifting the hours of light exposure 12 hours. Several investigators have found that the period when ovulation can be blocked in proestrous rats by pentobarbital is not fixed, but is synchronized to environmental lighting. When the period of light exposure is moved forward several hours, the onset of the critical period is changed by an equal number of hours, after two or three estrous cycles.

Strauss and Meyer have examined the relationship between ambient lighting schedules and the release of "ovulating hormone" (presumed to be LH) in the immature rat treated with serum gonadotropin (PMS). If rats are given PMS on the thirtieth day of life, they usually ovulate 2½ days later, in the evening. This ovulation is presumably the consequence of a mechanism involving initial ovarian steroidogenesis, and subsequent stimulation of the brain and pituitary by circulating ovarian hormones. When rats were treated with pentobarbital on the afternoon of their thirty-second day, ovulation was completely blocked if the barbiturate was administered at 2 P.M., but proceeded normally if the animals were treated after 4 P.M. (Strauss and Meyer, 1962a). If the timing of the day-night cycle was shifted 5 hours, or if day and night were reversed, there was a corresponding shift in both the time of ovulation and the critical period, provided that the rats were exposed to the new lighting regimen for 6 days prior to receiving the PMS (Strauss and Meyer, 1962b). Exposure to constant darkness for several days prior to the administration of PMS did not change the time of the critical period, or the time of ovulation; its onset continued to be determined by the lighting schedule in use immediately prior to the start of darkness (Strauss and Meyer, 1964). When rats were kept in constant light, starting on the twenty-sixth day of life, and given PMS as usual, on the thirtieth day, the critical period and ovulation were delayed for 12–48 hours, and ovulation appeared to occur at random times during the day (Strauss, 1964). These authors concluded that there is an endogenous "clock" mechanism which regulates the time of pituitary release of ovulating hormone in the PMS-treated immature rat, as well as in the adult female. This rhythm has a period of approximately 24 hours, and is ordinarily synchronized by light. The relation of the ovulation clock to lighting appears to be similar in many ways to that of the adrenal clock (Section I,C), and to the pineal clock which regulates 5-hydroxytryptamine (serotonin) content but not hydroxyindole-*O*-methyl transferase (HIOMT) activity (Section V,D).

III. The Responses of Animals to Light

A. Direct Effects of Light

Photic stimuli influence the physiology and behavior of animals in a variety of ways. In some species, light acts directly on effector cells; it stimulates germ cell maturation in ascidians (Rose, 1939) and hydrozoans (Ballard, 1942), and enhances tyrosinase activity in the dermal melanocytes of some vertebrates (Rothman *et al.*, 1946), possibly by a direct effect on sulfhydryl bonds in the enzyme protein. In most animals, however, light stimulates only a small population of highly specialized photoreceptor cells located in the retina, in the dorsal diencephalon of some species (e.g., the pineal complex of frogs), and possibly in the hypothalamus of others (the duck).

B. Visual, Reflex, and "Neurovegetative" Functions of Light

Photic information serves at least three functions in higher animals: (1) it provides the raw material of the complex physiological-psychological phenomenon of vision; (2) it stimulates the optic autonomic reflexes, such as those regulating pupillary size, and (3) it controls, to an extent which varies among species, certain "neurovegetative functions" such as gonadal maturation and the endocrine rhythms described above. This last category is usually used to describe mechanisms which involve a direct neural-endocrine link. It should be recognized, however, that visual and reflex responses to light may also affect endocrine function, even though they directly involve only the neural apparatus. For example, it is well known that an isolated pigeon will not lay eggs unless it sees another pigeon, or its own reflection in a mirror (Matthews,

1939); the presence of the male accelerates estrogen release in the female canary (Warren and Hinde, 1961); and the sight of the brooding female can direct the synthesis of "crop milk" by the male dove (A. J. Marshall, 1961). It is possible that these phenomena are also influenced by olfactory or auditory stimuli. The endocrine role of light-induced alterations in sympathetic nervous tone is discussed in Section V,E.

Each of these three functions of light is subserved by a more or less specific neuroanatomic pathway. Full vision in mammals requires the integrity of the retinas, the optic nerves and tracts, the superior colliculi and lateral geniculate bodies, and the occipital cortex. The ocular reflexes remain intact in the absence of the geniculate bodies and the cortex, but are damaged following transection of the optic tracts or removal of the superior colliculi. It has been shown that the destruction of the optic tract does not block such "neurovegetative" effects of light as the stimulation of premature estrus in the ferret (le Gros Clarke *et al.*, 1939), or the induction of the "persistent estrus syndrome" in the rat (Critchlow, 1963). The neuroanatomic basis of the photic regulation of mammalian endocrine function is discussed in Section V,A.

C. Nonretinal Photoreceptors in Vertebrates

The dorsal diencephalic region of lower vertebrates contains a highly specialized photoreceptive apparatus, consisting of a saclike pineal organ or epiphysis, whose cavity is continuous with the brain ventricle, and a parapineal organ (also called the parietal organ, or Stirnorgan, in the frog), usually situated just beneath the skin. Electron- and light-microscopic studies have shown that this system contains subcellular photoreceptive elements indistinguishable from those found in the retina (Kelly, 1962), as well as ganglion cells (Oksche, 1955). By recording electrical impulses along the frog pineal nerve (i.e., the nerve from the Stirnorgan), Dodt and Heerd (1962) showed that this structure served as a wavelength discriminator. Electrical activity was stimulated by darkness or long wavelengths, and inhibited by white light or short wavelengths. The frog epiphyseal stalk is also photoreceptive. Photic stimulation of this region in animals deprived of a Stirnorgan depresses diencephalic electrical activity (Dodt and Jacobson, 1963).

The amphibian pineal complex is probably involved in endocrine function, but it is not clear whether its role is simply photoreceptive and neural, or whether it also serves as a gland. If the pineal complex of lizards is damaged or is shielded from light, the behavioral and thyroidal responses of the animal to cold are altered (Eakin *et al.*, 1959). The ability of *Xenopus* tadpoles to blanch upon exposure to darkness is blocked following pinealectomy (Bagnara, 1963). It has been suggested that this blockade is related to the inability of the operated animal to synthesize and secrete melatonin, a highly potent melanophore-lightening agent. [This compound is found in large quantities in mammalian pineal glands (Lerner *et al.*, 1959), and is produced only in this organ in mammals (Axelrod *et al.*, 1961).] The melatonin-forming enzyme, hydroxyindole-*O*-methyl transferase (HIOMT) is indeed present in the amphibian pineal; however it is not confined to this structure: HIOMT activity has also been identified in frog brain and eye (Axelrod *et al.*, 1965a). It has not yet been demonstrated that melatonin (or any other methoxyindole) is actually secreted into the circulation of the amphibian from *any* of its possible sites of synthesis. Hence it is not certain that pinealectomy would deprive the amphibian of a unique source of hormonal melatonin. The ability of the *mammalian* pineal to synthesize melatonin is controlled by environmental lighting; darkness increases (and light inhibits) HIOMT activity (Wurtman *et al.*, 1963b). However ambient lighting conditions appear to have no effect on melatonin synthesis in the amphibian (R. J. Wurtman, unpublished observations, 1966). The morphology of the pineal changes dramatically with phylogenetic development. In mammals, the pineal has lost virtually all of its photoreceptor elements (Kelly, 1962), and instead contains cells whose appearance suggests a secretory function. The relation of the mammalian pineal to light and endocrine function is described in Section V,D and in Chapter 32.

Benoit (1961) and Benoit and Assenmacher (1959) found that if light was projected directly upon the hypothalamus of blinded ducks by a quartz rod implanted in the eye socket, or if these birds were placed in very strong room light, they responded by developing testicular hypertrophy. He concluded that the hypothalamus of the duck contains a photoreceptor, and that the response of this receptor to the long-wavelength light rays which normally penetrate the skull is involved in mediating the "photosexual reflex."

It has not been possible to demonstrate an effect of environmental lighting on the gonads of blinded mammals. Ganong *et al.* (1963) demonstrated that measurable quantities of natural light do penetrate into the mammalian brain. Photic energy reaching the hypothalamus was attenuated 10^{-6}–10^{-9}-fold by the skull and soft tissues of the sheep, dog, and rabbit. The degree of attenuation could not be determined precisely in the single rat studied, but was probably of the order of 10^{-3}. Lisk and Kannwischer (1964) reported that if artificial light was allowed to impinge directly on the suprachiasmatic region of blinded rats, by means of glass rods implanted stereotaxically in individual hypothalamic neurons, the incidence of vaginal smears showing estrous phases was moderately elevated (80%, compared to 62% in similarly prepared animals whose glass rods were shielded from the light by dental cement). The presence of light in this region of the hypothalamus for short periods did not influence the weight of the ovary or pituitary. Six weeks of continuous light exposure did produce ovarian enlargement when the glass rods were placed in the arcuate nuclei; the incidence of estrus among these animals was only 48%.

In view of the extensive evidence that electrical stimulation of the anterior hypothalamus influences the secretion of gonadotropins, it is not surprising that the application of *energy*, per se, to impaled hypothalamic neurons should affect ovary growth and function. It remains to be determined whether the gonadal changes described by Lisk and Kannwischer (1964) were simply the consequence of the local application of heat to hyperexcitable neurons, or bore a specific relationship to light. The nonspecificity of this response is suggested by the apparent absence of photopigments or morphological photoreceptor units in the anterior hypothalamus, and by the fact that the exposure of blinded rats to even very intense light has not been reported to produce ovarian changes. Such changes would be expected if the attenuation of light through the rat cranium were of the order indicated by Ganong and coworkers (1963) and if functioning hypothalamic photoreceptors existed in this species.

IV. Methods Used to Study the Endocrine Effects of Light, and Common Problems in the Interpretation of Data

A. General Methods

In general, studies of the relations between ambient lighting and endocrine function have been concerned with two distinct phenomena: (1) the ability of experimental lighting conditions to *perturb* endocrine function, and (2) the likelihood that natural lighting cycles participate in the *physiological regulation* of several glands (i.e., the onset of gonadal maturation, the synchrony of adrenal rhythms). In the former case, animals have been maintained under a standardized lighting stress, such as continuous light or dark, or multiple on-off periods per day. This has generated a reproducible endocrine response such as the adrenal-dependent eosinopenia of dark-adapted rats and humans placed in bright light (Radnot *et al.*, 1962), or the persistent estrus syndrome of rats kept in constant light. The endocrine response has then been used as a "model system" for the study of the mechanisms involved.

In the latter case, it has been necessary to show that some naturally occurring change in the level of endocrine function ordinarily depends upon the response of the animal to its particular lighting schedule. This has usually been demonstrated by altering the "lighting geography" of the animal—that is, by changing the daily length of light exposure, or the time the light photoperiod starts, to one that could conceivably exist at another point in the animal's history—and observing that, as a consequence, gonadal maturation takes place prematurely, or that endocrine rhythms become "entrained" to the new lighting schedule (Sections I,A and I,C).

Modifications of these two methods of applying experimental lighting have formed the basis for most of the studies on photic-neuroendocrine interactions reported to date. Once the reproducibility of either type of endocrine response has been demonstrated, the persistence of the ability to respond has been tested following various experimental procedures, such as lesions, drug and hormone treatment, or application of monochromatic lighting.

B. Experimental Pitfalls: Other Environmental Cues and Activity Rhythms, Selection of Controls, Problems of Sampling

It has often proved difficult to devise experiments on the mechanisms of photic effects on endocrine function which could yield unambiguous information. There are a number of common pitfalls encountered in experimental design and in the interpretation of data. It is possible that external stimuli other than light (i.e., sound, smell, temperature or humidity, presence of food, or other animals) are providing the relevant cue to the neuroendocrine apparatus. Thus, olfactory stimuli from males of a slightly different strain can block implantation in mice (Bruce, 1959), and cyclic variations in environmental noise or odors, or in the time of feeding, can "drive" the adrenal secretory rhythm (Halberg *et al.*, 1954). It is possible that light primarily influences the level of muscular activity, and that this nonspecifically stimulates adrenal and gonadal function. This hypothesis was first suggested by Rowan (1938), who noted that enforced activity (jumping to avoid a swinging bar) was associated with premature gonadal development in a few juncos. More recent studies on activity rhythms in mammals, and their relation to environmental lighting, have been reviewed by Aschoff (1960).

In most species, voluntary motor activity is concentrated in a 12-hour period, the onset of which is related to day or night; thus rats and hamsters are nocturnally active animals, humans and most birds are diurnal, and mice may be either. Aschoff (1960) has characterized these activity cycles by three parameters: the ratio of active time to rest time, the total activity per period, usually measured by the distance run in an activity cage, and the length of the total active-rest cycle, or its inverse, the frequency of cycles. In animals active in light, increased illumination leads to more active time per cycle, greater total activity, and more frequent cycles. Among nocturnal animals, light has the opposite, and darkness the same, effects. Thus, when rats, a nocturnal species, are kept in constant light, the period of each running cycle increases by about 45 minutes per day (Folk, 1959). After 16 days of constant illumination, the time of onset of the daily activity period has shifted a full 12 hours. Aschoff (1958) noted an opposite effect of light on cycle length in birds. Activity rhythms persist following blinding; this suggests either that they are truly "endogenous," or that they can be synchronized to a hierarchy of known and unknown external "Zeitgebern" which have a periodicity of about 24 hours.

In general, changes in light exposure which alter circadian endocrine rhythms exert a parallel influence on activity rhythms; hence it is likely that some components of both mechanisms are shared. This does not necessarily imply that light-induced changes in endocrine function *depend on* alterations in activity cycles, as has been suggested. Hammond (1954) and others have summarized the evidence against this hypothesis: (1) in no experimental situation thus far described has it been possible to induce precocious puberty by an external stimulus operating in darkness; (2) in some species, light alters the activity rhythm without influencing endocrine cycles, whereas in others it produces the opposite effects; (3) high ambient temperatures greatly increase the activity of the white-crowned sparrow, but have little or no effect on gonad growth; low temperatures depress muscular activity, but do not interfere with the gonadal response to added light (Farner *et al.*, 1953); (4) F. H. A. Marshall (1942) pointed out that ferrets used in the winter for fowling remain in diestrus, in spite of their high level of activity, whereas other animals kept in cages develop premature estrus if exposed to extra lighting; (5) Bissonette (1933), unlike Rowan (1925), found no gonadal activation in birds subjected to a forced increase in activity, although light was an effective stimulus to other birds trussed up in cages; (6) Holmquest and his collaborators (1966) showed that, when rats were exposed to a random lighting schedule, 24-hour rhythms in adrenal and plasma corticosterone levels persisted long after activity rhythms were extinguished. Finally, at least one surgical procedure (bilateral superior cervical ganglionectomy in the rat) blocks the early effects of light on gonad cycles but has no effect on either the normal activity cycle or its perturbation by constant light (R. J. Wurtman, unpublished observations, 1964). The relation between activity and adrenal secretion is discussed in Sections V,B, and V.E.

Frequently, investigators have utilized individual animals as their own controls in studying the effects of experimental procedures on the capacity of an endocrine function to respond to light. Animals have been exposed to light for a period (e.g., the time necessary for a full estrous response in the ferret), and then "good responders" have been selected out, subjected to surgical or other procedures, and tested again for their light response. This type of experimental design can yield misleading data, for several reasons. First, there is good evidence that the gonadal responses of rats (Critchlow, 1963), ferrets (Van der Werff ten Bosch, 1963), and mink (*Mustela*) (Hammond, 1951) to light are conditioned by the age of the animal, the season of the year, and the duration of the animal's domestication. Most birds, and possibly some mammals, demonstrate a seasonal "refractory period" to light. For instance, the gonads of the white-crowned sparrow regress in late summer, even though the bird is still in an environment of long days (see Farner, 1962). The assumption that the responses of the same animal to a given light stimulus at two different times are comparable is open to question. Second, the use of only "good responders" is statistically unsound. It practically ensures that the conclusions will be applicable to only a segment of the population, and it may mask meaningful phenomena. If the distribution curve of the endocrine response under study happens to be bi- or triphasic, whole populations are omitted from the study. Even if the curve is normally distributed, there is no guarantee that animals whose first response to light places them in one "tail" of the curve would still be found in that "tail" on subsequent tests. Hence it is probable that almost any procedure being tested for its ability to block the light effect will appear to work.

If blinding changed the period of a particular circadian rhythm from 24 to 25 hours (by blocking the effect of the photic "Zeitgeber"), and if maxima and minima had previously occurred at noon and midnight, it is apparent that continued sampling of the blind group only at these two times would make it appear, 6 days after blinding, that the rhythm had become extinct when in fact it might still be present but shifted 6 hours. Similarly, the response of the rat ovary to light is multiphasic (Fiske, 1941); ovarian weight is increased after 1–2 months' exposure to constant light, depressed after 6 months, and about the same as that of rats kept in darkness in the intervening months. If the relation between constant light and rat ovary weight were studied only after 3 months, it might be concluded that light had no effect on the ovary.

V. Mechanisms by Which Light Influences Selected Neuroendocrine Functions

A. Neural Pathways Involved in the Interaction of Light and the Mammalian Gonad

The only photoreceptive structure definitely known to function in the mammal is the retina (see Section III,C). Impulses generated by photic stimuli are transmitted via the optic nerves to the optic chiasm, where a large fraction of the nerve fibers decussate. Caudal to the chiasm, most of the light information travels with the "classic" optic tracts to the superior colliculus, pretectal nuclei, and lateral geniculate bodies, and then to the occipital cortex. At least four other nerve bundles have been described which may transmit photic information in mammals. These fibers, referred to collectively as the "accessory optic system," are the posterior accessory optic tract, the transpeduncular tract, the anterior accessory optic tract, and direct retinal-hypothalamic fibers. The posterior accessory optic tract (Marburg, 1903) leaves the main optic tract just before the lateral geniculate body and passes over the cerebral peduncles to a nucleus in the tegmentum of the midbrain. This tract has been described in primates, as well as in carnivores and rodents. The transpeduncular tract (Gudden, 1870) departs from the optic tract at the level of the superior colliculi and then courses over the cerebral peduncles to follow a path similar to that described for the posterior optic tract. The anterior accessory optic tract (Bochenek, 1908) leaves the optic tract just after the optic chiasm and then travels through the cerebral peduncle to Bochenek's nucleus, in the ventral tegmental-subthalamic region. This tract has been identified in rats and cats (Hayhow, 1959; Hayhow *et al.*, 1960). Direct retinal-hypothalamic connections were described by Krieg (1932), who delineated a paramedian fiber group which emerged from the caudal border of the optic chiasm and entered the infundibular region of the rat hypothalamus. Frey (1937) claimed to find evidence of a similar tract, the "hypothalamic optic root," in the guinea pig. Most subsequent workers have failed to support these earlier claims. Bilateral orbital enucleation in the rat failed to produce a significant decrease in the number of fibers in Frey's optic root (Nauta, 1943). Bodian (1940) believed that this tract was really an intrahypothalamic fiber bundle, whose longitudinal course brought it in close contact with the dorsal surface of the optic chiasm. Direct connections between the optic tract and the supraoptic and suprachiasmatic nuclei of rats were described by Rieke (1958), but this observation has not been confirmed. Knoche (1957) described a tract that left the optic chiasm in several mammals, and then passed on to the paraventricular nucleus, the arcuate nucleus, and the neural lobe of the pituitary. The presence of this tract could not be confirmed in the cat (Hayhow, 1959). At the present time, it must be concluded that the evidence for tracts which carry light information directly from the mammalian retina to the hypothalamus is inadequate. Before such pathways are accepted as proved, they should be demonstrated by electrophysiological studies (e.g., their electrical activity should be rapidly altered following photic stimulation of the retina).

In order to demonstrate that a particular neural locus is part of the special pathway that mediates an endocrine effect of light, it should be necessary to show that destruction of that locus blocks the light effect without interfering with normal endocrine function. Such a lesion is orbital enucleation; blind ferrets generally come into estrus at the normal time of the year, whether or not they are exposed to added lighting, and blind rats can have normal estrous cycles, but do not develop the "persistent estrus syndrome" when exposed to extra lighting. No intracranial lesion has yet been described which satisfies this criterion. On the other hand, it is clear that all or most of the "classic" radiations posterior to the optic chiasm can be destroyed without interfering with gonadal effect of light in the ferret (le Gros Clarke *et al.*, 1939) and the rat (Critchlow, 1963). It may be inferred that the neuroendocrine effects of light depend upon information which leaves the optic tract in the region of the chiasm. It is possible, but certainly not proved, that it is transmitted by the anterior accessory optic tract described above.

It is probable that light information from the retinas eventually finds its way to the hypothalamus; it has been shown that the long-term exposure of female rats to continuous light is associated with morphological changes in the supraoptic nucleus (Fiske and Greep, 1959). These changes were thought to be related to the effects of light on the ovary. However, the supraoptic nucleus is not currently believed to play a significant role in rat ovarian function, and the only time that brains were examined (after 8 weeks of lighting) was long after the ovarian effects of light usually appear (see Section V,C). Once in the hypothalamus, light information could either be converted directly to an endocrine output (e.g., it could influence the release of the hypothalamic neurohumors which control secretion from the pituitary), or it could be transmitted neurally to other neuroendocrine effector organs. Two such organs are the adrenal medulla and the pineal gland. Both are regulated by a sympathetic nervous input which the hypothalamus modulates, in its capacity as the "chief ganglion" of the autonomic nervous system. It can be anticipated that more information will become available in the next decade on how lights acts on the neural arm of the neuroendocrine apparatus, as improved neurochemical and neuropharmacological techniques are applied to this study.

B. Light and Adrenal Secretion in the Mammal

The 24-hour rhythms in adrenal glucocorticoid secretion and in consequent metabolic phenomena, such as the blood eosinophile level, have already been described (Sections I,C and II,B,2), and it has been shown that, although these rhythms are ordinarily tied to the day-night light cycle, they can persist in the absence of such cycles. Bartter *et al.*, have described a diurnal cycle in aldosterone secretion (1962) which is thought to be influenced by, but not dependent on, diurnal postural changes. The neural centers which control both the endogenous adrenal rhythm and its response to photic cues are largely unknown. Migeon *et al.* (1956) reported that the diurnal adrenal rhythm persisted in blind subjects, but Landau and Feldman (1954) observed a marked decrease in morning eosinopenia in similar patients. The adrenal rhythm has been found to persist in bed-ridden patients after one year of near-total inactivity (Perkoff *et al.*, 1959); hence it is not dependent upon activity rhythms. Diurnal changes in pituitary adrenocorticotropic hormone (ACTH) release appear to be independent of the blood glucocorticoid feedback apparatus (Graber *et al.*, 1964). In the female rat, continuous light is associated with a decrease in adrenal weight (Fiske and Lambert, 1962). This decrease has been attributed (Critchlow, 1963) to the loss of the 24-hour rhythm in ACTH release (Halberg, 1953). In males, both adrenal weight and the amplitude of the daily rhythm in glucocorticoid secretion are less than in females; constant light has little effect on either.

C. Light and Gonad Function in Monoestrous and Polyestrous Mammals

1. *Monoestrous Mammals*

Extra light can induce premature gonadal development in many birds and monoestrous mammals (Table II), although at least one such animal, the ferret, does not appear to be dependent upon a response to environmental lighting for gonad growth (Section I,B). The relation between lighting and the avian gonad is discussed in detail in Chapter 30.

In 1954, Abrams and his collaborators showed that the removal of both superior cervical ganglia blocked the estrous response of the ferret to light. This effect was confirmed by Donovan and Van der Werff ten Bosch (1956), who suggested that it was a consequence of the ptosis which followed sympathectomy. They argued that the fallen eyelids diminished the amount of light impinging on the retina to an intensity which was below a critical level. Subsequently, W. A. Marshall (1962) showed that ptosis was not the cause of the sympathectomy effect, since surgical removal of the eyelids did not restore the capacity of the ferret to respond to light, and sewing the lateral lids shut did not block the gonad effect in unoperated animals. Marshall conjectured that sympathectomy blocked the transmission of the light stimulus to some critical endocrine organ. This organ was shown not to be the thyroid (W. A. Marshall, 1963). On the basis of studies in the rat described below (Section V,D), it is possible that it may be the pineal gland.

2. *Polyestrous Animals*

When immature female rats are grown in an environment of continuous light, gonadal maturation, as indicated by vaginal opening, occurs earlier than in animals reared in normal light (Fiske, 1941). When groups of young adults are placed in constant light, the incidence of daily vaginal smears showing estrous phases increases rapidly. Within 7–10 days, it rises from 45% to 70–90% (Wurtman *et al.*, 1964b). Among individual animals, there is a good deal of variation in the vaginal response to illumination. Some show only estrous smears for long periods (hence this phenomenon has been termed the persistent estrus syndrome). Others continue to have vaginal estrous cycles, but the estrous phase is prolonged. Still others show no vaginal response, or even prolonged diestrus. There appears to be an imperfect correlation between estrous vaginal smears in light-treated rats and the presence or absence of ovulation (I. Lawton and N. B. Schwartz, personal communication, 1965); hence the significance of this phenomenon in reproductive physiology is difficult to assess. Nonetheless, it is reproducible, and has lent itself to use as a model system for the study of light-gonad interactions.

When animals are exposed to light for relatively short periods (1–3 months, depending on their age), ovarian weight is increased; this stimulation has been termed the early effect of light. Exposure for longer periods leads to a depression in ovarian weight, if the animals are compared to littermates kept in normal light or darkness (Fiske,

1941). Increases in pituitary weight and gonadotropin content (Lawton and Schwartz, 1965), and in uterine weight, also characterize the early response. These effects also disappear after prolonged light exposure (Maric *et al.*, 1965). Critchlow (1963) suggested that the apparent fall in follicle-stimulating hormone (FSH) secretion and the consequent ovarian atrophy in rats kept in light for long periods were the result of a feedback response to continued high levels of estrogen secretion. Evidence that circulating estrogen levels are persistently elevated in light-exposed rats is lacking, as is a precedent for a gonadal feedback which requires several months to operate.

It has been postulated (Critchlow, 1963) that the effects of light on the rat ovary are mediated by direct retinal-hypothalamic fibers, and that in the hypothalamus this information controls the release of neurohumors which regulate gonadotropin secretion via the hypophyseal portal system. Critchlow found that, in thirteen of twenty-three animals that had been preselected as "good light responders," electrolytic lesions of the brain which damaged the medial preoptic region, the suprachiasmatic nuclei, and the optic chiasm partly blocked the vaginal response to light. The other ten animals were discarded from the study because they showed persistent vaginal estrus even without being exposed to light. Interpretation of this lesion data is complicated by the fact that the animals were preselected both before and after surgery, and by the evidence that the lesions alone interfered with normal vaginal cycling. McCann and Ramirez (1964) have found that continuous light differs from suprachiasmatic lesions in that it does not block the elevation in plasma LH levels which follows castration in the rat. Bilateral superior cervical ganglionectomy blocks the early effect of continuous light on the vaginal cytology (Wurtman *et al.*, 1964b), but not the persistent estrous state seen after 2–4 months of illumination. It is thus possible that the increase in estrous smears seen after relatively short periods of light results from the operation of one physiologic mechanism, and the vaginal changes (and decline in pituitary gonadotropins) seen after prolonged treatment result from another. It is possible that the early effect of light on the rat gonad may be mediated in part by the pineal gland and the sympathetic nervous system; this is discussed in Section V,D.

Early blindness due to orbital pathology is associated with premature menarche in humans; this effect is exaggerated when the blindness is accompanied by loss of light perception (Zacharias and Wurtman, 1964). Chronic blindness has also been reported to decrease the size of the human sella turcica (Hollwich, 1955). It is noteworthy that the human, a day-active animal, responds to blinding with earlier gonadal development, whereas the rat, a nocturnal species, shows delayed maturation (Browman, 1940).

D. Light and the Mammalian Pineal Gland

The remarkable shift from photoreceptor to glandular structure seen in the phylogenetic development of the pineal has already been described (Section III,C). In the mammal, the pineal retains its responsiveness to environmental lighting, but it now receives information about the state of the environment indirectly, via a neural pathway involving the retina, the brain, and the peripheral sympathetic nervous system. The mammalian pineal gland appears to be a highly specialized "factory" for making methoxyindoles; it may also have other functions (see Chapter 32). Several steps in pineal methoxyindole synthesis have been shown to be influenced by light (Fig. 1). Prolonged illumination increases the activity of 5-hydroxytryptophan decarboxylase (5-HTPD), the enzyme which makes serotonin, (Snyder *et al.*, 1964), and decreases the activity of hydroxyindole-*O*-methyl transferase (HIOMT), the melatonin-forming enzyme (Wurtman *et al.*, 1963b). It also depresses pineal weight (Fiske *et al.*, 1960), and the levels of serotonin (Quay and Halevy, 1962) and melatonin (Quay, 1964) in this organ. The most important effect of light is probably on the *O*-methylating enzyme (HIOMT), since this enzyme is found only in the pineal (Axelrod *et al.*, 1961), and probably rate-limits the biosynthesis of methoxyindoles such as melatonin and methoxytryptophol (Wurtman *et al.*, 1963b). Both of these compounds have been shown to influence the rat ovary (Chu *et al.*, 1964; McIsaac *et al.*, 1964); melatonin has also been shown to be released from the mammalian pineal (Barchas and Lerner, 1964), and to be concentrated within endocrine glands, especially the ovary and pituitary (Wurtman *et al.*, 1963a, 1964c), and taken up by the brain.

There is a diurnal cycle in HIOMT activity, as long as rats are maintained on a physiological lighting schedule. The activity of this enzyme rises two- to threefold during the 5 hours after the daily onset of darkness (Axelrod *et al.*, 1965b). If, however, animals are blinded, kept in continuous darkness, or even deprived of a single photoperiod of darkness, the daily rhythm in HIOMT activity is completely abolished. Hence it may be conjectured that this rhythm is truly "exogenous." When rats are placed in continuous light or darkness, the diurnal changes in HIOMT activity are exaggerated. Enzyme activity in dark-treated animals may rise to 4–10 times that of littermates kept in light (Wurtman *et al.*, 1963b; Wurtman and Axelrod, 1965). The content of serotonin in the pineal also varies diurnally (Quay, 1963), falling

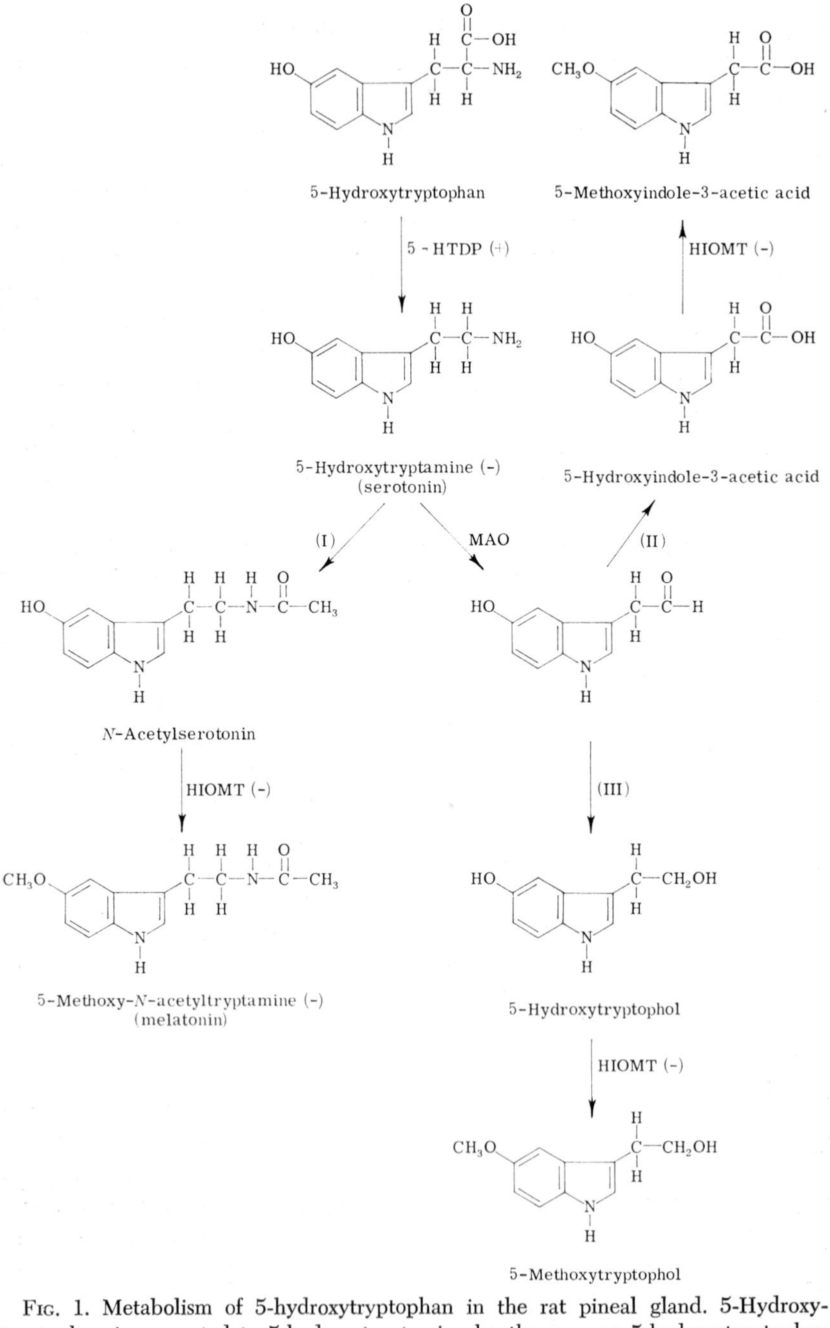

5-Hydroxytryptophan

5-HTDP (+)

5-Hydroxytryptamine (-)
(serotonin)

(I)

N-Acetylserotonin

HIOMT (-)

5-Methoxy-N-acetyltryptamine (-)
(melatonin)

MAO

(III)

5-Hydroxytryptophol

HIOMT (-)

5-Methoxytryptophol

(II)

5-Hydroxyindole-3-acetic acid

HIOMT (-)

5-Methoxyindole-3-acetic acid

FIG. 1. Metabolism of 5-hydroxytryptophan in the rat pineal gland. 5-Hydroxytryptophan is converted to 5-hydroxytryptamine by the enzyme 5-hydroxytryptophan sharply at the same time that HIOMT activity is rising. The serotonin rhythm is the consequence of cyclic alterations in the release of the amine from its binding sites within the pineal (Snyder and Axelrod, 1965). Some of the serotonin released after the onset of darkness is acetylated to form *N*-acetylserotonin (see Fig. 1); this compound is an excellent substrate for HIOMT, which converts it to melatonin.

In 1960, Kappers showed that, although the rat pineal derives embryologically from the roof of the third ventricle, its innervation in the adult is largely, if not entirely, sympathetic, consisting of fibers which originate in the superior cervical ganglia. Studies were subsequently undertaken to determine whether information about the state of lighting was transmitted to the pineal via this neural route. It was found that bilateral superior cervical ganglionectomy, like blinding, completely extinguished the 24-hour HIOMT cycle (Axelrod *et al.*, 1965b) and the ability of this enzyme to respond to continuous illumination (Wurtman *et al.*, 1964b). The removal of various endocrine glands was without effect on HIOMT. The rise in HIOMT activity in darkness was also inhibited by treatment with actinomycin D or puromycin (Axelrod *et al.*, 1965b), two drugs which block DNA-dependent protein synthesis. On the basis of these studies, it appears likely that light, perceived by the retina, regulates the activity of the sympathetic nerves to the pineal. These nerves then release a neurotransmitter (i.e., norepinephrine or serotonin) which controls the formation of HIOMT in the pineal (Wolfe *et al.*, 1962). This enzyme, in turn, controls melatonin synthesis.

The tracts in the brain which carry information about lighting from the retina to the central portion of the sympathetic nervous system are not fully known, but appear to include the medial forebrain bundle, a major component of the limbic system. The effect of light on the pineal, like the effect on the gonads, is not lost following transection of the optic tracts (Axelrod, J., Snyder, S. H., Wurtman, R. J., Heller, A., and Moore, R. Y., unpublished observations, 1966).

Interference with the sympathetic innervation of the pineal also blocks

---

decarboxylase (5-HTPD); this enzyme is probably the same as dopa decarboxylase. 5-Hydroxytryptamine (serotonin) is metabolized in the rat pineal by two pathways. Part of it is *N*-acetylated by a ubiquitous enzyme (I) to *N*-acetylserotonin, which is converted to 5-methoxy-*N*-acetyltryptamine (melatonin) by hydroxyindole-*O*-methyl transferase (HIOMT). Another fraction of the pineal serotonin is deaminated by monoamine oxidase (MAO), and then either oxidized to 5-hydroxyindole acetic acid (II) or reduced to 5-hydroxytryptophol (III). Both of these compounds may be converted to the corresponding methoxyindole by HIOMT. The plus (+) or minus (−) signs in parentheses describe the effects of continuous illumination on the enzyme or compound in the pineal.

the effect of continuous light on pineal weight (Wurtman *et al.*, 1964a) and 5-HTPD activity (Snyder *et al.*, 1965). These effects may be obtained by destroying the superior cervical ganglia, or simply by decentralizing them (i.e., cutting the preganglionic fibers from the spinal cord to the superior cervical ganglia).

When rats are blinded, the diurnal cycle in pineal serotonin content persists, even though this amine can no longer be influenced by continuous light or darkness (Snyder *et al.*, 1965). Cyclic biochemical processes in the rat pineal thus appear to be regulated by two kinds of mechanisms: a completely exogenous control system (e.g., the one regulating HIOMT activity), which depends upon neural stimuli triggered by day-night lighting shifts, and an endogenous system (e.g., serotonin content), which may be circadian, and which can function in the absence of rhythmic photic impulses, but is ordinarily entrained by environmental light. Both mechanisms operate via a sympathetic nervous route. It has recently been observed that the amount of the sympathetic neurotransmitter norepinephrine in the rat pineal also varies with a 24-hour cycle (Wurtman and Axelrod, 1966). Pineal norepinephrine levels rise during the dark period and reach their nadir at the end of the light period. This rhythm also appears to be exogenous.

The ability of light to inhibit methoxyindole synthesis in the pineal may be related to some of its effects on the rat ovary. When the light-induced decrease in pineal HIOMT activity is blocked by superior cervical ganglionectomy, the early effect of light on the vaginal estrous cycle is also lost (Wurtman *et al.*, 1964b), even though these ganglia do not innervate the gonads. This observation is consistent with the blocking effect of cervical ganglionectomy on the premature estrus which can be induced in ferrets by light (Section V,C,1) (Abrams *et al.*, 1954), and suggests that the sympathetic nervous system may participate in the environmental control of gonad function in several species.

The melatonin-forming enzyme in the monkey pineal varies with a 24-hour cycle which is similar to that described in the rat (Quay, 1966). Light appears to *stimulate* pineal HIOMT in the hen (Axelrod *et al.*, 1964).

E. Light, the Sympathetic Nervous System, and Renal Function

The path by which light influences pineal weight and serotonin content, and the activity of several pineal enzymes, has been shown to involve the sympathetic nervous system. Activation of the sympathetic nervous system by any stimulus probably results in neural discharge in more than one end organ. It is thus possible that light, acting via the retina, modifies the tone of a large portion of the sympathetic nervous system. This hypothesis is consistent with the 24-hour rhythm in pineal norepinephrine content described above, and with observations on the effect of blindness on the diurnal cycle of urinary catecholamine excretion. In the study of Januszewicz and Wocial (1960), the day was divided into three intervals: 10 P.M. to 6 A.M., when all subjects slept; 6 A.M. to 2 P.M., when all engaged in limited activity; and 2 P.M. to 10 P.M., a period of full activity. Normal subjects excreted an average of 2, 8, and 12 μg of norepinephrine in each of the test periods. Convalescent patients, who remained in bed all day, excreted 2, 5, and 8 μg. Blind patients, pair-matched for activity with their controls, excreted 7, 6, and 7 μg. Since most of the norepinephrine in the urine originates in sympathetic nerve endings (Wurtman, 1966), these data can be interpreted as indicating that the "tone" of at least a portion of the human sympathetic nervous system responds to environmental lighting, mediated via the retina.

The demonstration that environmental lighting influences sympathetic nervous discharge may help to explain the mechanisms of the well-known diurnal rhythms in human renal function. It has been recognized for some time that the volume of urine formed per hour is markedly diminished at night. Sodium, chloride, bicarbonate, and water clearances all vary diurnally in a parallel fashion (Stanbury and Thomson, 1951). Potassium excretion generally follows the same pattern, but is more variable, perhaps because of its extreme sensitivity to changes in the level of circulating mineralocorticoids. Several theories have been advanced to explain these phenomena. One holds that the rhythms are a consequence of diurnal cycles of orthostasis and activity. This hypothesis is not consistent with the observation that they persist in subjects who are deprived of sleep and forced to continue physical activity at night (Stanbury and Thomson, 1951), but are largely extinguished in blind people without light perception who maintain normal activity (Lobban and Tredre, 1964). The rhythms have also been said to be a consequence of the diurnal adrenal secretory cycle. They have been found to be absent in some Addisonian patients, but have clearly persisted in others (Garrod and Burston, 1952), including at least one patient who was subjected to bilateral adrenalectomy (Nabarro, 1956). The administration of ACTH did not interfere with the rhythms in normal subjects (Stanbury and Thomson, 1951). The sodium-excretion rhythm is clearly 180° out of phase with the rhythm in aldosterone secretion—i.e., at a time when blood mineralocorticoid levels are rising, sodium is being excreted, not retained (Bartter *et al.*, 1962). A third theory holds that the rhythms are a consequence of the 24-hour lighting cycle. Borst and DeVries (1950) observed that the excretion of chloride between 6 and 9 A.M. was higher in summer than in winter in hospitalized patients on a standardized activity regimen. They attributed this to the earlier appearance of sunlight on the ward in the summer. Sharp (1960) found that the morning rises in urine flow and sodium and potassium excretion could be blocked in normal subjects on a standard activity regimen if they were blindfolded and kept in darkness. When the subjects were exposed to light 3 hours later, cyclic renal function rapidly returned to normal. Martel *et al.* (1962) studied the amount of time required for adrenal and renal rhythms in young men to become synchronized to a 12-hour shift in lighting. They found that the shift in sodium excretion was complete within 4 days. Glomerular filtration (creatinine clearance) and water excretion required 5–6 days to resynchronize, whereas urinary ketogenic steroid output (presumed to be a measure of cortisol secretion) did not shift during 8 days of exposure to the new lighting conditions. They concluded that light controls the renal rhythms of salt and water excretion, and that its influence is not mediated by the adrenal cortex.

The autonomic nervous system participates in the regulation of renal blood flow (Balint *et al.*, 1952; Nahmod and Lanari, 1964; Kamm and Levinsky, 1965). It is possible that diurnal, light-induced variations in sympathetic motor tone may alter renal blood flow and glomerular filtration, or the distribution of blood within the kidney. These alterations could conceivably bring about the diurnal rhythms in water, and perhaps sodium excretion.

VI. Summary

In the 40 years since the discovery that the annual pattern of avian testicular activation could be induced prematurely by exposing juncos to artificial long days, a large body of evidence has accumulated showing that environmental lighting influences endocrine function. Continuous exposure to light alters the rate of sexual maturation in many mammals. It also interferes with normal ovarian periodicity in both monoestrous and polyestrous species. Constant darkness or blindness frequently has opposite effects. The natural lighting cycle of day and night serves as a "Zeitgeber," or synchronizer, of a variety of circadian biological rhythms, including those of adrenal steroid secretion, renal excretion of salt and water, and pineal serotonin content, as well as the time during the day of proestrus that the hypothalamic LH-release mechanism is activated. In addition, this daily lighting cycle may be the direct cause of 24-hour rhythms in pineal hydroxyindole-*O*-methyl transferase activity, and perhaps in sympathetic nervous "tone."

The entire spectrum of visible light appears to activate neuroendocrine photoreceptors. The intensity of photic energy required is well within the level provided by sunlight or by the artificial light sources in general use. The retina probably contains the only neuroendocrine photoreceptors of physiological significance in the mammal, although there is evidence that under laboratory conditions, stimulation of the hypothalamus by transmitted light can influence ovarian function in blinded animals. In lower vertebrates, the activity of the pineal region responds directly to light. In rodents, light continues to exert a marked influence on pineal function, but by an indirect neural route involving the sympathetic innervation of this gland. The neural pathway by which photic information influences hypothalamo-hypophyseal function must involve an accessory optic tract, but its precise location is not known.

Acknowledgment

The author acknowledges with thanks the assistance of Drs. Leona Zacharias, Julius Axelrod, and Walle Nauta, who made helpful criticisms of this manuscript.

References

Abrams, M. E., Marshall, W. A., and Thomson, A. P. D. (1954). Effect of cervical sympathectomy on the onset of oestrus in ferrets. *Nature* **174,** 311.

Allanson, M., and Deanesley, R. (1934). Reaction of anoestrus hedgehogs to experimental conditions. *Proc. Roy. Soc.* **B116,** 170–185.

Aschoff, J. (1958). Tierische Periodik unter dem Einfluss von Zeitgebern. *Z. Tierpsychol.* **15,** 1–30.

Aschoff, J. (1960). Exogenous and endogenous components in circadian rhythms. *Cold Spring Harbor Symp. Quant. Biol.* **25,** 11–28.

Axelrod, J., MacLean, R. D., Albers, R. W., and Weissbach, H. (1961). Regional distribution of methyl transferase enzymes in the nervous system and glandular tissues. *In* "Regional Neurochemistry" (S. S. Kety and J. Elkes, eds.), pp. 307–311. Pergamon Press, Oxford.

Axelrod, J., Wurtman, R. J., and Winget, C. M. (1964). Melatonin synthesis in the hen pineal gland and its control by light. *Nature* **201,** 1134.

Axelrod, J., Quay, W. B., and Baker, P. C. (1965a). Enzymatic synthesis of the skin-lightening agent, melatonin, in amphibians. *Nature* **208,** 386.

Axelrod, J., Wurtman, R. J., and Snyder, S. H. (1965b). Control of hydroxyindole-*O*-methyl transferase activity in the rat pineal gland by environmental lighting. *J. Biol. Chem.* **240,** 949–954.

Bagnara, J. T. (1963). The pineal and the body lightening reaction of larval amphibians. *Gen. Comp. Endocrinol.* **3,** 86–100.

Baker, J. R., and Ranson, R. M. (1932). Factors affecting the breeding of the field mouse (*Microtus agrestis*). *Proc. Roy. Soc.* **B110,** 313–322.

Bakke, J. L., and Lawrence, N. (1965). Circadian periodicity in thyroid stimulating hormone titer in the rat hypophysis and serum. *Metabolism* **14,** 841–843.

Balint, P., Fekete, A., and Szalay, Z. S. (1952). The nervous regulation of renal adaptation. *Acta Physiol. Acad. Sci. Hung.* **10,** 263–276.

Ballard, W. W. (1942). The mechanism for synchronous spawning in hydractinia and pennaria. *Biol. Bull.* **82,** 329–339.

Barchas, J. D., and Lerner, A. B. (1964). Localization of melatonin in the nervous system. *J. Neurochem.* **11,** 489–491.

Barnum, C. P., Jardetzky, C. O., and Halberg, F. (1958). Time relations among metabolic and morphologic 24-hour changes in mouse liver. *Am. J. Physiol.* **195,** 301–310.

Bartholomew, G. A. (1949). The effect of light intensity and day length on reproduction in the English sparrow. *Bull. Museum Comp. Zool. Harvard Coll.* **101,** 433–476.

Bartter, F. C., Delea, C. S., and Halberg, F. (1962). A map of blood and urinary changes related to circadian variations in adrenal cortical function in normal subjects. *Ann. N.Y. Acad. Sci.* **98,** 969–983.

Benoit, J. (1961). Opto-sexual reflex in the duck: physiological and histological aspects. *Yale J. Biol. Med.* **34,** 97–116.

Benoit, J., and Assenmacher, I. (1959). The control by visible radiations of the gonadotropic activity of the duck hypophysis. *Recent Progr. Hormone Res.* **15,** 143–164.

Benoit, J., Walter, F. X., and Assenmacher, I. (1950). Nouvelles recherches relatives à l'action de lumières de différentes longueurs d'onde sur la gonadostimulation du canard mâle impobère. *Compt. Rend. Soc. Biol.* **144,** 1206–1211.

Bissonette, T. H. (1932). Modification of mammalian sexual cycles; reactions of ferrets (*Putoris vulgaris*) of both sexes to electric light added after dark in November and December. *Proc. Roy. Soc.* **B110,** 322–336.

Bissonette, T. H. (1933). Light and sexual cycles in starlings and ferrets. *Quart. Rev. Biol.* **8,** 201–208.

Bissonette, T. H., and Chapnick, M. N. (1930). Studies on the sexual cycle in birds. *Am. J. Anat.* **45,** 307–344.

Bissonette, T. H., and Csech, A. G. (1937). Modification of the mammalian sexual cycle: fertile matings of raccoons in December instead of February induced by increasing daily periods of light. *Proc. Roy. Soc.* **B122,** 246–254.

Bliss, E. L., Sandberg, A. A., Nelson, D. H., and Eik-Nes, K. (1953). The normal levels of 17-hydroxycorticosteroids in the peripheral blood of man. *J. Clin. Invest.* **32,** 818–823.

Bochenek, A. (1908). Über zentrale Endigungen des Nervus Opticus. *Anz. Akad. Wiss. Krakau* (*Bull. Intern. Acad. Polon. Sci. Lett., Cl. Sci. Math. Nat.*) No. 1, 91–95.

Bodian, D. (1940). Studies on the diencephalon of the Virginia opposum. II. The fiber connections in normal and experimental material. *J. Comp. Neurol.* **72,** 207–297.

Borst, J. G. G., and DeVries, C. A. (1950). The three types of "Natural Diuresis." *Lancet* **II,** 1–6.

Browman, L. C. (1937). Light in its relation to activity and estrous rhythms in the albino rat. *J. Exptl. Zool.* **75,** 375–388.

Browman, L. G. (1940). The effect of optic enucleation on the male albino rat. *Anat. Record* **78,** 59–77.

Bruce, H. M. (1959). An exteroceptive block to pregnancy in the mouse. *Nature* **184,** 105.

Bünning, E. (1964). "The Physiological Clock: Endogenous Diurnal Rhythms and Biological Chronometry," p. 145. Academic Press, New York.

Chu, E. W. (1965). Effect of environmental illumination on estrous cycles of rodents. *Acta Cytologica* **9,** 221–227.

Chu, E. W., Wurtman, R. J., and Axelrod, J. (1964). An inhibitory effect of melatonin on the estrous phase of the estrous cycle of the rodent. *Endocrinology* **75,** 238–242.

Clark, R. H., and Baker, B. L. (1964). Circadian periodicity in the concentration of prolactin in the rat hypophysis. *Science* **143,** 375.

Critchlow, V. (1958). Ovulation induced by hypothalamic stimulation in the anesthetized rat. *Am. J. Physiol.* **195,** 171–174.

Critchlow, V. (1963). The role of light in the neuroendocrine system. *In* "Advances in Neuroendocrinology" (A. V. Nalbandov, ed.), pp. 377–402. Univ. of Illinois Press, Urbana, Illinois.

Critchlow, V., and Sawyer, C. H. (1955). Electrical activity of the rat brain, correlated with neurogenic stimulation of the adenohypophysis. *Federation Proc.* **14,** 32–33.

Dempsey, E. W., Meyers, H. J., Young, W. C., and Jennison, D. B. (1934). Absence of light and the reproductive cycle in the guinea pig. *Am. J. Physiol.* **109,** 307–311.

Dobie, J. B. (1946). Poultry lighting for egg production. *Wash. State Coll. Agr. Expt. Sta. Bull.* **471.**

Dodt, E., and Heerd, E. (1962). Mode of action of pineal nerve fibers in frogs. *J. Neurophysiol.* **25,** 405–429.

Dodt, E., and Jacobson, M. (1963). Photosensitivity of a localized region of the frog diencephalon. *J. Neurophysiol.* **26,** 752–758.

Donovan, B. T., and Van der Werff ten Bosch, J. J. (1956). The cervical sympathetic system and light-induced oestrus in the ferret. *J. Physiol.* (*London*) **132,** 123–129.

Eakin, R. M., Stebbins, R. C., and Wilhoft, D. C. (1959). Effects of parietalectomy and sustained temperature on thyroid of lizard, *Sceloporus occidentalis. Proc. Soc. Exptl. Biol. Med.* **101,** 162–164.

Everett, J. W. (1956). The time of release of ovulating hormone from the rat hypophysis. *Endocrinology* **59,** 580–585.

Everett, J. W., and Sawyer, C. H. (1949). A neural timing factor in the mechanism by which progesterone advances ovulation in the cyclic rat. *Endocrinology* **45,** 581–595.

Everett, J. W., and Sawyer, C. H. (1950). A 24-hour periodicity in the "LH-Release Apparatus" of female rats, disclosed by barbiturate sedation. *Endocrinology* **47,** 198–218.

Everett, J. W., Sawyer, C. H., and Markee, J. E. (1949). A neurogenic timing factor in control of the ovulatory discharge of luteinizing hormone in the cyclic rat. *Endocrinology* **44,** 234–250.

Farner, D. S. (1959). Photoperiodic control of annual gonadal cycles in birds. *In* "Photoperiodism and Related Phenomena in Plants and Animals," Publ. No. 55, pp. 717–750. Am. Assoc. Advance. Sci., Washington, D.C.

Farner, D. S. (1961). Comparative physiology: photoperiodicity. *Ann. Rev. Physiol.* **23,** 71–96.

Farner, D. S. (1962). Hypothalamic neurosecretion and phosphatase activity in relation to the photoperiodic control of the testicular cycle of *Zonotrichia leucophrys gambelii*. *Gen. Comp. Endocrinol.* Suppl. 1, 160–167.

Farner, D. S., Mewaldt, L. R., and Irving, S. D. (1953). The roles of darkness and light in the activation of avian gonads. *Science* **118**, 351–352.

Fiske, V. M. (1941). Effect of light on sexual maturation, estrous cycles, and anterior pituitary of the rat. *Endocrinology* **29**, 187–196.

Fiske, V. M., and Greep, R. O. (1959). Neurosecretory activity in rats under conditions of continuous light or darkness. *Endocrinology* **64**, 175–185.

Fiske, V. M., and Lambert, H. H. (1962). Effect of light on the weight of the adrenal in the rat. *Endocrinology* **71**, 667–668.

Fiske, V. M., Bryant, G. K., and Putnam, J. (1960). Effect of light on the weight of the pineal gland in the rat. *Endocrinology* **66**, 489–491.

Folk, G. E., Jr. (1959). Modification by light of 24-hour activity of white rats. *Proc. Iowa Acad. Sci.* **66**, 399–406.

Foreman, D. (1962). The normal reproductive cycle of the prairie dog and the effects of light. *Anat. Record* **121**, 391–405.

Fraps, R. M. (1954). Diurnal periodicity in the release of ovulation-inducing hormone. *Proc. Natl. Acad. Sci. U.S.* **40**, 348–356.

Frey, E. (1937). Vergleichend-anatomische Untersuchungen über die basale optische Wurzel, die Commissure Transversa Gudden und über eine Verbindung der Netzhaut mit dem vegatativen Gebiet im Hypothalamus durch eine "Dorsale Hypothalamische Wurzel" des Nervus Opticus bei Amnioten. *Schweiz. Arch. Neurol. Psychiat.* **39**, 255–290.

Ganong, W. F., Shepherd, M. D., Wall, J. R., van Brunt, E. E., and Clegg, M. T. (1963). Penetration of light into the brain of mammals. *Endocrinology* **72**, 962–963.

Garrod, O., and Burston, R. A. (1952). The diuretic response to injected water in adrenal disease and panhypopituitarism and the effect of cortisone therapy. *Clin. Sci.* **11**, 113–128.

Glick, J. L., and Cohen, W. D. (1964). Nocturnal changes in oxidative activities of rat liver mitochondria. *Science* **143**, 1184.

Gordon, R. D., Wolfe, L. K., Island, D. P., and Liddle, G. W. (1966). Diurnal variation in plasma renin activity (PRA) of normal subjects. *Clin. Res.* **14**, 108.

Graber, A. L., Nicholson, W. E., Island, D. P., Givens, J. R., and Liddle, G. W. (1964). Persistence of a diurnal rhythm in plasma ACTH concentrations of cortisol-deficient patients. *Program 46th Meeting Endocrine Soc., Chicago*, p. 41.

Greenwald, G. S. (1963). Failure of continuous light to induce constant oestrus in the hamster. *J. Endocrinol.* **28**, 123–124.

Gudden, B. (1870). Über einen bisher nicht beschreiben Nervenfasernstrang im Gehirne der Säugetiere und des Menschen. *Arch. Psychiat.* **2**, 364–366.

Guillemin, R., Dear, W. E., and Liebelt, R. A. (1959). Nycthemeral variations in plasma free corticosteroid levels in the rat. *Proc. Soc. Exptl. Biol. Med.* **101**, 394–395.

Hague, E., ed. (1964). Photo-neuro-endocrine effects in circadian systems. *Ann. N.Y. Acad. Sci.* **117**, 1–645.

Halberg, F. (1953). Some physiological and clinical aspects of 24-hour periodicity. *J. Lancet* **73**, 20–28.

Halberg, F. (1959a). Physiological 24-hour periodicity: general and procedural considerations with reference to the adrenal cycle. *Z. Vitamin-, Hormon-, Fermentforsch.* **10**, 225–296.

Halberg, F. (1959b). Physiological 24-hour periodicity in human beings and mice, the lighting regimen, and daily routine. *In* "Photoperiodism and Related Phenomena in Plants and Animals," Publ. No. 55, 803–878. Am. Assoc. Advance. Sci., Washington, D.C.

Halberg, F., and Visscher, M. B. (1950). Regular diurnal physiological variation in eosinophil levels in 5 stocks of mice. *Proc. Soc. Exptl. Biol. Med.* **75**, 846–847.

Halberg, F., Visscher, M. B., and Bittner, D. J. (1954). Relation of visual factors to eosinophil rhythm in mice. *Am. J. Physiol.* **179**, 229–235.

Halberg, F., Peterson, R. E., and Silber, R. H. (1959). Phase relationships of 24-hour periodicities in blood corticosterone, mitoses in cortical adrenal parenchyma, and total body activity. *Endocrinology* **64**, 222–230.

Hammond, J., Jr. (1951). Control by light of reproduction in ferrets and mink. *Nature* **167**, 150–151.

Hammond, J., Jr. (1954). Light regulation of hormone secretion. *Vitamins Hormones* **12**, 157–204.

Hart, D. S. (1951). Photoperiodicity in the female ferret. *J. Exptl. Biol.* **28**, 1–12.

Hayhow, W. R. (1959). An experimental study of the accessory optic fiber system in the cat. *J. Comp. Neurol.* **113**, 281–313.

Hayhow, W. R., Webb, C., and Jervie, A. (1960). The accessory optic fiber system in the rat. *J. Comp. Neurol.* **115**, 187–216.

Hemmingsen, A. M., and Krarup, N. B. (1937). Rhythmic diurnal variations in the oestrus phenomena of the rat and their susceptibility to light and dark. *Kgl. Danske Videnskab. Selskab, Biol. Medd.* **13**, No. 7.

Hendricks, S. B. (1956). Control of growth and reproduction by light and darkness. *Am. Scientist* **44**, 229–247.

Hill, M., and Parkes, A. S. (1934). Effect of absence of light on the breeding season of the ferret. *Proc. Roy. Soc.* **B115**, 14–17.

Hollwich, F. (1955). Der Einfluss des Augenlichtes auf die Regulation des Stoffwechsels. *Klin. Monatsbl. Augenheilk.* **23**, 95–125.

Hollwich, F., and Tilgner, S. (1961). Experimentelle Untersuchungen über den photosexuellen Reflex bei der Ente. *Ophthalmologica* **142**, 572–576.

Hollwich, F., and Tilgner, S. (1963). Das Verhalten der Eosinophilen-Zahl als Indikator der okularen Lichtreizwirkung. *Klin. Monatsbl. Augenheilk.* **142**, 531–540.

Holmquest, D. L., Retiene, K., and Lipscomb, H. S. (1966). Circadian rhythms in rats: the effects of random lighting. *Science* **152**, 662–664.

Januszewicz, W., and Wocial, B. (1960). Wplyw Pracy, Rytmu Dobowego Oraz Bodzca Wzrokowego Na Wydalanie Katecholamin A Moczem. *Arch. Med. Wiss.* **30**, 207–216.

Kamm, D. E., and Levinsky, N. G., 1965). The mechanism of denervation natiuresis. *J. Clin. Invest.* **44**, 93–102.

Kappers, J. A. (1960). The development, topographical relations, and innervation of the epiphysis cerebri in the albino rat. *Z. Zellforsch. Mikroskop. Anat.* **52**, 163–215.

Kelly, D. E. (1962). Pineal organs: photoreception, secretion and development. *Am. Scientist* **50**, 597–625.

Knoche, H. (1957). Die retino-hypothalamische Bahn von Mensch, Hund, und Kaninchen. *Mikroskop. Anat. Forsch.* **63**, 461–486.

Krieg, W. J. S. (1932). The hypothalamus of the albino rat. *J. Comp. Neurol.* **55**, 19–89.

Landau, J., and Feldman, S. (1954). Diminished endogenous morning eosinopenia in blind subjects. *Acta Endocrinol.* **15**, 53–60.

Lawton, I. E., and Schwartz, N. B. (1965). Pituitary LH content in rats exposed to continuous illumination. *Endocrinology* **77**, 1140–1142.

le Gros Clarke, W. E., McKeown, T., and Zuckerman, S. (1939). Visual pathways concerned in gonadal stimulation in ferrets. *Proc. Roy. Soc.* **B126**, 449–468.

Lerner, A. B., Case, J. D., and Heinzelman, R. V. (1959). Structure of melatonin. *J. Am. Chem. Soc.* **81**, 6084–6085.

Lisk, R. D., and Kannwischer, L. R. (1964) Light: Evidence for its direct effect on hypothalamic neurons. *Science* **146**, 272–273.

Lobban, M. C., and Tredre, B. (1964). Renal diurnal rhythms in blind subjects. *J. Physiol.* (*London*) **170**, 29P.

McCann, S. M., and Ramirez, V. D. (1964). The neuroendocrine regulation of hypophyseal luteinizing hormone secretion. *Recent Progr. Hormone Res.* **20**, 143, 148–150.

McIntosh, H. W. (1966). Circadian variation in serum calcium levels. *Clin. Res.* **14**, 178.

McIsaac, W. M., Taborsky, R. G., and Farrell, G. L. (1964). 5-Methoxytryptophol: effect on estrus and ovarian weight. *Science* **145**, 63–64.

Marburg, O. (1903). Basale Opticuswurzel und Tractus Penduncularis Transversus. *Arb. Neurol. Inst. Wien. Univ.* **10**, 66–80.

Maric, D. K., Matsuyama, E., and Lloyd, C. W. (1965). Gonadotrophin content of pituitaries of rats in constant estrus induced by continuous illumination. *Endocrinology* **77**, 529–536.

Marshall, A. J. (1961). Reproduction. *In* "Biology and Comparative Physiology of Birds" (A. J. Marshall, ed.), Vol. II, pp. 169–213. Academic Press, New York.

Marshall, F. H. A. (1940). The experimental modification of the oestrus cycle in the ferret by different intensities of light irradiation and other methods. *J. Exptl. Biol.* **17**, 139–146.

Marshall, F. H. A. (1942). Exteroceptive factors in sexual periodicity. *Biol. Rev. Cambridge Phil. Soc.* **17**, 68–90.

Marshall, F. H. A., and Bowden, F. P. (1936). Further effects of irradiation on oestrous cycle of ferret. *J. Exptl. Biol.* **13**, 383–386.

Marshall, F. H. A., and Bowden, F. P. (1934). The effect of irradiation with different wave-lengths on the estrous cycle of the ferret, with remarks on the factors controlling sexual periodicity. *J. Exptl. Biol.* **11**, 409–422.

Marshall, W. A. (1962). The effect of altering the size of the palpebral fissure on the induction of oestrus by light in normal ferrets after removal of both superior cervical sympathetic ganglia. *J. Physiol.* (*London*) **165**, 27–28P.

Marshall, W. A. (1963). The effect of autotransplantation of the thyroid gland on the onset of the oestrus in ferrets. *J. Endocrinol.* **26**, 279–285.

Martel, P. J., Sharp, G. W. G., Slorach, S. A., and Vipond, H. J. (1962). A study of the roles of adrenocortical steroids and glomerular filtration rate in the mechanism of the diurnal rhythm of water and electrolyte excretion. *J. Endocrinol.* **24**, 159–169.

Matthews, L. H. (1939). Visual stimulation and ovulation in pigeons. *Proc. Roy. Soc.* **B126**, 557–560.

Migeon, C. V., French, A. B., Samuels, L. T., and Bowers, J. Z. (1955). Plasma 17-hydroxycorticosteroid levels and leukocyte values in the rhesus monkey, including normal variations and the effect of ACTH. *Am. J. Physiol.* **182**, 462–468.

Migeon, C. V., Tyler, F. H., Mahoney, J. P., Florentin, A. A., Castle, H., Bliss, E. L., and Samuels, L. T. (1956). The diurnal variation of plasma levels and urinary excretion of 17-hydroxycortoids in normal subjects, night workers and blind subjects. *J. Clin. Endocrinol. Metab.* **16,** 622–633.

Morris, T. R., and Fox, S. (1958). Light and sexual maturity in the domestic fowl. *Nature* **181,** 1453–1454.

Nabarro, J. D. N. (1956). "Modern Views of the Secretion of Urine," Cushny Memorial Lectures (F. R. Winton, ed.), p. 148. Churchill, London.

Nahmod, V. E., and Lanari, A. (1964). Abolition of autoregulation of renal blood flow by acetylcholine. *Am. J. Physiol.* **207,** 123–127.

Nauta, W. J. H. (1943). Bestaat de hypothalamische Opticuswortel. *Versl. Koninkl. Ned. Akad. Wetenschap.* **52,** 633–636.

Oksche, A. (1955). Untersuchungen über die Nervenzellen und Nervenverbindungen des Stirnorgans, der Epiphyse, und des Subkommissuralorgans bei anuren Amphibien. *Morphol. Jahrbuch* **95,** 393–425.

Ortavant, R. (1958). Le cycle spermatogénétique chez le Belier. Thesis, Fac. Sci. Univ. de Paris, pp. 128. Inst. Natl. Recherche Agron, Paris.

Perkoff, G. T., Eik-Nes, K., Nugent, C. A., Fred, H. L., Nimer, R. A., Rush, L., Samuels, L. T., and Tyler, F. H. (1959). Studies on the diurnal variation of plasma 17-hdyroxycorticosteroids in man. *J. Clin. Endocrinol. Metab.* **19,** 432–443.

Pincus, G. (1943). A diurnal rhythm in the excretion of urinary ketosteroids by young men. *J. Clin. Endocrinol. Metab.* **3,** 195–199.

Quay, W. B. (1963). Circadian rhythm in rat pineal serotonin and its modifications by estrous cycle and photoperiod. *Gen. Comp. Endocrinol.* **3,** 473–479.

Quay, W. B. (1964). Circadian and estrous rhythms in pineal melatonin and 5-hydroxy indole-3-acetic acid. *Proc. Soc. Exptl. Biol. Med.* **115,** 710–713.

Quay, W. B. (1966). 24-Hour rhythms in pineal 5-hydroxytryptamine and hydroxyindole-O-methyl transferase activity in the macaque. *Proc. Soc. Exptl. Biol. Med.* **121,** 946–948.

Quay, W. B., and Halevy, A. (1962). Experimental modification of the rat pineal's content of serotonin and related indole amines. *Physiol. Zool.* **35,** 1–7.

Radnot, M., Wallner, E., and Honig, M. (1962). Topographical relations of retinal defects to the optico-vegetative function. *Acta Biol. Acad. Sci. Hung.* **4,** Suppl. 12, 47 (Abstract).

Ramirez, V. D., and McCann, S. M. (1964). Fluctuations in plasma luteinizing hormone concentrations during the estrous cycle in rats. *Endocrinology* **74,** 814–816.

Rieke, W. O. (1958). Optico-hypothalamic pathways in the rat. *Anat. Record* **130,** 363–364.

Rose, S. M. (1939). Embryonic induction in the ascidia. *Biol. Bull.* **77,** 216–231.

Rothman, S., Krysa, H. F., and Smiljanic, A. M. (1946). Inhibitory action of human epidermis on melanin formation. *Proc. Soc. Exptl. Biol. Med.* **62,** 208–209.

Rowan, W. (1925). Reaction of light to bird migration and developmental changes. *Nature* **115,** 494–495.

Rowan, W. (1938). Light and seasonal reproduction in animals. *Biol. Rev. Cambridge Phil. Soc.* **13,** 374–402.

Sade, D. S. (1964). Seasonal cycle in size of testes of free-ranging *Macaca mulatta. Folia Primat.* **2,** 171–180.

Scharrer, E., and Scharrer, B. (1963). "Neuroendocrinology" pp. 51–56. Columbia Univ. Press, New York.

Schatz, D. L., and Volpe, R. (1959). Lack of diurnal variation in the level of serum protein-bound iodine. *J. Clin. Endocrinol. Metab.* **19,** 1495–1497.

Schindler, W. J., Critchlow, V., Krause, D. M., and McHorse, T. S. (1965). 24-Hour pattern of pituitary-thyroid function in male and female rats. *Program 6th Pan-American Congr. Endocrinology, Mexico City, 1965.* Abstr. #138.

Schwartz, N. B., and Bartosik, D. (1962). Changes in pituitary LH content during the rat estrous cycle. *Endocrinology* **71,** 756–762.

Scott, P. P., and Lloyd-Jacob, L. (1959). Reduction in the anoestrus period of laboratory cats by increased illumination. *Nature* **184,** 2022.

Sharp, G. W. G. (1960). The effect of light on the morning increase in urine flow. *J. Endocrinol.* **21,** 219–223.

Simmons, D. J. (1962). Diurnal periodicity in epiphyseal growth cartilage. *Nature* **195,** 82–83.

Skreb, N. (1954). Experimentelle Untersuchungen über die äusseren Ovulationsfaktoren bei der Fledermaus *Nyctalus noctula. Naturwiss.* **41,** 484.

Snyder, S. H., and Axelrod, J. (1965). Circadian rhythm in pineal serotonin: Effect of monoamine oxidase inhibition and reserpine. *Science* **149,** 542–544.

Snyder, S. H., Axelrod, J., Fischer, J. E., and Wurtman, R. J. (1964). Neural and photic regulation of 5-hydroxytryptophan decarboxylase in the rat pineal gland. *Nature* **203,** 981–982.

Snyder, S. H., Zweig, M., Axelrod, J., and Fischer, J. E. (1965). Control of the circadian rhythm in serotonin content of the rat pineal gland. *Proc. Natl. Acad. Sci. U.S.* **53,** 301–305.

Stanbury, S. W., and Thomson, A. E. (1951). Diurnal variations in electrolyte excretion. *Clin. Sci.* **10,** 267–293.

Stevens, V. C., Owen, C., Fukushima, M., and Vorys, N. (1964). Diurnal variation in the ascorbic acid content of the pseudopregnant rat. *Endocrinology* **74,** 493–494.

Strauss, W. F. (1964). Neural timing of ovulation in immature rats treated with gonadotrophin. *Dissertation Abstr.* (*Physiol. Sect.*) **24,** 11.

Strauss, W. F., and Meyer, R. K. (1962a). Neural timing of ovulation in immature rats treated with gonadotrophin. *Science* **137,** 860–861.

Strauss, W. F., and Meyer, R. K. (1962b). Neural timing of ovulation in immature rats treated with gonadotrophin: effect of light. *Am. Zoologist* **2,** 219.

Strauss, W. F., and Meyer, R. K. (1964). Neural timing of rats in continuous darkness: shift by prior lighting. *Program 46th Meeting Endocrine Soc., Chicago,* p. 23.

Thomson, A. P. D. (1954). The onset of oestrus in normal and blinded ferrets. *Proc. Roy. Soc.* **B142,** 126–135.

Van der Werff ten Bosch, J. J. (1963). Effects of cerebral lesions, blinding, and domestication on gonadal functions of the male ferret. *J. Endocrinol.* **26,** 113–123.

Warren, R. P., and Hinde, R. A. (1961). Does the male stimulate oestrogen secretion in female canaries? *Science* **133,** 1354–1355.

Wells, L. J. (1959). Experiments of light and temperature in a wild mammal with an annual breeding season. *In* "Photoperiodism and Related Phenomena in Plants and Animals," Publ. No. 55, pp. 801–802. Am. Assoc. Advance. Sci., Washington, D.C.

Wilson, W. O., Woodard, W. E., and Abplanalp, H. (1956). The effect and after-effect of varied exposure to light on chicken development. *Biol. Bull.* **111,** 415–422.

Wislocki, G. B., Aub, J. C., and Waldo, C. M. (1947). The effects of gonadectomy and the administration of testosterone propionate on the growth of antlers in male and female deer. *Endocrinology* **40,** 202–224.

Withrow, R. B., ed. (1959). "Photoperiodism and Related Phenomena in Plants and Animals," Publ. No. 55. Am. Assoc. Advance. Sci., Washington, D.C.

Wolfe, D. E., Potter, L. T., Richardson, K. C., and Axelrod, J. (1962). Localizing tritiated norepinephrine in sympathetic axons by electron microscopic autoradiography. *Science* **138,** 440–442.

Woods, J. W., Wayt, H. J., and Baker, H. J. (1966). Cyclic fluctuations in I^{131} content of thyroid glands of cats and monkeys. *Proc. Soc. Exptl. Biol. Med.* **122,** 211–214.

Wurtman, R. J. (1966). "Catecholamines." Little, Brown, Boston, Massachusetts.

Wurtman, R. J., and Axelrod, J. (1965). The pineal gland. *Sci. Am.* **213,** 50–59.

Wurtman, R. J., and Axelrod, J. (1966). A 24-hour rhythm in the content of norepinephrine in the pineal and salivary glands of the rat. *Life Sci.* **7,** 665–669.

Wurtman, R. J., Axelrod, J., and Chu, E. W. (1963a). Melatonin, a pineal substance: effect on the rat ovary. *Science* **141,** 277–278.

Wurtman, R. J., Axelrod, J., and Phillips, L. (1963b). Melatonin synthesis in the pineal gland: control by light. *Science* **142,** 1071–1073.

Wurtman, R. J., Axelrod, J., and Fischer, J. E. (1964a). Melatonin synthesis in the pineal gland: effect of light mediated by the sympathetic nervous system. *Science* **143,** 1328–1330.

Wurtman, R. J., Axelrod, J., Chu, E. W., and Fischer, J. E. (1964b). Mediation of some effects of illumination on the rat estrous cycle by the sympathetic nervous system. *Endocrinology* **75,** 266–272.

Wurtman, R. J., Axelrod, J., and Potter, L. T. (1964c). The uptake of H^3-melatonin in endocrine and nervous tissue and the effects of constant light exposure. *J. Pharmacol. Exptl. Therap.* **142,** 314–318.

Zacharias, L., and Wurtman, R. J. (1964). Blindness: its relation to menarche. *Science* **144,** 1154–1155.

CHAPTER 19

Modifications in Reproductive Function after Exposure to Hormones during the Prenatal and Early Postnatal Period

CHARLES A. BARRACLOUGH

I. General Introduction

Since the early theoretical proposals of Lillie (1916, 1917) and Keller and Tandler (1916) on the possible cause of the freemartin condition in cattle, innumerable studies have been made on the role of hormones in the differentiation of sex. As a consequence of these studies it can be stated that the genetic sex of mammals cannot be altered by hormones although many permanent aberrancies can be produced by prenatal hormone treatment. It is not feasible, nor is it within the scope of this chapter, to consider these abnormal developmental changes nor will this chapter attempt to present all the minutiae which have led to our current concepts of how pre- and postnatal hormone treatment alters the normal maturation of the reproductive system. Furthermore, several excellent reviews have recently been written on these subjects (Leathem, 1958; Burns, 1961). Rather, this contribution will attempt to critically evaluate what the author considers to be the pertinent studies which have led to the present understanding of how the hypothalamo-hypophyseal-gonadal system matures. Since the major portion of our current concepts were derived from studies of the abnormal, it is necessary also to consider the mechanisms by which hormonal imbalances, produced early in the undifferentiated or quiescent period of reproductive development, permanently alter the normal reproductive neuro-endocrine relationships.

II. The Effect of Pre- and Postnatal Hormone Treatment on Subsequent Reproduction

A. The Age Factor

The responses of the gonads, the accessory reproductive organs, and the brain to exogenous hormones depend not only upon the hormones administered, the length of treatment, and the dosage employed but also upon the age of the treated animals. To carefully assess the response of the reproductive tract to a hormone it is first necessary to establish if the organ to be studied is responsive at a given age. If one quickly scans the literature it becomes immediately apparent that the prepubertal pituitary, gonad, and the sex accessories do not react in a fashion that at all resembles the responses that can be observed in the mature animal. This is true for most of the common laboratory animals and may be related to the degree of organ maturation at the time of birth. The relationships between prepubertal age and gonadal responsiveness have been studied by transplantation of gonadal tissue and by the administration of exogenous steroids and gonadotropins. From such studies it has been determined that there is a wide variability in different species, the duration of unresponsiveness being short in the rat and longer in the monkey (Krohn, 1955). For example, the rat ovary is relatively insensitive to gonadotropins immediately after birth, and reactivity is gained only gradually during the first 14 days of postnatal life (Price and Ortiz, 1944). Price and Ortiz (1944) observed that administration of serum gonadotropin (PMS) would increase rat ovarian weight at 10 days of age, but the maximum weight increase did not occur until 20–25 days. Similar observations were made when the newborn ovary was transplanted to a castrate adult. Concomitant steroid release by the 10-day-old rat ovary could also be induced with gonadotropins, as attested by a uterine weight increase, but only after 15 days of age could follicular growth be induced. Thus prior to 15 days of age the main ovarian response to gonadotropin is from the thecal or interstitial cells. However, it should be noted that during this period of maturation (1–15 days of age) the normal reproductive changes are principally further differentiation and somatic growth, and there is no evidence that sex steroids are being secreted.

In the prepubertal male, exogenous gonadotropin increases testis weight and seminiferous tubule diameter and stimulates the interstitial tissue, but spermatogenesis is not hastened. Even gonadotropin treatment from birth to puberty fails to accelerate the appearance of spermatozoa. Of more importance is the response of the interstitial tissue prior to puberty. Gonadotropin will stimulate the interstitial cells to secrete androgens in sufficient concentration to enlarge the responsive seminal vesicles (Price and Ortiz, 1944; Hooker, 1948).

Normally, the alterations in size, morphology, and/or chemical composition of the sex accessory organs have been employed as indices of sex steroid secretion. Does the infantile reproductive tract truly indicate that the gonad is quiescent or again is this related to the reactivity of these target organs at different ages? Ortiz (1947) and Price and Ortiz (1944) have carefully evaluated the relationship of age to reactivity in the reproductive systems of the rat and hamster. Steroid treatment consisted of six daily injections starting at birth and at 4, 8, 10, 12, 20, and 30 days of age. Autopsy was performed 24 hours after the last injection. Estradiol benzoate caused maximal uterine stimulation in the hamster at 10 days of age and in the rat at 26 days of age. Vaginal opening occurred in 6-day-old hamsters and 18-day-old rats. Testosterone propionate stimulated both ventral prostate and seminal vesicles of the hamster maximally at 16 days of age. The rat ventral prostate responded maximally on day 14 and the seminal vesicles on day 26. It should be noted that some responsiveness was obtained in the early age groups as well, indicating that both the seminal vesicle and the prostate are responsive even at 6 days of age, but to a lesser degree. An analysis of the normal weight changes of the seminal vesicles and concomitant histochemical studies of sudanophilic lipid and cholesterol content of the testes of 10-, 20-, and 30-day-old mice would suggest that detectable androgen secretion begins at 18–20 days of age and rises sharply thereafter. Prior to this time, few changes occur which cannot be considered as somatic growth (Barraclough and Leathem, 1959). As will be discussed later, the initial testicular secretions of androgen must begin much earlier (at 1–3 days of age) than the suggestive evidence of sex accessory weight changes indicate. This undetectable release seems to be the single determining factor in the sexual differentiation of the hypothalamic-gonadotropin controlling mechanism.

The contribution of the secretions of the prepubertal ovary and testes (or lack thereof) to the subsequent fertility of the animal was originally studied by Pfeiffer (1936). He observed that ovaries, transplanted to adult males which had been castrated at birth, would show normal follicular and corpora lutea development. Similarly, adult female rats, ovariectomized at birth, exhibited normal vaginal cycles when an ovary was transplanted into the eye. In contrast, when testes were transplanted into newborn females, the ovaries of these animals, when adult, contained only follicles (no corpora lutea), and persistent vaginal cornification ensued after puberty. It was originally proposed by Pfeiffer that the mechanism by which androgen (secreted from testes) produced this anovulatory persistent estrous condition was by "masculinization" of the adenohypophysis so that a permanent imbalance in gonadotropin secretion resulted. This author suggested that the pituitary of the newborn rat was undifferentiated. If it differentiated in the presence of androgen, only follicle-stimulating hormone (FSH) was elaborated, whereas if it differentiated normally, both FSH and luteinizing hormone (LH) were secreted. With the identification and crystallization of testosterone, different investigators have studied the effects of postnatal injections of this androgen on subsequent fertility. The studies have involved different regimens of treatment and variable doses of hormone. Shay *et al.* (1939) observed that female rats treated from birth to either 44 or 175 days of age were permanently sterile. Bradbury (1941) injected 0.25 mg of testosterone propionate on alternate days from 6 to 38 days of age and then sacrificed the animals 10 weeks after treatment. The ovaries of these rats contained few follicles but lacked corpora lutea and mating attempts were unsuccessful. In contrast to the response of female rats treated at birth are those effects produced by androgen treatment of the adult female rat. Such animals, injected with 2.0 mg of testosterone propionate daily throughout a 4-week period and caged with normal males, did not mate and vaginal plugs were absent. One month after treatment was discontinued, remating was attempted with 98% success (Huffman, 1941). Thus only temporary abnormalities could be produced in adult animals treated with androgen, whereas prepubertal exposure resulted in permanent aberrancies.

The interpretations of different investigators as to the cause of these various abnormalities closely paralleled the original hypothesis of Pfeiffer. Treatment of infantile rats with androgen permanently altered the normal secretion of the adenohypophysis. It should be noted that little was known until 1949 of the central nervous regulation of adenohypophyseal function, so at that time these interpretations were reasonable.

To evaluate more carefully the effect and duration of effect of a hormone administered at a given time in development, a single injection of testosterone propionate was administered to different groups of female mice (Barraclough and Leathem, 1954; Barraclough, 1955) or rats (Barraclough, 1961) at 2, 5, 10, or 20 days of age. The mice were autopsied at 10-day intervals to 60 days of age, and all rats were sacrificed at 100 days of age. The ovaries of all adult animals treated with a single injection of 1.25 mg of testosterone propionate at 2 or 5 days of age lacked corpora lutea, exhibited an increase in follicular atresia, and interstitial tissue hypertrophy was evident. Androgen treatment at 10 days of age had a less drastic effect as the ovaries of only 4 of 10 rats lacked corpora lutea at 100 days of age. In mice treated at 10 days of age, ovulation and formation of corpora lutea were delayed approximately 10 days (from 50 to 60 days of age), but at 60 days of age 85% of the ovaries contained corpora lutea as compared with 90% of the littermate controls. All ovaries of rats or mice treated with androgen at 20 days of age were normal at autopsy. As a consequence of these studies, we proposed that a period of steroid sensitivity exists in the female rat and mouse between birth and the tenth day of age, during which administration of androgen will result in subsequent infertility.

The effects of androgen administered prior to birth on subsequent fertility have also been studied. Androgen injections to rats from days 19–20 of pregnancy produced female offspring which had abnormally masculinized external genitalia (Greene *et al.*, 1939; Swanson and Van der Werff ten Bosch, 1964b); when the ovaries were examined at 10, 21, and 26 weeks of age, however, all contained corpora lutea and mating behavior was normal. Surprisingly, the female young of rats treated on days 21 or 22 of pregnancy had normal external genitalia with normal vaginal canalization and normal ovaries when adult. It has been suggested that androgen treatment on days 21–22 of pregnancy failed to produce masculinized female offspring because of the delayed absorption and transplacental passage or inactivation of the steroid. Another explanation worthy of consideration is that the progesterone being secreted by the pregnant rat protects against the permanent "masculinizing" effect of prenatal androgen. A differential responsiveness of the pregnant and nonpregnant animal to the "masculinizing" action of androgen has been observed in the guinea pig by Diamond and Young (1963).

B. The Dosage Factor

Once the critical period of steroid sensitivity had been established, more detailed investigations were undertaken to establish the minimum dosage of androgen required to produce sterility. As is shown in Table I,

TABLE I

EFFECT OF VARIOUS DOSES OF TESTOSTERONE PROPIONATE ON INDUCTION OF STERILITY IN THE FEMALE RAT

Amount injected on day 5 (micrograms)	Number of rats injected	Number of rats sterile	Sterility (%)[a]
1250	1000	998	99.8
10	136	96	70.6
5	25	11	44.0
1	10	3	30.0

[a] These figures represent a compilation of data obtained in several studies (see Barraclough, 1961; Gorski and Barraclough, 1963).

as little as 10 μg, administered at 5 days of age, produced sterility in 70% of the treated animals. Since then many studies have been conducted on the age and dosage required to produce sterility. A summary of the results is presented in chronological order in Table II and provides a comparison of the results obtained in the prepubertal castrate male with an ovarian implant, with results obtained in prepubertal female rats injected with androgen. Some tentative conclusions may be made: (1) the testes of the prepubertal rat secrete sufficient androgen to permanently alter the hypothalamo-hypophyseal-gonadal axis between days 1–3 of age, and (2) the minimum dosage of androgen which is effective in producing sterility in over 60% of the animals injected at 5 days of age is of the order of 10 μg. Although the duration of time that androgen remains in the circulation is unknown, it is reasonable to presume that a 24–48-hour period of exposure to androgen is all that is necessary to permanently "imprint" the mechanisms controlling ovulation. However, it is impossible to extrapolate from these experimental values to the actual amount of hormone secreted by the prepubertal testes, as in these experiments androgen was administered subcutaneously in oil. Thus the concentration of androgen in circulation at the critical time is unknown. Furthermore, studies which attempt to determine the amount (micrograms) of androgen secreted by the 1–3-day-old testes will not, in the author's opinion, be solved by transplantation of varying amounts of testicular tissue. How can one determine the ratio of interstitium to seminiferous tubule in the testicular segment selected for implantation? Furthermore, Pfeiffer (1936) encountered different responses, depending upon the degree of revascularization of the graft. Because of the question of the protein-binding capacity of the serum in the prepubertal rat plus the indeterminate problems of liver inactivation, rate of absorption, etc., this is a difficult problem to solve. It is of interest to note that neither seminal vesicle, prostate, nor the testis itself gives any indication that androgen is being secreted. However, the threshold of reactivity of the sex accessories may be higher than the concentration of androgen necessary to produce the "masculinization" referred to earlier. Swanson and Van der Werff ten Bosch (1964b) have also suggested that, as maturation of the hypothalamo-hypophyseal-gonadal axis proceeds with age (from 1–10 days of age), "masculinization" may still be produced, provided that the dosage of administered hormone is increased. There are no data to support this hypothesis and it is just as likely that the brains of some animals mature more rapidly than others (or vice versa). Thus the 40% of the rats which are still susceptible to androgen at 10 days of age may not have completed their maturation.

III. The Persistent Estrus Syndrome, Its Cause, and Its Contribution to the Understanding of the Normal Estrous Cycle

As early as 1936 Pfeiffer observed that female rats with testes implanted at birth exhibited persistent cornification of the vaginal mucosa after puberty. This subsequently was attributed to the constant secretion of ovarian estrogen as a consequence of the imbalance produced in pituitary gonadotropin secretion by the early exposure to androgen. Concomitant with this persistent vaginal cornification is the continual succession of large ovarian follicles and the absence of corpora lutea. In female rats this anovulatory persistent estrus syndrome not only occurs naturally, as a function of old age, but can be produced by

TABLE II

SUMMARY OF EFFECTS OF PREPUBERTAL CASTRATION OF MALE RATS AND OF VARIOUS DOSES OF ANDROGEN ADMINISTERED AT DIFFERENT AGES TO FEMALE RATS ON THE PRODUCTION OF THE ANOVULATORY PERSISTENT ESTRUS SYNDROME

	Days before birth					Age at treatment (postnatal days; 1 = day of birth)										Ovaries with corpora lutea (age in weeks)[a]			
Treatment	5	4	3	2	1	1	2	3	4	5	6	10	11	20	49	10	14	21 or more	Reference
Castration of males with subsequent ovarian implants						x												+	Pfeiffer (1936)
													x			−			
											x					−			
								x								+			Kawashima (1960)
						x										+			
															x			−	
												x						−	
								x										−	
							x											+	
						x												+	Yazaki (1960)
								x										−	Harris (1964)
							x											−	
						x												+	
Testosterone propionate administered subcutaneously (in oil) in micrograms														1000		+			Barraclough and Leathem (1954),
												1000				+[b]			Barraclough (1955)
										1000						−			
														1250			+	(100)	
												1250					+[c]	(60)	Barraclough (1961)
										1250							−	(0)	
						1250											−	(0)	
										1							±	(70)	

					5	±	(56)	Gorski and Barraclough (1963)
					10	±	(19)	
					100	−	−	
					50	−	−	Swanson and Van der Werff ten Bosch (1964a)
					10	+	−	
					5	+	−	
				10		−	−	
				5		−	−	
			500			−	−	Swanson and Van der Werff ten Bosch (1964b)
		2500[d]				+	+	
	2500[d]					+	+	
2500[d]						+	+	

[a] +, presence; −, absence; values in parentheses are percent ovaries with corpora lutea.
[b] Data obtained in mouse.
[c] Data obtained in rat.
[d] Dosage administered to mother.

different experimental procedures such as continuous illumination, frequent intense auditory stimulation, transplantation of a testis into a newborn female, administration of various steroids during infancy, or by lesions of the hypothalamus. The causative factors of this syndrome are considered in a recent review by Everett (1964a).

Of particular importance are the mechanisms and sites of action by which androgen produces permanent sterility (and persistent estrus). Since the time of Pfeiffer's early observations, it has become apparent that the pituitary of the androgen-sterilized rat elaborates both FSH and LH. Seemingly, the particular adenohypophyseal malfunction is the failure to release sufficient gonadotropin to cause ovulation, a phenomenon now generally held to be regulated by the hypothalamus (Everett, 1964a). This suggested to us that either the pituitary of the androgen-sterilized rat is refractory to hypothalamic activation or, more likely, that the malfunction in the ovulatory mechanism is inherent within the hypothalamus itself. Some support for the latter hypothesis was offered by the observations of Harris and Jacobsohn (1951) and Martinez and Bittner (1956). Hypophyses from male rats restored normal estrous cycles when transplanted beneath the median eminence of hypophysectomized female rats. Apparently, the sex difference in gonadotropin secretion is not resident within the adenohypophysis as such but at a higher neural level. Many recent studies (since 1960) have interpreted the effects of prepubertal hormone treatment as producing malfunctions in the hypothalamic regulation of gonadotropin secretion, and yet only a few studies have actually approached this problem at the central nervous system level. By electrical stimulation of various regions of the hypothalamus of androgen-sterilized rats we demonstrated that the adenohypophysis of the sterile rat can function normally to cause ovulation provided: (1) proper gonadotropin storage is permitted and (2) an impetus for its release is supplied by the hypothalamus (Barraclough and Gorski, 1961; Gorski and Barraclough, 1963). Second, it was observed that transplantation of the pituitary from the sterile rat into proximity with the median eminence of an untreated hypophysectomized female rat restored normal cycles and ovulation. Transplantation of the normal pituitary into the sella turcica of the sterile rat failed to alter the anovulatory persistent estrous condition (Segal and Johnson, 1959). These studies prove that prepubertal androgen treatment alters normal hypothalamic rather than adenohypophyseal function.

Apparently, prepubertal androgen treatment so alters normal hypothalamic function as to render it incapable of activating the cyclic ovulatory discharge of gonadotropin (presumably LH). However, such treatment does not cause complete cessation of LH secretion. This is shown by the syndrome which ensues in the adult sterile rat: persistent vaginal cornification and ovarian interstitial cell, adrenal, and pituitary hypertrophy—all of which are either directly or indirectly (through estrogen secretion) the consequence of a tonic discharge of adenohypophyseal LH. Also, depending upon the age of treatment, other abnormalities, such as failure of the vagina to canalize, pyosalpinx, or salpingitis, occur.

To establish a hypothalamic locus which is deleteriously affected by androgen requires an evaluation of the specific hypothalamic areas proposed to be responsible for the control of ovulation in the normal rat. In 1958, Critchlow initially demonstrated that electrical stimulation of hypothalamic regions in the basal area extending from the optic chiasm to the infundibular stalk consistently induced ovulation in pentobarbital-blocked rats. The more recent studies of Everett (1964b) have extended these observations to include the septum and preoptic area rostral to the suprachiasmatic nuclei. Furthermore, when small specific lesions are made in the suprachiasmatic nuclei, the syndrome produced is almost identical to that observed in androgen-sterilized rats (Flerkó and Bardós, 1959; Barraclough *et al.*, 1964).

The hypothalamic locus thus implicated as the site of deleterious androgen action is the midline suprachiasmatic-preoptic area. Lesions of this region result in an imbalance in gonadotropin secretion which imitates that observed in the sterile rat. Ovulation can readily be induced by stimulation of this region in normal but not in androgen-sterilized animals.

On the basis of these observations we proposed that the hypothalamus exerts a *dual control* over the release of adenohypophyseal gonadotropin in the female rat (Barraclough and Gorski, 1961) (Fig. 1). The first level of hypothalamic control involves the *tonic* discharge of gonadotropin in sufficient quantity to maintain estrogen production but cannot independently initiate the ovulatory surge of gonadotropin. We suggested that this control is resident within the arcuate-ventromedial nuclear region of the hypothalamus. Evidence for this primary control and localization is based on the observations that estrogen is secreted in the anovulatory persistent estrous rat and that electrical stimulation of these structures in the sterile rat will induce LH secretion. Furthermore, destruction of these areas results in the cessation of estrogen production, ovarian atrophy, and anestrus (Flerkó and Bardós, 1959).

Of fundamental importance is the second and higher control which is responsible for the *cyclic* discharge of gonadotropin to cause ovulation. The specific region responsible for such control most likely resides within the preoptic area of the hypothalamus. This region of "ovulation control"

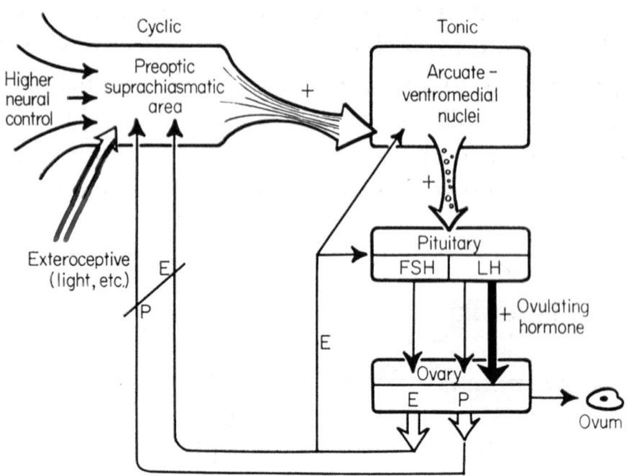

FIG. 1. Diagrammatic representation of the events which may occur at the hypothalamic, pituitary, and gonadal level to result in steroid secretion and ovulation. When proper estrogen (E) to progesterone (P) ratios are reached, the preoptic area becomes responsive to exteroceptive and interoceptive influences, is activated, and in turn it activates the arcuate-ventromedial nuclear area. Sufficient LRF is released to cause the ovulatory discharge of gonadotropin and ovulation.

is dependent for its activation on exteroceptive stimuli such as light (Critchlow, 1963), interoceptive stimuli such as steroids (Flerkó and Szentágothai, 1957), and other neural controlling influences.

It may be that the hypothalamic event which occurs during the normal cycle in the female rat is this: the preoptic (suprachiasmatic) area responds under proper environmental and hormonal circumstances (which are fulfilled on the day of proestrus), by an activation of the more terminal infundibular regions to cause an ovulatory discharge of gonadotropin from the adenohypophysis (Fig. 1). In the absence of this higher control, the terminal structures (arcuate-ventromedial nuclei) still function normally to stimulate LH secretion, but the ovulatory surge of gonadotropin is absent, so sterility results (Fig. 2).

This portion of the preoptic area of the prepubertal female rat is apparently undifferentiated at birth with regard to its subsequent control of gonadotropin secretion. When allowed to differentiate normally, it regulates the release of ovulating hormone. However, if it is exposed to androgen, it becomes refractory to both intrinsic and extrinsic activation, and the more tonic type of male gonadotropin secretion occurs. Thus, either the prepubertal secretions of the testis or the exogenous administration of androgen serve to effectively imprint the masculine pattern of control on the hypothalamic regulation of gonadotropin secretion during its undifferentiated period. In the male this is adequate for a normal function (Fig. 2), but if it occurs in the female then sterility is the result. It should be emphasized that the ovaries of the sterile rat respond to exogenous (Segal and Johnson, 1959) and endogenous LH (released after hypothalamic stimulation; Barraclough and Gorski, 1961) by releasing ova and forming corpora lutea. Whether or not there is a decrease in sensitivity of the sterile ovary to LH is not known.

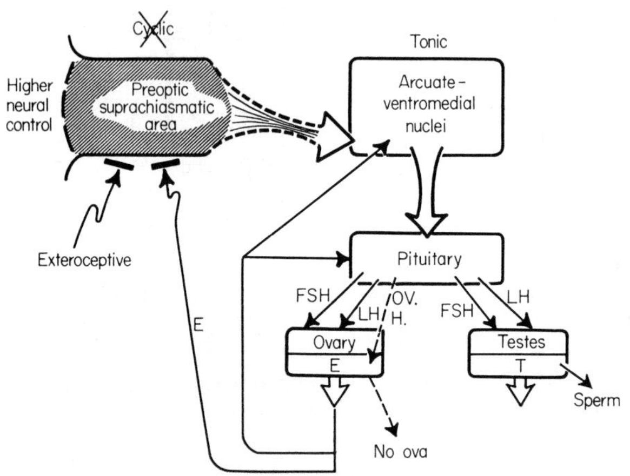

FIG. 2. Hypothalamic events which occur after prepubertal treatment of female rats with androgen, or destruction of the anterior preoptic area. In the absence of the cyclic control for the ovulatory discharge of gonadotropin, only tonic hypothalamic influences on adenohypophyseal function can be manifested. While sufficient FSH and LH are released to cause follicular development and estrogen secretion, ovulation does not occur and the persistent estrus syndrome ensues. In the male this control is adequate for maintenance of spermatogenesis and androgen production. E, estrogen; OV. H., ovulating hormone; T, testosterone.

Thus far only rats treated with 1.25 mg of androgen at 5 days of age have been considered. Similar studies in rats "sterilized" with 10 μg of androgen demonstrated that the degree of hypothalamic refractoriness was dosage-dependent (Gorski and Barraclough, 1963). High doses of androgen produced a refractory hypothalamus which could be activated only after progesterone priming plus extrinsic stimulation of the arcuate-ventromedial complex (Barraclough and Gorski, 1961). "Low" doses of androgen (10 μg) produced the same anovulatory persistent estrus syndrome, but the rats did not require progesterone priming in order to respond to electrical stimulation of the arcuate-ventromedial nuclear region with the release of ovulating hormone. Furthermore, when the rats treated with 10 μg of androgen were primed with progesterone, ovulation could be induced by stimulation of the preoptic area, a phenomenon never observed in the animals sterilized with 1.25 mg of androgen. It is evident that the sterility syndrome exhibited by the rats receiving the large dose of androgen is not identical with that in the rats receiving the smaller dose. The observations further suggest that the high dosage of androgen affects the arcuate-ventromedial nuclear region as well as the preoptic area, whereas the lower dosage alters only preoptic thresholds. The latter circumstance may represent the normal "physiological" state in male rats where cyclic regulatory processes are not necessary and only the tonic control is required. If one assumes that prepubertal androgen treatment alters *neuronal* responsiveness to a critical stimulus, it is then possible to visualize the differences between the two groups of animals (1.25 mg vs. 10 μg). Figure 3 is a diagrammatic

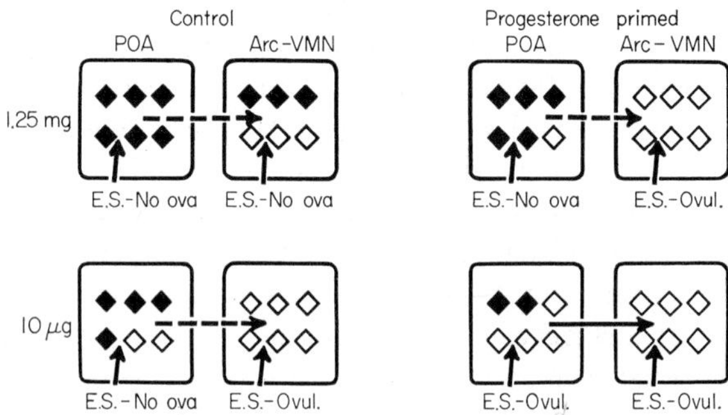

FIG. 3. Diagrammatic representation of one of many possible degrees of neuronal refractoriness which may occur as the consequence of prepubertal androgen treatment. The solid black diamonds indicate refractory neurons, and the open diamonds are neurons which are receptive to stimuli. Rats sterilized with 1.25 mg of androgen do not ovulate after electrical stimulation of either the preoptic area or arcuate-ventromedial nuclear regions. Progesterone-priming overcomes the refractoriness within the arcuate-ventromedial but not the preoptic area. In contrast, a lesser degree of refractoriness is produced in rats which received the 10 μg dose of androgen early in life. Stimulation of the arcuate-ventromedial nuclear region induces ovulation and after progesterone-priming the preoptic area also will respond and ovulation occurs. POA, preoptic area; Arc-VMN, arcuate-ventromedial nuclei; E.S., electrical stimulation; Ovul., ovulation.

representation of one of several possible degrees of neuronal refractoriness which may exist in a pool of six neurons after prepubertal androgen treatment (either 1.25 mg or 10 μg). The decrease in the thresholds of activation within this neuronal pool and the subsequent response to electrical stimulation also are indicated. With the high dosage, some neurons remain permanently refractory, and preoptic area stimulation does not induce ovulation. In contrast, sufficient refractoriness is overcome by the progesterone-priming of animals sterilized with 10 μg of androgen and extrinsic stimulation of the preoptic area induces ovulation. It should be noted that neither preparation will ovulate spontaneously, as some neurons remain permanently unresponsive.

IV. Effects of Prepubertal Androgen Treatment on Pituitary Gonadotropin

A. Luteinizing Hormone

Once established, the anovulatory persistent estrus syndrome promotes further alterations in the endocrine system. Initial assays on the LH content of the 60-day-old sterile rat pituitary (weaver finch method) indicated that the concentration of this gonadotropin was high, and comparable to that of the male rat (Segal and Johnson, 1959). However, assays performed on 150-day-old rats (ovarian ascorbic acid depletion technique) gave pituitary LH concentrations which were only one-third of the values found in normal female glands (Gorski and Barraclough, 1962a). The concentrations of LH in normal and sterile 150-day-old rat pituitaries prior to and after treatment with progesterone are shown in Table III. When persistent vaginal cornification is interrupted by progesterone, storage of LH occurs and the content of the sterile rat pituitary increases 75%. Electrical stimulation of the median eminence at this time induces the release of the stored LH to cause ovulation. Thus, the action of progesterone may be twofold: (1) as indicated previously, progesterone may facilitate the electrical stimulus by lowering thresholds of activation in the hypothalamus, and (2) progesterone may permit the pituitary to store sufficient LH to cause ovulation when released.

More recent studies indicate that prepubertal androgen treatment has other effects on the normal synthesis and/or storage of LH. A comparison of the changes in LH content with age in the normal and androgen-sterilized rat (1.25 mg) is shown in Fig. 4. As compared with the older rats, the normal 30-day-old rat pituitary has a high LH content, which may represent active synthesis and storage of this gonadotropin. There is no evidence that this stored LH is released from the 30-day-old pituitary. In comparison, the pituitary LH content of the 30-day sterile rat is abnormally low. Just prior to puberty (35 days) the normal pituitary content decreases, whereas an increase in gonadotropin is observed in the pituitary of the sterile rat. These changes most likely are related to the onset of puberty, but more data are required before any detailed explanation of such variations can be made. After puberty the LH content of the normal estrous rat and the anovulatory persistent estrous rat

TABLE III

ADENOHYPOPHYSEAL LUTEINIZING HORMONE CONTENT IN NORMAL, ANDROGEN STERILIZED, AND PROGESTERONE-PRIMED, STERILE FEMALE RATS

Treatment	Number of animals	Body weight[a] (grams)	Ovarian weight[a] (milligrams)	Anterior pituitary[a] (milligrains)	Pituitary LH[a] concentration (micrograms per gram net weight)	Total pituitary concentration (micrograms)
Normal proestrus	7	259 ± 6.0	60.4 ± 6.4	9.0 ± 0.4	2.20 ± 0.33	19.9 ± 3.2
Normal estrus	9	255 ± 6.0	73.8 ± 1.5	9.1 ± 0.7	1.08 ± 0.16	9.8 ± 1.4
Androgen sterile, persistent estrus	6	254 ± 6.0	32.2 ± 2.0	11.6 ± 0.6	0.69 ± 0.12	8.0 ± 1.3
Persistent estrus and progesterone	8	288 ± 13.0	37.6 ± 4.9	10.9 ± 1.1	1.19 ± 0.15	13.0 ± 1.6
Persistent estrus and progesterone and electrical stimulation	8	266 ± 19.0	33.2 ± 7.0	9.4 ± 1.7	0.77 ± 0.12	7.2 ± 1.1

[a] Mean ± standard error. Lambda = 0.271 for twenty-three assays. (From Gorski and Barraclough, 1962a.)

become more or less standardized and then do not vary appreciably with age. Thus, neonatal treatment with androgen may alter the adenohypophyseal mechanisms required for synthesis of LH prior to puberty, whereas the secondary feedback action of estrogen during persistent estrus may prevent the normal pituitary storage of LH at subsequent

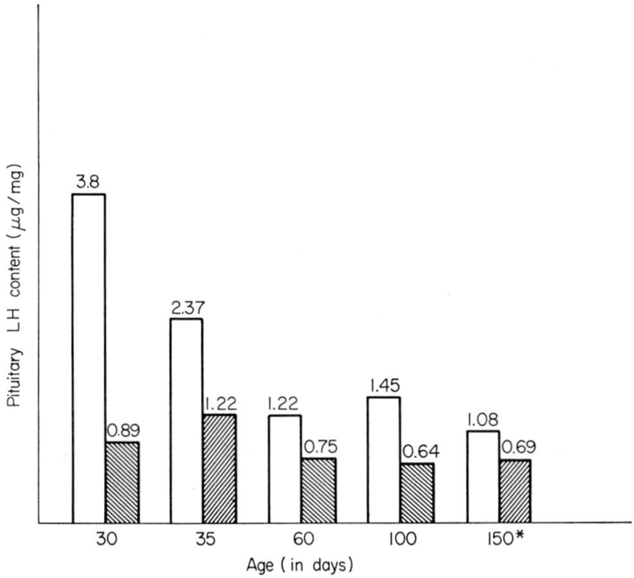

FIG. 4. Comparison of the adenohypophyseal LH content at different ages in the normal and androgen-sterilized female rat (1.25 mg at 5 days of age). The striped bars are the androgen-sterilized animals and the open bars are the control values. The data presented for the 150-day-old group (asterisk) represent data obtained in a previous study and incorporated in this figure for comparison with the earlier ages (see Table III).

ages (Barraclough, 1966a). Questions still to be answered relate to the secretion on demand of the gonadotropin stored in the pituitary of the sterile rat. If the LH content of sterile rat pituitaries is expressed as the total content, then sufficient gonadotropin seemingly is present to cause ovulation. However, can this material be released? Some answers should be forthcoming after a comparative analysis of the pituitary LH content of rats sterilized with 10 μg or 1.25 mg of androgen. Also, is sufficient LH-releasing factor (LRF) present in the hypothalamus of the sterile rat to cause the discharge of LH and ovulation?

B. Follicle-Stimulating Hormone

To date no quantitative studies have been conducted on the effects of prepubertal androgen treatment on the FSH content of the pituitary. However, the ovarian compensatory hypertrophy response after unilateral ovariectomy has been used as a qualitative index of the hypothalamic regulation of FSH secretion in the androgen-sterilized rat. Comparable degrees of ovarian hypertrophy were observed in androgen-sterilized and normal rats (Gorski and Barraclough, 1962b). Furthermore, estrogen treatment of both groups of animals prevented the release of FSH which would ordinarily occur on the demand of unilateral ovariectomy (Barraclough, 1966b). Swanson and Van der Werff ten Bosch (1964a) have reported similar observations in rats prepubertally treated with comparable dosages of androgen. However, when low dosages of androgen (10 μg) were administered, a smaller degree of compensatory hypertrophy was observed than with the "high" sterilizing dosage. Destruction of the anterior hypothalamus markedly curtailed the release of FSH from the adenohypophysis after hemispaying of the sterile rat (Gorski and Barraclough, 1962b). These data support Flerkó's hypothesis (1963) that discrete FSH and LH areas of control exist within the rat hypothalamus and also indicate that the FSH-controlling mechanism is not altered by prepubertal androgen treatment.

C. Luteotropic Hormone

Kikuyama (1963a) employed the pigeon crop-sac response to determine the luteotropic hormone (LTH) content of the androgen-sterilized rat pituitary and failed to note any significant change in concentration. Whereas the normal gland contained 0.44 IU at estrus and 0.43 IU at diestrus, the pituitary glands of 150–210-day-old persistent estrous rats had a value of 0.38 IU. Furthermore, reserpine treatment of sterile rats, previously ovulated with exogenous gonadotropins, resulted in a release of LTH from the adenohypophysis. The criteria used to determine this release was mucification of the vaginal mucosa after estradiol treatment and stimulation of the lobuloalveolar system of the mammary gland. Attempts to induce pseudopregnancy by vaginal cervix stimulation and to produce a uterine decidual reaction (after estrogen and progesterone treatment) have not been successful in the androgen-sterilized rat (Zeilmaker, 1964). In contrast, Burin *et al.* (1963) have obtained a decidual reaction in androgen-sterilized rats treated with progesterone, and the corpora lutea induced by exogenous chorionic gonadotropin (HCG) have become functional after pituitary isografts were placed under the kidney capsule (Zeilmaker, 1964).

It should be noted that after artificial induction of ovulation the timing sequence which relates to the release of LTH in response to reserpine and to the sensitization of the uterine epithelium may differ from that observed in the normal animal. By varying the interval to uterine trauma after administration of reserpine in "ovulated" sterile rats, we have successfully obtained a decidual response in 25% of the tested rats (Barraclough, unpublished data, 1966). However, the 75% which failed to respond support Zeilmaker's (1964) observation that the uterine sensitivity to traumatic stimuli is very low in the sterile rat.

V. Comparative Effects of Prepubertal Treatment with Hormones Other Than Androgen on Subsequent Fertility

A. Estrogen (Including the Persistent Diestrus Syndrome)

Simultaneously with the early studies on the effects of pre- and postnatal treatment of female animals with androgen, investigations were also being conducted on the responses produced by prepubertal estrogen treatment. Like the androgen studies, the general experimental approach consisted of multiple injections administered at different ages after birth. Turner (1941) administered 100–200 IU of estrogen to newborn female rats from days 1–10 of age. At autopsy 10 months later, he observed that the ovaries of these animals lacked corpora lutea and that many follicles were in various stages of atresia. When such ovaries were transplanted to untreated female hosts, corpora lutea were formed. Hale (1944) extended these studies and injected either diethylstilbestrol or estrone into lactating mothers (days 1–14 of lactation) or into the female young, beginning on 7, 14, 21, or 28 days of age. One to fourteen injections were administered. The vaginae of the young rats which suckled the lactating females treated with estrone opened at 9–10 days; in the young injected with estrogen, vaginal opening occurred on days 10–13. Vaginal cycles began at the same time as the littermate controls, but they were either abnormal from the beginning or became so after 4–10 months. The usual abnormality was persistent vaginal cornification. Although the majority of rats treated before 15 days copulated, only one animal became pregnant. This is in contrast to rats treated after 21 days of age which had normal vaginal cycles, copulated, and bore normal litters. Examination of the reproductive tract of adult rats treated with estrogen before 15 days revealed abnormal changes in the periovarial bursa or oviducts (pyosalpinx or salpingitis). The ovaries lacked corpora lutea but contained a few developing follicles and hypertrophied interstitial tissue. The ovaries of animals treated after 21 days of age were normal. Takasugi (1963) observed that five daily injections of estrone, beginning at birth, produced a similar syndrome, and Kikuyama (1963b) established that on this 5-day schedule, the minimum daily dose necessary to produce persistent estrus in rats ranged between $\frac{1}{960}$–$\frac{1}{1920}$ mg. However, at least $\frac{1}{160}$ mg was required to prevent luteinization of the ovaries.

Gorski (1963a) has studied the frequency of occurrence of the anovulatory persistent estrus syndrome when varying amounts of estradiol benzoate were administered as a single injection to the 5-day-old rat. The results of these studies are shown in Table IV. They show that 5 μg

TABLE IV

Effect on Sterility of Single Injections of Different Dosages of Estradiol Benzoate Administered to 5-Day-Old Rats[a]

Amount estrogen injected (micrograms)	Number of rats injected	Number of rats sterile	Sterility (%)
100	110	103	93.4
10	13	11	84.6
5	48	41	85.4
1	12	5	41.7
0.5	8	0	0

[a] From Gorski (1963a).

of estradiol benzoate may be considered the minimum dosage necessary to produce sterility in over 60% of the treated rats. This is compared to the 10 μg of testosterone propionate necessary to produce a similar syndrome. Gorski (1963a) also confirmed and extended the earlier observations of Hale (1944) that estrogen-sterilized female rats would mate, but such mating behavior could not be correlated with the stage of the vaginal cycle. Furthermore, neither progesterone therapy nor the mating stimulus induced ovulation, and ovulation only infrequently occurred as a consequence of electrical stimulation of the median eminence region of the hypothalamus (one of nine rats ovulated). Progesterone priming of these animals, followed by electrical stimulation of the hypothalamus, resulted in only one of six rats ovulating the next day. Thus, the mechanism and site of action of estrogen in producing sterility remains unresolved. It is possible that prepubertal estrogen treatment of female rats not only alters the hypothalamic ovulation-controlling mechanisms, but may also affect the adenohypophysis and gonad as well.

In persistent estrous rats, Arai (1963a) has compared the effects of intrapituitary injections of acid extracts of ventromedial hypothalamus versus temporal cortex of adult male rats on the pituitary-gonadal system. He observed that only the ventromedial hypothalamic extracts induced ovulation. The extract was without effect when injected into central nervous system centers. While this is secondary evidence, it would seem that the adenohypophysis retains its responsiveness to LRF after prepubertal estrogen treatment. The ovary responds to the LH released and ovulation occurs. Hale (1944) also observed ovulation in the ovaries of estrogen-sterilized rats after transplantation into adult rats. Some question still exists concerning the thresholds of responsiveness to gonadotropin of these sterile, polyfollicular ovaries. The failure of such animals to ovulate may also be due to the direct deleterious action of estrogen on the ovary at a critical stage in maturation so that subsequent thresholds are elevated.

While early postnatal treatment of female rats subsequently produces persistent estrus, continued treatment of rats with increasing doses of estrogen to 30 days of age produces persistent diestrus. In the majority of these animals, vaginal diestrus persists after puberty (no cornification), and the ovaries resemble those of immature rats as neither follicles beyond the stage of antrum formation nor corpora lutea are formed in them. However, some rats given identical treatment exhibit persistent vaginal cornification which continues even after ovariectomy or after hypophysectomy followed by ovariectomy and adrenalectomy (Takewaki, 1964a). Similar observations have been reported previously in mice (for references see Takasugi, 1963). The gonadotropin content of the adenohypophysis of persistent estrous and diestrous rats has been measured by Noumura (1958) using the immature rat assay to determine total gonadotropins (GTH). He reported that GTH potency of the estrogen-induced, persistent estrous rat is normal whereas in persistent anestrous animals the GTH potency is low and is not altered by ovariectomy. A more critical analysis of the LH content of the pituitary in persistently anestrous animals (by the ovarian ascorbic acid depletion technique) revealed similar low concentrations. Furthermore, the LRF content in the hypothalami of persistent diestrous rats was less than that of normal rat hypothalami (Arai, 1963b).

Although the corpora lutea forming after exogenous gonadotropin therapy spontaneously do not become functional in the persistent diestrous rat, the injection of reserpine causes the secretion of LTH in both the persistent estrous and diestrous rat. Assays of the LTH content of the adenohypophyses of these two preparations demonstrated that such content was significantly lower in persistent diestrous rats than in persistent estrous or normal rats (Kikuyama, 1963a; Takewaki, 1964b).

The persistent diestrus syndrome has been interpreted by various investigators as indicating the occurrence of an irreversible alteration in some controlling center in the brain. Why does estrogen treatment from days 1–5 of age produce persistent estrus and treatment from days 1–30 produce persistent diestrus? Although specific experimental data are lacking, sufficient evidence is at hand to permit further interpretation of the hypothalamic sites affected by differential estrogen treatment. It is probable that the estrogen treatment which produces persistent estrus permanently elevates the thresholds of responsiveness in the preoptic area so that the cyclic regulation of the ovulatory discharge of gonadotropin is absent and the anovulatory, persistent estrus syndrome occurs. On the other hand, the increase in both dosage and length of treatment apparently deleteriously alters the tonic controlling mechanisms which we have suggested as being resident in the arcuate-ventromedial nuclear area. With the loss of this control, LH secretion ceases, and permanent diestrus ensues. What evidence is there to suggest this site of action? As early as 1932, Hohlweg and Junkmann noted that anterior pituitary transplants into the anterior chamber of the eye did not develop castration cells after ovariectomy and suggested that a "sex centrum" was present in the hypothalamus. The studies of Flerkó (1963) have shown that after gonadectomy only those pituitaries which are transplanted in the "hypophysiotropic" area of the hypothalamus develop "castration cells" and that the arcuate-basal ventromedial nuclei region corresponds fairly well to the center of this "hypophysiotropic" area. Similar transplants elsewhere in the central nervous system fail to develop "castration cells." The adenohypophysis of the "estrogen-induced" persistent diestrous rat does not develop castration cells after gonadectomy, which suggests a malfunction in the arcuate-ventromedial nuclear area of the hypothalamus (quoted by Arai, 1963b). Second, the LRF content of this region is less than normal (Arai, 1963a). Third, lesions of this median eminence region also produce persistent diestrus and decrease both FSH and LH activity in the pituitary, an observation also made in the persistent diestrous rat (Flerkó, 1963). Finally, electrical stimulation of this region fails to induce ovulation, even in progesterone-primed rats (Gorski, 1963a). Thus, it would appear that, as dosage and length of treatment are increased, a major portion of the gonadotropin-controlling region of the hypothalamus is permanently altered and anestrus occurs.

B. Other Steroid Derivatives and Gonadotropin

A few studies on the permanent effects produced by prepubertal administration of progesterone, deoxycorticosterone, and cholesterol have been published. In general, large pharmacological doses of these compounds are required to produce an effect. Selye and Friedman (1940) found that after 50 mg of deoxycorticosterone acetate was administered over a 40-day period, starting from birth, corpora lutea were not formed in the rat ovary. Turner (1941) reported persistent estrus after treatment with progesterone, and Takasugi (1953) observed that 83 μg of progesterone per day for 20 days, or 62 μg of deoxycorticosterone acetate per day for 20 days, or 8 mg of cholesterol per day administered over a 50-day period produced the anovulatory persistent estrus syndrome. Apparently most steroids, if given in sufficiently high dosages for prolonged periods, can permanently alter the undifferentiated prepubertal hypothalamus. No studies characterizing the site of action of these substances have been performed.

In a more recent study, Revesz *et al.* (1960) administered progesterone, 17α-ethinyl-19-nortestosterone, or 6α-methyl-17α-acetoxyprogesterone to pregnant female or newborn rats. They observed that, whereas progesterone (200 mg daily) caused no abnormalities, both synthetic compounds produced pseudohermaphrodism. Unfortunately, all animals were autopsied at 20 days of age, so the effects on subsequent reproductive physiology are not known. Androgenic activity has been attributed to the 19-nortestosterone compound (Wilkins *et al.*, 1958) but not to the acetoxyprogesterone (Lyster *et al.*, 1959). Gorski (1963b) has also studied the effects of a variety of different steroids on development of normal adult patterns of ovulatory estrous cycles in the rat. He observed that the following compounds, administered as a single injection at 5 days of age, failed to alter the normal reproductive pattern: 0.05 cm^3 peanut oil, 1 mg androstenedione, 1.25 mg norethandralone, 6.25 mg hydroxyprogesterone caproate (Delalutin), 1.25 mg cortisone acetate, 2.5 mg hydrocortisone, 5 mg cholesterol, and 1 mg of conjugated estrogens. In contrast, Jacobsohn (1964) has observed that a variety of "anabolic steroids" will induce sterility if injected into neonatal rats.

The observations made by Turner (1941) and Bradbury and Gaensbauer (1939) further complicate the picture of the mechanisms underlying differentiation of the hypothalamus. They found that daily administration of human chorionic gonadotropin during the first 2–4 weeks of life masculinized the external genitalia in the female rat and produced the persistent estrus syndrome. Turner concluded that the production of large amounts of any sex steroid in the very young rat is capable of permanently altering the pattern of gonadotropin secretion.

C. Protection against Steroid-Induced Sterility

In a series of interesting experiments, Kikuyama (1961, 1962) observed that the simultaneous administration of reserpine or chlorpromazine with testosterone propionate or estrone prevented the development of many of the expected abnormalities of gonadotropin secretion. All 4–8-day-old rats treated with estrone and with either reserpine or chlorpromazine were cyclic when adult. Complete protection was not gained in rats receiving androgen since only two of five animals were normal after puberty. On the other hand, reserpine adequately protected against the masculine-imprinting action of the endogenous androgen secreted normally by the prepubertal rat testes. Kawashima (1964) administered reserpine to male rats 1–10-days-old and then orchidectomized the animals; 20 days later ovarian and vaginal grafts were placed under the skin. When the rats were sacrificed at 80 days of age, the implanted ovaries contained corpora lutea, and the vaginae gave evidence of cyclic estrogen secretion. The grafted ovaries of rats treated with only the reserpine vehicle lacked corpora lutea, and the vaginae showed persistence of cornification.

The dosage of reserpine is a critical factor in the end result as attested by the observation that a single injection of 50 μg, given to 4-day-old rats, permanently decreased pituitary LH content and induced a modified persistent diestrus syndrome (Corbin *et al.*, 1964). Although it is not known how these tranquilizing compounds afford protection, this procedure should prove to be a fruitful approach to the further study of sexual differentiation.

VI. Effects of Prepubertal Steroid Treatment on Mating Behavior

Although the various neuroendocrine aspects of sexual behavior are considered in detail in Chapters 21 and 22, this chapter would be incomplete without a brief discussion of the effects of prepubertal hormone treatment on subsequent mating behavior.

Most female rats that are exposed to steroids at an early age develop the anovulatory persistent estrus syndrome, but persistence of vaginal cornification does not necessarily imply persistent sexual receptivity. However, no general statement can be made about the receptivity of persistent estrous animals to the male. For example, we have studied the mating behavior of adult female rats treated with either 1.25 mg or 10 μg of testosterone propionate at 5 days of age (Barraclough, 1961; Barraclough and Gorski, 1962). We observed that animals receiving the 1.25 mg dosage were sexually unreceptive to the male, whereas other rats (10 μg dosage) exhibiting the same syndrome mated readily. The mating responses of rats treated with 10 μg of androgen at 5 days of age are shown in Fig. 5. These animals exhibited, in certain cases, persistent heat as well as persistent vaginal cornification. One rat accepted the male for 9 consecutive days whereas other rats would mate for 3 successive days and still others mated every other day. These bizarre patterns of mating behavior could in no way be correlated with a vaginal cycle since all rats continued to exhibit persistent vaginal cornification, and copulation did not induce ovulation. Attempts to restore mating behavior to the animals treated with the high dose of androgen by the administration of estrogen and progesterone were unsuccessful.

Rat number \ Days	1	2	3	4	5	6	7	8	9
1	+	+	+	+	+	+	+	+	+
2	-	-	+	-	-	-	-	-	-
3	-	+	-	+	+	-	-	+	-
4	+	-	+	+	+	-	+	-	-
5	+	-	+	-	+	-	+	-	-
6	-	-	-	+	-	-	-	+	-
7	+	+	-	-	-	-	-	-	+
8	-	-	-	+	+	+	-	-	-

FIG. 5. Mating response of rats treated with 10 μg of androgen at 5 days of age. The plus signs indicate presence of spermatozoa in the vaginal washings.

A similar dichotomy in the mating behavior of rats injected with estrogen early in life has been observed. As indicated previously, rats treated with estrone or diethylstilbestrol in infancy would accept the male when they became adult, but did not ovulate and no pregnancies occurred. If estrogen treatment was delayed until 21 days of age, then the rats mated, became pregnant, and bore normal litters (Hale, 1944). Similar observations have been made in androgen-sterilized rats (Barraclough, 1961). Rats treated with 100 μg of estradiol benzoate at 5 days of age resembled rats sterilized with 10 μg of androgen; no consistent pattern of sexual receptivity could be detected. The "estrogenized" rats mated repeatedly, and on nine occasions spermatozoa were detected in the vaginal washings during the diestrous interval of the vaginal cycle (Gorski, 1963a).

Differences exist in the reproductive physiology of animals subjected to different doses of androgen and estrogen before 10 days of age which might, in part, explain this dichotomy in mating behavior. As described earlier, there is evidence to suggest that steroids which produce the anovulatory persistent estrus syndrome also deleteriously affect the preoptic-suprachiasmatic area of the hypothalamus. Furthermore, the degree of refractoriness produced is dosage dependent. Such prepubertal treatment also alters the responsiveness of the hypothalamus to the feedback action of certain steroid hormones. Progesterone therapy does not induce ovulation in the androgen- or estrogen-sterilized rat, and in the sexually unreceptive animal it does not restore mating behavior (Barraclough *et al.*, 1964).

Since the site of hypothalamic regulation of the ovulatory discharge of gonadotropin and the neurons responsive to progesterone may be located in the anterior preoptic region, it is not unlikely that this same region is also involved in the regulation of mating behavior in the rat. Large lesions which produce persistent estrus also abolish mating behavior (Hillarp *et al.*, 1954), and progesterone will not "ovulate" these animals (Barraclough *et al.*, 1964). On the other hand, rats which spontaneously develop persistent estrus ovulate in response to progesterone, and both these and rats with light-induced persistent estrus accept the male and ovulate in response to the stimulus of copulation (Everett, 1939, 1940). These responses suggest that the hypothalamus of the spontaneous or light-induced persistent estrous rat is less refractory to extrinsic stimuli than is the hypothalamus of the androgen- or estrogen-sterilized rat. Prepubertal administration of estrogen or of low doses of androgen produces a degree of hypothalamic refractoriness greater than that observed as a consequence of old age, but less than that observed in rats which received "high" doses of androgen. Law and Meagher (1958) have destroyed delineated areas in the hypothalamus of the rat and attempted to correlate the localization of the lesion with mating behavior in both spayed and nonspayed rats. They observed that central lesions in the region of the posterior border of the optic chiasm diminished or abolished a female mating response (lordosis) although such lesions only rarely produced persistent estrus. In contrast, rats with lesions in the premammillary region or anterior hypothalamus mated in vaginal diestrus. On the basis of these studies, Law and Meagher (1958) suggest that the neural mechanisms necessary for sexual receptivity are independent of the hormonal factors which regulate cyclic behavior. However, one must question the size and localization of the lesions in their study, since they failed to observe the common consequence of basal medial anterior hypothalamic lesions, namely persistent estrus. Furthermore, if hormonally regulated cyclic behavior and neurally regulated mating responses exist independently of one another, how does one explain the loss of mating behavior in the spayed or steroid-sterilized rat? It is unlikely that the anterior hypothalamus is solely responsible for the regulation of mating behavior but it may represent a locus of integration of the component activities of a total pattern. This locus is influenced by afferent and humoral mechanisms both from the periphery and by projections from higher levels, but it is also capable of basic independent activity after extirpation of the higher controls.

VII. Influence of Exogenous Hormone Administration in Adult Female Rats Pretreated with Sex Steroids before Puberty

Since rats receiving steroids during infancy do not ovulate, corpora lutea are not formed and the source of progesterone, thought to be necessary for ovulation, is absent. With this reasoning, Everett (1940) was able to show that progesterone could restore normal ovulatory cyclic behavior to the spontaneous persistent estrous rat. Initial attempts by Pfeiffer (1941) to induce ovulation by treatment of sterile rats with progesterone were unsuccessful, and in more recent studies we confirmed these preliminary observations. As is shown in Fig. 6, vaginal cycles could be restored by progesterone but ovulation never occurred, regardless of the dosage employed or the sequence of treatment (Barraclough *et al.*, 1964).

This observation, considered along with our information on the site of hypothalamic malfunction in the "androgenized" rat, suggested that the anterior preoptic area may be the area through which progesterone acts

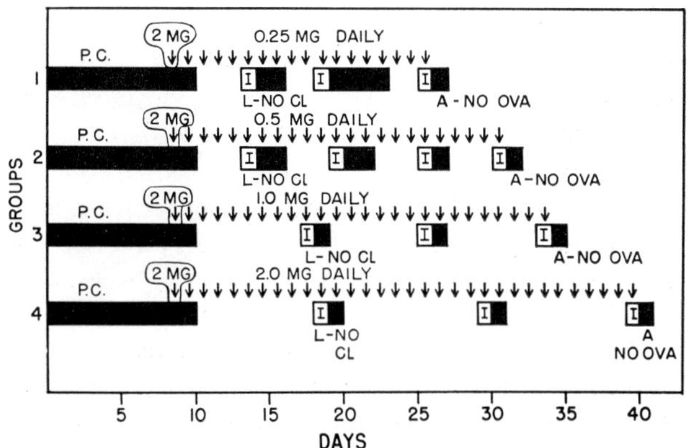

FIG. 6. Effects of daily injections of various doses of progesterone on the vaginal cycle of the androgen-sterilized rat. Note that the 0.5 mg dose induced a 5-day vaginal cycle, but at autopsy 33 days later no ova were found in the fallopian tubes and corpora lutea were absent from the ovaries. P.C., persistent vaginal cornification; L., laparotomy; NO CL, no corpora lutea; A., autopsy; I, proestrus. The black areas represent vaginal cornification.

to facilitate ovulation. To test this hypothesis, lesions were made in the anterior hypothalamus of normal cycling female rats. Three weeks after persistent estrus had become established, the response of these animals to progesterone was tested. Rats with lesions of the suprachiasmatic nuclei exhibited persistent estrus and ovulated in response to progesterone. Destruction of the suprachiasmatic nuclei and the major portion of the medial preoptic area produced persistent estrus, but progesterone did not induce ovulation. The smallest lesions which prevented progesterone-induced ovulation destroyed a part of the suprachiasmatic nuclei and the periventricular portion of the medial preoptic area. That the median eminence, tuberal region, and the adenohypophysis could still respond was demonstrated by ovulation following electrical stimulation of these hypothalamic areas in rats with preoptic lesions (Fig. 7).

From these studies it would appear that a primary site of action of progesterone is the preoptic area. However, due consideration must also be given a second hypothesis. It may be that the site of origin of the *intrinsic stimulus* which activates the components of the hypothalamo-pituitary axis actually resides within the preoptic-suprachiasmatic region. If this region contains the generator of the active stimulus, ovula-

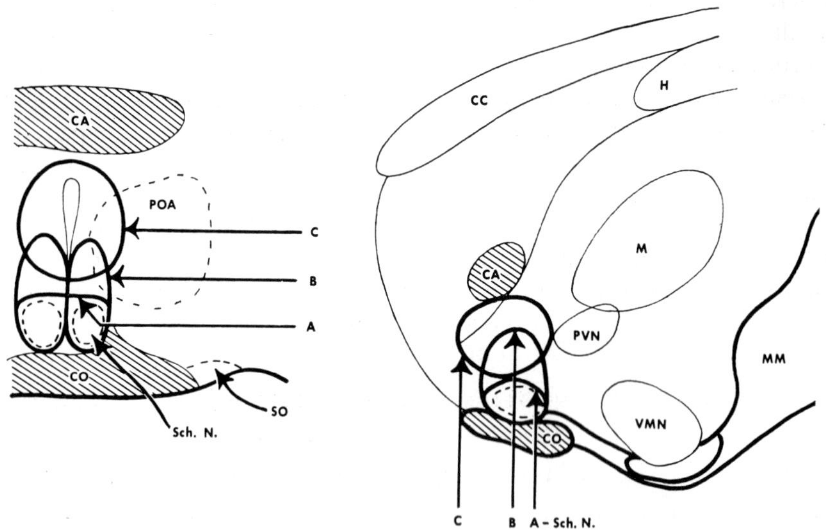

FIG. 7. Coronal and sagittal reconstructions of lesions produced in the anterior hypothalamus of the rat. Lesion A produced persistent estrus, but progesterone therapy induced ovulation. Lesion B produced persistent estrus and the animal did not ovulate in response to progesterone. Lesion C failed to produce persistent estrus and progesterone advanced ovulation 24 hours. CA, anterior commissure; POA, medial preoptic area; CO, optic chiasm; Sch. N., suprachiasmatic nuclei; SO, supraoptic nuclei; CC, corpus callosum; M, massa intermedia; PVN, paraventricular nuclei; MM, mammillary bodies, VMN, ventromedial nucleus; H, hippocampus.

tion cannot occur when the area is destroyed, even when all hormonal balances are correct and the remaining structures intact. It should be noted parenthetically that experiments on localization of the feedback site of any steroid by the lesion technique are open to similar alternate interpretations. Thus, the possibility that progesterone may act secondarily to facilitate preoptic activation of the median eminence structures and subsequently the adenohypophysis deserves consideration. This effect is suggested from the data obtained in the androgen-sterilized rat (see Fig. 4) and from the observations of Kawakami and Sawyer (1959) who noted that thresholds of activation within the ventromedial nuclei could be lowered by progesterone. However, if the "intrinsic stimulus" originates within the preoptic area, where do neuropharmacological agents such as pentobarbital or atropine sulfate act to block ovulation and the progesterone advancement of ovulation? Ovulation can easily be induced in such preparations by electrical stimulation of the preoptic area or septum (Everett, 1964b). If these were the depressed areas, such events should not occur. Obviously, the answers to these questions await further information.

The effects of other hormones in the adult sterile rat have been considered in other portions of this chapter. The ovaries of immature or adult anovulatory persistent estrous rats (either androgen- or estrogen-sterilized) respond to LH, HCG, or PMS by releasing ova and forming corpora lutea (Segal and Johnson, 1959; Harris, 1964; Schuetz and Meyer, 1963). Changes in the levels of circulating estrogen produced by unilateral or bilateral ovariectomy of the androgen- or estrogen-sterilized rat increase FSH secretion, and estrogen injections decrease FSH secretion (Gorski and Barraclough, 1962b; Gorski, 1963a). Courrier *et al.* (1961) and Arai (1963a) have observed that LRF extracts cause sufficient release of gonadotropin from the adenohypophysis of estrogen- or androgen-sterilized rats to induce ovulation.

VIII. Influence of Prepubertal Hormone Treatment on Subsequent Ovarian Steroidogenesis

The principal information on the secretions (or lack thereof) of the anovulatory polyfollicular ovary is based on the effects produced after transplantation into a host animal. Hale (1944) observed that the ovary of the estrogen-sterilized rat secreted sufficient steroids to stimulate the male sex accessory organs. Whether or not this was androgenic stimulation is not known. However, it has been conclusively shown that these polyfollicular ovaries, when placed in an environment where the female pattern of gonadotropin is secreted, will again ovulate and secrete estrogen in a cyclic pattern. This is true if the host animal is a normal ovariectomized female or a prepubertally castrate male (Yazaki, 1959, 1960; Harris, 1964). That the corpora lutea, once formed, can secrete progesterone has been shown by Zeilmaker (1964) and Kikuyama (1963a). Goldzieher and Axelrod (1963) have incubated the polyfollicular ovary of the androgen-sterilized rat with pregnenolone-4-C^{14} as the substrate. In Table V are presented the results of one such study. Gold-

TABLE V

STEROIDOGENESIS IN OVARIAN TISSUE OF PERSISTENT ESTROUS RATS[a]

Metabolite	Total counts per minute
Unconverted pregnenolone	391,540
Δ^5-Pregnen-3β,20β-diol	10,870
17α-Hydroxyprogesterone	6,890
Dehydroepiandrosterone	8,620
Δ^4-Androstenedione	20,100
Testosterone	12,470
Estrogens	None

[a] From Goldzieher and Axelrod (1963). Substrate is pregnenlone-4-C^{14}.

zieher indicates that, although there is ample conversion of the pregnenolone to androgens, no aromatization to estrogens is detectable. This does not imply that no estrogen is secreted by this ovary but rather that the ratio of androgen to estrogen is high. These investigators have also noted a similar pattern of secretion from the polycystic ovaries of the human female. It is this author's opinion that, if the anovulatory polyfollicular ovary of the rat does secrete more androgen than the normal ovary *in vivo,* the abnormality is more directly due to the imbalance in gonadotropin secretion than to the direct effect of the androgen or estrogen on the ovary during its phase of maturation. Otherwise, these ovaries would not resume normal function when placed under the influence of the cyclic pattern of gonadotropin secretion. It would be interesting to study steroidogenesis by these ovaries after a period of normal function in a host animal.

IX. Influence of Prepubertal Administration of Sex Steroids on Reproductive Physiology of the Male

A. Androgen

The effects of androgenic hormones on the male reproductive system have been extensively investigated. The diversified effects produced by androgen depend upon the age, length of treatment, and dosage employed. They have been considered in detail in "Sex and Internal Secretions" by Albert (1961) and by Price and Williams-Ashman (1961). For example, in the immature rat, small doses of androgen depress testicular weight (Greene and Burrill, 1940), whereas large doses actually stimulate the testis. In both cases, however, there is Leydig cell atrophy. The differential responsiveness of the testes depends upon the direct stimulatory effect of high doses of exogenous androgen on the gonad (Nelson and Merckel, 1937). Small doses of androgen do not stimulate the testes directly, but they inhibit gonadotropin production and/or release, and thus testis weight is decreased. The effect of a single injection of androgen at a given time in development on subsequent reproductive system maturation has been studied by Barraclough and Leathem (1959). Male mice 5, 10, or 20 days of age were given a single injection of 1.0 mg of testosterone propionate and then autopsied at 10-day intervals between treatment and 60 days of age. Mice treated at 5 or 10 days of age had a suppressed testicular growth rate throughout the 60 days of study. Furthermore, normal differentiation of spermatids to spermatozoa was delayed from 30 to 40 days of age. Testes weights in mice treated at 20 days of age were initially depressed but at 40 days they were comparable to the littermate controls. Androgen also initially stimulated the seminal vesicles of mice treated at 5 or 10 days of age, but this organ was significantly smaller than the controls at 60 days of age. Seemingly, prepubertal androgen treatment of the male delays onset of puberty by approximately 10 days, but eventually (by 60 days of age) normal reproduction is established. This is contrasted to the female, in which identical treatment permanently alters reproductive performance.

B. Estrogens

It is now generally agreed that in most forms studied (viz., rat, guinea pig, bull, man, etc.), estrogen induces atrophy of the male gonad (Albert, 1961). Furthermore, if estrogen treatment is begun early in life, then testicular descent is impaired and spermatogenesis is inhibited. However, such effects of estrogen seem to be temporary when administered to adult animals, and regeneration is complete within 6 weeks (Lynch, 1952). The effect of estrogen in the rat is to induce atrophy of the Leydig cells and germinal epithelium so that only spermatocytes, Sertoli cells, and spermatogonia remain. Little information is available on the permanent effects produced by single injections of estrogen to prepubertal male animals. Harris and Levine (1962) injected 4-day-old male rats with 100 μg of estradiol benzoate and observed a retardation of growth and a marked disorganization of spermatogenesis at puberty. Kincl *et al.* (1963) have reported that male rats injected with 120 μg of estradiol dipropionate before 10 days of age would not mate when adult, and that there was a complete loss of the germinal epithelium of the seminiferous tubule and a decreased seminal vesicle and prostate weight. In contrast, males treated at 10 or 20 days of age were normal when adult. By reducing the dosage of estrogen it was further noted that 10 μg of estrogen was insufficient to produce testicular atrophy, and normal litters were obtained in the breeding studies. A single injection of 30 μg of estradiol produced a significant decrease in accessory sex gland weight, and infertility, but spermatogenesis was not arrested. Because of the paucity of information on the influence of prepubertal estrogen treatment in the male, it is not possible to attempt any major conclusions on the mechanism or site of action of estrogens in the male. Since the weights of the prostate and seminal vesicles are markedly decreased, it would seem that androgen secretion has been attenuated, and consequently libido is decreased and no mating occurs. Thus these estrogen-sterilized male rats may, to some degree, resemble the persistent diestrous female rats. If prepubertal estrogen treatment alters normal function of the tonic hypothalamic controlling area, gonadotropin secretion decreases, and either the abnormal male or female syndrome is produced. However, this hypothesis is contradicted by the effects produced by a single injection of estrogen in the female rat where the persistent estrus syndrome occurs. The many undetermined factors which may be important to the final effect include the changes produced by estrogen in the reactivity of the male gonad and sex accessory glands to gonadotropin and endogenous androgen as well as the differential effects of different dosages of estrogen and the age of the treated animal.

X. Other Effects of Prepubertal Steroid Treatment

A. Growth

It is well recognized that castration of the neonatal rat markedly reduces growth rate. Conversely, 2- or 5-day-old rats treated with 1.25 mg of testosterone propionate exhibit an increased growth rate, whereas similar treatment of the 10- or 20-day-old animal does not produce this effect (Barraclough, 1961). Similarly, Harris (1964) has noted a significant difference in growth rate between 50 and 100 days of age of animals sham-operated or castrated during the first day of life. However, animals which were castrated on the third to seventh day of life were indistinguishable from sham-operated groups. While androgens have a protein anabolic action, this in itself does not seem to account for the body weight differences among normal and experimental groups. Swanson and Van der Werff ten Bosch (1963) have carefully evaluated the effects of prepubertal androgen treatment on the growth rates of male and female rats. They observed that the testosterone-treated female rats grow heavier than their controls and that the difference in body weight increases with age. Furthermore, when weight gain per week is plotted against age, the curve for the androgen-sterilized female rats runs parallel to but generally above the controls, indicating that a persistently higher growth rate is initiated by the androgen treatment. In contrast, prepubertal treatment of male rats causes a depression of growth rate but eventually a normal growth rate is resumed. Determinations of specific gravity and weights of heart, liver, and kidneys indicate that the changes in weight due to androgen treatment are attributable to overall differences in size and not to specific differences in any particular body component. Thus, there is a possibility that the hypothalamic regulation of growth hormone secretion might be affected by such treatment so that a male pattern of control is imprinted before 10 days of age. Rats 10–20-days-old fail to show an increased growth rate after prepubertal androgen treatment.

B. Activity Cycles

Richter (1933) and Richter and Hartman (1934) observed that normal adult male rats show low irregular running behavior in activity cages, whereas high peaks of activity are observed in female rats during estrus, and activity decreases in the diestrous phase of the cycle. Harris (1964) noted that males castrated at birth and implanted with an ovary when adult show the female pattern of running behavior. Males sham-operated at birth and castrated and implanted with ovarian tissue when adult exhibit the male behavior. Kennedy (1964) found that injection of androgen into pregnant rats during the last 5 days of gestation caused genital abnormalities in female young but did not affect their estrous cycle or activity. Injection of androgen into 2–6-day-old female rats did not reduce running activity, and he concludes that the disorganization of female behavior by prepubertal exposure to androgen does not lower running activity to the male level.

C. Time of Vaginal Opening and Vaginal Cycles in Androgen-Sterilized Rats

We have observed that vaginal opening in the sterile rat generally occurs 2–3 days earlier than the littermate controls. In our colony, vaginal opening generally occurs between 38–42 days of age. Jacobsohn (1964) has reported that the vaginal lavages from female rats receiving 1.5 mg of testosterone propionate at 5 days of age contained cornified cells 5 days earlier than the control (38 vs. 43 days of age). Swanson and Van der Werff ten Bosch (1964b) noted that neonatal rats treated with 5 μg of androgen were ovulating when they reached 10 weeks of age, but became sterile at 21 weeks of age.

XI. General Comments and Conclusions

It is apparent to the reader that the majority of the data presented in this chapter involve studies on the rat or mouse. This has not been arbitrarily decided but rather emphasizes the lack of information in other species. The author has informally spoken with many investigators who have indicated that they have also attempted to produce a syndrome similar to that seen in rats in a variety of other species, but without success. These species include the rabbit and cat. There was one case in which a newborn female beagle puppy was given a very large dose of androgen; when last observed (1 year later) this animal had not come into heat. Recently, Young *et al.* (1964) have reported the production of three pseudohermaphrodite female rhesus monkeys by prenatal androgen treatment. These animals were still immature at the time of the report, and little is known of the neuroendocrine imbalance which may subsequently develop. In reflex-ovulating species it does not seem required that a steroid imprinting mechanism be present, since the neural reflex component becomes the determining factor in the release of ovulating hormone. The picture in humans is confused and uncertain, but the experimental observations on the permanent effects produced in animals by prepubertal exposure to a wide variety of the currently popular synthetic steroids suggests a need for cautious and educated use of these drugs.

In conclusion, there is now available sufficient evidence to conclude that the hypothalamus of some ovulating forms (rat, mouse, etc.) is undifferentiated in terms of its subsequent control of adenohypophyseal gonadotropin secretion. The period of undifferentiation is variable from species to species, depending upon the degree of maturation of the brain at the time of birth. The normal process by which the male imprints its type of regulation within the brain is by the secretion of androgen during the late prenatal or early postnatal period. In contrast, insufficient estrogen is secreted by the ovary in pre- or postnatal animals to affect the undifferentiated hypothalamus and maturation proceeds to the cyclic type of regulation characteristic of the adult female.

Acknowledgment

The support for many of the previously unpublished research data, as well as the "in press" publications was made possible by an award from the USPHS, Grant No. NB–04199–01. The author also wishes to express his appreciation to Samuel Fava for his assistance in the preparation of this manuscript.

References

Albert, A. (1961). The mammalian testis. *In* "Sex and Internal Secretions" (W. C. Young, ed.), Vol. I, pp. 305–365. Williams & Wilkins, Baltimore, Maryland.

Arai, Y. (1963a). Induction of luteinization by intrapituitary injection of hypothalamic extract in persistent-estrous rats. *J. Fac. Sci. Univ. Tokyo, Sect. IV* **10,** 243–248.

Arai, Y. (1963b). The content of luteinizing hormone of the anterior pituitary and the luteinizing hormone releasing factor of the hypothalamus in estrogen-induced persistent-diestrous rats. *Proc. Japan Acad.* **39,** 605–609.

Barraclough, C. A. (1955). Influence of age on the response of preweaning female mice to testosterone propionate. *Am. J. Anat.* **97,** 493–522.

Barraclough, C. A. (1961). Production of anovulatory, sterile rats by single injections of testosterone propionate. *Endocrinology* **68,** 62–67.

Barraclough, C. A. (1966a). *Endocrinology* (in press).

Barraclough, C. A. (1966b). Modifications in the CNS regulation of reproduction after exposure of prepubertal rats to steroid hormones. *Rec. Progr. Hormone Res.* **22,** 503–539.

Barraclough, C. A., and Gorski, R. A. (1961). Evidence that the hypothalamus is responsible for androgen-induced sterility in the female rat. *Endocrinology* **68,** 68–79.

Barraclough, C. A., and Gorski, R. A. (1962). Studies on mating behavior in the androgen-sterilized female rat in relation to the hypothalamic regulation of sexual behavior. *J. Endocrinol.* **25,** 175–182.

Barraclough, C. A., and Leathem, J. H. (1954). Infertility induced in mice by a single injection of testosterone propionate. *Proc. Soc. Exptl. Biol. Med.* **85,** 673–674.

Barraclough, C. A., and Leathem, J. H. (1959). Influence of age on the response of male mice to testosterone propionate. *Anat. Record* **134,** 239–255.

Barraclough, C. A., Yrarrazaval, S., and Hatton, R. (1964). A possible hypothalamic site of action of progesterone in the facilitation of ovulation in the rat. *Endocrinology* **75,** 838–845.

Bradbury, J. T. (1941). Permanent after-effects following masculinization of the infantile female rat. *Endocrinology* **28,** 101–106.

Bradbury, J. T., and Gaensbauer, F. (1939). Masculinization of the female rat by gonadotropic extracts. *Proc. Soc. Exptl. Biol. Med.* **41,** 128–129.

Burin, P., Thevenot-Duluc, A. J., and Mayer, G. (1963). Exploration des potentialities de l'hypophyse et des effecteurs des hormones génitales chez les rattes en oestrus permanent provoqué par une injection postnatale de testosterone. *Compt. Rend. Soc. Biol.* **157,** 1258–1260.

Burns, R. K. (1961). Role of hormones in the differentiation of sex. *In* "Sex and Internal Secretions" (W. C. Young, ed.), Vol. I, pp. 76–158. Williams & Wilkins, Baltimore, Maryland.

Corbin, A., Fraschini, F., Carraro, A., and Martini, L. (1964). Effects of prepubertal reserpine treatment on pituitary LH and the estrous cycle of the rat. *Program 46th Meeting Endocrine Soc., San Francisco* p. 24 (Abstract).

Courrier, R., Guillemin, R., Jutisz, M., Sakiz, E., and Aschheim, P. (1961). Présence dans un extrait d'hypothalamus d'une substance qui stimule la sécrétion de l'hormone antéhypophysaire de lutéinisation (LH). *Compt. Rend. Soc. Biol.* **253,** 922–927.

Critchlow, B. V. (1958). Ovulation induced by hypothalamic stimulation of the anesthetized rat. *Am. J. Physiol.* **195,** 171–174.

Critchlow, B. V. (1963). The role of light in the neuroendocrine system. *In* "Advances in Neuroendocrinology" (A. V. Nalbandov, ed.), pp. 377–402. Univ. of Illinois Press, Urbana, Illinois.

Diamond, M., and Young, W. C. (1963). Differential responsiveness of pregnant and nonpregnant guinea pigs to the masculinizing action of testosterone propionate. *Endocrinology* **72,** 429–438.

Everett, J. W. (1939). Spontaneous persistent estrus in a strain of albino rats. *Endocrinology* **25,** 123–127.

Everett, J. W. (1940). The restoration of ovulatory cycles and corpus luteum formation in persistent estrous rats by progesterone. *Endocrinology* **27,** 681–686.

Everett, J. W. (1964a). Central neural control of reproductive functions of the adenohypophysis. *Physiol. Rev.* **44,** 373–431.

Everett, J. W. (1964b). Preoptic stimulative lesions and ovulation in the rat: Thresholds and LH-release time in late diestrus and proestrus. *In* "Major Problems in Neuroendocrinology" (E. Bajusz and G. Jasmin, eds.), pp. 346–366. Karger, Basel.

Flerkó, B. (1963). The central nervous system and the secretion and release of luteinizing hormone and follicle stimulating hormone. *In* "Advances in Neuroendocrinology" (A. V. Nalbandov, ed.), pp. 211–224. Univ. of Illinois Press, Urbana, Illinois.

Flerkó, B., and Bardós, V. (1959). Zwei verschiedene Effekte experimenteller Läsion des Hypothalamus auf die Gonaden. *Acta Neuroveget. (Vienna)* **20,** 248–262.

Flerkó, B., and Szentágothai, J. (1957). Oestrogen sensitive nervous structures in the hypothalamus. *Acta Endocrinol.* **26,** 121–127.

Goldzieher, J. W., and Axelrod, L. R. (1963). Clinical and biochemical features of polycystic ovarian disease. *Fertility Sterility* **14,** 631–653.

Gorski, R. A. (1963a). Modification of ovulatory mechanisms by postnatal administration of estrogen to the rat. *Am. J. Physiol.* **205,** 842–844.

Gorski, R. A. (1963b). The specificity of the hypothalamic steroid sensitive period. *Anat. Record* **145,** 234.

Gorski, R. A., and Barraclough, C. A. (1962a). Adenohypophyseal LH content in normal, androgen-sterilized and progesterone-primed sterile female rats. *Acta Endocrinol.* **39,** 13–21.

Gorski, R. A., and Barraclough, C. A. (1962b). Studies on hypothalamic regulation of FSH secretion in the androgen-sterilized female rat. *Proc. Soc. Exptl. Biol. Med.* **110,** 298–300.

Gorski, R. A., and Barraclough, C. A. (1963). Effects of low dosages of androgen on the differentiation of hypothalamic regulatory control of ovulation in the rat. *Endocrinology* **73,** 210–216.

Greene, R. R., and Burrill, M. W. (1940). The recovery of testes after androgen induced inhibition. *Endocrinology* **26,** 516–518.

Greene, R. R., Burrill, M. W., and Ivy, A. C. (1939). Experimental intersexuality. The effect of antenatal androgens on sexual development of female rats. *Am. J. Anat.* **65**, 415–470.

Hale, H. B. (1944). Functional and morphological alterations of the reproductive system of the female rat following prepuberal treatment with estrogens. *Endocrinology* **35**, 499–506.

Harris, G. W. (1964). Sex hormones, brain development and brain function. *Endocrinology* **75**, 627–648.

Harris, G. W., and Jacobsohn, D. (1951). Functional grafts of the anterior pituitary gland. *J. Physiol.* (*London*) **113**, 35P–36P.

Harris, G. W., and Levine, S. (1962). Sexual differentiation of the brain and its experimental control. *J. Physiol.* (*London*) **163**, 42P (Abstract).

Hillarp, N. Å., Olivecrona, H., and Silfverskiold, W. (1954). Participation of the preoptic area in male mating behavior. *Experiential* **10**, 224–225.

Hohlweg, W., and Junkmann, K. (1932). Die hormonal-nervose Regulierung der Funktion des Hypophysenborderlappens. *Klin. Wochschr.* **11**, 321–323.

Hooker, C. W. (1948). The biology of the interstitial cells of the testis. *Recent Progr. Hormone Res.* **3**, 173–195.

Huffman, J. W. (1941). Effect of testosterone propionate upon reproduction in the female rat. *Endocrinology* **29**, 77–79.

Jacobsohn, D. (1964). Development of female rats injected shortly after birth with testosterone or "anabolic steroids". *Acta Endocrinol.* **45**, 402–414.

Kawakami, M., and Sawyer, C. H. (1959). Induction of behavioral and electroencephalographic changes in the rabbit by hormone administration or brain stimulation. *Endocrinology* **65**, 631–643.

Kawashima, S. (1960). Secretion of androgen by ovarian grafts in males castrated at birth. *J. Fac. Sci. Univ. Tokyo, Sect. IV* **9**, 117–125.

Kawashima, S. (1964). Inhibitory action of reserpine on the development of the male pattern of secretion of gonadotropins in the rat. *Annotationes Zool. Japon.* **37**, 79–85.

Keller, K., and Tandler, J. (1916). Über das Verhalten der Eihäute bei der Zwillingssträchtigkeit des Rindes. Untersuchungen über die Entstehungsursache der geschlechtlichen Unterentwicklung von weiblichen Zwillingskälbern welche neben einem männlichen Kalbe zur Entwicklung gelangen. *Wien. Tierärztl. Wochschr.* **3**, 513.

Kennedy, G. C. (1964). Mating behavior and spontaneous activity in androgen-sterilized female rats. *J. Physiol.* (*London*) **172**, 393–399.

Kikuyama, S. (1961). Inhibitory effect of reserpine on the induction of persistent estrus by sex steroids in the rat. *Annotationes Zool. Japon.* **34**, 111–116.

Kikuyama, S. (1962). Inhibition of induction of persistent estrus by chlorpromazine in the rat. *Annotationes Zool. Japon.* **35**, 6–11.

Kikuyama, S. (1963a). Secretion of luteotropic hormone by the anterior hypophysis in persistent-estrous and diestrous rats. *J. Fac. Sci. Univ. Tokyo, Sect. IV* **10**, 231–242.

Kikuyama, S. (1963b). Doses of estrone effective in securing persistent-estrous rats. *Annotationes Zool. Japon.* **36**, 145–148.

Kincl, F. A., Folch Pi, A., and Lasso, L. H. (1963). Effect of estradiol treatment in the newborn male rat. *Endocrinology* **72**, 966–968.

Krohn, P. L. (1955). Tissue transplantation techniques applied to the problem of the aging of the organs of reproduction. *Ciba Found. Colloq. Aging* **1**, 141–162.

Law, T., and Meagher, W. (1958). Hypothalamic lesions and sexual behavior in the female rat. *Science* **125**, 1626–1627.

Leathem, J. H. (1958). The effects of aging on reproduction. *In* "The Endocrinology of Reproduction" (J. T. Velardo, ed.), pp. 315–329. Oxford Univ. Press, London and New York.

Lillie, F. R. (1916). The theory of the freemartin. *Science* **43,** 611–613.

Lillie, F. R. (1917). The freemartin: a study of the action of sex hormones in the fetal life of cattle. *J. Exptl. Zool.* **23,** 371–452.

Lynch, K. M. (1952). Recovery of the rat testis following estrogen therapy. *Ann. N.Y. Acad. Sci.* **55,** 734–741.

Lyster, S. C., Lund, C. H., Dulin, W. E., and Stafford, R. O. (1959). Ability of some progestational steroids to stimulate male accessory glands of reproduction in the rat. *Proc. Soc. Exptl. Biol. Med.* **100,** 540–543.

Martinez, C., and Bittner, J. J. (1956). A non-hypophyseal sex difference in estrous behavior of mice bearing pituitary grafts. *Proc. Soc. Exptl. Biol. Med.* **91,** 506–509.

Nelson, W. O., and Merckel, C. (1937). Maintenance of spermatogenesis in testis of the hypophysectomized rat with steroid derivatives. *Proc. Soc. Exptl. Biol. Med.* **36,** 825–828.

Noumura, T. (1958). Hypophyseal-ovarian relationship in persistent-estrous and persistent-anaestrous rats. *J. Fac. Sci. Univ. Tokyo, Sect. IV* **8,** 317–335.

Ortiz, E. (1947). The postnatal development of the golden hamster (*Cricetus auratus*) and its reactivity to hormones. *Physiol. Zool.* **20,** 45–66.

Pfeiffer, C. A. (1936). Sexual differences of the hypophyses and their determination by the gonads. *Am. J. Anat.* **58,** 195–226.

Pfeiffer, C. A. (1941). Hormonal factors in the formation and maintenance of corpora lutea in "constant" estrous rats. *Anat. Record* **79,** 50 (Abstract).

Price, D., and Ortiz, E. (1944). The relationship of age to reactivity of the reproductive systems of the rat. *Endocrinology* **34,** 215–239.

Price, D., and Williams-Ashman, H. G. (1961). The accessory reproductive glands of mammals. *In* "Sex and Internal Secretions" (W. C. Young, ed.), Vol. I, pp. 366–448. Williams & Wilkins, Baltimore, Maryland.

Revesz, C., Chappel, C. I., and Gaundry, R. (1960). Masculinization of female fetuses in the rat by progestational compounds. *Endocrinology* **66,** 140–143.

Richter, C. P. (1933). The effect of early gonadectomy on the gross body activity of rats. *Endocrinology* **17,** 445–450.

Richter, C. P., and Hartman, C. G. (1934). The effect of injection of amniotin on the spontaneous activity of gonadectomized rats. *Am. J. Physiol.* **108,** 136–143.

Schuetz, A. W., and Meyer, R. K. (1963). Effect of early postnatal steroid treatment on ovarian function in prepubertal rats. *Proc. Soc. Exptl. Biol. Med.* **112,** 875–880.

Segal, S. J., and Johnson, D. C. (1959). Inductive influence of steroid hormones on the neural system. Ovulation controlling mechanisms. *Arch. Anat. Microscop. Morphol. Exptl.* **48,** 261–274.

Selye, H., and Friedman, S. M. (1940). The action of various steroid hormones on the ovary. *Endocrinology* **27,** 857–866.

Shay, H., Gershon-Cohen, J., Paschkis, K. E., and Fels, S. S. (1939). The effect of large doses of testosterone propionate (Oreton) on the female genital tract of the very young rat. Production of ovarian cysts. *Endocrinology* **25,** 933–943.

Swanson, H. E., and Van der Werff ten Bosch, J. J. (1963). Sex differences in growth of rats and their modification by a single injection of testosterone propionate shortly after birth. *J. Endocrinol.* **26,** 197–207.

Swanson, H. E., and Van der Werff ten Bosch, J. J. (1964a). The "Early-Androgen" syndrome; its development and the response to hemispaying. *Acta Endocrinol.* **45,** 1–12.

Swanson, H. E., and Van der Werff ten Bosch, J. J. (1964b). The "Early-Androgen" syndrome; differences in response to prenatal and postnatal administration of various doses of testosterone propionate in female and male rats. *Acta Endocrinol.* **47,** 37–50.

Takasugi, N. (1953). Einflusse von Progesteron, Desoxykortikosteron Acetat und Cholestrin auf die Ovarien der neugeborenen, weiblichen Ratten. *Annotationes Zool. Japon.* **26,** 52–56.

Takasugi, N. (1963). Vaginal cornification in persistent-estrous mice. *Endocrinology* **72,** 607–619.

Takewaki, K. (1964a). Persistent changes in uterus and vaginal in rats given injections of estrogen for the first thirty postnatal days. *Proc. Japan Acad.* **40,** 42–47.

Takewaki, K. (1964b). Secretion of luteotropin in persistent-diestrous rats. *Endocrinol. Japon.* **11,** 1–8.

Turner, C. D. (1941). Permanent genital impairments in the adult rat resulting from administration of estrogen during early life. *Am. J. Physiol.* **133,** 471–472 (Abstract).

Wilkins, L., Jones, H. W., Holman, G. H., and Stempfel, R. S. (1958). Masculinization of the female fetus associated with administration of oral and intramuscular progestins during gestation: non-adrenal female pseudohermaphrodism. *J. Clin. Endocrinol. Metab.* **18,** 559–585.

Yazaki, I. (1959). Effect of adrenalectomy, injections of hormonic steroids or gonadotropins and subjection to stressful stimuli on subcutaneous ovarian grafts in castrated male rats as studied by daily examination of vaginal smears. *Japan. J. Zool.* **12,** 267–277.

Yazaki, I. (1960). Further studies on endocrine activity of subcutaneous ovarian grafts in male rats by daily examination of smears from vaginal grafts. *Annotationes Zool. Japon.* **33,** 217–225.

Young, W. C., Goy, R. W., and Phoenix, C. H. (1964). Hormones and sexual behavior. *Science* **143,** 212–218.

Zeilmaker, G. H. (1964). Aspects of the regulation of corpus luteum function in androgen-sterilized female rats. *Acta Endocrinol.* **46,** 571–579.

CHAPTER 20

Control of the Onset of Puberty[1]

VAUGHN CRITCHLOW[2] and MILDRED ELWERS BAR-SELA

I. Introduction

"We find in the records that at Salamis the son of Euthymenes grew to 4 ft. 6 in. in his third year; he walked slowly, was dull of sense, became sexually quite mature, had a bass voice, and was carried off by a sudden attack of paralysis when he turned three." (From Pliny, "Natural History")

Although somewhat less dramatic than the usual case of cerebral pubertas praecox, with which the above description was probably concerned, the sequence of events which characterizes normal transition from infancy to adulthood is no less impressive. In spite of the fact that the physiological basis for this transition early attracted the attention of many prominent pioneers in endocrinology, advances in the understanding of the control of puberty have been sporadic and relatively slow. However, it is a measure of the progress achieved that the significance

[1] The original research cited was supported by USPHS grants A-3385 and B-4645.

[2] Supported by the National Institute of General Medical Sciences Research Career Program Award 3K3-GM-15, 364.

of the neurological signs described by Pliny would today be generally appreciated, even though the details of the underlying mechanisms which relate neuropathology to sexual maturation remain largely obscure.

It is now recognized that attainment of sexual maturation is a complex process which requires maturation and interaction not only of gonads and reproductive tract, but also of the pituitary and, importantly, of the neuroendocrine mechanisms which ultimately control gonadotropin secretion in the adult animal. In accordance with available information and with the views expressed by Harris (1955), it appears that a maturational sequence is involved and that the gonads, reproductive tract, and hypophysis are normally capable of adult activities prior to puberty; initiation of functions in these structures awaits only the activation of the pituitary by appropriate hormonal stimuli from the brain. Since the final events which culminate in sexual maturation appear to a large extent to be dependent upon the activation of neuroendocrine mechanisms which control gonadotropin secretion in the adult, information and concepts regarding these mechanisms are immediately relevant. In addition to appropriate sections in this book, several excellent and recent reviews of the role of the nervous system in regulating reproductive functions are available (e.g., Harris, 1955; Everett, 1961, 1964; Szentágothai *et al.,* 1962; Flerkó, 1963; Sawyer, 1964).

It is the purpose of this review to examine and summarize the evidence which forms the basis for the current views, summarized above, regarding the sequence of maturation in organs and systems which participate in reproductive functions and to explore in some detail the possible roles of the neural mechanisms that have been implicated. A recent and interesting review by Donovan (1963) on the timing of puberty has been particularly helpful in this regard. We will use the term puberty to denote the stage of development at which the ability to reproduce sexually is achieved, although this term is often used to include events which precede this capability.

II. Prepubertal Development of the Gonads

Concepts related to the control of puberty have undergone profound changes during the past 50 years; part of this evolution has been a consequence of the gradually expanding list of organs and systems which have been implicated in the control of reproductive processes. Thus, following the discovery of the role of the gonads and their secretions in the development and maintenance of the reproductive organs, attention was focused on the gonads as the principal puberty-inducing structures. Subsequently, with the realization of the contributions of the hypophysis and, finally, of the central nervous system, theories were expanded to include these in the hierarchy of puberty-controlling mechanisms and attention has gradually shifted away from the role of the gonads per se. However, considerable evidence indicates that the immature gonads are not inert or passive structures and that they may in fact participate importantly, through their secretions, in the integration and maturation of hypophyseal and neural functions. It is in view of these latter findings that an effort will be made to summarize the development of ovaries and testes with regard to both gametogenic and hormonal activities and to consider the developmental stages which are correlated with the appearance of responsivity to gonadotropins.

A. Testis

1. *Normal Development*

In general, the postnatal development of the vertebrate testis follows a fairly definite pattern which has been described in several reviews (Moore, 1939; Sohval, 1958; Albert, 1961). Since the testis has two major functional activities, gametogenic and hormonal, the following discussion of its normal maturation will differentiate between the developmental histories of these two facets of testicular morphology and physiology.

With regard to gametogenic functions, the age at which sperm appear varies tremendously among vertebrates, and the greatest range in age of appearance is observed in mammals. Whereas the rat testis usually contains sperm at approximately 45 days of age (Clermont and Perey, 1957), about 15 years are normally required for the same stage of maturation in the human.

Morphologically, the testis of the newborn contains small, solid, and nonconvoluted cordlike structures which are the primordia of seminiferous tubules. These sex cords contain numerous cells of two types, gonocytes or primordial germ cells, and supporting cells (Clermont and Perey, 1957), which form a palisadelike layer along a thin basement membrane. As the male matures, a gradual series of changes is instituted which results in marked enlargement and increased tortuosity of the tubules, formation of a thin tunica propria external to the basement membrane, and organization of the cellular components of the tubules into the complex stratification which is characteristic of the mature germinal epithelium. Finally, lumens appear in the tubules. There is considerable individual and species variation in the rapidity, in relation to age, with which these changes occur. The process is relatively most rapid in species in which males reach sexual maturity early.

Recent studies which have examined and defined the quantitative aspects of the spermatogenic cycle have greatly facilitated the understanding of the dynamics of spermatogenesis. Although most of these studies have dealt with the rat and mouse, the general plan of spermatogenesis appears to be similar in the several species that have been investigated (Albert, 1961; Roosen-Runge, 1962). According to Clermont and Perey (1957), spermatogenesis in the rat is initiated in most tubules at 4–6 days of age and a majority of tubules contain spermatozoa at 45 days of age. Thus, spermatogenesis in this species appears to have a duration of approximately 40 days. Interestingly, it seems that despite wide disparities in the age at which sexual maturity is normally attained, the duration of spermatogenesis in all species thus far studied is 4–7 weeks (Roosen-Runge, 1962). In the rat the 40-day duration of spermatogenesis, added to the 13–14 days required for transport of sperm to the vas deferens (Clegg, 1960), approximates the 55–60-day period normally required for puberty. This total duration, coupled with the probability that most of the 40-day period includes stages of spermatogenesis which are independent of gonadotropins (Clermont and Morgentaler, 1955), may be relevant to some of the outstanding questions regarding control of puberty in the male and will be discussed in Section II,A,2.

With respect to endocrine function, there appears to be little doubt that the testis achieves this capability very early. In fact, it has been established in several species that the testis secretes androgenic substances prenatally (Albert, 1961; Burns, 1961). In mammals this secretion may be essential for sexual differentiation in the male by allowing retention and development of male structures and preventing differentiation of female structures. Ablation of fetal testes in the rabbit (Jost, 1953) and mouse (Raynaud and Frilley, 1947) reportedly disrupts masculinization of the reproductive tract and results in retention of Müllerian duct derivatives. A more variable atresia of Wolffian ducts occurs in fetal male rats following castration (Wells and Fralick, 1951). Interstitial cells, the presumptive source of androgen, are present in many species (Moore, 1939; Albert, 1961; Burns, 1961), including the human (Gillman, 1948; Sniffen, 1950), in abundant numbers during the prenatal period. However, these interstitial cells regress within a relatively short time following birth and do not reappear until the age of puberty is approached. The recent studies of Niemi and Ikonen (1963) confirm this view. The secretions of the interstitial elements during the immediate postnatal period, prior to their regression, are evidently responsible for the induction or differentiation of a male-type neuroendocrine mechanism which causes acyclic gonadotropin secretion (Harris. 1964).

In spite of the postnatal regression of testicular interstitial tissue, there is considerable evidence that the testis secretes effective amounts of androgen during most of the prepubertal period. Neonatal castration inhibits the growth and differentiation of accessory glands (Wiesner, 1932, 1934; Price, 1947). Several other observations relative to the effects of castration on gonadotropic functions of the pituitary also indicate that infant testes secrete androgen during this period of relative quiescence (Section III,C).

In summarizing the prepubertal development and activity of the testis of the rat, it appears that the processes involved in gamete formation are activated independently of gonadotropins early in the prepubertal period; the terminal steps of spermatogenesis, which are gonadotropin dependent, are completed at approximately 45 days of age; mature sperm reach the vas deferens at the time of puberty, about 55–60 days of age. In contrast, the endocrine components of the testis are active in the fetus, they regress during the postnatal period, and they are reactivated immediately prior to puberty.

The factors which regulate the normal processes of testicular maturation are not altogether known; however, chief among the influences that have been implicated are those exerted by pituitary gonadotropins. The roles of these hormones on testicular maturation are discussed below.

2. *Responsivity to Gonadotropins*

There is no doubt that full maturation of the male gonad and accessory organs normally requires an intact pituitary. Hypophysectomy, without replacement therapy, prevents testicular maturation and produces a state of persistent sexual infantilism (Crowe *et al.*, 1910; Aschner, 1912a; Walker *et al.*, 1952). Although the extent to which the developing testis is influenced by gonadotropins and the potential roles of individual gonadotropins have been subjects of much investigation and conjecture for many years, information relating to the basic mechanisms involved in attainment of sexual maturity in the male is extremely limited.

In general, the situation is most clear with regard to testicular hormonal function and it seems well established that prenatal endocrine activity of the testis in the rabbit (Jost, 1953) is dependent upon pituitary hormones. Hypophysectomy in this species produces adverse effects on male reproductive tract structures which are similar to those produced by castration, and administration of appropriate gonadotropic materials corrects these deficiences. The situation is less clear in the rat (Wells, 1959) and mouse (Raynaud, 1959), and there is less evidence that the activity of the fetal testis in these species is dependent upon pituitary gonadotropins. However, it is well established that the testis of the immature rat secretes androgenic hormones in response to implantation of pituitaries (P. E. Smith and Engle, 1927a) and following administration of pituitary extracts (Woods and Simpson, 1961), purified luteinizing hormone (LH) (Greep *et al.*, 1936; Woods and Simpson, 1961), and chorionic gonadotropin (HCG) (Gaarenstroom, 1941). In the rat, administration of gonadotropin to immature males led to evidence of secretion of androgen between birth and 6 days of age (Price and Ortiz, 1944).

Thus, the secretory elements of testicular interstitial tissue are capable of responding to appropriate gonadotropic stimulation very early, and their postnatal regression and relative quiescence during the prepubertal period appear to be due to the absence of sufficient levels of LH.

The role of gonadotropins in the initiation and regulation of spermatogenesis is much more obscure. Although it is classically recognized that follicle-stimulating hormone (FSH) acts chiefly on the tubular germinal epithelium for maintenance of its activity, it appears that this hormone plays a less important role in testicular function than believed previously. It has been demonstrated repeatedly in several species that LH (Greep and Fevold, 1937; Woods and Simpson, 1961) or androgens (Walsh *et al.*, 1934; Nelson and Merckel, 1938; Cutuly and Cutuly, 1940; Wells, 1942; P. E. Smith, 1944) maintain complete spermatogenesis following hypophysectomy. It is presumed that the effectiveness of LH is based on the induction of androgen secretion. Although testes maintained with LH or androgen following hypophysectomy are small and the seminiferous tubules do not retain their normal diameter (P. E. Smith, 1944; Woods and Simpson, 1961), the spermatogenic process appears normal. Relevant to the important role that LH plays in testicular maturation and function, the results obtained in immature rats treated with anti-LH serum are of particular interest. Administration of this serum for 9 days produced marked reduction in testicular weight and withdrawal of the testes into the inguinal canal accompanied by complete suppression of spermiogenesis and atrophy of interstitial tissue (Hayashida, 1963). In spite of the fact that purified FSH has only a limited capacity to maintain spermatogenesis in the hypophysectomized male rat, small doses demonstrate a marked synergistic action with LH or androgen in such maintenance and in the repair of posthypophysectomy regression of the testis (Woods and Simpson, 1961). On this basis it seems clear that FSH plays a role in the male reproductive system, but its contribution is complex and the mechanism by which it facilitates spermatogenesis and spermiogenesis is unknown.

The problem of control of puberty in the male is further complicated by the difficulty with which precocious spermatogenesis is induced experimentally. Although several submammalian forms, such as amphibians (Burns and Buyse, 1931, 1934) and birds (Domm, 1931), demonstrate premature spermatogenesis following administration of gonadotropic substances, the effects of such treatments have been notably unimpressive in mammals other than the ground squirrel (*Citellus tridecemlineatus*) (Wells and Moore, 1936). The consensus is that treatment with gonadotropic agents which produce precocious puberty in females is ineffective in male rats (Smith and Engle, 1927a; Moore, 1936; Price and Ortiz, 1944; Woods and Simpson, 1961) and monkeys (Engle, 1932), although such treatment markedly increases the size of the testes and sex accessories. Some effects of gonadotropins on spermatogenesis have been noted, but they have generally been subtle. For example, administration of serum gonadotropin (PMS) to intact prepubertal rats affected only the late steps of spermiogenesis, resulting in some advancement of spermatid development (Wakeling, 1959). Woods and Simpson (1961) observed that, whereas treatment with a combination of purified FSH and LH did not cause precocious spermatogenesis in normal weanling rats, such treatment following hypophysectomy resulted in some acceleration of spermatogenesis, and sperm were found in the testes of treated rats but not in those of controls at 44 days of age. The presence of sperm in 44-day-old rats, however, is not a sign of marked precocity.

Current concepts regarding the basis for the refractoriness of the spermatogenic process of most immature mammals to artificial acceleration must still acknowledge the existence of unknown factors which influence maturation of the testis and, hence, the age at which spermatogenesis is initiated. However, such lack of responsivity may in part be related to the fixed time course and degree of hormonal autonomy exhibited by spermatogenesis.

Because of time course and hormonal autonomy, available information suggests that the rat is not the best species for studying the influence of hormonal factors on initiation of spermatogenesis. First, as indicated above, spermatogenesis is initiated in this species at approximately 4 days of age, and its duration, i.e., the period between activation of primordial germ cells and the appearance of resulting spermatozoa, is approximately 40 days. Since the period from birth to puberty is only 55–60 days, most of the prepubertal period is normally occupied by the first spermatogenic cycle and the time required for sperm transport to the vas deferens. Second, the duration of the spermatogenic process appears to be largely fixed and inflexible; gonadotropins seem to have little if any effect on most of the stages in this process, and hypophysectomy, although resulting in considerable degeneration of germinal epithelial elements and a consequent decrease in number of spermatids, is compatible with spermatogenesis up to stage 7 of spermiogenesis, which normally occurs at 33 days of age (Clermont and Morgentaler, 1955). If only the late stages of spermatogenesis, those that occur from days 33 to 40, are facilitated or accelerated by pituitary hormones, obvious precocity of the degree which is elicitable in female rats would be an unlikely result of such treatment. Consequently, only slight shifts in late stages of spermiogenesis, such as those observed by Wakeling (1959), would be expected. In this species, therefore, it may be as Albert (1961) proposes: ". . . no amount of exogenous gonadotropin could be expected to produce precocious spermatogenesis because a certain minimum of time may be required for the series of divisions which *in toto* constitutes the spermatogenic cycle."

Although the limitations outlined above may help to explain the inability to induce precocious puberty in the male rat and in other forms in which the duration of the spermatogenic cycle plus the time required for sperm transport approximates the period between birth and normal sexual maturation, they do not furnish an explanation in species where the prepubertal period greatly exceeds the duration of gametogenesis. If, as it appears in all species studied (Roosen-Runge, 1962), the duration of spermatogenesis is between 4–7 weeks, the age of onset of puberty would depend entirely upon those factors or mechanisms which control maturation of the testis and which set the stage for initiation of gamete formation. The nature of these factors or mechanisms is unknown. The pituitary may yet be implicated since administration of gonadotropins or androgens induces precocious spermatogenesis in several submammalian vertebrates and in the ground squirrel. Furthermore, there is a considerable wealth of well-documented clinical evidence which indicates that some forms of isosexual precocity in boys are due to a variety of neuropathological processes; such pathologies presumably effect increased gonadotropin secretion, and in some cases increased urinary excretion of gonadotropic hormones has been demonstrated (Wilkins, 1950; McCullagh *et al.*, 1960). By focusing attention on forms with appropriately long prepubertal periods, it may be possible to find the correct dosage, time of administration, and combination of pituitary hormones that will induce precocious spermatogenesis in species that have heretofore proved refractory.

B. Ovary

1. *Normal Development*

The normal development of the ovary has been the subject of many studies in a large number of species (Brambell, 1956; Franchi *et al.*, 1962). Although considerable species variation exists in the stage of ovarian development at birth and in the duration of the prepubertal period, these are not necessarily related, and discrepancies in the behavior of ovaries of various species under normal and abnormal conditions may be more apparent than real. Ovarian development is remarkably consistent among species if birth is regarded as merely an incidental event. In general, complete functional maturity is not reached until some time after birth; however, in none of the species studied does the ovary show a steady, progressive development. Rather, ovarian maturation is characterized by several distinct periods which vary in duration among species and which culminate in a period during which the ovary is morphologically and functionally ready for the relatively rapid maturational events associated with release of the first ova.

It is now generally agreed that proliferation of germ cells and oogonia ceases before birth in all mammals and most vertebrates (Franchi *et al.*, 1962). The initial changes of meiotic prophase also occur prenatally. Ovogenesis differs from spermatogenesis in that in the former prophase is interrupted by a "resting" period which persists until the oocyte has undergone a period of cytoplasmic increase without apparent nuclear changes. The factors which initiate the growth phase in only a small portion of the total oocyte population at any one time are unknown. Only after the oocyte has attained its maximum size will the hormonally dependent completion of meiosis occur.

In summarizing the maturation of the ovary, the rat will be used as the reference species, and, for convenience, three periods of postnatal development will be considered: infantile, from birth to 10 days of age; early juvenile, from 10 to 20 days of age; and late juvenile, from 20 days to puberty at approximately 40 days of age. This classification of the developmental periods of ovarian maturation is a composite based on the observations of several investigators. The terms infantile and juvenile were first applied by Clauberg (1932) to immature rabbit ovaries that were nonresponsive or responsive, respectively, to gonadotropins. Hertz and Hisaw (1934) adopted these terms and correlated responsivity with the appearance of antral follicles. Subsequently, these designations were applied to similar periods of development in the rat (Hisaw, 1947). Further subdivision of the juvenile period into early and late periods was proposed by Dawson and McCabe (1951) and Rennels (1951) on the basis of more subtle changes in follicular structure, histological evidence of secretory activity, and responsivity to gonadotropins. It should be noted that the age limits of these periods as stated for the rat have been derived from a number of sources and are only approximations; they represent an attempt to reconcile primarily descriptive accounts of ovogenesis and follicular development (Arai, 1920; Cowperthwaite, 1925; Hargitt, 1930; Sneider, 1940) with histochemical studies of the follicle and interstitial tissue (Dawson and McCabe, 1951; Rennels, 1951; Falck, 1953) and with responses to gonadotropins (Section II,B,2). In addition, since the duration of gestation varies as much as 3 days (21–23 days) in the rat, infantile ovaries show some interlitter differences in the state of development during the first few postnatal days. For the same reason, the terminations of the infantile and early juvenile periods are usually stated as covering a 3-day range.

At birth, the beginning of the infantile period, the rat ovary contains primary oocytes scattered throughout the cortex, each surrounded by a single flattened layer of epithelial cells. Remnants of the disappearing ovarian medulla form bundles of stroma between these primordial follicles, and an indistinct tunica albuginea separates the germinal epithelium from the ovarian cortex. Although some oocytes have attained the resting stage of development at birth, all reach this stage within 2–3 days. Some oocytes then acquire a follicular covering of cuboidal epithelial cells. As individual oocytes begin the period of cytoplasmic growth, they induce rapid proliferation of these follicular cells. Some follicles have a granulosum of 4–6 cell layers by the fourth postnatal day, and by the sixth day the ovarian stroma condenses into a primitive, undivided theca around each of the growing follicles. A rapid decrease in the total number of oocytes and follicles through atresia occurs in the infantile as well as successive periods of prepubertal development (Ingram, 1962). This atretic process consists of breakdown of the oocyte and granulosa, and, as in the case with atresia of small-to-medium follicles in the adult, no contribution to the substance of the ovary is evident.

The development of the primary interstitial tissue during the infantile period has been described by Dawson and McCabe (1951), Rennels (1951), and Falck (1953). Cells with positive histochemical reactions for cholesterol can be identified as early as the sixth postnatal day. These cells are believed to arise from granulosal bridges which connect adjacent follicles during the infantile period. Although initially lacking morphological features of secretory cells, these primary interstitial cells assume a characteristic epithelioid appearance by the tenth to twelfth day, when cholesterol storage also increases and histochemical reactions for other steroids become positive. Meanwhile, the growing oocytes attain near-maximum size, granulosal proliferation increases, and antra, signaling the end of the infantile period, begin to appear in the growing follicles by the tenth day.

During the early juvenile period, the primary interstitial tissue increases in volume, and there is histochemical evidence of increasing synthesis of steroids or steroid precursors (Dawson and McCabe, 1951; Rennels, 1951; Falck, 1953). Characteristic of this period are the marked changes which occur in the follicles; these show rapid growth due to mitotic activity in the cells of the granulosa as well as to an increase in size of antra. As follicles develop, the theca becomes differentiated into its internal and external components. This subdivision seems to occur somewhat later with respect to development of the antrum than in the adult ovary (Dawson and McCabe, 1951). With the appearance of follicles with a large antrum and a distinct theca interna (Graafian follicles) at 18–20 days of age, the early juvenile period comes to a close.

The late juvenile period is characterized by continuing growth and atresia of follicles. In the beginning, Graafian follicles undergo atresia as soon as they appear and the process becomes more complex. Abortive maturation spindles occur in the oocyte, and the granulosa before disappearing may show a transient period of positive histochemical reactions for steroids. Also, the theca interna hypertrophies, and histochemical reactions for steroids increase; these so-called "thecal bodies," which may represent abortive attempts at corpora lutea formation (Dawson and McCabe, 1951), become the secondary or definitive interstitial tissue. As the volume of this tissue increases concomitant with continuing growth and atresia of Graafian follicles, the late juvenile ovary of the rat differs morphologically from pubertal and adult ovaries only in that it lacks corpora lutea.

The secretory activity of the immature ovary is difficult to assess since the initial development of the secondary reproductive organs is not dependent upon the ovary. Fetal gonadectomy does not inhibit the differentiation of Müllerian duct or urogenital sinus derivatives nor does if affect development of female external genitalia. Since exogenous estrogens have been reported to hasten the differentiation of these structures, it appears that the fetal ovary does not secrete sufficient amounts of estrogens to stimulate their development (Burns, 1961).

Even in the early postnatal period, gonadectomy fails to furnish evidence of estrogen secretion. No significant decrease in uterine weight was seen at 8 days following gonadectomy at birth (Price, 1947), although neonatal ovariectomy results in significant inhibition of uterine growth by the tenth day (Plagge, 1956), i.e., at the end of the infantile period. The effects of gonadectomy on uterine weight are more pronounced during the early juvenile period (Price, 1947; Rennels, 1951). The presence of histochemically demonstrable steroids in the primary interstitial tissue suggests that synthesis of steroids occurs late in the infantile and increases during the early juvenile periods (Dawson and McCabe, 1951; Rennels, 1951; Falck, 1953). Since the uterus is responsive to exogenous steroids during the first postnatal week and becomes increasingly sensitive to estrogen during the next 3 weeks, reaching a maximum at the twenty-sixth day, its slow rate of growth during most of the prepubertal period suggests that estrogen secretion by the ovary is low (Price, 1947).

Much less is known concerning the prepubertal secretion of progesterone. Rennels (1951) reported that Hooker-Forbes assays for serum progesterone were negative in the early juvenile period. However, on the basis of the appearance of cholesterol in the uterine epithelium, Alden (1947) suggested that progesterone secretion may occur as early as 20 days of age. As pointed out by Dawson and McCabe (1951), this indication of progesterone secretion appears at the age when the first fully developed Graafian follicles begin to undergo atresia and the granulosa temporarily contains histochemically demonstrable steroids.

From the information that is available, the ovary and reproductive tract show few morphological changes between 25 days of age and the final events associated with puberty. The ovarian changes which immediately precede the first ovulation apparently have the same temporal characteristics (Blandau and Money, 1943) as those associated with ovulation in the adult (Boling *et al.*, 1941; Odor, 1955). Although sometimes out of phase, the first ovulation is generally appropriately timed in relation to vaginal opening and heat for fruitful mating: vaginal opening, onset of heat, and ovulation usually occur in this sequence within a 24-hour-period (Blandau and Money, 1943).

Several observations suggest that hormonal activity of the ovary increases immediately prior to vaginal opening and ovulation. In our experience (Bar-Sela and Critchlow, unpublished observations, 1964), a rapid increase in uterine weight occurs during the 3 days prior to ovulation. Accompanying this increase in weight there occurs an accumulation of fluid which culminates in ballooning of the uterus on or 1 day preceding vaginal opening. A proestrous vaginal smear occurs with this ballooning. When the latter precedes vaginal opening, the smear at opening is cornified. According to Astwood's data (1939), sufficient estrogen to produce a fluid-filled uterus is probably released 24–30 hours before this event, and Zondek (1940) has shown that the ovary can be removed 48–72 hours before vaginal cornification without preventing cornification. From these data, it appears that a rapid rise in estrogen secretion is triggered about 3 days prior to vaginal opening. The situation with regard to progesterone secretion at first ovulation is unknown; however, this steroid has been implicated in the induction of heat and ovulation in the adult (Everett 1961, 1964).

The ova produced at the first ovulation are fully capable of being fertilized and developing into normal offspring and the number and size of offspring born and reared are comparable to those of the adult female (Blandau and Money, 1943). Regular estrous cycles follow vaginal opening in those animals which are not immediately mated (Bar-Sela and Critchlow, unpublished observations, 1964). The rat does not usually show an adolescent period of irregular cycles or relative infertility following puberty.

The temporal features of ovarian maturation in the mouse (Engle, 1931; Brambell, 1956) and hamster (Ortiz, 1947) are similar to those described for the rat. On the other hand, a number of common laboratory and domestic animals are born with ovaries which compare with the late fetal ovary of the rat and show subsequent patterns of development which differ markedly. Guinea pig, rabbit, and pig ovaries are morphologically comparable to those of the fetal rat until the second (Allen, 1904; Bookhout, 1945), third (Hertz, 1963), and seventh (Casida, 1935) postnatal weeks, respectively. The immature guinea pig ovary compares to the infantile rat ovary until late in the third week, early juvenile until the eighth, and late juvenile until puberty at about the twelfth week (Freed and Coppock, 1936). These three postnatal periods of ovarian development, based on morphology and responsivity to gonadotropins, extend to the eleventh, twelfth, and fifteenth weeks respectively in the rabbit (Allen, 1904; Hertz and Hisaw, 1934) and to the eleventh, fifteenth, and thirty-second weeks in the pig (Casida, 1935). Thus, it is apparent that the absolute and relative durations of the different periods vary considerably between these species.

In marked contrast to the late development described above, a number of species show ovarian maturation prior to birth which is comparable to that found in infantile and early juvenile rat ovaries. Ovaries of the horse (Cole *et al.*, 1933; Amoroso and Rowlands, 1951) and seal (Amoroso *et al.*, 1951) show marked development of the interstitial tissue during fetal life, but contain only primordial follicles. Graafian follicles have been observed at birth in the cow (Marden, 1952) and appear in the late fetal giraffe (Kellas *et al.*, 1958) and human (Block,

1953; Potter, 1963). Corpora lutea have even been described in the late human fetus (Witschi, 1963). Despite the early development of the ovary, these species exhibit relatively late puberty and a prolonged adolescence characterized by irregular cyclicity and relative infertility (Hartman, 1931).

2. *Response to Gonadotropins*

Foá (1900) first demonstrated the ability of the prepubertal ovary to respond to an adult environment with follicular maturation, ovulation, and corpora lutea formation by transplanting the immature rabbit ovary into an adult host. Subsequently, Long and Evans (1922) confirmed these observations with similar studies in the rat and further demonstrated that the ovarian implants were hormonally active, as evidenced by the restoration of vaginal cyclicity in ovariectomized adult hosts. Aschheim (1926), P. E. Smith (1926), and Zondek (1926) independently associated maturation of the ovary with the pituitary by showing that precocious ovarian development followed daily implantation of pituitaries into immature rats or mice. During the next few years these same workers amplified their early reports with studies of dose and age relationships (P. E. Smith, 1927; P. E. Smith and Engle, 1927a,b) and with the important finding that not only the anterior pituitary but placenta and urine of pregnancy contain specific gonad-stimulating substances (Aschheim and Zondek, 1927, 1928; Zondek and Aschheim, 1927). These maturational responses became the standard test for assaying pituitaries or body fluids from animals in various physiological states for the presence of gonadotropins. It soon became apparent that responses differed not only with respect to types of preparation used, but with age and species of the recipient. It was early recognized that developing ovaries show an initial refractory period when no amount of any gonadotropin produces a detectable response. Subsequently, there occurs a gradual development of responsivity, with various components of the ovary becoming competent at different times. Apparent conflicts in the development of responsivity of different species can be resolved by considering the stages of ovarian development, outlined above, with respect to their onset and relative duration. In all species, full maturational responses are obtained from ovaries containing Graafian follicles with a well-developed theca interna (Hisaw, 1947), whether this stage is reached prenatally or at a considerable time after birth.

It is generally agreed that maturation of the oocyte through the resting stage of meiosis and the growth period is hormonally autonomous (Brambell, 1956; Franchii *et al.*, 1962). Similarly, initial differentiation of the follicle proceeds independently of the pituitary (P. E. Smith, 1930; Dempsey, 1937; Hertz, 1963). In fact, follicles of the fetal and infantile ovary are refractory to exogenous gonadotropin in the rat (Corey, 1928, 1930; Saunders and Cole, 1936) and mouse (Engle, 1931) as are the follicles of comparable stages in the pig (Casida, 1935), guinea pig (Freed and Coppock, 1936), and rabbit (Hertz and Hisaw, 1934).

In contrast to the lack of responsivity of the follicle, infantile interstitial tissue responds to exogenous gonadotropins with hypertrophy (Saunders and Cole, 1936; Price and Ortiz, 1944; Picon, 1956; Pavic, 1963) and some evidence of estrogen synthesis (Falck, 1953) and secretion (Price and Ortiz, 1944). These responses were obtained in the rat only after the seventh postnatal day and were increased by the tenth day (Dawson and McCabe, 1951; Rennels, 1951; Falck, 1953). The hypertrophy of ovarian interstitial tissue in the fetal horse (Cole *et al.*, 1933; Amoroso and Rowlands, 1951), and seal (Amoroso *et al.*, 1951) are well known, but the fetal ovaries of these species are morphologically comparable to those in the infantile rat.

During the early juvenile period in the rat, the secretory response of the primary interstitial tissue to exogenous gonadotropin becomes more pronounced (Price and Ortiz, 1944; Gaarenstroom and de Jongh, 1946), and not only is estrogen apparently secreted in large amounts, but cholesterol storage is concomitantly depleted by the administration of PMS (Rennels, 1951) or HCG (Falck, 1953). This mobilization of cholesterol is not seen in the infantile ovary (Falck, 1953). During the early juvenile period PMS or HCG may cause changes in the theca, described as "luteinization," which may be premature transformation into a reactive secondary interstitial tissue (Rennels, 1951).

The follicles of the late juvenile ovary respond completely to appropriate gonadotropic stimulation with final maturation, ovulation, and corpus luteum formation. Although these have been reported to occur in response to PMS or HCG as early as the nineteenth day (Freed and Coppock, 1936; Hohlweg, 1936; McCormack and Meyer, 1964), the response is not consistent before the twenty-second day, and the number of ova recovered from younger animals is low (Leonard and Smith, 1934; Gaarenstroom *et al.*, 1960; McCormack and Meyer, 1964). Since there is no sharp line of demarcation between the early and late juvenile stages, due to differences in rates of follicular development, it is not surprising that some responsive Graafian follicles appear early in isolated instances.

Once the ovary becomes responsive and ovulation consistently occurs, there appears to be a direct relation between age and the number of ova shed in response to a given low dose of PMS-HCG, while at a given age more ova are shed with increasing doses of PMS in rats (Zarrow and Quinn, 1963) or hamsters (Bodemer *et al.*, 1959). Implications of the age factor in terms of release of FSH will be discussed later. With respect to responsivity of the ovary, the ability to increase ovulations with increasing levels of PMS is of interest. Apparently it is not only the Graafian follicle which becomes responsive to follicle-stimulating preparations in the late juvenile ovary. Superovulation, which depends on stimulation of growth and differentiation of small- and medium-sized follicles, occurs in response to implantation of pituitary tissue (Smith and Engle, 1927a) or administration of PMS (Cole, 1937), FSH (Evans and Simpson, 1940), or PMS-HCG combinations. The medium-sized follicles are not, however, responsive during the early juvenile period. Hisaw (1947) states that, although the morphological difference between a follicle which does not respond to gonadotropins and one that has gained competence is not obvious, responsivity appears to be correlated with the time at which the theca interna normally starts differentiating into epithelioid tissue. As has been pointed out, this differentiation is not apparent in the early juvenile ovary until the follicle has reached maximum size. In the adult ovary, by contrast, follicles in the early stages of antrum formation already have a distinct theca interna (Boling *et al.*, 1941; Harrison, 1962). This raises the interesting question as to whether the follicles of the late juvenile ovary display adult timing in differentiation of the theca.

The temporal characteristics of induced ovulation in the late juvenile period, in terms of polar body formation by the oocyte, preovulatory swelling of the follicle, and extrusion of the secondary oocyte, are comparable to those associated with ovulation in the adult (Blandau and Money, 1943). Furthermore, the ova are fully capable of being fertilized and producing normal offspring (Evans and Simpson, 1940).

Sex steroids may modify responses to exogenous gonadotropins. Their influence may be exerted on mechanisms which control gonadotropin secretion, as will be discussed later, or directly on the ovary. Estrogens administered to intact or hypophysectomized rats increase ovarian weight through the development of medium-sized prevesicular follicles (Gaarenstroom and de Jongh, 1946; J. E. Meyer and Bradbury, 1960; B. D. Smith, 1961). In the hypophysectomized rat, estrogen treatment causes both a decrease in the atresia of large follicles which usually follows hypophysectomy and an increase in mitoses, indicative of active granulosal proliferation (Williams, 1944, 1945a; Gaarenstroom and de Jongh, 1946; de Wit, 1953; Payne and Hellbaum, 1955; J. E. Meyer and Bradbury, 1960). Furthermore, responses to exogenous gonadotropins are increased. Williams (1945b) found that stilbestrol-treated hypophysectomized rats were more responsive to some dose levels of PMS than were intact controls. Diethylstilbestrol increased responses of hypophysectomized animals to FSH (Gaarenstroom and de Jongh, 1946; Payne and Runser, 1958; Payne *et al.*, 1959), LH (J. E. Meyer and Bradbury, 1960), and HCG (Gaarenstroom and de Jongh, 1946). Simpson *et al.* (1941) stated that the FSH-estrogen effects reflect a synergistic action on the follicles whereas the LH-estrogen response is additive, with estrogen affecting the follicles and LH, the interstitial tissue. Bradbury (1961) further substantiated the direct effect by demonstrating unilateral augmentation of follicular responses to FSH or HCG following direct application of stilbestrol to one ovary. These effects may relate to development of responsivity to endogenous FSH (Hisaw, 1947).

In summary, postnatal ovarian development in the rat can be divided into infantile, early juvenile, and late juvenile periods on the basis of morphological development and responses to exogenous and endogenous hormones. The infantile ovary is characterized by hormonally independent development of secondary follicles and by the appearance of a primary interstitial tissue which is not only responsive to HCG, but is apparently morphologically matured under the influence of endogenous LH. During the early juvenile period, this interstitial tissue becomes capable of secreting increasing amounts of estrogen under gonadotropic stimulation, but the follicular apparatus is still essentially refractory until an antrum and a theca interna have developed. With the appearance of these structures, which can be hastened at most by only a few days, the ovary becomes completely competent to respond to gonadotropins. This responsivity also coincides with the first evidence of progesterone secretion.

Ovarian development in many species progresses through similar stages at different rates and the degree of maturation at parturition varies greatly. Since the ovaries of cows and humans contain Graafian follicles at birth, and thus correspond to the responsive late juvenile ovary of the rat, it is not surprising that ovulation can be induced by PMS in the cow at 3 weeks of age (Casida *et al.*, 1943; Howe *et al.*, 1962) or that it may occur at 21 months of age in the human (Jolly, 1955).

III. The Pituitary and Puberty

As indicated previously, current concepts hold that the immature pituitary is capable of supporting complete reproductive functions prior to the physiological age of puberty. This view was firmly established by the experiments of Harris and Jacobsohn (1952) which demonstrated that transplantation of immature hypophyses into the subarachnoid space under the median eminence of hypophysectomized adult females caused the restoration of normal ovarian function. Although the above experiments clearly demonstrated the adult capabilities of immature pituitaries in an appropriate adult environment, numerous other observations point to the fact that immature hypophyses contain significant quantities of gonadotropins, that these are secreted in limited quantities during the prepubertal period, and, further, that the immature gland may markedly increase the secretion of gonadotropins under certain conditions.

A. Gonadotropin Content of Immature Pituitaries

In their early experiments on the response of the immature ovary to pituitary implants, P. E. Smith and Engle (1927a) found that immature rat pituitaries were nearly twice as effective as adult glands on a weight basis. Evidently the very young rat pituitary contains gonadotropins since responses were obtained even when 5-day-old glands were used. Female pituitary glands contain more gonadotropins than those of males from birth to shortly before puberty, and although the levels increase with age in both sexes, female glands show a sharp drop in gonadotropic potency at puberty while potency of male pituitaries continues to rise (Clark, 1935a; McQueen-Williams, 1935; Lauson *et al.*, 1939). These changes in hormone content are paralleled by changes in the basophiles of the developing hypophyses (Wolfe, 1935; Severinghaus, 1938, 1939; Siperstein *et al.*, 1954).

The observation that the pituitary of the late juvenile female rat contains more gonadotropin than does that of the adult rat has been confirmed in more recent studies. De Jongh and Paesi (1958) reported that glands from immature females contain more FSH than those of adults, even though the latter are four times heavier. Although content of LH was lower in the immature pituitary, its concentration was higher. Hypophyseal concentrations of both hormones were lower in immature than in mature males. Ramirez and McCann (1963a) found LH concentration of 26-day-old female pituitaries as high as those of adult females, while the glands from 26-day-old males had lower concentrations of LH than those of immature females or adults of either sex. Parlow (1964a,b) states that the major change in pituitary concentration of gonadotropin at puberty in the rat is a decrease in FSH. Earlier, Siperstein *et al.* (1954) reported that rapid degranulation of pituitary basophiles occurred at puberty in the female rat and that the degranulation occurred first in the peripheral (FSH) and then in the central (LH) gonadotrophs.

The immature rabbit pituitary also contains LH, as determined by the ability of the 3-month-old and to a lesser extent, the 4-week-old pituitary to induce ovulation in the estrous rabbit (Wolfe and Cleveland, 1931). Pituitary stores of FSH are extremely high in the infantile female pig (Parlow *et al.*, 1964). Although FSH concentrations increase insignificantly with age, LH rises to a level at 110 days that surpasses that of the adult female. Male pigs at 108 days have concentrations of both hormones equivalent to those in the 110-day-old female (Parlow *et al.*, 1964).

Human pituitaries from infancy through childhood have been assayed. Follicle-stimulating activity has been detected in glands of very young children (Saxton and Loeb, 1937; Bahn *et al.*, 1953) and Ryan (1962) found measurable quantities of LH in pituitaries of young girls. Apparently total gonadotropic potency is low in childhood and gradually increases during adolescence (Henderson and Rowlands, 1938; Witschi and Riley, 1940; Bahn *et al.*, 1953).

B. Secretion of Gonadotropins in Immature Animals

The presence of measurable quantities of gonadotropins in the immature pituitary does not, however, indicate the extent to which these hormones are released. Few direct measurements of serum or urinary gonadotropins in immature animals have been reported. Soliman and Ghanem (1956) found the serum of immature rabbits almost as potent as that of the adult in increasing testicular weight in immature chicks. Ramirez and McCann (1963a) could not detect LH in the serum of normal 26-day-old rats of either sex. Results in children are somewhat conflicting. Nathanson *et al.* (1941), using the mouse ovarian response, found that urine of boys contained no FSH before age 13, while it could be detected in girls as early as 11 years. Brown (1958) studied pooled urine of three age groups of boys and girls. Total potency and FSH were higher in 11-year-old girls than in boys and the approach of puberty in girls was marked by a decrease in FSH and an increase in total potency and LH. Urinary concentrations of both hormones increased gradually in boys.

Because the sensitivity of currently available assay procedures precludes direct measurement of circulating levels of gonadotropins in intact immature animals, most evidence pertaining to the prepubertal release of pituitary gonadotropins has been obtained indirectly. Such indirect evidence is based largely on alterations in gonadal morphology and function produced by hypophysectomy and on gonadal responses to exogenous gonadotropins in intact and hypophysectomized animals.

The effects of pituitary removal on the development of the gonads and accessory organs vary with the age at hypophysectomy and with species and sex. Interpretation of the alterations produced by pituitary ablation, in terms of the qualitative and quantitative aspects of the hormonal deficits produced, is complicated at early stages of development by the relative autonomy of some elements of the reproductive system and by the possible influences of pituitary hormones other than gonadotropins. In the fetus, Wells (1947, 1959) and Jost (1953) found that hypophysectomy by decapitation *in utero* did not cause gonadal atrophy in rats of either sex, although the same operation in the fetal rabbit (Jost, 1953) produced adverse effects on the male reproductive system similar to those produced by castration. These effects were corrected by the administration of gonadotropins.

Hypophysectomy during the prepubertal period in several species results in the failure of gonads and accessory organs of both sexes to reach full maturity (Crowe *et al.*, 1910; Aschner, 1912a; P. E. Smith, 1927; Fluhmann, 1934; Walker *et al.*, 1950, 1952). Walker and coworkers noted that after hypophysectomy at 6 days of age, testes and accessory organs of male rats atrophied, while the ovaries and uteri of females increased slightly in weight. They suggested that the pituitary does not influence growth of the ovaries and uterus during the first postnatal week. Atrophy occurred in males and females after hypophysectomy performed at 28 days. Although injection of growth hormone caused growth of reproductive organs in hypophysectomized rats of both sexes, the authors considered this to be due to contamination of the preparation with gonadotropin. However, growth hormone is reported to have direct effects on the uterus and male secondary organs (Li, 1956). That the pituitary may influence accessory organs without mediation of the ovary is also suggested by reports that early growth and differentiation of the uterus is not affected by ovariectomy (Wiesner, 1932, 1934, 1935), although it is adversely affected by hypophysectomy. Even vaginal opening may occur in the absence of the ovaries (Long and Evans, 1922; Pfeiffer, 1936) but not in the absence of the pituitary (Smith, 1927; Walker *et al.*, 1950, 1952).

The changes produced by prepubertal hypophysectomy suggest that there is sufficient LH secretion to influence ovarian development some weeks before effects attributable to FSH are seen. Removal of the pituitary at birth in the guinea pig (Perry and Rowlands, 1963) or at 18 days in the rat (Selye, 1933) does not prevent normal development of the follicular apparatus, and a newborn rat ovary implanted under the kidney capsule of a hypophysectomized adult shows normal follicular development to the 21-day stage (Hertz, 1963). However, the primary interstitial tissue of similarly transplanted ovaries fails to develop and will not secrete estrogen in response to exogenous gonadotropins, suggesting that development of this tissue is dependent upon hypophyseal secretions (Rennels, 1951). Falck (1953) noted that the primary interstitial cells of the infantile ovary resemble the deficiency cells seen in the hypophysectomized adult, and that estrogen secretion with associated cholesterol depletion cannot be obtained with HCG until the interstitial tissue has become epithelioid in structure at 10–12 days postpartum. Falck suggests that this morphological change indicates endogenous LH secretion.

In summarizing the effects of prepubertal hypophysectomy, it appears that pituitary removal before 21 days of age postpartum furnishes no evidence concerning the secretion of FSH because follicular development of the ovary is not influenced by this hormone until approximately 21 days of age. On the other hand, alterations produced in ovarian interstitial tissue by hypophysectomy suggest that some LH is secreted as early as 10–12 days of age; whether it appears earlier cannot be determined since the responsive tissue is not present during the first week. In the male, early secretion of gonadotropins is suggested by the atrophic changes of the testes and accessory organs that result from hypophysectomy at 6 days of age (Walker *et al.*, 1952).

Follicular responses of the ovary to exogenous gonadotropins vary in such a way as to indicate that before the late juvenile period of ovarian development the animal's own pituitary contributes little FSH to the response. Thus, PMS or HCG administered singly or in combination before the twentieth day of age do not normally induce ovulation. From the responses of hypophysectomized and intact late juvenile (over 20 days of age) animals to combinations of exogenous gonadotropins, it appears that follicle-stimulating activity determines the number of follicles which will respond to LH or HCG. During the fourth week, the number of responsive follicles increases with the dose of PMS used in the hamster (Bodemer *et al.*, 1959) and rat (McCormack and Meyer, 1964). However, if the dose levels are kept constant in the intact animal, the number and size of corpora lutea produced (Engle, 1938; Fevold, 1939) and the number of ova recovered (Bodemer *et al.*, 1959; Zarrow and Wilson, 1961; Zarrow and Quinn, 1963) increase until approximately the thirtieth day. These findings suggest that during the fourth week, endogenous FSH gradually increases to provide increasing numbers of large follicles responsive to luteinizing preparations. Since beyond the fourth week there is no further increase in number of ova shed in response to a given dose of PMS-HCG, FSH secretion appears to remain relatively constant until immediately before puberty.

During the fourth week, purified FSH preparations result in follicular growth in the rat unless injections are continued for 10 days, in which case luteinization occurs. Such luteinization is attributed to endogenous LH release, since hypophysectomy prevents its occurrence (Hisaw *et al.*, 1938; Fevold, 1939) unless massive doses are used (Velardo, 1960). Thus, LH-releasing mechanisms can be activated during the fourth week of life, presumably by the feedback of ovarian steroids.

C. Gonadal-Pituitary Interrelationships

Although the immature pituitary contains large quantities of gonadotropins that are normally released at only low levels, under certain circumstances increased secretion can be induced. That secretion of pituitary gonadotropins in the immature animal is held in check by the immature as well as the mature gonad has long been known. Kallas (1929a,b, 1930) first presented evidence that castration of an immature rat results in an increase in gonadotropin secretion sufficient to induce follicular development and luteinization in an intact parabiotic partner. This work has been repeatedly confirmed in the rat (Martins and de Mello, 1934; R. K. Meyer and Hertz, 1937; Biddulph *et al.*, 1940; Byrnes and Meyer, 1951a,b; Schuetz *et al.*, 1964) and in the mouse (Mühlbock, 1953).

Several other observations also offer indirect evidence for postcastration elevation of gonadotropin secretion in the immature rat. Ovariectomy followed by implantation (Hohlweg and Dohrn, 1931; Mandel, 1933) or autotransplantation (Pfeiffer, 1936; Greep and Jones, 1950) of an ovary results in early vaginal opening, presumably due to stimulation of the implanted ovary by increased levels of gonadotropin resulting from temporary absence of the gonads. Probably by a similar mechanism, intrasplenic ovarian grafts in gonadectomized immature rats undergo rapid maturation (Maekawa, 1960). Also, prepubertal gonadectomy is followed by development of castration cells (Hohlweg and Dohrn, 1931, 1932; Severinghaus, 1938, 1939) and an increase in gonadotropic potency of the hypophysis (Clark, 1935b; Presl *et al.*, 1963).

Recently, direct evidence for the inhibition of pituitary secretion by gonadal hormones has been obtained. Ramirez and McCann (1963a) determined both pituitary and plasma concentrations of LH in rats of both sexes gonadectomized at 10–12 days and killed at 26 days of age. Pituitary concentration of LH in the female was not increased by gonadectomy whereas that of the male was raised significantly. Plasma LH, not detectable in normal animals of either sex, was increased by gonadectomy in both.

All of the above pituitary responses to castration, including changes in cytology and content and release of gonadotropins, have been prevented by the administration of gonadal steroids. The amount of estrogen required to suppress the changes in the immature female is extremely small compared with that needed in the adult (Hohlweg and Dohrn, 1932; Byrnes and Meyer, 1951b; Ramirez and McCann, 1963a) and pituitary suppression occurs at estrogen levels below those causing uterine stimulation (Byrnes and Meyer, 1951a; Maekawa, 1960). Immature females require considerably less estrogen for suppression than do immature males (Hohlweg and Dohrn, 1931; Meyer and Hertz, 1937; Biddulph *et al.*, 1940). Testosterone requirements for suppression are lower in immature than adult males (McCann and Ramirez, 1964) and lower than those required to stimulate the seminal vesicles (Maekawa, 1960). Testosterone also suppressed the postcastration effects in immature rats of either sex (Schuetz *et al.*, 1964).

Although these studies indicate that hypophyseal cytology as well as content and release of gonadotropins can be manipulated by removal of the gonads and substitution of their secretions in the late juvenile rat (over 20 days of age), relatively little is known concerning the age at which these pituitary-gonadal relations are established. Clark (1935b) reported that castration at birth increased total gonadotropic potency of the male pituitary by the twenty-first day, but did not affect the already high levels in the female gland. An increase in pituitary basophiles at 21 days of age following neonatal castration was observed only in the male (Severinghaus, 1939). Recently, however, Presl *et al.* (1963) presented evidence which suggests that the ovary also influences pituitary activity between birth and 22 days of age. A more precise definition of the times at which the feedback mechanism is established awaits investigation with more sensitive methods.

IV. The Brain and Puberty

Clinically, concepts linking the brain with mechanisms controlling sexual maturation are not new. Shortly after the turn of the century, Erdheim (1904) associated Fröhlich's syndrome, which includes arrested sexual development, with pathology located at the base of the brain. Similarly, various and heterogeneous cerebral diseases, including hydrocephalus, encephalitis, nonspecific inflammations, neoplasms, and tumors have for many years been causally related to the appearance of precocious puberty in children. Several reviews summarize and treat the considerable literature on this subject (Weinberger and Grant, 1941; Lange-Cosack, 1951, 1952; Bauer, 1954, 1959). It is of interest that the cerebral pathology first related to pubertas praecox involved tumors of, or in the region of, the pineal. This clinicopathological relationship led Marburg to conclude (1908) that the pineal is a gland of internal secretion involved in the inhibition of sexual maturation. This concept of pineal function long furnished the basis for the widespread view that damage to the pineal was responsible for cerebral sexual precocity and it stimulated much experimentation involving this structure.

Although considerable research activity was early directed to the pineal, the disparate and conflicting results obtained raised many questions concerning the validity of conclusions which related epiphyseal dysfunction to pubertas praecox. In acknowledgment of contemporary physiological findings (Aschner, 1912b; Camus and Roussy, 1920), attention eventually was focused on the possibility that other neural structures might influence reproductive functions. Bailey and Jelliffe (1911) and Bailey and Bremer (1921) were impressed with the multiplicity of neurological signs which usually accompanied pineal tumors and were among the first to suggest that such tumors might affect sexual development through pressure exerted on adjacent neural centers. Somewhat later, it was observed that pineal tumors which result in precocity usually involve the adjacent hypothalamus (Bing *et al.*, 1938). Since tumors of the hypothalamus which do not involve the pineal result in precocity as frequently as those that do (Bing *et al.*, 1938; Weinberger and Grant, 1941; Bauer, 1954, 1959), and, because physiologists had failed to offer definitive experimental evidence supporting earlier views of pineal function, attention was shifted to the hypothalamus at a time when bases for concepts of hypothalamo-pituitary-gonadal relationships were tenuous indeed. Several careful reviews of the literature noted that most cerebral pathology associated with pubertas praecox is located in the posterior hypothalamus (Weinberger and Grant, 1941; Lange-Cosack, 1951, 1952; Bauer, 1954, 1959). It was postulated that the effects of such lesions are due to destruction of hypothalamic mechanisms which normally inhibit the secretion of gonadotropins (Dott, 1938; Weinberger and Grant, 1941). Lesions that produce hypogonadism tend to involve more anterior parts of the hypothalamus (Bauer, 1954, 1959).

A. Hypothalamus

Experimental confirmation of the above prescient clinical extrapolations was not to be available for many years and only recently has experimental evidence been obtained which (1) supports the inclusion of the hypothalamus in mechanisms that control the endocrine events which culminate in puberty and (2) indicates the existence of neural mechanisms which normally restrain or inhibit the secretion of pituitary gonadotropins during the prepubertal period.

Although 30 years ago Hohlweg and Junkmann (1932) ingeniously arrived at the conclusion that a neural *Sexualzentrum* was involved in the control of puberty and reproductive cycles, this conclusion was considerably premature and it was eclipsed by the popular theory of Moore and Price (1932) which considered pituitary-gonadal interrelationships sufficient to explain phenomena associated with reproductive functions. It was approximately 20 years later that Harris and Jacobsohn (1952) furnished the major stimulus for reconsidering the role of the nervous system in relation to puberty. These investigators demonstrated that immature rat hypophyses transplanted under the median eminence of hypophysectomized adult female rats not only restored vaginal cyclicity but also supported mating, pregnancy, and delivery of normal young. In addition to illustrating the importance of the hypophyseal portal system in pituitary-ovarian functions, these experiments demonstrated that 12- to 16-day-old pituitaries are capable of adult function. Hence, that portion of the prepubertal period which follows the attainment of gonadal responsivity to gonadotropins may result from the inactivity of those hypthalamic mechanisms which regulate pituitary-gonadal function in the adult animal. Evidence that this inactivity stems, at least in part, from the influence of inhibitory mechanisms had to await subsequent developments; it was Donovan and Van der Werff ten Bosch (1956, 1959a) who put the concept of neural inhibition of gonadotropin secretion in the prepubertal animal on a firm basis. These investigators found that electrolytic lesions placed in the anterior hypothalamus resulted in premature vaginal opening and ovulation in the female rat. The effectiveness of lesions placed in the anterior hypothalamus in producing signs of accelerated sexual maturation in the female rat has been amply confirmed (Bogdanove and Schoen, 1959; Elwers and Critchlow, 1960; Horowitz and Van der Werff ten Bosch, 1962; Schiavi, 1964). However, Gellert and Ganong (1960) found posterior tuberal, not anterior hypothalamic, destruction effective in this regard. Recently, Schiavi (1964) found that both anteriorly and posteriorly placed lesions resulted in precocious ovarian activity. The implications of these several attempts to localize the hypothalamic structures involved are discussed below.

Although several criteria for lesion-induced precocity have been used singly or in combination, i.e., date of vaginal opening, increased uterine weight, early initiation of vaginal cyclicity and ovulation, the results have consistently pointed toward early activation of the pituitary-ovarian axis. If puberty is considered as the stage of development at which reproduction becomes possible, true precocious puberty probably results from hypothalamic lesions since on several occasions animals with early vaginal opening have mated at first estrus and produced normal litters (Bar-Sela and Critchlow, unpublished observations, 1964). Previously, Gellert and Ganong (1960) considered the early initiation of estrous cyclicity as indicative of true precocious puberty. In confirmation of Donovan and Van der Werff ten Bosch (1959a), we have found that with the exception of some animals which show persistent vaginal cornification, many rats with accelerated sexual development following hypothalamic lesions demonstrate normal reproductive cycles and functions, including mating, pregnancy, and delivery and rearing of litters (Bar-Sela and Critchlow, unpublished observations, 1964).

It is of interest with regard to the mode of action of hypothalamic lesions that the degree of precocity appears to be independent of the age at which the lesions are placed. Horowitz and Van der Werff ten Bosch (1962) found that the advancement of the age at which the vagina opened in rats operated upon at 3 or 4 days of age was similar to that caused by lesions placed at 10, 14, or 15 days. These authors favor the view that such lesions interfere with some physiological process which occurs shortly before puberty, the effect being due to the presence of the lesions at a particular stage of development.

Brain destruction in the male, similar to that which induces premature ovarian stimulation in the female, has thus far proved ineffective in causing sexual precocity (Bogdanove and Schoen, 1959; Bar-Sela and Critchlow, unpublished observations, 1964), although some effects on the development of the seminal vesicle and ventral prostate have been noted in a preliminary report (Bar-Sela, 1964). It is not surprising that the male rat has proved refractory since, as discussed previously (Section II,A,2), it has not been possible to induce precocious puberty even with the administration of exogenous gonadotropins.

Whereas the lesions described above resulted in acceleration of sexual development in female rats, destruction localized to the region of the ventromedial and arcuate nuclei prevented or delayed puberty in the rabbit (Bustamante, 1942; Bustamante *et al.*, 1942). A similar delay in sexual maturation was recently reported in conjunction with electrolytic lesions placed in the ventromedial-mammillary body region of female (Corbin and Schottelius, 1960, 1961a) and male (Corbin, 1963) rats. These observations were interpreted as indicating the presence of a gonadotropin-stimulating mechanism in this part of the diencephalon. However, the lesions were large and produced rather severe atrophy of the hypophysis. Because other tropic functions of the pituitary were not examined and since the extent of involvement of the hypophyseal-portal system was not made clear, conclusions regarding the specificity of the delaying effects may be somewhat premature. On the other hand, consistent with the interpretation of the significance of the delaying effects of these lesions, the region of the arcuate nucleus has been implicated as a facilitatory area for gonadotropin release in adults of several species (Sawyer, 1964).

Attempts to localize and identify the hypothalamic structures involved in the control of puberty have been of little avail. Clinically there appears to be some consensus that destruction of the anterior portions of the hypothalamus is most often associated with hypogonadism (Bauer, 1954, 1959), whereas posterior tuberal lesions usually result in sexual precocity (Dott, 1938; Weinberger and Grant, 1941). In addition, there is some reason to believe that hamartomas attached to the floor of the hypothalamus induce puberty at a very early age, while lesions elsewhere or more diffuse pathological processes cause puberty at 6 years or older (Lange-Cosack, 1951, 1952). Experimental studies have neither confirmed the above clinical observations nor have they added much pertinent information regarding the identity of the hypothalamic structures operant in the control of puberty. In fact, it is apparent that some discrepancies have arisen and need to be resolved.

First, although Donovan and Van der Werff ten Bosch (1956, 1959a) originally emphasized the anterior hypothalamus as the site involved in the restraint of puberty in the female rat, there now seems to be little reason for considering this part of the diencephalon unique in this regard. On the basis of the information now available, it seems clear that much of the medial and ventral hypothalamus, with the possible exception of the mammillary bodies, is equipotential in this respect. The recent report of Schiavi (1964) best supports this view since his is one of the few studies which systematically examined the effects of focal destruction in both the anterior and posterior hypothalamus. This investigator found that lesions variously placed from the suprachiasmatic region and anterior hypothalamus to the premammillary area were effective in promoting precocious ovarian activity.

This view of the widespread potential of hypothalamic lesions to induce precocious puberty is seemingly complicated by the failure of Gellert and Ganong (1960) to observe precocity associated with "anterior" hypothalamic destruction. However, as pointed out by Schiavi (1964), this failure may be attributed to the small number of animals used and to the variations in lesions designated as "anterior"; some of the latter were located medial to the posterior part of the dorsomedial nucleus. Also, complications may have arisen from the use of mean dates of vaginal opening and first estrus to describe the effects produced by a heterogeneous group of lesions. In a preliminary report, Ganong (1961) acknowledged that some rats with anterior hypothalamic lesions might be considered to have experienced precocious puberty, but these were considered insignificant in view of the group average. In view of the several reports of precocious ovarian activation produced by hypothalamic lesions located in the anterior hypothalamus or outside of the posterior tuberal region, the discrepancy suggested by the findings of Gellert and Ganong may be more apparent than real. In spite of the diffuseness of the hypothalamic localization observed in the rat, some anatomic specificity is indicated since lesions placed in several other diencephalic and telencephalic sites have proved ineffective in causing premature sexual development (Donovan and Van der Werff ten Bosch, 1959a; Elwers and Critchlow, 1960, 1961; Gellert and Ganong, 1960; Schiavi, 1964).

Another point of some disagreement regarding lesion localization and puberty involves an observation of Bogdanove and Schoen (1959). These authors confirmed the findings of Donovan and Van der Werff ten Bosch (1959a) and found anterior hypothalamic destruction effective in causing precocious sexual development in female rats, but they also reported that lesions involving the arcuate nucleus were specifically associated with luteinization of prematurely stimulated ovaries. This relationship was not confirmed in two subsequent reports (Elwers and Critchlow, 1960; Schiavi, 1964). However, the findings of Bogdanove and Schoen may be subject to another interpretation. Rather than destruction in the region of the arcuate nucleus specifically causing LH release and ovulation, it is possible that the more anteriorly placed lesions in their series disrupted mechanisms responsible for the ovulatory discharge of LH. Several workers have described persistent vaginal cornification in some rats subsequent to lesion-induced precocious vaginal opening (Donovan and Van der Werff ten Bosch, 1959a; Horowitz and Van der Werff ten Bosch, 1962; Schiavi, 1964). At present, it is not known whether such animals ovulate in association with vaginal opening, although the findings of Schiavi suggest that some do not. By definition, such animals, despite precocious sexual development, would fail to attain true puberty. Consistent with localization achieved in adult rats by Hillarp (1949) and others, lesions which cause persistent vaginal cornification seem to involve principally the basal portions of the anterior hypothalamus.

An additional source of conflict relating to the localization of hypothalamic structures involved in the control of puberty concerns the "posterior tuberal" (Gellert and Ganong, 1960) or premammillary (Schiavi, 1964) lesions which cause precocity and those in the "ventromedial nucleus-mammillary body" area (Corbin and Schottelius, 1960, 1961a; Corbin, 1963) which cause delayed puberty. Anatomically these areas are practically coextensive and closer examination of the morphological characteristics of the lesions will be necessary in order to resolve this apparent paradox. As indicated above, the lesions of Corbin and Schottelius may have produced their effects through encroachment upon the hypophyseal-portal system.

B. Extrahypothalamic Structures

In addition to implicating the hypothalamus in mechanisms that control sexual development in the female rat, recent experimental evidence also points to possible roles for certain extrahypothalamic structures such as the amygdaloid nuclear complex and other components of the limbic system as well as the ubiquitous pineal.

1. *Amygdala and Other Limbic System Structures*

Electrolytic destruction localized to the amygdala, a temporal lobe component of the limbic system, produced premature ovarian activation, uterine stimulation, and vaginal opening that was similar in all respects to that observed following placement of lesions in the hypothalamus (Elwers and Critchlow, 1960). As is the case with many rats with hypothalamic lesions, animals which demonstrate premature ovarian activity following destruction in the amygdala show completely normal vaginal cycles, responses to constant illumination, and the capacity to mate successfully and rear the resulting litters (Bar-Sela and Critchlow, unpublished observations, 1964).

In contrast to the rather diffuse distribution of effective lesion sites in the hypothalamus, localization in the amygdala appears relatively discrete. In our experience, only lesions that involve a restricted part of the basomedial region, in the area of the corticomedial nuclear complex, produce precocious ovarian stimulation. The effectiveness of amygdaloid lesions has been confirmed by Ganong (1961). Lesions placed in the pyriform lobe, which contains the amygdaloid complex, have been reported to produce premature appearance of the upsurge in running activity that is usually associated with puberty in rats (Riss *et al.*, 1963).

The amygdala is in intimate anatomical relationship with the hypothalamus via both direct and indirect fiber connections. Bilateral interruption of the stria terminalis, an amygdalo-hypothalamic tract, also resulted in premature ovarian activation, offering further evidence for participation of the amygdaloid complex in mechanisms that control gonadotropin release in immature female rats (Elwers and Critchlow, 1961).

Although the acceleration of sexual development observed in association with focal destruction in the hypothalamus, amygdala, or stria terminalis has been interpreted in terms of removal of neural mechanisms which normally inhibit gonadotropin secretion, it is possible that such lesions produce their effects through stimulation or irritation (Everett and Radford, 1961). However, there are some data which suggest that the latter is not the case. Donovan and Van der Werff ten Bosch (1959b) found that chronic electrical stimulation failed to duplicate the effects of lesions in advancing the seasonal estrus of the ferret. A further indication that the effects of lesions on sexual maturation stem from removal of inhibition was furnished by the results obtained following electrical stimulation applied through electrodes implanted in the brains of young female rats. In these studies (Bar-Sela and Critchlow, 1966), stimulation applied to the amygdala for 6 hours per day, starting at 25 days of age, resulted in significant delay of vaginal opening and first ovulation. By demonstrating reciprocal effects with electrical stimulation, these studies furnish additional evidence that lesion-induced precocity is due to ablation and not irritation, and the results support inclusion of the amygdala in neural mechanisms that restrain gonadotropin secretion in immature female rats. Theories concerning these inhibitory mechanisms have been advanced and will be discussed below (Section V,C).

The effectiveness of lesions placed in the amygdala and stria terminalis may also offer some explanation for the lack of discrete localization of puberty-inducing lesions in the hypothalamus. As has been pointed out (Elwers and Critchlow, 1960, 1961), the locations of hypothalamic lesions reported to cause precocious ovarian activation correspond approximately to the distribution of the stria terminalis. Interruption of these fibers may be the common factor in these variously placed hypothalamic lesions.

Evidence that other limbic system structures influence puberty is intriguing but not clear. Riss *et al.* (1963), on the basis of altered patterns of running activity and decreased gonadal weights, suggested that hippocampal lesions cause decreased secretion of gonadotropins. Kling (1964) also found decreased ovarian weights associated with destruction in the hippocampus, but such lesions failed to influence significantly the age of vaginal opening or testicular weights. In addition, Kling reported delayed vaginal opening as well as decreased ovarian and testicular weights in rats with olfactory stalk and medial olfactory area lesions. If confirmed and expanded, such findings will be important in further clarifying the relationships between limbic and hypothalamic functions.

2. *Pineal*

As indicated previously, the pineal is another intracranial structure that has been implicated in the control of puberty. As a result of the early clinical findings and theories, laboratory investigations concerned with the functional relationship between the epiphysis and mechanisms involved with sexual development and functions were initiated many years ago. Although historic and current concepts regarding the pineal are treated elsewhere in this book, some of the recent investigations bear directly on the problem of control of puberty and will be mentioned briefly in this context.

In his excellent review of the early period of pineal research, Krabbe (1923) noted that much of the experimental work was poorly controlled and technically faulty and made the laconic observation that ". . . one has very often the impression that the authors' desire to consider the organ incretory in function is greater than their critical judgment regarding published researches." A general disinterest in the pineal followed the discovery of pituitary-gonadal relationships; nevertheless, a few reports continued to appear. The data and conclusions presented, however, continued to be as conflicting as those described by Krabbe. More recently, Kitay and Altschule (1954a) reviewed the literature on the pineal and noted that many of the reports were of questionable validity because the presentations of data did not permit statistical analysis. However, on the basis of the papers considered satisfactory, it was concluded that the accumulated evidence favored pineal inhibition of gonadal activity. In a review of clinical cases, Kitay (1954a) focused attention on the relationship between nonparenchymal tumors of the pineal and precocious puberty; he suggested that such tumors cause their effects by interfering with the secretory functions of the pineal. These conclusions restimulated interest in this organ and a number of recent papers again point to a relationship between epiphyseal and gonadal functions.

Consistent with the premise that the pineal in some way inhibits gonadal function, Kitay (1954b) reported that pinealectomy increased ovarian weight in immature female rats operated at 26–30 but not 21 days of age. Kitay and Altschule (1954b) also found that pineal extracts produced marked ovarian atrophy and apparent inhibition of ovulation if treatments were started at 30 days of age. Subsequently, Wurtman *et al.* (1959) confirmed the effects of pineal ablation and extracts on ovarian weights. An inhibitory role for the pineal was also suggested by the report that pineal extracts prevented the increase in weight of the immature rat ovary that follows exposure to constant light (Wurtman *et al.*, 1961). However, somewhat paradoxically, Jöchle (1956) reported that administration of pineal extract induced early vaginal opening in rats kept in either rhythmic or constant light. Based on the chronic effects of these injections, this investigator envisioned a "braking" effect which prevented extreme excursions of the cycling mechanism in response to environmental stimuli.

Following the recent discovery that melatonin (5-methoxy-*N*-acetyltryptamine) is synthesized in the pineal glands of all mammals that have been studied (Lerner *et al.*, 1959, 1960), and with the finding that the enzyme involved in its synthesis, 5-hydroxyindole-*O*-methyl transferase, is found only in the pineal (Axelrod and Weissbach, 1961), there has been a relative flurry of investigations to determine the effect of melatonin on gonadal function under a variety of conditions. Relative to the control of puberty, it has been reported that small doses of melatonin depress growth of the immature rat ovary and delay vaginal opening (Wurtman *et al.*, 1963). The site and mode of action of melatonin are still obscure.

If these experimental observations are confirmed, the long list of proponents of the pineal as a gland of internal secretion with gonad-inhibiting functions may yet have their day, and newer concepts concerning mechanisms controlling puberty will have to acknowledge the contributions of this enigmatic structure. In the meantime, the present review and consideration of mechanisms involved in the control of puberty will concentrate on hypothalamo-pituitary-gonadal relationships.

V. Control of Puberty

The causal relationship between certain brain lesions and precocious sexual development in both clinical and experimental situations adds considerable support to other presumptive evidence which indicates that the latency between attainment of functionally competent gonads and the onset of puberty results from the relative inactivity of those neural systems which control gonadotropic functions in the adult animal. In view of the paucity of information relating to the maturation of the brain, full understanding of the processes involved in the initiation of function in these nueroendocrine mechanisms and in the transition from the prepubertal to the adult state is not yet possible. However, some insight may be gained by considering some of the conditions or stimuli which modify the age of puberty. Because little is known concerning mechanisms which regulate puberty in the male and since it generally has not been possible to accelerate the age of sexual maturation with exogenous gonadotropins in male mammals, the following discussion will necessarily be almost exclusively limited to the female. It should be emphasized, however, that pubertas praecox in the human male, as well as in the female, is a definite and dramatic clinical entity: in some cases enlarged genitalia are present at birth and mature sperm have been found in boys less than 4 years of age (Driggs and Spatz, 1939).

A. Environmental Factors and Puberty

For many years it has been recognized that certain manipulations result in premature sexual maturation of the female rat. The effects of several of these procedures are clearly mediated through the central nervous system since exteroreceptors and neural pathways are involved, while others are less obviously linked to neural mechanisms and are related to alterations in hormonal environments and/or metabolic processes.

1. *External Environmental Factors*

In this category, constant illumination (Luce-Clausen and Brown, 1939; Fiske, 1941), cold (Mandl and Zuckerman, 1952), stimulation of the uterine cervix (Swingle *et al.,* 1951; Aron and Aron-Brunetière, 1953), handling in infancy (Morton *et al.,* 1963), and a stressful combination of sound, light, and electrical shock (Nagy and Árvay, 1958; Árvay and Nagy, 1959) are reported to cause early pituitary-ovarian function in rodents. As a clinical correlate of the latter experimental observations, Nagy and Árvay (1958) noted that the stresses of war or of "Americanization" exert profound effects on the onset of puberty in girls of several nations. Interestingly, whereas darkness (Luce-Clausen and Brown, 1939; Fiske, 1941) or blinding (Browman, 1940; Truscott,

1944) appear to retard sexual development in the rat, blindness in the human may be associated with early menarche (Zacharias and Wurtman, 1964).

Although it is reasonable to expect that the above exteroceptive stimuli affect gonadal function through intermediation of the hypothalamo-pituitary axis, the details of the mechanisms involved are for the most part unknown. The effects of constant light have been explored in most detail and it is well established that in many species this afferent modality occupies a somewhat unique position among environmental factors which influence pituitary-gonadal function (Harris, 1955; Amoroso and Marshall, 1960; Critchlow, 1963). According to Fiske (1941), constant light produces alterations in pituitary content and secretion of both FSH and LH in immature rats.

The diversity of neurogenic stimuli which induce premature sexual development is intriguing and lends credence to the suggestion of Nagy and Árvay (1958) and Árvay and Nagy (1959) that sensory inflow from the environment influences the maturation of neural systems responsible for the control of gonadotropin secretion. These workers accentuated sensory input by means of a constant barrage of environmental stimuli, the severe "psychic" trauma of their experiments, and found either advancement or delay of puberty, depending upon the age of the animal. It does not seem, however, that these various puberty-inducing stimuli qualify as "nonspecific" stresses since altered diets or rough handling (Mandl and Zuckerman, 1952) and the stresses associated with a variety of inappropriately placed neural lesions (Donovan and Van der Werff ten Bosch, 1959a; Elwers and Critchlow, 1960, 1961; Gellert and Ganong, 1960; Schiavi, 1964) do not cause early sexual development. Of interest with respect to the wide spectrum of stimuli which induce early pituitary-ovarian function, electrophysiological recordings in rats (Barraclough and Cross, 1963) and cats (Cross and Green, 1959; Brooks *et al.*, 1962) indicate that there is considerable convergence of sensory input in the hypothalamus and that individual units may respond to stimuli of several afferent modalities.

2. *Internal Environmental Factors*

Other experimental manipulations, less obvious in their involvement of the nervous system, also affect the onset of pituitary-gonadal functions. Some of these procedures entail hormonal alterations. For example, administration of estrogens (Hohlweg, 1934; Desclin, 1935; Lane, 1935; Mazer *et al.*, 1936; Hohlweg and Chamorro, 1937; Herold and Effkemann, 1938; Westman and Jacobsohn, 1938; Price and Ortiz, 1944; Cole, 1946) and androgens to rats (Hohlweg, 1937; Nathanson *et al.*, 1938; Salmon, 1938) or monkeys (van Wagenen, 1949) and transplantation of ovaries (Pfeiffer, 1936; Greep and Jones, 1950) cause premature ovarian stimulation and/or ovulation. The above responses to hormonal administration appear to reflect a surfeit of gonadal steroids; premature vaginal opening following transplantation of ovaries is presumed to result from a transient decrease in circulating levels of sex steroids which reflexly triggers increased pituitary-ovarian secretory activity (Greep and Jones, 1950). Some of the implications of these observations will be discussed below (Section V,B).

Treatment with yet another hormone has been reported to prematurely activate the pituitary-gonadal axis. Corbin and Schottelius (1961b) described precocious sexual maturation in rats following intraventricular injection of oxytocin and suggested that this hormone may function as a neurohumoral stimulus to cause gonadotropin secretion in the immature rat. Similar injections of epinephrine and vasopressin failed to accelerate sexual development.

In addition to hormonal treatments, certain pharmacological agents also exert effects on puberty. Robson and Botros (1961) reported that administration of 5-hydroxytryptamine (serotonin) or iproniazid and other monoamine oxidase inhibitors to mice delayed vaginal opening and first vaginal estrus and caused decreased weight of reproductive organs; slight or no effects were observed in males. Since these drugs did not interfere with ovarian responses to exogenous gonadotropins or with uterine and vaginal responses to estrogen, it was postulated that they act on brain or pituitary to inhibit gonadotropin secretion. These authors considered the possibility that reserpine, which blocks ovulation in adult rats (Barraclough and Sawyer, 1957) and which reportedly delays puberty when administered intraventricularly in immature rats (Corbin and Schottelius, 1961b), may exert its effects by causing liberation of serotonin from body depots, while monoamine oxidase inhibitors may act by decreasing the enzymic breakdown of serotonin. Setnikar *et al.* (1960) previously noted that iproniazid delayed sexual maturation in female rats and caused lengthened estrous cycles, absence of corpora lutea, decreased uterine development, and the appearance of "deficiency cells" in and atrophy of ovarian interstitial tissue. Again, no effects were noted in males. It was postulated that these results were due to partial blockade of LH release.

Another type of manipulation which exerts profound effects on puberty involves alterations in nutritional status. There is considerable evidence that rats raised in large litters or fed on a restricted diet not only show drastic retardation of somatic growth but also exhibit delayed puberty; conversely, rats that are unusually well nourished because of being placed in small litters show marked somatic growth and sexual precocity (Asdell and Crowell, 1935; Engle *et al.*, 1937; Kennedy, 1957; Widdowson and McCance, 1960; Kennedy and Mitra, 1963; Widdowson *et al.*, 1964).

With regard to the specific effects of nutrition on reproductive functions, several interesting aspects of this long-established relationship have been featured in recent papers. It appears that underfeeding in pigs (Dickerson *et al.*, 1964) and rats (Widdowson *et al.*, 1964) produces signs of a preferential blockade of LH release, while FSH secretion seems little affected. The endocrine changes described by Kennedy and Mitra (1963) are consistent with this interpretation of a specific blockade of LH. Thus, as a consequence of the apparent failure in cyclic LH release mechanisms, young rats whose vaginas opened late due to underfeeding show persistent vaginal cornification associated with follicular ovaries that are devoid of corpora lutea. Interestingly, initiation of rehabilitative feeding serves to synchronize ovulation in these animals. Furthermore, it is intriguing that in affecting mechanisms responsible for cyclic LH release, inanition in the female rat produces effects which resemble those associated with neuroendocrine dysfunctions produced by certain hypothalamic lesions (Hillarp, 1949), constant light (Browman, 1937; Hemmingsen and Krarup, 1937), and prepubertal administration of androgen (Barraclough, 1961; Barraclough and Gorski, 1961).

Although the marked correlation between nutrition, growth, and reproductive functions has long been recognized, only recently has this correlation been considered in context with neural mechanisms involved in attainment of puberty. Kennedy and Mitra (1963), acknowledging the apparent role of the hypothalamus, suggested that food intake, or its correlated effects on metabolic processes, may act as the normal signal to initiate puberty. However, instead of being the definitive signal, it seems more likely that food intake is but one of many influences which can affect neuroendocrine systems concerned with gonadotropin secretion since several of the manipulations described previously modify the onset of puberty without obviously distorting general metabolic or growth patterns. As shown by Donovan and Van der Werff ten Bosch (1959a), sexual maturation may be achieved prematurely in the absence of signs of accelerated growth in rats with hypothalamic lesions.

B. Role of Gonadal Steroid Feedback

Numerous investigations into functional interrelationships between gonads and pituitary have clearly established that under many conditions secretion of gonadotropins is controlled by circulating levels of ovarian and testicular hormones. There is overwhelming evidence, based on a variety of indices and approaches in a number of species, that gonadectomy results in a compensatory increase in the secretion of both FSH and LH. Furthermore, it is the generally accepted view, although some modification may be necessary because of recent findings, that physiological levels of estrogen and androgen are capable of suppressing postcastration elevations in gonadotropin secretion. These interrelationships, unified under concepts of negative feedback, have long been implicated in the regulation of reproductive cycles in adult animals (Moore and Price, 1932).

Similarly, theories concerned with the control of sexual maturation early focused on the reciprocal relationships between the secretion of gonadal steroids and pituitary gonadotropins. On the basis of their studies of changes in castration cells induced by pituitary transplantation, Hohlweg and Junkmann (1932), clearly ahead of their time, suggested that suppression of secretion of gonadotropin is dependent upon neural connections of the pituitary and speculated that a *Sexualzentrum* in the nervous system might play an essential role in the prepubertal inhibition of gonadotropin secretion. Hohlweg and Dohrn (1932) found that pituitary cytological changes associated with gonadectomy in infant rats were prevented by estrogen administered in a dose that was approximately one-hundredth of that required in the adult. As a result of these studies, Hohlweg (1936) suggested that the extreme sensitivity of the *Sexualzentrum* to inhibition by estrogen serves to keep the secretion of FSH at a low level. With approaching puberty, he postulated that the center becomes progressively less sensitive to estrogen and, as a result of these elevated thresholds, stimulates the pituitary to increase the secretion of FSH. Later, Byrnes and Meyer (1951b), relying on ovarian and uterine changes, also reported that less estrogen is required to inhibit gonadotropin secretion in immature than in postpubertal rats and postulated that it is the increasing refractoriness of the pituitary which permits accelerated release of FSH and eventual attainment of puberty. It was concluded in these studies that estrogen inhibits FSH and facilitates LH secretion.

The original ideas of Hohlweg and his associates, because they envisioned participation of neural structures, are in amazing accord with present-day concepts. Thus, Donovan and Van der Werff ten Bosch (1959a), in considering the effects of neural lesions, postulated that the main difference between the immature and adult animal is the extreme sensitivity of the brain of the former to gonadal hormones. In the same vein, Ramirez and McCann (1963a) and McCann and Ramirez (1964), on the basis of differences in the suppressive effects of estrogen and androgen on pituitary and plasma levels of LH in immature and adult gonadectomized rats, suggested that onset of puberty results from resetting of a hypothalamic "gonadostat." Because of this presumed change in threshold, circulating levels of gonadal hormones which are effective in restraining gonadotropin secretion in the immature animal are rendered ineffective at puberty. These authors found no evidence that estrogen facilitates LH secretion as postulated by Byrnes and Meyer (1951b).

Thus, the current consensus is that gonadotropin-regulating mechanisms of the immature animal are markedly more sensitive to the negative feedback influences of both estrogen and androgen than are those of the adult. However, it is not clear whether this hypersensitivity extends to the secretion of both LH and FSH. The question with respect to LH seems resolved since Ramirez and McCann (1963a) and McCann and Ramirez (1964) measured this hormone in the blood of gonadectomized rats and found that smaller doses of estradiol and testosterone were required to suppress the high levels of circulating LH in immature than in adult rats. To our knowledge, similar studies have not been performed with specific assays for plasma FSH. Byrnes and Meyer (1951b) concluded on the basis of indirect indices that the hypersensitivity of the infant rat chiefly involved the secretion of FSH; conversely, because certain doses of estrogen caused increased ovarian weight, it was postulated that estrogen facilitates the secretion of LH. Recent evidence, however, suggests that the hypersensitivity of the prepubertal animal to sex steroids may pertain primarily to the secretion of LH. Parlow (1964a), using slightly older rats which reached and exceeded the age of puberty during the course of the experiment, found that, whereas 0.4 or 0.1 μg of estradiol inhibited postovariectomy increase in pituitary and serum LH concentration, these same doses failed to inhibit a similar elevation in hypophyseal content of FSH. At a higher daily dose (2.0 μg), estradiol caused significant inhibition of both pituitary and serum FSH. These data were interpreted as indicating that LH is far more responsive than FSH to the inhibitory action of physiological doses of estrogen. In a preliminary report, Bogdanove (1964) also reported on the differential effects of testosterone treatment in castrated adult male rats. Again, this sex steroid produced a decrease in plasma levels of LH but had little or no effect on circulating levels of FSH. In addition, Schuetz *et al.* (1964) recently presented evidence obtained from parabiosed immature rats which suggests that testosterone preferentially inhibits the postcastration rise in circulating LH but not FSH.

Although it seems clear that less estrogen and testosterone are required to suppress the postcastration elevation in LH secretion in immature than in adult rats, the same difference in sensitivity may not be present in mechanisms controlling FSH secretion. If an increase in FSH secretion is the major hormonal event associated with the triggering of puberty, as suggested by Parlow (1964a,b), the available data are not entirely consistent with the premise that hypersensitivity of negative feedback mechanisms is the essential basis for maintenance of the prepubertal state.

Another inconsistency which raises questions about the role of sex steroid inhibition of gonadotropin secretion during the prepubertal period pertains to the effects of steroid administration. As indicated previously, it has been demonstrated repeatedly that administration of gonadal steroids may result in precocious ovulation. Apparently this phenomenon is not elicitable before the late juvenile period (Price and Ortiz, 1944). Furthermore, it occurs in response to doses of estrogen only slightly greater than those which lead to ovarian regression (Cole, 1946), and it requires more than 3 and less than 4 days in the presence of an intact pituitary (Westman and Jacobsohn, 1938). Evidence of facilitation of gonadotropin release following the injection of gonadal steroids is not unique to the immature animal; numerous examples of similar responses in adults are available (Everett, 1961, 1964; Greep, 1961; Sawyer, 1964). Such facilitation may reflect the effects of positive feedback, although the possibility of a "rebound" phenomenon should be considered. The latter is a manifestation of negative feedback. Sex steroid-induced ovulation in the immature rat as an effect of rebound would be compatible with the presence of a hypersensitive negative feedback system. On the other hand, premature gonadotropin release stemming from positive feedback would not be consistent with this view. Thus, indicative of the complexities of feedback influences, estrogen, especially in combination with progesterone (Ramirez and McCann, 1963b), suppresses LH in the plasma of gonadectomized rats, while it apparently facilitates LH release under certain conditions in intact adult and immature rats. To be sure, the doses of sex steroids used in many of the early experiments to induce precocious ovulation were massive and undoubtedly nonphysiological, and postulations of the existence of positive feedback mechanisms on such bases would be tenuous indeed. However, Ramirez and Sawyer (1965) recently obtained important evidence which suggests the occurrence of positive feedback; a series of small doses of estrogen induced precocious vaginal opening, early initiation of estrous cycles, and stimulation of LH release in the immature female rat.

These paradoxical effects of estrogen on LH release are made even more intriguing when considered in conjunction with those of progesterone. Although estrogen and testosterone have figured prominently in concepts related to the feedback regulation of gonadotropin release, it has been apparent for some time that progesterone might exert significant influences. Again, the situation is complex because both inhibition and facilitation of gonadotropin secretion have been observed to result from progesterone administration. There is extensive evidence which indicates that progesterone is capable of suppressing the secretion of LH. Indeed, as pointed out by Everett in his excellent review (1961), most attention and emphasis has been focused on the inhibitory effects of this steroid hormone. On the other hand, Everett also cites numerous observations in several species which indicate that progesterone facilitates the secretion of LH under certain conditions of timing, dose, ovarian status, and estrogen priming.

The paradoxical feedback effects of progesterone on LH release may also operate in the immature animal. Bradbury (1947) found that progesterone administered concurrently with estrogen to the immature rat prevented the increase in ovarian weight and decrease in pituitary content of gonadotropin, presumably due to LH release, that resulted from treatment with estrogen alone. Also, because it appeared that it took more exogenous estrogen to suppress LH release in ovariectomized immature and adult rats than is normally secreted by the ovary, Ramirez and McCann (1963a) postulated that progesterone may synergize with estrogen to inhibit LH release in the intact animal and subsequently designed an assay in which progesterone was combined with estrogen to furnish a rat in which endogenous LH release was blocked (1963b). Conversely, McCormack and Meyer (1963, 1964) reported that progesterone increased the PMS-induced ovulatory responses of immature rats. This response of the immature rat ovary to a single dose of PMS is age dependent (Zarrow and Quinn, 1963), requires approximately 56 hours (Quinn and Zarrow, 1964a), and probably involves the participation of neuroendocrine mechanisms that control LH release since several neural blocking agents (Zarrow and Quinn, 1963; Quinn and Zarrow, 1964a) and lesions placed in the medial preoptic region (Quinn and Zarrow, 1964b) inhibit the ovulatory response. The age dependency of the response to PMS may be related to attainment of responsivity of the ovary and its ability to secrete estrogen and progesterone in amounts sufficient to facilitate the activity of neural structures that control LH release. Whether estrogen and progesterone act only on the brain or whether direct effects on the pituitary are also involved will be treated in other chapters of this book. However, considerable evidence indicates that some of the effects of both estrogen and progesterone (Everett, 1961, 1964; Sawyer, 1964; Barraclough and Gorski, 1961) may be mediated through the brain. In view of the facilitatory effects of progesterone on PMS-induced ovulation, and because phenobarbital blocked these effects, there appears to be considerable merit in considering the suggestion of McCormack and Meyer (1964) that progesterone plays a facilitative role in the functional maturation of mechanisms that control pituitary gonadotropin secretion.

Although there is no definitive experimental evidence to explain the paradoxical effects of estrogen and/or progesterone on gonadotropin secretion, some light might be shed on this problem by considering the effects of the biphasic actions of progesterone which have been described in several experimental systems. For example, in the estrogen-primed rabbit, Sawyer and Everett (1959) found that progesterone treatment 4 hours prior to mating facilitated ovulation, whereas administration of this steroid 24 hours in advance of mating inhibited this response. Kawakami and Sawyer (1959) showed that this biphasic pattern in ovulatory response was correlated with similar patterns in thresholds of electroencephalogram arousal and sexual behavior.

The presence of such biphasic effects in the rat might furnish an explanation for the finding that progesterone inhibits estrogen-induced LH release (Bradbury, 1947) while it facilitates PMS-induced ovulation (McCormack and Meyer, 1963, 1964) in immature rats. In the first case, Bradbury administered progesterone subcutaneously at the time estrogen was injected. Since in his studies and in the experiments of Westman and Jacobsohn (1938) an approximate 72–96-hour period was required for evidence of estrogen-induced LH release, it is possible that inhibitory effects of progesterone were being exerted at the time of the "critical period." This period, extrapolating from the adult rat (Everett *et al.*, 1949) and from studies of PMS-induced ovulation (McCormack and Meyer, 1963, 1964), probably occurs approximately 10–12 hours prior to ovulation. In contrast to the above inhibitory effects, McCormack and Meyer observed facilitation of ovulation with progesterone. Although these workers used PMS to induce ovulation, the time course of the response, as described previously, is approximately the same as that observed with estrogen. Progesterone was administered to the majority of their immature animals 2 days following PMS injection. Under these circumstances, only a few hours separated progesterone treatment from the critical period and it is possible that the facilitatory effects of progesterone were being manifested at that crucial time. Earlier administration of progesterone might inhibit rather than facilitate PMS-induced ovulation.

Like many aspects of hormonal feedback, the bases for the biphasic actions of progesterone are obscure. These actions might reflect dose-dependent phenomena in which low levels of circulating progesterone in combination with estrogen facilitate, while higher levels inhibit, LH release. On this basis, it is possible that the biphasic effects that have been observed are more closely related to blood levels than to time. Time may be incidental and related primarily to the artifical conditions imposed by the placement of a subcutaneous pool of progesterone in oil. It is conceivable that facilitation during the first few hours following the injection of such a pool of progesterone reflects the time course of absorption and the effects of gradually increasing levels of circulating steroid, while subsequent inhibition results from progesterone titers exceeding certain critical levels. In the intact animal with endogenous hormone secretion, absolute levels rather than time per se may determine the actions of progesterone: low titers of progesterone resulting from the secretory activity of maturing follicles or waning corpora lutea (Everett, 1961) may facilitate LH release, while higher titers from functional corpora lutea may inhibit it.

In the immature rat, attainment of competence of the ovary to secrete progesterone in addition to estrogen may be related to the age dependency of the ovulatory response that follows treatment with estrogen or PMS. Ovulation cannot be induced consistently by either of the above hormonal treatments before the late juvenile period, in the fourth week of life. There is some evidence (Alden, 1947; Dawson and McCabe, 1951) to indicate that the rat ovary begins to secrete progesterone late in the third week and since this steroid facilitates PMS-induced ovulation, it may be that progesterone in low levels, in combination with estrogen, is the factor which determines whether neural mechanisms responsible for LH release are activated in response to either PMS or estrogen treatment.

Some of the complex actions of progesterone could be involved in the paradoxical effects of gonadal steroid feedback in gonadectomized versus intact rats. In line with the above considerations, it may be possible with appropriate timing and dosage of estrogen and progesterone to facilitate rather than inhibit LH release in ovariectomized rats.

C. Mode of Action of Puberty-Inducing Neural Lesions

It is apparent that more information is essential before meaningful conclusions can be reached regarding the role of circulating gonadal steroids on the control of puberty. However, the long-recognized hypersensitivity of the immature animal to the suppressive effects of gonadal steroids and the several studies which suggest the presence of estrogen-sensitive, FSH-inhibiting structures in the anterior hypothalamus (Flerkó, 1954; Flerkó and Szentágothai, 1957; Szentágothai *et al.*, 1962) of the adult rat have been used to support an attractive explanation for the puberty-inducing effects of lesions in this part of the brain. Donovan and Van der Werff ten Bosch (1959a) postulated that such lesions hasten the onset of puberty by destroying neural structures, presumably located in the anterior hypothalamus, which normally act to inhibit the secretion of gonadotropins and that the release from inhibition stems from interference with the negative feedback of gonadal hormones upon the hypothalamus.

Concerning the localization of estrogen-sensitive structures in the nervous system, recent observations indicate that feedback mechanisms for the control of FSH may not be discretely localized in the anterior hypothalamus. From the work of Lisk in the female rat (1960), it appears that estrogen-sensitive structures involved in the control of both FSH and LH are also located in the region of the arcuate nucleus and mammillary body. Based on the total distribution of these structures as pictured by both Lisk and Flerkó, and making the assumptions that (1) the indirect indices used by both authors reflect decreased FSH secretion and (2) the effects of intrahypothalamically administered estrogen are at least in part mediated through direct actions on neural components, it seems that much of the longitudinal extent of the medial hypothalamus of the rat may contain structures which respond to estrogen by decreasing the secretion of FSH. In contrast to the situation in the rat, Davidson and Sawyer found the basal-tuberal posterior median eminence region to be the focus for the gonadotropin-suppressing actions of estrogen in the female rabbit (1961a) and for the similar actions of androgen in the male dog (1961b). It is possible that the diffuseness of these steroid-sensitive structures in the rat explains the widespread distribution of hypothalamic lesions which induce sexual precocity. On the other hand, if neural lesions cause premature puberty through disruption of negative feedback of gonadal hormones, it is surprising that many such lesions are compatible with subsequent normal reproductive functions. A possible explanation of these findings would be that most of such destruction involves only a portion of the "feedback center" and that the residuum is capable of compensating for the loss in the adult animal. The behavior of the feedback system in rats with lesion-induced precocity to the challenge of exogenous estrogen or of unilateral or bilateral gonadectomy has not, to our knowledge, been studied. Such manipulations, which would exaggerate the effective signals and place increased demand on feedback elements, might furnish additional information as to the integrity of this function in the effectively lesioned rat.

As an alternative to the view that interference with negative feedback of gonadal hormones is the feature common to lesions of the amygdala, stria terminalis, and hypothalamus which cause early onset of ovarian function, we suggest that lesions induce sexual precocity by interrupting an influence exerted by or through the amygdaloid complex and stria terminalis which is inhibitory to the secretion of gonadotropin. In contrast to the view of Donovan (1963), we speculate that this inhibition from the amygdala is distinct from influences exerted by circulating titers of gonadal steroids.

The following considerations are offered to summarize evidence which relates to this hypothesis and to explore some of its implications. As mentioned above (Section IV,B,1), results obtained with lesions in the amygdala and stria terminalis, as well as the effects of chronic amygdaloid stimulation, suggest that this nuclear complex is in some way involved in the inhibition of gonadotropin secretion in the immature female rat. The amygdala has been implicated previously in the control of gonadotropin secretion; however, the gonadal atrophy observed in rats following placement of massive lesions (Yamada and Greer, 1960) and the effectiveness of electrical stimulation in causing ovulation in the rabbit (Koikegami *et al.*, 1954), cat (Shealy and Peele, 1957), and "persistent estrous" rat (Bunn and Everett, 1957) suggest a facilitatory role for this structure in this aspect of pituitary regulation in the adult. The inhibitory influence indicated in the prepubertal female rat is seemingly paradoxical, but is consistent with the observation relating an inhibitory influence from amygdala to the control of sexual behavior (Schreiner and Kling, 1953; Green *et al.*, 1957; Wood, 1958) and food intake (Morgane and Kosman, 1959, 1960; Wood, 1958). It is perhaps significant that all animals in which ovulation was induced following electrical stimulation of this nuclear complex were either primed with estrogen (rabbit and cat) or in persistent estrus (rat); such a hormonal background may be instrumental in establishing the qualitative difference in responses of mature versus immature animals. Like afferent input (Stuart *et al.*, 1964), estrogen levels may determine the nature of the responses of hypothalamic units to influences exerted by the amygdaloid complex. Variations in responsiveness of hypothalamic units during the stages of the estrous cycle and following progesterone treatment have been described (Barraclough and Cross, 1963).

Since discrete lesions of the amygdala and stria terminalis induce changes which appear identical to those produced by focal destruction located in many parts of the hypothalamus, and because the stria terminalis on approaching the hypothalamus fans out in the longitudinal plane to connect with most of the medial group of nuclei (Gurdjian, 1928; Krieg, 1932), it is likely that all hypothalamic lesions which have been described in association with precocious puberty involve projections of this fiber system. Therefore, it is postulated that lesions placed in these three sites produce one common functional deficit, interference with a gonadotropin-inhibiting influence mediated through amygdalo-hypothalamic connections.

The observation, now confirmed in several laboratories, that puberty-inducing lesions may be compatible with normal reproductive functions encourages further speculation regarding the role of the amygdala and its presumptive inhibitory influence. First, on the assumption that the complex sequence of hormonal events which characterizes the estrous cycle, pregnancy, and lactation requires more than token utilization of mechanisms responsible for the fine regulation and coordination of the secretion of all gonadotropins, it would appear that hormonal feedback is essentially intact in rats which show no deficits in reproductive functions subsequent to lesion-induced precocious puberty. Therefore, it is suggested that the influence of the amygdala is distinct from and complimentary to that of the hormonal feedback system and that the former can be removed without compromising the latter. The apparently extensive distribution of gonadal steroid-sensitive elements may preclude their complete destruction with discrete hypothalamic lesions and may allow for the survival of sufficient feedback components to support normal reproductive processes in the presence of many lesions which induce precocious sexual maturation.

Another possible implication of the retention of normal reproductive functions in rats with lesion-induced precocity relates to the duration of the inhibitory influence of the amygdala. The temporary nature of the deficit produced in these animals suggests that the inhibitory influence mediated by the amygdalo-hypothalamic system is itself transient and is manifested only in the prepubertal state. If such is the case, the extraordinary sensitivity that undoubtedly exists in at least some of the gonadal-steroid feedback systems of the immature animal could be a reflection of the additional influence of this limbic system structure. That lesions of the amygdala which result in precocious ovarian stimulation do not cause disturbances in subsequent reproductive functions is also in keeping with the view that while this nuclear complex plays a modulatory role in many hypothalamic functions, it is not essential to their normal occurrence (Gloor, 1960).

D. Concluding Remarks

It is clearly much too premature to attempt to formulate a unified theory to explain the control of onset of puberty. However, in the belief that working hypotheses are useful, if only as targets, the following is offered in an effort to apply a portion of the existing information to the situation in the female rat. It appears in this species that the ovaries, reproductive tract, and pituitary are in a state of complete readiness to assume adult activities at approximately 25 days of age. Likewise, it would seem on the basis of the ovulatory responses of the immature rat to PMS, FSH, or estrogen during the fourth week of life, that the neural and pituitary substrates for LH release are essentially intact and ready to function at this time. Consistent with this view of the early competence of LH-controlling mechanisms, the stalk-median eminence region contains adult levels of LH-releasing factor (Ramirez and McCann, 1963a) and the mechanisms which control the cyclic release of LH are evidently present as early as 24 days of age (McCormack and Meyer, 1962; Strauss and Meyer, 1962, 1964). The only functional element that appears to be missing is the neural mechanism which furnishes the humoral stimulus for the increased secretion of FSH. The latent period, approximately 15 days in our colony, between this stage of readiness at 25 days of age and the age of normal puberty may be occupied by processes involved with the functional maturation of neuroendocrine mechanisms which control the secretion of FSH. The nature of these processes of maturation is unknown, but they can be influenced to some extent by the hormonal and diverse environmental stimuli described previously. The fact that a considerable variety of manipulations induce a standardized degree of precocious puberty, i.e., puberty at approximately 30–35 days of age instead of at 40 days, implies that the neural apparatus which controls FSH secretion is at least partially competent and ready to function at 30–35 days of age and not before. The latency between this stage of readiness and puberty may reflect a restraining or inhibitory influence of the amygdala.

Although mechanisms subserving FSH secretion can be induced to function at 30–35 days of age, normally more time, approximately 5–10 days, is required for further maturation of hypothalamic "FSH centers." Such maturation may be related to an increase in afferent inflow and/or alterations in hormonal background which result in lowering of neural thresholds to levels where the amygdaloid influence is no longer effective; the system is consequently "released" and normal function ensues. In this schema, removal of the inhibition exerted by the amygdala, through destruction of the nucleus per se or of its projections to the hypothalamus, prematurely lowers neural thresholds and removes the necessity for further maturation; the result is an unencumbered hypothalamic mechanism which functions fully at 30–35 days of age to cause the secretion of FSH. According to these views, and consistent with the findings of Horowitz and Van der Werff ten Bosch (1962), it would be expected that puberty-inducing lesions would cause the same advancement of vaginal opening regardless of the age at operation. Conversely, electrical stimulation of the amygdalo-hypothalamic system should maintain elevated thresholds and consequently delay puberty. This view of the nature of the influence exerted by the amygdala is compatible with the recent electrophysiological studies of Stuart *et al.* (1964) which indicate that afferent "bias" to the hypothalamus is a major determinant of the direction of the effects exerted by limbic structures on somatovisceral and endocrine mechanisms. Thus, afferent input may be an important factor in determining the susceptibility of hypothalamic neurons to amygdaloid influence.

At this stage, it seems reasonable to suspect, in agreement with many previous workers, that an increase in FSH secretion is the principal stimulus for puberty. Extrapolating from the PMS experiments discussed earlier, an increase in FSH secretion occurring at a time when the ovary is competent to respond may lead to the secretion of estrogen and progesterone in quantities sufficient to trigger the first ovulatory upsurge in LH release.

Addendum

Recently, a useful addition to the literature on puberty has appeared in the form of a monograph by B. T. Donovan and J. J. Van der Werff ten Bosch: "Physiology of Puberty." Williams & Wilkins, Baltimore, Maryland (1965).

Acknowledgment

We would like to express our gratitude to our colleagues Drs. J. Wagner and W. Schindler for their constructive criticisms that have proved so helpful in the preparation of this manuscript.

REFERENCES

Albert, A. (1961). The mammalian testis. *In* "Sex and Internal Secretions" (W. C. Young, ed.), 3rd ed., Vol. I, pp. 305–365. Williams & Wilkins, Baltimore, Maryland.

Alden, R. H. (1947). Implantation of the rat egg. II. Alteration in osmiophilic epithelial lipids of the rat uterus under normal and experimental conditions. *Anat. Record* **97**, 1–19.

Allen, B. M. (1904). The embryonic development of the ovary and testes in mammals. *Am. J. Anat.* **3**, 89–153.

Amoroso, E. C., and Marshall, F. H. A. (1960). External factors in sexual periodicity. *In* "Marshall's Physiology of Reproduction" (A. S. Parkes, ed.), 3rd ed., Vol. I, Part 2, pp. 707–831. Longmans, Green, New York.

Amoroso, E. C., and Rowlands, I. W. (1951). Hormonal effects in the pregnant mare and foetal foal. *J. Endocrinol.* **7**, l-lii.

Amoroso, E. C., Harrison, R. J., Matthews, L. H., and Rowlands, I. W. (1951). Reproductive organs of near-term and new-born seals. *Nature* **168**, 771–772.

Arai, H. (1920). On the postnatal development of the ovary (albino rat) with especial reference to the number of ova. *Am. J. Anat.* **27**, 405–462.

Aron, C., and Aron-Brunetière, R. (1953). Effets de la stimulation mécanique du vagin et du segment supracervical de l'utérus sur l'ovaire du Cobaye. *Compt. Rend.* **237**, 846–848.

Árvay, A., and Nagy, T. (1959). Der Einfluss belastender Nervenreize auf den Zeitpunkt des Eintrittes der Geschlechtsreife. *Acta Neuroveget.* (*Vienna*) **20**, 57–75.

Aschheim, S. (1926). Über die Funktion des Ovariums. *Z. Geburtshilfe Gynaekol.* **90**, 387–392.

Aschheim, S., and Zondek, B. (1927). Hypophysenvorderlappenhormon und Ovarialhormon im Harn von Schwangeren. *Klin. Wochschr.* **6**, 1322.

Aschheim, S., and Zondek, B. (1928). Schwangerschaftsdiagnose aus dem Harn (durch Hormonnachweiss). *Klin. Wochschr.* **7**, 8–9.

Aschner, B. (1912a). Über die Funktion der Hypophyse. *Arch. Ges. Physiol.* **146**, 1–146.

Aschner, B. (1912b). Zur Physiologie des Zwischenhirns. *Wien. Klin. Wochschr.* **25**, 1042–1043.

Asdell, S. A., and Crowell, M. F. (1935). The effect of retarded growth upon sexual development of rats. *J. Nutr.* **10**, 13–24.

Astwood, E. B. (1939). Changes in the weight and water content of the uterus of the normal adult rat. *Am. J. Physiol.* **126**, 162–170.

Axelrod, J., and Weissbach, H. (1961). Purification and properties of hydroxyindole-O-methyl transferase. *J. Biol. Chem.* **236**, 211–213.

Bahn, R. C., Lorenz, N., Bennett, W. A., and Albert, A. (1953). Gonadotrophins of the pituitary gland during infancy and early childhood. *Endocrinology* **52**, 605–606.

Bailey, P., and Bremer, F. (1921). Experimental diabetes insipidus. *Arch. Internal Med.* **28**, 773–803.

Bailey, P., and Jelliffe, S. E. (1911). Tumors of the pineal body. *Arch. Internal Med.* **8**, 851–880.

Barraclough, C. A. (1961). Production of anovulatory, sterile rats by single injections of testosterone propionate. *Endocrinology* **68**, 62–67.

Barraclough, C. A., and Cross, B. A. (1963). Unit activity in the hypothalamus of the cyclic female rat: effect of genital stimuli and progesterone. *J. Endocrinol.* **26,** 339–359.

Barraclough, C. A., and Gorski, R. A. (1961). Evidence that the hypothalamus is responsible for androgen-induced sterility in the female rat. *Endocrinology* **68,** 68–79.

Barraclough, C. A., and Sawyer, C. H. (1957). Blockade of the release of pituitary ovulating hormone in the rat by chlorpromazine and reserpine: possible mechanisms of action. *Endocrinology* **61,** 341–351.

Bar-Sela, M. E. (1964). Sexual development in male rats bearing amygdaloid and hypothalamic lesions. *Anat. Record* **148,** 359.

Bar-Sela, M. E., and Critchlow, V. (1966). Delayed puberty following electrical stimulation of amygdala in female rats. *Am. J. Physiol.* **211,** in press.

Bauer, H. G. (1954). Endocrine and other clinical manifestations of hypothalamic disease. *J. Clin. Endocrinol. Metab.* **14,** 13–31.

Bauer, H. (1959). Endocrine and metabolic conditions related to pathology in the hypothalamus: a review. *J. Nervous Mental Disease* **128,** 323–338.

Biddulph, C., Meyer, R. K., and Gumbreck, L. G. (1940). The influence of estriol, estradiol and progesterone on the secretion of gonadotropic hormones in parabiotic rats. *Endocrinology* **26,** 280–284.

Bing, J. F., Globus, J. H., and Simon, H. (1938). Pubertas praecox: A survey of the reported cases and verified anatomical findings (with particular reference to tumors of the pineal body). *J. Mt. Sinai Hosp.* **4,** 935–965.

Blandau, R. J., and Money, W. L. (1943). The attainment of sexual maturity in the female albino rat as determined by the copulatory response. *Anat. Record* **86,** 197–215.

Block, E. (1953). A quantitative morphological investigation of the follicular system in newborn female infants. *Acta Anat.* **17,** 201–206.

Bodemer, C. W., Rumery, R. E., and Blandau, R. J. (1959). Studies on induced ovulation in the intact immature hamster. *Fertility Sterility* **10,** 350–360.

Bogdanove, E. M. (1964). Differential effects of testosterone treatment on the secretion of FSH and LH. *Program 46th Meeting Endocrine Soc., San Francisco* p. 25.

Bogdanove, E. M., and Schoen, H. C. (1959). Precocious sexual development in female rats with hypothalamic lesions. *Proc. Soc. Exptl. Biol. Med.* **100,** 664–669.

Boling, J. L., Blandau, R. J., Soderwall, A. L., and Young, W. C. (1941). Growth of the Graafian follicle and the time of ovulation in the albino rat. *Anat. Record* **79,** 313–331.

Bookhout, C. G. (1945). The development of the guinea pig ovary from sexual differentiation to maturity. *J. Morphol.* **77,** 233–263.

Bradbury, J. T. (1947). Ovarian influence on the response of the anterior pituitary to estrogens. *Endocrinology* **41,** 501–513.

Bradbury, J. T. (1961). Direct action of estrogen on the ovary of the immature rat. *Endocrinology* **68,** 115–120.

Brambell, F. W. R. (1956). Ovarian changes. *In* "Marshall's Physiology of Reproduction" (A. S. Parkes, ed.), 3rd ed., Vol. I, Part 1, pp. 397–542. Longmans, Green, New York.

Brooks, C. McC., Ushiyama, J., and Lange, G. (1962). Reactions of neurons in or near the supraoptic nuclei. *Am. J. Physiol.* **202,** 487–490.

Browman, L. G. (1937). Light in its relation to activity and estrous rhythms in the albino rat. *J. Exptl. Zool.* **75**, 375–388.

Browman, L. G. (1940). The effect of optic enucleation on the male albino rat. *Anat. Record* **78**, 59–73.

Brown, P. S. (1958). Human urinary gonadotrophins. I. In relation to puberty. *J. Endocrinol.* **17**, 329–336.

Bunn, J. P., and Everett, J. W. (1957). Ovulation in persistent-estrous rats after electrical stimulation of the brain. *Proc. Soc. Exptl. Biol. Med.* **96**, 369–371.

Burns, R. K. (1961). Role of hormones in the differentiation of sex. *In* "Sex and Internal Secretions" (W. C. Young, ed.), 3rd ed., Vol. I, pp. 76–158. Williams & Wilkins, Baltimore, Maryland.

Burns, R. K., and Buyse, A. (1931). The effects of extracts of the mammalian hypophysis upon immature salamanders. *Anat. Record* **51**, 155–185.

Burns, R. K., and Buyse, A. (1934). The effect of an extract of the mammalian hypophysis upon the reproductive system of immature male salamanders after metamorphosis. *J. Exptl. Zool.* **67**, 115–135.

Bustamante, M. (1942). Experimentelle Untersuchungen über die Leistungen des Hypothalamus, besonders bezüglich der Geschlechtsreifung. *Arch. Psychiat.* **115**, 419–468.

Bustamante, M., Spatz, H., and Weisschedel, E. (1942). Die Bedeutung des Tuber cinereum des Zwischenhirns für das Zustandekommen der Geschlechtsreifung. *Deut. Med. Wochschr.* **68**, 289–292.

Byrnes, W. W., and Meyer, R. K. (1951a). The inhibition of gonadotrophic hormone secretion by physiological doses of estrogen. *Endocrinology* **48**, 133–136.

Byrnes, W. W., and Meyer, R. K. (1951b). Effect of physiological amounts of estrogen on the secretion of follicle stimulating and luteinizing hormones. *Endocrinology* **49**, 449–460.

Camus, J., and Roussy, G. (1920). Experimental researches on the pituitary body. *Endocrinology* **4**, 507–522.

Casida, L. E. (1935). Prepuberal development of the pig ovary and its relation to stimulation with gonadotropic hormones. *Anat. Record* **61**, 389–396.

Casida, L. E., Meyer, R. K., McShan, W. H., and Wisnicky, W. (1943). Effects of pituitary gonadotropins on the ovaries and the induction of superfecundity in cattle. *Am. J. Vet. Res.* **4**, 76–94.

Clark, H. M. (1935a). A prepubertal reversal of the sex difference in the gonadotrophic hormone content of the pituitary gland of the rat. *Anat. Record* **61**, 175–192.

Clark, H. M. (1935b). A sex difference in the change in potency of the anterior hypophysis following bilateral castration in newborn rats. *Anat. Record* **61**, 193–202.

Clauberg, C. (1932). Schwangerschaftsreaktion am Ovar des infantilen Kaninchens, eine Erleichterung der hormonalen Diagnose des Chorioepithelioms. *Zentr. Gynaekol.* **56**, 964–971.

Clegg, E. J. (1960). The age at which male rats become fertile. *J. Reprod. Fertility* **1**, 118–119.

Clermont, Y., and Morgentaler, H. (1955). Quantitative study of spermatogenesis in the hypophysectomized rat. *Endocrinology* **57**, 369–382.

Clermont, Y., and Perey, B. (1957). Quantitative study of the cell population of the seminiferous tubules in immature rats. *Am. J. Anat.* **100**, 241–267.

Cole, H. H. (1937). Superfecundity in rats treated with mare gonadotropic hormone. *Am. J. Physiol.* **119**, 704–712.

Cole, H. H. (1946). Estrogen in late pregnancy mare serum and ovarian inhibition. *Endocrinology* **39**, 177–182.

Cole, H. H., Hart, G. H., Lyons, W. R., and Catchpole, H. R. (1933). The development and hormonal content of fetal horse gonads. *Anat. Record* **56**, 275–293.

Corbin, A. (1963). Testicular and accessory organ depression in immature rats with posterior hypothalamic lesions. *Am. J. Physiol.* **204**, 129–132.

Corbin, A., and Schottelius, B. A. (1960). Effects of posterior hypothalamic lesions on sexual maturation of immature female albino rats. *Proc. Soc. Exptl. Biol. Med.* **103**, 208–210.

Corbin, A., and Schottelius, B. A. (1961a). Estrogen therapy in immature female rats with posterior hypothalamic lesions. *Proc. Soc. Exptl. Biol. Med.* **106**, 841–844.

Corbin, A., and Schottelius, B. A. (1961b). Hypothalamic neurohormonal agents and sexual maturation of immature female rats. *Am. J. Physiol.* **201**, 1176–1180.

Corey, E. L. (1928). Effect of prenatal and postnatal injections of the pituitary gland in the white rat. *Anat. Record* **41**, 40.

Corey, E. L. (1930). Foetal and early postnatal responses of rat gonads to pituitary injections. *Physiol. Zool.* **3**, 379–391.

Cowperthwaite, M. H. (1925). Observations on pre- and postpubertal oogenesis in the white rat, *Mus norvegicus albinus. Am. J. Anat.* **36**, 69–89.

Critchlow, V. (1963). The role of light in the neuroendocrine system. *In* "Advances in Neuroendocrinology," (A. V. Nalbandov, ed.), pp. 377–402. Univ. of Illinois Press, Urbana, Illinois.

Cross, B. A., and Green, J. D. (1959). Activity of single neurones in the hypothalamus: Effect of osmotic and other stimuli. *J. Physiol.* (*London*) **148**, 554–569.

Crowe, S. J., Cushing, H., and Homans, J. (1910). Experimental hypophysectomy. *Bull. Johns Hopkins Hosp.* **21**, 127–169.

Cutuly, E., and Cutuly, E. C. (1940). Observations on spermatogenesis in rats. *Endocrinology* **26**, 503–507.

Davidson, J. M., and Sawyer, C. H. (1961a). Effects of localized intracerebral implantation of oestrogen on reproductive function in the female rabbit. *Acta Endocrinol.* **37**, 385–393.

Davidson, J. M., and Sawyer, C. H. (1961b). Evidence for a hypothalamic focus of inhibition of gonadotropin by androgen in the male. *Proc. Soc. Exptl. Biol. Med.* **107**, 4–7.

Dawson, A. B., and McCabe, M. (1951). The interstitial tissue of the ovary in infantile and juvenile rats. *J. Morphol.* **88**, 543–571.

de Jongh, S. E., and Paesi, F. J. (1958). The ICSH-concentration in the hypophysis of immature and adult rats: additional remarks on somatotrophin and FSH. *Acta Endocrinol.* **29**, 413–418.

Dempsey, E. W. (1937). Follicular growth rate and ovulation after various experimental procedures in the guinea pig. *Am. J. Physiol.* **120**, 126–132.

Desclin, L. (1935). Action de fortes doses d'hormone folliculaire sur la structure de l'ovaire et du lobe antérieur de l'hypophyse chez le rat blanc. *Compt. Rend. Soc. Biol.* **120**, 526–528.

de Wit, J. C. (1953). The effect of oestradiol monobenzoate on follicles of various sizes in the ovary of the hypophysectomized rat. *Acta Endocrinol.* **12**, 123–139.

Dickerson, J. W. T., Gresham, G. A., and McCance, R. A. (1964). The effect of undernutrition and rehabilitation on the development of the reproductive organs: pigs. *J. Endocrinol.* **29,** 111–118.

Domm, L. V. (1931). The precocious development of sexual characters in the fowl by homeoplastic hypophyseal implants. I. The male. *Anat. Record* **51,** 20–21.

Donovan, B. T. (1963). The timing of puberty. *Sci. Basis Med. Ann. Rev.* pp. 53–75.

Donovan, B. T., and Van der Werff ten Bosch, J. J. (1956). Precocious puberty in rats with hypothalamic lesions. *Nature* **178,** 745.

Donovan, B. T., and Van der Werff ten Bosch, J. J. (1959a). The hypothalamus and sexual maturation in the rat. *J. Physiol.* (*London*) **147,** 78–92.

Donovan, B. T., and Van der Werff ten Bosch, J. J. (1959b). The relationship of the hypothalamus to oestrus in the ferret. *J. Physiol.* (*London*) **147,** 93–108.

Dott, N. M. (1938). Surgical aspects of the hypothalamus. *In* "The Hypothalamus," pp. 131–185. Oliver & Boyd, Edinburgh and London.

Driggs, M., and Spatz, H. (1939). Pubertas praecox bei einer hyperplastischen Missbildung des Tuber cinereum. *Arch. Pathol. Anat. Physiol.* **305,** 567–592.

Elwers, M., and Critchlow, V. (1960). Precocious ovarian stimulation following hypothalamic and amygdaloid lesions in rats. *Am. J. Physiol.* **198,** 381–385.

Elwers, M., and Critchlow, V. (1961). Precocious ovarian stimulation following interruption of stria terminalis. *Am. J. Physiol.* **201,** 281–284.

Engle, E. T. (1931). Prepubertal growth of the ovarian follicle in the mouse. *Anat. Record* **48,** 341–350.

Engle, E. T. (1932). Experimentally induced descent of the testis in the *Macacus* monkey by hormones from the anterior pituitary and pregnancy urine. *Endocrinology* **16,** 513–520.

Engle, E. T. (1938). The relation of the anterior pituitary gland to problems of puberty and of menstruation. *Res. Publ. Assoc. Res. Nervous Mental Disease* **17,** 298–320.

Engle, E. T., Crafts, R. C., and Zeithaml, C. E. (1937). First estrus in rats in relation to age, weight, and length. *Proc. Soc. Exptl. Biol. Med.* **37,** 427–432.

Erdheim, J. (1904). Über Hypophysenganggeschwülste und Hirncholesteatome. *Sitzber. Akad. Wiss. Wien., Math.-Naturw. Kl., Abt. III* **113,** 537–726.

Evans, H. M., and Simpson, M. E. (1940). Experimental superfecundity with pituitary gonadotropins. *Endocrinology* **27,** 305–308.

Everett, J. W. (1961). The mammalian female reproductive cycle and its controlling mechanisms. *In* "Sex and Internal Secretions" (W. C. Young, ed.), 3rd ed., Vol. I, pp. 497–555. Williams & Wilkins, Baltimore, Maryland.

Everett, J. W. (1964). Central neural control of reproductive functions of the adenohypophysis. *Physiol. Rev.* **44,** 373–431.

Everett, J. W., and Radford, H. M. (1961). Irritative deposits from stainless steel electrodes in the preoptic rat brain causing release of pituitary gonadotropin. *Proc. Soc. Exptl. Biol. Med.* **108,** 604–609.

Everett, J. W., Sawyer, C. H., and Markee, J. E. (1949). A neurogenic timing factor in control of the ovulatory discharge of luteinizing hormone in the cyclic rat. *Endocrinology* **44,** 234–250.

Falck, B. (1953). Occurrence of cholesterol and formation of oestrogen in the infantile rat ovary. *Acta Endocrinol.* **12,** 115–122.

Fevold, H. L. (1939). The follicle stimulating and luteinizing hormones of the anterior pituitary. *In* "Sex and Internal Secretions" (E. Allen, *et al.*, eds.), 2nd ed., pp. 966–1002. Williams & Wilkins, Baltimore, Maryland.

Fiske, V. M. (1941). Effect of light on sexual maturation, estrous cycles, and anterior pituitary of the rat. *Endocrinology* **29**, 187–196.

Flerkó, B. (1954). Zur hypothalamischen Steuerung der gonadotropen Funktion der Hypophyse. *Acta Morphol. Acad. Sci. Hung.* **4**, 475–492.

Flerkó, B. (1963). The central nervous system and the secretion and release of luteinizing hormone and follicle stimulating hormone. *In* "Advances in Neuroendocrinology" (A. V. Nalbandov, ed.), pp. 211–224. Univ. of Illinois Press, Urbana, Illinois.

Flerkó, B., and Szentágothai, J. (1957). Oestrogen sensitive nervous structures in the hypothalamus. *Acta Endocrinol.* **26**, 121–127.

Fluhmann, C. F. (1934). The nature of ovary-stimulating hormones. *Am. J. Obstet. Gynecol.* **28**, 668–681.

Foá, C. (1900). La greffe des ovaires en relation avec quelques questions de biologie générale. *Arch. Ital. Biol.* **34**, 43–73.

Franchi, L. L., Mandl, A. M., and Zuckerman, S. (1962). The development of the ovary and the process of oogenesis. *In* "The Ovary" (S. Zuckerman, ed.), Vol. 1, pp. 1–88. Academic Press, New York.

Freed, S. C., and Coppock, A. (1936). Fundamental similarity in the development of gonadotropic response in the immature guinea pig and rat. *Endocrinology* **20**, 81–85.

Gaarenstroom, J. H. (1941). An analysis of the effect of chorionic gonadotropic hormone on the rat testis. *Arch. Intern. Pharmacodyn.* **66**, 121–129.

Gaarenstroom, J. H., and de Jongh, S. E. (1946). "A Contribution to the Knowledge of the Influences of Gonadotropic and Sex Hormones on the Gonads of Rats." Elsevier, Amsterdam.

Gaarenstroom, J. H., Smelik, P. G., and De Wied, D. (1960). The ovarian response to chorionic gonadotrophin in immature rats with lesions in basal hypothalamus. *Mem. Soc. Endocrinol.* **9**, 65–69.

Ganong, W. F. (1961). *In* "Control of Ovulation" (C. A. Villee, ed.), p. 183. Pergamon Press, Oxford.

Gellert, R. J., and Ganong, W. F. (1960). Precocious puberty in rats with hypothalamic lesions. *Acta Endocrinol.* **33**, 569–576.

Gillman, J. (1948). The development of gonads in man, with a consideration of the role of fetal endocrines and the histogenesis of ovarian tumors. *Carnegie Inst. Wash. Publ.* **32**, 81–131.

Gloor, P. (1960). Amygdala. *In* "Handbook of Physiology" (Am. Physiol. Soc., J. Field, ed.), Sect. 1, Vol. II, pp. 1395–1420. Williams & Wilkins, Baltimore, Maryland.

Green, J. D., Clemente, C. D., and de Groot, J. (1957). Rhinencephalic lesions and behavior in cats. *J. Comp. Neurol.* **108**, 505–545.

Greep, R. O. (1961). Physiology of the anterior hypophysis in relation to reproduction. *In* "Sex and Internal Secretions" (W. C. Young, ed.), 3rd ed., Vol. I, pp. 240–301. Williams & Wilkins, Baltimore, Maryland.

Greep, R. O., and Fevold, H. L. (1937). The spermatogenic and secretory function of the gonads of hypophysectomized adult rats treated with pituitary FSH and LH. *Endocrinology* **21**, 611–618.

Greep, R. O., and Jones, I. C. (1950). Steroid control of pituitary function. *Recent Progr. Hormone Res.* **5**, 197–254.

Greep, R. O., Fevold, H. L., and Hisaw, F. L. (1936). Effects of two hypophyseal gonadotropic hormones on the reproductive system of the male rat. *Anat. Record* **65**, 261–271.

Gurdjian, E. S. (1928). Corpus striatum of the rat. *J. Comp. Neurol.* **45**, 249–281.

Hargitt, G. T. (1930). The formation of the sex glands and germ cells of mammals. III. The history of the female germ cells in the albino rat to the time of sexual maturity. *J. Morphol. Physiol.* **49**, 277–331.

Harris, G. W. (1955). "Neural Control of the Pituitary Gland." Edward Arnold, London.

Harris, G. W. (1964). Sex hormones, brain development and brain function. *Endocrinology* **75**, 627–648.

Harris, G. W., and Jacobsohn, D. (1952). Functional grafts of the anterior pituitary gland. *Proc. Roy. Soc.* **B139**, 263–276.

Harrison, R. J. (1962). The structure of the ovary—mammals. *In* "The Ovary" (S. Zuckerman, ed.) Vol. 1, pp. 143–187. Academic Press, New York.

Hartman, C. G. (1931). On the relative sterility of the adolescent organism. *Science* **74**, 226–227.

Hayashida, T. (1963). Inhibition of spermiogenesis, prostate and seminal vesicle development in normal animals with antigonadotrophic hormone serum. *J. Endocrinol.* **26**, 75–83.

Hemmingsen, A. M., and Krarup, N. B. (1937). Rhythmic diurnal variations in the oestrous phenomena of the rat and their susceptibility to light and dark. *Kgl. Danske Videnskab, Selskab, Biol. Medd.* **13**, 1–61.

Henderson, W. R., and Rowlands, I. W. (1938). Gonadotropic activity of anterior pituitary gland in relation to increased intracranial pressure. *Brit. Med. J.* I, 1094–1097.

Herold, L., and Effkemann, G. (1938). Die Bedeutung des vegetativen Nervensystems für die innersekretorische Funktion des Hypophysenvorderlappens. *Arch. Gynaekol.* **167**, 389–396.

Hertz, R. (1963). Pituitary independence of the prepubertal development of the ovary of the rat and rabbit and its pertinence to hypo-ovarianism in women. *In* "The Ovary" (H. G. Grady and D. E. Smith, eds.), pp. 120–127. Williams & Wilkins, Baltimore, Maryland.

Hertz, R., and Hisaw, F. L. (1934). Effects of follicle-stimulating and luteinizing pituitary extracts on the ovaries of infantile and juvenile rabbit. *Am. J. Physiol.* **108**, 1–13.

Hillarp, N. Å. (1949). Studies on the localization of hypothalamic centres controlling the gonadotrophic functions of the hypophysis. *Acta Endocrinol.* **2**, 11–23.

Hisaw, F. L. (1947). Development of the Graafian follicle and ovulation. *Physiol. Rev.* **27**, 95–119.

Hisaw, F. L., Fevold, H. L., and Greep, R. O. (1938). The pituitary gonadotropic hormones. *Res. Publ. Assoc. Res. Nervous Mental Disease* **17**, 247–256.

Hohlweg, W. (1934). Veränderungen des Hypophysenvorderlappens und des Ovariums nach Behandlung mit grossen Dosen von Follikelhormon. *Klin. Wochschr.* **13**, 92–95.

Hohlweg, W. (1936). Der Mechanismus der Wirkung von gonadotropen Substanzen auf das Ovar der infantilen Ratte. *Klin. Wochschr.* **15**, 1832–1835.

Hohlweg, W. (1937). Männliche Wirkstoffe und Corpus luteum-Bildung. *Klin. Wochschr.* **16**, 586–587.

Hohlweg, W., and Chamorro, A. (1937). Über die luteinisierende Wirkung des Follikelhormons durch Beeinflussung der luteogenen Hypophysenvorderlappensekretion. *Klin. Wochschr.* **16,** 196–197.

Hohlweg, W., and Dohrn, M. (1931). Beziehungen zwischen Hypophysenvorderlappen und Keimdrüsen. *Wien. Arch. Inn. Med.* **21,** 337–350.

Hohlweg, W., and Dohrn, M. (1932). Über die Beziehungen zwischen Hypophysenvorderlappen und Keimdrüsen. *Klin. Wochschr.* **11,** 233–235.

Hohlweg, W., and Junkmann, K. (1932). Die hormonal-nervöse Regulierung der Funktion des Hypophysenvorderlappens. *Klin. Wochschr.* **11,** 321–323.

Horowitz, S., and Van der Werff ten Bosch, J. J. (1962). Hypothalamic sexual precocity in female rats operated shortly after birth. *Acta Endocrinol.* **41,** 301–313.

Howe, G. R., Black, D. L., Foley, R. C., and Black, W. G. (1962). Ovarian activity in prepuberal dairy calves. *J. Animal Sci.* **21,** 82–90.

Ingram, D. L. (1962). Atresia. *In* "The Ovary" (S. Zuckerman, ed.), Vol. 1, pp. 247–273. Academic Press, New York.

Jöchle, W. (1956). Über die Wirkung eines Epiphysenextraktes (Glanepin) auf Sexualentwicklung and Sexualcyklus junger weiblicher Ratten unter normalen Haltungsbedingungen und bei Dauerbeleuchtung. *Endokrinologie* **33,** 287–295.

Jolly, H. (1955). "Sexual Precocity." Thomas, Springfield, Illinois.

Jost, A. (1953). Problems of fetal endocrinology: the gonadal and hypophyseal hormones. *Recent Progr. Hormone Res.* **8,** 379–418.

Kallas, H. (1929a). Puberté précoce par parabiose. *Compt. Rend. Soc. Biol.* **100,** 979–980.

Kallas, H. (1929b). Sur le passage de substances hypophysaires pendant la parabiose. *Compt. Rend. Soc. Biol.* **102,** 280–282.

Kallas, H. (1930). Zur Frage nach der Innersekretorischen Tätigkeit des infantilen Eierstockes. *Klin. Wochschr.* **9,** 1345–1346.

Kawakami, M., and Sawyer, C. H. (1959). Neuroendocrine correlates of changes in brain activity thresholds by sex steroids and pituitary hormones. *Endocrinology* **65,** 652–668.

Kellas, L. M., van Lenrep, E. W., and Amoroso, E. C. (1958). Ovaries of some foetal and prepubertal giraffes (*Giraffa camelopardalis* Linnaeus). *Nature* **181,** 487–488.

Kennedy, G. C. (1957). The development with age of hypothalamic restraint upon the appetite of the rat. *J. Endocrinol.* **16,** 9–17.

Kennedy, G. C., and Mitra, J. (1963). Body-weight and food intake as initiating factors for puberty in the rat. *J. Physiol.* (*London*) **166,** 408–418.

Kitay, J. I. (1954a). Pineal lesions and precocious puberty: a review. *J. Clin. Endocrinol. Metab.* **14,** 622–625.

Kitay, J. (1954b). Effects of pinealectomy on ovary weight in immature rats. *Endocrinology* **54,** 114–116.

Kitay, J., and Altschule, M. D. (1954a). "The Pineal Gland." Harvard Univ. Press, Cambridge, Massachusetts.

Kitay, J., and Altschule, M. D. (1954b). Effects of pineal extract administration on ovary weight in rats. *Endocrinology* **55,** 782–784.

Kling, A. (1964). Effects of rhinencephalic lesions on endocrine and somatic development in the rat. *Am. J. Physiol.* **206,** 1395–1400.

Koikegami, H., Yamada, T., and Usui, K. (1954). Stimulation of amygdaloid nuclei and periamygdaloid cortex with special reference to its effects on uterine movements and ovulation. *Folia Psychiat. Neurol. Japon.* **8,** 7–31.

Krabbe, K. H. (1923). The pineal gland, especially in relation to the problem on its supposed significance in sexual development. *Endocrinology* **7**, 379–414.

Krieg, W. J. S. (1932). The hypothalamus of the albino rat. *J. Comp. Neurol.* **55**, 19–89.

Lane, C. E. (1935). Some influences of oestrin on the hypophyseal-gonad complex of the immature female rat. *Am. J. Physiol.* **110**, 681–685.

Lange-Cosack, H. (1951). Verschiedene Gruppen der hypothalamischen Pubertas praecox. *Deut. Z. Nervenheilk.* **166**, 499–545.

Lange-Cosack, H. (1952). Verschiedene Gruppen der hypothalamischen Pubertas praecox. *Deut. Z. Nervenheilk.* **168**, 237–266.

Lauson, H. D., Golden, J. B., and Severinghaus, E. L. (1939). Gonadotrophic content of the hypophysis throughout the life cycle of the normal female rat. *Am. J. Physiol.* **125**, 396–404.

Leonard, S. L., and Smith, P. E. (1934). Responses of the reproductive system of hypophysectomized rats to injections of pregnancy-urine extracts. II. The female. *Anat. Record* **58**, 175–203.

Lerner, A. B., Case, J. D., and Heinzelman, R. V. (1959). Structure of melatonin. *J. Am. Chem. Soc.* **81**, 6084–6085.

Lerner, A. B., Case, J. D., and Takahashi, Y. (1960). Isolation of melatonin and 5-methoxyindole-3-acetic acid from bovine pineal glands. *J. Biol. Chem.* **235**, 1992–1997.

Li, C. H. (1956). Pituitary growth hormone as a metabolic hormone. *Science* **123**, 617–619.

Lisk, R. D. (1960). Estrogen-sensitive centers in the hypothalamus of the rat. *J. Exptl. Zool.* **145**, 197–208.

Long, J. A., and Evans, H. M. (1922). The oestrous cycle in the rat and its associated phenomena. *Mem. Univ. Calif.* **6**, 1–148.

Luce-Clausen, E. M., and Brown, E. F. (1939). The use of isolated radiation in experiments with the rat. III. Effects of darkness, visible and infra red radiation on three succeeding generations of rats. *J. Nutr.* **18**, 551–562.

McCann, S. M., and Ramirez, V. D. (1964). The neuroendocrine regulation of hypophyseal luteinizing hormone secretion. *Recent Progr. Hormone Res.* **20**, 131–170.

McCormack, C. E., and Meyer, R. K. (1962). Ovulating hormone release in gonadotrophin treated immature rat. *Proc. Soc. Exptl. Biol. Med.* **110**, 343–346.

McCormack, C. E., and Meyer, R. K. (1963). Ovulation induced by progesterone in immature rats pretreated with pregnant mare serum gonadotropin. *Gen. Comp. Endocrinol.* **3**, 300–307.

McCormack, C. E., and Meyer, R. K. (1964). Minimal age for induction of ovulation with progesterone in rats: evidence for neural control. *Endocrinology* **74**, 793–799.

McCullagh, E. P., Rosenberg, H. S., and Norman, N. (1960). Tumor of the tuber cinereum with precocious puberty: case report with hormone assays. *J. Clin. Endocrinol. Metab.* **20**, 1286–1293.

McQueen-Williams, M. (1935). Sex comparison of gonadotropic content of anterior hypophyses from rats before and after puberty. *Proc. Soc. Exptl. Biol. Med.* **32**, 1051–1052.

Maekawa, K. (1960). Hypophysis-inhibitory action of endogenous androgen and estrogen in infantile rats. *Endocrinol. Japon.* **7**, 53–56.

Mandel, J. L. (1933). Influence of ovarian grafts upon immature castrate rats. *Proc. Soc. Exptl. Biol. Med.* **30,** 1415–1417.

Mandl, A. M., and Zuckerman, S. (1952). Factors influencing the onset of puberty in albino rats. *J. Endocrinol.* **8,** 357–364.

Marburg, O. (1908). Die Adipositas cerebralis. Ein Beitrag zur Kenntnis der Pathologie der Zirbeldrüse. *Deut. Z. Nervenheilk.* **36,** 114–121.

Marden, W. G. R. (1952). The hormone control of ovulation in the calf. *Endocrinology* **50,** 456–461.

Martins, T., and de Mello, R. F. (1934). Sur les résultats de la parabiose de Rats femelles avec des Rats chartrés et hypophysectomisés. *Compt. Rend. Soc. Biol.* **117,** 1258–1260.

Mazer, C., Israel, S. L., and Alpers, B. J. (1936). The time element in the pituitary-ovarian response to large doses of the estrogenic hormone. *Endocrinology* **20,** 753–761.

Meyer, J. E., and Bradbury, J. T. (1960). Influence of stilbestrol on the immature rat ovary and its response to gonadotrophin. *Endocrinology* **66,** 121–128.

Meyer, R. K., and Hertz, R. (1937). The effect of oestrone on the secretion of the gonadotropic complex as evidenced in parabiotic rats. *Am. J. Physiol.* **120,** 232–245.

Moore, C. R. (1936). Responses of immature rat testes to gonadotropic agents. *Am. J. Anat.* **59,** 63–88.

Moore, C. R. (1939). Biology of the testes. *In* "Sex and Internal Secretions" (E. Allen *et al.*, eds.), 2nd ed., pp. 353–451. Williams & Wilkins, Baltimore, Maryland.

Moore, C. R., and Price, D. (1932). Gonad hormone functions, and the reciprocal influence between gonads and hypophysis with its bearing on the problem of sex hormone antagonism. *Am. J. Anat.* **50,** 13–71.

Morgane, P. J., and Kosman, A. J. (1959). A rhinencephalic feeding center in the cat. *Am. J. Physiol.* **197,** 158–162.

Morgane, P. J., and Kosman, A. J. (1960). Relationship of the middle hypothalamus to amygdalar hyperphagia. *Am. J. Physiol.* **198,** 1315–1318.

Morton, J. R. C., Denenberg, V. H., and Zarrow, M. X. (1963). Modification of sexual development through stimulation in infancy. *Endocrinology* **72,** 439–442.

Mühlbock, O. (1953). Gonadotrophic function of the hypophysis in parabiotic triplet mice. *Acta Endocrinol.* **12,** 47–55.

Nagy, T., and Árvay, A. (1958). The aspects of pubertal age with special regard to nervous stimuli. *Acta Med. Acad. Sci. Hung.* **11,** 435–454.

Nathanson, I. T., Franseen, C. C., and Sweeney, A. R., Jr. (1938). Nature of the action of testosterone on genital tract of the immature female rat. *Proc. Soc. Exptl. Biol. Med.* **39,** 385–388.

Nathanson, I. T., Towne, L. E., and Aub, J. C. (1941). Normal excretion of sex hormones in childhood. *Endocrinology* **28,** 851–865.

Nelson, W. O., and Merckel, C. E. (1938). Maintenance of spermatogenesis in hypophysectomized mice with androgenic substances. *Proc. Soc. Exptl. Biol. Med.* **38,** 737–740.

Niemi, M., and Ikonen, M. (1963). Histochemistry of the Leydig cells in the postnatal prepubertal testis of the rat. *Endocrinology* **72,** 443–448.

Odor, D. L. (1955). The temporal relationship of the first maturation division of rat ova to the onset of heat. *Am. J. Anat.* **97,** 461–491.

Ortiz, E. (1947). The postnatal development of the reproductive system of the golden hamster (*Cricetus auratus*) and its reactivity to hormones. *Physiol. Zool.* **20,** 45–66.

Parlow, A. F. (1964a). Differential action of small doses of estradiol on gonadotrophins in the rat. *Endocrinology* **75,** 1–8.

Parlow, A. F. (1964b). *Recent Progr. Hormone Res.* **20,** 171–172.

Parlow, A. F., Anderson, L., and Melampy, R. (1964). Pituitary follicle-stimulating hormone and luteinizing hormone concentrations in relation to reproductive stages of the pig. *Endocrinology* **75,** 365–376.

Pavic, D. (1963). The effects of gonadotrophic hormones on young rat ovaries grown in organ culture. *J. Endocrinol.* **26,** 531–538.

Payne, R. W., and Hellbaum, A. A. (1955). The effect of estrogens on the ovary of the hypophysectomized rat. *Endocrinology* **57,** 193–199.

Payne, R. W., and Runser, R. H. (1958). The influence of estrogen and androgen on the ovarian response of hypophysectomized immature rats to gonadotropins. *Endocrinology* **62,** 313–321.

Payne, R. W., Runser, R. H., Hagans, J. A., and Morrison, R. D. (1959). Assay of follicle-stimulating hormone in the hypophysectomized estrogen-treated immature female rat. *Endocrinology* **65,** 389–394.

Perry, J. S., and Rowlands, I. W. (1963). Hypophysectomy of the immature guinea pig and the ovarian response to gonadotrophins. *J. Reprod. Fertility* **6,** 393–404.

Pfeiffer, C. A. (1936). Sexual differences of the hypophyses and their determination by the gonads. *Am. J. Anat.* **58,** 195–225.

Picon, L. (1956). Sur le rôle de l'âge dans la sensibilité de l'ovaire à l'hormone gonadotrope chez le rat. *Arch. Anat. Microscop. Morphol. Exptl.* **45,** 311–341.

Plagge, J. C. (1956). Effect of prepuberal castration on body and thymus weight in the immature albino rat. *Anat. Record* **124,** 101–110.

Potter, E. L. (1963). The ovary in infancy and childhood. *In* "The Ovary" (H. G. Grady and D. E. Smith, eds.), pp. 11–23. Williams & Wilkins, Baltimore, Maryland.

Presl, J., Horský, J., Henzl, M., and Jirásek, J. (1963). The development of a feedback mechanism between the ovary and the diencephalic-hypophysial system in the rat. *J. Endocrinol.* **26,** 287–294.

Price, D. (1947). An analysis of the factors influencing growth and development of the mammalian reproductive tract. *Physiol. Zool.* **20,** 213–247.

Price, D., and Ortiz, E. (1944). The relation of age to reactivity in the reproductive system of the rat. *Endocrinology* **34,** 215–239.

Quinn, D. L., and Zarrow, M. X. (1964a). Inhibition of pregnant mare's serum-induced ovulation in the immature rat. *Endocrinology* **74,** 309–313.

Quinn, D. L., and Zarrow, M. X. (1964b). Inhibition of PMS-induced ovulation following hypothalamic lesions. *Program 46th Meeting Endocrine Soc., San Francisco* p. 24.

Ramirez, V. D., and McCann, S. M. (1963a). Comparison of the regulation of luteinizing hormone (LH) secretion in immature and adult rats. *Endocrinology* **72,** 452–464.

Ramirez, V. D., and McCann, S. M. (1963b). A highly sensitive test for LH-releasing activity: the ovariectomized, estrogen progesterone-blocked rat. *Endocrinology* **73,** 193–198.

Ramirez, V. D., and Sawyer, C. H. (1965). Advancement of puberty in the female rat by estrogen. *Endocrinology* **76,** 1158–1168.

Raynaud, A. (1959). Effects of destruction of the fetal hypophysis by X-rays upon sexual development of the mouse. *In* "Comparative Endocrinology" (A. Gorbman, ed.), pp. 452–478. Wiley, New York.

Raynaud, A., and Frilley, M. (1947). Destruction des glandes génitales de l'embryon de souris par une irradiation au moyen des rayons x, à l'âge de 13 jours. *Ann. Endocrinol. (Paris)* **8**, 400–419.

Rennels, E. G. (1951). Influence of hormones on the histochemistry of ovarian interstitial tissue in the immature rat. *Am. J. Anat.* **88**, 63–107.

Riss, W., Burstein, S. D., and Johnson, R. W. (1963). Hippocampal or pyriform lobe damage in infancy and endocrine development of rats. *Am. J. Physiol.* **204**, 861–866.

Robson, J. M., and Botros, M. (1961). The effect of 5-hydroxytryptamine and of monoamine oxidase inhibitors on sexual maturity. *J. Endocrinol.* **22**, 165–175.

Roosen-Runge, E. C. (1962). The process of spermatogenesis in mammals. *Biol. Rev. Cambridge Phil. Soc.* **37**, 343–377.

Ryan, R. J. (1962). The luteinizing hormone content of human pituitaries. I. Variations with sex and age. *J. Clin. Endocrinol. Metab.* **22**, 300–303.

Salmon, U. J. (1938). Gonadotropic effect of androgens upon the immature rat ovary. *Proc. Soc. Exptl. Biol. Med.* **38**, 352–353.

Saunders, F. J., and Cole, H. H. (1936). Age and qualitative ovarian response of the immature rat to mare gonadotropic hormone. *Proc. Soc. Exptl. Biol. Med.* **33**, 504–505.

Sawyer, C. H. (1964). Control of secretion of gonadotropins. *In* "Gonadotropins" (H. H. Cole, ed.), pp. 113–159. Freeman, San Francisco, California.

Sawyer, C. H., and Everett, J. W. (1959). Stimulatory and inhibitory effects of progesterone on the release of pituitary ovulating hormone in the rabbit. *Endocrinology* **65**, 644–651.

Saxton, J., and Loeb, L. (1937). Thyroid stimulating and gonadotropic hormones of human anterior pituitary gland at different ages and in pregnant and lactating women. *Anat. Record* **69**, 261–279.

Schiavi, R. C. (1964). Effect of anterior and posterior hypothalamic lesions on precocious sexual maturation. *Am. J. Physiol.* **206**, 805–810.

Schreiner, L., and Kling, A. (1953). Behavioral changes following rhinencephalic injury in cat. *J. Neurophysiol.* **16**, 643–659.

Schuetz, A. W., Sager, D. B., and Meyer, R. K. (1964). Effect of testosterone on human chorionic gonadotrophin (HCG)-induced ovarian augmentation in parabiotic rats. *Endocrinology* **75**, 383–388.

Selye, H. (1933). Effect of hypophysectomy on the ovary of immature rats. *Proc. Soc. Exptl. Biol. Med.* **31**, 262–264.

Setnikar, I., Murmann, W., and Magistretti, M. J. (1960). Retardation of sexual development in female rats due to iproniazid treatment. *Endocrinology* **67**, 511–520.

Severinghaus, A. E. (1938). The cytology of the pituitary gland. *Res. Publ. Assoc. Res. Nervous Mental Disease* **17**, 69–117.

Severinghaus, A. E. (1939). Anterior hypophyseal cytology in relation to the reproductive hormones. *In* "Sex and Internal Secretions" (E. Allen *et al.*, eds.), 2nd ed., pp. 1045–1087. Williams & Wilkins, Baltimore, Maryland.

Shealy, C. N., and Peele, T. L. (1957). Studies on amygdaloid nucleus of cat. *J. Neurophysiol.* **20**, 125–139.

Simpson, M. E., Evans, H. M., Fraenkel-Conrat, H. L., and Li, C. H. (1941). Synergism of estrogens with pituitary gonadotropins in hypophysectomized rats. *Endocrinology* **28**, 37–41.

Siperstein, E. C., Nichols, C. W., Jr., Griesbach, W. E., and Chaikoff, I. L. (1954). Cytological changes in the rat anterior pituitary from birth to maturity. *Anat. Record* **118**, 593–619.

Smith, B. D. (1961). The effect of diethylstilbestrol on the immature rat ovary. *Endocrinology* **69**, 238–245.

Smith, P. E. (1926). Hastening development of female genital system by daily homoplastic pituitary transplants. *Proc. Soc. Exptl. Biol. Med.* **24**, 131–132.

Smith, P. E. (1927). The induction of precocious sexual maturity by pituitary homeotransplants. *Am. J. Physiol.* **80**, 114–125.

Smith, P. E. (1930). Hypophysectomy and a replacement therapy in the rat. *Am. J. Anat.* **45**, 205–273.

Smith, P. E. (1944). Maintenance and restoration of spermatogenesis in hypophysectomized Rhesus monkeys by androgen administration. *Yale J. Biol. Med.* **17**, 281–287.

Smith, P. E., and Engle, E. T. (1927a). Experimental evidence regarding the rôle of the anterior pituitary in the development and regulation of the genital system. *Am. J. Anat.* **40**, 159–217.

Smith, P. E., and Engle, E. T. (1927b). Induction of precocious sexual maturity in the mouse by daily pituitary homeo- and hetero-transplants. *Proc. Soc. Exptl. Biol. Med.* **24**, 561–562.

Sneider, M. E. (1940). Rhythms of ovogenesis before sexual maturity in the rat and cat. *Am. J. Anat.* **67**, 471–499.

Sniffen, R. C. (1950). The testis. I. The normal testis. *Arch. Pathol.* **50**, 259–284.

Sohval, A. R. (1958). The anatomy and endocrine physiology of the male reproductive system. *In* "The Endocrinology of Reproduction" (J. T. Velardo, ed.), pp. 243–312. Oxford Univ. Press, London and New York.

Soliman, F. A., and Ghanem, Y. S. (1956). Levels of thyrotrophic and gonadotrophic hormones in the blood of mature and immature female rabbits. *Nature* **178**, 745.

Strauss, W. F., and Meyer, R. K. (1962). Neural timing of ovulation in immature rats treated with gonadotrophin. *Science* **137**, 860–861.

Strauss, W. F., and Meyer, R. K. (1964). Neural timing of ovulation in rats in continuous darkness: shift by prior lighting. *Program 46th Meeting Endocrine Soc., San Francisco* p. 23.

Stuart, D. G., Porter, R. W., and Adey, W. R. (1964). Hypothalamic unit activity. II. Central and peripheral influences. *EEG. Clin. Neurophysiol.* **16**, 248–258.

Swingle, W. W., Seay, P., Perlmutt, J., Collins, E. J., Fedor, E. J., and Barlow, G., Jr. (1951). Effect of electrical stimulation of uterine cervix upon sexual development in prepuberal rats. *Am. J. Physiol.* **167**, 599–604.

Szentágothai, J., Flerkó, B., Mess, B., and Halász, B. (1962). "Hypothalamic Control of the Anterior Pituitary." Akad. Kiado, Budapest.

Truscott, B. L. (1944). Physiological factors in hypophysial-gonadal interaction. I. Light and the follicular mechanism of the rat. *J. Exptl. Zool.* **95**, 291–305.

van Wagenen, G. (1949). Accelerated growth with sexual precocity in female monkeys receiving testosterone propionate. *Endocrinology* **45**, 544–546.

Velardo, J. T. (1960). Induction of ovulation in immature hypophysectomized rats. *Science* **131**, 357–359.

Wakeling, A. (1959). The effect of gonadotrophins and androgen on spermiogenesis in the immature rat. *J. Endocrinol.* **19**, 263–273.

Walker, D. G., Simpson, M. E., Asling, C. W., and Evans, H. M. (1950). Growth and differentiation in the rat following hypophysectomy at 6 days of age. *Anat. Record* **106**, 539–554.

Walker, D. G., Asling, C. W., Simpson, M. E., Li, C. H., and Evans, H. M. (1952). Structural alterations in rats hypophysectomized at six days of age and their correction with growth hormone. *Anat. Record* **114**, 19–47.

Walsh, E. L., Cuyler, W. K., and McCullagh, D. R. (1934). The physiologic maintenance of the male sex glands. The effect of androtin on hypophysectomized rats. *Am. J. Physiol.* **107**, 508–512.

Weinberger, L. M., and Grant, F. C. (1941). Precocious puberty and tumors of the hypothalamus. *AMA Arch. Internal Med.* **67**, 762–792.

Wells, L. J. (1942). The response of the testis to androgens following hypophysectomy. *Anat. Record* **82**, 565–585.

Wells, L. J. (1947). Progress of studies designed to determine whether the fetal hypophysis produces hormones that influence development. *Anat. Record* **97**, 409.

Wells, L. J. (1959). Functioning of the anterior hypophysis in the fetal rat. *In* "Comparative Endocrinology" (A. Gorbman, ed.), pp. 444–451. Wiley, New York.

Wells, L. J., and Fralick, R. L. (1951). Production of androgen by the testes of fetal rats. *Am. J. Anat.* **89**, 63–107.

Wells, L. J., and Moore, C. R. (1936). Hormonal stimulation of spermatogenesis in the testis of the ground squirrel. *Anat. Record* **66**, 181–200.

Westman, A., and Jacobsohn, D. (1938). Endokrinologische Untersuchungen an Ratten mit durchtrenntem Hypophysenstiel. III. Über die luteinisierende Wirkung des Follikelhormons. *Acta Obstet. Gynecol. Scand.* **18**, 115–123.

Widdowson, E. M., and McCance, R. A. (1960). Some effects of accelerating growth. I. General somatic development. *Proc. Roy. Soc.* **B152**, 188–206.

Widdowson, E. M., Mavor, W. O., and McCance, R. A. (1964). The effect of undernutrition and rehabilitation on the development of the reproductive organs: rats. *J. Endocrinol.* **29**, 119–126.

Wiesner, B. P. (1932). Effects of early oöphorectomy in rats. *J. Physiol.* (*London*) **75**, 39P.

Wiesner, B. P. (1934). The post-natal development of the genital organs in the albino rat, with a discussion of a new theory of sexual differentiation. *J. Obstet. Gynaecol. Brit. Empire* **41**, 867–922.

Wiesner, B. P. (1935). The post-natal development of the genital organs in the albino rat with a discussion of a new theory of sexual differentiation. VI. Effects of sex hormones in the heteronomous sex. *J. Obstet. Gynaecol. Brit. Empire* **42**, 8–78.

Wilkins, L. (1950). "The Diagnosis and Treatment of Endocrine Disorders in Childhood and Adolescence," Chapter 10, p. 208. Thomas, Springfield, Illinois.

Williams, P. C. (1944). Ovarian stimulation by oestrogens: effects in immature hypophysectomized rats. *Proc. Roy. Soc.* **B132**, 189–199.

Williams, P. C. (1945a). Ovarian stimulation by oestrogens. 2. Stimulation in the absence of hypophysis, uterus, and adrenal glands. *J. Endocrinol.* **4**, 125–126.

Williams, P. C. (1945b). Studies of the biological action of serum gonadotrophin. 2. Ovarian response after hypophysectomy and oestrogen treatment. *J. Endocrinol.* **4**, 131–136.

Witschi, E. (1963). Embryology of the ovary. *In* "The Ovary" (H. G. Grady and D. E. Smith, eds.), pp. 1–10. Williams & Wilkins, Baltimore, Maryland.

Witschi, E., and Riley, G. M. (1940). Quantitative studies on the hormones of human pituitaries. *Endocrinology* **26**, 565–576.

Wolfe, J. M. (1935). The normal level of the various cell types in the anterior pituitaries of mature and immature rats and further observations on cyclic histologic variations. *Anat. Record* **61**, 321–330.

Wolfe, J. M., and Cleveland, R. (1931). Comparison of capacity of anterior hypophyseal tissue of mature and immature female rabbits to induce ovulation. *Anat. Record* **51**, 213–218.

Wood, C. D. (1958). Behavioral changes following discrete lesions of temporal lobe structures. *Neurology* **8**, 215–220.

Woods, M. C., and Simpson, M. E. (1961). Pituitary control of the testis of the hypophysectomized rat. *Endocrinology* **69**, 91–125.

Wurtman, R. J., Altschule, M. D., and Holmgren, U. (1959). Effects of pinealectomy and of a bovine pineal extract in rats. *Am. J. Physiol.* **197**, 108–110.

Wurtman, R. J., Roth, W., Altschule, M. D., and Wurtman, J. J. (1961). Interactions of the pineal and exposure to continuous light on organ weights of female rats. *Acta Endocrinol.* **36**, 617–624.

Wurtman, R. J., Axelrod, J., and Chu, E. W. (1963). Melatonin, a pineal substance: effect on the rat ovary. *Science* **141**, 277–278.

Yamada, T., and Greer, M. A. (1960). The effect of bilateral ablation of the amygdala on endocrine function in the rat. *Endocrinology* **66**, 565–574.

Zacharias, L., and Wurtman, R. J. (1964). Blindness: its relation to age of menarche. *Science* **144**, 1154–1155.

Zarrow, M. X., and Quinn, D. L. (1963). Superovulation in the immature rat following treatment with PMS alone and inhibition of PMS-induced ovulation. *J. Endocrinol.* **26**, 181–188.

Zarrow, M. X., and Wilson, E. D. (1961). The influence of age on superovulation in the immature rat and mouse. *Endocrinology* **69**, 851–855.

Zondek, B. (1926). Über die Funktion des Ovariums. *Z. Geburtshilfe Gynaekol.* **90**, 372–380.

Zondek, B. (1940). On the mechanism of action of gonadotrophin from pregnancy urine. *J. Endocrinol.* **2**, 12–20.

Zondek, B., and Aschheim, S. (1927). Das Hormon des Hypophysenvorderlappens. 1. Testobjekt zum Nachweis des Hormons. *Klin. Wochschr.* **6**, 248–252.

CHAPTER 21

Sexual Behavior: General Aspects

CHARLES H. PHOENIX, ROBERT W. GOY, and WILLIAM C. YOUNG[1]

I. Introduction

A. Definition

The term sexual behavior refers to a complex series of responses directly associated with genital stimulation and copulation whether homosexual or heterosexual. For each species there is a generally recognizable sequence of postural configurations which, taken together, constitutes a sexual behavior pattern. The sequence of responses shows considerable intraspecies and intraindividual variability and does not suggest any automatic running off of stereotyped responses. Some components of sexual behavior show greater variability than others, but even the most stereotyped components manifest a degree of variability.

The sexual behavior pattern of a species is therefore a somewhat idealized concept of sexual behavior characteristic of a species. Verbal

[1] Publication No. 92 of the Oregon Regional Primate Research Center supported in part by Grant MH 08634 of the National Institutes of Health, and in part by Grant FR 00163.

descriptions or photographic representations of specific sexual behavior components are consequently attempts at representing modal forms of the response, and as such are statistical concepts of what is normal. In addition to the particular bodily configuration adopted by the animal, the sequence of events is likewise based on a probability continuum. Not all behavior sequences have the same probability of occurrence. Intromission by the male, for example, is invariably preceded by a mount of some description, but ejaculation need not be preceded by an intromission, although it usually is.

Obviously, descriptions of sexual behavior patterns differ in the amount of detail which is included. Early studies of sexual behavior in the male rat (Stone, 1927) did not distinguish between intromission with ejaculation and intromission without accompanying ejaculation; both responses were referred to simply as copulation. There are no rules for deciding a priori on the degree of refinement necessary for adequate behavioral description. The extent of refinement is largely limited by the techniques available and its usefulness in solving the particular problem under study. On the one hand, there is a danger of such superficial observation and analysis that potentially significant aspects of the behavior are missed; on the other hand, finer and finer analysis of obscure details may provide only monumental irrelevancies. Good description is, in fact, an abstraction from behavior.

B. Terminology

There has been little standardization of terminology in designating the various components of sexual behavior, but some uniformity has been achieved. What is particularly important is that workers describe with care the particular behavior to which a term refers. This requirement differs in no way from standard scientific procedure. A considerable amount of work has been carried out on the sexual behavior of the rat and guinea pig, and substantial uniformity in terminology has been achieved over the years. There has been no particular problem of relating one component of sexual behavior in the guinea pig to a similar component of sexual behavior in the rat. However, when the behavior is used to make inferences about the level of drive, then the same behavioral end points do not have the same inferential validity across different species. In other instances as well, the cross-species comparisons of particular behaviors are cumbersome or difficult to interpret. Attempts to compare components of sexual behavior in the rodent with sexual behavior in the primate can be expected to present difficulties. Estrus, for example, has been used to refer to both the vaginal condition and to behavior. The distinction is not always made between the two reference points, but if estrous behavior is referred to in the rodent, its meaning is relatively clear. When estrus is used with reference to behavior in the monkey, its meaning is obscure. There is no question but that the physiological state of the female monkey when it is receptive to the male need not be comparable to the physiological state in the rodent when it is receptive. Some attention by those working with primates to a broad background of research and terminology in sexual behavior and reproduction already existing for lower mammals should reduce the probability of confusion in terminology.

C. Conceptualization

Sexual behavior has been commonly classified as instinctive. The basis for the classification is that the behavior is presumably unlearned. In a chapter entitled, "Instinctive Behavior: Reproductive Activities," Beach (1951) rejected the dichotomy of instinctive versus learned behavior and pointed to the need for the study of factors determining development and organization of the behavior in question. In a later review of the history of the concept of instinct, Beach (1955) concluded that when behavior has been appropriately studied and analyzed "the concept of instinct will disappear to be replaced by scientifically valid and useful explanations."

The rejection of the instinct concept by most psychologists was based primarily on its vagueness and its failure as an explanatory concept. Morgan (1943) dismissed the concept as "a conventional rubric for referring to rather complex motivated behavior." For most psychologists the concept of drive replaced the older instinct concept. Some sought to "explain" sexual behavior as that behavior resulting from a sex drive, just as eating was "explained" by the presence of a hunger drive. Stone (1939) defined sex drive as "aroused action tendencies . . . that . . . lead to satisfaction or alleviation of dominant physiological 'urges' associated with reproduction." The concept of drive was essentially free of burdensome connotation and preconceptions that had built up around the instinct concept and in that respect offered a fresh approach, but to a large extent "drive" was simply substituted for instinct and little advance was made in conceptualization.

The term drive has persisted in the literature although its meaning has not always been made clear. In experimental literature, males particularly are frequently classified as "low-drive" or "high-drive" without any implication as to inner states or urges (Valenstein *et al.*, 1954). Used in this sense drive refers only to the relative amount of sexual behavior displayed. Sex drive, sex instinct, or libido are frequently used interchangeably, especially in medical literature. Semantically the problem is to find a term that relates to the animal's sexual performance without the necessity of making assumptions about the factors governing performance. By and large the problems under study by students of sexual behavior involve finding and evaluating those variables that determine the frequency and kind of sexual behavior displayed. In psychological terms the problem falls within the area referred to as motivation. One may ask what motivates a male rat to mount the female. The answer that the motivation is sex instinct, sex drive, or libido is in fact no answer—it explains nothing. Explanation of the behavior can be found without any reference to the concepts mentioned. The questions asked by the experimenter become, for example, what role does the nervous system, hormone level, method of rearing, conditions of housing, genetic background, or condition of the female play in regulating male mounting behavior. When these and related questions have been answered, postulation of innate or learned sex urges, needs, drives, action tendencies, propensities, or instincts will no longer be necessary. The terms can then be used in a purely denotative manner.

Not only is there much about animal sexual behavior that is poorly understood, but the behavior itself has been described for relatively few species. Conceptualization, however, need not await extensive behavioral description. Because all descriptions of behavior represent some degree of abstraction, approach to description with a conceptual system is more likely to engender useful observations.

D. Methods

Field observations generally attempt to introduce the least possible modification into the behavior setting and therefore tend to be restricted to descriptive studies. The hope in such work is to observe the behavior as it occurs in nature without the artificial restrictions of the laboratory. In fact, very few observations are possible today in field situations unaffected by man. More often than not the characteristics of the variation introduced by man's encroachment on "nature" are not known or are ignored. Islands, parks, or preserves where much field work is carried out provide at best quasi-natural settings for controlled behavioral observations.

The laboratory frequently introduces many fundamental variables into the behavioral setting. Most, if not all of the variables are, in principle at least, subject to manipulation by the experimenter. Laboratory observations may not be generalizable to the field situation, but the converse is also true. Some questions concerning sexual behavior that arise in the field may be studied in greater detail in the laboratory, and it is also true that still other questions, such as why a particular species fails to mate in the laboratory situation, may be answered by looking to the environment in which mating normally occurs. Description, whether obtained in the field or in the laboratory, can serve as a first step in the process of achieving an understanding of phenomena so that prediction and control become possible.

Good descriptions are reliable and capable of verification. Motion pictures of sexual behavior patterns provide a document that can be studied repeatedly and observed by many, but photographic documentation without frequency data and controlled sampling techniques leaves much to be desired.

With the development of valid and reliable measures of sexual behavior, the experimental approach to sexual behavior becomes feasible. Any of a number of components of sexual behavior or the total pattern may serve as a dependent variable. Frequency of mounting, intromission, and ejaculation for the male, and the ratio of lordosis responses to mounts for the female, have been used in many studies as dependent variables. With more detailed and intensive studies, especially in the rat, time intervals between series of intromissions and between successive ejaculations have been studied as a function of the previous occurrence of the response (Larsson, 1958).

The number and kinds of independent variables have involved surgical manipulation such as castration, brain lesions, enucleation of the eyes, denervation of the genitalia, and injection of hormones or drugs, or manipulation of the environment such as changes of sex of the partner, unusual heat or cold, prolonged or reversed light-dark cycles, and many more.

The aim of experimental studies of sexual behavior is to determine those factors, biological or environmental, that control its form and display. Simple determination of relevant variables, however, is not enough. The hope is to obtain quantitative information concerning each variable such that functional relationships can be established between relevant variables and the form and extent of sexual behavior displayed.

II. Gonadal Hormones and Activation of Sexual Behavior in Adult Mammals

A. Administration of the Homologous Hormone

Steroid hormones are one of the major variables controlling the display of sexual behavior in the adult. The adult female, especially among subprimate mammals, seldom or never displays the characteristic female pattern of sexual behavior in the absence of gonadal hormone stimulation. Behavioral heat or estrus is dependent on the presence of estrogen or estrogen and progesterone, whether it is supplied from endogenous or exogenous sources. Changes in levels of circulating estrogen and progesterone are presumed to account for the cyclic, or in some species seasonal, periods of receptivity.

The specific posture adopted by the female varies widely from one species to another, but the postures have in common a stance that facilitates mounting and intromission by the male. Spaying leads to the immediate and complete cessation of female sexual behavior. In rodents such as rats and guinea pigs, injection of suitable amounts of estrogen followed by progesterone induces a complete estrous response indistinguishable from the estrous behavior displayed prior to spaying. In some species such as the rabbit and cat, estrogen alone will induce heat in the spayed animal. In sheep a "priming" dose of progesterone followed by estrogen is essential for induction of the complete estrous pattern. The exact mechanism of action of these hormones in producing the behavior is not understood, but the hormones are presumed to act on the central nervous system, particularly the hypothalamus. It is very likely that the hormones or their metabolites act on central neural tissues other than the hypothalamus, but where and how the hormones act to give rise to the behavior remains problematical.

In the adult, estrogen and progesterone function to activate preexisting patterns of behavior. The particular quality and quantity of behavior displayed following injection of a given amount of hormone varies among species, individuals, and strains (Fig. 1).

The relationship between estrogen and progesterone in the induction of female sexual behavior has been subject to question inasmuch as a good deal of evidence suggests that progesterone inhibits estrous behavior. The administration of progesterone concurrently with estrogen suppresses estrus in the ferret (Marshall and Hammond, 1945), and progesterone following estrogen is said to inhibit sexual response in the ovariectomized rhesus monkey (Ball, 1941). Endogenous progesterone produced during the luteal phase of the ovarian cycle prevents the behavioral conditioning action of estrogen in guinea pigs (Dempsey *et al.*, 1936; Goy *et al.*, 1966), cows (Melampy *et al.*, 1957), and swine (Baker *et al.*, 1954). In addition, sexual responses of the intact female chimpanzee (Young and Orbison, 1944) decline or disappear during the luteal phase.

The reconciliation of these antagonistic and synergistic (facilitating) effects of progesterone has been attempted in several ways. One hypothesis proposes that the "normal" action of progesterone is antagonistic, and the facilitating actions of progesterone depend upon prior conditioning of the individual with an estrogen. In addition, the antagonistic and facilitating actions of progesterone at every stage of the ovarian cycle are believed to depend upon the balance between estrogen and progesterone. Such an hypothesis would explain the facilitating actions in the intact female on the basis of the relatively small amounts of progesterone secreted from the preovulatory follicle compared to the amounts of estrogen present. After ovulation and the formation of a corpus luteum, the larger amounts secreted at that time would act antagonistically.

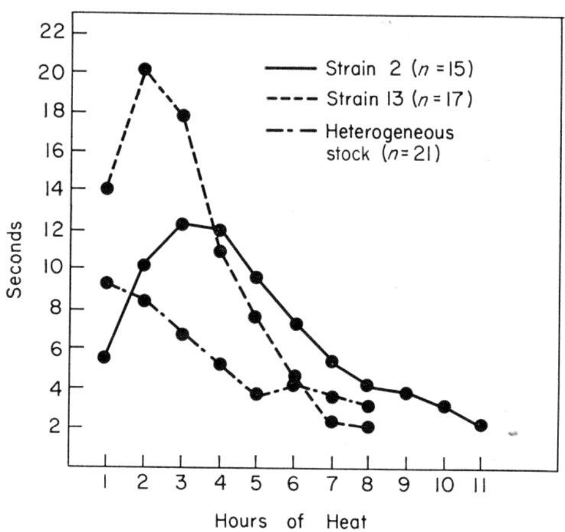

FIG. 1. Changes in the duration of the lordosis response as a function of time since the onset of heat in different genetic strains of female guinea pigs. The curves end at the time when 50% of the subjects failed to display the response, that is, were no longer in heat. *n*-number of animals in each group. (From Goy and Young, 1957.)

In studies which we have carried out on spayed female guinea pigs, the quantitative balance hypothesis has not been supported. When ten times the quantity necessary for the induction of estrus was administered to the same inbred females (Group I), no inhibition of the behavior was found. In a second study when two independent groups of genetically heterogeneous females were tested concurrently, an amount of progesterone (25 mg, Group III) more than sixty times that used for Group II (0.4 mg) also was without any measurable inhibiting action (Table I).

An alternate hypothesis which is aimed at reconciling the antagonistic and facilitating actions of progesterone was advanced by Sawyer and

TABLE I

LACK OF RELATIONSHIP BETWEEN ESTROUS BEHAVIOR IN SPAYED GUINEA PIGS AND AMOUNT OF PROGESTERONE INJECTED FOLLOWING A CONSTANT AMOUNT OF ESTRADIOL

	Amount of progesterone (mg)	Interval from progestrone to heat (hours)	Duration of heat (hours)	Duration of maximum lordosis (seconds)	Mean number of mounts
Inbred strain Group I (n = 7)					
Control test	0.2	4.1	6.3	19.8	23.4
Retest	2.0	5.7	6.1	20.1	28.6
Heterogeneous stock					
Group II (n = 9)	0.4	4.6	7.8	10.9	5.0
Group III (n = 8)	25.0	5.6	6.4	8.9	4.4

Everett (1959). The results of their study suggest that the two actions of progesterone are properties of the hormone itself. In estrogen-primed rabbits the facilitating effect is followed in the course of time by antagonistic or inhibitory effects. Insofar as this conception of a biphasic action of progesterone suggests that the sequence of the phases is from facilitation to inhibition, it would require modification. In spayed guinea pigs progesterone is antagonistic to the induction of estrous behavior when administered at any time within 24 hours prior to the conditioning estrogen (Table II). Moreover, as the results in the table indicate,

TABLE II

EFFECT OF PRIOR PROGESTERONE ON HORMONAL INDUCTION OF ESTROUS BEHAVIOR IN SPAYED GUINEA PIGS

Group	n	Percentage of females in heat	Mean latency to heat (hours)	Mean number of mounts
Test: administration of 1 mg progesterone at varying times prior to conditioning injection of estradiol				
72 hours	10	90	5.6	1.6
48 hours	8	88	4.8	2.9
24 hours	6	17	6.0	1.5
16 hours	6	0	—	0
8 hours	6	0	—	0.1
4 hours	6	0	—	0.2
2 hours	5	0	—	0
0 hours (simultaneous)	6	0	—	0
Controls (No prior progesterone)	10	90	3.7	4.5

progesterone is inhibitory even when administered simultaneously with estrogen. Accordingly, the antagonistic phase does not necessarily follow the facilitating phase except when the conditioning action of estrogen is completed. As Zucker has shown in unpublished studies (1966) of the guinea pig, the inhibitory effects of progesterone are evident when administered following estrogen provided that the estrogen-conditioning action is incomplete. Stated otherwise, the inhibitory effect will develop if progesterone is given any time between the administration of estrogen and the completion of its conditioning action. Only when the conditioning action of estrogen is complete (18 hours according to the data in Table III) does the inhibitory phase follow the facilitating effect of progesterone.

What emerges from this brief consideration of the problem is that none of the hypotheses outlined can account for the variety of facilitating and antagonistic actions of progesterone. Little attention has been paid in earlier work to the temporal relations that modify the interactions between the hormones. It is likely that parts of each of the hypotheses discussed will have to be incorporated into any more general statement which attempts to reconcile these divergent actions of progesterone and to account for the conspicuous differences between species.

Unlike the female, whose display of sexual behavior is generally cyclic, the male characteristically shows a constant readiness to engage in sexual behavior. The distinction between cyclicity for the female and relative constancy for the male is valid even among species breeding seasonally, and for males of many species mating can occur during any season and viable sperm are continuously produced. Systematic studies show that considerable variation exists among species with respect to various measures of the sexual behavior pattern. The variation (Table IV) in the number of intromissions which normally precede ejaculation extends from a mean of 3.7 in the rhesus monkey to 23.0 or more in the mouse. Other quantitative measures of the relationship between components show as marked variation. These differences cannot be accounted for by differences in kind of circulating hormone nor can intraspecies differences be accounted for in this way. When males from these different species are castrated and treated with threshold amounts of chemically pure testosterone, the same type and magnitude of behavioral differences result.

Males, unlike females, do not terminate all sexual behavior following castration. The diminution in sexual activity occurs more gradually, with the ejaculatory response being the first response lost from the behavioral repertoire. Intromission is the next response lost, and it is followed by a decline in mounting frequency. In the guinea pig, mounting behavior was observed in 40% of the animals studied 31 weeks after castration, at which time observations were discontinued (Grunt and Young, 1953). The sexually experienced male cat has been observed to mount for 2 or 3 years after castration. In the male rhesus monkeys, castrated at 3 months of age, the normal double-foot-clasp mount was seen to develop and persist over what is now a 4-year period of observation (Goy, 1964). The effects of castration in the adult monkey and chimpanzee are unclear, but available evidence suggests that sexual

TABLE III

INTERACTIONS OF ESTROGEN AND PROGESTERONE IN THE ACTIVATION AND SUPPRESSION OF ESTRUS IN SPAYED GUINEA PIGS[a,b]

Group	n	Time (hours) and amount (mg) of first progesterone	Percentage in heat	Time of second estrogen	Time (hours) and amount (mg) of second progesterone	Percentage in heat	Type of progesterone action
I	8	36, 1.0	100	—	—	—	Facilitation
II	9	6, 1.0	0	—	36, 0.4	0	Inhibition
III	10	18, 1.0	100	—	36, 0.4	0	Facilitation followed by inhibition
IV	10	36, 0.4	100	—	207, 0.4	30	Recovery from inhibition
V	9	36, 0.4	100	42	78, 0.4	22	Facilitation followed by inhibition
VI	8	36, 0.4	100	94	130, 0.4	75	Recovery from inhibition

[a] Material supplied from studies in progress by Zucker.
[b] Treatment of all groups at 0 hours with estradiol benzoate (6 μg).

TABLE IV

QUANTITATIVE CHARACTERISTICS OF SEXUAL BEHAVIOR IN LABORATORY STUDIES OF MAMMALS

Species	Number of intromissions preceding ejaculation	Duration of interval between intromissions (seconds)	Duration of interval between first intromission and ejaculation (seconds)	Source
Guinea pig	3 to 4; 6.4	44	285	Young and Grunt (1951); Gerall (1958)
Hamster	10.4	10.3	112.5	Beach and Rabedeau (1959)
Rat	10.6	51.5	430 (estimated)	Beach and Jordan (1956)
Mouse[a]	23.0	56	1764	McGill (1962)
Cat	7.2	306.9[b]	—	Whalen (1963)
Rhesus monkey	3.7	42	124	R. Kuehn, unpublished data (1966)

[a] The data from McGill were based on studies of three different inbred strains. Values reported in the table are the intermediate ones in each case.

[b] This measure varies markedly with the serial order of the intromission. The value given is the shortest possible and represents the average interval between the first and second intromission.

behavior tends to persist for periods longer than those characteristic of nonprimate species.

Rats and guinea pigs that have reached a consistently low level of sexual activity after castration will show a restoration of behavior with injection of androgen. The full behavior is not reinstated immediately but shows a gradual return over time as injections are continued. The behavioral components are reinstated in the reverse order to which they are lost. Mounting is the first component to return and ejaculation the last. The precastration level is re-established in the guinea pig after approximately 9 weeks of treatment with 25.0 μg testosterone propionate per 100 gm body weight per day (Grunt and Young, 1953). When threshold doses of androgen are administered, increasing the dosage does not bring about increases in sexual activity. In this respect the guinea pig and mouse (Champlin *et al.*, 1963) may differ from the rat and hamster whose sexual activity may be increased by increasing the dosage level above the threshold necessary to permit ejaculation (Young, 1961).

B. Administration of the Heterologous Hormone

Intact male rats and guinea pigs seldom display female components of sexual behavior. The male guinea pig at birth will display the lordosis response when stimulated in an appropriate manner, but the response cannot be evoked after a few hours and is seldom or never observed in the intact adult. Beach has reported one case of a male rat with normal testicular function that displayed female behavior, but such display by males is indeed infrequent (Beach, 1941, 1945a).

Castration of the adult male and treatment with estrogen or estrogen and progesterone rarely induces the complete female pattern of behavior. Occasional brief responses have been observed when high doses of estrogen were injected, but the pattern characteristic of females has not been observed in male rats or guinea pigs castrated and tested as adults (Ball, 1939; Goy *et al.*, 1964).

Observations of subhuman primates indicate that the lordosis response, or "present," as the receptive posture is termed, is commonly displayed by the intact adult male *Macaca*. Not only does the response appear to be independent of estrogen and progesterone but independent of any gonadal hormone. The presence of the response in 4-year-old males castrated at 3 months of age and in adult ovariectomized females observed in our laboratory attests to the relative independence of the behavior from gonadal hormone control. The presence of the response in infant male and female monkeys further indicates that the "present" posture in *Macaca mulatta* and *Macaca nemestrina* is more independent of gonadal hormones for its expression in these primates than is the homologous behavior pattern in nonprimate species. It is possible that the administration of estrogen and progesterone might result in a greater increase in the frequency of the "present" in females than in males, but data on this problem are not available at the present time.

Mounting is generally thought of as a component of male behavior but is not infrequently observed in a number of female mammals, including rodents, dogs, cattle, and monkeys. Mounting frequency can be expected to vary widely among individuals, strains, and species. In the guinea pig mounting is associated with estrus, whereas in the rat the behavior is not necessarily associated with any point in the ovarian cycle. The injection of exogenous estrogen and progesterone will induce mounting in the spayed guinea pig to a level comparable to that displayed at the time of spontaneously occurring estrus in intact females.

Injection of testosterone propionate will induce mounting behavior in spayed female guinea pigs and rats comparable with or somewhat in excess of that displayed during estrus. The mounting is frequently accompanied by pelvic thrusts, and the pattern is indistinguishable from that displayed by the normal male. Thus, in the female guinea pig or rat either estrogen and progesterone or testosterone can induce mounting with pelvic thrusts. The response of the female to testosterone, however, generally shows two characteristics which differentiate it from the response of the genetic male. Both the average frequency of mounting displayed in a 10-minute test and the sensitivity to exogenous androgen are lower in the genetic female than in the genetic male. These characteristics of lower response to androgen are not determined by interactions between the injected testosterone and endogenous secretions. The same relationships between the sexes and response to androgen are found even when the heterotypic hormones are injected into gonadectomized subjects.

The effects of testosterone on mounting behavior in the female primate are not yet known, but preliminary work in our laboratory based on the study of three pairs of female rhesus monkeys indicates that testosterone injections do not increase mounting rate directly. In the cases recently studied in our laboratory, mounting was more influenced by the sexual and dominance condition of the partner than it was by the injection of amounts of testosterone propionate as large as 10 mg per day. Mounting was not conspicuously influenced in any of the subordinate members of the pairs treated with testosterone. Dominant individuals mounted without testosterone (mean = 0.90 mounts per test). During the period of testing when their subordinate partners were being injected, dominant females mounted 1.53 times per test on the average.

Later, when they themselves were injected with testosterone, the mean number of mounts per test was only 1.45.

The principal effect of testosterone on the rhesus female appears to be an augmentation of those characteristics and behavior normally associated with the establishment or maintenance of a dominant relationship. One of the display gestures normally associated with dominant males in tests involving the pairing of males with females consists of hyperextension of the mandible and retraction of the lips, exposing all of the teeth. The expression closely resembles that of the yawn as displayed by human beings. As shown in Table V, the frequency of display of this facial expression (designated as dominance display) increases greatly during administration of exogenous testosterone. In contrast to the mounting behavior shown in the same table, the effect of the hormone is not limited to the dominant females.

TABLE V

EFFECTS OF TESTOSTERONE PROPIONATE (TP) ON DOMINANCE DISPLAY AND MOUNT'NG BEHAVIOR IN RHESUS FEMALES[a]

	Mean number of displays per animal per test		Mean number of mounts per animal per test	
	Prior to TP	During TP	Prior to TP	During TP
Dominant females	0.17	5.54	0.93	1.45
Subordinate females	0.05	1.62	0	0.02

[a] Three animals used in each group.

From the study of sexual behavior following the injection of homotypic and heterotypic hormone, it appears that bisexual potentiality among nonprimates is higher in the female than it is in the male. Among primates, however, bisexual potential is more pronounced in the male than in the female, or at least more conspicuous than it is in the male nonprimate. Accordingly, any theory of the genesis of sexuality which derives its standards for maleness and femaleness from the study of normal males and females must give adequate consideration to these taxonomic differences. Despite these differences between primates and other mammals, nothing in the evidence reviewed suggests that these taxonomic groups differ extensively with respect to the importance of developmental processes. In the determination of whether predominantly masculine or feminine modes of conduct will be activated or expressed during adulthood, for primates as for nonprimates, the hormonal environment during early development is critical.

III. Gonadal Hormones and Organization of Sexual Behavior

A. Activation versus Organization

Insofar as reproductive behavior is concerned, the role of the gonadal hormones in the adult male or female has been conceptualized as one of activation (Young, 1961). That is, the gonadal hormones in the adult activate or bring to expression previously established patterns of sexual behavior. In the psychosexually undifferentiated individual, testicular hormones act to organize or differentiate the pattern of sexual behavior which will be displayed by the adult. The testicular hormones therefore may act in either of two ways with respect to sexual behavior. In the immature, psychosexually undifferentiated animal, the role of the testicular hormones is organizational; in the adult their role is activational (Phoenix *et al.*, 1959).

The manner in which testicular hormones act to organize patterns of sexual behavior is a matter of conjecture. It is assumed that the patterning occurs in central neural structures, but neither the nature nor loci of the changes is known. There is considerable evidence implicating the hypothalamus as one locus, especially in view of what is known concerning its control of pituitary function and sexual behavior, but the entire central nervous system, including the spinal cord, cannot be discounted. This is especially true when it is realized that organizational action is not restricted to behavior that is purely sexual but includes other sex-related behavior as well (Young *et al.*, 1964).

We have emphasized the action of testicular hormones on central neural structures in the organization of patterns of behavior but we do not mean to imply that other tissues are of no consequence in the full expression of sexual behavior. An analogy between the action of androgen on the embryonic differentiation of the genital tract and the action of similar hormones on central neural structures was suggested several years ago (Phoenix *et al.*, 1959). The exact contribution of peripheral structures, including peripheral receptors, to the full display of male behavior versus the contribution of central factors has not been evaluated here nor is it crucial to the concept of the dual role of androgen function—organization and activation.

B. Effects of Early Androgen Administration

To date there have been no reports inconsistent with the hypothesis that during a rather well-defined period in development, depending upon the species, testosterone produces behavioral masculinization of the genetic female. The concept of the organizational action of the gonadal hormones on sexual behavior was given impetus by the results of our work with experimentally produced female pseudohermaphroditic guinea pigs. In the initial experiments pregnant guinea pigs were given a single injection of 5 mg of testosterone propionate on either day 10, 15, 18, or 24 of gestation followed by 1 mg per day to the end of the 68-day gestation period. The treatments produced offspring that at birth were macroscopically indistinguishable from males.

When these animals were spayed as adults and treated with estradiol benzoate and progesterone, they failed to respond in typical female fashion. Not only was responsiveness to the female hormones suppressed, but the animals showed an increased responsiveness to testosterone propionate in the manner in which the frequency of display of malelike behavior was increased following injection of the male hormone. The effects of the prenatal treatment were permanent or at least showed no lessening of the prenatal treatment effect when tested at 1 year of age. When testosterone was administered postnatally, from birth to 80 days of age, no such lasting effects were found. The differences in permanence of effect, especially, pointed to the differential role of the hormone depending upon when in development the hormone was administered. From the initial work it also became obvious that dosage levels and the time when the hormone was administered, even within the fetal period, were crucial.

An extensive follow-up study (Goy *et al.*, 1964) in which testosterone was injected during different stages of pregnancy revealed that the degree of modification both in genital morphology and sexual behavior varied with the time of treatment and amount of hormone injected. The behavior displayed by offspring from the various treatment groups varied from normal female responsiveness at one extreme, to behavior indistinguishable from that of castrated male control subjects at the other extreme. The greatest degree of modification of sexual behavior and genital morphology in the guinea pig occurred when treatment was initiated on postcoital day 30 and the gestational period from day 30 to 35 was determined to be the "period of maximal susceptibility" to the masculinizing actions of exogenous testosterone.

Further refinement in dosage and time of treatment conceivably might have resulted in a somewhat different period of maximal susceptibility, but one of the significant facts derived from this study is that all degrees of modification in sexual behavior are obtained (Fig. 2). This empirical finding of a continuum from normal male to normal female provides the basis for our current view that the organization of sexual behavior is not an "all-or-none" phenomenon. Accordingly, the pattern of sexual behavior displayed by any individual need not be conceptualized as either masculine or feminine in its organization. Intermediate "types" can be produced and more than two organizations of sexuality have been empirically demonstrated. The scatter plot in Fig. 2 illustrates the means for mounting and duration of heat for twelve different groups of prenatally androgenized female guinea pigs. The numbers in parenthesis in the plot refer to the gestational interval when androgen was administered. For each treatment 5 mg of androgen was given daily

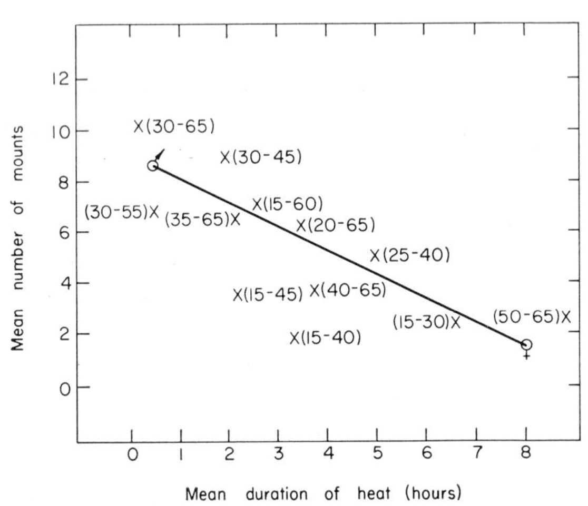

FIG. 2. Scatter plot based on the means for mounting frequency and duration of heat in standardized tests of twelve different groups of prenatal androgen treatments (x). The control values are indicated by (♂) and (♀). The slope of the line is not based on empirical correlation, but is merely drawn for illustrative purposes. See text.

for 6 days, followed by 1 mg thereafter. Only the 5-mg dosage was critical to the induction of profound masculine alterations. The standards for male (♂) and female (♀) performance were obtained from untreated control animals. It is clear from Fig. 2 that when treatment ends prior to gestational day 30, or begins as late as day 50, the mean values for mounting and duration of heat do not differ greatly from those for normal females. Treatments begun on day 30, however, all produce significant deviation toward the values characteristic for males.

Of some theoretical consequence is the finding that masculinization of behavior is obtainable without apparent change in external genital structures and that some animals with pronounced modification of genital structures, such as the absence of a vaginal orifice, displayed behavior patterns characteristic of the normal female. In general, however, morphological masculinization and suppression of estrous behavior were correlated.

The observation that prenatal treatments which profoundly influence the genetic female guinea pig are without measurable effect on the genetic male is pertinent to our present consideration of androgen as a fetal organizing substance for behavior. The development of male sexual behavior occurs at a normal rate in males treated prenatally with testosterone. No evidence for a psychosexual precocity or an increase in vigor or capacity has been obtained in any of our studies of the male guinea pig. What may be of even greater theoretical importance is that no damaging effect of the prenatal treatment on the male behavioral characteristics has been observed. In this respect the effects of early androgen on the homotypic sex are quite different from the effects of early estrogen on the homotypic sex as described in a later section.

Thus far we have discussed the effects of prenatally injected testosterone on the organization of patterns of sexual behavior. However, the effects of such injections on the offspring extend to behavior beyond that which is immediately associated with reproduction, as our studies of pseudohermaphroditic rhesus monkeys indicate. Pregnant rhesus monkeys were injected with 20 mg of testosterone propionate per day from day 40 to day 69 of pregnancy following a procedure described by van Wagenen and Hamilton (1943) and Wells and van Wagenen (1954). The degree of morphological modification produced by the treatment is illustrated in Fig. 3. These original treatment parameters have since been modified in an attempt to maximize behavioral as well as morphological changes.

Because of the high abortion rate associated with the testosterone treatments employed, only eight pseudohermaphroditic females and ten males from treated mothers have been obtained. This number represents offspring from approximately seventy-four treated pregnant females.

Present findings with additional animals confirm previously described results based on the study of two female pseudohermaphrodites (Young *et al.*, 1964). Infant pseudohermaphroditic female monkeys initiate play, threaten others, and engage in rough-and-tumble play more frequently than do female control subjects, and in this respect resemble the normal male and differ little from the neonatally castrated male rhesus.

With respect to behavior which is considered more specifically sexual in nature, mounting and the "present" posture, the female pseudohermaphrodites display these behaviors with a frequency intermediate between that of the female and the prepubertally castrated male (Table VI).

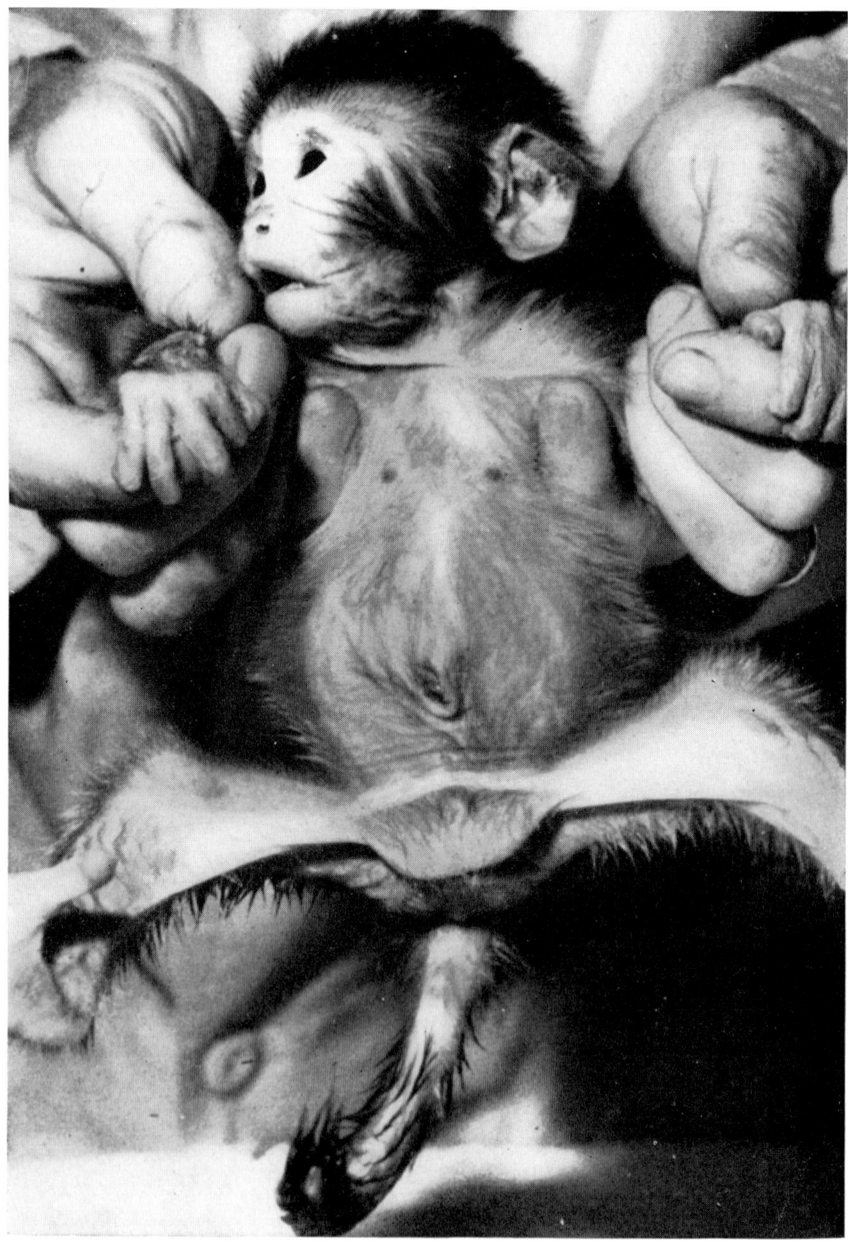

FIG. 3. Female pseudohermaphrodite #828. At birth there was a well-developed scrotum, a small and nonpendulous phallus, and no external vaginal orifice. During subsequent development the infant showed conspicuous psychological masculinization.

Qualitatively, the character of mounting displayed by pseudohermaphroditic monkeys is also intermediate between the male and female criterion groups. Double-foot-clasp mounts are displayed very rarely, and single-foot-clasp mounts infrequently. Similar qualitative distinctions cannot be made for the "present" posture which, insofar as we have been able to determine, does not differ between normal males and females.

TABLE VI

TOTAL FREQUENCY OF TWO ITEMS OF SEXUAL BEHAVIOR DURING 100 CONSECUTIVE 5-MINUTE OBSERVATION PERIODS IN JUVENILE RHESUS MONKEYS

	n	Mean mounts	Mean "presents"
Intact females	16	1.6	37.2
Female pseudohermaphrodites	4	10.0	28.1
Prepubertally castrated males[a]	7	21.8	26.2
Intact males	9	67.0	13.3

[a] Includes data from two males castrated on the day of birth and five males castrated at 3 months of age.

Genetic male offspring from testosterone-treated mothers have been observed over a 6-month period and have not yet shown any signs of differing from males from untreated mothers with respect to development of social and sexual behavior. These results are in agreement with those found in studies of sexual behavior in male guinea pigs born of testosterone-treated mothers.

In the monkey and guinea pig, both long-gestational animals, the period of organization of the neural tissues mediating mating behavior occurs during the fetal period. In the rat, sexual organization is not complete until after birth. In terms of periods of maximum susceptibility, however, the monkey, rat, and guinea pig bear a remarkable similarity when postfertilization age is taken as a criterion. Only in the guinea pig have details of this period been evaluated (Goy *et al.*, 1964). Most of the work on the rat has been confined to assessment of the postnatal period of susceptibility and for the monkey, where large samples are not easily obtained, only a beginning has been made in determining optimum time and dosage values for modification of morphology and sexual behavior (van Wagenen and Hamilton, 1943; Wells and van Wagenen, 1954; Phoenix and Goy, unpublished observations, 1965).

Female rats treated with small amounts of testosterone propionate during the late prenatal period showed essentially normal sexual behavior as adults, and large doses of testosterone propionate (30–50 mg) produced noncyclic low intensity mating behavior in the females when tested as adults (Wilson *et al.*, 1940). Further experiments in which female rats were treated pre- and postnatally and postnatally only demonstrated that the early postnatal period was most effective in producing permanent changes (decrements or abolition) of female sexual behavior. When treatment involving multiple injections of testosterone propionate was started as late as 15 days postnatally, no permanent modification in sexual behavior was observed (Wilson *et al.*, 1941).

A single injection of 1.25 mg of testosterone propionate administered to the 5-day-old female rat produces permanent changes in the organization of patterns of sexual behavior. Such females show persistent vaginal cornification but they do not mate. Injections of progesterone into these androgen-sterilized female rats does not induce mating behavior nor do these females mate when spayed and injected with estrogen and progesterone (Barraclough and Gorski, 1962). However, when 5-day-old female rats were injected with 10 μg of testosterone, although sterile as adults, they displayed wide variations in periods of sexual receptivity. There was no correlation between the display of sexual behavior and vaginal cornification which persisted.

Injection of 1.25 mg of testosterone into the 5-day female rats unquestionably reduces or abolishes responsiveness of the tissues mediating female behavior to estrogen and progesterone. The extent to which early treatment with testosterone masculinizes the female rat in the sense of enhancing malelike behavior and increasing responsiveness to testosterone in adulthood has not been studied systematically. Five-day-old female rats treated with 500 μg of testosterone and later spayed and injected with estradiol and progesterone failed to show estrous behavior. When treated with testosterone, they displayed "marked male behavior patterns" when placed with a receptive female or normal male (Harris and Levine, 1962). Quantification of the malelike behavior was not reported, however, nor was any assessment made of normal females similarly treated with testosterone in adulthood beyond the qualitative remark that their masculine behavior was "less marked."

C. Deprivation of Gonadal Androgen during Development

Considerable evidence now exists supporting the theory that in the genetic male some androgenic substance secreted by the developing testes acts on neural tissues during the period of psychosexual differentiation to organize the male pattern of behavior. In the absence of this testicular support, development of male behavioral patterns is deficient, and female patterns are developed or retained instead.

Male rats castrated the day of birth and injected as adults with relatively small amounts of estradiol and progesterone displayed the complete pattern of female sexual behavior, including darting, crouching, and ear wiggling. Little or no female behavior was displayed by rats castrated at 10, 20, 30, 50, and 90 days of age when tested following injection of up to fifty times the amount of estradiol sufficient to evoke the female response in males castrated the day of birth (Fig. 4). Males

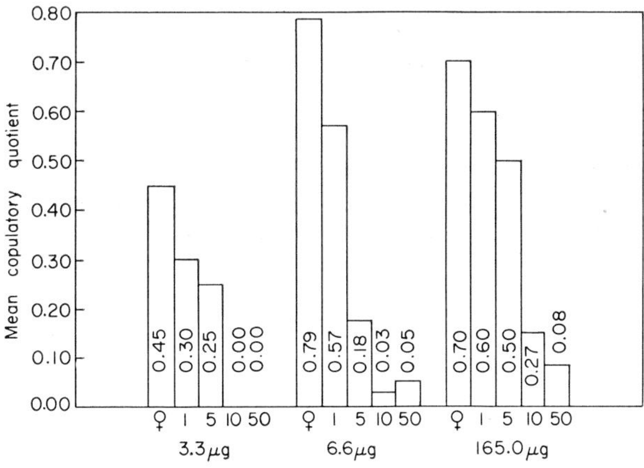

FIG. 4. Mean copulatory quotients of male rats castrated at 1, 5, 10, and 50 days of age and of spayed female rats tested following injection of various amounts of estradiol benzoate. (Data adapted from Grady *et al.*, 1965, as reported by Goy, 1964.)

castrated at 5 days of age resembled spayed females and males castrated the day of birth with respect to the frequency of display of the lordosis response, but they resembled males castrated at 10 days of age and older with respect to the display of other components of female sexual behavior (Grady and Phoenix, 1963; Grady *et al.*, 1965).

Not only is the rat castrated the day of birth capable of displaying the full female pattern of sexual behavior, but, when an ovary is transplanted into the animal, it will ovulate and form corpora lutea in a cyclic manner (Pfeiffer, 1936; Harris, 1964). Based largely on activity of ovaries transplanted into neonatally castrated male rats, Harris (1964) has concluded that early castration "results in failure of differentiation of the central nervous system into that of the male type."

Although castration on the day of birth permits the display of estrous behavior following injection of estrogen and progesterone, it does not prevent the induction of mounting behavior with testosterone replacement therapy. Males castrated the day of birth displayed higher mounting rates per minute than males castrated at 5, 10, 30, or 90 days of age with comparable hormone treatment. However, males castrated on day 1 displayed virtually no intromissions and they did not ejaculate (Grady *et al.*, 1965). No suitable explanation of the high mounting rate is readily available. Two facts may be relevant: mounting is a component of sexual behavior commonly found in the female repertoire and is enhanced by treatment of the normal adult female with testosterone; the testis in the rat is endocrinologically active about 5 days prior to birth, and accordingly, males castrated at birth may possess some potential for masculine behavior.

Castration of the male guinea pig at birth does not alter its later responsiveness to androgen or estrogen. In order to modify the male pattern of sexual organization in this species, the prediction can be made that castration of the fetus would be necessary. This has not been accomplished, but the male guinea pig fetus has been treated with an antiandrogen. At present the behavior is incompletely assessed, but the results indicate that effective quantities of antiandrogen can prevent complete masculine development of the external genital structures, as well as prevent the display of intromission and ejaculation components of sexual behavior in adulthood (Table VII). Moreover, the period when treatment is effective for the "feminizing" action of antiandrogen

TABLE VII

ABILITY TO DISPLAY INTROMISSION AND EJACULATION IN ADULT GUINEA PIGS TREATED PRENATALLY WITH ANTIANDROGEN[a]

		n	Mean number of intromissions	Mean proportion of tests on which ejaculation occurred
Males treated on gestation days 27 through 57	3 mg daily	4	3.2	0.85
	5 mg daily	5	4.8	0.84
	10 mg daily	3	14.8	0.80
	15 mg daily	3	0	0
Control males	No treatment	8	3.8	0.84

[a] The data presented are from current studies in our laboratory by Zucker and R. E. Kuehn. The antiandrogen used was cyproterone acetate (1,2α-methylene-6-chloro-$\Delta^{4,6}$-prenadiene-17α-ol-3,20-dione-17-acetate) kindly provided for these studies by Schering AG, Berlin.

in the male appears to correspond with the period in development for the masculinizing actions of androgen on the genetic female.

Thus far the experiments carried out on the rhesus monkey do not parallel those already described for the rat and guinea pig. The principal methodological difference is that for the monkey no replacement therapy of any kind has as yet been attempted. In addition, the study of the monkey is limited to observations during the period of infancy and preadolescence. Accordingly, direct comparisons are not possible between the data on the monkey and those for the rat and guinea pig in which adults treated with exogenous hormones were studied.

Rhesus monkeys castrated at 3 months of age ($n = 5$) mount the partner with characteristic double foot clasps. They achieve erection although the penis remains infantile, and they engage in those activities of play behavior characteristic of the male. Two rhesus males castrated the day of birth have not achieved the same level of sexual performance displayed by the males castrated at 3 months of age. In 5-minute observation periods over 100 consecutive days when the animals were approximately 3 years old, the mean number of mounts displayed by the 3-month castrates was 27. One male castrated the day of birth did not mount over the same time period and one mounted 16 times. In contrast, the mean number of mounts for nine intact males of comparable age observed in a similar situation was 67 (Table VI), although 1 intact male did not mount at all. Variations in the degree of compatability with test partners, methods of rearing, dominance status, and the small sample size make the absolute values difficult to interpret. There is little doubt that prepubertally castrated rhesus monkeys develop with a strong bias for masculine behavior, but the character of their sexual behavior appears to be intermediate between that of intact males on the one hand and that of the pseudohermaphroditic females on the other.

D. Effects of Early Estrogen Administration

Pregnant female guinea pigs have been injected with estradiol benzoate in an effort to evaluate the effects on the sexual behavior of the offspring. Unfortunately, in the guinea pig such treatment was found to be incompatible with pregnancy. Any conclusion concerning the effects of estradiol on organization of the pattern of sexual behavior must be drawn exclusively from experiments on the rat.

Injection of estradiol benzoate into 5-day-old female rats reduced or abolished the capacity to display estrous behavior in adulthood (Whalen and Nadler, 1963; Levine and Mullins, 1964). Similar results were found when males castrated the day of birth were injected with estrogen at 5 days of age and later tested for display of female behavior (Feder and Whalen, 1965). Thus, estrogen administered to either genetic males or females during the period of psychosexual differentiation blocks the capacity for the display of female behavior in adulthood. Moreover, the damaging effects of estrogen are not limited to the organization of feminine behavior. In our laboratory, H. H. Feder (1965) has shown that the same hormone (estradiol) administered early in the neonatal period to genetic males prevents the organization of normal masculine sexual behavior. Even when supplemental androgen is given in adulthood (Whalen, 1964), males treated neonatally with estrogen are unable to achieve intromission and ejaculation.

The point deserves special emphasis, however, that this detrimental effect of early estrogen on the male is not an organizing action of the hormone in the sense that we have used that term. In the studies dealing with the organizing action of androgen, its effect on the genetic female not only interfered with feminine behavior but also augmented masculine behavioral characteristics. Moreover, early androgen had no deleterious or "paradoxical" effects on the genotypic male fetus. In contrast, early estrogen appears to interfere with the development of both feminine behavior in females and masculine behavior in males. In addition, when it interferes with the development of masculine behavior in males, no evidence has been obtained that it promotes or augments the capacity for feminine behavior in the same individuals. Accordingly, the conclusion with regard to the organizing properties of the gonadal hormones appears to be the same for behavior as for the organization and differentiation of the genital tracts (Burns, 1961). For both sets of characteristics, androgen has effects which are compatible with the development of normal maleness or promotes the development of masculine characteristics in genetic females. Estrogen, in contrast, is equally incompatible with the development of normal female characteristics in females and normal male characteristics in genetic males.

Apparently, it is the absence of male hormone rather than the action of the female hormone that permits the organization of the female pattern of sexual behavior. Beach (1945b) described normal sexual behavior in a genetic female rat with congenital absence of gonadal tissue following injection of estrogen and progesterone. This observation suggested to Beach that gonadal secretions "do not act as embryonic organizers insofar as the behavioral mechanisms are concerned." Present evidence indicates that this may be true for estrogen but not for androgen, at least among mammals.

IV. Genetic and Hormonal Interaction

A. Chromosomal Influences

The influence which the genome exerts upon the sexuality of the individual is less completely understood for mammals than for a number of other vertebrate forms. Nevertheless, a significant number of developments have established the importance of both chromosomal and genic factors in the regulation of sex and behavior. In the human the rapid development of knowledge of chromosomal structure has led to the identification of specific chromosomal abnormalities associated with definite sexual disorders. Individuals showing one of three human disorders in particular, the Klinefelter syndrome in men and either the Turner or the superfemale syndrome in women, generally show departures from the normal number of chromosomes. The Klinefelter male and the superfemale both possess 47 chromosomes and the Turner female possesses 45. Moreover, in all three abnormalities, a sex chromosome of the X type is involved. For the male disorder as well as the superfemale, an additional or supernumery X chromosome is present, making the genomes XXY + 2A and XXX + 2A respectively. For Turner's syndrome involving gonadal agenesis, one of the customary X chromosomes is missing from an abnormally high proportion of somatic cells so that the genome is conventionally designated XO + 2A. It should be noted in passing that when the genome for Turner's syndrome is described as deficient in one X chromosome, some appeal to the phenotype is being made to aid in the designation of the deficiency. Logically the missing factor could as easily be a Y chromosome, and the significant aspect of the genome, broadly speaking, is that only one sex chromosome is present. According to these interpretations, at least two sex chromosomes are essential for the development of any gonad at all. When less than two are present, no gonad develops. When more than two are present, a gonad develops but does not display normal functional characteristics. Nevertheless, if a Y chromosome is present at all, male influences are expressed in the developing gonad. A female gonad, however abnormal, develops only in the absence of the Y chromosome.

Much of what has been said regarding the aberrations of sex chromosome structure is abstracted and oversimplified. In actual fact, in studying individual somatic cells from cases that are clinically classified as Klinefelter, superfemale, or Turner syndromes, a variety of sex-chromosome abnormalities have been found. Chiefly these abnormalities are represented in the form of mosaics, and the general types indicated above are believed to represent the predominant or most frequently encountered karyotype associated with each syndrome, although the problem is by no means settled. For more detailed accounts of the karyotype-sexual phenotype relationship, the reader is referred to three excellent reviews (Gowen, 1961; Sohval, 1963; Beatty, 1964). What is clear from the broad survey is that most chromosomal irregularities involving the sex chromosomes result in some type of defective gonadogenesis. The clinical and anatomical features associated with the abnormal karyotype depend more on the extent to which the defective gonad secretes androgens than on the sex-chromosome contribution per se.

Important in the context of present interests is the accumulation of reports indicating that sex orientation and libido are normal in the Turner female, provided that appropriate estrogen therapy is supplied to stimulate the development of the secondary sexual characters in adulthood. The information available suggests that for the human, as Beach (1945b) found for the rat, the presence of an ovary during fetal and prepubertal development is unessential to the development of normal female psychosexual adequacy.

B. Specific Autosomal Factors

More difficult to explain for the hypothesis of androgenic regulation of male sexual development is the syndrome called testicular feminization. In this syndrome, chromosomal studies generally have shown a normal number of chromosomes with an XY genotype. Cryptorchid testes in either an abdominal or inguinal location, absence or suppression of uterine development, and nearly normal external female genital structures and a normal female sexual orientation are additional characteristics of the syndrome. As Gowen (1961) has pointed out, the syndrome can only be accounted for genetically by a simple autosomal dominant with its action limited to the genotypic male. Moreover, it can only be made compatible with the results obtained on psychosexual differentiation if the action of the gene is postulated as antiandrogenic (French *et al.*, 1965; David *et al.*, 1965). Obviously more than one way exists for genes to express antiandrogenicity, and until much more work has been done, it is not possible to suggest which of the alternatives is more probable. It is possible, however, to conclude that the antiandrogenic action of the gene does not involve a simple elevation of target-organ thresholds. Individuals afflicted with the disorder fail to show any response to androgens, even when large amounts are supplied by injection (Wilkins, 1957; Morris and Mahesh, 1963).

An autosomal recessive has been implicated in the inheritance of adrenal virilization. The action of this gene causes the secretion of abnormal amounts of androgen from the fetal or postnatal adrenal. The expressivity of the gene is variable both with respect to the quantity of androgen secreted and the age when the abnormal secretory activity begins. In males it produces the syndrome of macrogenitosomia praecox, and in females it results in pseudohermaphroditism if the abnormality commences prenatally and in secondary virilization if it commences postnatally. The factors which modify the expressivity of the gene are not known.

Autosomal factors apparently influence the characteristics of the sexual behavior pattern in still other ways. The vigor or level of sexual behavior characteristic of the individual is closely regulated by genetic mechanisms, and the frequency and duration measures commonly used in laboratory studies are highly heritable. For females, the intensity of estrus has been shown to vary greatly with the breed in cattle (Rottensten and Touchberry, 1957; Lagerlöf, 1951), and with the genetic strain among guinea pigs (Goy and Young, 1957). Similar strain differences and genetical influences have been shown for the sexual behavior of male mice (McGill, 1962), rats (Whalen, 1961), guinea pigs (Valenstein *et al.*, 1954), and bulls (Bane, 1954). Moreover, for both males and females, when studies of the inheritance of the different behavioral components have been carried out, independence of the separate behaviors has been demonstrated (Jakway, 1959; Goy and Jakway, 1959, 1962; McGill and Blight, 1963). That is, sexual behavior is not inherited as a unitary trait. In the male, mounting, intromission, and ejaculation all show separate modes of inheritance. Inheritance of the behavior has been shown to display phenotypic dominance, heterosis, or additivity, depending on the particular component studied, and similar relations have been demonstrated for the female.

When the sexual behavior pattern is considered in its entirety, the complex nature of the genetic control and its balance with the endocrine factors provide for the production of a vast array of types. In the set of autosomal influences studied, certain genes seem to fix the upper limits for independent male and female components, whereas other genes determine whether the behavior displayed will be predominantly masculine or feminine in character by regulating the secretion of androgen on the one hand and the responsiveness of the substrate on the other.

The limitation of expression of male behavioral genes to the genotypic male, and of female behavioral genes primarily to the genotypic female, has to be interpreted as our knowledge of the gene-hormone relationship develops. The sex-limited character of the behavioral traits, however, seems clearly related to the presence or absence of androgens during the period for organization of sexual behavior, and the evidence from both genetic and endocrinological studies of the problem provide consistent support for such an hypothesis.

V. Summary

Sexual behavior is conceptualized as a complex of responses directly associated with genital stimulation and copulation regardless of its role in facilitating the union of gametes or preservation of the species.

Historically there has been considerable debate as to whether or not sexual behavior is learned or innate, whether or not it is an instinct or a drive. Progress in the understanding of sexual behavior has been made to the extent that researchers have concerned themselves with studying the variables controlling the behavior rather than engaging in debate as to its "proper" classification.

The specific nature of the relationship of the gonadal hormones to sexual behavior has been in dispute for many years. Although a thorough understanding of the many complex interactions remains to be achieved, considerable advance has been made. A direct relationship has been demonstrated between the action of gonadal hormones and the display of sexual behavior in all adult laboratory and domestic animals studied. However, the role of these hormones in activating sexual behavior in primates, including man, has not yet been delineated. It is widely assumed that the higher the order of mammal, the less the dependence on gonadal hormones for the activation of sexual behavior, but experimental evidence supporting this conclusion is meager.

The role of gonadal hormones in the adult has been designated as one of activation in that they activate previously established patterns of sexual behavior. In the morphologically and psychosexually undifferentiated mammal, however, a different function of the male hormone (androgen) has been demonstrated. During this early developmental period, pre- or postnatal depending upon the species, the male hormone organizes the tissues, presumably neural, that mediate the display of sexual behavior in the adult. Evidence supporting the concept of a dual function of the male hormone has been obtained in studies carried out on the rat and guinea pig and is currently being tested in the rhesus monkey. Present evidence obtained from research on the monkey supports the hypothesis and suggests that the organizational function extends to aspects of behavior not generally considered to be sexual in nature.

Fundamental in establishing the form and extent of sexual behavior displayed by the individual are the actions of the genes and chromosomes. The pattern of sexual behavior displayed, including the presence or absence of specific components of sexual behavior or the vigor of display, has been shown to be heritable. Morphological abnormalities of the reproductive system in man have been associated with chromosomal abnormalities, but disorders of sexual behavior have not. The type of behavior associated with abnormal sex chromosomes depends more on the functional characteristics of the developing gonad than on the chromosomal factors per se.

References

Baker, L. N., Ulberg, L. C., Grummer, R. H., and Casida, L. E. (1954). Inhibition of heat by progesterone and its effects on subsequent fertility in gilts. *J. Animal Sci.* **13**, 648–657.

Ball, J. (1939). Male and female mating behavior in prepuberally castrated male rats receiving estrogens. *J. Comp. Psychol.* **28**, 273–283.

Ball, J. (1941). Effect of progesterone upon sexual excitability in the female monkey. *Psychol. Bull.* **38**, 533.

Bane, A. (1954). Studies on monozygous cattle twins. XV. Sexual functions of bulls in relation to heredity, rearing intensity and somatic conditions. *Acta Agr. Scand.* **4**, 95–208.

Barraclough, C. A., and Gorski, R. A. (1962). Studies on mating behaviour in the androgen-sterilized female rat in relation to the hypothalamic regulation of sexual behaviour. *J. Endocrinol.* **25**, 175–182.

Beach, F. A. (1941). Female mating behavior shown by male rats after administration of testosterone propionate. *Endocrinology* **29**, 409–412.

Beach, F. A. (1945a). Bisexual mating behavior in the male rat: effects of castration and hormone administration. *Physiol. Zool.* **18**, 390–402.

Beach, F. A. (1945b). Hormonal induction of mating responses in a rat with congenital absence of gonadal tissue. *Anat. Record* **92**, 289–292.

Beach, F. A. (1951). Instinctive behavior reproductive activities. *In* "Handbook of Experimental Psychology" (S. S. Stevens, ed.), pp. 387–434. Wiley, New York.

Beach, F. A. (1955). The descent of instinct. *Psychol. Rev.* **62**, 401–410.

Beach, F. A., and Jordan, L. (1956). Sexual exhaustion and recovery in the male rat. *Quart. J. Exptl. Psychol.* **8**, 121–133.

Beach, F. A., and Rabedeau, R. G. (1959). Sexual exhaustion and recovery in the male hamster. *J. Comp. Physiol. Psychol.* **52**, 56–61.

Beatty, R. A. (1964). Chromosome deviations and sex in vertebrates. *In* "Intersexuality in Vertebrates Including Man" (C. N. Armstrong and A. J. Marshall, eds.), pp. 17–143. Academic Press, New York.

Burns, R. K. (1961). Role of hormones in the differentiation of sex. *In* "Sex and Internal Secretions" (W. C. Young, ed.), 3rd ed., pp. 76–158, Williams & Wilkins, Baltimore, Maryland.

Champlin, A. K., Blight, W. C., and McGill, T. E. (1963). The effects of varying levels of testosterone on the sexual behaviour of the male mouse. *Animal Behaviour* **11**, 244–245.

David, R. R., Wiener, M. Ross, L., and Landau, R. L. (1965). Steroid metabolism in the syndrome of testicular feminization. *J. Clin. Endocrinol. Metab.* **25**, 1393–1402.

Dempsey, E. W., Hertz, R., and Young, W. C. (1936). The experimental induction of oestrus (sexual receptivity) in the normal and ovariectomized guinea pig. *Am. J. Physiol.* **116**, 201–209.

Feder, H. H. (1965). Specificity of estradiol and testosterone preparations in the differentiation of sexual function in rats. Unpublished doctoral dissertation. University of Oregon Medical School, Portland, Oregon.

Feder, H. H., and Whalen, R. E. (1965). Feminine behavior in neonatally castrated and estrogen treated male rats. *Science* **147**, 306–307.

French, F. S., Blaggett, B., Van Wyk, J. J., Talbert, L. M., Hubbard, W. R., Johnston, F. R., and Weaver, R. P. (1965). Testicular feminization: clinical, morphological and biochemical studies. *J. Clin. Endocrinol. Metab.* **25**, 661–677.

Gerall, A. A. (1958). Effect of interruption of copulation on male guinea pig sexual behavior. *Psychol. Rept.* **4**, 215–221.

Gowen, J. W. (1961). Genetic and cytologic foundations for sex. *In* "Sex and Internal Secretions" (W. C. Young, ed.), 3rd ed., pp. 3–75. Williams & Wilkins, Baltimore, Maryland.

Goy, R. W. (1964). Reproductive behavior in mammals. *In* "Human Reproducti and Sexual Behavior" (C. W. Lloyd, ed.), pp. 409–441. Lea & Febiger, Philadelphia, Pennsylvania.

Goy, R. W., and Jakway, J.(1959). The inheritance of patterns of sexual behaviour in female guinea pigs. *Animal Behaviour* **7**, 142–149.

Goy, R. W., and Jakway, J. (1962). Role of inheritance in determination of sexı behavior patterns. *In* "Roots of Behavior" (E. L. Bliss, ed.), pp. 96–112. Harper, New York.

Goy, R. W., and Young, W. C. (1957). Strain differences in the behavioural responses of female guinea-pigs to alpha-oestradiol benzoate and progesteron *Behaviour* **10**, 340–354.

Goy, R. W., Bridson, W. E., and Young, W. C. (1964). Period of maximal susceptibility of the prenatal female guinea pig to masculinizing actions of testosterone propionate. *J. Comp. Physiol. Psychol.* **57**, 166–174.

Goy, R. W., Phoenix, C. H., and Young, W. C. (1966). Inhibiting action of the corpus luteum on the hormonal induction of estrous behavior in the guinea pig. *Gen. Comp. Endocrinol.* **6**, 267–275.

Grady, K. L., and Phoenix, C. H. (1963). Hormonal determinants of mating behavior; the display of feminine behavior by adult male rats castrated neonatally. *Am. Zoologist* **3**, 482–483.

Grady, K. L., Phoenix, C. H., and Young, W. C. (1965). Role of the developing rat testis in differentiation of the neural tissues mediating mating behavior. *J. Comp. Physiol. Psychol.* **59**, 176–182.

Grunt, J. A., and Young, W. C. (1953). Consistency of sexual behavior patterns in individual male guinea pigs following castration and androgen therapy. *J. Comp. Physiol. Psychol.* **46**, 138–144.

Harris, G. W. (1964). Sex hormones, brain development and brain function. *Endocrinology* **75**, 627–648.

Harris, G. W., and Levine, S. (1962). Sexual differentiation of the brain and its experimental control. *J. Physiol.* (*London*) **163**, 42–43.

Jakway, J. (1959). Inheritance of patterns of mating behaviour in the male guinea pig. *Animal Behaviour* **7**, 150–162.

Lagerlöf, N. (1951). Hereditary forms of sterility in Swedish cattle breeds. *Fertility Sterility* **2**, 230–242.

Larsson, K. (1958). "Conditioning and Sexual Behavior in the Male Albino Rat," p. 269. Almquist & Wiksell, Stockholm.

Levine, S., and Mullins, R., Jr. (1964). Estrogen administered neonatally affects adult sexual behavior in male and female rats. *Science* **144**, 185–187.

McGill, T. E. (1962). Sexual behavior in three inbred strains of mice. *Behaviour* **19**, 341–350.

McGill, T. E., and Blight, W. C. (1963). The sexual behaviour of hybrid male mice compared with the sexual behaviour of males of the inbred parent strains. *Animal Behaviour* **11**, 480–483.

Marshall, F. H. A., and Hammond, J., Jr. (1945). Experimental control by hormone action of the oestrous cycle in the ferret. *J. Endocrinol.* **4**, 159–168.

Melampy, R. M., Emerson, M. A., Rakes, J. M., Hanka, L. J., and Eness, P. G. (1957). The effect of progesterone on the estrous response of estrogen-conditioned ovariectomized cows. *J. Animal Sci.* **16**, 967–975.

Morgan, C. T. (1943). "Physiological Psychology," 1st ed., p. 396. McGraw-Hill, New York.

Morris, J. M., and Mahesh, V. B. (1963). Further observations on the syndrome, "testicular feminization." *Am. J. Obstet. Gynecol.* **87**, 731–745.

Pfeiffer, C. A. (1936). Sexual differences of the hypophyses and their determination by the gonads. *Am. J. Anat.* **58**, 195–226.

Phoenix, C. H., Goy, R. W., Gerall, A. A., and Young, W. C. (1959). Organizing action of prenatally administered testosterone propionate on the tissues mediating mating behavior in the female guinea pig. *Endocrinology* **65**, 369–382.

Rottensten, K., and Touchberry, R. W. (1957). Observations on the degree of expression of estrus in cattle. *J. Dairy Sci.* **40**, 1457–1465.

Sawyer, C. H., and Everett, J. W. (1959). Stimulatory and inhibitory effects of progesterone on the release of pituitary ovulating hormone in the rabbit. *Endocrinology* **65**, 644–651.

Sohval, A. R. (1963). Chromosomes and sex chromatin in normal and anomalous sexual development. *Physiol. Rev.* **43**, 306–356.

Stone, C. P. (1927). The retention of copulatory ability in male rats following castration. *J. Comp. Psychol.* **7**, 369–387.

Stone, C. P. (1939). Sex drive. *In* "Sex and Internal Secretions" (E. Allen *et al.*, eds.), 2nd ed., pp. 1213–1262. Williams & Wilkins, Baltimore, Maryland.

Valenstein, E. S., Riss, W., and Young, W. C. (1954). Sex drive in genetically heterogeneous and highly inbred strains of male guinea pigs. *J. Comp. Physiol. Psychol.* **47**, 162–165.

van Wagenen, G., and Hamilton, J. B. (1943). The experimental production of pseudohermaphroditism in the monkey. *In* "Essays in Biology, in Honor of Herbert M. Evans," pp. 581–607. Univ. of California Press, Berkeley, California.

Wells, L. J., and van Wagenen, G. (1954). Androgen-induced female pseudohermaphroditism in the monkey (*Macaca mulatta*); anatomy of reproductive organs. *Carnegie Inst. Wash., Contribs. Embryol.* **35**, 93–106.

Whalen, R. E. (1961). Strain differences in sexual behavior of the male rat. *Behaviour* **18**, 199–204.

Whalen, R. E. (1963). Sexual behavior of cats. *Behaviour* **20**, 321–342.

Whalen, R. E. (1964). Hormone-induced changes in the organization of sexual behavior in the male rat. *J. Comp. Physiol. Psychol.* **57**, 175–182.

Whalen, R. E., and Nadler, R. D. (1963). Suppression of the development of female mating behavior by estrogen administered in infancy. *Science* **141**, 273–274.

Wilkins, L. (1957). "The Diagnosis and Treatment of Endocrine Disorders in Childhood and Adolescence," 2nd ed., p. 276. Thomas, Springfield, Illinois.

Wilson, J. G., Young, W. C., and Hamilton, J. B. (1940). A technic suppressing development of reproductive function and sensitivity to estrogen in the female rat. *Yale J. Biol. Med.* **13**, 189–202.

Wilson, J. G., Hamilton, J. B., and Young, W. C. (1941). Influence of age and presence of the ovaries on reproductive function in rats injected with androgens. *Endocrinology* **29**, 784–789.

Young, W. C. (1961). The hormones and mating behavior. *In* "Sex and Internal Secretions" (W. C. Young, ed.), 3rd ed., pp. 1173–1239. Williams & Wilkins, Baltimore, Maryland.

Young, W. C., and Grunt, J. A. (1951). The pattern and measurement of sexual behavior in the male guinea pig. *J. Comp. Physiol. Psychol.* **44**, 492–500.

Young, W. C., and Orbison, W. D. (1944). Changes in selected features of behavior in parts of oppositely sexed chimpanzees during the sexual cycle and after ovariectomy. *J. Comp. Psychol.* **37**, 593–629.

Young, W. C., Goy, R. W., and Phoenix, C. H. (1964). Hormones and sexual behavior. *Science* **143**, 212–218.

CHAPTER 22

Sexual Behavior: Hormonal Control

ROBERT D. LISK[1]

I. Introduction

All behavior ultimately depends upon interactions occurring in the central nervous system. In adult vertebrates, with the possible exception of man (Money, 1961), the sex hormones are necessary for the elicitation of the complete mating response. This implies that neuronal systems exist which can be influenced by specific hormones, and this may lead to an overt behavioral act.

The material presented in this chapter will be limited to the evidence for the participation of specific neural elements in sexual behavior. Due to the paucity of investigations concerning the other classes of vertebrates, discussion is limited almost entirely to the mammals. Emphasis is on the adult animal, although some reference will be made to the influence of hormones on behavior, when given to the neonate animal; for further discussion of this subject, see Chapter 19.

The specific pattern shown by the female mammal at mating usually involves a postural adjustment of the perianal region, which results in a presentation of this region to the male in such a manner that he has access to the vaginal canal. This postural response, generally known as lordosis, has repeatedly been demonstrated to be under hormonal con-

[1] The work reported from author's laboratory was supported by the National Science Foundation through grants G-14580 and GB-914.

trol, ovariectomy resulting in its precipitous loss. There are other behavioral reactions shown by the female which may conveniently be termed "enticement reactions." They are useful in providing cues to the male concerning the female's presence as well as her intentions. Very little work has been done on the neural correlates of these responses; however, a general discussion of "enticement reactions" will be found in Chapter 21.

The male mammal has to proceed through a more complicated series of reactions to achieve a complete mating response. Here there are necessary elements of recognition, orientation, mounting, pelvic thrusting, intromission, and ejaculation. Different levels of hormone stimulation are necessary for expression of the various parts of this sequence. Following castration there is no precipitous loss of this behavior sequence but a gradual decline in function with the most specific, consumatory responses of ejaculation and intromission disappearing first. Some of the more general components of this behavior pattern may never disappear.

Although it is recognized that the genetic makeup of the individual and the environment in which the animal was raised can profoundly influence the behavior expressed, how such factors influence the central nervous system is as yet unknown. A general discussion of these factors can be found in Young (1957).

Discussion has thus been limited to the role of the central nervous system in activation of sexual behavior patterns in adult mammals. Unless otherwise stated, it is assumed that no experimental manipulations have been performed before an animal reached sexual maturity and that normal environmental and sociological conditions prevailed during the maturation process.

Since the components of the pattern for sexual behavior are radically different for male and female, it seems apparent that various regions of the central nervous system will be involved to a different extent in the two sexes. Thus, it seems best, when discussing the various areas of the central nervous system, to keep the data for the male and female separate. At various points, summaries are made, which attempt to compare hormone-sensitive loci and the probable pathways and regions of the central nervous system involved in the expression of sexual behavior for both sexes.

There are available several recent excellent reviews of the literature on reproductive behavior. Coverage is provided in comprehensive manner both for the general aspects and more specific neuronal involvement in reproductive behavior in the vertebrates (Young, 1961; Young *et al.*, 1964; Sawyer, 1960).

II. The Nervous System: Role in Sexual Behavior

A. Neural Mechanisms as Revealed by Lesion Experiments

1. *Peripheral and Spinal Mechanisms*

a. The Male. Stimulation of sensory nerve endings or spinal reflexes appear relatively unimportant to the maintenance of sexual behavior patterns in the male. Beach (1952) and his colleagues have shown that removal of the penile bone in the rat, either by surgery or as the result of castration on the day of birth, did not interfere with attempts to copulate. Bard (1940) and his co-workers have shown that following removal of the lower end of the spinal cord, sexual aggressiveness remains undiminished in the male cat. Spinal male animals, including the dog and man, maintain the capacity for penile erection and ejaculation on manipulation of the genitalia (Fulton, 1939).

b. The Female. Sex behavior in the lower mammals does not appear to depend on afferent impulses from the genitalia. Brooks (1937) showed that anesthetizing or deafferentiation of the vagina did not prevent rabbits from mating. In the rat, Ball (1934) showed that surgical removal of the vagina and uterus was compatible with mating. Bard (1939) found that female cats still show sex behavior after removal of the sacral region of the spinal cord or abdominal sympathetics.

2. *Neocortical and Rhinencephalic Mechanisms*

a. The Male. The cortex appears to have an essential role for the initiation of mating behavior in most male mammals. Beach (1940) showed that, while removal of 20% of the cortex had no effect on the number of rats copulating, no male mated if 60% of its cortex had been removed. In a more recent study of the male cat, Goldstein (1957) reported that large cortical lesions do not result in a loss of interest in the female but rather appear to exert their effects by interference with the motor patterns necessary for copulation.

The results of this work led to the suggestion by Beach and his colleagues that in the rodent the main action of the cerebral cortex is to facilitate the arousal of behavior, whereas in the more complex brain of the cat the cortex functions in the specific patterns of coordination required for the execution of mating.

The problem has recently been reinvestigated for the rat (Larsson, 1962a). Bilateral ablations by suction were made in either the dorsolateral or the medial cortex. Following dorsolateral lesions (Fig. 1A), four animals showed no sexual behavior and sixteen animals showed less sexual activity than previously. Within this group there was no significant correlation between extent of cortical injury and the decrease in ejaculation frequencies. Although no abnormalities of testis or interstitial tissue occurred, hormone replacement therapy was tried. This resulted in the reappearance of ejaculatory patterns in one out of four inactive

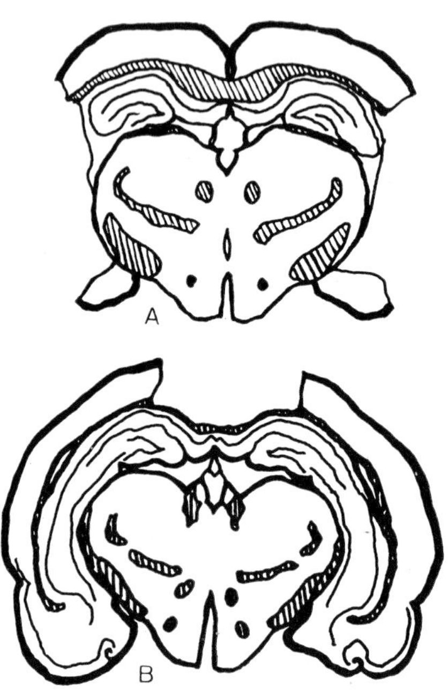

FIG. 1. Cross-section of rat brain indicating the extent of dorsolateral (A) and medial cortical (B) lesions made in the male. Severe depression of sexual behavior resulted only from the dorsolateral lesions. (From Larsson, 1962a.)

animals. Lesions of the medial cerebral cortex did not eliminate sex behavior in any of the animals (Fig. 1B). Two animals, however, showed a failure to ejaculate; this was restored by 10 mg testosterone treatment in one animal, but the other did not respond.

Thus, following dorsolateral lesions in which only 7–21% of the surface was destroyed, sexual behavior was depressed in all animals and completely eliminated in three. Following destruction of 7–17% of the medial cortex, sex behavior was not eliminated. These experiments do not support the earlier studies for the rat but suggest that relatively small lesions can profoundly affect behavior, depending upon the locus involved.

Further extension of this work (Larsson, 1964) shows that lesions in the frontal lobes permanently eliminated sex activity in eight of twenty rats. The absence of activity resulted from removal of 20% or more of the frontal lobes, removal of 13% or less having no effect on sexual activity. Removal of up to 54% of the posterior part of the cerebral hemispheres did not eliminate sex behavior in any animal. Some of these animals showed disturbances in sensory-motor adjustment and thus had some difficulties in locating the female and maintaining bodily contact with her.

A summary of these findings indicates that extensive destruction of the occipital cortex, parietal, or temporal cortex does not interfere with normal mating in the male rat but damage to the frontal lobes results in severe damage. A diagram of these lesions (Fig. 2) indicates that those

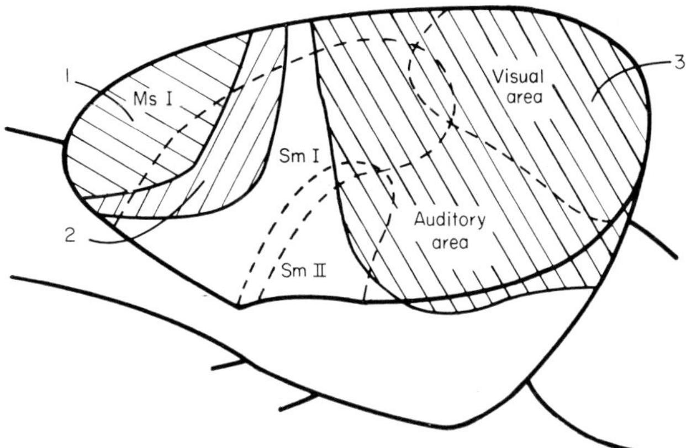

Fig. 2. Diagrammatic outline of rat cortex showing the location of the somatic sensory areas I (Sm I) and II (Sm II), and the precentral motor area (Ms I) plus the gross localizations of the visual and auditory regions. The area labeled 1 indicates the limits of the smallest lesions which produced sexual failure. Areas 1 and 2 indicate the largest rostral area destroyed without a resultant depression in sexual behavior. Area 3 represents the largest posterior portion of cortex destroyed. No posterior lesions resulted in complete elimination of sexual behavior. (Based on Larsson, 1964.)

lesions effective for elimination of sexual behavior included the main part of the motor-sensory area and parts of the overlapping sensory-motor area. These results are thus in line with the studies on the cat by Beach and his collaborators (Beach *et al.*, 1955, 1956; Zitrin *et al.*, 1956) showing the relative importance of frontal areas for mating behavior.

The male rabbit does not lose interest in the female if either the neocortex or the olfactory bulbs are removed (Brooks, 1937; Stone,

1939). However, the combined removal of the olfactory bulbs and the cortical regions for somesthetic, auditory, and visual sensations results in prompt disappearance of sexual behavior.

The rhinencephalon appears to influence sexual activity in the male. Hypersexuality in the male monkey was reported by Klüver and Bucy (1937) following removal of the temporal lobes. A series of studies by Schreiner and Kling (1953, 1954, 1956) extended these observations to include the male cat, agouti, and lynx as well as the monkey. Hypersexuality resulted from the removal of the amygdala along with the overlying piriform cortex. The reaction was dependent upon the presence of male sex hormone.

Green *et al.* (1957) investigated hypersexuality in the cat following small electrolytic or surgical lesions. They were unable to produce hypersexuality by destruction of the amygdala alone, but small lesions in the piriform cortex just medial to the rhinal fissure and situated beneath the basolateral amygdaloid nucleus induced hypersexual changes in the absence of damage to the amygdala. These animals would mate in a strange territory, a most unusual feature for the cat. The hypersexual behavior was again found to be under hormonal control, both androgen and estrogen restoring this behavior following castration.

b. The Female. The cerebral cortex appears to be dispensable as far as sex behavior is concerned in the female mammal. In the cat, Bard (1939) found that removal of all the neocortex, most of the rhinencephalon, and a large part of the striatum and thalamus was still compatible with estrous behavior in response to estrogen. The female rabbit will still mate following removal of the neocortex and rhinencephalic cortex plus the receptors for olfaction, vision, and audition (Brooks, 1937). Davis in 1939 showed that the female rat would continue to cycle, mate, become pregnant, and deliver young following removal of the neocortex. This result has been confirmed many times. It is interesting to note that mounting activity in the male ceases following decortication, the pattern of behavior similarly being lost by the female following this operation (Beach, 1943).

Larsson (1962b) reinvestigated the role of the cortex in estrous behavior in the female rat using the technique of spreading cortical depression by application of 25% KCl solution to various cortical areas. The results indicate a temporary inhibition of ear wiggling, lordosis, and acceptance of the male, lasting approximately 1 hour in 50% of the animals. Hopping responses and pursuit of the male were entirely eliminated. Thus, the cortex of the female is functional in spontaneous incentive regarding mating behavior.

De Groot (1962) noted that rats with lesions which produced complete destruction of the habenular nuclei or which had large bilateral lesions in the amygdala or stria terminalis showed mating behavior during diestrous or while pregnant. Sawyer (1959) found in experiments with the rabbit that there was a tendency toward the state of hypersexualism following section of the fornix plus removal of the olfactory bulbs (Fig. 3). These rabbits showed repeated mounting and would

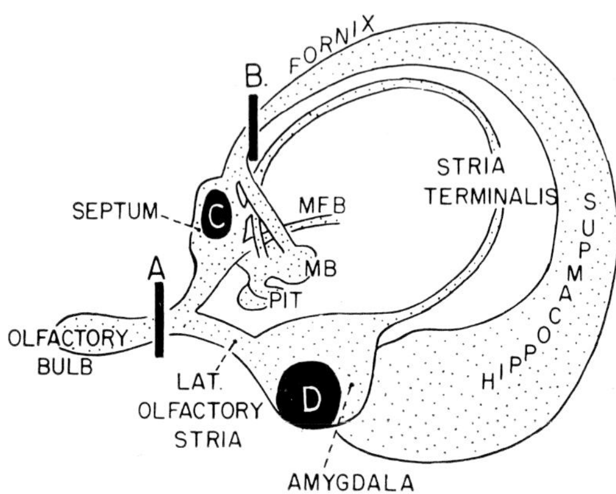

FIG. 3. Diagram of rhinencephalon of the rabbit. Removal of olfactory bulbs (A) plus transection of the fornix (B) in females resulted in a tendency to hypersexualism. MB, mammillary body; MFB, medial forebrain bundle; PIT, pituitary. (From Sawyer, 1959.)

accept the male at any time. Gestaut (1952) has described sexual activity in female cats following rhinencephalic lesions, at the same time that the reproductive tract was anestrous.

3. *Diencephalic and Hypothalamic Mechanisms*

a. The Male. Brookhart and Dey in 1941 showed that lesions in the anterior hypothalamus could result in a decrease in sex behavior or its permanent and irreversible elimination in the male guinea pig. These animals did not show any changes of the testes, either in spermatogenesis, or interstitial cells. An extensive series of investigations by the Soulairacs summarized in 1963 by M. L. Soulairac indicate that bilateral lesions in the medial preoptic region in the male rat result in a fairly rapid progressive disappearance of sexual behavior. By about 10 to 15 days following lesioning, the male shows no interest in an estrous female. No change in sex behavior resulted from a unilateral lesion. When bilateral lesions were placed in the posterior hypothalamus, Soulairac found that bilateral destruction of the lateral mammillary nuclei resulted in complete disappearance of the motor patterns necessary for copulation within 3–5 days. After this, the males maintained a state of hyperactivity in the presence of the estrous female, but it was nondirected activity. In contrast to the anterior lesions which did not result in any change in gonads or hypophysis, many of the animals bearing the posterior lesions showed atrophic changes in spermatogenesis, the interstitial tissue, and the deferent canal. Lesions which destroyed the median eminence also resulted in the disappearance of sexual behavior. In this case, the testes atrophied and showed aspermia. The pituitary was similarly atrophic and often disorganized.

The Soulairacs suggest their lesion experiments show the indispensability of both the median preoptic region and the lateral mammillary region for sexual behavior in male rats. Normally these two regions function synergistically, with the anterior region acting as a motivational center, receiving impulses from the neocortex and rhinencephalon. Probably information from many sources is integrated here and transmitted to the posterior region which intervenes directly in the motor patterns necessary for copulation. The posterior regions would also appear to have elements for regulating the gonads and genital organs.

A recent investigation by Larsson and Heimer (1964) showed that in sixteen rats with small medial preoptic lesions, two were normal, six had a marked depression of sexual behavior, and eight showed no sexual activity. Histological examinations showed normal testes. Following castration, testosterone replacement therapy failed to restore sexual activity in five of the eight animals. Following placement of large lateral preoptic lesions in eleven animals, nine remained sexually normal. The areas of the brain involved in these lesions are shown in Figs. 4A and B. Destruction of the septal region resulted in aggressive behavior, but no changes were noted in sexual behavior. K. Larsson and L. Heimer feel (personal communication, 1964) that neural structures in the medial preoptic region are essential to mating since this is a neuronal system sensitive to hormones. This would explain why sexual behavior was permanently abolished in some cases whereas in others enough neurons remained intact so that an increase in the amount of hormone available resulted in complete copulatory responses once again. Beach (1964) has reported that Rogers, while working in his laboratory, noted that injury to the posterior ventromedial tuberal region greatly reduced the occurrences of mating responses in the male rat. Androgen was without effect in restoring the behavior. On the other hand, Heimer and Larsson (1964) found that complete destruction of the mammillary bodies did

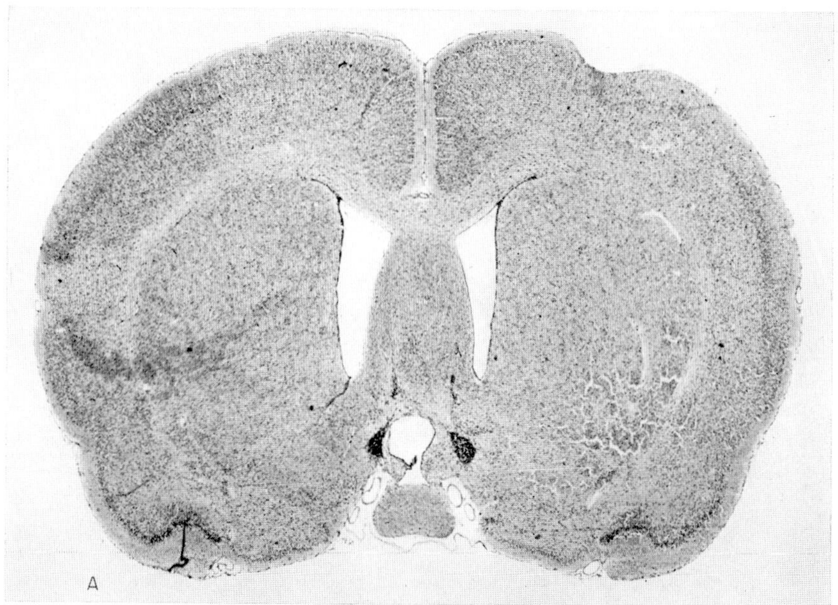

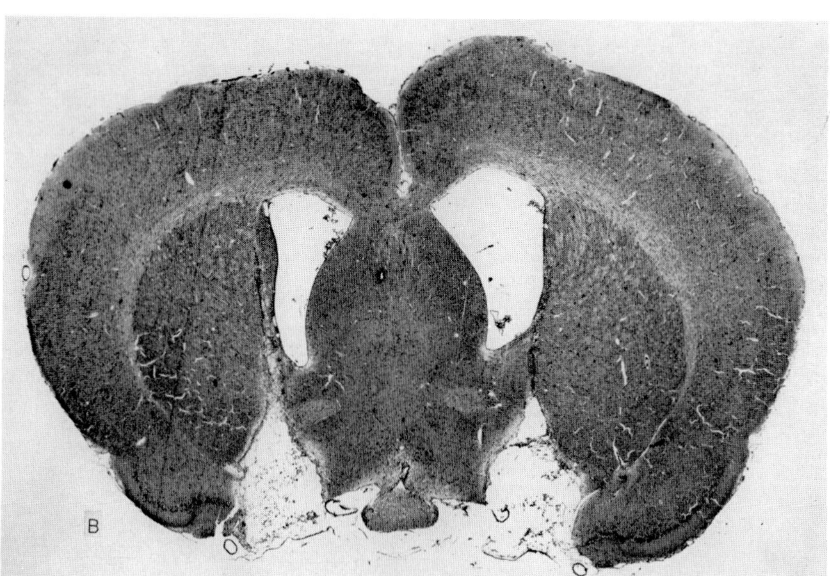

FIG. 4. Transverse sections of rat brains. A: Small bilateral lesions in the medial preoptic region of the male rat brain which resulted in complete elimination of sexual behavior. B: Extensive bilateral lesions of the lateral preoptic area which did not disturb mating behavior. (From Larsson and Heimer, 1964.)

not result in any depletion in sex activity; if anything, a slight enhancement may have occurred.

Phoenix (1961), working with the male guinea pig, reported that severe deficits in sex behavior resulted after lesions in the ventromedial hypothalamus. Damage to the periventricular fiber system appeared important for this result, with partial destruction also involving the posterior part of the arcuate nucleus, the ventromedial nucleus, and extending to part of the anterior and posterior median eminence.

Recent investigations in the author's laboratory of sexual activity in the male rat have been aimed at determining the importance of basal midline structures extending from the preoptic area to the beginning of the arcuate nucleus. Since none of this work has been published elsewhere and the testing procedure is different from that employed by other investigators, the experiments are reported in considerable detail.

All the rats used in this investigation were sexually experienced and had sired at least one litter. In all cases a single midline lesion was made with a platinum electrode insulated except for 0.5 mm at the tip. Current was anodal at 1.0 mA (milliamperes) for 15 seconds. Following a 1-week recovery period after lesioning, each male was placed with a behaviorally estrous female, made so by placement of a blob of estradiol in the anterior part of the arcuate nucleus. This resulted in a very reactive animal behaviorally, and the condition of this preparation remained unimpaired for months. Papers under the cages were examined daily, and the number of copulation plugs were counted. In this manner the total sexual activity culminating in ejaculation was calculated for a 4-week period.

Table I presents a comprehensive summary of the observations. It shows that four of five experienced rats without lesions copulate on over 50% of the nights when a suitable partner is available. An analysis of the data by 2-week intervals indicates the amount of copulation remained remarkably constant during equal time intervals.

Lesions in the basal medial structures, especially in the suprachiasmatic region, resulted in a severe depletion of sex activity so that ejaculation never occurred or did so on less than 25% of the nights. If the suprachiasmatic region was not completely destroyed, or the lesion was slightly more dorsal, some decrease in sex activity occurred, but copulation may have resulted on as many as 50% of the nights. Still more dorsal lesions did not interfere with sex behavior. The lesions are summarized in Fig. 5, which shows the largest areas common to all lesions resulting in severe, moderate, or no depletion of sexual behavior. Subtracting those areas in common to the various groups, one notes that midline structures in and around the suprachiasmatic nucleus appear to be highly important to sexual behavior. This extends the region involved in the complete execution of mating behavior from the medial preoptic area as shown by Larsson and Heimer (1964) to include the basal midline structures in the anterior hypothalamus. The general outline of the area in which lesions appear to suppress sexual behavior in the male rat thus conforms to the area noted for the female rat in which hormone implant facilitated lordosis (Lisk, 1962a).

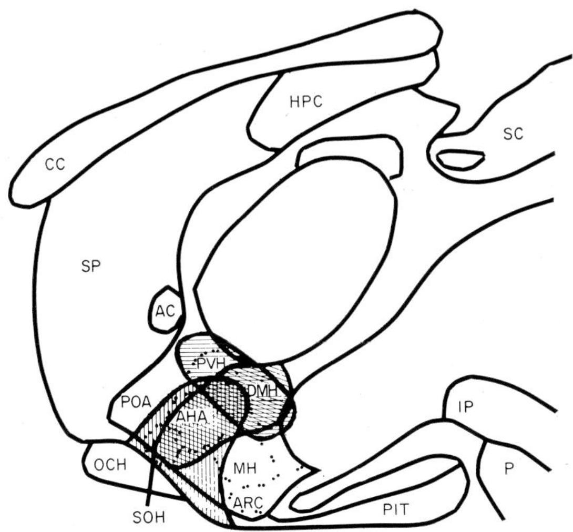

FIG. 5. Sagittal diagram of rat diencephalon showing superimposed the largest areas common to all lesions resulting in severe (vertical lines), moderate (slanted lines), and no (horizontal lines) depletion of sexual behavior. AC, anterior commissure; AHA, anterior hypothalamic area; ARC, arcuate nucleus; CC, corpus callosum; DMH, dorsomedian nucleus; HPC, hippocampal commissure; IP, interpeduncular nucleus; MH, ventromedial nucleus; OCH, optic chiasm; P, pons; PIT, pituitary; POA—preoptic area; PVH—paraventricular nucleus; SC, superior colliculus; SP, septum pellucidum; SOH, suprachiasmatic nucleus.

Analysis of the data for the experimental animals by 2-week intervals again showed a marked constancy for the total ejaculatory behavior in many animals over the 4-week period. However, eleven animals showed a marked increase in the percentage of days on which copulation occurred during the final 2 weeks. Examination of the brains indicates that most of these animals had lesions which were mostly confined to one side of the midline. It appears that a gradual accommodation occurred so that the remaining tissue could eventually carry out the ejaculatory function with little or no change from the preoperative level.

No change in gonad or pituitary weight resulted from these lesions. However, a significant increase in the weight of the seminal vesicles plus

TABLE I

PERCENTAGE OF DAYS ON WHICH COPULATION PLUGS WERE FOUND WHEN MALES REMAINED WITH STIMULUS FEMALES DURING A 4-WEEK PERIOD, ANALYZED IN SUCCESSIVE 2–WEEK INTERVALS

Animal	First 2 weeks after lesion		Second 2 weeks after lesion		Change in percentage of days of copulation from first to second period[a]	Location of lesions
	Percentage of days of copulation	Number of Copulation plugs	Percentage of days of copulation	Number of copulation plugs		
Control						
1	36 (5/14)	8	75 (9/12)	15	+	No lesions made
2	85 (12/14)	28	83 (10/12)	20	0	No lesions made
3	78 (11/14)	25	83 (10/12)	23	0	No lesions made
4	21 (3/14)	4	25 (3/12)	10	0	No lesions made
5	64 (9/14)	23	58 (7/12)	21	0	No lesions made
Experimental						
1	50 (7/14)	9	50 (7/14)[b]	8	0	Preoptic + part of suprachiasmatic
2	29 (4/14)	9	43 (6/14)[b]	9	+	Anterior hypothalamus + filiform + dorsomedian
3	14 (2/14)	2	0 (0/14)[c]	0	—	Suprachiasmatic complete destruction
4	21 (3/14)	3[d]	21 (3/14)[c]	5[d]	0	Suprachiasmatic + surrounding tissue destroyed
5	7 (1/14)	1	7 (1/14)[c]	1[d]	0	Suprachiasmatic + filiform + dorsomedian all partial
6	29 (4/14)	8	29 (4/14)[b]	5	0	Suprachiasmatic + filiform partial destruction
7	50 (7/14)	14	54 (8/14)	15	0	Filiform + reunions partial destruction
8	14 (2/14)	3	50 (7/14)[b]	14	+	Suprachiasmatic + filiform one side only
9	54 (8/14)	15	43 (6/14)[b]	9	—	Small lesion anterior hypothalamus
10	29 (4/14)	10	29 (4/14)[b]	10	0	Suprachiasmatic + filiform + dorsomedian all partial

11	54 (8/14)	16	77 (10/13)	16	+	Filiform + dorsomedian complete destruction
12	50 (7/14)	15	69 (9/13)	15	+	Suprachiasmatic + filiform partial + one side only
13	50 (7/14)	14	85 (11/13)	29	+	Filiform one side only
14	7 (1/14)	5	29 (4/14)[b]	5	+	Small lesion anterior hypothalamus
15	54 (8/14)	15 + 1[d]	69 (9/13)	19	+	No lesion found
16	50 (7/14)	18	77 (10/13)	22	+	Filiform + reunions partial
17	14 (2/14)	6	36 (5/14)[c]	2 + 5[c]	+	Suprachiasmatic all of posterior part
18	43 (6/14)	9	64 (8/14)	14	+	Filiform one side only
19	36 (5/14)	8	7 (1/14)[c]	1	−	Small midline lesion at level of dorsomedian
20	14 (2/14)	6	36 (5/14)[c]	8	+	Suprachiasmatic slight—dorsomedial + filiform almost complete destruction
21	0 (0/14)	0	0 (0/14)[c]	0	0	Midline lesion from filiform to dorsomedian
22	0 (0/14)	0	0 (0/14)[c]	0	0	Suprachiasmatic + anterior arcuate destroyed

[a] 0, no change; +, increase in percentage; —, decrease in percentage.
[b] Moderate depression of sexual behavior; mating occurred 26–50% of days together.
[c] Severe depression of sexual behavior; mating occurred 0–25% of days together.
[d] Small dried-up, very abnormal-appearing copulation plugs.

prostate did occur. Similar observations concerning increased weight of the male accessory organs following anterior hypothalamic lesions have been made (Bogdanove *et al.*, 1964). This suggests that, if anything, the activity of the pituitary-gonad axis in the male rat is enhanced following basal midline lesions in the preoptic and anterior hypothalamic region.

One rat in this series, upon recovering from the anesthetic, immediately began to attempt copulation with its cage mate, a male. When the cage mate was replaced by a stimulus female, sexual activity continued in an almost uninterrupted manner for about 2 hours. During this time two complete ejaculations occurred. This confirms an earlier observation of Hillarp *et al.* (1954) who noted that both male and female rats, following placement of anterior hypothalamic lesions, showed malelike mounting behavior immediately upon recovery from the anesthetic. The lesion in this animal was fairly extensive and involved the midline structures bilaterally from the preoptic region to the beginning of the arcuate nucleus. However, the suprachiasmatic nucleus was completely spared by the lesion. The continued mating performed by this animal over the following 4 weeks indicated a moderate depression of sexual activity.

Further comment on the testing method employed seems warranted, since providing the subject with a suitable partner at all times differs markedly from the usual procedure of a 10-minute or 1-hour mating test per day. My results showed that many experienced rats when provided with a suitable partner perform the complete copulatory act more than once per night and maintain this level of activity over long periods of time. This means an excellent baseline can be established for comparisons of total ejaculatory activity after experimental manipulation. Futhermore, this method of testing would appear to give excellent appraisal of the complete sexual performance of an animal over long periods of time and under relatively natural conditions. The constant presence of a suitable partner removes the sex act being tested from a conditioned stimulus to a simple consummatory act performed whenever the need arises on the part of the animal.

b. The Female. Beach (1952) found that mating still took place and normal reproduction was possible following removal of the thalamus in cats. In the rabbit, large thalamic lesions similarly do not prevent mating or ovulation (Sawyer, 1959).

Observations concerning the lack of mating following hypothalamic lesions have been repeatedly made during the past 25 years. C. Fisher *et al.* (1938) noted that cats would no longer mate following lesions in the anterior hypothalamus around the supraoptic nuclei. In the guinea pig (Brookhart *et al.*, 1940; Dey *et al.*, 1942), anterior hypothalamic lesions blocked mating behavior which could not be restored by the use of exogenous hormone. A decrease in sexual activity was found in the rat following anterior hypothalamic lesions (Clark, 1942).

Recently, these problems have been reinvestigated using more discrete lesions. Sawyer and Robison (1956) found that the female cat remained in permanent anestrus, even after exogenous hormone treatment, following anterior hypothalamic lesions rostral to the ventromedial nuclei and either medial to or within the area of the medial forebrain bundle. These lesions are entirely separate from those which result in gonad atrophy due to interference with the feedback mechanism between the gonad and pituitary. Lesions in the ventromedian nucleus, the premammillary region, or destruction of the mammillary body result in anestrus from ovarian atrophy. However, exogenous hormone returns these animals to a state of estrous behavior (Fig. 6).

Investigation of the rabbit indicates that the mammillary bodies are needed for estrous behavior (Sawyer, 1959). Destruction of this region eliminated mating, and sexual responsiveness could not be restored by exogenous hormone. Again, a separate area controlling gonadotropic function was found. Clegg *et al.* (1958) have shown that lesions in the anterior hypothalamus eliminate sexual behavior in the ewe.

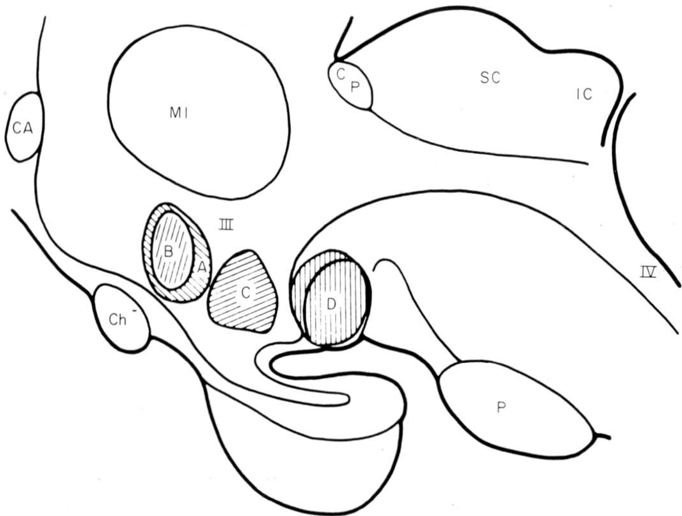

Fig. 6. Sites of lesions affecting sexual behavior and gonadotropin secretion in the cat. Diagram represents a midsagittal section of the hypothalamus. Lesions at A and B abolished sex behavior and exogenous hormone treatment did not restore it. A lesion at C and a lesion at D induced ovarian atrophy, but mating occurred when exogenous hormone was administered. CA, anterior commissure; MI, massa intermedia; Ch, optic chiasm; P, pons; CP, posterior commissure; SC, superior colliculus; IC, inferior colliculus; III, third ventricle; IV, fourth ventricle.

Recent work with the rat (A. Soulairac and Soulairac, 1956; Law and Meagher, 1958) indicates that an anterior hypothalamic center is necessary for sexual behavior. In their studies, Law and Meagher found that bilateral lesions at the posterior border of the optic chiasm resulted in mating in only two of nine animals; then they mated at diestrus. Following premammillary lesions, five of six rats mated at diestrus as well as estrus. This suggested to these authors that inhibitory centers existed in the hypothalamus, destruction of which allowed the expression of sex behavior at times in the hormonal cycles other than the estrous phase. However, their lesions were made with nicrome wire so there is the possibility of irritative deposits (Everett and Radford, 1961) having been induced, which may account for these results.

Averill and Purves (1963) have confirmed the fact that small medial lesions in the anterior hypothalamus result in a constantly cornified vaginal smear and a failure to mate, thus supporting earlier work (e.g., Clark, 1942; Hillarp, 1949; Greer, 1953). Whether this result is due to hormonal imbalance resulting from an upset in the pituitary-gonad axis or due to destruction of neural elements essential for integration of estrous behavior remains an open question.

Recent work with the guinea pig (Goy and Phoenix, 1963) showed that bilateral lesions which involved the complete destruction of the anterior median eminence and anterior arcuate nucleus in five of nine animals resulted in loss of lordosis. Another group of females which showed defects in sex behavior had lesions within the lateral extensions of the arcuate nucleus and ventrolateral part of the ventromedian. However, the actual destruction of these nuclei was less than 10%, the major portion of the lesion falling within the relatively cell-free zone between these nuclei. All females were castrated, and exogenous hormone was used in testing for behavioral estrus.

In marked contrast to these results, Goy and Phoenix found two animals bearing more anterior lesions in the supraopticus diffusus region which showed estrous behavior in the castrate condition. Hormone treatment did not result in any change in the level of behavior shown. Following lesioning, most of the animals failed to show any malelike mounting behavior, which is a usual element for the female guinea pig. Testosterone had no restorative value in any of these animals.

In conclusion, the lesion data for female mammals is consistent with the theory of dual hormone-sensitive systems within the hypothalamus. One system situated in the median eminence region appears to be the regulator of the pituitary-gonad axis. After its destruction, behavioral estrus is still possible, provided exogenous hormone is used. A second region, apparently hormone-sensitive, appears essential for the lordosis response in the female. This has been localized to the preoptic region and anterior hypothalamus for the cat, rat, guinea pig, the hamster, and ewe. Only the rabbit among the mammals so far investigated has a behavior-regulating region in the posterior hypothalamus.

There is no change in the pituitary gonad axis following destruction of the behavioral center, yet heat never occurs, even after application of exogenous hormone.

Recent investigations (Law and Meagher, 1958; Goy and Phoenix, 1963) indicate that certain discrete lesions in the anterior hypothalamus of guinea pigs or the premammillary region for the rat result in a constant behavioral estrus which is divorced from hormonal control. Thus, these authors feel that certain regions of the hypothalamus act as inhibitory regions to the display of sexual behavior. It does not seem necessary at this time to postulate sites at which the gonadal hormones inhibit behavior until other possibilities have been eliminated. It is important to note that all lesions which resulted in changes in estrous behavior other than its complete disappearance were made with iron compound electrodes. Hillarp *et al.* (1954) noted that 20–30 minutes after recovery from the ether anesthesia, rats of either sex bearing bilateral lesions of the preoptic area (made with nicrome wire) showed a strong drive for male-type copulatory behavior lasting several hours. Reynolds (1963) found that following radio-frequency current lesions to the ventromedial nuclei, no hyperphagia or obesity resulted, a finding diametrically opposed to the innumerable experimental results showing that electrolytic lesioning of this nucleus resulted in obesity. Everett and Radford (1961) found that electrical stimulation to the preoptic region of the rat brain was the most sensitive locus for ovulation. Further examination of the brain material showed that ovulation was always accompanied by a zone of inflammation at the end of the electrode tract. When platinum electrodes were used, no ovulation resulted. Microinjection of $FeCl_3$ into the preoptic tissue induced ovulation. Thus, ovulation was due to a deposit of iron salts and not to the current passed.

The failure of Reynolds to induce hyperphagia and Everett and Radford to get ovulation unless iron-bearing electrodes were used suggests that the iron deposits set up irritative foci in the central nervous system which result in the continued activity of the nervous elements affected. Since the lesions were made by iron-containing electrodes in both cases where unusual sexual behavior was found following lesions, it is possible that these results are again due to irritative foci. Since these lesions appear to be in the region where various responses are summated and integrated for the production of estrous behavior, it does not appear too farfetched to think of irritative foci resulting in maximal sensitization of this area, with the resulting display of behavior even in the absence of appropriate hormonal substrate.

A strong body of evidence has been accumulated for male mammals which indicates that the preoptic-anterior hypothalamus and especially the midline structures in this region must be intact for expression of sex behavior patterns. A second center also exists in the median eminence region which regulates gonadotropin release. Thus there is considerable agreement here with the picture presently available for the female. There is also some evidence that the ventromedial and posterior hypothalamus are involved in the mediation of sex behavior in the rat (Beach, 1964; M. L. Soulairac, 1963; Heimer and Larsson, 1964) and the guinea pig (Phoenix, 1961).

Investigations on the male are undoubtedly complicated by the fact that the previous experience of the animal is very important in determining the outcome of any experimental manipulation undertaken. The previous suggestion of caution in interpretation, based on the variability of lesioning techniques employed, applies equally here.

Recent experimental evidence from my laboratory indicating that malelike mounting behavior can occur immediately after recovery from anesthesia, when platinum electrodes are used rather than iron, supports the observations of Hillarp *et al.* (1954) and exonerates iron deposits as the mediating factor in this instance. Thus it appears that the destruction of neurons in the preoptic region is the causal factor for malelike mounting observed in both male and female rats immediately after this operation. This effect is transient and lasts at the longest for a few hours.

One must keep in mind, however, some further observations which indicate that sexual behavior can be elicited by a variety of stimuli. Electrical stimulation in the lateral anterior hypothalamic region can result in full display of sexual behavior in the male rat (Vaughan and Fisher, 1962). Why, then, should chemical stimulation from a deposit of iron salts not exert a similar stimulatory effect? Electrical or chemical stimulation (MacLean, 1957) has resulted in the display of various elements of sex behavior in male cats and rats. Thus the deposit of iron salts may provide a sufficient chemical stimulus to the mating center of both male and female.

The diencephalon and especially the hypothalamus do not serve alone in the regulation of sexual behavior in the mammal. Although ample proof has been presented that complete estrous behavior does not depend on the cortex, evidence has also been provided that the cortex in the female plays a role in the initiation of enticement reactions (Larsson, 1962b). Furthermore lesions in the cortex, thalamus, and amygdala can modify the conditions under which lordosis behavior may be obtained

(Sawyer, 1959; de Groot, 1962; Gestaut, 1952). Complete disappearance of estrous behavior has so far only resulted from hypothalamic lesions. Thus, the data indicate that, in the female, primary integration of all factors for the successful accomplishment of sexual behavior correlated with the gonadal state takes place in the hypothalamus. In the male, the cortex, especially the sensory and motor areas of the frontal region, appears to be essential for the proper execution of sexual behavior.

B. Neural Mechanisms as Revealed by Stimulation and Recording Experiments

1. *Peripheral and Spinal Mechanisms.*

a. The Male. It appears obvious that hormones not only act centrally but affect many peripheral structures on the body, which in turn brings about altered sensitivity of these structures and results in modifications of the central state. The problem of the relevance of peripheral versus central mechanisms has been discussed by Young (1961) and Lehrman (1961) and a full discussion of this subject can be found in Chapter 17.

b. The Female. Female mammals will sometimes show parts of their normal sex behavior pattern following grasping of the neck or back and prodding of the perineum with a glass rod. Ball (1937) used this method for quantifying sex behavior in the female rat. The cat responds to artificial stimulation of the vagina by ovulation and a species-specific after-reaction (Greulich, 1934); so does the estrogen-treated rabbit (Sawyer, 1949). Lissak (1962) has shown that olfaction plays an important role in estrous behavior in the cat. He observed that anestrous cats allowed mating which resulted in a complete after-reaction when they were exposed to the odor of valeric acid or the vaginal secretions of a cat made artificially estrous.

2. *Neocortical and Rhinencephalic Mechanisms*

a. The Male. Using a 25% KCl solution to produce localized depression of cortical activity, Larsson (1962b) found that copulatory activity was inhibited for approximately 2 hours regardless of whether the solution was applied over the parieto-occipital or the frontal regions. The inhibition of behavior appeared to be due to depression of the component responsible for spontaneous initiative of the animal.

MacLean (1957) found that, following chemical excitation of the dorsal hippocampus or following after-discharges induced by electrical stimulation, male cats showed a series of grooming reactions sometimes accompanied by penile erection that was suggestive of courtship behavior. Similar behavior could be elicited in rats. These were some of the first observations suggesting that cerebral excitation could elicit an overt sexual response.

Employing the techniques of electrical stimulation and using the squirrel monkey as the subject, MacLean and his co-workers have succeeded in outlining paths in the central nervous system both for penile erection and ejaculation (MacLean and Ploog, 1962; MacLean, 1962; MacLean *et al.*, 1963). The results of their findings, which are summarized in Fig. 7, indicate that in the squirrel monkey positive loci for erection are distributed within three cortico-subcortical divisions of the limbic system. At the highest level they coincide with known hippocampal connections with the septum, anterior thalamus, and hypothalamus. The medial septopreoptic region and medial part of the dorsomedial nucleus of the thalamus appear to be nodal points for erection. Stimulation of the septum or rostral diencephalon which caused erection was commonly associ-

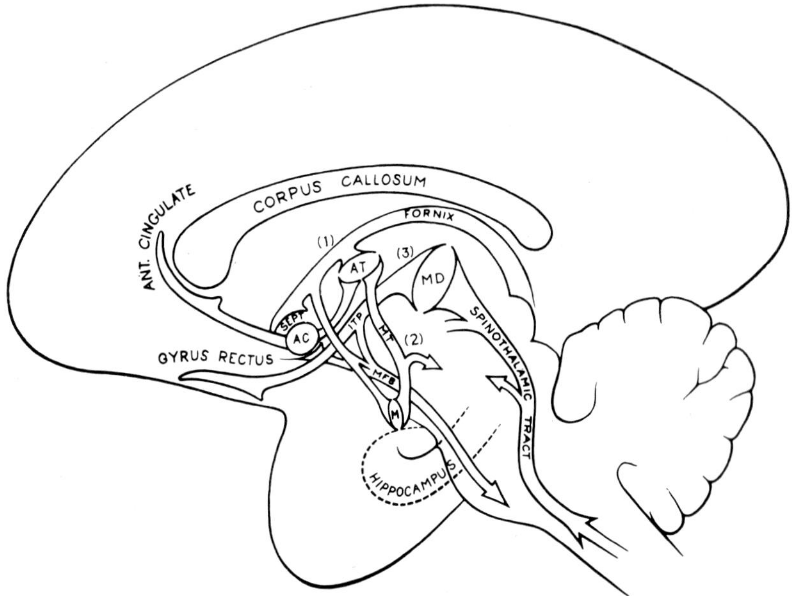

FIG. 7. Loci positive for penile erection have been found in three subdivisions of the limbic system as schematically represented above and labeled (1), (2), and (3). The septum (SEPT) and the medial part of the medial dorsal nucleus (MD) are nodal points for erection. The medial forebrain bundle (MFB) and inferior thalamic peduncle (ITP) form important descending pathways. The spinothalamic tract which connects with the medial dorsal nucleus also influences ejaculation and scratching of the genitals. AC, anterior commissure; AT, anterior thalamic nucleus; M, mammillary body; MT, mammillothalamic tract. (From MacLean, 1962.)

ated with after-discharges in the hippocampus. During these after-discharges, pronounced changes were noted in the erection, which suggests that the hippocampus modified the excitability of the effector neurons involved in penile erection.

Positive loci were also found in parts of the so-called Papez (1937) circuit, comprising the mammillary bodies, mammillothalamic tract, parts of the anterior thalamic nucleus, and the anterior cingulate gyrus. Such loci also occurred in parts of the medial orbital gyrus and along its connections with the medial part of the medial dorsal nucleus. The positive loci could be followed caudally along the course of the medial forebrain bundle and the periventricular fiber system. The medial forebrain bundle appears to provide the major descending pathway to the ventral tegmentum. From here the pathway goes to the dorsolateral part of the substantia nigra and then descends through the ventral lateral part of the pons.

Seminal discharge, it was found, could occur dissociated from erection; in the thalamus positive points for this response were in the ventromedial part of the medial dorsal nucleus and in the mid-dorsal portion of the parafascicular-centromedian complex. Thus genital sensation and ejaculation appear to lie in and articulate with that part of the medial dorsal nucleus that is nodal with respect to erection.

b. The Female. See discussion under diencephalic and hypothalamic mechanisms (Section II,B,3,b).

3. *Diencephalic and Hypothalamic Mechanisms*

a. The Male. In the male rat, Herberg (1963) showed that electrical self-stimulation of the ventromedial quadrant of the median forebrain bundle, (the electrode ending just above the lateral mammillary nucleus and lateral to the origin of the mammillothalamic tract) resulted in seminal discharge without inducing penile erection or other signs of sex drive. The result was also obtained by externally programmed stimulation. It was easily blocked by light anesthesia, which suggests that its mediation was by an extended polyneuronal system. Ejaculation can thus be separated from other sex mechanisms. Herberg went on to show that self-stimulation at some current strengths was enhanced by androgen and depressed by hunger.

Vaughan and Fisher (1962) found that three out of thirty rats responded to electrical stimulation in the anterior dorsolateral hypothalamus with mounting behavior. When currents of 0.8 to 1.0 mA were used, mounting began within seconds of onset and continued but stopped immediately when the current was turned off. During stimulation, penile erection was virtually constant. Electrical stimulation resulted in a greatly decreased postejaculatory interval. Furthermore, in a test lasting 7.5 hours with 5-minute on-off intervals of stimulation, during the actual 220 minutes of stimulation the subject mounted 174 times without intromission, 81 times with intromission, and had 45 ejaculations. When tested with a nonestrous female for 60 minutes, 15 mounts without intromission were noted, compared to 19 complete ejaculations when tested with an estrous female for a similar period. Thus, the estrous female appeared to play a necessary role for the high level of response shown by the subject.

The quick onset and termination suggests a direct neural mediation, not a humoral one, and indicates that in the lateral anterior hypothalamus, near the upper boundaries of the lateral preoptic region, there may be an excitatory area for male sexual behavior.

Stimulation or inhibition in the central nervous system can also result from the use of pharmacological agents. Thus, M. L. Soulairac (1963) has investigated a wide range of chemical agents as a means of unravelling the adrenergic and cholinergic components involved in male sexual behavior in the rat. It should be recalled that the anterior hypothalamus is thought of as being primarily parasympathetic (cholinergic) whereas the posterior hypothalamus is sympathetic (adrenergic).

Soulairac's findings indicate that proper functioning of both the adrenergic and cholinergic systems is important. A hyperactivity of the adrenergic system or hypofunction of the cholinergic system results in complete disappearance of sexual behavior. Studies with reserpine showed that low dosage, 25 μg per 100 gm per day, increased sexual behavior whereas a dose of 60 μg per 100 gm per day resulted in complete disappearance of sexual behavior. Histological study indicated lesions in the lateral mammillary nuclei and in the gonads. Fuller (1963) showed that long-term (8 weeks) application of reserpine at 53 μg per 100 gm per day resulted in depressed sexual behavior. M. L. Soulairac (1963) also found that treatment with 5-hydroxytryptamine (serotonin) resulted in an augmentation of the sexual reflexes, including increased numbers of ejaculations and decreased latency to ejaculation. This suggested that 5-hydroxytryptamine might be one of the humoral mediators involved in regulation of male sexual behavior.

b. The Female. In the estrous cat, electroencephalograph (EEG) recordings have been made from several hypothalamic regions during and after real or simulated copulatory activity. In the cat, vaginal stimulation is followed by a behavioral after-reaction lasting several minutes. The EEG recordings show bursts of high amplitude activity localized in the anterior lateral hypothalamus in and around the medial forebrain bundle (Fig. 8). Such changes never occur in the posterior hypo-

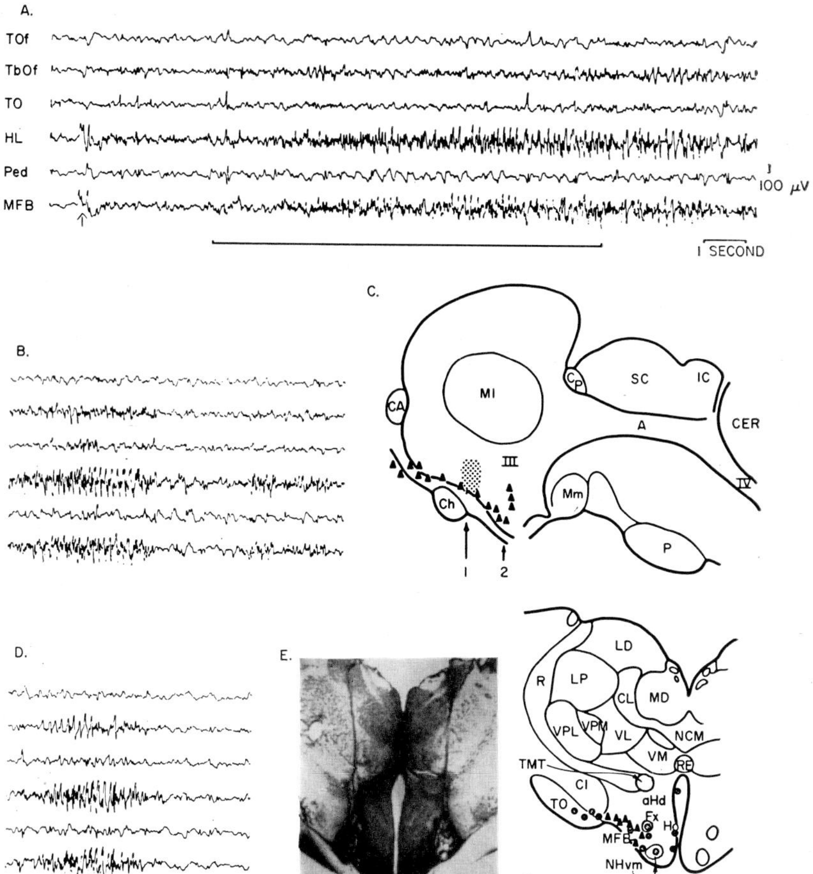

FIG. 8. Selected EEG tracings during vaginal stimulation (A) and the after-reaction (B,D) in an estrous cat. Note the dramatic changes in the lateral hypothalamic area (HL) and the medial forebrain bundle (MFB) channels. TOf, olfactory tract; TbOf, olfactory tubercle; TO, optic tract; Ped, cerebral peduncle. C shows in sagittal view the areas from which altered electrical activity was obtained; arrows 1 and 2 indicate levels of cross-section shown in E. E shows points with altered electrical activity (solid triangles) and points where no change was recorded (solid circles).

Sagittal section: A, aqueduct of Sylvius; CA, anterior commissure; CER, cerebellum; Ch, optic chiasm; CP, posterior commissure; IC, inferior colliculus; MI, massa intermedia; Mm, mammillary body; P, pons; SC, superior colliculus; III, third ventricle; IV, fourth ventricle.

Cross-section: aHd, dorsal hypothalamic area; Cl, internal capsule; CL, central lateral nucleus; Fx, fornix; Hp, posterior hypothalamic area; LD, dorsolateral nucleus; LP, lateral posterior nucleus; MD, dorsomedial nucleus; MFB, median forebrain bundle; NCM, central median nucleus; NHvm, ventromedian hypothalamic nucleus; R, reticular nucleus, Re, nucleus reuniens; TmT, mammillothalamic tract; TO, optic tract; VL, ventrolateral nucleus; VM, ventromedial nucleus; VPL, ventroposterior lateral nucleus; VPM, ventroposterior medial nucleus.

thalamus, and they are found only in estrous or estrogen-primed cats (Porter *et al.*, 1957).

Green (1954), using unrestrained rabbits with chronically implanted electrodes, noted heightened EEG activity in the anterior hypothalamus during courtship and mating. Barraclough (1959, 1960) noted that stimulation of the cervix in the rat in late proestrus and during estrus resulted in EEG changes localized to the lateral preoptic area and lateral hypothalamus.

Using the cat, Lissák (1962) showed that the odor of valeric acid or that of an estrous smear from another cat would produce changes in the EEG record confined to the lateral preoptic area and basal septal area. Both substances induced mating, which resulted in a complete after-reaction. He found that progesterone or testosterone at 0.5 mg per day for 3 days did not produce any change in behavior or electrical activity.

Sawyer and Kawakami (1961), in a series of investigations on the rabbit, noted that following coitus a change in the EEG record occurred which included spindle bursts from the frontal cortex and related areas. They called this the EEG after-reaction. Following this, a hyperarousal record was noted in those rhinencephalic areas related to the hippocampus. It was noted that the after-reaction response could be produced in the estrous rabbit by a 5-per-second electrical stimulation to the hypothalamus or rhinencephalon. The arousal response, it was noted, was elicited by a 300-per-second stimuli to the reticular formation. Thus, the effects of hormones on the EEG response to electrical stimulation could be studied (Kawakami and Sawyer, 1959).

Progesterone given to an estrogen-primed rabbit had biphasic effects. First, both thresholds to electrical stimulation were lowered. At their lowest point, the rabbit was in heat and would mate and ovulate as a result of mating (Fig. 9). Using 0.5 mg of estrogen or 5 mg of testosterone per day for 5 days, it was possible to get a lowered EEG arousal threshold to electrical stimulation while the EEG after-reaction threshold remained elevated. Such an animal mated readily but failed to ovulate as a result of mating. Thus, both behavioral changes and gonadotropin release are associated with definite EEG patterns.

Recently, the first studies of unitary activity in the hypothalamus in relation to sexual functions have been reported by Barraclough and Cross (1963). Using the female rat and recording from the lateral regions of the thalamus and hypothalamus, they found 47% of the units responded to probing of the cervix with a glass rod. For the most part, these units responded to several stimuli. Typically, acceleration of firing resulted from probing the cervix, pain, or cold. Inhibitory convergence was also noted. Smell appears to be intensified by hormones, since twice as many units responded to olfactory stimuli at proestrus as at any other stage of the cycle.

When 400 μg of progesterone was given intravenously, there was a selective inhibition of the units responsive to cervical probing which became maximal at 30 minutes, with full recovery by 1 hour. During the estrous phase of the cycle, there were relatively more neurons unresponsive or actually inhibited by the test stimuli employed.

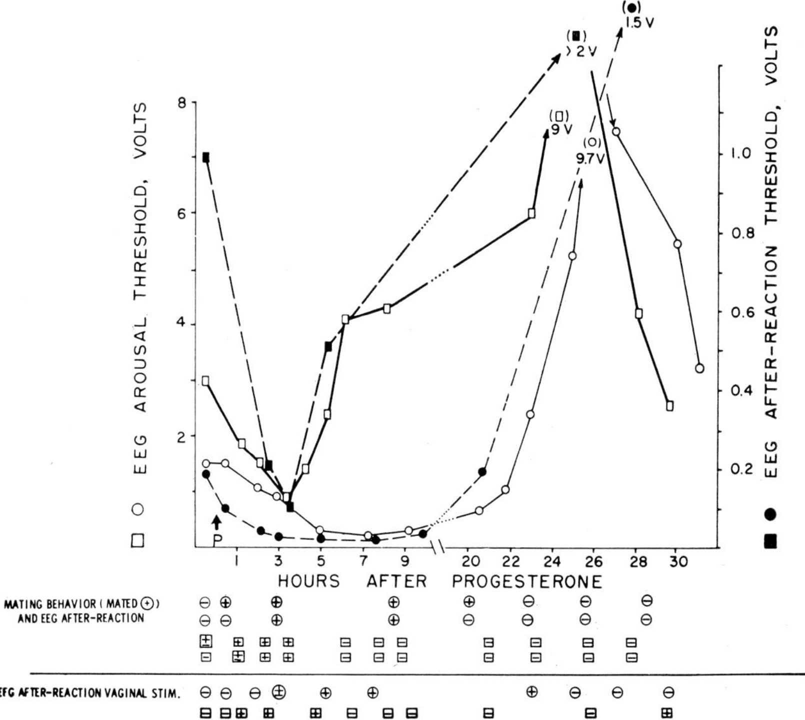

Fig. 9. Effect of progesterone on the threshold of EEG arousal and EEG after-reaction induced by stimulating, respectively, reticular formation and the ventromedial hypothalamus. The rabbits had been ovariectomized and treated with estrogen. Two different rabbits are shown, indicated by the square and round symbols. The mating behavior and sexually induced EEG after-reactions for both animals are indicated beneath the graph. (Adapted from Sawyer and Kawakami, 1961.)

In conclusion, studies of EEG records made during sexual activity suggest that hormones affect broad areas of the nervous system. However, there seems to be a focus of change in the preoptic and anterior hypothalamic regions. This appears to be true even in the rabbit, a species in which the mammillary bodies are essential for mating. In the hormone-treated animal, electrical stimulation to the reticular system and ventromedial hypothalamus can result in changes in the EEG pattern similar to those which occur following coitus; these regions therefore appear to be important in the relay of afferent impulses associated with coitus. Although the sensitivity of the EEG patterns to electrical stimulation can be altered by hormone treatment, it remains to be shown whether these changes result from hormone effects at the level of the hypothalamus or more diffuse effects of hormone on the entire central nervous system.

In 1937, Papez proposed a now-famous circuit in regard to emotional behavior involving the hippocampus, fornix, mammillary bodies, anterior thalamic nucleus, cingulate cortex, and entorhinal cortex back to the hippocampus. Green and Arduini (1954) demonstrated that afferent connections to the hippocampus include pathways from the reticular activating system, hypothalamus, preoptic region, and septum. Evidence has also been presented by Adey *et al.* (1956, 1957) for reverse connections running via the fornix, hippocampus, entorhinal cortex, septum and stria medullaris to the midbrain tegmentum. It now appears that these circuits are of great importance for the expression of sexual behavior. Whether all segments in these circuits are affected by the sex hormones or whether hormonal influence is limited to certain points remains an important question for future research.

C. Neural Mechanisms as Revealed by Hormone Implantation

1. *Diencephalic and Hypothalamic Mechanisms*

a. The Male. A. E. Fisher (1956) reported that water-soluble testosterone compounds injected into the preoptic area of male rats resulted in female sexual behavior following lateral injections or maternal behavior following medial placement.

Recent studies in the author's laboratory have attempted to find hormone-positive loci for male sexual behavior in the rat. Animals were castrated at 23 days of age and had testosterone implants, unilateral and bilateral, made in the preoptic region at 90 days of age. So far no complete mating patterns have been noted, and only an increase in excitability has been observed. There is increased following of the female, including sniffing and licking of the genital region. However, the male appears to be at a loss as to what to do at this point.

Barfield (1964), employing unilateral or bilateral implants of testosterone placed in the basal medial preoptic region, induced capons to show copulatory behavior which included mounting the hen, treading, and depression of the tail in the normal manner. The copulatory behavior produced was independent of aggressive and courting behavior.

b. The Female. Since lesions could result in the loss of sexual behavior, it became particularly important to ascertain if specific hormone-sensitive elements in the area of the central nervous system were destroyed. The fact that exogenous hormone was without effect in restoring sexual responses supported this conclusion. However, it was always possible that the lesion had destroyed an essential fiber tract or motor pathway for the function. Therefore, if a behavior pattern could be produced by localized application of hormone, one would be closer to the acceptance of hormonal mediation of behavior due to specific central effects.

The first evidence for central action of hormones for elicitation of behavioral estrus was supplied by Kent and Lieberman (1949) who showed that intraventricular injection of progesterone resulted in facilitation of the lordosis response whereas similar injections were ineffective if given subcutaneously. In 1958, Harris *et al.* showed that stilbesterol implants in the posterior hypothalamus of the spayed cat could bring about estrous behavior, although a peripheral effect was excluded, the genital tract remaining atrophic. In the rat, Lisk (1960a) found that intravenous injection of progesterone in the castrated, estrogen-primed animal resulted in elicitation of the lordosis response within 1.5 minutes of the injection, compared to a median of about 4 hours with subcutaneous application. Furthermore, one-sixtieth of the subcutaneous dosage was effective intravenously. Lisk (1962a) further demonstrated that minute implants of estradiol in the anterior hypothalamus or preoptic region were a sufficient stimulus to produce lordosis in the castrated rat (Fig. 10).

Hormone implantation experiments employing intact animals indicated that a second hormone-sensitive region existed in the hypothalamus, one which regulated the pituitary-gonad axis and in which estrogen implants resulted in gonadal atrophy due to failure of the pituitary to release sufficient gonadotropin to maintain the ovaries (Lisk, 1960b, 1962b; Davidson and Sawyer, 1961).

Although the original neural site for hormonal induction of estrous behavior in the cat (Harris, *et al.*, 1958) was noted to be the posterior hypothalamus, later work by Sawyer (1963) using more refined implants indicates that the anterior hypothalamus is the critical area. The earlier results were probably due to diffusion through the nervous tissue. Recently, Palka and Sawyer (1964) found that in the rabbit only hypothalamic implants of estrogen located in the posterior and central medial hypothalamus resulted in estrous behavior, which occurred within 1–2 days of implant. Daily injection of progesterone failed to block the estrous behavior in these animals although such treatment would normally do so in the estrogen-primed rabbit. These data imply that the mating center in the rabbit hypothalamus exists just anterior to the mammillary bodies.

In recent experiments in the author's laboratory, attempts have been made to influence mating behavior by hypothalamic hormone implants in intact rats. These experiments showed that large implants of estradiol resulted in constant mating behavior regardless of locus in the hypo-

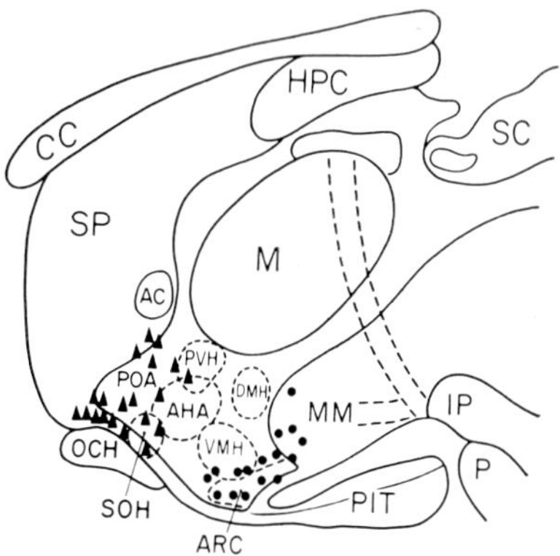

FIG. 10. Sagittal section of rat diencephalon indicating location of estradiol implants which induced the lordosis response in ovariectomized female rats (solid triangles) and location of estradiol implants which induced a significant decrease in weight of the reproductive tract (solid circles). AC, anterior commissure; AHA, anterior hypothalamic area; ARC, arcuate nucleus; CC, corpus callosum; DMH, dorsomedial nucleus; HPC, hippocampal commissure; IP, interpeduncular nucleus; M, massa intermedia, MM, mammillary bodies; OCH, optic chiasm; P, pons; PIT, pituitary; POA, preoptic area; PVH, paraventricular nucleus; SC, superior colliculus; SOH, suprachiasmatic nucleus; SP, septum pellucidum; VMH, ventromedial nucleus. (Adapted from Lisk, 1960b, 1962a.)

thalamus, and at the same time they blocked gonadotropin release, resulting in atrophic ovaries. More refined implants blocked gonadotropin release if placed at the correct locus (arcuate-mammillary area), but if placed in the anterior region (preoptic-suprachiasmatic region) they had no influence on mating behavior. Such animals mated once and had a normal pregnancy. Thus, the operational control of the mating center would appear to be influenced by the physiological state of the animal. Progesterone and testosterone were also implanted and found to have no influence on mating behavior in the intact rat (Lisk, 1965).

One of the difficulties in studies of mating behavior is the long latency between application of hormone to the castrated animal and the first appearance of estrous behavior. This period is usually about 3 days and is not changed whether the estrogen is given subcutaneously, intravenously, or into the brain. The Palka and Sawyer (1964) observation of mating in the rabbit within 1–2 days of hormone placement would seem to be the shortest latency thus far reported. In our studies (Lisk, 1962a), a latency of 3–5 days was usual after the intracranial placement of hormones in animals castrated a minimum of 2 weeks preceding hormone placement.

Most experiments which involve testing for estrous behavior by the use of exogenous hormone are carried out only after the animal has undergone a considerable period of hormone deprivation. It is thus possible that the latency observed between hormone application and the overt behavioral event represents the time necessary to re-engage machinery that has been forced to shut down due to lack of material—i.e., hormone —in the castrated state. One possible method for testing this hypothesis is to implant hormone in the mating center and at the same time spay animals at specific stages of the estrous cycle.

Two of five animals implanted during proestrus with estradiol in 200 μ lumen diameter tubes lordosed in response to the male mounting immediately on recovery from anesthesia. Complete data for the lordosis response and vaginal cycle are presented in Table II. Responses other than the two noted immediately after the operation were seen in one animal on day 3 and in one on day 7. On day 8, three of the animals accepted the male and lordosed. The two that did not were then given an intravenous injection of progesterone in propylene glycol (30 μg in 0.05 ml) via the femoral vein. One animal lordosed 7 minutes after the progesterone injection. The other animal did not respond. On day 9, four animals lordosed immediately on being mounted by the male. The remaining animal was given 60 μg of progesterone intravenously, but still no lordosis resulted. Table II shows that this animal never gave the lordosis response. The hormone-containing tube ended in or near the suprachiasmatic nucleus in all five animals. The only difference in the animal that would not lordose was the placement of the tube directly in the midline, resulting in the destruction of the peak of fibers located between the two suprachiasmatic nuclei. During the second week after hormone placement, the remaining four animals mated on nearly every occasion on which they were tested.

Of five animals receiving hormone placement at estrus, two mated immediately on recovery from the anesthetic. Again, the next lordosis was obtained on day 3. From day 4 to 14 none of the animals responded to the male. On day 14 a progesterone implant was made in the mating center bilaterally opposite to the estrogen implant. Between 2 and 6 hours after placment of the implant, four out of five animals accepted the male and lordosed. The remaining animal never showed lordosis. At autopsy it was found that in this animal one tube had been implanted in the midline and destroyed the peak of fibers just above the suprachiasmatic nuclei.

TABLE II

LORDOSIS RESPONSE (AND VAGINAL CYCLE) FOUND WHEN RATS WERE IMPLANTED, DURING PROESTRUS, AND SPAYED, ESTRADIOL BEING PLACED IN THE PREOPTIC-ANTERIOR HYPOTHALAMIC REGION[a]

	Hormone location				
Day	Suprachiasmatic	Suprachiasmatic	Suprachiasmatic	Suprachiasmatic	Anterior hypothalamus
0	(pe)	(p)	L(p)	(pe)	L(pd)
1	(ed)	(ep)	(pe)	(p)	(dpe)
2	(p)	(p)	(p)	(pe)	(pe)
3	(p)	(p)	L(pe)	(e)	(e)
4	(pe)	(pd)	(pe)	(pd)	(e)
7	L(dp)	(p)	(p)	(d)	(pd)
8	L(ep)	L(e)[b]	L(e)	(p)[c]	L(e)
9	L(e)	L(pe)	L(e)	(p)[c]	L(pe)
10	—	—	(p)	(d)	L(p)
11	L(pe)	L(p)			
14	L(pd)	L(p)	(e)	(d)	L(e)

[a] L, lordosis; d, leukocytes; p, nucleated epithelium, e, cornified epithelium; —, not tested. When two or more letters are used, the first one indicates the predominant cell type.

[b] Intravenous progesterone, animal lordosed in 7 minutes.

[c] Intravenous progesterone, animal never lordosed.

Following the initial mating response after the progesterone implant, only one animal continued to show lordosis. The vaginal cycle for this animal was fairly regular and mating occurred at all stages in this cycle (Fig. 11). As illustrated in Table II, when hormone implantation was performed at the time of spaying, some semblance of a vaginal cycle appears to be retained for at least 2–3 weeks, and mating is not correlated with any specific stage in this vaginal cycle (Lisk, unpublished observations, 1962).

These experiments indicate that the implant procedure itself does not block the lordosis response since four animals mated immediately on recovery from the anesthesia. However, these experiments still do not resolve the reason for the latency period. Since the neural elements are already in a primed state, the local supply of estrogen would be expected to maintain the overt response of lordosis. If anything, this work suggests that estrogen alone is not the ideal stimulus for estrous behavior in the rat. The addition of progesterone, however, brought about a rapid response in all but two animals. In these two, hormone placement was similar to the others, but there appeared to be a small lesion of the median peak of fibers between the suprachiasmatic nuclei produced by one of the hormone-bearing tubes.

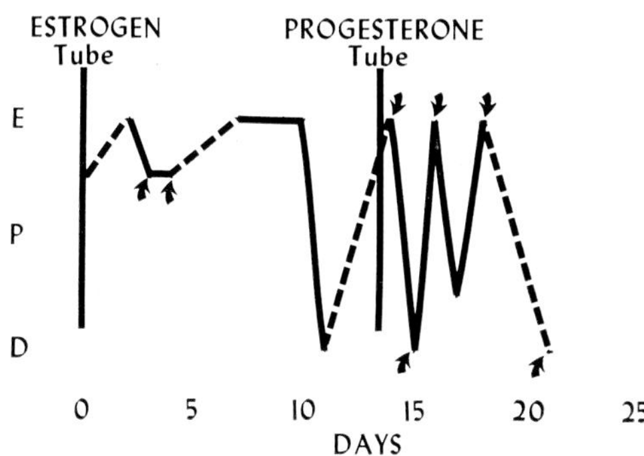

FIG. 11. Diagram of vaginal cycle for female rat with estrogen implant placed in mating center at estrus and animal immediately spayed. Following a bilaterally opposite implant of progesterone on day 14, a fairly regular vaginal cycle was noted, and the animal mated (curved arrows) without regard to the phase of the vaginal cycle. E, estrus; P, proestrus; D, diestrus.

In summary, it is apparent that hormone placement studies show unusually good agreement with the conclusions drawn on the basis of lesion studies in the hypothalamus. The hormonal induction of estrous behavior in the cat from posterior hypothalamic implants is the only report opposed to the definition of the mating center on the basis of lesion placement. Studies by Lisk (1965) with large estrogen implants in the rat indicate that the results in the cat were probably due to diffusion from implants with a large surface area. Later work in the cat supports this conclusion.

A question often asked in this type of study is how far does the implanted steroid diffuse. A second question is how do endogenously secreted steroids get across the blood-brain barrier. These are particularly important questions for all studies with estrogens, in which the latency of behavioral reactions tends to take days. Michael (1962a,b, 1965) has tackled both of these problems. Using implants of radioactive stilbesterol, he was able to show selective accumulation of this material by specific neurons. Activity was demonstrable for a distance of only

400–600 μ from the implant. Using systemically administered hexoestrol-H^3 of high specific activity (100–150 μc per microgram), Michael was able to show specific uptake in the various classical target organs plus certain regions of the brain. All of these areas showed a peak at the same time, approximately 5 hours postinjection. By 72 hours, when the cat became behaviorly estrus, no hormone activity could be detected in the brain. Localization of hormone in the brain was confined to a bilaterally symmetrical system involving the septal region, preoptic area, and hypothalamus in the cat. The primate showed an additional localization in the caudate nucleus. This indicates that hormones apparently exert their influence on a series of structures within the diencephalic region of the brain rather than being confined to one nuclear group. Such an interpretation is consistent with the findings on hormone implants in the rat (Lisk, 1962a), where both positive and inactive loci were noted within the preoptic-anterior hypothalamic region. It seems that a critical number of neurons within this system must be stimulated before the behavior pattern can be evoked. Such an interpretation is also the most plausible in view of the finding that some form of the behavior can still be elicited in some cases by giving exogenous hormone, even after lesions in this region which abolish mating behavior.

D. Effects of Neonatal Hormone Injection on Reproductive Behavior of the Adult

Discussion so far has been limited to sexual behavior shown by animals which have been allowed to develop normally and then tested in the adult stage following lesioning or hormone placement. Thus, the neural tissues mediating sexual behavior have had a chance to develop normally. In the adult, hormonal action is thought to activate behavior; it results in the display of behavior patterns which have already been established at an earlier time.

The question of the action of hormones during developmental processes in producing an appropriately organized substrate in the nervous system is an important one. What happens to the behavioral responses of the adult if an animal has been deprived of hormones from very early stages or if supplemental hormone treatment is given during the development of the nervous system? This question is answered in detail in Chapters 19 and 21, but certain aspects of it deserve discussion in this chapter.

Phoenix *et al.* (1959) injected pregnant guinea pigs with testosterone propionate during most of pregnancy. After the female young born of these mothers became adult, they were gonadectomized and treated with estrogen followed by progesterone. It was found that their capacity to display lordosis was greatly reduced, and many animals still showed male-like mounting behavior, even when lordosis could not be produced. These data lend strong support to the idea that androgen acting prenatally has an organizing action on the nervous tissues mediating sexual behavior in the guinea pig.

Barraclough (1961) found that treatment of female rats with a single injection of testosterone propionate on or before the fifth day of life resulted in the production of an anovulatory animal. When these animals became adults, progesterone, either when given daily or as a series of spaced injections, was without effect in bringing about mating behavior (Barraclough and Gorski, 1962). Following ovariectomy, injections of estrogn followed by progesterone did not result in mating behavior. However, if the animals were sterilized by a minimum dosage of testosterone (10 μg), mating did occur as often as every day. This suggests that the testosterone disrupted the normal development of neural tissue in the preoptic anterior hypothalamic region. Depending upon the degree of abnormality in the substrate, mating behavior was continued or permanently eliminated.

Whalen and Nadler (1963) have investigated the effect on behavior of injection of 200 μg of estradiol benzoate in female rats during the critical neonatal period of development. When adult, these animals were castrated and given estrogen followed by progesterone. The animals would not show lordosis. Gorski (1963) treated female rats with 5–100-μg doses of estradiol benzoate on the fifth day of life. He found that the animals were anovulatory in adulthood and showed lengthened estrous cycles, averaging 7.7 days. Ten of eighteen animals mated repeatedly but without correlation to the vaginal cycle. Sperm was found at diestrus nine times, and results were similar even at the 5-μg level. Levine and Mullens (1964) found that neonatal injections of estrogens affected sex behavior in both male and female rats.

These and other data show that hormones do act on neural circuits during development to produce a behavior pattern. Not only heterotypical but homotypical hormones given in excess amount can modify the development of the neural organization required for the display of behavior in the adult animal.

Recently we have begun an investigation of the problem of what happens if an animal is deprived of sex hormone before puberty and allowed to reach adulthood, then given hormones. The questions to be answered were whether hormonal stimulation at the neural level would lead to behavioral responses, and what constituted an adequate stimulus.

Our first experiments involved rats castrated at 23 days of age and then implanted with estradiol when 90 days of age. The estradiol was contained in the lumen of tubes 150 μ in diameter, and tubes were implanted either unilaterally or bilaterally in the preoptic mating center.

Two out of four animals bearing unilateral implants of estradiol showed lordosis after a latency of 27 and 31 days. The remaining two animals had not responded at the end of 2 months, even though the implant was in approximately the same location in all four animals. Following bilateral implantation of estradiol, one animal mated after an 8-day latency period, and a second animal after 9 days. Two animals did not lordose for the male until 30 days after implantation. The fifth animal, in which the tubes missed the mating center and ended in the dorsomedial nucleus, never showed lordosis (Lisk, unpublished observations, 1964).

When the experiment was terminated approximately 60 days after hormone implantation, autopsy showed that the uterus had remained in the anestrus condition following unilateral application of estradiol (mean wet weight 112 mg). However, following bilateral implantation of estradiol, uterine weight was affected. The two animals with the shortest latency to lordosis had a mean uterine weight of 365 mg, whereas the two animals that did not respond for 30 days had a mean uterine weight of 198 mg. This indicates that some estrogen was getting into the peripheral circulation and again demonstrates the importance of the surface area of the implants. However, one animal in which the hormone placement was too far posterior in the hypothalamus had a uterine weight of 191 mg and did not mate at any time. These results support the earlier findings that castration of the young does not interfere with mating behavior in the adult, provided exogenous hormone is supplied (Valenstein *et al.*, 1955; Beach, 1945; Wilson and Young, 1941). Thus, once the ciritical period for organization of the substrate is passed, absence of hormone does not prevent the maintenance of the basic pattern of response. The long latencies noted after unilateral implants suggest the possibility of reparitive processes being required before the neural circuits are capable of responding to the hormonal stimulus.

Following bilateral implants with one tube containing estradiol and the other progesterone, lordosis behavior appeared after a 5-day latency in one animal and after 10 days in a second. In the remaining two animals, the hormone implant was made too far posterior, outside of the mating center, and lordosis behavior never resulted. At autopsy the mean wet weights of the uteri for the animals which lordosed was 125 mg, whereas it was 139 mg for the animals not showing lordosis. Thus the combination of estrogen plus progesterone did not result in an increase in uterine weight. Most important is the observation of a latency of 5–10 days. This is a 300–400% decrease in latency time compared to the latency in animals with estrogen implants which did not produce uterine stimulation (Lisk, unpublished observations, 1964). This marked facilitation of lordosis in the prepubertally castrated rat by neural implantation of estrogen plus progesterone again demonstrates that, although estrogen can be a sufficient stimulus for the mediation of sexual behavior in the female rat, estrogen alone is not the most effective stimulus, and quite likely not the sole physiological stimulus normally activating this response in the intact animal.

III. Sexual Behavior in Nonmammalian Vertebrates

This chapter has been limited to a consideration of sexual behavior in mammals. There is very little knowledge concerning the other groups of vertebrates. In birds, it has been shown that hormones are necessary for reproductive behavior (Höhn, 1961). According to Rogers (1922), loss of the hyperstriatum eliminates reproductive behavior in pigeons. Recently, Barfield (1964) demonstrated that copulatory behavior, independent of aggressive and courting behavior, resulted from testosterone implants in the preoptic region of chickens. For the reptiles, there appear to be no published studies relevant to the neural regions involved in the control of reproductive behavior. Noble and Aronson (1945) found that, in the male leopard frog (*Rana Pipiens*), mating behavior ceases following lesions in the preoptic region.

This very small number of investigations suggests some unity of neural regions involved in reproductive behavior throughout the vertebrates. However, the comparative aspects of vertebrate reproductive behavior is obviously a much-neglected field which is ripe for proper exploration.

IV. Concluding Remarks

The following points appear worthy of re-emphasis. In the male the complete copulatory pattern depends upon an arousal mechanism which is normally conditioned to various cues provided by the female. When this mechanism reaches a threshold level, the consummatory phase—ejaculation—takes place. It appears likely that the consummatory phase is dependent upon androgen, but different degrees of the arousal mechanism appear to function in the castrated animal, depending on species and previous experience.

In adult animals, sex hormones are activational on a substrate which has been developed at an earlier age. Thus, the hormone provides an essential link to unlock a pattern of previously established behavior.

To carry out this pattern, the male mammal requires a cerebral cortex, especially the sensory-motor and the motor-sensory projection areas. These appear necessary to the arousal mechanism, and there may be some organization of the appropriate motor pattern at this level in some mammals. The female can carry on complete reproduction in the absence of the cortex, but there is evidence that the cortex can influence the time and degree of the behavioral responses.

The major facilitation of complete mating responses occurs at the level of the diencephalon. Here it appears that the preoptic region and the anterior hypothalamus are essential for mating behavior in both male and female rats and in the female cat, guinea pig, hamster, and ewe. In the rabbit the posterior hypothalamus is essential. For female rats, cats, and rabbits, it has been shown that implantation of estrogen can result in a complete behavioral response at the same locus that a lesion will irreversibly cause deletion of the behavior (Fig. 12).

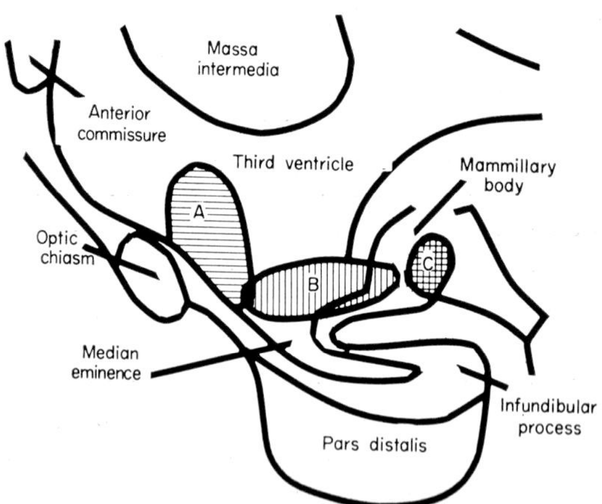

FIG. 12. Summary of data for diencephalic involvement in the mating behavior in the mammals. Lesioning of area A resulted in the reduction or elimination of mating behavior in the rat (male and female), and the female cat, guinea pig, hamster, and sheep. Hormone implant in area A results in mating behavior in the female cat and rat. Area B, lesioning results in gonad and reproductive tract atrophy for cats, rats, rabbits, etc.; however, following treatment with exogenous hormone, mating is still possible. Area C, lesions prevent mating in the female rabbit; hormone implant results in mating behavior.

In the male rat not only preoptic lesions but bilateral destruction of the lateral mammillary nuclei result in disappearance of sexual behavior.

Relatively little work has been done on the male, but there is a suggestion from the work on the rat that an integrating system in the preoptic region responds to the various modalities of exteroceptive and interoceptive stimuli. Summation of a sufficient number of afferent impulses initiates activity in the posterior hypothalamic region which results in the consummatory act of ejaculation.

While electrical stimulation of the anterior hypothalamic region has resulted in the display of complete sexual behavior by the male rat, the intensity and completeness of the behavior was dependent upon the presence of an estrous female. Similar stimulation in the posterior hypothalamus resulted in ejaculation without erections or overt signs of sexual behavior. Thus, ejaculation can apparently be separated from all other aspects of sex behavior.

Electrical stimulation in the female and EEG recordings during and after coitus point to a focus of activity in the preoptic and anterior hypothalamic region, but no changes have been found in the posterior regions. This may reflect the absence of a consummatory mechanism in the female. Electrical stimulation in the primate male indicates nodal points for erection and ejaculation in the thalamus and preoptic region. Both of these responses can be brought about separately by electrical stimulation. There appears to be a considerable degree of uniformity in the neural circuits involved in the expression of sexual behavior in male and female mammals. Brief reference has been made to the fact that during early developmental stages the sex hormones can influence developmental processes in the central nervous system to such a degree that sexual behavior patterns are completely repressed. This subject is discussed in detail in Chapter 19.

Important problems remain concerning the specific actions of hormones on the neurons and how behavior can be organized by the action of a hormone. There are many unanswered questions about sexual behavior in the male because in this sex a sequential series of events must occur to complete the mating reaction. Very little is known concerning how much of this sequence is actually hormone dependent and what regions of the nervous system are hormone sensitive in the male mammal.

References

Adey, W. R., Merrilles, N. C. R., and Sunderland, S. (1956). The entorhinal area, evoked potential, and histological studies of its interrelationships with brain-stem regions. *Brain* **79**, 414–439.

Adey, W. R., Sunderland, S., and Dunlop, C. W. (1957). The entorhinal area; electrophysiological studies of its interrelations with rhinencephalic structures and the brainstem. *EEG Clin. Neurophysiol.* **9**, 309–324.

Averill, R. L. W., and Purves, H. D. (1963). Differential effects of permanent hypothalamic lesions on reproduction and lactation in rats. *J. Endocrinol.* **26,** 463–477.

Ball, J. (1934). Sex behavior of the rat after removal of the uterus and vagina. *J. Comp. Physiol. Psychol.* **18,** 419–422.

Ball, J. (1937). A test for measuring sexual excitability in the female rat. *Comp. Psychol. Monogr.* **14,** No. 1.

Bard, P. (1939). Central nervous mechanisms for emotional behavior patterns in animals. *Res. Publ. Assoc. Res. Nervous Mental Disease* (*Proc.*) **19,** 190–218.

Bard, P. (1940). The hypothalamus and sexual behavior. *Res. Publ. Assoc. Res. Nervous Mental Disease* **20,** 551–579.

Barfield, R. J. (1964). Induction of copulatory behavior by intracranial placement of androgen in capons. *Am. Zoologist* **4,** 301.

Barraclough, C. A. (1959). Localized alterations in electrical activity of the hypothalamus associated with stimulation of the vaginal cervix in estrous rats. *Abstr. Commun. 21st Internat. Physiol. Congr. IUPS, Buenos Aires, 1959* p. 28. Excerpta Med. Found., Amsterdam.

Barraclough, C. A. (1960). Hypothalamic activation associated with stimulation of the vaginal cervix of proestrus rats. *Anat. Record* **136,** 159.

Barraclough, C. A. (1961). Production of anovulatory sterile rats by single injections of testosterone propionate. *Endocrinology.* **68,** 62–67.

Barraclough, C. A., and Cross, B. A. (1963). Unit activity in the hypothalamus of the cyclic female rat: effect of genital stimuli and progesterone. *J. Endocrinol.* **26,** 339–359.

Barraclough, C. A., and Gorski, R. A. (1962). Studies on mating behavior in the androgen-sterilized female rat in relation to the hypothalamic regulation of sexual behavior. *J. Endocrinol.* **25,** 175–182.

Beach, F. A. (1940). Effects of cortical lesions upon the copulatory behavior of male rats. *J. Comp. Psychol.* **29,** 193–239.

Beach, F. A. (1943). Effects of injury to the cerebral cortex upon the display of masculine and feminine mating behavior by female rats. *J. Comp. Psychol.* **36,** 169–199.

Beach, F. A. (1945). Hormonal induction of mating responses in a rat with congenital absence of gonadal tissue. *Anat. Record* **92,** 289–292.

Beach, F. A. (1952). Mechanisms of hormonal action upon behavior. *Ciba Found. Colloq. Endocrinol.* **3,** 209–215.

Beach, F. A. (1964). Biological bases for reproductive behavior. *In* "Social Behavior and Organization Among Vertebrates" (W. Etkin, ed.), pp. 117–142. Univ. of Chicago Press, Chicago, Illinois.

Beach, F. A., Zitrin, A., and Jaynes, J. (1955). Neural mediation of mating behavior in male cats. II. Contribution of the frontal cortex. *J. Exptl. Zool.* **130,** 381–401.

Beach, F. A., Zitrin, A., and Jaynes, J. (1956). Neural mediation of mating in male cats. I. Effects of unilateral and bilateral removal of the neocortex. *J. Comp. Physiol. Psychol.* **49,** 321–327.

Bogdanove, E. M., Parlow, A. F., Bogdanove, J. N., Bhargava, I., and Crabill, E. V. (1964). Specific LH and FSH bio-assays in rats with hypothalamic lesions and accessory sex gland hypertrophy. *Endocrinology* **74,** 114–122.

Brookhart, J. M., and Dey, F. L. (1941). Reduction of sexual behavior in male guinea pigs by hypothalamic lesions. *Am. J. Physiol.* **133,** 551–554.

Brookhart, J. M., Dey, F. L., and Ranson, S. W. (1940). Failure of ovarian hormones to cause mating reactions in spayed guinea pigs with hypothalamic lesions. *Proc. Soc. Exptl. Biol. Med.* **44,** 61–64.

Brooks, C. M. (1937). The role of the central cortex and of various sense organs in the excitation and execution of mating activity in the rabbit. *Am. J. Physiol.* **120,** 544–553.

Clark, G. (1942). Sexual behavior in rats with lesions in the anterior hypothalamus. *Am. J. Physiol.* **137,** 746–749.

Clegg, M. T., Santolucito, J. A., Smith, J. D., and Ganong, W. F. (1958). The effect of hypothalamic lesions on sexual behavior and estrous cycles in the ewe. *Endocrinology* **62,** 790–797.

Davidson, J. M., and Sawyer, C. H. (1961). Effects of localized intracerebral implantation of estrogen on reproductive function in the female rabbit. *Acta Endocrinol.* **37,** 385–393.

Davis, D. C. (1939). The effects of ablations of neocortex on mating, maternal behavior and the production of pseudopregnancy in the female rat and on copulation activity in the male. *Am. J. Physiol.* **127,** 374–380.

Dey, F. L., Leininger, C. R., and Ranson, S. W. (1942). The effects of hypothalamic lesions on mating behavior in female guinea pigs. *Endocrinology* **30,** 323–326.

De Groot, J. (1962). The influence of limbic brain structures on reproductive functions of female rats. *Abstr. Commun 22nd Internat. Congr. Physiol. Sci., Leiden, 1962, Excerpta Med., Intern. Congr. Ser.* **48.**

Everett, J. W., and Radford, H. M. (1961). Irritative deposits from stainless steel electrodes in the preoptic rat brain causing release of pituitary gonadotropin. *Proc. Soc. Exptl. Biol. Med.* **108,** 604–609.

Fisher, A. E. (1956). Maternal and sexual behavior induced by intracranial chemical stimulation. *Science* **124,** 228–229.

Fisher, C., Magoun, W. H., and Ranson, S. W. (1938). Dystocia in diabetes insipidus. *Am. J. Obstet. Gynecol.* **36,** 1–9.

Fuller, R. (1963). Sexual changes in the male rat following chronic administration of reserpine. *Nature* **200,** 585–586.

Fulton, J. F. A. (1939). Levels of autonomic function with particular reference to the cerebral cortex. *Res. Publ. Assoc. Res. Nervous Mental Disease* (*Proc.*) **19,** 219–236.

Gestaut, H. (1952). Corrélations entre le système nerveux végétatil et le système de la die de relation dans le rhinencéphale. *J. Physiol.* (*Paris*) **44,** 431–470.

Goldstein, A. C. (1957). The experimental control of sex behavior in animals. *In* "Hormones, Brain Function, and Behavior" (H. Hoagland, ed.), pp. 99–119. Academic Press, New York.

Gorski, R. A. (1963). Modification of ovulatory mechanisms by postnatal administration of estrogen to the rat. *Am. J. Physiol.* **205,** 842–844.

Goy, R. W., and Phoenix, C. H. (1963). Hypothalamic regulation of female sexual behavior: establishment of behavioral estrus in spayed guinea pigs following hypothalamic lesions. *J. Reprod. Fertility* **5,** 23–40.

Green, J. D. (1954). Electrical activity in hypothalamus and hippocampus of conscious rabbits. *Anat. Record* **118,** 304.

Green, J. D., and Arduini, A. A. (1954). Hippocampal electrical activity in arousal. *J. Neurophysiol.* **17,** 533–557.

Green, J. D., Clemente, C. D., and de Groot, J. (1957). Rhinencephalic lesions and behavior in cats. An analysis of the Klüver-Bucy syndrome with particular reference to normal and abnormal sexual behavior. *J. Comp. Neurol.* **108**, 505–545.

Greer, M. A. (1953). The effect of progesterone on persistent vaginal estrus produced by hypothalamic lesions in the rat. *Endocrinology* **53**, 380–390.

Greulich, W. W. (1934). Artificially induced ovulation in the cat (*Felis domestica*). *Anat. Record* **58**, 217–224.

Harris, G. W., Michael, R. P., and Scott, P. P. (1958). Neurological site of action of stilbesterol in eliciting sexual behavior. *Ciba Found. Symp., Neurol. Basis Behavior* pp. 236–254.

Heimer, L., and Larsson, K. (1964). Mating behavior in male rats after destruction of the mammillary bodies. *Acta Neurol. Scand.* **40**, 353–360.

Herberg, L. J. (1963). Seminal ejaculation following positively reinforcing electrical stimulation of the rat hypothalamus. *J. Comp. Physiol. Psychol.* **56**, 679–685.

Hillarp, N. Å. (1949). Studies on the localization of hypothalamic centers controlling the gonadotropic function of the hypophysis. *Acta Endocrinol.* **2**, 11–49.

Hillarp, N. Å., Olivercrona, H., and Silfverskiöld, W. (1954). Evidence for the participation of the preoptic area in male mating behavior. *Experientia* **10**, 224–227.

Höhn, E. O. (1961). Endocrine glands, thymus and pineal body. *In* "Biology and Comparative Physiology of Birds" (A. J. Marshall, ed.), Vol. II, pp. 87–114. Academic Press, New York.

Kawakami, M., and Sawyer, C. H. (1959). Induction of behavioral and electroencephalographic changes in the rabbit by hormone administration or brain stimulation. *Endocrinology* **65**, 631–643.

Kent, G. C., Jr., and Liberman, M. J. (1949). Induction of psychic estrus in the hamster with progesterone administered via the lateral brain ventricle. *Endocrinology* **45**, 29–32.

Klüver, H., and Bucy, P. C. (1937). "Psychic blindness" and other systems following bilateral temporal lobectomy in Rhesus monkeys. *Am. J. Physiol.* **119**, 352–353.

Larsson, K. (1962a). Mating behavior in male rats after cerebral cortex ablation. I. Effects of lesions in the dorsolateral and the median cortex. *J. Exptl. Zool.* **151**, 167–176.

Larsson, K. (1962b). Spreading cortical depression and the mating behavior in male and female rats. *Z. Tierpsychol.* **19**, 321–331.

Larsson, K. (1964). Mating behavior in male rats after cerebral cortex ablation. II. Effects of lesions in the frontal lobes compared to lesions in the posterior half of the hemispheres. *J. Exptl. Zool.* **155**, 203–224.

Larsson, K., and Heimer, L. (1964). Mating behavior of male rats after lesions in the preoptic area. *Nature* **202**, 413–414.

Law, T., and Meagher, W. (1958). Hypothalamic lesions and sexual behavior in the female rat. *Science* **128**, 1626–1627.

Lehrman, D. S. (1961). Hormonal regulation of parental behavior in birds and infrahuman mammals. *In* "Sex and Internal Secretions" (W. C. Young, ed.), 3rd ed., Vol. II, pp. 1268–1382. Williams & Wilkins, Baltimore, Maryland.

Levine, S., and Mullens, R. (1964). Estrogen administered neonatally affects adult sexual behavior in male and female rats. *Science* **144**, 185–187.

Lisk, R. D. (1960a). A comparison of the effectiveness of intravenous, as opposed to, subcutaneous injection of progesterone for the induction of estrous behavior in the rat. *Can. J. Biochem. Physiol.* **38**, 1381–1383.

Lisk, R. D. (1960b). Estrogen-sensitive centers in the hypothalamus of the rat. *J. Exptl. Zool.* **145**, 197–208.

Lisk, R. D. (1962a). Diencephalic placement of estradiol and sexual receptivity in the female rat. *Am. J. Physiol.* **203**, 493–496.

Lisk, R. D. (1962b). Testosterone-sensitive centers in the hypothalamus of the rat. *Acta Endocrinol.* **41**, 195–204.

Lisk, R. D. (1965). Reproductive capacity and behavioral estrus in the rat bearing hypothalamic implants of sex steroids. *Acta Endocrinol.* **48**, 209–219.

Lissák, K. (1962). Olfactory-induced sexual behavior in female cats. *Proc. 22nd Intern. Physiol. Congr. IUPS, Leiden, 1962* Vol. 1, Part 2, pp. 653–656. Excerpta Med. Found., Amsterdam.

MacLean, P. D. (1957). Chemical and electrical stimulation of hippocampus in unrestrained animals. Part II. Behavioral findings. *Arch. Neurol. Psychiat.* **78**, 128–142.

MacLean, P. D. (1962). New findings relevant to the evolution of psychosexual functions of the brain. *J. Nervous Mental Disease* **135**, 289–301.

MacLean, P. D., and Ploog, D. W. (1962). Cerebral representation of penile erection. *J. Neurophysiol.* **25**, 29–55.

MacLean, P. D., Sushil, D., and Denniston, R. H. (1963). Cerebral localization for scratching and seminal discharge. *Arch. Neurol.* **9**, 485–497.

Michael, R. P. (1962a). Estrogen-sensitive neurons and sexual behavior in female cats. *Science* **136**, 322–323.

Michael, R. P. (1962b). Estrogen-sensitive systems in mammalian brains. *Proc. 22nd Intern. Physiol. Congr. IUPS, Leiden, 1962* Vol. 1, Part 2, pp. 650–652. Excerpta Med. Found., Amsterdam.

Michael, R. P. (1965). The selective accumulation of estrogens in the neural and genital tissues of the cat. *Proc. 1st Intern. Congr. Hormonal Steroids, Milan, 1962* Vol. 2, pp. 469–481. Academic Press, New York.

Money, J. (1961). Sex hormones and other variables in human eroticism. *In* "Sex and Internal Secretions" (W. C. Young, ed.), 3rd ed., Vol. II, pp. 1383–1400. Williams & Wilkins, Baltimore, Maryland.

Noble, G. K., and Aronson, L. R. (1945). The sexual behavior of Anura. 2. Neural mechanisms controlling mating in the male leopard frog, *Rana pipiens*. *Bull. Am. Museum Nat. Hist.* **86**, 85–139.

Palka, Y. S., and Sawyer, C. H. (1964). Induction of estrous behavior in the ovariectomized rabbit by estrogen implants in the hypothalamus. *Am. Zoologist* **4**, 289.

Papez, J. W. (1937). A proposed mechanism of emotion. *Arch. Neurol. Psychiat.* **38**, 725–743.

Phoenix, C. H. (1961). Hypothalamic regulation of sexual behavior in male guinea pigs. *J. Comp. Physiol. Psychol.* **54**, 72–77.

Phoenix, C. H., Goy, R. W., Gerall, A. A., and Young, W. C. (1959). Organizing action of prenatally administered testosterone propionate on the tissues mediating mating behavior in the female guinea pig. *Endocrinology* **65**, 369–382.

Porter, R. W., Cavanaugh, E. B., Critchlow, B. V., and Sawyer, C. H. (1957). Localized changes in electrical activity of the hypothalamus in estrous cats following vaginal stimulation. *Am. J. Physiol.* **189**, 145–151.

Reynolds, R. W. (1963). Ventromedial hypothalamic lesions without hyperphagia. *Am. J. Physiol.* **204**, 60–62.

Rogers, F. T. (1922). Studies of the brain stem. VI. An experimental study of the corpus striatum of the pigeon as related to various instinctive types of behavior. *J. Comp. Neurol.* **35**, 21–60.

Sawyer, C. H. (1949). Reflex induction of ovulation in the estrogen-treated rabbit by artificial vaginal stimulation. *Anat. Record* **103**, 502.

Sawyer, C. H. (1959). Effects of brain lesions on estrous behavior and reflexogenous ovulation in the rabbit. *J. Exptl. Zool.* **142**, 227–246.

Sawyer, C. H. (1960). Reproductive behavior. *In* "Handbook of Physiology" (Am. Physiol. Soc., J. Field, ed.), Sect. 1, Vol. II, pp. 1225–1240. Williams & Wilkins, Baltimore, Maryland.

Sawyer, C. H. (1963). Induction of estrus in the ovariectomized cat by local hypothalamic treatment with estrogen. *Anat. Record* **145**, 280.

Sawyer, C. H., and Kawakami, M. (1961). Interactions between the central nervous system and hormones influencing ovulation. *In* "Control of Ovulation" (C. A. Villee, ed.), pp. 79–100. Pergamon Press, Oxford.

Sawyer, C. H., and Robison, B. (1956). Separate hypothalamic areas controlling pituitary gonadotropic function and mating behavior in female cats and rabbits. *J. Clin. Endocrinol.* **16**, 914–915.

Schreiner, L., and Kling, A. (1953). Behavioral changes following rhinencephalic injury in cat. *J. Neurophysiol.* **16**, 643–659.

Schreiner, L., and Kling, A. (1954). Effects of castration on hypersexual behavior induced by rhinencephalic injury in cat. *Arch. Neurol. Psychiat.* **72**, 180–186.

Schreiner, L., and Kling, A. (1956). Rhinencephalon and behavior. *Am. J. Physiol.* **184**, 486–490.

Soulairac, A., and Soulairac, M. L. (1956). Effects of hypothalamic lesions on the sexual behavior and genital tract of the male rat. *Ann. Endocrinol.* (*Paris*) **17**, 731–745.

Soulairac, M. L. (1963). Étude expérimentale des régulations hormono-nerveuses du comportement sexuel du Rat male. *Ann. Endocrinol.* (*Paris*) **24**, Suppl., 1–94.

Stone, C. P. (1939). Sex drive. *In* "Sex and Internal Secretions" (E. Allen *et al.*, eds.), 2nd ed., pp. 1213–1262. Williams & Wilkins, Baltimore, Maryland.

Valenstein, E. S., Riss, W., and Young, W. C. (1955). Experiential and genetic factors in the organization of sexual behavior in male guinea pigs. *J. Comp. Physiol. Psychol.* **48**, 397–403.

Vaughan, E., and Fisher, A. E. (1962). Male sexual behavior induced by electrical stimulation. *Science* **137**, 758–760.

Whalen, R. E., and Nadler, R. D. (1963). Suppression of the development of female mating behavior by estrogen administered in infancy. *Science* **141**, 273–274.

Wilson, J. G., and Young, W. C. (1941). Sensitivity to estrogen studied by means of experimentally induced mating responses in the female guinea pig and rat. *Endocrinology* **29**, 779–783.

Young, W. C. (1957). Genetic and psychological determinants of sexual behavior patterns. *In* "Hormones, Brain Function and Behavior" (H. Hoagland, ed.), pp. 75–98. Academic Press, New York.

Young, W. C. (1961). The hormones and mating behavior. *In* "Sex and Internal Secretions" (W. C. Young, ed.), 3rd ed., Vol. II, pp. 1173–1239. Williams & Wilkins, Baltimore, Maryland.

Young, W. C., Goy, R. W., and Phoenix, C. H. (1964). Hormones and sexual behavior. *Science* **143**, 212–218.

Zitrin, A., Jaynes, J., and Beach, F. A. (1956). Neural mediation of mating in male cats. III. Contribution of the occipital, parietal and temporal cortex. *J. Comp. Neurol.* **105**, 111–125.

CHAPTER 23

Melanocyte-Stimulating Hormone and the Intermediate Lobe of the Pituitary: Chemistry, Effects, and Mode of Action

RONALD R. NOVALES

I. Introduction

The study of the regulation of vertebrate color change is rich in examples of interest to neuroendocrinology. A complete neuroendocrine sequence of events has been established, relating background coloration to chromatophore response in certain lower vertebrates. Thus, in a frog on an illuminated dark background, a certain part of the retina is stimulated. The brain then brings about the release of melanocyte-stimulating hormone (MSH) from the intermediate lobe of the pituitary gland. This hormone produces dispersion of melanin in the melanophores of the skin, with a consequent darkening of the animal, resulting in adaptive color change. Among the many problems of interest to neuroendocrinologists are the mode of regulation of the intermediate lobe by the brain and the nature of the pathway between the retina and the pituitary. These problems as they relate to MSH are discussed in Chapter 24. This chapter is primarily concerned with the effects of MSH in the organism and the mechanisms by which it may affect target cells. It will be seen that MSH apparently affects the sodium permeability of the membranes of pigment-containing cells and other cells, so that the target cells affected by MSH have some similarities to neurons. Furthermore, there may even be similarities between the mode of action of MSH and neurohumors, e.g., acetylcholine, since both disperse melanin in the melanophores of bony fishes.

The textbooks by Gorbman and Bern (1962), Barrington (1963), and Turner (1966) provide background information on the control of skin color. Detailed reviews on MSH can be found in the books by Parker (1948), Fingerman (1963), and Waring (1963). Comparative aspects have been reviewed by Karkun and Landgrebe (1963), and the endocrinology has been kept up-to-date by the reviews of Waring and Landgrebe (1950), Landgrebe *et al.* (1955), and Barrington (1964).

II. Chemistry of Melanocyte-Stimulating Hormone

A. Early Developments

Melanocyte-stimulating hormone was discovered in tadpoles by the extirpation experiments of P. E. Smith and B. M. Allen (for references, see Waring, 1963). These results were later extended to the adult frog by Hogben and Winton, and Swingle demonstrated that the hormone is secreted by the intermediate lobe. Active extracts from ox pituitary powder were described in 1932 by B. Zondek and H. Krohn. Waring (1963) has reviewed the methods used in making these early preparations. They usually involved extraction with dilute acetic acid, followed by various procedures. Assays were commonly performed on intact or hypophysectomized frogs, utilizing the response of the web melanophores.

B. Isolation, Purification, and Structure

A homogeneous, highly active MSH was isolated from hog pituitary glands by Lerner and Lee (1955) and named α-MSH. This hormone consists of a sequence of thirteen amino acids with an N-terminal acetyl group, according to Harris and Lerner (1957). Another MSH (β-MSH) was also isolated from hog pituitary material by Geschwind *et al.* (1956) and Harris and Roos (1956). This molecule contains eighteen amino acids, and has less melanin-dispersing activity than α-MSH. The structures of these hormones are shown in Table I. Initially, there was considerable uncertainty about the relationship between MSH and adrenocorticotropic hormone (ACTH) because of the difficulties encountered

TABLE I

THE RELATIONSHIP BETWEEN THE STRUCTURE OF MELANOCYTE-STIMULATING HORMONE AND AMINO ACIDS 1–19 OF THE 39 AMINO ACIDS IN ADRENOCORTICOTROPIC HORMONE[a]

ACTH								Ser-	Tyr-	Ser-	Met-	Glu-	His-	Phe-	Arg-	Try-	Gly-	Lys-	Pro-	Val-	Gly-	Lys-	Lys-	Arg-	Arg-	Pro
(pig, sheep, beef)								1	2	3	4	5	6	7	8	9	10	11	12	13	14	15	16	17	18	19
α-MSH							CH_3CO-	Ser-	Tyr-	Ser-	Met-	Glu-	His-	Phe-	Arg-	Try-	Gly-	Lys-	Pro-	Val-	NH_2					
(pig, beef, horse)								1	2	3	4	5	6	7	8	9	10	11	12	13						
β-MSH					Asp-	Glu-	Gly-	Pro-	Tyr-	Lys-	Met-	Glu-	His-	Phe-	Arg-	Try-	Gly-	Ser-	Pro-	Pro-	Lys-	Asp				
(pig)					1	2	3	4	5	6	7	8	9	10	11	12	13	14	15	16	17	18				
β-MSH					Asp-	Ser-	Gly-	Pro-	Tyr-	Lys-	Met-	Glu-	His-	Phe-	Arg-	Try-	Gly-	Ser-	Pro-	Pro-	Lys-	Asp				
(beef)					1	2	3	4	5	6	7	8	9	10	11	12	13	14	15	16	17	18				
β-MSH					Asp-	Glu-	Gly-	Pro-	Tyr-	Lys-	Met-	Glu-	His-	Phe-	Arg-	Try-	Gly-	Ser-	Pro-	Arg-	Lys-	Asp				
(horse)					1	2	3	4	5	6	7	8	9	10	11	12	13	14	15	16	17	18				
β-MSH	Ala-	Glu-	Lys-	Lys-	Asp-	Glu-	Gly-	Pro-	Tyr-	Arg-	Met-	Glu-	His-	Phe-	Arg-	Try-	Gly-	Ser-	Pro-	Pro-	Lys-	Asp				
(human)	1	2	3	4	5	6	7	8	9	10	11	12	13	14	15	16	17	18	19	20	21	22				

[a] (From Li, 1961.)

in the separation of the two hormones (Sulman, 1952; Reinhardt *et al.*, 1952). It was later found that ACTH has inherent melanin-dispersing activity and a structure resembling that of the MSH's. The structure of α-MSH appears to be the same in all mammalian species, but there are slight differences in the β-MSH's (see Karkun and Landgrebe, 1963). These differences usually involve amino acid substitutions, but human β-MSH is also longer than hog β-MSH; it contains twenty-two amino acids (Harris, 1959). All the MSH's and the ACTH's in various mammalian species studied possess a "heptapeptide core" (Met-Glu-His-Phe-Arg-Try-Gly), which has some melanin-dispersing activity by itself. Although little is known about the MSH of cold-blooded vertebrates, Burgers (1963) has shown by electrophoretic methods that cod and bullfrog pituitaries contain some MSH components similar to the known mammalian hormones. In addition, bullfrog pituitaries contain an unknown component and pituitaries of the lizard *Anolis carolinensis* contain three components that do not correspond to any mammalian hormone tested. The biochemistry of the natural MSH's has been reviewed by Li (1957) and by Lee and Lerner (1959).

C. Synthesis

The great advances which have been made in this exciting and demanding field in recent years have been reviewed by Hofmann (1962), Hofmann and Yajima (1962), Li (1962), and Schwyzer (1964). Both α-MSH and bovine β-MSH have been synthesized and shown to have biological activities essentially like the natural hormones. Studies with peptides related to the hormones have provided information about the amino acid sequences required for melanin dispersion in the melanophores of isolated frog skin. This work has made use of the reflectometric technique of Shizume *et al.* (1954), which proved very useful in the isolation experiments. The studies have shown that melanin-dispersing activity probably resides largely in the last five amino acids of the "heptapeptide core," although some caution is in order in interpreting results of experiments such as those in which high concentrations of peptides were used (Schwyzer, 1964). Furthermore, the full structure of α-MSH is required for maximum activity. It is worth noting that tryptophan is present in the core. It is probable that tryptophan is important for receptor occupation by MSH, since MSH is competitively antagonized by melatonin (*N*-acetyl-5-methoxytryptamine) in its darkening effect on frog skin (Novales and Novales, 1965). The terminal acetyl group is important for α-MSH activity, since Guttmann and Boissonnas (1961) found that analogs lacking this group have greatly reduced biological activity. Furthermore, removal of the acetyl group from α-MSH or melatonin produces approximately the same degree of reduction in their respective darkening or lightening activity (Lerner and Lee, 1962); this provides further evidence that they may act on similar receptors in the frog melanophore.

D. Properties

Properties of the MSH's have been reviewed by Li (1957). Optical rotation studies show that β-MSH exists in an unfolded form; thus interaction with the receptor probably does not require coiling of the molecule. It has long been known that exposure of pituitary preparations to hot alkali increases their ability to disperse melanin (potentiation) and results in their having a more prolonged effect in the animal (protection). The early work on this subject has been reviewed by Waring (1963). Recently, the true nature of the effects of hot alkali has been revealed to some degree. Raben (1955) reported that these effects are accompanied by an increased resistance to proteolytic enzymes and decreased optical activity, suggesting racemization as the most reasonable explanation for them. Alkali-heat treatment of pure porcine α-MSH (Lee and Buettner-Janusch, 1963) or ACTH (Pickering and Li, 1964) causes substantial racemization of certain amino acids in the molecule. This is accompanied by increased resistance to tryptic or chymotryptic digestion in the case of α-MSH. Thus, protection can reasonably be explained as the result of racemization, rendering the hormone more resistant to enzymic destruction and permitting it to remain longer in the circulation. However, potentiation cannot be explained solely on this basis, for this effect requires the presence of a free N-terminal serine, not present in the MSH's (Pickering and Li, 1962).

Although the exact nature of the alkali-heat effect on the serine residue is still unknown, potentiation of pituitary extracts is probably due to the ACTH contained in them. A final interesting property is the susceptibility of the MSH's to reversible inactivation by oxidation. The available results indicate that formation of methionine sulfoxide is responsible for this effect (Hofmann, 1962), even though methionine is not required for melanin-dispersing activity. It is possible that fully effective binding of the hormone to receptor sites requires an intact methionine residue, as suggested by Hofmann.

III. Effects of Melanocyte-Stimulating Hormone

A. Chromatophores and Pigmentation

The most widely studied effect of MSH on chromatophores is the ability to produce melanin dispersion in the melanophores of cold-blooded vertebrates. A chromatophore is a pigment cell that is able to disperse or aggregate its pigment in response to appropriate stimuli. Melanophores are melanin-containing chromatophores. Melanocytes are melanin-producing and melanin-containing cells found in all vertebrates but the melanin in melanocytes cannot be dispersed or aggregated in response to stimuli, as it can in melanophores. In the vertebrates, melanophores are only found in fishes, amphibians, and reptiles. The melanin-containing cells of the skin of mammals and birds are melanocytes, rather than melanophores. They seem to possess the ability to donate melanin to other cells in feathers, hairs, or epidermis.

The effect of MSH on melanophores is most clearly seen in those vertebrate classes in which functional innervation of melanophores is lacking, e.g., the Agnatha, Chondrichthyes, and Amphibia. In the Osteichthyes (Pickford and Atz, 1957) and Reptilia, melanin dispersion does not occur in some species in response to MSH, presumably as a result of the largely nervous control of their melanophores. Another type of chromatophore usually responds to MSH by pigmentary dispersion; this is the lipophore, classically exemplified by the erythrophores of teleost fishes. However, the chemical identity of the lipophore-stimulating hormone with MSH has not yet been established with certainty.

Melanocyte-stimulating hormone is also able to increase the melanin content of the skins of cold-blooded vertebrates. Frieden and Bozer (1951) found that 8 weeks of MSH injections were required to increase the melanin content of frog skin by 41%. Karkun and Mukerji (1953) obtained a similar result using MSH that by their determinations was free of ACTH. The situation in fishes is more complicated. An MSH injection stimulates melanogenesis in *Fundulus heteroclitus* (Pickford and Kosto, 1957), but is unable to stimulate the formation of new melanophores in xanthic goldfish (Chavin, 1956). However, ACTH is effective in the latter process. The effect on guanophores, guanine-containing chromatophores, should also be mentioned; MSH produces guanophore contraction and a reduction in the guanine content of tadpole skin (Bagnara, 1958), the opposite of its effect on melanophores. Furthermore, the amino acid requirements for this effect parallel those for melanin dispersion (Bagnara, 1964). The same author has also shown that hypophysectomy reduces the pteridine content of the skin of frog tadpoles. This effect is partially repaired by MSH treatment for 2 weeks (Bagnara, 1961). It may be related to the effect on lipophores, since lipophore-containing skin of reptiles (Ortiz *et al.*, 1963) and amphibians (Obika and Bagnara, 1964) contains pteridines, often intimately associated with lipophores.

Since mammals and birds possess melanocytes, rather than melanophores, different methods must be used to study the pigmentary effects of MSH in these forms. This is the result of the virtual inability of melanocytes to disperse or aggregate their melanin. Lerner *et al.* (1954) found that natural MSH with no appreciable ACTH activity produces a darkening of human skin and nevi similar to that seen in patients with adrenal insufficiency. Similar results were obtained with synthetic α-MSH by McGuire and Lerner (1963). Darkening was accompanied by a decrease in skin reflectance in the latter experiments. The exact mechanism of this effect has not yet been clarified, but it presumably involves increased melanin synthesis in the melanocytes, followed by passage of melanin into overlying epidermal cells. In the guinea pig, in addition to increasing the number of melanocytes and amount of melanin in the abdominal wall, β-MSH increases the length, width, and complexity of the dendritic processes of the melanocytes (Snell, 1962). The latter effect was attributed to increased melanogenesis and was probably not the result of any melanin dispersion in the melanocytes. Finally, it should be pointed out that MSH increases the melanin content of hamster melanoma (Foster, 1959).

B. Extrachromatophoral Effects

A number of effects of the MSH's have been described that are comparable to the extraadrenal effects of ACTH (Engel, 1961). Some of these are shared with ACTH as a result of common amino acid sequences. Some of the effects can be roughly classified as hormonal. For example, natural or synthetic MSH's stimulate the thyroid gland of guinea pigs (Čehović, 1962) or mice (Bowers *et al.*, 1964), there being histological evidence for stimulation in the guinea pig similar to that obtained with thyrotropin (TSH). If these are direct effects, they may mean that TSH shares some amino acid sequences with the MSH's, but only determination of the structure of TSH will reveal whether or not this is the case; α-MSH is also closely related to α-corticotropin-releasing factor (α-CRF), although not necessarily identical to it (Schally *et al.*, 1960). It has been suggested that α-MSH may serve as a precursor for ACTH in the anterior pituitary. This is a reasonable possibility in view of the identity of the first thirteen amino acids in the two hormones. Various aspects of the complex problem posed by CRF have recently been reviewed by Hofmann (1962) and Schwyzer (1964). As to ACTH activity per se, α-MSH has many of the properties of ACTH *in vitro* (Steelman and Guillemin, 1959), although it is inactive *in vivo* (Hofmann, 1962). In addition, the MSH's have an adipokinetic effect, as does ACTH. *In vivo,* MSH has less adipokinetic activity than ACTH (Steelman and Smith, 1960). However, ACTH, TSH, α-MSH, and β-MSH all have a comparable degree of adipokinetic activity on guinea pig adipose tissue *in vitro,* according to Rudman *et al.* (1963). In view of the thyrotropic activity of MSH, it is of great interest that TSH also has lipolytic activity.

In addition, a variety of other effects of the MSH's are known. Several of these are on the nervous system itself, and thus of great potential interest to neuroendocrinology. For example, Ferrari and co-workers have found that injection of MSH or ACTH into the cisterna magna of dogs produces muscular hypertonus (stretching). A number of other hormones and drugs are ineffective in this regard. Ferrari *et al.* (1963) reviewed this work and reported on the inability of melatonin to antagonize the stretching response to MSH, even at high doses. This result suggests that there are differences in the receptors for melanophore stimulation and the stretching effect. The effect is not due to a contaminant, since a synthetic peptide related to MSH is also effective. It may have some relation to the regulation of sleeping and yawning behavior, of which little is known from an endocrine point of view. An effect on the electrical activity of neurons was first reported by Guillemin and Krivoy in 1960 and reviewed by Krivoy *et al.* (1963). Injection of β-MSH into cats increases the amplitude of spinal monosynaptic reflex potentials. Other hormones, e.g., α-MSH, ACTH, oxytocin, or vasopressin, are ineffective in this regard. These results were viewed as a clue that β-MSH may function as a neurohumor in mammals. This hypothesis received support from the finding that brain extracts produce an enzymic inactivation of β-MSH. Liver or muscle extracts are ineffective. Chlorpromazine was reported to reversibly antagonize the effect of β-MSH on the positive intermediary potential in the cat spinal cord. It was concluded that chlorpromazine may act to lower the central excitatory state of the nervous system by modifying the action of β-MSH. These results all demonstrated that β-MSH facilitates submaximally induced spinal reflexes in the cat, but did not reveal any modification of behavior associated with the effect. Krivoy *et al.* (1963) also noted that placing β-MSH in the aquarium water reduces the frequency of change of amplitude in the spontaneous discharge of the transparent knife fish, *Gymnotidae eigenmannia,* indicating a possible effect on the excitability of the nervous system of this fish. Krivoy *et al.* (1963) discussed these results in the light of the possibility that β-MSH and certain other peptides are neurohumors. If correct, this view would require production of β-MSH by neurons, and this is clearly different from the possibility that pituitary β-MSH affects nervous function.

Another effect which is not clearly nervous is the ability of ACTH or α-MSH to increase the heart rate in the dog heart-lung preparation (Krayer *et al.*, 1961). This effect does not depend upon intact stores of norepinephrine, since it occurs after reserpine pretreatment. The effect is almost exclusively upon the heart rate, in contrast to that of the sympathomimetic amines and those of agents which cause their release. The authors pointed out that these hormones may constitute a new class of substances with effects on the heart.

Effects on the eyes have also been described. To date, conflicting results have been obtained on dark adaptation. Hanaoka (1951) followed up earlier work and reported that MSH shortens the time required for dark adaptation in man. On the other hand, Kalant *et al.* (1959) failed to confirm this work in a careful study, using MSH prepared in a manner similar to that used by Hanaoka. Hanaoka (1953) also reported that MSH enhances the regeneration of bleached visual purple extracted from amphibian eyes, but this work has not been repeated with pure hormones. Another visual effect has recently been described by Dyster-Aas and Krakau (1964). They found that both MSH's and other related peptides are able to cause an "aqueous flare response" in the rabbit eye when administered systemically. Since the aqueous flare response is due to the presence of macromolecules in the aqueous humor, this may be evidence that MSH increases the permeability of the blood-aqueous humor barrier in the eye. The effect was correlated with the melanin-dispersing activity of the hormones and was elicited more readily in pigmented than in albino animals.

IV. Mode of Action of Melanocyte-Stimulating Hormone

A. Melanin Dispersion

The cellular mechanisms involved in producing melanin dispersion have been studied from a number of viewpoints, some referred to already. Useful reviews of this problem have been published by Lerner and Takahashi (1956), Lerner and Case (1959) and Novales (1962). The subject is also discussed in the books by Fingerman (1963) and by Barrington (1963). The most generally useful system for studies of MSH action has been the isolated frog skin. Frog skin pales when rinsed in Ringer's solution and darkens upon addition of MSH. Darkening can be measured as a decrease in transmission (P. A. Wright, 1948; Frieden *et al.*, 1948) or reflectance (Shizume *et al.*, 1954). The skin of other cold-blooded species is also suitable, but frog skin has been used most widely.

Melanophores in tissue culture have permitted studies not possible with skin. The most valuable cells for this purpose have been embryonic salamander melanophores from *Taricha* (Novales, 1960), *Ambystoma* (Zimmerman and Dalton, 1961), or *Xenopus* (Kulemann, 1960). These cells are in an intermediate state of expansion; addition of pituitary powder (Twitty, 1945), natural β-MSH (Novales, 1960), synthetic α-MSH (Novales, 1963), or ACTH (Zimmerman and Dalton, 1961) produces melanin dispersion accompanied usually by cellular expansion. There is also an increase in the cellular perimeter in *Ambystoma* melanophores (Novales and Novales, 1962, 1965). This effect is in contrast to the responses of melanophores in fish scales (Matthews, 1931) or frog skin (Hewer, 1923); in these melanophores, as revealed by the light microscope, the melanin granules disperse in a cell of fixed outline. The difference in response may be the result of the isolated condition in culture, since Kulemann (1960) found that isolated melanophores respond by shape changes, whereas those in an epithelial sheet respond only with melanin dispersion. On the other hand, Hu (1963) claims that cultured fish melanocytes respond by shape changes but melanophores respond only by pigment movements. Thus, it is possible that the cultured melanophores studied from salamanders are really melanocytes, but this would be difficult to prove. In any case, MSH may be bringing about a net synthesis of cell membrane in the responding cells.

Quite a bit has been learned bearing on the mechanism of melanin dispersion. The need for various amino acids in α-MSH has been clarified, as referred to in Section II,C. Physicochemical aspects have also been studied. The force which propels the melanin granules during dispersion is still largely unknown, but some educated guesses can be made about it. Work on fish scale melanophores by Marsland (1944) showed that there is solation of peripheral cytoplasm during melanin dispersion. Presumably, the melanin granules move outward during dispersion into the cytoplasm of the processes, which is more fluid in the sol state. Gelation, on the other hand, involves a solidifying of the cytoplasm, and there is evidence that cytoplasm is in the gel state in the central region of fish melanophores with concentrated melanin. Forsdahl (1959) obtained electron-microscopic evidence in *Anolis carolinensis* for the movement of melanin within a cell of fixed outline. She also obtained evidence for a solation during melanin dispersion, which is produced by MSH in this species. The ground cytoplasm is clear in the processes of melanophores with dispersed melanin. On the other hand, the ground cytoplasm of the central region of such a melanophore is electron dense. These results support the view that melanin dispersion results from the expulsion of melanin granules by dense central cytoplasm into the less-dense cytoplasm of the processes.

The converse is true in melanophores with aggregated melanin, resulting from the removal of MSH. These have dense cytoplasm in the processes and less-dense central cytoplasm. Assuming that the electron density of cytoplasm is related to its physical state, this view now requires an explanation of just precisely how MSH produces peripheral solation and central gelation of the ground cytoplasm to produce melanin dispersion. On the other hand, other possible mechanisms of melanin dispersion must be kept in mind, such as the electrophoretic mechanism proposed by Kinosita (1963) or the melanin-containing "intracellular sac" described by Falk and Rhodin (1957) with the electron microscope. Furthermore, the probability is high that both membrane and cytoplasmic changes occur during melanin dispersion in response to MSH.

Several theories of MSH action have been proposed which are based on studies with metabolic inhibitors. Thus, P. A. Wright (1955) suggested that MSH may produce melanin dispersion by inhibiting glycolysis, since inhibitors of glycolysis such as iodoacetate inhibit paling. It has been postulated that MSH produces melanin dispersion by inhibiting the glycolysis necessary for the maintenance of the aggregated state. On the other hand, Horowitz (1957) advanced the suggestion that MSH acts by tying up sulfhydryl (SH) groups necessary for the maintenance of the aggregated state. Evidence consisted in the finding that SH-binding agents (e.g., mersalyl) mimic MSH action on *Anolis* skin and SH-donors (e.g., cysteine) inhibit MSH action. These theories have shed interesting light on the problem but have not stimulated much further work. Barrington's (1963) discussion of the conflicting evidence regarding metabolic aspects of melanophore responses clearly shows the need for further research in this area.

Another approach has been to focus on the change in cytoplasmic state, rather than on the role of metabolism in the response. Lerner and Takahashi (1956) felt that MSH might be producing cytoplasmic solation by changing the permeability of the melanophore membrane to ions. Suggestions such as this and that of Jöchle (1958) are in accord with the view that an ionic mechanism is involved in MSH action. The first clear evidence for such a mechanism was the demonstration by Novales (1959) that sodium is necessary for the response of frog melanophores to MSH or ACTH. The sodium requirement is specific to MSH or ACTH action, since mersalyl or caffeine can darken frog skin in sodium-free media. Since melanin dispersion can occur in the absence of sodium, it is likely that sodium is involved in the primary event or events by which MSH acts on the cell to produce melanin dispersion. Further evidence for the crucial role played by sodium came from the demonstration that frog skin will even *pale* in the presence of MSH in a sodium-free medium. This eliminates the possibility that MSH produces melanin dispersion directly, without the participation of sodium. The sodium requirement was confirmed in frog skin by M. R. Wright and Lerner (1960) and extended to cultured melanophores by Novales and Novales (1961). Cultured melanophores contract in sodium-free potassium medium and this even occurs in the presence of MSH. Further work showed that the requirement for sodium is *absolute,* since neither lithium nor any other of a large series of monovalent or divalent cations will replace sodium (Novales *et al.,* 1962). Dikstein *et al.* (1963) have reported that calcium at a concentration of 10 m*M* will replace sodium in permitting the response of *Hyla arborea* skin to MSH, but R. R. Novales (unpublished observations, 1964) was unable to confirm this observation in *Rana pipiens* skin.

The implications of the sodium dependence of MSH action have been thoroughly discussed by Novales (1959, 1962). The most likely interpretation is that MSH increases the permeability of the melanophore membrane to sodium, although the possibility exists that MSH inhibits the extrusion of sodium from the cell. The result of either effect would be the net accumulation of sodium in the cell, resulting in the triggering of melanin dispersion. Unfortunately, no direct evidence is available that MSH increases the sodium content of melanophores; the assumption is based on the fact that the sodium-dependent excitation of nerve and muscle involves the movement of sodium into the cell. Several possible mechanisms exist by which sodium entry might be coupled to melanin dispersion. Water entry could be the means. Sodium accumulation in cells is known to be accompanied by water accumulation. Water entry produces melanin dispersion in frog melanophores (Shizume *et al.,* 1954; Novales, 1959) and expansion of tissue-cultured melanophores (Kulemann, 1960; Novales and Novales, 1965). Melanin dispersion could also result from the bioelectric change which might accompany sodium entry, as a result of intracellular electrophoresis. A third method of coupling sodium entry to melanin dispersion is the possibility that sodium entry produces a direct solation of the peripheral cytoplasm. The sodium permeability mechanism is analogous to the mechanism by which acetylcholine probably produces melanin dispersion in teleost melanophores, by analogy with the mechanism of action of acetylcholine in muscle and nerve. The possibility that sodium is required for an action on the nucleus is rendered unlikely by recent work. R. R. Novales (unpublished observations, 1964) found that actinomycin D, an inhibitor of messenger RNA synthesis, is without any consistent effect on the response of frog melanophores to MSH. Puromycin, an inhibitor of protein synthesis, is also without effect. Results obtained in studies with calcium tend to support the view that MSH action involves a change in sodium permeability. Thus, the frog melanophore response to MSH is heightened by a reduction in the calcium content of the tissue (Novales *et al.,* 1962). Caffeine action is not similarly enhanced. Since calcium ion reduces sodium permeability, this result is in accord with the view that MSH is enhancing permeability. Furthermore, cultured melanophores do not respond to MSH in a calcium-free medium (Novales and Novales, 1965), recalling the inexcitability of neurons in the absence of calcium.

Tercafs (1963) found that there is no direct relation between the modification of frog skin permeability by an agent and its effect on frog melanophores. This is to be expected even if the above theory were correct, since melanophore cellular membranes are not necessarily responsive to the same agents as frog epithelial cells. As Tercafs points out, the action of MSH on the melanophore is highly specific. There is also no relationship between the effect of an agent on frog skin sodium transport and its effect on melanophores, but one cannot necessarily argue on this basis that MSH is not affecting sodium extrusion from the melanophore. The ionic and osmotic requirements are not confined solely to vertebrate melanophore responses, for Fingerman *et al.* (1963) have shown that the response of fiddler crab (*Uca*) melanophores to sinus gland hormone requires the presence of a monovalent cation and is influenced by the osmotic pressure of the medium. Potassium or lithium will replace sodium in the *Uca* response, in contrast to the frog system. Finally, van de Veerdonk (1962) has suggested that MSH may act on the ground substance of the dermal connective tissue to liberate potassium, which then brings about melanin dispersion by exchanging between the melanophore and the extracellular fluid. This view is rendered unlikely on three counts: (1) MSH will act on cultured melanophores apart from connective tissue (*vide supra*); (2) although van de Veerdonk (1962) showed that potassium has a slight darkening effect on *Xenopus* skin, it can only darken *Rana* skin one-fifth as effectively as MSH, even when all the sodium of Ringer's solution is replaced by potassium (Novales, 1959); (3) there is no potassium requirement for MSH action on frog skin, since MSH is effective in isotonic sodium chloride lacking any potassium (Novales, 1959). In summary, the view that MSH is modifying sodium permeability is in accord with much of the available evidence and explains many aspects of the response, even the graded nature of the log-dose response curve (Novales, 1959).

B. Melanin Synthesis

The mechanism for enhancement of melanin synthesis by MSH's is probably related to prolonged melanin dispersion, according to Odiorne (1948). Lerner (1959) has amplified this view and suggested that increased melanin synthesis occurs as a consequence of bringing the tyrosinase-bearing melanin granules into contact with more substrate. Treatment with MSH does not increase the extractable tyrosinase content of frog skin (Purvis and Denstedt, 1957). However, MSH treatment does enhance the ability of *Fundulus* skin to darken in solutions containing dihydroxyphenylalanine at the same time that it is increasing the melanophore content of the skin (Kosto *et al.*, 1959). Interesting work has recently appeared bearing on the mechanism of formation of melanophores in xanthic goldfish. Chavin *et al.* (1963) found that stress-induced melanogenesis is accompanied by an increase in both absolute and particulate tyrosinase activity in the skin. Furthermore, Kim *et al.* (1961) have obtained evidence by the use of colchicine that the formation of melanophores from promelanophores by ACTH involves a nuclear division. Recent work by Tchen *et al.* (1964) has shown that both α- and β-MSH are active in this regard, although earlier reports by Hu and Chavin (1960) had stated that MSH is inactive in promoting melanogenesis *in vitro*.

V. Concluding Remarks

The significant advances of the past decade in the chemistry of the MSH's have made possible great progress in the physiology of these hormones. Demonstration of extrachromatophoral effects has both illuminated and complicated the question of the function of these hormones, but it is not certain that the MSH's have any physiological functions other than control of pigmentation. However, the existence of extrachromatophoral effects reinforces the view that consideration of function should extend beyond the immediate area covered by the name of a tropic hormone to include other possible functions. The demonstration of effects on the nervous system may eventually lead to the delineation of a role for MSH in nerve physiology. Finally, the real possibility that MSH acts on melanophores by an ionic and osmotic mechanism indicates that there is a similarity between melanophores and neurons. The field of neuroendocrinology should rightly be concerned with possible common mechanisms of cellular control by neurohumors and hormones, as well as the more traditional topics of neurosecretion and the nervous control of endocrine function.

References

Bagnara, J. T. (1958). Hypophyseal control of guanophores in anuran larvae. *J. Exptl. Zool.* **137**, 265–284.

Bagnara, J. T. (1961). Chromatotrophic hormone, pteridines, and amphibian pigmentation. *Gen. Comp. Endocrinol.* **1**, 124–133.

Bagnara, J. T. (1964). Stimulation of melanophores and guanophores by melanophore-stimulating hormone peptides. *Gen. Comp. Endocrinol.* **4**, 290–294.

Barrington, E. J. W. (1963). "An Introduction to General and Comparative Endocrinology," p. 257. Oxford Univ. Press (Clarendon), London and New York.

Barrington, E. J. W. (1964). Hormones and the control of color. *In* "The Hormones" (G. Pincus *et al.*, eds.) Vol. IV, pp. 299–363. Academic Press, New York.

Bowers, C. Y., Redding, T. W., and Schally, A. V. (1964). Effects of α- and β-melanocyte stimulating hormones and other peptides on the thyroid in mice. *Endocrinology* **74**, 559–566.

Burgers, A. C. J. (1963). Melanophore stimulating hormones in vertebrates. *Ann. N.Y. Acad. Sci.* **100**, 669–677.

Čehović, G. (1962). Action des hormones mélanophorétiques (MSH) sur la fonction thyroïdenne chez la cobaye. *Compt. Rend.* **254**, 1872–1874.

Chavin, W. (1956). Pituitary-adrenal control of melanization in xanthic goldfish, *Carassius auratus* L. *J. Exptl. Zool.* **133**, 1–46.

Chavin, W., Kim, K., and Tchen, T. T. (1963). Endocrine control of pigmentation. *Ann. N.Y. Acad. Sci.* **100**, 678–685.

Dikstein, S., Weller, C. P., and Sulman, F. G. (1963). Effect of calcium ions on melanophore dispersal. *Nature* **200**, 1106.

Dyster-Aas, K., and Krakau, C. E. T. (1964). Increased permeability of the blood-aqueous humor barrier in the rabbit's eye provoked by melanocyte stimulating peptides. *Endocrinology* **74**, 255–265.

Engel, F. L. (1961). Extra-adrenal actions of adrenocorticotropin. *Vitamins Hormones* **19**, 189–227.

Falk, S., and Rhodin, J. (1957). Mechanism of pigment migration within teleost melanophores. *Proc. Reg. Conf. (Eur.) Electron Microscopy, Stockholm, 1956* pp. 213–215. Academic Press, New York.

Ferrari, W., Gessa, G. L., and Vargui, L. (1963). Behavioral effects induced by intracisternally injected ACTH and MSH. *Ann. N.Y. Acad. Sci.* **104**, 330–343.

Fingerman, M.(1963). "The Control of Chromatophores." Pergamon Press, Oxford.

Fingerman, M., Miyawaki, M., and Oguro, C. (1963). Effects of osmotic pressure and cations on the response of the melanophores in the fiddler crab, *Uca pugnax*, to the melanin-dispersing principle from the sinus gland. *Gen. Comp. Endocrinol.* **3**, 496–504.

Forsdahl, K. A. (1959). Mechanism of pigment-granule movement in melanophores of the lizard *Anolis carolinensis*. *Nytt Mag. Zool.* **8**, 37–44.

Foster, M. (1959). Physiological studies of melanogenesis. *In* "Pigment Cell Biology" (M. Gordon, ed.), pp. 301–313. Academic Press, New York.

Frieden, E. H., and Bozer, J. M. (1951). Effect of administration of intermedin upon melanin content of the skin of *Rana pipiens*. *Proc. Soc. Exptl. Biol. Med.* **77**, 35–37.

Frieden, E. H., Fishbein, J. W., and Hisaw, F. L. (1948). An *in vitro* bioassay for intermedin. *Arch. Biochem.* **17**, 183–189.

Geschwind, I. I., Li, C. H., and Barnafi, L. (1956). Isolation and structure of melanocyte-stimulating hormone from porcine pituitary glands. *J. Am. Chem. Soc.* **78**, 4494–4495.

Gorbman, A., and Bern, H. A. (1962). "A Textbook of Comparative Endocrinology," p. 86. Wiley, New York.

Guttman, S., and Boissonnas, R. A. (1961). Influence of the structure of the N-terminal extremity of α-MSH on the melanophore stimulating activity of this hormone. *Experientia* **17**, 265–270.

Hanaoka, T. (1951). Effect of melanophore hormone on the scotopic vision of human eye. *Japan. J. Physiol.* **2**, 9–16.

Hanaoka, T. (1953). Potency of melanophore hormone toward the regeneration of visual purple. *Japan. J. Physiol.* **3**, 219–230.

Harris, J. I. (1959). Structure of a melanocyte-stimulating hormone from the human pituitary gland. *Nature* **184**, 167–169.

Harris, J. I., and Lerner, A. B. (1957). Amino-acid sequence of the α-melanocyte-stimulating hormone. *Nature* **179**, 1346–1347.

Harris, J. I., and Roos, P. (1956). Amino-acid sequence of a melanophore-stimulating peptide. *Nature* **178**, 90.

Hewer, H. R. (1923). Studies in amphibian colour change. *Proc. Roy. Soc.* **B95**, 31–41.

Hofmann, K. (1962). Chemistry and function of polypeptide hormones. *Ann. Rev. Biochem.* **31**, 213–246.

Hofmann, K., and Yajima, H. (1962). Synthetic pituitary hormones. *Recent Progr. Hormone Res.* **18**, 41–83.

Horowitz, S. B. (1957). The effect of sulfhydryl inhibitors and thiol compounds on pigment aggregation and dispersion in the melanophores of *Anolis carolinensis*. *Exptl. Cell Res.* **13**, 400–402.

Hu, F. (1963). Hormonal influence on goldfish pigment cells *in vitro*. *In* "Cinemicrography in Cell Biology" (G. C. Rose, ed.), pp. 339–356. Academic Press, New York.

Hu, F., and Chavin, W. (1960). Hormonal stimulation of melanogenesis in tissue culture. *J. Invest. Dermatol.* **34**, 377–391.

Jöchle, W. (1958). Melanophorotrope Wirkstoffe im Säugetierorganismus und ihre mögliche Bedeutung. *In* "Hormone und Psyche: Die Endokrinologie des alternden Menschen," pp. 351–355. Springer, Berlin.

Kalant, H., Ogilvie, J. C., Smith, L. C., Taylor, N. B. G., and Walker, I. G. (1959). Effect of melanophore-stimulating hormone on human dark adaptation. *Can. J. Biochem. Physiol.* **37**, 829–841.

Karkun, J. N., and Landgrebe, F. W. (1963). Pituitary hormones affecting the chromatophores. *In* "Comparative Endocrinology" (U. S. von Euler and H. Heller, eds.), Vol. I, pp. 81–110. Academic Press, New York.

Karkun, J. N., and Mukerji, B. (1953). Studies on chromatophorotropic hormone of the pituitary gland. III. The influence of melanophore hormone upon the synthesis of melanin pigments in the skin of frogs (*Rana tigrina*). *Indian J. Med. Res.* **41**, 467–471.

Kim, K., Tchen, T. T., and Hu, F. (1961). Studies on ACTH-induced melanocyte formation: Effect of colchicine. *Exptl. Cell Res.* **25**, 454–457.

Kinosita, H. (1963). Electrophoretic theory of pigment migration within fish melanophore. *Ann. N.Y. Acad. Sci.* **100**, 992–1003.

Kosto, B., Pickford, G. E., and Foster, M. (1959). Further studies of the hormonal induction of melanogenesis in the killifish, *Fundulus heteroclitus*. *Endocrinology* **65**, 869–881.

Krayer, O., Astwood, E. B., Waud, D. R., and Alper, M. H. (1961). Rate-increasing action of corticotropin and of α-intermedin in the isolated mammalian heart. *Proc. Natl. Acad. Sci. U.S.* **47**, 1227–1236.

Krivoy, W. A., Lane, M., and Kroeger, D. C. (1963). The actions of certain polypeptides on synaptic transmission. *Ann. N.Y. Acad. Sci.* **104**, 312–329.

Kulemann, H. (1960). Untersuchungen der Pigmentbewegungen in embryonalen Melanophoren von *Xenopus laevis* in Gewebekulturen. *Zool. Jahrb., Abt. Algem. Zool. Physiol. Tiere* **69**, 169–197.

Landgrebe, F. W., Ketterer, B., and Waring, H. (1955). Hormones of the posterior pituitary. *In* "The Hormones" (G. Pincus and K. V. Thimann, eds.), Vol. III, pp. 389–431. Academic Press, New York.

Lee, T. H., and Buettner-Janusch, V. (1963). On the mechanism of sodium hydroxide modification of α-melanocyte-stimulating hormone. *J. Biol. Chem.* **238**, 2012–2015.

Lee, T. H., and Lerner, A. B. (1959). Melanocyte-stimulating hormones from pituitary glands. *In* "Pigment Cell Biology" (M. Gordon, ed.), pp. 435–442. Academic Press, New York.

Lerner, A. B. (1959). Mechanism of hormone action. *Nature* **184**, 674–677.

Lerner, A. B., and Case, J. D. (1959). Pigment cell regulatory factors. *J. Invest. Dermatol.* **32**, 211–221.

Lerner, A. B., and Lee, T. H. (1955). Isolation of homogeneous melanocyte stimulating hormone from hog pituitary glands. *J. Am. Chem. Soc.* **77**, 1066–1067.

Lerner, A. B., and Lee, T. H. (1962). The melanocyte-stimulating hormones. *Vitamins Hormones* **20**, 337–346.

Lerner, A. B., and Takahashi, Y. (1956). Hormonal control of melanin pigmentation. *Recent Progr. Hormone Res.* **12**, 303–320.

Lerner, A. B., Shizume, K., and Bunding, I. (1954). The mechanism of endocrine control of melanin pigmentation. *J. Clin. Endocrinol. Metab.* **14**, 1463–1490.

Li, C. H. (1957). Hormones of the anterior pituitary gland. II. Melanocyte-stimulating and lactogenic hormones. *Advan. Protein Chem.* **12**, 269–317.

Li, C. H. (1961). Some aspects of the relation of peptide structure to activity in pituitary hormones. *Vitamins Hormones* **19**, 313–329.

Li, C. H. (1962). Synthesis and biological properties of ACTH peptides. *Recent Progr. Hormone Res.* **18**, 1–32.

McGuire, J. S., and Lerner, A. B. (1963). Effects of tricosapeptide "ACTH" and alpha-melanocyte-stimulating hormone on the skin color of man. *Ann. N.Y. Acad. Sci.* **100**, 622–629.

Marsland, D. A. (1944). Mechanism of pigment displacement in unicellular chromatophores. *Biol. Bull.* **87**, 252–261.

Matthews, S. A. (1931). Observations on pigment migration within the fish melanophore. *J. Exptl. Zool.* **58**, 471–486.

Novales, R. R. (1959). The effects of osmotic pressure and sodium concentration on the response of melanophores to intermedin. *Physiol. Zool.* **32**, 15–28.

Novales, R. R. (1960). Responses of tissue-cultured embryonic newt melanophores to epinephrine and intermedin. *Trans. Am. Microscop. Soc.* **79**, 25–33.

Novales, R. R. (1962). The role of ionic factors in hormone action on the vertebrate melanophore. *Am. Zoologist* **2**, 337–352.

Novales, R. R. (1963). Responses of cultured melanophores to the synthetic hormones, α-MSH, melatonin and epinephrine. *Ann. N.Y. Acad. Sci.* **100,** 1035–1047.

Novales, R. R., and Novales, B. J. (1961). Sodium dependence of intermedin action on melanophores in tissue culture. *Gen. Comp. Endocrinol.* **1,** 134–144.

Novales, R. R., and Novales, B. J. (1962). Dynamics of tissue-cultured melanophore responses to hormones, as revealed by frame analysis. *Am. Zoologist* **2,** 545.

Novales, R. R., and Novales, B. J. (1965). The effects of osmotic pressure and calcium deficiency on the response of tissue-cultured melanophores to melanocyte-stimulating hormone. *Gen. Comp. Endocrinol.* **5,** 568–576.

Novales, R. R., and Novales, B. J. (1965). Analysis of antagonisms between pineal melatonin and other agents which act on amphibian melanophores. *Progr. Brain Res.* **10,** 507–519.

Novales, R. R., Novales, B. J., Zinner, S. H., and Stoner, J. S. (1962). The effects of sodium, chloride, and calcium concentration on the response of melanophores to melanocyte-stimulating hormone (MSH). *Gen. Comp. Endocrinol.* **2,** 286–295.

Obika, M., and Bagnara, J. T. (1964). Pteridines as pigments in amphibians. *Science* **143,** 485–487.

Odiorne, J. M. (1948). Morphological color changes in vertebrates. *In* "Biology of Melanomas," Spec. Publ. No. 4 (M. Gordon, ed.), pp. 288–308. N.Y. Acad. Sci. New York.

Ortiz, E., Büchli, E., Price, D., and Williams-Ashman, H. G. (1963). Red pteridine pigments in the dewlaps of some anoles. *Physiol. Zool.* **36,** 97–103.

Parker, G. H. (1948). "Animal Colour Changes and their Neurohumors." Cambridge Univ. Press, London and New York.

Pickering, B. T., and Li, C. H. (1962). Some aspects of the relationship between chemical structure and melanocyte-stimulating properties of several peptides related to adrenocorticotropin, *Biochim. Biophys. Acta* **62,** 475–482.

Pickering, B. T., and Li, C. H. (1964). Adrenocorticotropins. XXIX. The action of sodium hydroxide on adrenocorticotropin. *Arch. Biochem. Biophys.* **104,** 119–127.

Pickford, G. E., and Atz, J. W. (1957). "The Physiology of the Pituitary Gland of Fishes," p. 32. N.Y. Zool. Soc., New York.

Pickford, G. E., and Kosto, B. (1957). Hormonal induction of melanogenesis in hypophysectomized killifish (*Fundulus heteroclitus*). *Endocrinology* **61,** 177–196.

Purvis, J. L., and Denstedt, O. F. (1957). The extraction and assay of the tyrosinase from frog skin. A study on the influence of the melanophore-stimulating hormone on the synthesis of the enzyme. *Can. J. Biochem. Physiol.* **35,** 961–975.

Raben, M. S. (1955). The nature of the effect of alkali on intermedin. *J. Clin. Endocrinol. Metab.* **15,** 842–843.

Reinhardt, W. O., Geschwind, I. I., Porath, J. O., and Li, C. H. (1952). Significance of intermedin activity in adrenocorticotropic hormone preparations. *Proc. Soc. Exptl. Biol. Med.* **80,** 439–442.

Rudman, D., Brown, S. J., and Malkin, M. F. (1963). Adipokinetic actions of adrenocorticotropin, thyroid-stimulating hormone, vasopressin, α- and β-melanocyte-stimulating hormones, fraction H, epinephrine and norepinephrine in the rabbit, guinea pig, hamster, rat, pig, and dog. *Endocrinology* **72,** 527–543.

Schally, A. V., Andersen, R. N., Lipscomb, H. S., Long, J. M., and Guillemin, R. (1960). Evidence for the existence of two corticotrophin-releasing factors, α and β. *Nature* **188,** 1192–1193.

Schwyzer, R. (1964). Chemistry and metabolic action of nonsteroid hormones. *Ann. Rev. Biochem.* **33,** 259–286.

Shizume, K., Lerner, A. B., and Fitzpatrick, T. B. (1954). *In vitro* bioassay for the melanocyte-stimulating hormone. *Endocrinology* **54**, 553–560.

Snell, R. S. (1962). Effect of the melanocyte stimulating hormone of the pituitary on melanocytes and melanin in the skin of guinea pigs. *J. Endocrinol.* **25**, 249–258.

Steelman, S. L., and Guillemin, R. (1959). Adrenocorticotropic activity of alpha melanocyte stimulating hormone (α-MSH). *Proc. Soc. Exptl. Biol. Med.* **101**, 600–601.

Steelman, S. L., and Smith, W. W. (1960). The adipokinetic activities of corticotrophins and melanocyte stimulating hormones. *Acta Endocrinol.* **33**, 67–72.

Sulman, F. G. (1952). Chromatophorotropic effect of adrenocorticotrophic hormone. *Nature* **169**, 588–589.

Tchen, T. T., Ammeraal, R. N., Kim, K., Wilson, C. M., Chavin, W., and Hu, F. (1964). Studies on the hormone-induced differentiation of melanoblasts in explants from xanthic goldfish tailfin. *Natl. Cancer Inst. Monogr.* **13**, 67–80.

Tercafs, R. R. (1963). Comparative study of the action of some pharmacological substances on chromatophores and on permeability characteristics of amphibian skin. *Gen. Comp. Endocrinol.* **3**, 734–735.

Turner, C. D. (1966). "General Endocrinology," 4th ed., p. 157. Saunders, Philadelphia, Pennsylvania.

Twitty, V. C. (1945). The developmental analysis of specific pigment patterns. *J. Exptl. Zool.* **100**, 141–178.

van de Veerdonk, F. C. G. (1962). Mechanism of hormone action in color change in amphibia. *Gen. Comp. Endocrinol.* **2**, 623–624.

Waring, H. (1963). "Color Change Mechanisms of Cold-Blooded Vertebrates." Academic Press, New York.

Waring, H., and Landgrebe, F. W. (1950). Hormones of the posterior pituitary. *In* "The Hormones" (G. Pincus and K. V. Thimann, eds.), Vol. II, pp. 427–514. Academic Press, New York.

Wright, M. R., and Lerner, A. B. (1960). On the movement of pigment granules in frog melanocytes. *Endocrinology* **66**, 599–609.

Wright, P. A. (1948). Photoelectric measurement of melanophoral activity of frog skin induced *in vitro. J. Cellular Comp. Physiol.* **31**, 111–123.

Wright, P. A. (1955). Physiological responses of frog melanophores *in vitro. Physiol. Zool.* **28**, 204–218.

Zimmerman, S. B., and Dalton, H. C. (1961). Physiological responses of amphibian melanophores. *Physiol. Zool.* **34**, 21–33.

CHAPTER 24

Relation of the Pars Intermedia to the Hypothalamus

WILLIAM ETKIN

I. Introduction

The relationship of the pars intermedia of the pituitary (hereafter called intermedia) to the brain has received much less attention than the pars anterior at the hands of experimentalists, chiefly because no important functional activity for this organ is known in mammals. In poikilothermic vertebrates the intermedia is one of the factors in chromatic adaptation and has been studied extensively from this point of view (see Chapter 23). The amphibians, in which the intermedia predominates in color regulation, have received the bulk of the attention, particularly with respect to neural regulation and to the developmental relation to the brain. Thus this chapter will of necessity deal largely with lower vertebrates, particularly amphibians. The polypeptides, α- and β-melanocyte-stimulating hormone [MSH (see Chapter 23)] are found in the intermedia of mammals, but the secretion of the intermedia in most other vertebrates has not been characterized chemically. Hence, the more general term "intermedin" is used here to refer to this secretion.

II. Morphological Considerations

A. Variation in General Structure

The comparative morphology of the intermedia has been comprehensively treated in Romeis' volume on the pituitary (1940) and brought up to date in many aspects by Diepen (1962). Extensive treatments of the literature on the pituitary in different vertebrate groups are available for fish in Pickford and Atz (1957), for birds in Wingstrand (1951) and Grignon (1956), and for mammals in H. D. Purves (1961). A very brief summary of those morphological considerations deemed to be of physiological significance is included here, with emphasis on recent work. The older literature will not be cited insofar as it is readily available in the above reviews.

The intermedia arises during development from the deeper or most posterior tip of the adenohypophyseal primordium (Rathke's pouch). This region early makes close contact with the posterior tip of the prospective infundibular region of the brain. Although in some forms, such as birds, there is a later separation of the two primordia by mesenchyme, in most vertebrates the two tissues remain intimately fused in the adult. In those tetrapods where the intermedia forms a lobe separate from the pars nervosa, the two tissues maintain intimate contact at their common boundary. Electron-microscope studies of some species reveal extensive invasion of the intermedia by fibers from the pars nervosa (Ribas-Mujal, 1958; Iturriza, 1964; J. D. Green, 1964). In fish, the nervous tissue characteristically sends extensive digitations into the epithelium, forming an intimate fusion of the two tissues. This lobe is called the neurointermediate lobe or meta-adenohypophysis (Meurling, 1963; Mellinger, 1964).

In birds generally and in some mammals (cetaceans, elephants, beavers, etc.) the intermedia fails to develop. In others (man, anthropoid apes) it regresses during the individual's lifetime so that often only remnants remain. It is not uncommon to find cords or nests of epithelial cells penetrating the pars nervosa in mammals. Recently, as will be detailed below, it has become possible to identify intermedin-secreting cells cytologically in birds and mammals. Tixier-Vidal *et al.* (1962) have described such cells in the cephalic portion of the anterior lobe of ducks, a region known to be rich in the hormone. H. D. Purves and Bassett

(1963) similarly found the anterior lobe of mammals which lack a distinct intermedia to have intermedia cells. They also believe that the cell cords invading the pars nervosa are intermedia cells. It is thus evident that the absence of a distinct intermedia does not preclude the presence of intermedin-secreting tissue. Indeed, the anterior lobe of birds and cetaceans has long been known to yield large amounts of intermedin upon extraction. These facts suggest that despite the morphological variability of the intermedia in birds and mammals it may be playing an important physiological role in these classes as well as in lower forms.

B. Cytology

In routine light microscopy the intermedia cells are generally chromophobic or slightly basophilic without the marked granulations seen in various anterior lobe cell types. In many animals they appear to be periodic acid-Schiff (PAS) positive, although not strongly so. In the anuran, *Rana pipiens,* Ortman (1954) has described fine PAS-positive granulation prominent in white-adapted frogs and coarser phospholipid granules in dark-adapted animals. However, there is much variability in cytological appearance among vertebrates, and no criterion seems applicable universally to the identification of these cells. In birds (Tixier-Vidal *et al.,* 1962) and in mammals (H. D. Purves and Bassett, 1963), intermedin-secreting cells have been identified by differential staining methods. It appears likely that the tinctorial characteristics shown in any animal are related to carrier substances or other components rather than to the hormone molecule of the gland, since this is a small-chain polypeptide (see Chapter 23).

In many animals, e.g. anurans (Mazzi, 1959) and mammals (Kurosumi *et al.,* 1961; Duchen, 1962; Ziegler, 1963), two kinds of cells are identifiable in the gland. One of these is small and angular, with scanty dense cytoplasm, and is generally located peripherally. The other has a more abundant vacuolated protoplasm and usually borders the capillaries adjacent to the pars nervosa. In a dogfish (*Scyliorhinus stellaris*) the cells exhibit a basophilic pole rich in endoplasmic reticulum and an opposite pole with vacuolated cytoplasm (Knowles, 1963). In several species of anurans and elasmobranchs, droplets of acidophilic colloid are commonly seen, often extending in chains to the capillary border. Some investigators feel that the colloid contains the glandular secretion (Della Corte, 1961; Nayar and Pandalai, 1963; Titlbach, 1963; Iturriza and Koch, 1964). On the other hand, Voitkevich and Soboleva (1962) found an inverse correlation between the acidophilic droplets and intermedin secretion in frogs. In his extensive electron-microscopic study of the gland in a dogfish, Mellinger (1964) was led to regard the droplets as products of cellular degeneration, an interpretation to which our own observations of organs degenerating in organ culture lend support.

It is possible to view the cytology of the intermedia in terms of two separate processes, synthesis and storage. These may be represented in the two poles of a single cell or as two histologically distinguishable kinds of cells—one in the secretory, the other in the storage phase of the activity cycle. Although such a representation may be satisfying as a tentative ordering concept, at present it can hardly be regarded as supported by substantial evidence. Some observations indicate storage of hormone in the intermedia of animals adapted to a white background (Waring and Landgrebe, 1949; Burgers *et al.*, 1963), and, conversely, lack of storage in dark animals (Voitkevich and Soboleva, 1962), but other workers fail to find changes in hormone content correlated with background (Metuzals, 1951; Ortman, 1954) or even a reduction of hormone content in light animals (Masselin, 1939; Chavin, 1959). Recently Kastin and Ross (1965) have provided clear evidence of loss of intermedin content after frogs have been darkened by hypothalamic lesions. However, in no animal is a clear correlation of hormone content and cytological change available.

The interpretation of the cytology of the intermedia, therefore, remains largely obscure. It is possible that two kinds of cells secreting different materials such as the two known MSH molecules are present or that one cell represents the storage, the other the synthetic phase, of a single cell type. Synthetic activity may be associated with basophilia, whereas storage may be characterized by vacuolation of the cytoplasm. No cytochemical identification of hormone content is available, although intermedin cells may be differentially stained in certain animals. Finally, the electron-microscopic finding by Titlbach (1963) of cilia in intermedia cells of the rat should be mentioned, although no rationale for their presence can be offered, and their occurrence in many different kinds of cells, including neurons, discourages speculation concerning their functional significance.

C. Vascularization

In tetrapods the intermedia is generally described as poorly vascularized. Where the tissue forms a flat plate a few cell layers in thickness, as in some amphibians, all capillaries may lie on the surface. Even in more massive glands, relatively few capillaries are seen in the parenchyma, and it would appear that many cells do not make contact with capillary walls. An exceptionally vascular gland has been described in a lizard (Nayar and Pandalai, 1963). In contrast, the neurointermediate lobe of fish is generally richly vascularized, presumably in relation to its endocrine and neurohemal character.

The vascular supply is generally shared with the pars nervosa rather than with the pars anterior. Often the large capillaries on the surface of the gland are common to the nervosa and intermedia. Blood draining the brain stem passes into the capillaries of the neurointermediate lobe in a shark (Mellinger, 1964) and in anurans (Cruz, 1956) and thus forms a kind of portal circulation in these animals. However, the primary capillary bed of the system does not appear to drain a distinctive neurohemal area of the brain. Hence the significance of this portal system is obscure. No important blood flow from the median eminence or equivalent neurohemal area enters the intermedia of the frog (Etkin, 1962a) or other vertebrate as far as known.

D. Innervation

In contrast to the pars anterior, the intermedia is provided with many nonmyelinated nerve fibers. In fish, where the parenchyma of the intermedia is generally extensively penetrated by projections of neural tissue, the fibers are numerous and pervade the gland, often ending in basketlike or other terminals associated with the cells (Bargmann and Knoop, 1960; Della Corte, 1961; Meurling, 1963; Mellinger, 1964). In tetrapods the fibers are relatively few, but here too they are acknowledged to penetrate among the cells and show synaptic endings (J. D. Green, 1947; Stutinsky, 1950; Dawson, 1953; Collin, 1954; Ribas-Mujal, 1958; Dierickx, 1963; Ziegler, 1963; J. D. Green, 1964). Thus the fibers are regarded as being related to the secretory activity of the cells rather than being vasomotor. It is also clear that the fibers are substantially all derived from the hypothalamus through the pars nervosa rather than from the cervical sympathetics by way of the blood vessels (Schürmeyer, 1926; Hillarp and Jacobsohn, 1943; Fuxe, 1964). Recent reports confirm older studies in which retinal fibers were reported to pass directly into the hypothalamus, thus providing the anatomical basis for direct regulation of the intermedia by lighting conditions (Knoche, 1956; Knapp and Riss, 1964).

The earlier light-microscopic studies mentioned above have indicated that at least some of the fibers to the intermedia in fish, amphibians, and mammals are neurosecretory—that is, that the fibers are made visible by standard neurosecretory stains. Electron-microscopic studies have confirmed the presence of fibers bearing typical elementary vesicles of neurosecretion (diameter of 1000–3000 Å) in fish and mammals (Bargmann and Knoop, 1960; Ziegler, 1963; J. D. Green, 1964; Mellinger,

1964). On the other hand, two recent studies failed to find fibers carrying such granules in frogs and toads (Iturriza, 1964; F. Knowles, personal communication, 1965). It will be convenient to refer to such fibers as large-granule fibers. The conflict of the light- and electron-microscopic evidence in amphibians is difficult to evaluate since the light-microscope studies reveal typical "beaded fibers" characteristic of neurosecretory axons in the intermedia (Dawson, 1953; Etkin, 1962a; Dierickx, 1963). Dierickx, indeed, not only found such fibers but also noted that they disappeared after ablation of the magnocellular preoptic nucleus. Unfortunately, the electron-microscopic studies have not as yet been correlated with light-microscope studies of animals under varied physiological conditions of background adaptation. It is possible that the glands studied with the electron-microscope were not under inhibition at the time of fixation. This would appear to be the case in Iturizza's study since his animals were removed from hibernation, at which time amphibians generally are dark and show no background response. In the study by Knowles the animals were anesthetized before fixation. Such anesthesia likewise darkens the animals. In any case it is clear that, with the possible exception of the amphibians, the intermedia is innervated in part by typical neurosecretory (large-granule) fibers which make synaptic contact with some of the cells.

Perhaps the most significant finding of the electron-microscopic studies has been the demonstration of fibers carrying small vesicles, about 700 Å in diameter, with electron-dense centers (Knowles, 1963; Iturriza, 1964; Mellinger, 1964). These will here be called small-granule fibers. The presence of fibers not staining with neurosecretory stains had long been recognized by light-microscopic studies (Hillarp and Jacobsohn, 1943; J. D. Green, 1947; Stutinsky, 1950; Ribas-Mujal, 1958). However, the extent to which these might be simply neurosecretory fibers temporarily depleted of granules is not clear. The electron-microscopic evidence makes it evident that, at least in the animals studied, the small-granule fibers are distinct from large-granule fibers. (By the criteria given in Chapter 5, both types of fibers may be considered to be neurosecretory, although the small-granule fibers do not stain with the usual neurosecretory stains.) In any event, where both fibers are present, the small-granule fibers appear to be more numerous and more constant in appearance than the large-granule fibers.

In summary, the intermedia in all forms is innervated by numerous small-granule or non-neurosecretory-staining fibers. In all forms, with the possible exception of amphibians, a smaller number of large-granule fibers staining typically with neurosecretory stains are also present. Both types of fibers appear to be in synaptic relation with intermedia cells.

III. Developmental Interactions

A. Inductive Influence of Neural Plate upon Adenohypophyseal Primordium

In the wood frog (*Rana sylvatica*) embryo at the open neural plate stage, the presumptive adenohypophyseal area is not capable of self-differentiation if transplanted into the tail fin of a hypophysectomized tadpole. However, if the anterior tip of the neural plate (with pre-chordal mesoderm) is included in the graft, both anterior lobe and intermedia differentiate and the intermedia produces intermedin (Etkin, 1958a). At a slightly later stage of development, the tailbud stage, when the primordium is recognizable as a nubben of cells, it is self-differentiating in both *Rana sylvatica* and *Rana pipiens,* and capable of forming both pars anterior and intermedia in the absence of neural tissue (Atwell, 1937; Etkin, 1958b). These results are consonant with the general findings regarding other head placodes. For example, the olfactory placode is dependent upon inductive influences from the anterior head region in early preprimordial stages and is self-differentiating before the definitive primordium is formed (Zwilling, 1940).

On the other hand, there is a large body of evidence indicating that in various salamanders and anurans even the definitive primordium is limited in its self-differentiating capacities. It can form the pars anterior when transplanted in isolation from the nervous system but requires that some of the adjacent infundibular floor be included in the graft in order to form the intermedia (for literature see Eakin, 1956; Pehlemann, 1962). Comparable findings are reported for the chick (Stein, 1933) and rabbit (Gaillard, 1937). Pehlemann (1962), working with two European frogs, found that the early definitive primordium isolated from brain fails to form morphologically recognizable pituitary tissue. The late primordium, after reaching the infundibulum, acquires the capacity to differentiate into pituitary tissue which secretes intermedin. Isolated at later stages, it secretes growth factor, and finally thyrotropin. The above authors regard the hypothalamic floor as the source of an inductive influence upon the primordium which continues for some time after the formation of the definitive primordium. Pehlemann regards successively more posterior areas of the hypothalamic floor as responsible for the induction of specific hormone-secreting capacities. The other authors emphasize the inductive effect of the infundibulum on the intermedia.

It seems unlikely that the difference in results regarding the dependence of the intermedia upon the brain in development is to be ascribed entirely to species differences. Important differences in technique exist between the experimenters. Etkin (1958b) emphasizes minimal manipulation of the primordium. He attempts to remove the primordium as cleanly as possible without excess manipulation and immediately inserts it into the previously prepared pocket in the host tissue. He therefore judges the absence of neural tissue in the transplant on the basis of failure of neural differentiation in the developed graft. The other authors prefer to clean off any supposed neural cells before transplanting the primordium. Both procedures have obvious limitations. Clearly it is possible that some neural cells are included in Etkin's transplants. On the other hand, the primordium in *Rana pipiens* and *Rana sylvatica* is closely adherent to the neural tissues. [In some mammals and reptiles it is described as actually fused to the hypothalamic floor when first formed (Gilbert, 1934; Sprankel, 1956).] It is possible therefore that the primordium is injured in any attempt to clean off neural cells. It must be recalled that it is the deepest part of the primordium which forms the firmest attachment to the brain wall and that this part forms the intermedia. This is the region described as missing in the differentiation of the cleaned primordium. Pehlemann's results on differential determination of functional capacities, insofar as the functional tests he used can be considered adequate, are open to the interpretation of differential injury of the primordium transplanted at different stages. Therefore this reviewer favors the concept that the embryonic determination of the adenohypophysis is dependent upon inductive influences from the anterior tip of the neural plate only in preprimordial stages. This point is of some theoretical interest since the neural tissue exerting this inductive effect is that which gives rise to the preoptic hypothalamus rather than the infundibulum. It is, of course, in the preoptic region that the neurosecretory nuclei later differentiate.

B. Development of Function in Intermedia

All experimenters agree that the late primordium of the adenohypophysis is self-differentiating. It then becomes of some interest to determine when it begins to secrete its specific hormones. Evidence that thyrotropin is secreted early, possibly even at primordial stages, was afforded by the evidence that the close apposition of the primordia of the pituitary and thyroid leads to precocious activation of the latter in the tadpole (Etkin, 1939). With respect to the intermedia, Kleinholz (1940) attempted to answer this question by extracting the heads of embryos of *Rana pipiens* at various stages and testing them for intermedin. He obtained positive responses as early as the tailbud stage, when the adenohypophyseal primordium has only just formed. His data, however, are not entirely convincing. Working with the same species, Etkin (1959) transplanted the tailbud primordium into the tail fin of hypophysectomized hosts. He found that the primordium at first shows no pigmentary potency even in quadruple quantity, whether alive or after killing by freezing. However, a single live primordium after 2.5 days *in situ* begins to secrete hormone. This is made evident by the expansion of the melanophores of the host, first immediately around the graft and then, after a few hours, throughout the body. Since the morphological development of the graft parallels that of the normal gland, it was concluded that secretion begins in normal development at the early postprimordial stage (Shumway stage 22–23). This is shortly before the target cells, the melanophores, differentiate. A similar although less definitive conclusion is reached from the study of the earliest color response to hypophysectomy in *Ambystoma* (Drager and Blount, 1941) and in *Xenopus* (Etkin, 1941a). A comparable early appearance of intermedin is found by extraction methods in the chick embryo (Chen *et al.*, 1940; Rahn and Drager, 1941) and in the fetal mouse (Enemar, 1963). It is noteworthy that in all cases the intermedia is seen to become functional at an early stage when cytological differentiation is not yet apparent.

C. Time of Development of Neural Regulation

The early tadpoles of the common American species of anurans are dark in color and unable to adapt to a white background. Background response appears rather abruptly in the tadpole in some species [*Rana pipiens, Rana sylvatica* (Etkin, 1959)] and at the time of metamorphic climax in others [*Bufo americanus, Bufo terrestris* (Etkin, unpublished observations, 1963)]. These facts indicate that the production of intermedin is at first unrestrained by neural inhibition (see Section IV). Regulation of intermedia activity through the nervous system becomes established much later than the initiation of hormone production.

D. Dependence of Median Eminence Development upon the Adenohypophysis

In the tadpole of several American anurans it has been shown that the differentiation of the median eminence is dependent upon thyroid hormone action (Etkin, 1963). However, although exogenous thyroxin will induce the differentiation of the median eminence in thyroidectomized animals, it will not do so in animals deprived of their adenohypophyses. This dependence of neural differentiation upon the epithelial tissue appears to be exerted at the local level rather than through circulating hormones. For example, hypophysectomized animals in parabiosis with normals do not develop a median eminence even though they metamorphose simultaneously with their normal parabiotic partners (Etkin, 1964).

In summary of the developmental interactions of brain and pituitary the following conclusions seem justified.

1. The presumptive adenohypophyseal area is dependent upon an inductive influence from the anterior margin of the neural plate. In some species it is possible that inductive influences from the brain floor continue to be active and necessary, particularly for intermedia differentiation after the early primordial stage.

2. Initiation of specific hormone production begins early in the post-primordial period but is not subject to regulation by the brain in coordination with background adaptation in anurans until a considerably later period of development.

3. A reciprocal inductive influence of the adenohypophysis upon neurohypophyseal development is shown in tadpoles by the dependence of the thyroid-induced development of the median eminence upon a local factor produced by the adenohypophysis.

IV. Neural Inhibition of the Intermedia

A number of early reports indicated that injury to the ventral hypothalamus or infundibulum in amphibians and elasmobranchs leads to darkening of the animal and loss of background response (Vunder, 1931; Houssay *et al.*, 1935; Stutinsky, 1939; Abramowitz, 1939). Such results are subject to a number of interpretations. Vunder regarded the injury as an irritation of the nerves which then stimulate intermedia activity. He sought to confirm this interpretation by showing that direct injury to the gland itself also induces darkening. Since the pigmentary response of these animals is subject to many other controlling factors besides intermedin, it is also possible that the lesion operates through one of these. For example, the pineal was early known to possess a factor, since identified as melatonin (Lerner *et al.*, 1960), which lightens the animal by inducing aggregation of the melanin in the melanophores. There is some evidence that melatonin is a physiological factor in the background response of amphibians (McCord and Allen, 1917; Simonnet *et al.*, 1952; Bagnara, 1963). Hence it is conceivable that hypothalamic injury may inactivate the pineal mechanism.

A further complication in interpretation of lesion experiments arises from the concept developed in extensive studies by Hogben and collaborators that the pars tuberalis is the source of a whitening substance ("W" substance) and that the pigmentary system of amphibians is regulated by the interplay of the antagonistic actions of intermedin and "W" substance (for summary see Waring 1963). Thus, after operations intended to remove the pars tuberalis in *Xenopus* (Hogben and Slome, 1931) or *Rana pipiens* (Steggerda and Sodewall, 1939), the animals become dark. In the lungfish, *Protopterus,* removal of the pars anterior leads to permanent darkening (Godet, 1961). In each of these experiments some injury appears to have been done to the hypothalamus. Nevertheless, the interpretation put upon the experiments is that the darkening results from the elimination of the source of a "W" substance. The possibility that the lesion of the hypothalamus induced the darkening was not considered.

The concept of a "W" substance from the adenohypophysis in anurans and elasmobranchs has been largely discredited (for a summary of the evidence see Parker, 1945; Jørgensen and Larsen, 1960; Mellinger, 1963). It would be of only historical interest except for the fact that it continues to appear in the literature (Godet, 1961; Waring, 1963). Such discussions fail to take into account the definitive evidence for inhibitory control of the intermedia by the hypothalamus (see below).

Several lines of evidence leave little doubt that the hypothalamus directly inhibits the intermedia in amphibians and elasmobranchs. Transplantation of the epithelial primordium in frog embryos results in an animal that remains permanently dark. Such animals become intensely black and show no ability to respond to a light background. Similar results follow grafting of differentiated pituitaries into hypophysectomized tadpoles. Furthermore, the intermedias of such grafts are considerably larger than normal. Their cells are larger and show a marked increase in amount and density of cytoplasm. The inference is therefore clear that this hyperactivity and hypertrophy cannot be interpreted as the result of traumatic stimulation but must be regarded as a release from inhibitory control by some hypothalamic influence (Etkin, 1935, 1941b).

Further support for this conclusion is derived from an experiment in which the hypothalamic lobes of young tadpoles were cut and partially destroyed, leaving the pituitary in place. Such experimental animals turn dark continuously until metamorphosis (about 3 weeks of age). The glands are hypertrophied with dense basophilic cytoplasm (Etkin and Rosenberg, 1938; Etkin, 1941b). These experiments indicate an inhibitory effect of the hypothalamus upon intermedia activity and growth of the gland in tadpoles.

Injury to the hypothalamus in adult anurans also leads to hyperactivity of the intermedia (Rowlands, 1954; Jørgensen and Larsen, 1960; Etkin *et al.*, 1961; Guardabassi, 1961; Etkin, 1962a). Similar results for larval anurans were reported by Voitkevich (1963), and for larval salamanders by Etkin and Sussman (1961). The early findings of the same kind for elasmobranchs by Abramowitz (1939) have been confirmed and extended by the elegant studies of Mellinger (1964). These authors favor the interpretation that the effect is to be understood in terms of a release from inhibition rather than traumatic stimulation. In these studies the effect is persistent and accompanied by histological evidence of high activity. Etkin, for example, reports a case of progressive blackening lasting over 15 months in a bullfrog. Mellinger's electron-microscopic studies clearly show cellular hyperactivity in the intermedia in the dogfish.

Although no physiological evidence for hyperactivity of the intermedia can be expected in mammals since no clear-cut function for intermedin is known in this class (see Chapter 23), the morphological evidence from transplantation and lesion experiments is consistent in indicating that the intermedia maintains itself well and shows signs of hypertrophy when freed of its hypothalamic connection (Barrnett and Greep, 1951; Bogdanove and Halmi, 1953; Siperstein and Greer, 1956). Apparently the mammalian gland does not recover from the trauma of transplantation or operative disruption of its vascular supply as readily as does the gland in lower vertebrates. Consequently, the positive response to the dissociation from the hypothalamus is less constant or evident in these forms although, in contrast to the pars anterior, the intermedia is well maintained (Campbell and Harris, 1957; László *et al.*, 1962; Daniel *et al.*, 1964). In view of the recent identification of intermedin-secreting cells in the anterior lobe of birds and certain mammals, the question of the effect of isolation of this tissue is now open to investigation in these animals.

Indirect evidence supporting the view that hypothalamic activity is associated with inhibition of the intermedia is furnished by experiments with drugs. Tranquilizing drugs which are believed to act by inhibiting hypothalamic function are reported to darken light-adapted frogs (Khazan and Sulman, 1961; Scott and Nading, 1961). Morphological studies on the hypothalamic neurosecretory system, known to be the source of antidiuretic hormone (ADH), show a consistent inverse relation between the amount of neurosecretory material appearing in this system and the size of the intermedia in mammals. Thus intermedia enlargement and cytological evidence of hyperactivity were found to follow dehydration stress in rodents (Roux, 1962; Soboleva, 1964). In extensive studies Legait (1963) reports a relation between the hypothalamic

ADH mechanism and intermedia size in various mammals. However, he regards intermedia activity as acting upon the hypothalamic neurosecretory system rather than the reverse. In anurans Voitkevich (1963) likewise found a relation between hypothalamic neurosecretion and intermedia activity and interpreted this as indicating hypothalamic control of intermedia function through neurosecretion.

In summary, it may be stated that in amphibians and elasmobranchs the evidence clearly supports the concept that the hypothalamus controls intermedia activity by inhibitory influences. The evidence from mammals is consistent with this concept but not definitive.

V. Nature of Neural Control

A. General Considerations

Much recent work on the intermedia of lower vertebrates has concentrated upon the question of the nature of the inhibitory control mechanism. Three possibilities are suggested by contemporary concepts in neuroendocrinology: (1) Control might be exerted by a blood-borne factor reaching the intermedia through the median eminence and thus be independent of the nerves; (2) control might be exerted by way of the nerve fibers, staining with neurosecretory stains, which we have designated above as large-granule fibers; or (3) control may be exerted by other nerve fibers, including those we have called small-granule fibers.

Before discussing the evidence on these points, it would be well to ecognize the distinctive features which must characterize any mechanism exerting inhibitory control over the intermedia. It is evident that to be effective such control must be completely pervasive of the tissue. Unlike positive stimulation, inhibitory control must reach substantially all the cells, since even a small remnant left uncontrolled would produce enough intermedin to obscure the inhibited state of the remainder of the gland. Direct evidence for this statement is seen in the fact that even minor lesions in the hypothalamus produce a darkening of considerable duration (Etkin, 1962b; Jørgensen and Larsen, 1963). As described above, the nerve fibers of the intermedia in tetrapods are generally conceded to be few compared to the number of cells. The vascularity of the gland is also relatively poor. It would appear, therefore, that the controlling substance, if indeed it is a chemical mechanism, must be one which readily diffuses among the cells. These requirements of pervasiveness and diffusibility suggest that the gland cells must be bathed in an inhibitory substance when under neural inhibition.

B. Control through the Median Eminence

The first suggestion listed above of control through substances released in the median eminence and conveyed to the gland by the portal circulation would satisfy the criteria of pervasiveness and diffusibility. However, an analysis of the control in the frog, *Rana pipiens,* shows that the median eminence is not directly involved (Etkin, 1962a). It was shown, for example, that contrary to previous descriptions there is no important blood flow from the median eminence to the intermedia, that circulation through the median eminence can be eliminated without interfering with background adaptation of the animal, and that a lesion of the nerve tract posterior to the median eminence has the same effect on pigmentation as the more familiar lesion in the hypothalamic lobes anterior to that structure. This latter point has also been reported for a toad (*Bufo bufo*) by Jørgensen and Larsen (1960). Voitkevich and Ovchinnikova (1963) reported that the removal of the anterior hypothalamus in tadpoles inhibits metamorphosis and leads to hyperactivity of the intermedia. Restoration of the neural tissue by implantation repairs the metamorphic defect but not the hyperpigmentation. They interpret this as indicating that whereas thyroid-stimulating hormone production can be stimulated by neurosecretion released into the cerebrospinal fluid, inhibition of the pars intermedia cannot be so achieved. They therefore regard the penetration of nerve fibers into the gland as essential for its control. Similar results were obtained in our early experiments with hypothalamic lesions where the darkened tadpoles were found to metamorphose normally (Etkin, 1941b). The evidence from these studies appears to eliminate the possibility of control through the portal circulation from the median eminence in anurans. Such control is probably exercised by nerve fibers penetrating into the substance of the gland. A comparable conclusion was drawn by Mellinger (1963) from his analysis of control in the elasmobranch, *Scyliorhinus canaliculus.* Jørgensen and Larsen (1963) found that small lesions in the hypothalamus of various amphibians led to darkening from which the animals eventually recovered. They regarded this as evidence that control was effected by "ordinary" nerves which regenerated rather than neurosecretory fibers. We have had similar experimental results in *Rana pipiens.* However, we believe that this experiment does not distinguish between the two kinds of nerve fibers. Rather, it supports the concept developed above that inhibitory control is effected by penetrating nerve fibers which regenerate after injury rather than through chemicals transmitted by way of portal vessels or cerebrospinal fluid.

C. Role of Innervation

The evidence discussed above supports the conclusion that the inhibitory control exerted over intermedia function is probably effected by nerves which penetrate the substance of the gland, at least in amphibians and elasmobranchs. In elasmobranchs, as noted in the discussion of innervation, two kinds of fibers have been revealed by electron-microscopic studies; they are here designated large-granule and small-granule fibers. Knowles (1963) has suggested that the small-granule fibers, which he regards as probably containing catecholeamine granules, are associated with the storage region of the cell. The large-granule fibers he finds related to the synthetic region of the cytoplasm. He has therefore offered the hypothesis that the small-granule fibers are inhibitory, acting by promoting storage of the hormone, whereas the large-granule fibers control the synthetic mechanism. It will be convenient to discuss present knowledge regarding neural control of the intermedia in terms of this tentative but attractive hypothesis.

If storage of hormone plays a considerable role in inhibition of intermedia function, it would be expected that the gland in light animals would contain more stored hormone than that of dark animals. As mentioned above, several relevant studies have been made of this phenomenon with discordant results. However, two recent studies have provided convincing evidence that the pituitary of the dark animal does indeed contain less intermedin than that of the light animal, as the concept of storage requires. Burgers *et al.* (1963) found that glands from white background-adapted *Xenopus* adults had about four times as high a ratio of intermedin to adrenocorticotropic hormone (ACTH) as did those of dark-adapted animals. Kastin and Ross (1965) obtained similar results and an absolute decrease in intermedin content in frogs darkened by hypothalamic lesions as compared to normals. Further evidence for storage of hormone is seen in the fact that the effects of hypothalamic lesions are apparent within minutes after the operation (Etkin, 1962b; Jørgensen and Larsen, 1963). It seems likely that this results from release of stored hormone.

Storage and release of stored hormone can account for only the initial effects of denervation. As shown above, in amphibians and elasmobranchs the denervated gland is capable of indefinite production of abundant hormone. It is clear, therefore, that the neural inhibition must restrain the autonomous activity of the gland in addition to promotion of storage. In Knowles' theory this function would fall upon the large-granule fibers. Little evidence is available to support this concept. The failure of Knowles and Iturriza (see Section II,D) to find large-granule fibers in the intermedia of amphibians argues against the role of these fibers in regulating synthesis. However, as pointed out above, the evidence for the absence of such fibers is not fully convincing. Iturriza has suggested that the intimate fusion of the nervosa and intermedia would allow the diffusion of neurosecretion from the former to control intermedin production. Nayar and Pandalai (1963) made a similar suggestion for a lizard in which they found no nerves in the intermedia. However, our results with grafts in the frog (Etkin, 1962a) indicate that the intermedia becomes hyperactive before neurosecretory material is lost from the graft. Furthermore, in an extensive series of transplants of intermedia with and without nervosa, we were able to detect no influence of the nervosa on the activity of the grafted gland (Etkin, unpublished results, 1963). We therefore think it unlikely that the neurosecretory materials stored in the frog pars nervosa contain the inhibitory substance. As mentioned above, several workers have stressed a reciprocal relation between the amount of neurosecretory material in the neurohypophysis and intermedia size or activity (Voitkevich, 1963; Roux, 1962; Legait, 1963). Such a correlation might be interpreted in terms of neurosecretory inhibition of the intermedia, but other alternatives seem equally probable. In conclusion, it may be stated that the concept of two separate functions for the two kinds of fibers, although remaining an open possibility, is not strongly supported by the available indirect evidence.

As an alternative concept, it may be suggested that chemical substances released by the two kinds of fibers work together to inhibit the over-all activity of the cell. In this connection, the analogy to a possible mechanism in the control of the anterior lobe through the median eminence should be pointed out. There the presence of catecholamines from small-granule fibers and neurosecretion from large-granule fibers seems clearly established (Fuxe, 1964; Kobayashi, 1965). It is possible that the two classes of chemicals acting through the portal circulation influence the activity of the cells of the anterior lobe. It may be that in the intermedia the same result is achieved by penetrating fibers bearing both types of chemicals. An interesting consequence of this view is that the spreading of the intermedia cells in the anterior lobe in birds and some mammals may not signify a reduction in physiological importance of intermedin in these forms but simply a change in control from the direct invasion of the intermedia tissue by nerve fibers to more diffuse control through the portal circulation. If this interpretation is valid, the resolution of the exact interrelation of small-granule and large-granule fibers in the intermedia may throw further light on the nature of the control of all adenohypophyseal functions.

VI. Summary

Intermedia tissue either as a distinct lobe or as a distinguishable cell type distributed in other lobes appears to be characteristic, although perhaps not universal, among vertebrates. Often two cell types are distinguishable in the lobe, but the functional significance of the differentiation is unknown.

The forebrain and the adenohypophysis show developmental interdependence. The neural plate of the early embryo appears to exert an inductive influence upon the presumptive adenohypophyseal area. Continued contact of the primordium with the floor of the forebrain has been claimed to be necessary for the complete determination of the intermediate lobe in some species but not in others.

The rate of secretion of intermedin in many fish and amphibians is under inhibitory control by the hypothalamus. The isolated gland commonly shows hypertrophy as well as hyperactivity. A comparable but less clearly established relationship appears to obtain in mammals. Inhibitory control does not become established in frog larvae until some time after the gland becomes functional during development.

Hypothalamic control appears to be mediated by way of penetrating nerve fibers derived from the hypothalamus. Two types of fibers have been distinguished by electron-microscopic studies. One type, reported as lacking in frogs, shows typical elementary neurosecretory granules; the other type shows similar but smaller granules. The specific role of each type is unknown. One suggestion is that the large granule fibers regulate secretion and the small granule fibers storage. Another possibility is that the two types of fibers cooperate in some way in the inhibition of the otherwise autonomous activity of intermedia cells.

References

Abramowitz, A. (1939). The pituitary control of chromatophores in the dogfish. *Am. Naturalist* **73**, 208–218.

Atwell, W. (1937). Functional transplantation of the primordium of the epithelial hypophysis in amphibia. *Anat. Record* **68**, 431–447.

Bagnara, J. (1963). The pineal and the body lightening reaction of larval amphibians. *Gen. Comp. Endocrinol.* **3**, 86–100.

Bargmann, W., and Knoop, A. (1960). Über die morphologischen Beziehungen des neurosecretorischen Zwischenhirnsystems zum Zwischenlappe der Hypophyse (Licht- und Electronenmikroskopische Untersuchungen). *Z. Zellforsch. Mikroskop. Anat.* **52**, 256–277.

Barrnett, R., and Greep, R. (1951). The pituitary gonadotropic activity of stalk-sectioned male rats. *Endocrinology* **49**, 337–348.

Bogdanove, E., and Halmi, N. (1953). Effects of hypothalamic lesions and subsequent propylthiouracil treatment on pituitary structure and function in the rat. *Endocrinology* **53**, 274–292.

Burgers, A., Imar, K., and Van Oordt, G. J. (1963). The amount of melanophore-stimulating hormone in single pituitary glands of *Xenopus laevis* kept under various conditions. *Gen. Comp. Endocrinol.* **3**, 53–57.

Campbell, H., and Harris, G. (1957). The volume of the pituitary and median eminence in stalk-sectioned rabbits. *J. Physiol. (London)* **136**, 333–343.

Chavin, W. (1959). Pituitary hormones in melanogenesis. *In* "Pigment Cell Biology" (M. Gordon, ed.), pp. 63–73. Academic Press, New York.

Chen, G., Oldham, F., and Geiling, E. (1940). Appearance of the melanophore expanding hormone of pituitary gland in developing chick embryo. *Proc. Soc. Exptl. Biol. Med.* **45**, 810–813.

Collin, R. (1954). Les rélations du matériel Gomori-positif d'origine hypothalamique avec la "pars intermedia" chez quelques mammifères. *Compt. Rend. Assoc. Anat.* **81**, 693–703.

Cruz, A. (1956). Sur l'existence de deux systems portes dans l'hypophyse des amphibiens anoures. *Acta Anat.* **36**, 153–168.

Daniel, P., Duchen, L., and Prichard, M. (1964). The effect of transection of the pituitary stalk on the cytology of the pituitary gland of the rat. *Quart. J. Exptl. Physiol.* **49**, 235–242.

Dawson, A. (1953). Evidence for the termination of neurosecretory fibers within the pars intermedia of the hypophysis of the frog, *Rana pipiens. Anat. Record* **115**, 63–70.

Della Corte, F. (1961). Struttura, tipi cellulari e dati istochimici della ipofisi di *Scylliorhinus stellaris* (L.) anche in rapporto all'attivita sessude. *Arch. Zool. Ital.* **46**, 227–271.

Diepen, R. (1962). Hypothalamus. *In* "Handbuch der mikroskopischen Anatomie des Menschen" (W. Von Möllendorff, ed.), Vol. IV, Part 7. Springer, Berlin.

Dierickx, K. (1963). The extirpation of the neurosecretory preoptic nucleus and the reproduction of *Rana temporaria. Arch. Intern. Pharmacodyn.* **145**, 580–589.

Drager, G., and Blount, R. (1941). The time of the appearance of melanophore-expanding hormone in the development of *Amblystoma maculatum. Anat. Record* **8**, Suppl. p. 92.

Duchen, L. (1962). The effects of ingestion of hypertonic saline on the pituitary gland of the rat: A morphological study of the pars intermedia and posterior lobe. *J. Endocrinol.* **25**, 161–168.

Eakin, R. (1956). Differentiation of the transplanted and explanted hypophysis of the amphibian embryo. *J. Exptl. Zool.* **131**, 263–290.

Enemar, A. (1963). Appearance of the hypophysial melanophore expanding activity in the fetal laboratory mouse. *Arch. Zool.* **16**, 169–178.

Etkin, W. (1935). Hyperactivity of the pars intermedia as a graft in the tadpole. *Anat. Record* **64**, Suppl. 1, 5.

Etkin, W. (1939). A thyrotropic field effect in the tadpole. *J. Exptl. Zool.* **82**, 463–495.

Etkin, W. (1941a). The first appearance of functional activity in the pars intermedia in the frog, *Xenopus. Proc. Soc. Exptl. Biol. Med.* **47**, 425–428.

Etkin, W. (1941b). On the control of growth and activity of the pars intermedia of the pituitary by the hypothalamus in the tadpole. *J. Exptl. Zool.* **86**, 113–137.

Etkin, W. (1958a). Embryonic determination of the adenohypophysis in the wood frog, *Rana sylvatica.* *Anat. Record* **131**, 548.

Etkin, W. (1958b). Independent differentiation in components of the pituitary complex in the wood frog. *Proc. Soc. Exptl. Biol. Med.* **97**, 388–393.

Etkin, W. (1959). Development of function in the pars intermedia of the pituitary of the frog. *Anat. Record* **134**, 559.

Etkin, W. (1962a). Hypothalamic inhibition of pars intermedia activity in the frog. *Gen. Comp. Endocrinol.* Suppl. 1, 148–152.

Etkin, W. (1962b). Neurosecretory control of the pars intermedia. *Gen. Comp. Endocrinol.* **2**, 161–169.

Etkin, W. (1963). The metamorphosis activating mechanism in the frog. *Science* **139**, 810–814.

Etkin, W. (1964). Developmental dependence of the median eminence upon the epithelial pituitary. *Am. Zoologist* **4**, 392–393.

Etkin, W., and Rosenberg, L. (1938). Infundibular lesion and pars intermedia activity in the tadpole. *Proc. Soc. Exptl. Biol. Med.* **39**, 332–334.

Etkin, W., and Sussman, W. (1961). Hypothalamo-pituitary relations in metamorphosis of *Ambystoma.* *Gen. Comp. Endocrinol.* **1**, 70–79.

Etkin, W., Levitt, G., and Masur, M. (1961). Inhibitory control of pars intermedia by brain in adult frog. *Anat. Record* **139**, 300–301.

Fuxe, K. (1964). Cellular localization of monoamines in the median eminence and the infundibular stem of some mammals. *Z. Zellforsch. Mikroskop. Anat.* **61**, 710–724.

Gaillard, P. (1937). An experimental contribution to the origin of the pars intermedia of the hypophysis. *Acta Neerl. Morphol. Norm. Pathol.* **1**, 3–11.

Gilbert, M. (1934). The development of the hypophysis: Factors influencing the formation of the pars neuralis in the cat. *Am. J. Anat.* **54**, 287–313.

Godet, R. (1961). La livrée pigmentaire du Protoptère et le problème des antagonismes intra-hypophysaires. *Compt. Rend.* **252**, 2148–2150.

Green, J. D. (1947). Vessels and nerves of amphibian hypophysis. *Anat. Record* **99**, 21–54.

Green, J. D. (1964). Electronmicroscopy of rat posterior pituitary. *Anat. Record* **148**, 286.

Grignon, G. (1956). Développement du complex hypothalamo-hypophysaire chez l'embryon du poulet. Soc. Impr. Typogr., Nancy.

Guardabassi, A. (1961). The hypophysis of *Xenopus laevis* Dandin larvae after removal of the anterior hypothalamus. *Gen. Comp. Endocrinol.* **1**, 348–363.

Hillarp, N. Å., and Jacobsohn, D. (1943). Über die Innervation der Adenohypophyse und ihre Beziehungen zur Gonadotropen Hypophysenfunktion. *Kgl. Fysiograf. Sallskap. Handl.* **54**, 1–25.

Hogben, L., and Slome, D. (1931). The pigmentary effector system VI. The dual character of endocrine coordination in amphibian color change. *Proc. Roy. Soc.* **B108**, 10–53.

Houssay, B., Biasotti, A., and Sammartino, R. (1935). Modifications fontionnelles de l'hypophyse après les lésions infundibulo-tuberiennes chez le crapaud. *Compt. Rend. Soc. Biol.* **120**, 725–727.

Iturriza, F. (1964). Electron-microscopic study of the pars intermedia of the pituitary of the toad, *Bufo arenarum.* *Gen. Comp. Endocrinol.* **4**, 492–502.

Iturriza, F., and Koch, O. (1964). Effect of the administration of D-lysergic acid diethylamide (LSD) on the colloid vesicles of the pars intermedia of the toad pituitary. *Endocrinology* **75**, 615–616.

Jørgensen, C., and Larsen, L. (1960). Control of colour change in amphibians. *Nature* **186**, 641–642.

Jørgensen, C., and Larsen, L. (1963). Nature of the nervous control of pars intermedia function in amphibians. *Gen. Comp. Endocrinol.* **3**, 468–472.

Kastin, A., and Ross, G. (1965). MSH and ACTH activities in pituitaries of frogs with hypothalamic lesions. *Endocrinology* **77**, 45–49.

Khazan, M., and Sulman, F. (1961). Melanophore-dispersing activity of reserpine in rana frogs. *Proc. Soc. Exptl. Biol. Med.* **107**, 282–284.

Kleinholz, L. (1940). The distribution of intermedin: First appearance in the early ontogeny of *Rana pipiens*. *Biol. Bull.* **79**, 432–438.

Knapp, H., and Riss, W. (1965). Optic pathways of *Rana pipiens*. *Anat. Record* **148**, 290.

Knoche, H. (1956). Morphologisch-experimentelle Untersuchungen über eine Faserverbindung der Retina mit den vegetativen Zentren des Zwischenhirnes und der Hypophyse. *Z. Zellforsch.* **45**, 201–264.

Knowles, F. (1963). The ultrastructure of the neurointermedia lobe of the pituitary of the dogfish, *Scylliorhinus stellaris*. *Gen. Comp. Endocrinol.* **3**, 712.

Kobayashi, H. (1965). Electron microscopic and pharmacological studies on the median eminence and pars nervosa. *Arch. Anat. Microscop. Morphol. Exptl.* **54**, 277–294.

Kurosumi, K., Matsuzawa, T., and Shubasaki, S. (1961). Electron microscopic studies on the fine structure of the pars nervosa and pars intermedia, and their morphological interrelation in the normal rat hypophysis. *Gen. Comp. Endocrinol.* **1**, 433–452.

László, F. A., Dávid, M. A., and Kovács, K. (1962). Changes in the pituitary volume of rats following destruction of the pituitary stalk. *Med. Exptl.* **7**, 368–378.

Legait, E. (1963). Cytophysiologie du lobe intermediaire de l'hypophyse des mamiferes. *In* "Cytologie de l'adenohypophyse." (J. Benoit and C. DaLage, eds.), pp. 215–230. C.N.R.S., Paris.

Lerner, A., Case, J., and Takahashi, Y. (1960). Isolation of melatonin and 5-methoxyindole-3-acetic acid from bovine pineal glands. *J. Biol. Chem.* **235**, 1992–1997.

McCord, C., and Allen, F. P. (1917). Evidences associating pineal gland function with alterations in pigmentation. *J. Exptl. Zool.* **23**, 207–224.

Masselin, J. (1939). Influence of light and darkness on the melanophore dilating action of the hypophysis. *Rev. Soc. Argent. Biol.* **15**, 28–34.

Mazzi, V. (1959). Esistono due tipi cellulari nel lobo intermedio degli anfibi? *Monitore Zool. Ital.* **67**, 109–115.

Mellinger, J. (1963). Étude histophysiologique du système hypothalamo-hypophysaire de *Scyliorhinus caniculus* (L.) en état de mélanodispersion permanente. *Gen. Comp. Endocrinol.* **3**, 26–45.

Mellinger, J. (1964). "Les relations neuro-vasculo-glandulaires dans l'appareil hypophysaire de la roussette, *Scyliorhinus caniculus* (L.)." Imprimerie Alsatia, Strasbourg.

Metuzals, J. (1951). Cytologische Studien über die Hypophysis cerebri des normalen und in Dunkelheit gehaltenen Grasfrosches (*Rana temporaria* L.) *Z. Zellforsch. Mikroskop. Anat.* **35**, 550–578.

Meurling, P. (1963). Nerves of the neurointermediate lobe of *Etmopterus spinax,* (Elasmobranchi). *Z. Zellforsch. Mikroskop. Anat.* **61,** 181–201.

Nayar, S., and Pandalai, K. (1963). Pars intermedia of the pituitary gland and integumentary colour changes in the garden lizard, *Calotes versicolor. Z. Zellforsch. Mikroskop. Anat.* **58,** 837–845.

Ortman, R. (1954). A study of the effect of several experimental conditions on the intermedin content and cytochemical reactions of the intermediate lobe of the frog (*Rana pipiens*). *Acta Endocrinol.* **23,** 437–447.

Parker, G. (1945). Melanophore activators in the common American eel, *Anguilla rostrata,* Le Sueur. *J. Exptl. Zool.* **98,** 211–234.

Pehlemann, F. (1962). Experimentelle Untersuchungen zur Determination und Differenzierung der Hypophyse bei anuren (*Pelobates fuscus, Rana esculenta*). *Arch. Entwicklungsmech. Organ.* **153,** 551–602.

Pickford, G., and Atz, J. W. (1957). "The Physiology of the Pituitary Gland of Fishes." N.Y. Zool. Soc., New York.

Purves, H. D. (1961). Morphology of the hypophysis related to its function. *In* "Sex and Internal Secretions" (W. C. Young, ed.), 3rd ed., pp. 161–239. Williams & Wilkins, Baltimore, Maryland.

Purves, H. D., and Bassett, E. G. (1963). The staining reactions of pars intermedia cells and their differentiation from pars anterior cells. *In* "Cytologie de l'adenohypophyse" (J. Benoit and C. DaLage, ed.), pp. 231–242. C.N.R.S. Paris.

Rahn, H., and Drager, G. (1941). Quantitative assay of the melanophore-dispersing hormone during the development of the chicken pituitary. *Endocrinology* **29,** 725–730.

Ribas-Mujal, D. (1958). Contribucion al estudio de la inervacion hipofisaria en la buey. *Z. Zellforsch. Mikroskop. Anat.* **48,** 356–380.

Romeis, B. (1940). Hypophyse. *In* "Handbuch der mikroskopischen Anatomie des Menschen" (W. Von Möllendorff, ed.), Vol. VI, Part 3. Springer, Berlin.

Roux, M. (1962). Modifications d'activité de l'hypothalamus neurosécrétoire et variations volumétriques des lobes hypophysaires ches la souris blanche au cours d'epreuves prolongées de vie sans eau. *Compt. Rend. Soc. Biol.* **156,** 1664–1666.

Rowlands, A. (1954). The influence of water and light and the pituitary upon the pigmentary system of the common toad (*Bufo bufo bufo*). *J. Exptl. Biol.* **31,** 151–160.

Schürmeyer, A. (1926). Über die Innervation der Pars Intermedia der Hypophyse der Amphibien. *Klin. Wochschr.* **5,** 2311–2312.

Scott, G., and Nading, L. (1961). Relative effectiveness of phenothiazine tranquilizing drugs causing release of MSH. *Proc. Soc. Exptl. Biol. Med.* **106,** 88–90.

Simonnet, H., Thieblot, L., and Segal, V. (1952). Interrelation epiphyso-hypophysaire et effet expanso-mélanophorique. *Ann. Endocrinol.* (*Paris*) **13,** 340–344.

Siperstein, E., and Greer, M. (1956). Observations on the morphology and histochemistry of the mouse pituitary implanted into the anterior eye chamber. *J. Natl. Cancer Inst.* **17,** 569–583.

Soboleva, E. (1964). The pars intermedia of the hypophysis during salt loading. *Bull. Exptl. Biol. Med.* **55,** 577–580.

Sprankel, H. (1956). Beiträge zur Ontogenese der Hypophyse von *Testudo graeca* L. und *Emys orbicularis* L. mit besonderer Berücksichtigung ihrer Beziehungen zu Praechordalplatte. *Z. Mikroskop.-Anat. Forsch.* **62,** 587–660.

Steggerda, F., and Soderwall, A. (1939). Relationship of the pars tuberalis to melanophore response in amphibia (*Rana pipiens*). *J. Cellular Comp. Physiol.* **13**, 31–37.

Stein, K. (1933). The localization and differentiation of the presumptive ectoderm of the forebrain and hypophysis as shown by chorio-atlantoic grafts. *Physiol. Zool.* **6**, 205–235.

Stutinsky, F. (1939). Le reflexe "opto-pituitaire" chez la grenouille. *Bull. Biol. France Belg.* **73**, 385–407.

Stutinsky, F. (1950). Colloide, corps de Herring et substance Gomori-positive de la neurohypophyse. *Compt. Rend. Soc. Biol.* **144**, 1357–1360.

Titlbach, M. (1963). Pars intermedia of the rat hypophysis (an electronmicroscopic study). *Cesk. Morfol.* **11**, 85–90.

Tixier-Vidal, A., Herlant, M., and Benoit, J. (1962). La préhypophyse du canard Pekin mâle au cours du cycle annuel. *Arch. Biol.* (*Liège*) **73**, 317–368.

Voitkevich, A. (1963). On the relation of neurosecretion to growth and cell differentiation in the amphibian adenohypophysis. *Gen. Comp. Endocrinol.* **3**, 554–567.

Voitkevich, A., and Ovchinnikova, G. (1963). Differentiation of the regulating effect of the hypothalamus on the anterior and intermedia lobes of the hypophysis. *Bull. Exptl. Biol. Med.* **55**, 100–104.

Voitkevich, A., and Soboleva, E. (1962). Data on the histophysiology of the pars intermedia of the hypophysis in connection with hypothalamic neurosecretion. *Bull. Exptl. Biol. Med.* (*USSR*) (*Engl. Transl.*) **51**, No. 3, 96–101.

Vunder, P. (1931). The effect of trauma and transplantation on the activity of the pituitary gland. *Trans. Dynam. Develop.* **6**, 73–86.

Waring, H. (1963). "Color Change Mechanisms of Cold-blooded Vertebrates." Academic Press, New York.

Waring, H., and Landgrebe, F. (1949). The melanophore excitant properties of extracts of various pituitary glands. *Australian J. Exptl. Biol. Med. Sci.* **27**, 331–336.

Wingstrand, K. G. (1951). "The Structure and Development of the Avian Pituitary." Gleerup, Lund.

Ziegler, B. (1963). Licht- und elektronenmikroskopische Untersuchungen an Pars intermedia und Neurohypophyse der Ratte. *Z. Zellforsch. Mikroskop. Anat.* **59**, 486–506.

Zwilling, E. (1940). An experimental analysis of the development of the anuran olfactory organ. *J. Exptl. Zool.* **84**, 291–323.

CHAPTER 25

Adrenal Medullary Secretion and Its Neural Control

U. S. von EULER

I. Morphological Considerations

A. Development of Adrenal Medullary Cells

Although it is generally agreed that the chromaffinoblasts which differentiate into the chromaffin cells of the adrenal medulla originate from the neural crest or the neural tube and hence from the ectoderm, it is not known in detail what determines the contacts between the nerve fibers and the chromaffin cells, or the local arrangements of these cells in the adrenal medulla. According to Palkama (1964), certain groups of chromaffin cells in the adrenal medulla in some animals lack innervation (see Section IV,A). For details concerning the development of the chromaffin cells in general and the adrenal medullary cells in particular, reference is made to the review of Boyd (1960).

While a typical regression occurs in the extra-adrenal chromaffin cell groups after birth, the adrenal medulla shows a rapid and conspicuous development at the same time (Fig. 1). As shown recently by Lempinen

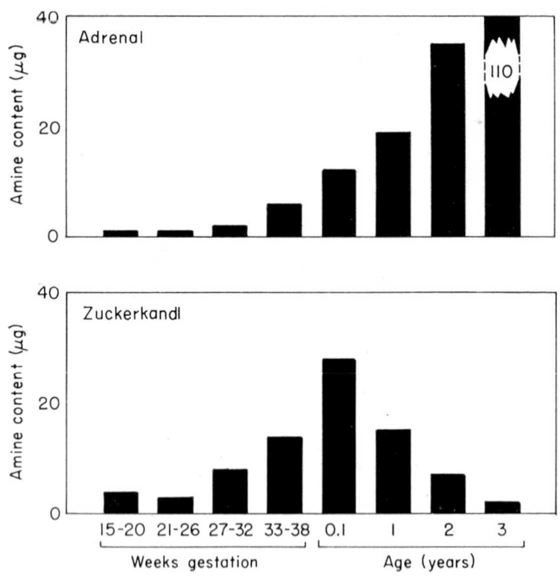

FIG. 1. Influence of age on the amount of catecholamines in one adrenal gland and one organ of Zuckerkandl of human fetuses and infants. (From West *et al.*, 1953.)

(1964), administration of cortisone or cortisol prevents the postnatal disappearance of extra-adrenal chromaffin tissue and brings about formation of new chromaffin cells in such tissue. The lack of regression in the adrenal medulla may therefore be due to the occurrence of the cortical tissue in close proximity to the medullary cells.

Wide differences are noted in the morphological disposition of the adrenomedullary cells in different phyla and animal species. This is illustrated in Fig. 2, which shows that the chromaffin cells can occur in very different patterns in relation to cortical cells.

Phylogenetically, the adrenal medulla develops gradually from scattered groups of chromaffin cells to a well-defined special organ. Chromaffin cells are found in different locations in poikilothermic vertebrates, including fish. Thus in the lungfish, *Protopterus*, chromaffin tissue is located in the walls of the intercostal branches of the dorsal aorta (Holmes, 1950). In teleosts such as *Salmo* and *Esox*, chromaffin tissue occurs separated from interrenal tissue while in *Cottus* it is em

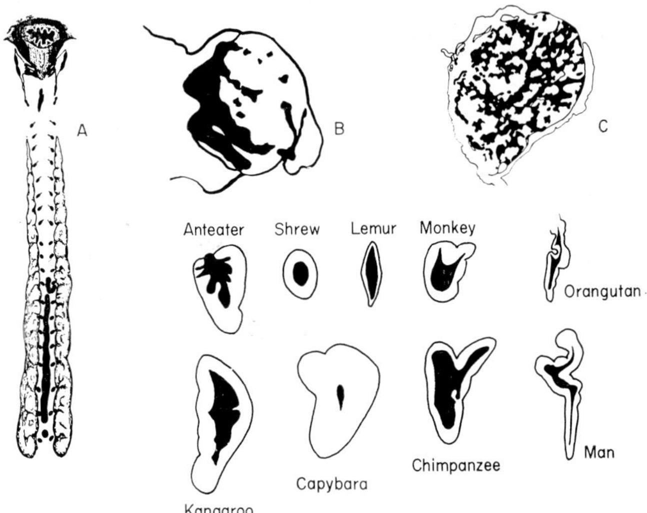

FIG. 2. Adrenal homologs and adrenals in (A) *Mustelis canis* (smooth dogfish), (B) *Anolis carolinensis* (American chameleon), (C) *Accipiter cooperi* (Cooper's hawk), and in various mammals. Chromaffin tissue in black. (From Hartman and Brownell, 1949.)

bedded in it (Nandi, 1961). Both norepinephrine and epinephrine have been found in large quantities in chromaffin cells of a special type in the hearts of the cyclostomes *Myxine* and *Petromyzon* (Bloom *et al.*, 1961). Even in annelids neurosecretory cells of a chromaffin-like type have been demonstrated (Scharrer and Brown, 1961) in the supraesophageal ganglion, which contains catecholamines. For further data see U. S. von Euler (1963).

B. Epinephrine and Norepinephrine Cells

The chromaffin cells occur in at least two varieties, producing either epinephrine or norepinephrine (Hillarp and Hökfelt, 1953; cf. Eränkö,

1960), with different functions, and connected with the centers in such a way that impulses may go specifically to one or the other kind of cells, at least in some species. The mechanism of this selection of contact is so far entirely obscure.

The two kinds of medullary cells can be differentiated in sections of the gland by different means, e.g., by treatment with iodate, which stains the norepinephrine-containing cells dark, while the epinephrine cells are unstained (Hillarp and Hökfelt, 1955). Figure 3 shows a typical

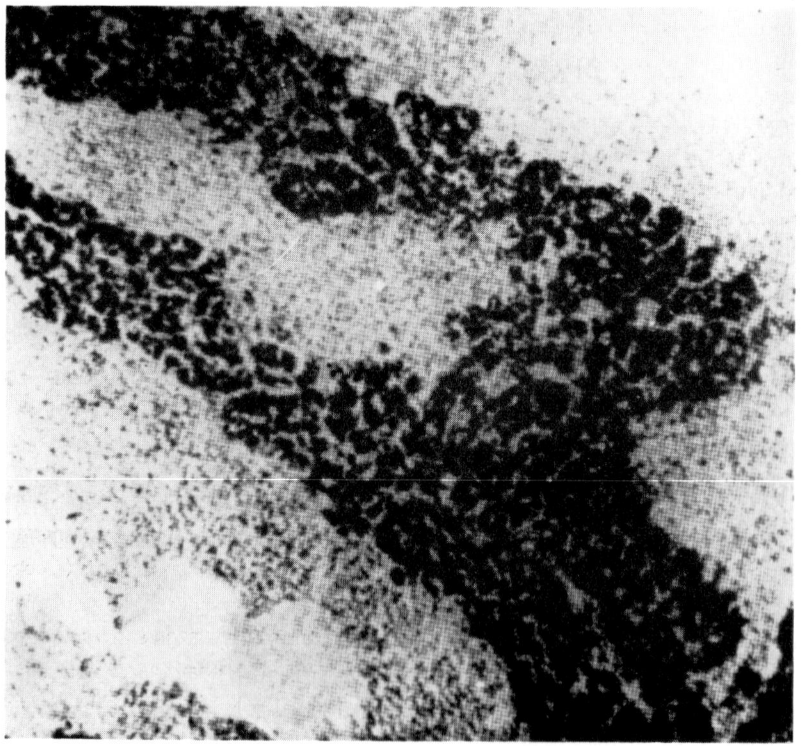

FIG. 3. Section of cat adrenal medulla, treated with potassium iodate. Dark areas, norepinephrine; light areas, epinephrine. (From Hillarp and Hökfelt, 1953.) × 130.

picture of the distribution of the two kinds of cells in the cat adrenal medulla which is known to contain about equal amounts of the two hormones.

Characteristic locations of the two kinds of cells within the gland have been described (Wright and Chester Jones, 1955). Large variations in the relative amounts of norepinephrine and epinephrine are found in birds. The proportions of the two amines were found to be similar in juvenile and adult specimens (Ghosh and Ghosh, 1964) except for the crow *Corvus splendens* in which the norepinephrine content was much higher in the medulla of juvenile birds than in adults. For further references see Eränkö (1960).

C. Subcellular Storage Particles

The chromaffin cells contain subcellular inclusions, stainable with osmium, as demonstrated in sections from the organ (Cramer, 1919). From these early observations it was further concluded that the particles contained the specific product of the cells, since different functional states of the medulla were correlated with the stainability of the particles. These findings passed largely unnoticed, however, and it was only many years later, in 1953, that two research groups, Hillarp, Lagerstedt, and Nilson in Sweden and Blaschko and Welch in England, gave conclusive evidence that the hormones of the adrenal medulla were mainly located in small granules or vesicles with a diameter of 0.1–0.6 μ. Isolated particles as well as particles *in situ* have subsequently been demonstrated by several groups (Lever, 1955; Wetzstein, 1957; cf. De Robertis, 1964, and others) using electron microscopic techniques. Recent studies have revealed characteristic differences in size and membrane appearance in the norepinephrine and epinephrine-containing granules (Wassermann and Tramezzani, 1963) (Fig. 4). The structure of the particles has not been elucidated in detail, but it has been reported that they are covered by a membrane and also show substructures of a size of about 200 Å in diameter (Lever, 1955; Wetzstein, 1962, and others).

The chemistry of the subcellular particles has been studied in considerable detail (see Blaschko, 1959; Hillarp, 1960a; Hagen and Barrnett, 1960). From these studies it has emerged that the particles contain proteins and phospholipids in relatively high proportions, as well as the specific amines. The amines occur in a concentration exceeding 0.5 M, or more than 80 mg per milliliter (Carlsson and Hillarp, 1958). Of particular interest is the finding that the particles are rich in adenosine triphosphate (ATP) which normally occurs in an amount of approximately 1 mole per 4 moles of amine (cf. Hillarp and Thieme, 1959). Since this proportion corresponds to an equal amount of positive and negative charges, it has been assumed that the amines are bound to the ATP. Under certain conditions the proportion of ATP to amines deviates from this value, however. The granules also have a high ATPase activity (Hillarp, 1958). The composition of the granules is given in Table I (Hillarp, 1959).

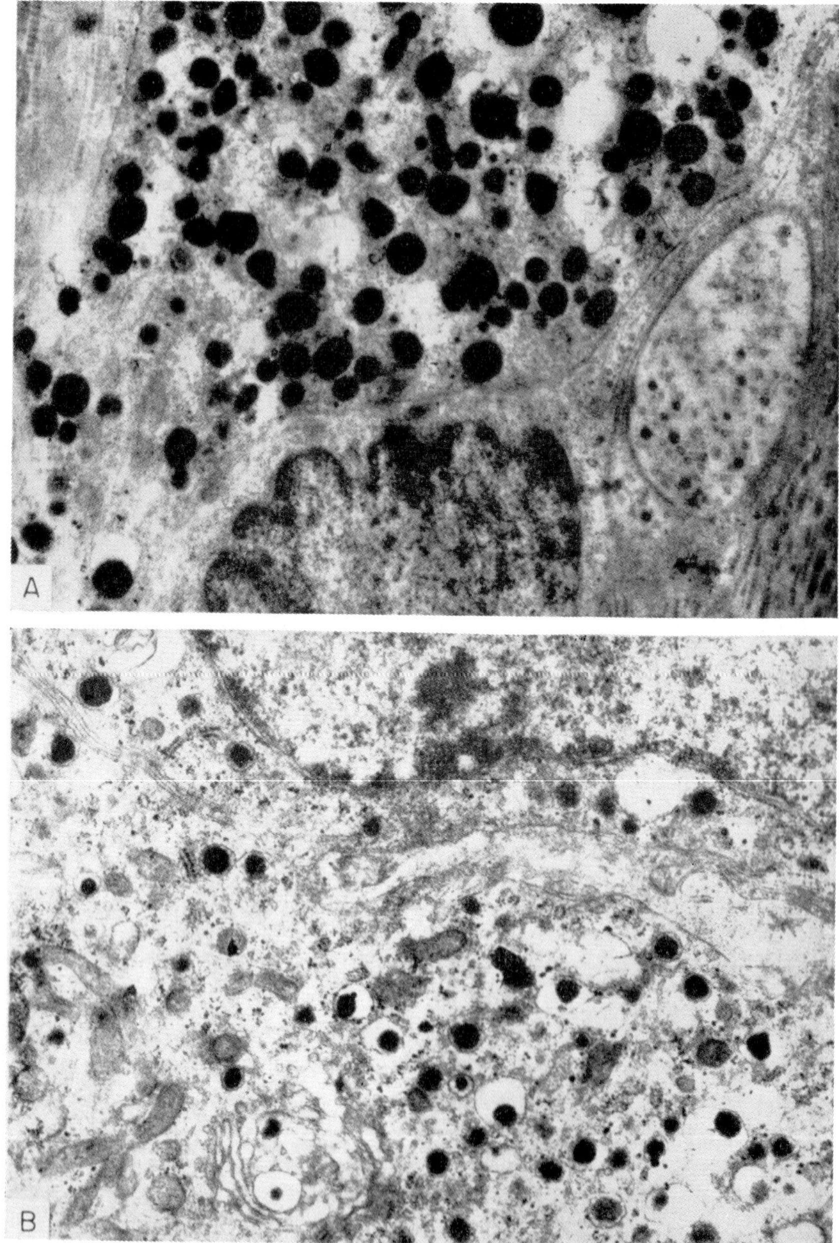

FIG. 4. Electron micrographs of parts of norepinephrine- (A) and epinephrine- (B) secreting adrenal cells from the snake *Zenodon merremii* showing osmiophilic catecholamine-containing granules. × 26,000. (From Wassermann and Tramezzani, 1963.)

The particles are stable in isotonic solution at low temperature but lose their amine content rapidly in hypotonic media, during exposure to heat, detergents, and certain drugs, presumably as a result of membrane damage (Hillarp and Nilson, 1954).

TABLE I

GENERAL CHEMICAL COMPOSITION OF AMINE GRANULES ISOLATED FROM OX ADRENAL MEDULLA[a]

	Percentage of wet weight	Percentage of dry weight
Water	68.5	
Amines	6.7	21
Adenosine phosphates	4.5	15
Proteins	11.5	35
Lipids	7	22
	98.2	

[a] See Hillarp (1959).

When incubated at 37°C in sucrose or phosphate buffer media, the adrenal medullary particles give off amines and ATP at about equal rates. The release rate is, however, relatively low and only about one-tenth of that of the corresponding particles from adrenergic nerves (Fig. 5). This fact may have physiological significance for the type of action of the two catecholamine-producing tissues (Stjärne, 1964).

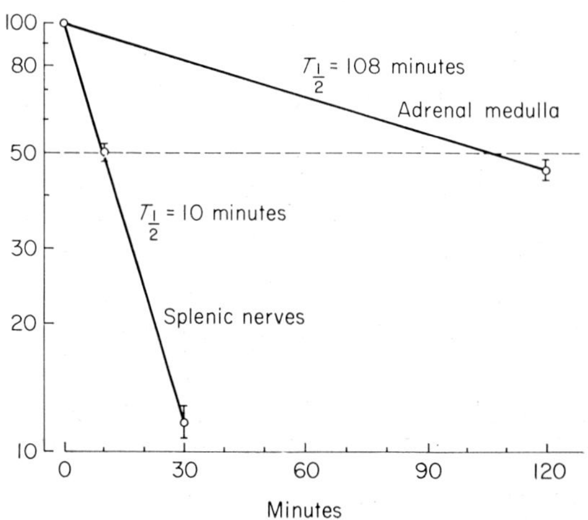

FIG. 5. Catecholamine release from isolated granules of bovine adrenal medulla and splenic nerves, incubated at 37°C in phosphate buffer, pH 7.5. $T_{1/2}$ = half-time.

In the presence of amines in the incubation media, the particles can take up amines, not only the specific amine occurring originally in the particles but also other amines, such as the precursor dopamine, and 5-hydroxytryptamine (Bertler *et al.*, 1961). The nature of the binding of the amines to the granules is still largely unknown. It has been discussed in detail in the review by Green (1962).

The presence of particles is required for the last step in the biosynthesis chain, i.e., the conversion of dopamine to norepinephrine (see Kirshner, 1959). The pathway of biosynthesis is shown in Fig. 6

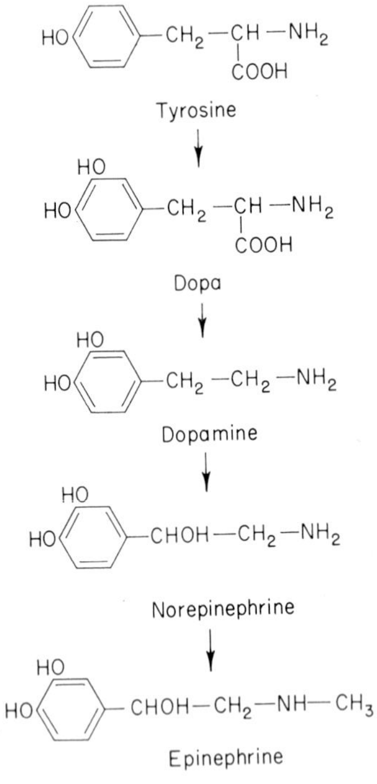

HO–C$_6$H$_4$–CH$_2$–CH(COOH)–NH$_2$

Tyrosine

↓

(HO)$_2$C$_6$H$_3$–CH$_2$–CH(COOH)–NH$_2$

Dopa

↓

(HO)$_2$C$_6$H$_3$–CH$_2$–CH$_2$–NH$_2$

Dopamine

↓

(HO)$_2$C$_6$H$_3$–CHOH–CH$_2$–NH$_2$

Norepinephrine

↓

(HO)$_2$C$_6$H$_3$–CHOH–CH$_2$–NH–CH$_3$

Epinephrine

FIG. 6. Main pathway of biosynthesis of norepinephrine and epinephrine.

(Blaschko, 1939; Holtz, 1939). It is generally assumed that the whole synthesis is taking place in the chromaffin cell itself, from tyrosine to norepinephrine and epinephrine.

Extensive studies have been made of the action of a large variety of drugs on the release and uptake of amines in the particles. Since a review of these actions is outside the scope of this article, the reader is referred to papers by Carlsson *et al.* (1963) and Weil-Malherbe and Posner (1963). Only a few examples of possible special interest for the physiological release and uptake phenomena will be mentioned here.

Schümann (1960b) has reported that tyramine releases amines from isolated medullary particles and has later shown that this release is accompanied by an equimolar uptake of tyramine. This observation has aided in clarifying the pharmacological effects of tyramine *in vivo* and supports the concepts expressed by Fleckenstein (1953) and by Burn and Rand (1958). In the presence of ribonuclease the particles give off amines and ATP in equivalent amounts (Philippu and Schümann, 1963).

Another drug which has come to play an important role in the analysis of storage granule function is the Rauwolfia alkaloid, reserpine. As shown by Carlsson and Hillarp (1956), this compound depletes the adrenal gland of its catecholamine stores. Kroneberg and Schümann (1958) further showed that the action is dependent on the innervation of the gland and may therefore be mediated by central impulses to a great extent.

The uptake process is further greatly enhanced by ATP in the presence of Mg^{2+} (Carlsson *et al.*, 1963). On the other hand, no effect on release or uptake has been observed by acetylcholine, histamine, 5-hydroxytryptamine, nicotine, or angiotensin II which have profound effects *in vivo*.

II. Hormones of the Adrenal Medulla

A. Chemistry and Biosynthesis

The demonstration of specific chemical compounds in the adrenal medulla dates back to Vulpian (1856) who found that treatment of fresh sections of the gland with ferric compounds causes a green color and to Henle (1865) who observed a brownish staining of these cells with bichromate solutions. Not before 1895 did it become clear, however, that the adrenal medulla contained biologically highly active compounds, when Oliver showed, in a demonstration before Schäfer, that an extract of the adrenal medulla caused a dramatic rise in blood pressure of an anesthetized dog when injected intravenously (Oliver and Schäfer 1895). The isolation of the active compound was accomplished a few years later by Takamine (1901) after the basic studies by Abel and E. M. K. Geiling (see Abel, 1899).

The chemical composition of the active compound was soon afterward elucidated by Friedmann (1904). The synthesis followed in 1904 by Stolz, who also synthetized the nonmethylated compound norepinephrine, later identified as a second hormone of the adrenal medulla.

For a long time epinephrine was considered to be the only medullary hormone, although observations by Schild (1933) suggested that some other compound might occur. In 1944 (published 1947) Holtz *et al.* showed that extracts of the cat's adrenals contained a catecholamine which had the properties of norepinephrine. This finding was soon confirmed and the two amines separated chemically in extracts of the bovine medulla (Bergström *et al.*, 1950).

Epinephrine, or α-3,4-dihydroxyphenyl-β-methylaminoethanol is a secondary base with a molecular weight of 183.2. The natural compound is the *levo*-isomer with the structural formula shown in Fig. 6. The *dextro*-isomer possesses only about one-twentieth of the biological activity of the *levo*-isomer.

Norepinephrine is the corresponding nonmethylated compound with the molecular weight 169.2 and the structural formula seen in Fig. 6.

Although dopamine has been found to be a regular constituent in the sheep adrenal medulla, as discovered by Goodall (1951), and in the ox, there is no evidence of its occurrence as a secretory product of the chromaffin medullary cells. Apparently its presence is due to its role as precursor to norepinephrine. It has been claimed that isopropylnorepinephrine occurs in small amounts in the adrenal medulla, but the evidence is controversial.

The biosynthesis follows the pathway shown in Fig. 6. The various steps involve oxidation of tyrosine to dopa (Nagatsu *et al.*, 1964) decarboxylation of dopa to dopamine, β-hydroxylation of the side chain to norepinephrine and *N*-methylation of this compound to epinephrine, each step requiring a specific enzyme (cf. Blaschko, 1959; Kirshner, 1960).

The rate of biosynthesis has been estimated during different conditions and depends to a large extent on the activity of the gland, as determined by neural or chemical stimuli (Schümann, 1960b).

It appears that after depletion, e.g., after insulin, the resynthesis is a relatively slow process requiring about a week (Hökfelt, 1951). However, by estimating the secretion as well as the content of the gland after stimulation, it has been shown that resynthesis may be more rapid (Holland and Schümann, 1956), even after insulin (Bygdeman *et al.*, 1960).

B. Assay

For the quantitative estimation of the two catecholamines both biological and chemical methods have been used. In most cases the extracts of the adrenal glands, and particularly the medullary tissue, can be used without further purification; the extracts usually contain the hormones in high concentration, allowing the use of highly diluted solutions with only small amounts of impurities. Extracts may be made with dilute perchloric, trichloroacetic, hydrochloric, acetic, or other acids, or even with saline, although the latter is less efficient.

In the majority of cases the adrenal extracts contain a mixture of epinephrine and norepinephrine. The two hormones can be separated by paper or column chromatography (Häggendal, 1962; Gunne, 1962) and estimated separately, or differentially in a mixture.

For the biological assay, a variety of methods have been utilized, such as the blood pressure of the cat or the rat, the isolated rabbit jejunum, rat colon, chicken rectal cecum, rat uterus, rabbit aortic strip, isolated iris, and several others. In the case of a mixture of the two hormones a suitable pair of test preparations has to be selected in such a way that the activity ratios of the two hormones is sufficiently different on the two preparations (Gaddum and Lembeck, 1949). Of such pairs may be mentioned rat colon and rat uterus, or blood pressure in the cat and chicken rectal cecum (U. S. von Euler, 1948).

The chemical assay may be carried out using colorimetric or fluorimetric procedures. In the former case oxidation with iodine to iodo-adrenochrome has been widely used (U. S. von Euler and Hamberg, 1949a), and for fluorimetric assay the trihydroxyindole reaction of Ehrlén (1948) as adapted by Lund (1949); Bertler *et al.* (1958); U. S. von Euler and Lishajko (1961) and Häggendal (1963) has proved very useful. Also, condensation with ethylenediamine yields strongly fluorescent products, suitable for assay (Weil-Malherbe and Bone, 1954). All of these methods have been described in detail in the quoted papers.

C. Inactivation and Excretion

The medullary hormones, including dopamine, are good substrates for monoamine oxidase and it is generally agreed that this enzyme plays an important role in the metabolic inactivation of the hormones *in vivo*. This conclusion is reached by the finding of the corresponding metabolites of acidic character in the urine. Thus dihydroxyphenylacetic acid was demonstrated in large amounts in normal human urine (C. von Euler *et al.*, 1955). More recently it has been shown (Armstrong *et al.*, 1957; Axelrod, 1959) that the catecholamines are inactivated to a large extent by the enzyme catechol-*O*-methyltransferase, which methylates the 3-hydroxy group in the catechol ring. The principal inactivation paths are shown in Fig. 7. Table II shows the metabolic fate of epinephrine in man (Axelrod, 1960). Inactivation also occurs by conjugation, mainly to ether sulfates and glucuronides (Richter, 1940; Clark *et al.*, 1951).

TABLE II

METABOLIC FATE OF EPINEPHRINE IN MAN

Compounds found in urine	Compound administered		
	H^3(−)-Epinephrine[a]	C^{14}-Metanephrine[a]	Ratio $H^3:C^{14}$
Epinephrine	3.3	—	—
Metanephrine (free)	7.1	11.8	0.60
Metanephrine (conjugated)	27.3	40.2	0.68
3-Methoxy-4-hydroxymandelic acid	45.0	30.4	1.5
3-Methoxy-4-hydroxyphenylglycol sulfate	5.8	4.4	1.3
3,4-Dihydroxymandelic acid	1.5	—	—
Total	90.0	86.8	

[a] Results are expressed as percentage of administered dose excreted.

Apart from the metabolites shown in Fig. 7, which have been demonstrated in urine, a small proportion of the catecholamines released from the adrenal medulla is excreted in urine as free amines. The proportion excreted in this way depends on several factors, such as the catecholamine "load" and diuresis, and is generally of the order of 2–4% of the administered amount. The influence of diuresis is relatively small when urine secretion is within normal limits. During increased diuresis, how-

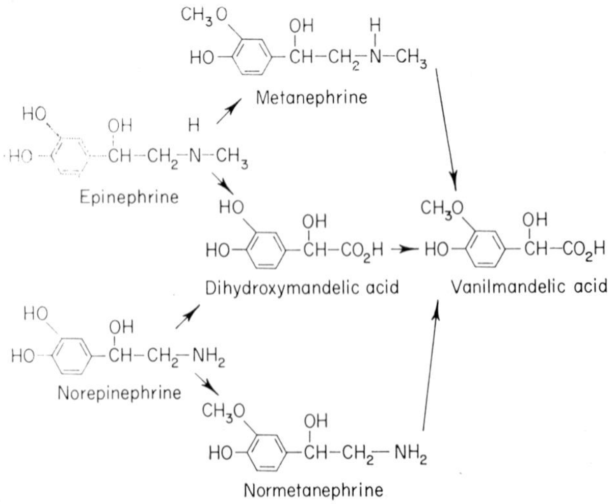

FIG. 7. Inactivation of epinephrine and norepinephrine by catechol-*O*-methyltransferase and by monoamine oxidase.

ever, the proportion excreted in urine may be considerably increased (Perman, 1961).

Under normal conditions most of the epinephrine excreted is derived from the adrenal glands and a smaller part from other chromaffin cells. Of the norepinephrine found in urine, presumably only a minor portion comes from the adrenal gland, while the larger part is derived from sympathetic nerves. The epinephrine excretion in urine has been used as an indicator of the relative activity of the adrenal medulla during various conditions (see Section IV,E–J).

D. Distribution in Various Species

A large number of studies have been made of the epinephrine and norepinephrine content of the adrenal glands of various animals. From these investigations it has emerged that not only do large differences occur in the amount of catecholamines per unit weight of gland, but also that the proportions of epinephrine and norepinephrine differ widely. Thus the rabbit adrenal gland contains almost exclusively epinephrine, whereas the whale medulla contains mostly norepinephrine. Table III gives the hormone content of the medullary glands of a variety of animals (U. S. von Euler, 1963). The relative constancy of the two hormones in different species is readily understood as a result of the morphological differentiation of the epinephrine and the norepinephrine-producing cells. Since the proportion of the cortical tissue shows wide variations between different animals, it is often preferable to refer hormone content of the medulla to the body weight of the animal.

Of considerable interest is the finding by Butterworth and Mann (1957a) that the proportion of norepinephrine as well as the total medullary hormone content of the two glands of an animal show close agreement, which facilitates controls. The members of a litter also show very similar values in this respect.

III. Action of Medullary Hormones

A. General Considerations

Since the basic investigations of Cannon (1928), the role of the adrenal medullary hormones as specific activators of a variety of physiological mechanisms in emergency situations has become generally recognized. A brief survey of the main biological effects of epinephrine also bears out the validity of this concept. The stimulating effect on the heart, vasodilatation of the coronary and skeletal muscle vessels, veno-

TABLE III

CATECHOLAMINES IN THE ADRENAL GLANDS OF ADULT MAMMALS

Animal	Norepinephrine (%)	Total amount of catecholamines (milligrams per gram of whole gland)	References[a]
Whale	83; 68	4.0; 2.1	1
Lion	55	0.53	2
Pig	49	2.2	3
Wildebeest	42	1.4	2
Cat	41	1.0	3
Gazelle	39	0.92	2
Hedgehog	39	0.48	9
Goat	37	2.2	7
Sheep	33; 33	0.75; 1.6	3, 2
Cow	29; 28	1.8; 4.2	3, 6
Dog	27	1.5	3
Mouse	25	1.0	3
Squirrel	24	0.84	5
Fox	23	1.4	5
Horse	20	0.84	3
Monkey (*Macacus*)	19	0.33	5
Man	17; 16	0.60; 0.58	3, 4
Zebra	17	1.9	2
Hare	12	0.35	3
Rat	9	1.2	3
Hamster	8	0.4	3
Guinea pig	2; 11	0.15; 0.63	3, 8
Rabbit	2	0.48	3

[a] Key to references:

1. Burn *et al.* (1951), Rastgeldi (1951).
2. Goodall (1951).
3. West (1955).
4. U. S. von Euler *et al.* (1954).
5. U. S. von Euler, unpublished work (1955).
6. U. S. von Euler and Hamberg (1949b).
7. Ozaki (1955).
8. U. S. von Euler and Hökfelt (1953).
9. Uuspää and Suomalainen (1954).

constriction, immobilization of the gut, bronchiolar muscle relaxation, pupillary dilatation and piloerection, are all actions which contribute to increased efficiency of the organism in states of flight or fight. The metabolic actions, such as mobilization of glucose and of fat (Dole, 1956) are further important factors subserving the same goal.

A functional differentiation of the two hormones is obvious on comparing certain circulatory and metabolic actions which are clearly different, as shown in Table IV.

TABLE IV[a]

COMPARISON OF THE PHYSIOLOGICAL ACTIVITY OF EPINEPHRINE AND NOREPINEPHRINE

System	Function	Effect: Epinephrine	Effect: Norepinephrine	Relative activity epinephrine to norepinephrine)
Vascular	Blood pressure: systolic	Raised	Raised	0.5
	Blood pressure: diastolic	None	Raised	—
	Skeletal muscle	Dilatation	Constriction	—
	Peripheral resistance	Decreased	Increased	—
Heart	Heart rate	Increased	Slightly increased or decreased	—
	Cardiac output	Increased	Unchanged	—
	Coronary vessels	Dilatation	Dilatation	1
Respiratory	Bronchial muscle	Inhibition	Slight inhibition	20
Carbohydrate metabolism	Blood sugar	Raised	Slightly raised	4
Eye	Pupillary dilator	Stimulation	Stimulation	15
Alimentary	Intestine	Inhibition	Inhibition	1–2
Reproductory organs	Uterine muscle	Inhibition	Inhibition	100
Skin smooth muscle	Arrectores pilorum	Stimulation	Stimulation	—

[a] Modified after P. F. Hall (1959).

On the other hand, more recent observations have brought out more similarities in action than were suspected at a time when it was believed that norepinephrine chiefly acted on heart and smooth muscle, whereas epinephrine had important metabolic actions (Celander, 1954). Thus it is now known that both hormones mobilize fat and increase the plasma level of free fatty acids, activate phosphorylase, and raise oxygen consumption.

It has been suggested that norepinephrine acts as a specific stimulating agent in carnivores (Goodall, 1951), and the high proportion of this hormone in feline animals supports this view. It is conceivable that animals exerting sudden, brief but forceful attacks on their prey may draw upon a circulating mixture of the two hormones.

As mentioned above, the qualitative actions of epinephrine and norepinephrine are, as a rule, quite similar, although the relative potency of the two amines varies widely. In some instances the relative efficiency is almost the same while in others it may differ as much as 300 times. These differences have been utilized for the biological differentiation and assay of the two hormones when they occur in a mixture.

Table IV gives some examples of the activity ratio for a number of functions. It should also be emphasized that the activity ratio for a given action is by no means a constant figure but may vary considerably.

Observations on the relative potency of epinephrine, norepinephrine and some other sympathomimetic amines have led to the concept of specific receptors on the target cells which respond to one or the other of the active agents (Ahlquist, 1948). These concepts have been greatly aided by results obtained with specific blocking substances acting on one or the other of the receptor types. Furchgott (1959) in his review on the subject proposes the following scheme (Table V).

TABLE V

RECEPTOR TYPES AND FUNCTION[a]

Receptor	Function
Alpha	Contraction of smooth muscle
Beta	Relaxation of smooth muscle other than that of intestine
	Increase in rate and strength of cardiac contraction
Gamma	Glycogenolysis
Delta	Inhibition of smooth muscle

[a] From Furchgott (1959).

Schematically, phentolamine and phenoxybenzamine (PBA) are α-blockers, while the action on β-receptors are antagonized by substances like dichloroisoproterenol (DCI) or pronethalol.

It has thus been established for the heart that norepinephrine primarily acts on the α-receptors and adrenaline on the β-receptors of the heart. The norepinephrine action is consequently readily inhibited by the α-blocker phentolamine, while DCI blocks the epinephrine action. The actions of the adrenergic blocking agents have been extensively analyzed and reviewed by Nickerson (1959).

The mechanism of action of the catecholamines on the effector cell is still unknown, but interesting attempts to recognize binding patterns at the receptor levels have been made (Belleau, 1960).

A complete survey of the biological actions of the medullary hormones is beyond the scope of this article and the reader is referred to pertinent treatises on this subject. Here only a few fundamental actions on circulation will be briefly considered.

B. Action on Heart and Circulation and on Smooth Muscle Organs

Both epinephrine and norepinephrine exert important actions on heart and circulation. In some instances, e.g., on the heart, the two hormones have similar effects, but in certain vascular regions they differ widely in action. When considering the actions of adrenal medullary hormones, it should be kept in mind that since norepinephrine in most species constitutes a relatively smaller part of the amines, its action is, as a rule, less conspicuous than that of epinephrine. On the other hand, adrenal medullary secretion is not infrequently combined with increased sympathetic nerve activity in general. This causes a pronounced effect to occur, because norepinephrine is liberated directly at the nerve endings. A comparison of the norepinephrine actions from these two sources would probably show the relative inefficiency of the former, for instance, during central stimulation, hypotension, or following gangliotropic drugs. However, the possibility of an active participation of norepinephrine secretion from the medulla should not be entirely overlooked, especially not in the cat.

As shown in Fig. 8, the inotropic action of epinephrine and norepinephrine is quite similar, while the effects on the blood pressure differ conspicuously. Thus norepinephrine raises both the systolic and the diastolic pressure, thereby increasing the mean blood pressure. Epinephrine on the other hand, in moderate doses, increases the systolic pressure but leaves the diastolic pressure unchanged or even slightly lowered. The resulting mean blood pressure is often unchanged or very moderately increased. The reason for this difference in action of the two amines on the blood pressure is the vasodilating effect of epinephrine on important sections of the vascular bed such as in the striated muscle and in the liver. Norepinephrine exerts a general vasoconstrictor action, with few exceptions, e.g., on the coronary vessels.

The cardiac output is increased by some 40% after moderate doses of epinephrine, whereas norepinephrine causes only little change. It can therefore be concluded that while norepinephrine causes a net increase in peripheral resistance, the net effect of epinephrine is one of decreased peripheral resistance (Goldenberg *et al.*, 1948).

The pulse rate is generally increased after administration of epinephrine, while the effect of norepinephrine is to cause a moderate reflex decrease in heart frequency.

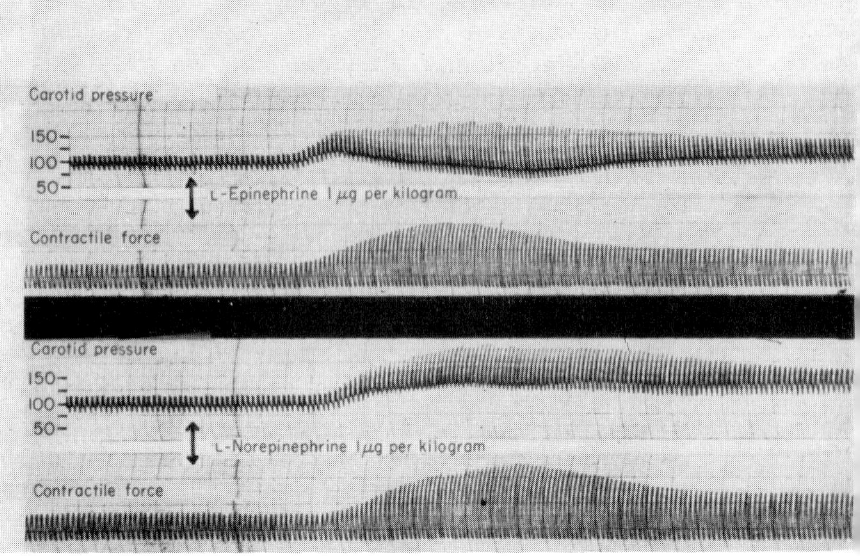

FIG. 8. Effect of epinephrine (upper curves) and norepinephrine (lower curves) in doses of 1 μg per kilogram on arterial blood pressure and contractile force of the heart in the dog. (From Cotten and Pincus, 1955.)

Table VI illustrates some of the actions of epinephrine and norepinephrine on the blood flow in various vascular beds.

On smooth muscle organs epinephrine and norepinephrine have, with few exceptions, the same kind of action, independently of whether it is stimulating or inhibiting. The two kinds of actions are associated with

TABLE VI

EFFECT OF EPINEPHRINE AND NOREPINEPHRINE ON REGIONAL BLOOD FLOW[a]

		Flow during administration of amines			
		Epinephrine		Norepinephrine	
Organ	Initial flow (liters per minute)		Percent change		Percent change
Liver	1.5	3.0	+100	1.5	0
Kidneys	1.5	0.9	− 40	1.2	−20
Skeletal muscle	1.0	2.0	+100	1.0	0
Brain	0.75	0.9	+ 20	0.7	−10
Total	4.75	6.8	+ 40	4.4	− 8

[a] After P. F. Hall (1959).

electrical changes of such a kind that contraction is accompanied by depolarization and the appearance of action potentials, while relaxation is associated with hyperpolarization and cessation of electrical activity. The early studies of Bozler (1940) led him to assume a dual effect of nervous impulses rather than a dual sympathetic innervation. By the use of the sucrose gap method of Stämpfli (1954) it has been possible to record mechanical responses simultaneously with changes in membrane potential and spontaneous electrical activity (cf. Bülbring, 1960). From these and other studies it emerged that epinephrine has a dual action, one directly on the membrane and the other primarily metabolic and depending on an increase in phosphorylase activity (Fig. 9). The direct

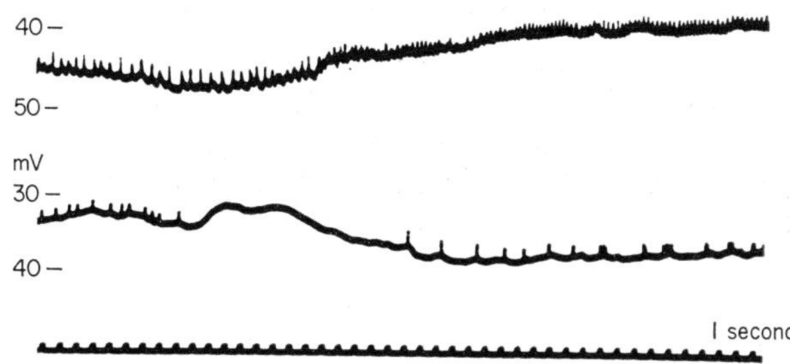

FIG. 9. Effects of acetylcholine, 3×10^{-6} gm per milliliter (upper record) and epinephrine, 10^{-8} gm per milliliter (lower record) on membrane potential and spike frequency of taenia coli of the guinea pig. (From Bülbring, 1954.)

action depolarizes the membrane, making it less stable and more excitable while the other may be utilized for energy-consuming active ion transport, tending to stabilize the membrane and making it less excitable. Depending on the muscle, or on the prevailing conditions in one and the same muscle, epinephrine may cause stimulation or relaxation. Direct evidence for a stimulation of the sodium pump by epinephrine, leading to hyperpolarization and relaxation has been obtained in intestinal smooth muscle (Axelsson and Bülbring, 1960).

Table IV gives a survey of some of the more important actions of the two amines on heart and circulation and on smooth muscle organs.

C. Action on Nervous Structures

Epinephrine exerts biological activity on ganglia and on the central nervous system. The effects of norepinephrine are similar but generally weaker. As shown by Bülbring and Burn (1942), epinephrine in small doses facilitates the impulse transmission in sympathetic ganglia, while larger doses have an inhibitory action. Lundberg (1952) found only inhibitory actions of epinephrine as well as norepinephrine, the latter compound being about 4 times weaker.

On the central nervous system, epinephrine causes subjective sensations of apprehension, discomfort, and even anxiety, thereby presumably reinforcing the emotional background for activity in emergency situations. The significance of the various effects described on different structures is not clear in its details. It has recently been claimed that epinephrine partakes in the central temperature regulation (Feldberg and Myers, 1964), and induces certain behavioral patterns in animals when topically administered at certain hypothalamic sites.

A comprehensive review of the actions of the catecholamines on central nervous mechanisms has been given by Rothballer (1959). The reader is also referred to articles by Dell (1960) and Bradley (1960).

Of particular interest is the effect of epinephrine on cortical structures and on the reticular system. Epinephrine in doses as low as 1 μg per kilogram produces an intense cortical arousal and also stimulates the mesencephalo-hypothalamic component of the descending facilitatory system. By this mechanism epinephrine causes a striking and long-lasting facilitation of monosynaptic (but not polysynaptic) reflex responses (Dell *et al.*, 1954).

Cells in the mesencephalic reticular system may increase or decrease their activity after epinephrine injections (Fig. 10). The main site of

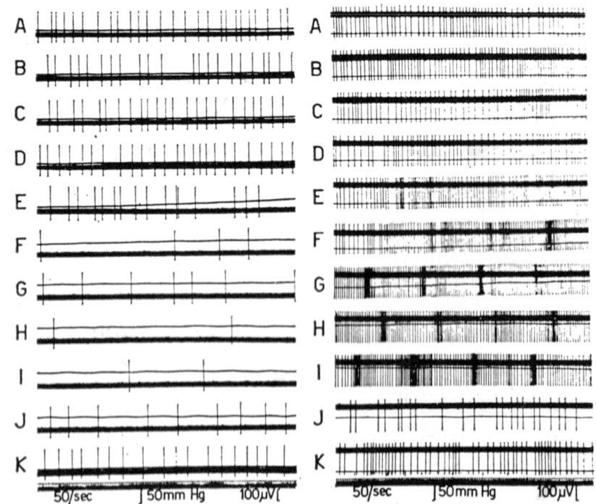

FIG. 10. Discharge rates from two mesencephalic neurons in the cat reacting to intravenous injection of 10 μg of epinephrine with increase (left) and decrease (right) in frequency. Injection made immediately before B. (From Bradley and Mollica, 1958.)

action of epinephrine is in a narrow region in the anterior part of the mesencephalon and the posterior part of the hypothalamus.

The electrical activity of the phrenic outflow is inhibited by epinephrine and norepinephrine, as observed by Krivoy *et al.* (1953), which may play a role in the development of epinephrine apnoea.

D. Metabolic Actions

1. *General Metabolism*

Epinephrine increases the oxygen consumption at rest by about 20–25%. This so-called calorigenic action has been extensively studied and many attempts to analyze this action have been made, using isolated organs, homogenates of organs, and soluble systems (cf. Ellis, 1956; Spoelstra, 1963). Part of the action observed may be ascribed to the glucose mobilization, phosphorylase activation, and increased fat metabolism. Norepinephrine is much less active in this respect (Goldenberg *et al.*, 1948).

Of considerable interest is the finding that norepinephrine strongly enhances the metabolism of rats exposed to cold (Hsieh and Carlson, 1957). It is interesting in this connection that Leduc (1961) found a strong increase in the norepinephrine release in such rats, as judged by the greatly increased output in urine. Epinephrine was also released under these conditions but only temporarily and in much smaller amounts.

In newborn animals it has been found (cf. Moore, 1960) that norepinephrine produces a strong increase in oxygen consumption, while epinephrine given in the same dose had no effect (Fig. 11).

The hormonal actions on metabolism have recently been integrated by Brodie *et al.* (1965) into a general system which plays an important role in stress situations of different kinds.

2. *Carbohydrate Metabolism*

The glucose-mobilizing and hyperglycemic action of epinephrine has been known for a long time. Thus glycosuria as a result of epinephrine injection was observed in 1901 by Blum. This action is also evident after administration of very low concentrations of epinephrine. The effect of norepinephrine in this respect is considerably smaller and is usually estimated to be about one-fifth to one-tenth of that of epinephrine.

The mechanism of the glycogenolytic effect of epinephrine has become clearer since it was discovered that this amine promotes the formation of a cyclic nucleotide, adenosine-3′5′-phosphate, which in its turn activates phosphorylase (Sutherland and Rall, 1960). The catecholamines stimulate the formation of cyclic adenylate in a number of tissues, thereby increasing the phosphorylase concentration. The enzyme catalyzes breakdown of glycogen with glucose formation in the liver and lactate in skeletal muscle. Epinephrine and norepinephrine are about equally active in stimulating the formation of cyclic adenylate, but since the glycemic effect of epinephrine is greater than that of norepinephrine, it appears doubtful whether the glucose-mobilizing effect of epinephrine is explicable only as a result of the above-mentioned mechanism.

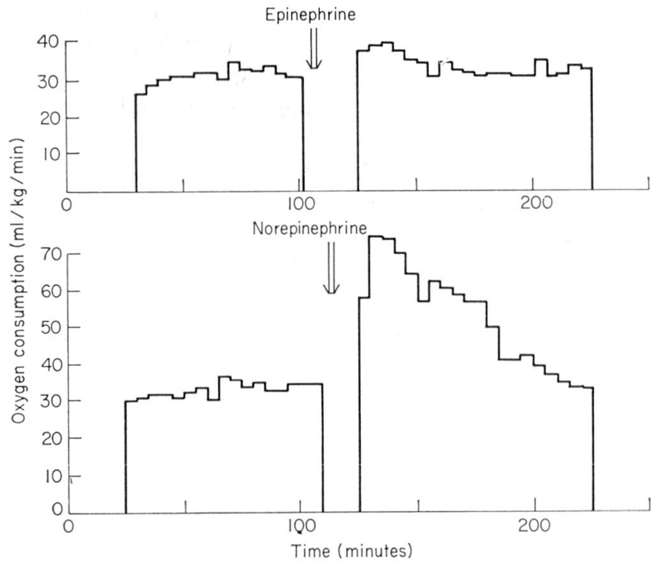

FIG. 11. Effects of epinephrine (above) and norepinephrine (below), 400 μg per kilogram in each case, on the oxygen consumption of 12-day-old rats. The P_{O_2} of the inspired air was near-atmospheric and the environmental temperature 35°C. (Moore and Underwood, 1963.)

3. *Fat Metabolism*

Epinephrine causes an increase in the free fatty acids (FFA) in plasma (Dole, 1956). The same kind of effect is seen on stimulation of the sympathetic system and on injection of norepinephrine (Havel and Goldfien, 1959). The effect of equimolar doses of the two amines is about equal. Prolonged infusions of norepinephrine in the dog (about 0.1 mg per kilogram per hour over 8 hours) causes a selective uptake and deposition of fat globules in red muscle fibers (Wirsén, 1964).

IV. Adrenal Medullary Secretion

A. Secretory Nerves to the Adrenal Medulla

The splanchnic fibers to the adrenal medulla originate from the lower thoracic and the lumbar sympathetic representation of the spinal cord and pass through the ventral roots. They are cholinergic in character and analogous to the presynaptic sympathetic neurons to other organs. They show only a small degree of cross-innervation or none (Inoue, 1959).

From the histochemical studies of Palkama (1964) it has emerged that the epinephrine-containing cells are surrounded by nerve fibers and probably innervated in all species. The norepinephrine-containing cells, on the other hand, show variations in this respect from species to species; they appear to be innervated in the dog, the cat, and rodents, but not in the horse and ox.

In view of the two different kinds of secretory cells, either secreting epinephrine or norepinephrine, and their differential activation by central stimuli, it must be assumed that the splanchnic nerve fibers innervate specific cells, at least in some species. It should therefore be theoretically possible to activate either type of cell by stimulation of the appropriate fibers. Since the splanchnic fibers are anatomically intermingled and not separable into their two groups, attempts have been made to achieve differential secretion by changing stimulation parameters (Mirkin, 1961). By raising the stimulation frequency range from 1–10 per second to 20 pulses per second, the epinephrine percentage rose from 65 ± 2 to 84 ± 2 in the dog. Thermal blockade of the splanchnic nerve decreased the total secretion and the percentage of epinephrine at any given frequency.

By intermittent peripheral stimulation, large quantities of the hormones may be secreted; the amounts secreted may be larger than the total content of the gland, indicating that synthesis has taken place as well (Hökfelt and McLean, 1950). According to Holland and Schümann (1956), synthesis and methylation rates are increased by splanchnic stimulation. The denervated medulla still shows a small secretion when measured in the cat under chloralose 17–56 days after nerve section. The mean secretion of the two glands was 21 ng of epinephrine and 34 ng of norepinephrine per minute (Vogt, 1952).

B. Resting Secretion

It has been much debated whether catecholamines are secreted continuously under resting conditions. This would seem likely since a certain reflex tone of the secretory nerves is to be expected. On the other hand, direct measurements of the adrenal secretion in the adrenal venous blood have shown that it is very small. When measuring is done under conditions of anesthesia, it should be remembered that many anesthetic agents elicit some adrenal secretion. In unanesthetized resting dogs Wada *et al.* (1935b) found a secretion of 0.015 μg per kilogram per minute (as epinephrine), and in cats anesthetized with pentobarbital (Nembutal), Dunér (1953) found 0.064 μg of norepinephrine per kilogram per minute and 0.012 μg of epinephrine per kilogram per minute from one suprarenal. Secretory rates of this order would also harmonize with the values obtained for the epinephrine level in human peripheral blood which has been estimated at about 0.1 ng per milliliter in man (Vendsalu, 1960) during resting conditions.

C. Central Stimulation

Beginning with the "piqûre diabetique" of Claude Bernard, the central representation of the nerve paths connected with the adrenal medulla has been extensively studied. The classical studies by Karplus and Kreidl (1909) showed the importance of the hypothalamus as a center for secretory stimuli. More precise information about the effect of various stimuli has been gained by direct estimation of the secretory rate of catecholamines in the adrenal medullary vein instead of observing secondary effects such as on the blood glucose and heart rate. Convenient methods for obtaining adrenal venous blood samples have been described by Bouckaert and van Loo (1947) and by Schapiro and Stjärne (1958). In this way it has been established that medullary secretion can be elicited by stimulation of widely different parts of the brain. Studies of this kind have shown that electrical stimulation can produce a release of medullary hormones not only from various areas in the hypothalamic and midbrain region but also from certain cortical areas (Brücke *et al.*, 1952; Redgate and Gellhorn, 1953; Folkow and von Euler, 1954; U. S. von Euler and Folkow, 1958). These experiments have also shown that a differential effect on the secretion of epinephrine and norepinephrine can be achieved by selecting specific points of stimulation. Furthermore, it has emerged that stimulation in some regions produces an increase while stimulation of other points causes an inhibition of the secretion (Fig. 12). Increased medullary secretion has also been observed by Goldfien and Ganong (1962) although they did not succeed in finding any stimulation points producing predominant norepinephrine secretion. The norepinephrine percentage during stimulation was approximately one-half of that during rest, indicating that chiefly epinephrine was secreted during stimulation. By stimulation of the hypothalamus (Grant *et al.*, 1958) and of the bulbar part of the sympathetic vasodilator outflow in the cat, an increased adrenal medullary secretion mainly consisting of epinephrine has been observed (Lindgren *et al.*, 1959).

Cerebral electrostimulation of subconvulsive intensity in man caused increased plasma epinephrine levels (Weil-Malherbe and Bone, 1954). Likewise, electroshock treatment in man causes a marked increase in medullary secretion and a plasma level of above 3 ng per milliliter (Havens *et al.*, 1959).

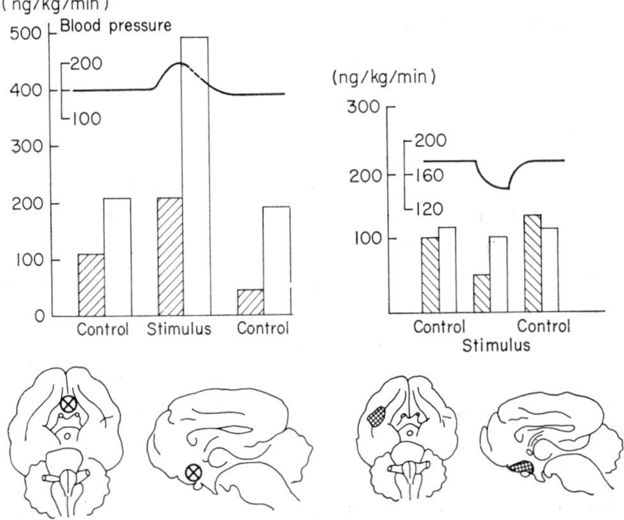

FIG. 12. Secretion from left suprarenal gland in the cat before, during, and after stimulation of the medial orbital cortex (left) and lateral orbital cortex (right) as indicated on the figure. Striped columns, epinephrine; plain columns, norepinephrine. (From U. S. von Euler and Folkow, 1958.)

The demonstration of specific localizations in the central nervous system at which stimulation leads to an output of epinephrine and norepinephrine has also aided in the understanding of the mechanism of increased adrenal medullary hormone secretion during situations of stress (Dougherty and White, 1944). In rats exposed to 50-volt shocks of 2 seconds duration for 1.5 hours the plasma FFA was significantly increased. This increase could be prevented by pretreatment with tranquilizers and other central depressants in the following order of potency: reserpine > benzquinamide > chlorpromazine > meprobamate > hydroxyzine > pentobarbital (Khan *et al.*, 1964).

Comparatively few studies have been made on the effect of hypothalamic lesions on the adrenal medullary response to various stimuli. Although no direct measurements of the secretion were made, the experiments of Cross and Silver (1962) indicated a loss or reduction of response of the medulla to hypercapnic stimuli when lesions were made in dorsal and posterior hypothalamus, and in the supramammillary area.

D. Reflex Stimulation of Medullary Secretion

A reflexly induced medullary secretion can be elicited by lowering the pressure in the baroceptor areas in the carotid sinus or in the aortic arch. Direct estimation of catecholamines in adrenal venous blood indicated increased secretion in the vagotomized cat (Kaindl and von Euler, 1951), but no consistent change in the composition of the secretion. Correspondingly, a rise of blood pressure causes a diminution of the adrenal medullary secretion (Robinson and Watts, 1962). Denervation of both carotid sinuses in vagotomized dogs caused a sevenfold increase in the total medullary output, without altering the proportion of epinephrine to norepinephrine (de Schaepdryver, 1959).

Several types of stress (see below) induce adrenal medullary secretion by reflex action. Thus the effects of cold, heat, and pain may be primarily regarded as reflex stimulation of the secretion. Electrical stimulation of afferent nerves in the anesthetized cat elicits adrenal medullary secretion. In their experiments U. S. von Euler and Folkow (1958) found that afferent stimulation of the sciatic or the brachial plexus increased the catecholamine output in the adrenal venous blood, and altered the relative amounts of the two hormones. The secretion during carotid occlusion in all cases contained more norepinephrine than epinephrine, whereas during afferent nerve stimulation the epinephrine secretion was higher than that of norepinephrine in one half of the experiments. The average epinephrine percentage during afferent nerve stimulation was about twice as high as that observed during carotid occlusion.

E. Hypo- and Hyperglycemia

The strong effect of hypoglycemia on adrenal medullary secretion first reported by Cannon *et al.* (1924) and by Houssay *et al.* (1924), has later been subjected to a more detailed analysis. From this it has emerged that the hypoglycemic stimulus has a selective effect upon medullary secretion in that practically only epinephrine is secreted. This has been shown both by analysis of the catecholamine excretion in urine during insulin hypoglycemia (U. S. von Euler and Luft, 1952) and by direct measurement of the secretory products in the adrenal venous blood (Dunér, 1954). The urinary excretion of epinephrine induced by 0.1 U of insulin per kilogram in man corresponded to that observed after infusion of 0.15 μg per kilogram per minute according to Elmadjian *et al.* (1956). Dunér was able to show not only that hypoglycemia increased the epinephrine secretion but also that hyperglycemia reduced it (Dunér, 1953) (Fig. 13). The effect is abolished by splanchnic nerve section and consequently elicited centrally as indicated in Section IV,C. A further analysis of the nervous pathways has been made by Crone

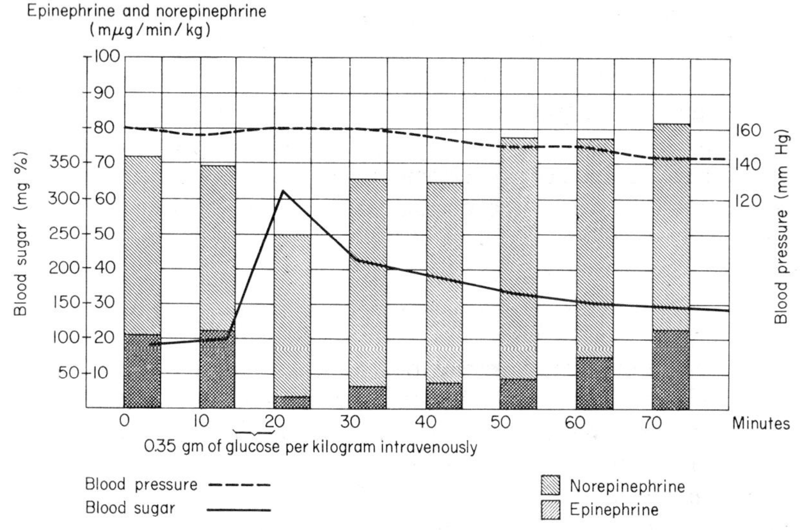

FIG. 13. Epinephrine and norepinephrine secretion from left adrenal in the cat before and after 0.35 gm of glucose per kilogram intravenously. (From Dunér, 1953.)

(1963) who found that the secretory effect was abolished in spinal sheep but remained after decerebration at the superior collicular level. The critical blood glucose level at which the epinephrine secretion is elicited lies between 0.05 and 0.07%. Cantu *et al.* (1963) observed that transection of the midbrain and the cervical spinal cord in dogs did not eliminate the increase in catecholamine secretion after insulin, whereas removal of the midthoracic portion of the spinal cord abolished it. Glucagon from the pancreas is not an obligatory mediator of the adrenal medullary response to hypoglycemia in the dog (Strand *et al.*, 1964).

As shown by Udenfriend *et al.* (1953) and by Hökfelt (1951) insulin hypoglycemia causes a very marked depletion of the epinephrine stores of the gland, which require about a week to become repleted. Although this seemed to indicate a slow turnover of epinephrine, later experiments by Bygdeman *et al.* (1960) indicate that the urinary secretion remains high during hypoglycemia, even at a stage when the epinephrine content of the gland is low.

Intravenous injection of 0.6 gm of glucose over 30 minutes in man causes a decrease in FFA concentration which can be prevented by ganglionic or adrenergic blockers (Goodner and Tustison, 1964). This suggests a central sympathetic nervous control similar to that found by Dunér (1953) for the adrenal medullary secretion.

The mechanism of the secretory effect of hypoglycemia has not been elucidated in detail, but it appears likely that the plasma glucose level exerts a regulating effect on central stimulatory pathways, presumably via specific receptors sensitive to the glucose level. By administration of 2-deoxyglucose, a strong medullary secretion is elicited, followed by depletion of the gland, apparently owing to a substitution of the authentic glucose for a chemically similar compound which is still sufficiently different to be inactive on the postulated receptors (Hökfelt and Bygdeman, 1961).

F. Medullary Secretion during Cold Exposure and Hypothermia

Exposure to cold produces an increased secretion of medullary hormones and hyperglycemia. As shown by Saito (1928), a fall in body temperature of 0.5°–1.7° does not increase medullary secretion, while a fall to about 30°C by immersion of a dog in cold water causes a considerable secretion, reaching a peak of about 0.3 μg per kilogram per minute (Wada *et al.*, 1935a). The heart rate in medulli-adrenalectomized dogs is still increased after exposure to cold, suggesting that this effect is partly caused by some other factor than secreted epinephrine.

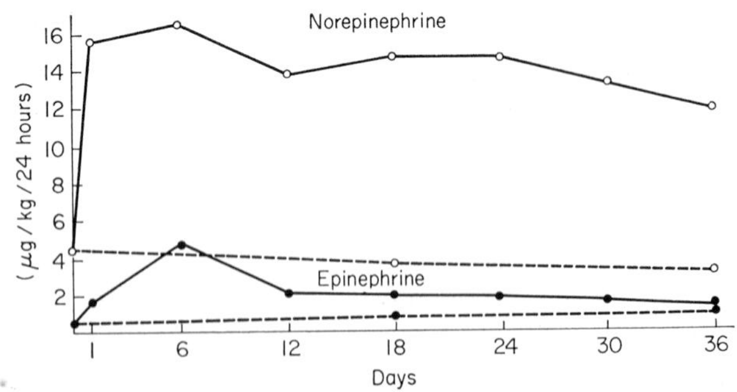

FIG. 14. Urinary excretion of epinephrine (●) and norepinephrine (○) in young rats at 3°C (solid lines) and 22°C (dotted lines). (From Leduc, 1961.)

In experiments by Leduc (1961) it was shown by urine catecholamine analysis that the epinephrine secretion during exposure of rats to cold is relatively much smaller than that of norepinephrine, which remains high in cold-exposed rats even after adrenalectomy (Fig. 14). It is also apparent that on prolonged exposure to cold the epinephrine excretion gradually diminishes over a period of a week, while the norepinephrine falls off much more slowly. The epinephrine secretion is regarded by Leduc as constituting a second line of defense. There is no indication that the norepinephrine secretion should emanate to any considerable degree from the adrenal medulla.

G. Heating and Burns

Saito (1928) has shown that surface heating of the dog, causing a rise of body temperature to above 41°C is accompanied by an increase in the epinephrine secretion of up to about 0.3 μg per kilogram per minute. A striking increase in the epinephrine and norepinephrine output in urine after burns, as a sign of increased medullary secretion, has been reported by Goodall *et al.* (1957) and by Birke *et al.* (1957b). This is illustrated by Table VII, from which it can be seen that the epinephrine excretion figures are very high during the first period after the burns. In fatal cases the values showed a marked decline in the prelethal period. The reason for the marked increase in medullary secretion following burns is still obscure.

TABLE VII

EPINEPHRINE AND NOREPINEPHRINE EXCRETION IN PATIENTS WITH SEVERE BURNS (FATAL CASES)[a]

	Female, 66 years 25% burn		Female, 12 years 88% burn		Female, 44 years 22% burn	
Days postburn	Epinephrine	Norepinephrine	Epinephrine	Norepinephrine	Epinephrine	Norepinephrine
Day 1	87	284	—	—	214	462
Day 4	106	309	—	—	244[b]	571
Day 10	100	308	91	120	—	—
Day 13	—	—	183	141	—	—
Day 18	—	—	224[b]	254	—	—
Day 26	261[b]	389	—	—	—	—

[a] After Goodall *et al.* (1957). Excretion in micrograms per 24 hours. Control values: epinephrine, 16 μg/24 hours; norepinephrine, 32 μg/24 hours.

[b] Died.

H. Hypoxia, Asphyxia, Hypercarbia, Hemorrhage

During hypoxia and anoxia the adrenal medullary secretion increases rapidly when desaturation has reached a certain value (cf. Saraké, 1954). Ludemann *et al.* (1955) observed a rise in arterial plasma epinephrine to the enormous values of 0.35 to 0.48 μg per milliliter at arterial oxygen saturation values of 0–20% after respiratory standstill in the dog. In order to cause a definite increase in the medullary secretion, the barometric pressure has to be lowered to levels corresponding to 7000–8000 meters altitude in the dog. While moderate hypercarbia alone had little action on the epinephrine secretion, and none when blood pH was maintained at a normal level with tris buffer (Nahas, 1959), hypersecretion of epinephrine can be elicited by exposing rabbits to 80% carbon dioxide–20% oxygen (Cross and Silver, 1962). Asphyxia causes a strong increase in medullary secretion. Even the fetal lamb responds with increased rate of the denervated heart after occlusion of the umbilical artery (Reynolds, 1953). Comline and Silver (1958) found that asphyxia in the fetal lamb caused predominantly norepinephrine secretion from the adrenal medulla, while the secretion after splanchnic stimulation was chiefly epinephrine.

Severe hemorrhage also increases medullary secretion which may reach values as high as 0.5 μg per kilogram per minute (Fig. 15), in the

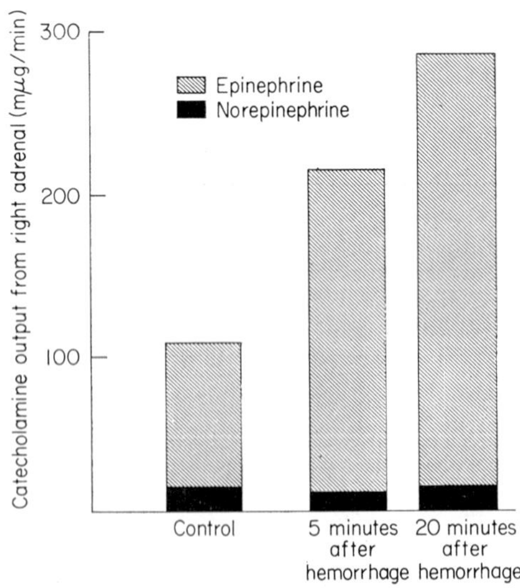

FIG. 15. Epinephrine and norepinephrine secretion from the right adrenal gland in dogs subjected to hemorrhage. (After Ganong, 1963.)

dog after removing one-third of the total blood volume. The increase may last for several hours and the total amount of oversecretion may reach 100 μg. These effects are largely, though not entirely, mediated through the splanchnic nerves (Satakė, 1954).

Carbon monoxide, 3% in air, administered for 2 minutes, and potassium cyanide, 2–2.5 mg per kilogram, injected intravenously, caused strong but transitory secretion of epinephrine (Satakė, 1954).

I. Physical and Emotional Stress

Adrenal medullary secretion is increased by muscular work, but only when this is of such an intensity that it involves a certain degree of exhaustion. This was first shown in the dog by Wada *et al.* (1935b). In agreement with these results, Munro and Robinson (1958) found no increase in the epinephrine plasma levels during moderate exercise in man, but in quarter-mile and long-distance runs, the plasma epinephrine was increased. The results also tally with the observations that only at considerable exercise rates (above 2 liters of oxygen consumption per minute) the epinephrine values in urine are increased (U. S. von Euler and Hellner, 1952). The mechanism of the secretory stimulation accompanying physical strain has not been analyzed, and it is still not clear whether the increase is due to irradiation effects, elicited by some humoral factor acting reflexly or directly on the secretory centers, or to other causes.

An increased adrenomedullary secretion during emotional stress has long been assumed and was experimentally proved by Cannon who induced emotional stress in cats by exposing them to barking dogs. The effect of psychic factors in causing secretion from the adrenal medulla has since been studied extensively, although chiefly by indirect methods such as measuring the epinephrine excretion in urine. With direct estimation methods it has been observed (Satakė, 1954) that in an unanesthetized dog in "furious emotional excitement" the epinephrine secretion was very greatly increased, from about 0.05 μg per kilogram per minute (resting secretion) to 6 μg per kilogram per minute or about 100 times. It appears very likely that between such excessive values and the resting levels all grades of secretory rates may occur as a result of emotional stimulation or mental stress.

The urine analysis method has found considerable use in the estimation of adrenal medullary secretion in psychic stress since it was introduced in 1954 (U. S. von Euler and Lundberg). A large number of stressful situations have been studied in this respect and some of the results are listed in Table VIII. As discussed previously, there is good evidence for the assumption that the greater part of the epinephrine excretion in the urine is derived from the adrenal medulla and thus may serve as relative measure of the medullary secretion.

Of particular interest is the anticipation stress which is clearly seen in the different effects of early and later runs in the human centrifuge (Frankenhaeuser *et al.*, 1962) as well as during mock runs when the actual *g*-value was negligible (Goodall and Berman, 1960). The same phenomenon was seen in the astronaut in the first United States

TABLE VIII

EPINEPHRINE EXCRETION IN URINE DURING VARIOUS KINDS OF STRESS

Situation	Epinephrine (nanograms per minute)	References
Normal, resting	4–8	U. S. von Euler, Hellner-Björkman and Orwèn (1955)
Mental work	11–15	Frankenhaeuser and Post (1962)
Examinations	6.5–21	Pekkarinen *et al.* (1961)
Routine work under stressful conditions (industrial stress)	18	Levi (1963)
Exciting films	11	Levi (1964)
Air transportation	24	U. S. von Euler and Lundberg (1954)
Centrifugation mock run	31	Goodall and Berman (1960)
Centrifugation first run	38	Frankenhaeuser *et al.* (1962)
Centrifugation sixth run	9	Frankenhaeuser *et al.* (1962)
Suborbital space flight		
Preflight 4 days	25	
Postflight 30 minutes	33	Jackson *et al.* (1961)
Postflight 45 hours	6	
Parachute jumping	18	Bloom *et al.* (1963)

suborbital manned space flight, whose epinephrine excretion was increased some 300–400% even 4 days before the actual flight. On the other hand, no adaptation seems to occur in cases involving an element of real danger such as parachute jumps, since the excretion figures were virtually the same in trainees who made their first jump and in the officers who had long experience (Fig. 16) (Bloom *et al.*, 1963).

From the results in Table VIII it can be seen that the emotional sphere is intimately related to the adrenal medullary secretory activity (cf. Elmadjian *et al.*, 1958). Since the nerve paths for this secretion have both cortical and hypothalamic connections, the morphological substrate is available, although the precise activation mechanism is still obscure.

Alterations in the epinephrine secretion during psychic disorders have been studied by Bergsman (1959) who observed characteristic patterns associated with various psychotic states.

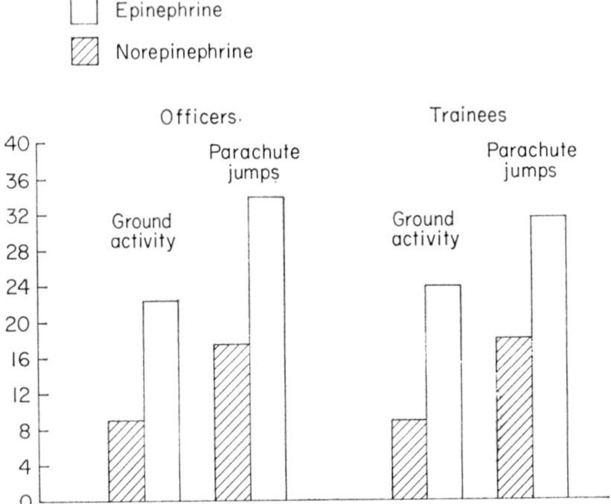

FIG. 16. Urinary excretion of epinephrine and norepinephrine, nanograms per minute, in officers and trainees during ground activity and during a period including parachute jumps. (From Bloom *et al.*, 1963.)

J. Drugs and Various Compounds

A large number of drugs which affect the autonomic nervous system or generally influence the functions of nerve cells and junctions will consequently alter the medullary secretion. Such effects have been actually confirmed by measuring the epinephrine secretion from the gland or by studying the plasma level or the urinary excretion. The effects vary greatly for different drugs with regard to intensity of effect, time course, and total amount of oversecretion. Space does not permit mentioning more than a few of the active compounds and the reader is referred to the comprehensive review of Sataké (1954) for details and references. Nicotine is a particularly potent stimulus, although the effect is usually short-lasting and followed by secretory block. Nicotine appears to cause a preferential secretion of epinephrine from the medulla, as first noted by Houssay and Rapela (1953). The secretory effect of nicotine is reduced by denervation, from which it is concluded that the action is partly central and partly on the gland itself (Sugawara, 1925).

The transmission between the splanchnic fibers and the chromaffin cells of the medulla is cholinergic, and drugs which facilitate or block cholinergic transmission have the corresponding effect on secretion. Examples are acetylcholine itself (Butterworth and Mann, 1957b) and eserine. Tetraethylammonium chloride stimulates adrenal medullary secretion through its direct effect on the chromaffin cells (Stone *et al.*, 1951).

A large number of drugs have been shown to cause various degrees of depletion of the adrenal medulla (cf. Hökfelt, 1951). Of these drugs, some have been extensively studied in recent years, particularly reserpine (Carlsson and Hillarp, 1956), guanethidine (Sheppard and Zimmerman, 1959), phenoxybenzamine (Schapiro, 1958), decaborane (Merritt *et al.*, 1964; U. S. von Euler and Lishajko, 1965), *N*-(3,3-diphenylpropyl)-α-methylphenethylamine (Segontin) (Schöne and Lindner, 1962). As regards reserpine, there is some evidence that it causes increased medullary secretion which is reduced by splanchnic nerve section and accordingly is of central nature (Kroneberg and Schümann, 1958). In some experiments the epinephrine secretion was small during depletion, suggesting that epinephrine secretion was not its only cause. Increased epinephrine excretion in urine after reserpine administration in man has been observed (Birke *et al.*, 1957a). It has been reported that reserpine in rats causes a preferential depletion of norepinephrine (Eränkö and Hopsu, 1958) and a similar effect has been observed in the pigeon (Ghosh and Ghosh, 1963). As for decaborane, it has not been established whether it lowers the catecholamine content of the adrenals after splanchnectomy or cord section. This is the case for the depleting action of carbon tetrachloride, however (Brody and Calvert, 1960). β-Tetrahydronaphthylamine has a comparatively small effect, which is abolished by splanchnectomy.

While some anesthetics and hypnotics tend to reduce the medullary secretion, others—such as ether, chloroform, and particularly urethan—increase it (Satake, 1954). Ethanol and acetaldehyde cause moderate increases in the adrenal medullary secretion as shown by Perman (1958a,b), who measured the secretory rate in adrenal venous blood and estimated the urinary excretion. Morphine increases adrenal medullary secretion.

It has been reported that diphtheria toxin (Kimura, 1927) increases the adrenal medullary secretion in the unanesthetized dog. After administration of *Salmonella* endotoxin the epinephrine excretion in urine was greatly increased, indicating increased secretion (Serafimov, 1962). Potassium chloride has a brief but strong stimulating effect on the secretion (Satake, 1954). The effect of calcium is discussed in Section V.

It has been reported that ferrous salts cause a release of catecholamines from the adrenal medulla (Eichholtz and Roesch, 1949). This effect appears to be a direct one on the cells since it is not influenced by drugs which block the specific receptor mechanisms. Thallium causes a marked release of epinephrine, as shown by increased urinary excretion (Tillman, 1952).

K. Hormonal Actions on Medullary Secretion

In hypothyroid patients Leak *et al.* (1962) have reported a decrease in the adrenal medullary secretion in response to insulin hypoglycemia, which has been taken to indicate that the medulla reacts less efficiently in such states. Hypothyroid rats respond to injections of deoxyglucose by increasing their blood glucose level to higher values than euthyroid or hyperthyroid rats and show less epinephrine excretion in urine (Johnson, 1965; cf. Harrison, 1964).

An increased norepinephrine proportion in the medulla has been observed during pregnancy in rats (Hökfelt, 1951) and in *Cholaepus* (Dresse and Goffart, 1963).

A striking finding has been reported recently by Feldberg and Lewis (1964) who observed that even minute doses of angiotensin II, as low as 0.1 μg, injected intra-arterially, produce a marked secretion of catecholamines from the adrenal medulla. This effect is abolished by section of the splanchnic nerves.

The releasing effect of histamine on the adrenal medullary hormones may also be mentioned in this context. This effect is apparently a direct one on the cell membrane (Burn and Dale, 1926). Hypophysectomy in the rat caused a slight decrease in the epinephrine content of the adrenals (Hökfelt, 1951).

L. Catecholamine Plasma Levels

While the estimation of epinephrine and norepinephrine in the adrenal venous blood generally presents no problems, the quantitative analyses of these hormones in plasma are more difficult, owing to the low concentrations. From the values obtained by Vendsalu (1960) which agree well with the equally careful studies by Price and Price (1957) and appear most acceptable, it can be seen that, in man, the levels during resting conditions are at the limit of accurate estimation. Thus Vendsalu (1960) found for femoral arterial plasma 0.24 ± 0.04 ng of epinephrine and 0.32 ng of norepinephrine per milliliter in healthy subjects. Following an insulin injection, Vendsalu found no change in the norepinephrine level but an increase in the epinephrine level to 0.8 ng per milliliter (Fig. 17). Price (1957) also showed that the resulting arterial plasma level of epinephrine was the same whether the epinephrine was infused in the adrenal vein in adrenalectomized patients or given by the antecubital venous route. For further references the reader is referred to the review by U. S. von Euler (1961, p. 553–578).

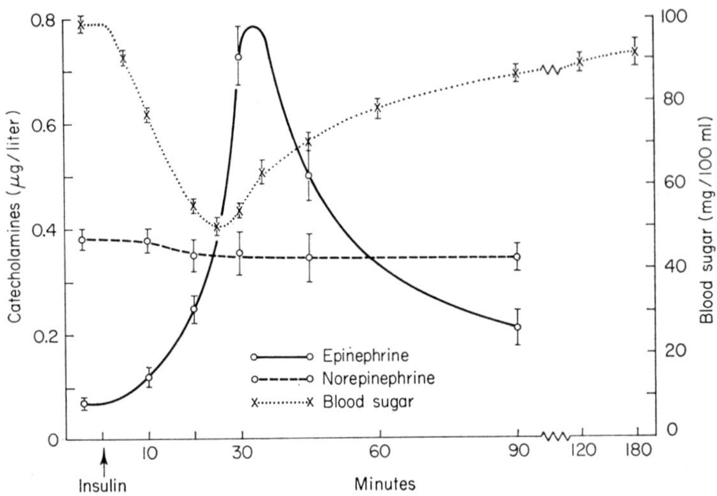

FIG. 17. Plasma catecholamine levels in micrograms per liter during insulin-induced hypoglycemia in man. (From Vendsalu, 1960.)

M. Differential Secretion

Analysis of the adrenal venous blood during varying experimental conditions has shown that the proportions of epinephrine and norepinephrine are not fixed and constant, particularly in the cat, whose adrenals contain about equal parts of the two hormones. It is hard to avoid the suspicion that norepinephrine, occurring in relatively large quantities in the cat's suprarenals, serves as a hormone in its own right, although the concept of differential secretion has been emphatically denied by some authors. In the foregoing sections, several examples of such differential secretion have been given, both as a result of hypothalamic stimulation (Redgate and Gellhorn, 1953; Folkow and von Euler, 1954) and following chemical stimuli (Dunér, 1953, 1954; Houssay and Rapela, 1953; Comline and Silver, 1958).

In animals secreting predominantly epinephrine, like the rabbit, the dog, or man, the evidence for a selective norepinephrine secretion is essentially lacking and would presumably be of minor importance as an adjuvant to the activity of the norepinephrine system. In view of the dominance of this system, an admixture of norepinephrine to the epinephrine secretion, as detected by urine analysis, would be hard to evaluate. The most striking example of a selective secretion from the adrenal gland is perhaps the action of hypoglycemia (Fig. 13) which has also been demonstrated in the dog (Hermann and Klepping, 1956). For further discussion of this point the reader is referred to the review of Malméjac (1964).

V. Mechanism of Release

The adrenomedullary cells, being innervated by cholinergic fibers (Feldberg and Minz, 1932), may in certain respects be regarded as homologs of postsynaptic adrenergic neurons. It is therefore generally accepted that acetylcholine serves as the physiological neurotransmitter. This substance is released on splanchnic stimulation and activates the adrenal chromaffin cells, presumably by depolarization. The cells also respond directly to acetylcholine, nicotine, and drugs with nicotine-like action.

In experiments on isolated perfused adrenals of cats Douglas and Rubin (1963) were able to show that acetylcholine releases catecholamines only in the presence of calcium ions. They also showed that calcium caused a catecholamine release by itself if the adrenals had been perfused previously with calcium-free Locke's solution.

In perfusion experiments on bovine adrenals, Philippu and Schümann (1962) also showed that calcium ions were necessary for the releasing effect action of acetylcholine, and they showed in addition that phenylethylamine was able to release catecholamines even in the absence of calcium (Fig. 18). This effect of calcium can also be demonstrated on isolated adrenal granules, as shown by the same authors. Thus a concentration of 2.5 mEq of calcium ions per liter increased the spontaneous release by 52%, and 5 mEq per liter by 125%. On the other hand, acetylcholine has no direct releasing effect on adrenal medullary granules (Blaschko *et al.*, 1955).

From his experiments on adrenal medullary granules Hillarp (1960b) has concluded that the granules are in equilibrium with a smaller free pool, and that on stimulation of the cells the free amines leave the cell, but not the granules.

The slow release of catecholamines from the adrenomedullary granules even at 37°C suggests that continuous and prolonged stimulation should release the amines in a slow rather than an "explosive" way. The experience from direct measurement of the secretion rate also seems to corroborate this assumption. High secretion rates only seem to be upheld for very brief periods and may correspond mainly to the release of the free pool. On splanchnic stimulation Rapela and Houssay (1952) found a secretion of 0.45 μg per kilogram per minute, a figure which is not incompatible with the concept of the release from granules as the rate-limiting factor. With a total catecholamine content of 1 mg in a 10-kg dog, 90% of which is in the granular fraction, and a release rate from granules of 0.5% per minute, the release rate would be 4.5 μg per minute or 0.45 μg per kilogram per minute.

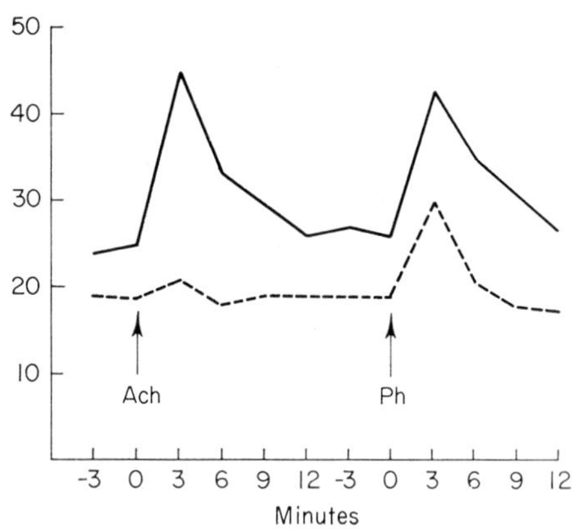

FIG. 18. Release of catecholamines in micrograms per minute from isolated perfused bovine adrenal perfused with normal (upper record) or calcium-free (lower record) Tyrode solution. At arrows, 0.03 μmole acetylcholine (Ach) and 16.5 μmoles β-phenylethylamine (Ph) were injected. (From Philippu and Schümann, 1962.)

VI. Chromaffin Cell Tumors

Since pheochrome cell tumors often originate from cells in the adrenal medulla, their secretory activity will be briefly considered here. Analysis of excised tumors and of the urinary catechol excretion (Engel and von Euler, 1950; U. S. von Euler and Ström, 1957) have revealed that the majority of tumors secrete a mixture of epinephrine and norepinephrine, but some of them secrete and contain selectively one or the other of the hormones. This suggests that they originated from different and specific cells producing only one type of hormone.

The hormone content of chromaffin cell tumor shows wide variations but may attain values similar to those of the adrenal medulla, i.e., about 10 mg per gram of tissue (U. S. von Euler and Ström, 1957).

An interesting difference with regard to the chemical composition of the storage granules has been noticed by Schümann (1960a) who found a relatively smaller ATP-content in the pheochrome cell granules. A study of the kinetics of amine release and uptake has been made by Stjärne *et al.* (1964).

The chromaffin cell tumors are not innervated and the factors causing secretion, which often occurs in brief outbursts, are not known. Diurnal variations in secretion rate have been observed in cases secreting continuously. Readers are referred for further literature to Sack and Koll (1963).

VII. Summary

Separate epinephrine and norepinephrine-containing cells have been demonstrated in the adrenal medulla. The major part of the catecholamines in the chromaffin cells is present in subcellular granules with a diameter of 0.1–0.6 μ.

The biosynthesis of the catecholamines proceeds in the chromaffin cell from tyrosine, dopa, and dopamine to norepinephrine and epinephrine. Quantitative assay of catecholamines can be made after purification of extracts on alumina or ion-exchange resins by biological assay or by fluorimetry. Catecholamines are chiefly inactivated by catechol-*O*-methyltransferase, by monoamine oxidase, or by conjugation. A few percent of the liberated amines are excreted in urine as free amines.

The adrenal catecholamine pattern varies in the animal series from almost pure epinephrine (rabbit) to almost pure norepinephrine (whale).

Characteristic differences in the action of epinephrine and norepinephrine on the cardiovascular apparatus and on smooth muscle organs are described. Metabolic actions are in general more marked for epinephrine than for norepinephrine, but on some occasions the reverse has been observed. The stimulating effect of catecholamines on the formation of a cyclic adenine nucleotide and the mobilization of free fatty acids should be especially mentioned.

Specific epinephrine and norepinephrine-secreting nerves with central representation have been described. Resting secretion is usually small. Catecholamine secretion can be reflexly induced by circulatory homeostatic mechanisms, by afferent nerve stimulation, and by a variety of factors acting centrally (hypoglycemia, hypothermia, heating and burns, hypoxia, hypercarbia, and various drugs). Physical exercise and emotional stress also cause an increased secretion of adrenal catecholamines.

The secretory activity of the adrenal medulla can be evaluated by assaying the plasma levels of catecholamines or the excretion in urine.

The catecholamine release from the chromaffin cell is mediated by cholinergic fibers. Calcium ions are of importance for the release process. Certain differences between the subcellular storage particles in adrenergic nerves and in chromaffin cells are emphasized.

Some properties of chromaffin cell tumors and their secretion products are briefly discussed.

Further references on the subject will be found in the following publications.

Symposia: C.N.R.S., 1957; Univ. of Montreal, 1958; Ciba, 1960; Bethesda, 1959. *Monographs* or *Chapters:* Bardelli, 1956; U. S. von Euler, 1956, 1961, 1963; Gaddum and Holzbauer, 1957; Hartman and Brownell, 1949, Sataké, 1954. *Reviews:* Axelrod, 1959; Bacq, 1949; Blaschko, 1954; Ellis, 1956; Elmadjian *et al.*, 1958; and Malméjac, 1964.

References

Abel, J. J. (1899). Über den blutdruckerregenden Bestandtheil der Nebenniere, das Epinephrin. *Z. Physiol. Chem.* **28,** 318–362.

Ahlquist, R. P. (1948). A study of the adrenotropic receptors. *Am. J. Physiol.* **153,** 586–600.

Armstrong, M. D., McMillan, A., and Shaw, K. N. F. (1957). 3-Methoxy-4-hydroxy-D-mandelic acid, a urinary metabolite of norepinephrine. *Biochim. Biophys. Acta* **25,** 422–423.

Axelrod, J. (1959). Metabolism of epinephrine and other sympathomimetic amines. *Physiol. Rev.* **39,** 751–776.

Axelrod, J. (1960). The fate of adrenaline and noradrenaline. *Ciba Found. Symp., Adrenergic Mechanisms* pp. 28–39.

Axelsson, J., and Bülbring, E. (1960). The metabolic basis for the inhibitory action of adrenaline on intestinal smooth muscle. *J. Physiol.* (*London*) **153,** 30P.

Bacq, Z. M. (1949). The metabolism of adrenaline. *Pharmacol. Rev.* **1,** 1–26.

Bardelli, S. (1956). Le amine adrenergiche. *Monografie Cardiol.* No. 6.

Belleau, B. (1960). Relationships between agonists, antagonists, and receptor sites. *Ciba Found. Symp., Adrenergic Mechanisms* pp. 223–245.

Bergsman, A. (1959). The urinary excretion of adrenaline and noradrenaline in some mental diseases. *Acta Psychiat. Scand.* **34,** Suppl. 133.

Bergström, S., von Euler, U. S., and Hamberg, U. (1950). Isolation of noradrenaline from suprarenal medulla. *Acta Physiol. Scand.* **20,** 101–108.

Bertler, Å., Carlsson, A., and Rosengren, E. (1958). A method for the fluorimetric determination of adrenaline and noradrenaline in tissues. *Acta Physiol. Scand.* **44,** 273–292.

Bertler, Å., Hall, G., Hillarp, N. Å., and Rosengren, E. (1961). Uptake of dopamine by the storage granules of the adrenal medulla *in vitro*. *Acta Physiol. Scand.* **52,** 167–170.

Bethesda (1959). Natl. Institutes of Health Symp. on Catecholamines. *Pharmacol. Rev.* **11,** 241–566.

Birke, G., Dunér, H., von Euler, U. S., and Plantin, L. O. (1957a). Studies on the adrenocortical, adreno-medullary and adrenergic nerve activity in essential hypertension. *Z. Vitamin-,Hormon- u. Fermentforsch.* **9,** 41–68.

Birke, G., Dunér, H., Liljedahl, S. O., Pernow, B., Plantin, L. O., and Troell, L. (1957b). Histamine, catechol amines and adrenocortical steroids in burns. *Acta Chir. Scand.* **114,** 87–98.

Blaschko, H. (1939). The specific action of 1-dopa decarboxylase. *J. Physiol.* (*London*) **96,** 50P–51P.

Blaschko, H. (1954). Metabolism of epinephrine and norepinephrine. *Pharmacol. Rev.* **6,** 23–28.

Blaschko, H. (1959). The development of current concepts of catecholamine formation. *Pharmacol. Rev.* **11,** 307–316.

Blaschko, H., and Welch, A. D. (1953). Localization of adrenaline in cytoplasmic particles of the bovine adrenal medulla. *Arch. Exptl. Path. Pharmakol.* **219,** 17–22.

Blaschko, H., Hagen, P., and Welch, A. D. (1955). Observations on the intracellular granules of the adrenal medulla. *J. Physiol.* (*London*) **129,** 27–49.

Bloom, G., Östlund, E., von Euler, U. S., Lishajko, F., Ritzén, M., and Adams-Ray, J. (1961). Studies on catecholamine-containing granules of specific cells in cyclostome hearts. *Acta Physiol. Scand.* **53, Suppl. 185.**

Bloom, G., von Euler, U. S., and Frankenhaeuser, M. (1963). Catecholamine excretion and personality traits in paratroop trainees. *Acta Physiol. Scand.* **58,** 77–89.

Blum, F. (1901). On adrenal diabetes. *Deut. Arch. Klin. Med.* **71,** 146–167.

Bouckaert, J. J., and van Loo, A. (1947). Au sujet de la mésure des modifications de l'adrénalino-sécrétion. *Experientia* **3,** 160.

Boyd, J. D. (1960). Origin, development and distribution of chromaffin cells. *Ciba Found. Symp., Adrenergic Mechanisms* pp. 63–82.

Bozler, E. (1940). An analysis of the excitatory and inhibitory effects of sympathetic nerve impulses and adrenaline on visceral smooth muscle. *Am. J. Physiol.* **130,** 627–634.

Bradley, P. B. (1960). Electrophysiological evidence relating to the role of adrenaline in the central nervous system. *Ciba Found. Symp., Adrenergic Mechanisms* pp. 410–420.

Bradley, P. B., and Mollica, A. (1958). The effect of adrenaline and acetylcholine on single unit activity in the reticular formation of the decerebrate cat. *Arch. Ital. Biol.* **96,** 168–186.

Brodie, B. B., Maickel, R. P., and Stern, D. N. (1965). Autonomic nervous system and adipose tissue. In press.

Brody, T. M., and Calvert, D. N. (1960). Release of catechol amines from the adrenal medulla by CCl_4. *Am. J. Physiol.* **198,** 682–685.

Brücke, F., Kaindl, F., and Mayer, H. (1952). Über die Veränderung in der Zusammensetzung des Nebennierenmarkinkretes bei elektrischer Reizung des Hypothalamus. *Arch. Intern. Pharmacodyn.* **88,** 407–412.

Bülbring, E. (1954). Membrane potentials of smooth muscle fibres of the taenia coli of the guinea-pig. *J. Physiol.* (*London*) **125,** 302–315.

Bülbring, E. (1960). Biophysical changes produced by adrenaline and noradrenaline. *Ciba Found. Symp., Adrenergic Mechanisms* pp. 275–287.

Bülbring, E., and Burn, J. H. (1942). An action of adrenaline on transmission in sympathetic ganglia, which may play a part in shock. *J. Physiol.* (*London*) **101,** 289–303.

Burn, J. H., and Dale, H. H. (1926). The vaso-dilator action of histamine, and its physiological significance. *J. Physiol.* (*London*) **61,** 185–214.

Burn, J. H., and Rand, M. J. (1958). The action of sympathomimetic amines in animals treated with reserpine. *J. Physiol.* (*London*) **144,** 314–336.

Burn, J. H., Langemann, H., and Parker, R. H. O. (1951). Noradrenaline in whale suprarenal medulla. *J. Physiol.* (*London*) **113,** 123–128.

Butterworth, K. R., and Mann, M. (1957a). A quantitative comparison of the sympathomimetic amine content of the left and right adrenal glands of the cat. *J. Physiol.* (*London*) **136,** 294–299.

Butterworth, K. R., and Mann, M. (1957b). The adrenaline and noradrenaline content of the adrenal gland of the cat following depletion by acetylcholine. *Brit. J. Pharmacol.* **12,** 415–421.

Bygdeman, S., von Euler, U. S., and Hökfelt, B. (1960). Resynthesis of adrenaline in the rabbit's adrenal medulla during insulin-induced hypoglycemia. *Acta Physiol. Scand.* **49,** 21–28.

Cannon, W. B. (1928). Die Notfallsfunktionen des Sympathicoadrenalen Systems. *Ergeb. Physiol.* **27,** 380–406.

Cannon, W. B., McIver, M. A., and Bliss, S. W. (1924). A sympathetic and adrenal mechanism for mobilizing sugar in hypoglycemia. *Am. J. Physiol.* **69,** 46–66.

Cantu, R. C., Wise, B. L., Goldfien, A., Gullixson, K. S., Fischer, N., and Ganong, W. F. (1963). Neural pathways mediating the increase in adrenal medullary secretion produced by hypoglycaemia. *Proc. Soc. Exp. Biol.* **114,** 10–13.

Carlsson, A., and Hillarp, N. Å. (1956). Release of adrenaline from the adrenal medulla of rabbits produced by reserpine. *Kgl. Fysiograf. Sallskap. Lund, Forhandl.* **26,** No. 8.

Carlsson, A., and Hillarp, N. Å. (1958). On the state of the catechol amines of the adrenal medullary granules. *Acta Physiol. Scand.* **44,** 163–169.

Carlsson, A., Hillarp, N. Å., and Waldeck, B. (1963). Analysis of the Mg++-ATP dependent storage mechanism in the amine granules of the adrenal medulla. *Acta Physiol. Scand.* **59,** Suppl. 215.

Celander, O. (1954). The range of control exercised by the "sympathico-adrenal system." *Acta Physiol. Scand.* **32,** Suppl. 116, 1–132.

Ciba (1960). *Ciba Found. Symp., Adrenergic Mechanisms, London.*

Clark, W. G., Akawie, R. I., Pogrund, R. S., and Geissman, T. A. (1951). Conjugation of epinephrine *in vivo*. *J. Pharmacol. Exptl. Therap.* **101,** 6–7.

C.N.R.S. (1957). L'adrénaline et la noradrénaline dans la régulation des fonctions homéostasiques. *Colloq. Natl. CNRS Lyon, 1957.*

Comline, R. S., and Silver, M. (1958). Response of the adrenal medulla of the sheep faetus to asphyxia. *Nature* **181,** 283–284.

Cotten, M. de V., and Pincus, S. (1955). Comparative effects of a wide range of doses of 1-epinephrine and of 1-norepinephrine on the contractile force of the heart in situ. *J. Pharmacol. Exptl. Therap.* **114,** 110–118.

Cramer, W. (1919). Observations on the functional activity of the suprarenal gland in health, and in disease. *Sci. Rept. Imp. Cancer Res. Fund* **6,** 1–23.

Crone, C. (1963). Which part of the central nervous system activates the adrenal medulla during hypoglycemia? *Acta Physiol. Scand.* **59,** Suppl. 213, 29.

Cross, B. A., and Silver, I. A. (1962). Central activation of the sympathetico-adrenal system by hypoxia and hypercapnia. *J. Endocrinol.* **24,** 91–103.

Dell, P. (1960). Intervention of an adrenergic mechanism during brain stem reticular activation. *Ciba Found. Symp., Adrenergic Mechanisms* pp. 393–409.

Dell, P., Bonvallet, M., and Hugelin, A. (1954). Tonus sympathique, adrénaline et controle réticulaire de la motricité spinale. *EEG Clin. Neurophysiol.* **6**, 599–618.

De Robertis, E. D. P. (1964). "Histophysiology of Synapses and Neurosecretion." Pergamon Press, Oxford.

de Schaepdryver, A. F. (1959). Physio-pharmacological effects on suprarenal secretion of adrenaline and noradrenaline in dogs. *Arch. Intern. Pharmacodyn.* **121**, 222–253.

Dole, V. P. (1956). Relation between non-esterified fatty acids in plasma and the metabolism of glucose. *J. Clin. Invest.* **35**, 150–154.

Dougherty, T. F., and White, A. (1944). Influence of hormones on lymphoid tissue structure and function. The role of the pituitary adrenotrophic hormone in the regulation of the lymphocytes and other cellular elements of the blood. *Endocrinology* **35**, 1–14.

Douglas, W. W., and Rubin, R. P. (1963). The mechanism of catecholamine release from the adrenal medulla and the role of calcium in stimulus-secretion coupling. *J. Physiol.* (*London*) **167**, 288–310.

Dresse, A., and Goffart, M. (1963). Les catécholamines de la médullosurrénale de l'Unau foetal ou nouveau-né (Cholaepus hoffmanni Peters). *Arch. Intern. Physiol. Biochim.* **71**, 271–273.

Dunér, H. (1953). The influence of the blood glucose level on the secretion of adrenaline and noradrenaline from the suprarenal. *Acta Physiol. Scand.* **28**, Suppl. 102.

Dunér, H. (1954). The effect of insulin hypoglycemia on the secretion of adrenaline and noradrenaline from the suprarenal of cat. *Acta Physiol. Scand.* **32**, 63–68.

Ehrlén, I. (1948). Fluorimetric determination of adrenaline. II. *Farm. Revy* **47**, 242–250.

Eichholtz, F., and Roesch, E. (1949). Pharmakologische Reaktionen an den Synapsen des NN-Marks. *Arch. Intern. Pharmacodyn.* **78**, 521–531.

Ellis, S. (1956). The metabolic effects of epinephrine and related amines. *Pharmacol. Rev.* **8**, 485–562.

Elmadjian, F., Lamson, E. T., Freeman, H., Neri, R., and Varjabedian, L. (1956). Excretion of epinephrine and norepinephrine after administration of insulin and methacholine. *J. Clin. Endocrinol.* **16**, 876–886.

Elmadjian, F., Hope, J. M., and Lamson, E. T. (1958). Excretion of epinephrine and norepinephrine under stress. *Recent Progr. Hormone Res.* **14**, 513–553.

Engel, A., and von Euler, U. S. (1950). Diagnostic value of increased urinary output of noradrenaline and adrenaline in phaeochromocytoma. *Lancet* **II**, 387.

Eränkö, O. (1960). Cell types of the adrenal medulla. *Ciba Found. Symp., Adrenergic Mechanisms* pp. 103–108.

Eränkö, O., and Hopsu, V. (1958). Effect of reserpine on the histochemistry and content of adrenaline and noradrenaline in the adrenal medulla of the rat and the mouse. *Endocrinology* **62**, 15–23.

Feldberg, W., and Lewis, G. P. (1964). The action of peptides on the adrenal medulla. Release of adrenaline by bradykinin and angiotensin. *J. Physiol.* (*London*) **171**, 98–108.

Feldberg, W., and Minz, B. (1932). Die Wirkung von Azetylcholin auf die Nebennieren. *Arch. Exptl. Pathol. Pharmakol.* **163**, 66–96.

Feldberg, W., and Myers, R. D. (1964). Effects on temperature of amines injected into the cerebral ventricles. A new concept of temperature regulation. *J. Physiol. (London)* **173**, 226–237.

Fleckenstein, A. (1953). Konstitution und Wirkung sympathomimetischer Amine. Neue Gesichtspunkte nach Versuchen an der normalen und denervierten Nickhaut der Katze. *Arch. Exptl. Pathol. Pharmakol.* **218**, 117–119.

Folkow, B., and von Euler, U. S. (1954). Selective activation of noradrenaline and adrenaline producing cells in the suprarenal gland of the cat by hypothalamic stimulation. *Circulation Res.* **2**, 191–195.

Frankenhaeuser, M., and Post, B. (1962). Catecholamine excretion during mental work as modified by centrally acting drugs. *Acta Physiol. Scand.* **55**, 74–81.

Frankenhaeuser, M., Sterky, K., and Jaerpe, G. (1962). Psycho-physiological relations in habituation to gravitational stress. *Percept. Motor Skills* **15**, 63–72.

Friedmann, E. (1904). Zur Kenntnis des Adrenalins (Suprarenins). *Beitr. Chem. Physiol. Pathol.* **6**, 92–93.

Furchgott, R. F. (1959). The receptors for epinephrine and norepinephrine (adrenergic receptors). *Pharmacol. Rev.* **11**, 429–441.

Gaddum, J. H., and Holzbauer, M. (1957). Adrenaline and noradrenaline. *Vitamins Hormones* **15**, 151–203.

Gaddum, J. H., and Lembeck, F. (1949). The assay of substances from the adrenal medulla. *Brit. J. Pharmacol.* **4**, 401–408.

Ganong, W. F. (1963). "Review of Medical Physiology." Lange Med. Publ., Los Altos, California.

Ghosh, I., and Ghosh, A. (1963). The effect of reserpine on adrenal medulla of the pigeon—a cytochemical investigation. *Cytologia* **28**, 146–153.

Ghosh, I., and Ghosh, A. (1964). Influence of age on cytochemically demonstrable avian catechol hormones. *Z. Biol.* **114**, 400–404.

Goldenberg, M., Pines, K. L., Baldwin, E. F., Greene, D. G., and Roh, C. E. (1948). The hemodynamic response of man to norepinephrine and epinephrine and its relation to the problem of hypertension. *Am. J. Med.* **5**, 792–806.

Goldfien, A., and Ganong, W. F. (1962). Adrenal medullary and adrenal cortical response to stimulation of diencephalon. *Am. J. Physiol.* **202**, 205–211.

Goodall, McC. (1951). Studies of adrenaline and noradrenaline in mammalian heart and suprarenals. *Acta Physiol. Scand.* **24**, Suppl. 85.

Goodall, McC., and Berman, M. L. (1960). Urinary output of adrenaline, noradrenaline, and 3-methoxy-4-hydroxymandelic acid following centrifugation and anticipation of centrifugation. *J. Clin. Invest.* **39**, 1533–1538.

Goodall, McC., Stone, C., and Haynes, B. W., Jr. (1957). Urinary output of adrenaline and noradrenaline in severe thermal burns. *Ann. Surg.* **145**, 479–487.

Goodner, C. J., and Tustison, W. A. (1964). Autonomic mediation of the effect of raised arterial glucose upon free fatty acids. *Science* **146**, 770–772.

Grant, R., Lindgren, P., Rosén, A., and Uvnäs, B. (1958). The release of catechols from the adrenal medulla on activation of the sympathetic vasodilator nerves to the skeletal muscles in the cat by hypothalamic stimulation. *Acta Physiol. Scand* **43**, 135–154.

Green, J. D. (1962). Binding of some biogenic amines in tissues. *Advan. Pharmacol* **1**, 349–422.

Gunne, L.-M. (1962). Relative adrenaline content in brain tissue. *Acta Physiol Scand.* **56**, 324–333.

Hagen, P., and Barrnett, R. J. (1960). The storage of amines in the chromaffin cell. *Ciba Found. Symp., Adrenergic Mechanisms* pp. 83–99.

Häggendal, J. (1962). On the use of strong exchange resins for determinations of small amounts of catechol amines. *Scand. J. Clin. Lab. Invest.* **14,** 537–544.

Häggendal, J. (1963). An improved method for fluorimetric determination of small amounts of adrenaline and noradrenaline in plasma and tissues. *Acta Physiol. Scand.* **59,** 242–254.

Harrison, T. S. (1964). Adrenal medullary and thyroid relationships. *Physiol. Rev.* **44,** 161–185.

Hartman, F. A., and Brownell, K. A. (1949). "The Adrenal Gland." Lea & Febiger, Philadelphia, Pennsylvania.

Havel, R. J., and Goldfien, A. (1959). The role of the sympathetic nervous system in the metabolism of free fatty acids. *J. Lipid Res.* **1,** 102–108.

Havens, L. L., Zileli, M. S., Dimascio, A., Boling, L., and Goldfien, A. (1959). Catechol amine responses to electrically induced convulsions in man. *In* "Biological Psychiatry" (J. H. Masserman, ed.), Vol. 1, pp. 120–129. Grune & Stratton, New York.

Henle, J. (1865). Über das Gewebe der Nebenniere und der Hypophyse. *Z. Ration. Med.* **24,** 143–152.

Hermann, H., and Klepping, J. (1956). Quelques aspects fonctionnels de la noradrénalino et adrénalino sécrétion par la médullo-surrénale. *Ann. Endocrinol. (Paris)* **17,** 692–694.

Hillarp, N. Å. (1958). Isolation and some biochemical properties of the catechol amine granules in the cow adrenal medulla. *Acta Physiol. Scand.* **43,** 82–96.

Hillarp, N. Å. (1959). Further observations on the state of the catechol amines stored in the adrenal medullary granules. *Acta Physiol. Scand.* **47,** 271–279.

Hillarp, N. Å. (1960a). Some problems concerning the storage of catechol amines in the adrenal medulla. *Ciba Found. Symp., Adrenergic Mechanisms* pp. 481–501.

Hillarp, N. Å. (1960b). Catecholamines: mechanisms of storage and release. *Proc. 1st Intern. Congr. Endocrinol., Acta Endocrinol. Copenhagen, 1960* pp. 181–185.

Hillarp, N. Å., and Hökfelt, B. (1953). Evidence of adrenaline and noradrenaline in separate adrenal medullary cells. *Acta Physiol. Scand.* **30,** 55–68.

Hillarp, N. Å., and Hökfelt, B. (1955). Histochemical demonstration of noradrenaline and adrenaline in the adrenal medulla. *J. Histochem. Cytochem.* **3,** 1–5.

Hillarp, N. Å., and Nilson, B. (1954). The structure of the adrenaline and noradrenaline containing granules in the adrenal medullary cells with reference to the storage and release of the sympathomimetic amines. *Acta Physiol. Scand.* **31,** Suppl. 113, 79–107.

Hillarp, N. Å., and Thieme, G. (1959). Nucleotides in the catechol amine granules of the adrenal medulla. *Acta Physiol. Scand.* **45,** 328–338.

Hillarp, N. Å., Lagerstedt, S., and Nilson, B. (1953). The isolation of a granular fraction from the suprarenal medulla, containing the sympathomimetic catechol amines. *Acta Physiol. Scand.* **29,** 251–263.

Hökfelt, B. (1951). Noradrenaline and adrenaline in mammalian tissues. Distribution under normal and pathological conditions with special reference to the endocrine system. *Acta Physiol. Scand.* **25,** Suppl. 92.

Hökfelt, B., and Bygdeman, S. (1961). Increased adrenaline production following administration of 2-deoxy-D-glucose in the rat. *Proc. Soc. Exptl. Biol. Med.* **106,** 537–539.

Hökfelt, B., and McLean, J. (1950). The adrenaline and noradrenaline content of the suprarenal glands of the rabbit under normal conditions and after various forms of stimulation. *Acta Physiol. Scand.* **21,** 258–270.

Holland, W. C., and Schümann, H. J. (1956). Formation of catechol amines during splanchnic stimulation of the adrenal gland of the cat. *Brit. J. Pharmacol.* **11,** 449–453.

Holmes, W. (1950). The adrenal homologues in the lungfish *Protopterus. Proc. Roy. Soc.* **B137,** 549–562.

Holtz, P. (1939). Dopadecarboxylase. *Naturwiss.* **27,** 724–725.

Holtz, P., Credner, K., and Kroneberg, G. (1947). Über das sympathicomimetische pressorische Prinzip des Harns ("Urosympathin"). *Arch. Exptl. Pathol. Pharmakol.* **204,** 228–243.

Houssay, B. A., and Rapela, C. E. (1953). Adrenal secretion of adrenalin and noradrenalin. *Arch. Exptl. Pathol. Pharmakol.* **219,** 156–159.

Houssay, B. A., Lewis, J. T., and Molinelli, E. A. (1924). Role de la sécrétion d'adrénaline pendant l'hypoglycémie produité par l'insuline. *Compt. Rend. Soc. Biol.* **91,** 1011.

Hsieh, A. C. L., and Carlson, L. D. (1957). Role of adrenaline and noradrenaline in chemical regulation of heat production. *Am. J. Physiol.* **190,** 243–246.

Inoue, M. (1959). Descending spinal pathway subserving adrenaline secretion of the adrenal gland in the toad. *Tohoku J. Exptl. Med.* **70,** 319–323.

Jackson, C. B., Jr., Douglas, W. K., Culver, J. F., Ruff, G., Knoblock, E. C., and Graybiel, A. (1961). Results of preflight and postflight medical examinations. *Proc. Conf. Results First U.S. Manned Suborbital Space Flight, June, 1961* pp. 31–36.

Johnson, D. G. (1965). Adrenomedullary response to 2-deoxyglucose in the hypothyroid, euthyroid, and hyperthyroid rat. *Acta Physiol. Scand.* **65,** 337–343.

Kaindl, F., and von Euler, U. S. (1951). Liberation of noradrenaline and adrenaline from the suprarenals of the cat during carotid occlusion. *Am. J. Physiol.* **166,** 284–288.

Karplus, J. P., and Kreidl, A. (1909). Gehirn und Sympathicus. I. Zwischenhirnbasis und Halssympathicus. *Arch. Ges. Physiol.* **129,** 138–144.

Khan, A. U., Forney, R. B., and Hughes, F. W. (1964). Plasma free fatty acids in rats after shock as modified by centrally active drugs. *Arch. Intern. Pharmacodyn.* **151,** 466–474.

Kimura, S. (1927). Zur Kenntnis der Wirkung des Tetrodongiftes. *Tohoku J. Exptl. Med.* **9,** 41–65.

Kirshner, N. (1959). Biosynthesis of adrenaline and noradrenaline. *Pharmacol. Rev.* **11,** 350–357.

Kirshner, N. (1960). Formation of adrenaline and noradrenaline. *Ciba Found. Symp., Adrenergic Mechanisms* pp. 17–24.

Krivoy, W. A., Hart, E. R., and Marrazzi, A. S. (1953). Inhibition of phrenic respiratory potentials by adrenaline and other sympathomimetic amines. *Federation Proc.* **12,** 337–338.

Kroneberg, G., and Schümann, H. J. (1958). Adrenalinsekretion und Adrenalinverarmung der Kaninchennebennieren nach Reserpin. *Arch. Exptl. Pathol. Pharmakol.* **234,** 133–146.

Leak, D., Brunjes, S., Johns, V. J., and Starr, P. (1962). Adrenal medullary response to insulin hypoglycemia in hypothyroid patients. *J. Lab. Clin. Med.* **60,** 811–817.

Leduc, J. (1961). Catecholamine production and release in exposure and acclimation to cold. *Acta Physiol. Scand.* **53,** Suppl. 183.

Lempinen, M. (1964). Extra-adrenal chromaffin tissue of the rat and the effect of cortical hormones on it. *Acta Physiol. Scand.* **62,** Suppl. 231.

Lever, J. D. (1955). Electron microscopic observations on the normal and denervated adrenal medulla of the rat. *Endocrinology* **57,** 621–635.

Levi, L. (1963). The urinary output of adrenalin and noradrenalin during experimentally induced emotional stress in clinically different groups. *Acta Psychotherap.* **11,** 218–227.

Levi, L. (1965). The urinary output of adrenaline and noradrenaline during different experimentally induced pleasant and unpleasant emotional states. *Psychosomat. Med.* **27,** 80–85.

Lindgren, P., Rosén, A., and Uvnäs, B. (1959). The release of catechols from the adrenal medulla on activation of the bulbar part of the sympathetic vasodilator outflow in cats. *Acta Physiol. Scand.* **47,** 233–242.

Ludemann, H. H., Filbert, M. G., and Cornblath, M. (1955). Application of a fluorometric method for adrenalinelike substances in peripheral plasma. *J. Appl. Physiol.* **8,** 59–66.

Lund, A. (1949). Fluorimetric determination of adrenaline in blood. I. Isolation of the fluorescent oxidation product of adrenaline. *Acta Pharmacol.* **5,** 75–94.

Lundberg, A. (1952). Adrenaline and transmission in the sympathetic ganglion of the cat. *Acta Physiol. Scand.* **26,** 252–263.

Malméjac, J. (1964). Activity of the adrenal medulla and its regulation. *Physiol. Rev.* **44,** 186–218.

Merritt, J. H., Schultz, E. J., and Wykes, A. A. (1964). Effect of decaborane on the norepinephrine content of rat brain. *Biochem. Pharmacol.* **13,** 1364–1366.

Mirkin, B. L. (1961). Factors influencing the selective secretion of adrenal medullary hormones. *J. Pharmacol. Exptl. Therap.* **132,** 218–225.

Moore, R. E. (1960). Thermoregulation in newborn animals. *Ciba Found. Symp., Adrenergic Mechanisms* pp. 469–471.

Moore, R. E., and Underwood, M. C. (1963). The thermogenic effects of noradrenaline in new-born and infant kittens and other small mammals. A possible hormonal mechanism in the control of heat production. *J. Physiol.* (*London*) **168,** 290–317.

Munro, A. F., and Robinson, R. (1958). Normal levels for plasma adrenaline and noradrenaline compared with those in subjects with complete transverse lesions of the spinal cord. *J. Physiol.* (*London*) **141,** 4P–5P.

Nagatsu, T., Levitt, M., and Udenfriend, S. (1964). Conversion of 1-tyrosine to 3,4-dihydroxyphenylalanine by cell-free preparations of brain and sympathetically innervated tissues. *Biochem. Biophys. Res. Commun.* **14,** 543–549.

Nahas, G. G. (1959). Influence du tamponnement du gaz carbonique sur les catécholamines du sang au cours de l'hypercapnie. *Compt. Rend.* **248,** 294–297.

Nandi, J. (1961). New arrangement of interrenal and chromaffin tissues of teleost fishes. *Science* **134,** 389–390.

Nickerson, M. (1959). Blockade of the actions of adrenaline and noradrenaline. *Pharmacol. Rev.* **11,** 443–461.

Oliver, G., and Schäfer, E. A. (1895). The physiological effects of extracts of the suprarenal capsules. *J. Physiol.* (*London*) **18,** 230–276.

Ozaki, T. (1955). Noradrenaline and adrenaline contents of suprarenal glands in various species of animals. *Tohoku J. Exptl. Med.* **61,** 345–352.

Palkama, A. (1964). The distribution of catecholamines and cholinesterases in the adrenal medulla. *J. Physiol. (London)* **175**, 13P–14P.

Pekkarinen, A., Castrén, O., Iisalo, E., Koivusalo, M., Laihinen, A., Simola, P. E., and Thomasson, B. (1961). The emotional effect of matriculation examinations on the excretion of adrenaline, noradrenaline, 17-hydroxycorticosteroids into the urine and the content of 17-hydroxycorticosteroids in the plasma. *In* "Biochemistry, Pharmacology and Physiology," pp. 117–137. Pergamon Press, Oxford.

Perman, E. S. (1958a). The effect of acetaldehyde on the secretion of adrenaline and noradrenaline from the suprarenal gland of the cat. *Acta Physiol. Scand.* **43,** 71–76.

Perman, E. S. (1958b). The effect of ethyl alcohol on the secretion from the adrenal medulla in man. *Acta Physiol. Scand.* **44,** 241–247.

Perman, E. S. (1961). Effect of ethanol and hydration on the urinary excretion of adrenaline and noradrenaline and on the blood sugar of rats. *Acta Physiol. Scand.* **51,** 68–74.

Philippu, A., and Schümann, H. J. (1962). Der Einfluss von Calcium auf die Brenzcatechinaminfreisetzung. *Experientia* **18,** 138–140.

Philippu, A., and Schümann, H. J. (1963). Ribonuclease- und Trypsinwirkung auf isolierte Nebennierenmark-Granula. *Experientia* **19,** 17–18.

Price, H. L. (1957). Circulating adrenaline and noradrenaline during diethyl ether anaesthesia in man. *Clin. Sci.* **16,** 377–387.

Price, H. L., and Price, M. L. (1957). The chemical estimation of epinephrine and norepinephrine in human and canine plasma. II. A critique of the trihydroxyindole method. *J. Lab. Clin. Med.* **50,** 769–777.

Rapela, C. E., and Houssay, B. A. (1952). Accion del nervio esplacnico mayor sobre la secrecion de adrenalina y noradrenalina suprarrenal del perro. *Rev. Soc. Argent. Biol.* **28,** 209–213.

Rastgeldi, S. (1951). Adrenaline and noradrenaline in the whale suprarenal gland. *Acta Physiol. Scand.* **23,** 44–46.

Redgate, E. S., and Gellhorn, E. (1953). Nature of sympatheticoadrenal discharge under conditions of excitation of central autonomic structures. *Am. J. Physiol.* **174,** 475–480.

Reynolds, S. R. M. (1953). Adrenal gland response to circulatory distress in fetal lambs. *Science* **118,** 248–249.

Richter, D. (1940). The inactivation of adrenaline *in vivo* in man. *J. Physiol. (London)* **98,** 361–374.

Robinson, R. L., and Watts, D. T. (1962). Inhibition of adrenal secretion of epinephrine during infusion of catecholamines. *Am. J. Physiol.* **203,** 713–716.

Rothballer, A. B. (1959). The effects of catecholamines on the central nervous system. *Pharmacol. Rev.* **11,** 494–547.

Sack, H., and Koll, J. F. (1963). Das Phäochromocytom. *Ergeb. Inn. Med. Kinderheilk.* **19,** 445–555.

Saito, S. (1928). Influence of application of cold or heat to the dog's body upon the epinephrine output rate. *Tohoku J. Exptl. Med.* **11,** 544–567.

Sataké, Y. (1954). Secretion of adrenaline and sympathins. *Tohoku J. Exptl. Med.* **60,** Suppl. II.

Schapiro, S. (1958). Effect of a catechol amine blocking agent (dibenzyline) on organ content and urine excretion of noradrenaline and adrenaline. *Acta Physiol. Scand.* **42,** 371–375.

Schapiro, S., and Stjärne, L. (1958). A method for collection of intermittent samples of adrenal vein blood. *Proc. Soc. Exptl. Biol. Med.* **99**, 414–415.

Scharrer, E., and Brown, S. (1961). Neurosecretion. XII. The formation of neurosecretory granules in the earthworm, *Lumbricus terrestris* L. *Z. Zellforsch. Mikroskop. Anat.* **54**, 530–540.

Schild, H. (1933). Adrenaline in the suprarenal medulla. *J. Physiol.* (*London*) **79**, 455–469.

Schöne, H.-H., and Lindner, E. (1962). Über die Wirkung von *N*-(3′-Phenyl-propyl-(2′))-1,1-diphenyl-propyl-(3)-amin auf den Katecholamin-Stoffwechsel. *Klin. Wochschr.* **40**, 1196–1200.

Schümann, H. J. (1960a). Hormon- und ATP-Gehalt des menschlichen Nebennierenmarks und des Phäochromocytomgewebes. *Klin. Wochschr.* **38**, 11–13.

Schümann, H. J. (1960b). Formation of adrenergic transmitters. *Ciba Found. Symp., Adrenergic Mechanisms* pp. 6–16.

Serafimov, N. (1962). Urinary excretion of catecholamines in endotoxin-induced fever in rabbits. *Acta Physiol. Scand.* **54**, 354–358.

Sheppard, H., and Zimmerman, J. (1959). Effect of guanethidine (SU-5864) on tissue catecholamines. *Pharmacologist* **1**, 69.

Spoelstra, A. J.-G. (1963). Calorigenic effects of adrenaline and noradrenaline. *J. Physiol.* (*Paris*) **55**, 677–696.

Stämpfli, R. (1954). A new method for measuring membrane potentials with external electrodes. *Experientia* **10**, 508–509.

Stjärne, L. (1964). Studies of catecholamine uptake storage and release mechanisms. *Acta Physiol. Scand.* **62**, Suppl. 228.

Stjärne, L., von Euler, U. S., and Lishajko, F. (1964). Catecholamines and nucleotides in phaeochromocytoma. *Biochem. Pharmacol.* **13**, 809–818.

Stolz, F. (1904). Über Adrenalin und Alkylaminoacetobrenzcatechin. *Ber. Deut. Chem. Ges.* **37**, 4149–4154.

Stone, C. A., Entwisle, G. E., and Loew, E. R. (1951). Effect of tetraethylammonium chloride on the adrenal medulla of cats. *J. Pharmacol. Exptl. Therap.* **101**, 34.

Strand, L. J., Goldfien, A., and Ganong, W. F. (1964). Effect of pancreatectomy on the adrenal medullary response to hypoglycemia in the dog. *Endocrinology* **74**, 656–657.

Sugawara, T. (1925). Effect of nicotine upon the rate of epinephrine output from the suprarenal glands. *Tohoku J. Exptl. Med.* **6**, 430–458.

Sutherland, E. W., and Rall, T. W. (1960). The relation of adenosine-3′,5′-phosphate to the action of catechol amines. *Ciba Found. Symp., Adrenergic Mechanisms* pp. 295–304.

Takamine, J. (1901). Adrenaline the active principle of the suprarenal glands and its mode of preparation. *Am. J. Pharmacol.* **73**, 523.

Tillman, S. (1952). Noradrenalinstegring vid thalliumförgiftning. *Svenska Lakartidn.* **49**, 1523–1525.

Udenfriend, S., Cooper, J. R., Clark, C. T., and Baer, J. E. (1953). Rate of turnover of epinephrine in the adrenal medulla. *Science* **117**, 663–665.

Univ. of Montreal (1958). Symp. on metabolism and biological significance of certain biogenic amines. *Rev. Can. Biol.* **17**, 265–411.

Uuspää, V. J., and Suomalainen, P. (1954). The adrenaline and noradrenaline content of the adrenal glands of the hedge-hog. *Ann. Acad. Sci. Fennicae, Ser. A* **IV**, 1–11.

Vendsalu, A. (1960). Studies on adrenaline and noradrenaline in human plasma. *Acta Physiol. Scand.* **49,** Suppl. 173.

Vogt, M. (1952). The secretion of the denervated adrenal medulla of the cat. *Brit. J. Pharmacol.* **7,** 325–330.

von Euler, C., von Euler, U. S., and Floding, I. (1955). Biologically inactive catechol derivatives in urine. *Acta Physiol. Scand.* **33,** Suppl. 118, 32–38.

von Euler, U. S. (1948). Preparation, purification and evaluation of noradrenaline and adrenaline in organ extracts. *Arch. Intern. Pharmacodyn.* **77,** 477–485.

von Euler, U. S. (1956). "Noradrenaline." Thomas, Springfield, Illinois.

von Euler, U. S. (1961). The catecholamines. Adrenaline; Noradrenaline. *In* "Hormones in Blood" (C. H. Gray and A. L. Bacharach, eds.), pp. 515–582. Academic Press, New York.

von Euler, U. S. (1963). Chromaffin cell hormones. *In* "Comparative Endocrinology" (U. S. von Euler and H. Heller, eds.), Vol. I, pp. 258–290. Academic Press, New York.

von Euler, U. S., and Folkow, B. (1958). The effect of stimulation of autonomic areas in the cerebral cortex upon the adrenaline and noradrenaline secretion from the adrenal gland in the cat. *Acta Physiol. Scand.* **42,** 313–320.

von Euler, U. S., and Hamberg, U. (1949a). Colorimetric determination of noradrenaline and adrenaline. *Acta Physiol. Scand.* **19,** 74–84.

von Euler, U. S., and Hamberg, U. (1949b). 1-Noradrenaline in the suprarenal medulla. *Nature* **163,** 642–643.

von Euler, U. S., and Hellner, S. (1952). Noradrenaline excretion in muscular work. *Acta Physiol. Scand.* **26,** 183–191.

von Euler, U. S., and Hökfelt, B. (1953). Colorimetric and biological estimation of adrenaline and noradrenaline in suprarenals of guinea-pigs. *Brit. J. Pharmacol.* **8,** 66–68.

von Euler, U. S., and Lishajko, F. (1961). Improved technique for the fluorimetric estimation of catecholamines. *Acta Physiol. Scand.* **51,** 348–355.

von Euler, U. S., and Lishajko, F. (1965). Catecholamine depletion and uptake in adrenergic nerve vesicles and in rabbit organs after decaborane. *Acta Physiol. Scand.* **65,** 324–330.

von Euler, U. S., and Luft, R. (1952). Effect of insulin on urinary excretion of adrenalin and noradrenalin. *Metabolism* **1,** 528–532.

von Euler, U. S., and Lundberg, U. (1954). Effect on flying on the epinephrine excretion in air force personnel. *J. Appl. Physiol.* **6,** 551–555.

von Euler, U. S., and Ström, G. (1957). Present status of diagnosis and treatment of pheochromocytoma. *Circulation* **15,** 5–13.

von Euler, U. S., Franksson, C., and Hellström, J. (1954). Adrenaline and noradrenaline content of surgically removed human suprarenal glands. *Acta Physiol. Scand.* **31,** 6–8.

von Euler, U. S., Hellner-Björkman, S., and Orwén, I. (1955). Diurnal variations in the excretion of free and conjugated noradrenaline and adrenaline in urine from healthy subjects. *Acta Physiol. Scand.* **33,** Suppl. 118, 10–16.

Vulpian, A. (1856). Note sur quelques réactions propres à la substance des capsules surrénales. *Compt. Rend.* **43,** 663–665.

Wada, M., Seo, M., and Abe, K. (1935a). Further study of the influence of cold on the rate of epinephrine secretion from the suprarenal glands with simultaneous determination of the blood sugar. *Tohoku J. Exptl. Med.* **26,** 381–411.

Wada, M., Seo, M., and Abe, K. (1935b). Effect of muscular exercise upon the epinephrine secretion from the suprarenal gland. *Tohoku J. Exptl. Med.* **27**, 65–86.

Wassermann, G., and Tramezzani, J. H. (1963). Separate distribution of adrenaline- and noradrenaline-secreting cells in the adrenal of snakes. *Gen. Comp. Endocrinol.* **3**, 480–489.

Weil-Malherbe, H., and Bone, A. D. (1954). On the occurrence of adrenaline and noradrenaline in blood. *Biochem. J.* **58**, 132–141.

Weil-Malherbe, H., and Posner, H. S. (1963). The effect of drugs on the release of epinephrine from adrenomedullary particles *in vitro*. *J. Pharmacol. Exptl. Therap.* **140**, 93–102.

West, G. B. (1955). The comparative pharmacology of the suprarenal medulla. *Quart. Rev. Biol.* **30**, 116–137.

West, G. B., Shepherd, D. M., Hunter, R. B., and Macgregor, A. R. (1953). The function of the organs of Zuckerkandl. *Clin. Sci.* **12**, 317–325.

Wetzstein, R. (1957). Elektronenmikroskopische Untersuchungen am Nebennierenmark von Maus, Meerschweinchen und Katze. *Z. Zellforsch. Mikroskop. Anat.* **46**, 517–576.

Wetzstein, R. (1962). Die phäochromen Granula des Nebennierenmarks im elektronenmikroskopischen Bild. *In* "Gewebs- und Neurohormone Physiologie des Melanophorenhormons" (H. Nowakowski, ed.), pp. 33–41. Springer, Berlin.

Wirsén, C. (1964). Histochemical observations of tissue changes in the noradrenaline-infused dog. *Acta Chir. Scand.* Suppl. 325, 26–30.

Wright, A., and Chester Jones, I. (1955). Chromaffin tissue in the lizard adrenal gland. *Nature* **175**, 1001–1002.

CHAPTER 26

Influence of Hormones on Brain Activity[1]

DIXON M. WOODBURY and ANTONIA VERNADAKIS

I. Introduction

It is the purpose of this chapter to summarize the available literature on the interrelationships of some hormones and the central nervous system (CNS). Homeostatic regulation in the body is controlled by the nervous and endocrine systems. Much research has been devoted to the physiology, biochemistry, and pharmacology of these two systems, but not to their interrelations. Since, however, each system is subject to the regulatory influence of the other, it is evident that the nervous system must influence the endocrine system and vice versa.

[1] Original investigations reported herein were supported by a U.S. Public Health Service research grant (NB–04553) and a career program award (5–K6–NB–13,838) from the National Institute of Neurological Diseases and Blindness, National Institutes of Health, Bethesda, Maryland.

In the present review, only the effects of hormones on the CNS will be emphasized. The effects of the CNS on hormonal secretions are extensively considered in other chapters of this book. This chapter also will not include the extensive subject of the relation between sex hormones and behavior. The subject is reviewed by Phoenix *et al.* and Lisk in this book (Chapters 21 and 22, respectively).

The hormones to be considered will include only those of the adrenal cortex, gonads, thyroid, parathyroid, pancreas, and growth hormone of the pituitary, since other hormones have not been studied sufficiently to merit their inclusion in this chapter.

II. Methods for Measuring Central Nervous System Activity

A. Electrical Stimulation of the Brain—Electroshock Seizures

The properties of electroshock seizures produced in animals have been extensively described by Toman *et al.* (1946), Toman and Goodman (1948), L. A. Woodbury and Swinyard (1952), and D. M. Woodbury and Esplin (1959). Toman *et al.* (1946) state, "that some properties of neuronal interaction in seizures elicited in animals are qualitatively similar to the properties of individual neurons in isolation, although the time-scale differs by several orders of magnitude at these two different levels of organization." The technique for measuring electroshock seizures in rats was first described by Spiegel (1937). Later, L. A. Woodbury and Davenport (1952) designed the apparatus and described the methods now widely used in many laboratories for electrically induced seizures in experimental animals.

In intact experimental animals, one of the properties of brain activity which can be conveniently determined quantitatively is the manifold overt motor manifestations of electrically induced seizures. The common forms of these motor movements are the clonic and the tonic discharges. The tonic component consists of two parts, flexion and extension. Threshold seizures, no matter how evoked, are characterized by localized clonic movements. Maximal seizures, no matter how evoked, are characterized by tonic flexion and extension and terminal clonus. The profile of experimentally induced electroshock seizures in rats expressed as a function of stimulus intensity is illustrated in Fig. 1. The ordinate represents the degree of motor activity and the abscissa the current in milliamperes (mA). The solid thick line represents the overt motor manifestations at the different current strengths. The variously labeled thin lines represent the underlying neurophysiological processes which take place in the brain as a result of the stimulation. The sequence of motor activity as a function of stimulus intensity is as follows. At low current values the motor response is due to sensory discharge as a result of stimulation of pain sensory receptors in the region of the stimulating electrodes. The hyperkinesia which occurs as the current increases appears to be due to a combination of maximal sensory discharge and stimulation of the "oscillator." The oscillator is defined as a collection of

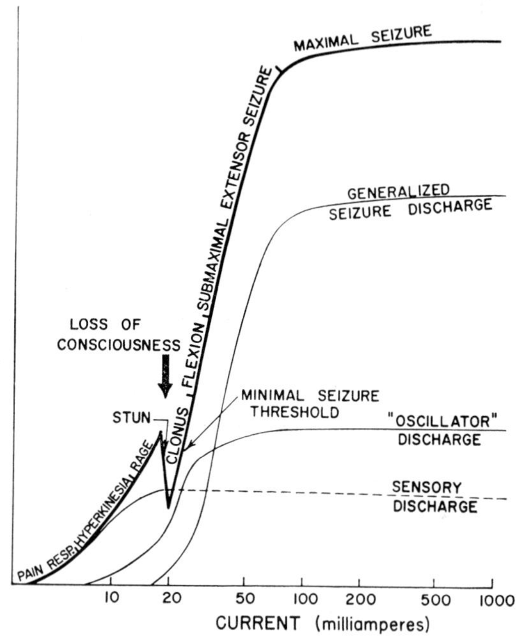

FIG. 1. Profile of experimentally induced seizures in rats as a function of stimulus intensity (see text for explanation). (D. W. Esplin and D. M. Woodbury, unpublished observations, 1964.)

neurons that discharge over a considerable period of time and cause hyperkinesia at low-intensity stimulation and minimal clonic seizures at higher current values (20 mA) (D. M. Woodbury and Esplin, 1959). When the current is increased to around 18 mA, a rage reaction is seen as a result of intense sensory discharge, more involvement of the oscillator and other subcortical areas involved in rage-type reactions. As the current strength is increased further, consciousness is lost and, although sensory discharge continues, sensation is lost, a stun reaction (catatonia) occurs, and motor activity decreases in this region. At current values slightly above this level minimal clonic seizures occur. Clonic activity sustained for 5 seconds is defined as the electroshock seizure threshold

(EST). The EST is a definite end point and can be easily measured since it is preceded by a stun reaction only slightly below the threshold and a rage reaction only slightly below the stun response. There is abundant evidence to indicate that the anatomical substratum of the oscillator, which is postulated to maintain seizure activity, may be that portion of the upper brain stem designated as the "centrencephalic system" by Penfield and Jasper (1954). Numerous investigations clearly show the role of specific components of this region (reticular activating system and thalamus) in the initiation and maintenance of minimal seizure discharge, for example, petit mal. Thus the manifestations of minimal seizure activity, namely, loss of consciousness and slight clonus, can be related to activity in the centrencephalic system including some involvement of the cortex.

As the stimulus intensity increases to values higher than threshold, flexion of the hindlimbs followed by clonus occurs as a result of maximal activity of the oscillator and generalized spread of seizure activity to involve other neuron networks and parts of the brain (seen in Fig. 1 on the curve labeled "generalized seizure discharge"). At still higher values maximal tonic flexor, tonic extensor, and clonic seizures occur. At this point the seizure seems to be a result of maximal discharge of the oscillator and apparently maximal discharge of the entire cerebrospinal axis.

B. Spinal Cord Convulsions

Direct stimulation of the spinal cord duplicates all the motor patterns seen during generalized motor seizure activity in the intact animal (Esplin and Laffan, 1957). The technique of direct spinal cord stimulation was first described by Esplin and Freston (1960) and modified for younger animals by Vernadakis (1962). The stimulating electrode is a stainless-steel wire or 26-gauge needle insulated except for the portion which is in contact with the spinal cord. Animals are decapitated at the cervical region, and the noninsulated portion is inserted into the cord from C_1 to C_4. The cord electrode is the cathode; the anode is attached to surrounding tissues. Square-wave stimuli are delivered by a Grass stimulator. Maximal stimulus parameters, in terms of the intensity, are 1–2 millisecond and 30–50 volts. With maximal parameters the entire cord is stimulated and both hindlimbs move in synchrony even if the electrode is placed along one side of the cord. Simple motor sequences, such as flexor-extensor convulsions, are timed. With supramaximal stimulation of the spinal cord, various responses, namely, phasic movements, flexion, and flexion followed by extension, are observed as a function of stimulus frequency.

C. Chemically Induced Seizures

As early as 1864, convulsions were produced in experimental animals by the injection of foreign substances (Morce, see Wortis, 1932). According to Moruzzi (1946), Landois in 1887 applied creatinine to the cerebral cortex of experimental animals, in the earliest attempt to produce focal seizures by chemical means. S. Baglioni and M. Magnini (1909, see Toman and Goodman, 1948) introduced the topical application of strychnine, which had been shown by Magendie in 1819 to produce seizures by its central nervous action. Pentylenetetrazol- (Metrazol), and strychnine-induced convulsions are most frequently used as test methods of assessing and evaluating CNS activity under a variety of conditions. A subcutaneous dose of 70 mg per kilogram of pentylenetetrazol will cause seizures in more than 97% of rats (Goodman *et al.*, 1946). This amount is approximately twice the threshold dose for 50% of animals. A threshold convulsion is defined as one episode of clonic spasms which persists for at least a 5-second period. Transient intermittent jerks or tremulousness are not considered as constituting a convulsion.

D. Audiogenic Seizures

In 1924 Donaldson reported that "The response of rats to some sensory stimuli, especially to sounds, is very marked—as is shown by jumping when the hands are clapped, and in some cases by an almost maniacal running and jumping—going on to exhaustion—when a bundle of keys is jingled before a cage."

Investigators of the effect of magnesium deficiency in the rat described as early as 1932 a convulsive sequence that occurred "spontaneously" or upon auditory stimulation (Kruse *et al.*, 1932; Greenberg and Tufts, 1935). Dice (1935) reported a similar pattern in "epileptic" mice exposed to the sound of jingling keys. Because of the apparent primacy of the auditory component in inducing the convulsive reaction, Morgan and Waldman (1941) suggested the descriptive phrase "audiogenic seizures," and this has become the most widely accepted term. In laboratory stocks of the house mouse, the occurrence of audiogenic seizures was first reported in a preliminary way by Mirsky *et al.* (1943) and was later studied by C. S. Hall (1947).

Various methods have been used to induce audiogenic seizures (C. S. Hall, 1947; Frings *et al.*, 1951). The most widely used sound source is a door bell generating 90–100 decibels of noise. Some workers, for a variety of special reasons, use pure tone stimuli produced by a variable-frequency oscillator or compressor-driven Galton whistle (Bevan,

1955). The components of the maximal audiogenic seizure (MAS) as described by Fink and Swinyard (1959) are: (1) latency, (2) running, (3) hindleg flexion, (4) hindleg extension, and (5) terminal clonus.

E. Electroencephalogram

The electroencephalogram (EEG) has been used as a method of assessing spontaneous electrical activity of the CNS. Detailed descriptions of methods in electroencephalography and the variables involved are found in Brazier (1958) and Ruch and Fulton (1960), and will not be given here.

The above-described methods of assessing CNS activity are those most pertinent to this chapter. Additional methods are summarized in Table I.

TABLE I

METHODS FOR EVALUATING THE EFFECTS OF HORMONES ON BRAIN ACTIVITY

I. Electrically-Induced Seizures
   - A. Generalized Stimulation
     1. Threshold (clonic)
     2. Flexor-Extensor
   - B. Local Stimulation
     1. Cortical, subcortical, etc.
     2. Spinal cord

II. Chemically Induced Seizures
   - A. Generalized Stimulation
     1. Pentylenetetrazol
        - a. Threshold
        - b. Flexor-extensor
     2. Other agents
        - a. Strychnine
        - b. Picrotoxin
        - c. Methionine sulfoximine
        - d. Thiosemicarbazide
   - B. Local Stimulation
     1. Convulsant drugs
     2. Irritant agents (penicillin, metals)

III. Sensory Stimulation
     1. Audiogenic
     2. Photic

IV. Metabolic Alterations
   - A. Water-Electrolyte (intraperitoneal glucose, vasopressin, etc.)
   - B. Carbon dioxide
   - C. Fever
   - D. Endocrine (ablation, administration)

III. Adrenal Gland

A. Hypofunction

1. *Effects on Electrically Induced Seizures*

The effects of adrenalectomy on brain excitability as measured by EST were studied by Davenport (1949) and Timiras *et al.* (1954), and summarized by D. M. Woodbury (1954). Davenport demonstrated that the EST of adrenalectomized rats given only water to drink decreased progressively (increased excitability) and after 4 days reached a minimum of 23% below the preoperative control threshold; the EST of rats maintained on 0.9% sodium chloride solution, deoxycorticosterone, or adrenocortical extract was the same as that of nonoperated controls. Administration of potassium chloride or magnesium chloride solutions accentuated the decrease in threshold produced by adrenalectomy alone; calcium chloride solution maintained the threshold approximately at the normal level. These results in rats have been extended to mice by Timiras *et al.* (1954) who found that adrenalectomized mice given water to drink showed a progressive decrease in EST, to both 60-cycle AC (25% decrease) and low-frequency unidirectional current (25% decrease); adrenalectomized mice given 0.9% sodium chloride to drink exhibited no change in threshold as compared to intact animals. The changes in brain excitability noted by these investigators were found to be correlated with changes in brain and plasma electrolyte concentrations. This interrelationship has been extensively discussed by D. M. Woodbury (1958), and only a brief summary will be given here. The brain of the adrenalectomized animal exhibits an increased concentration of intracellular sodium and a decreased ratio of extracellular to intracellular sodium concentration; total brain concentration is unchanged, but the ratio of intracellular to extracellular potassium concentration is decreased. These changes in electrolyte concentration correlate with a decrease in EST (increased brain excitability).

2. *Effects on Chemically Induced Seizures*

The influence of adrenocortical hypofunction on susceptibility to pentylenetetrazol-induced seizures was measured by Torda and Wolff (1952) in adrenalectomized rats maintained on sodium chloride; no change from control values was observed. Cicardo (1945, 1946) also noted that the dose of pentylenetetrazol necessary to produce minimal convulsions was the same in adrenalectomized rats and adrenalectomized and hypophysectomized toads as in the intact controls. Adrenocortical hypofunction, therefore, does not appear to increase susceptibility to pentylenetetrazol-induced convulsions as it does to seizures produced electrically. However, the problem of chemically induced convulsions in adrenalectomized animals is complicated by alterations in the absorption, fate, and excretion of the convulsant drug, and it is likely that adrenalectomy influences one or more of these factors; for example, if absorption of the convulsant is delayed, a larger dose would be required to produce a given effect. Although the experiments of Torda and Wolff rule out this particular factor of absorption since the pentylenetetrazol was administered intravenously, other factors such as those discussed by Swinyard *et al.* (1955) are involved even when the convulsant is injected intravenously. More precise studies are necessary for a complete solution of the problem.

In contrast to the results with pentylenetetrazol adrenalectomy was found to lower the threshold for seizures induced by intravenous infusion of strychnine in rats. (De Salva, 1960).

The average minimal convulsant dose of insulin was determined in normal, adrenalectomized, adrenodemedullated (with transplant of cortex), and hypophysectomized rats by Swann and Fitzgerald (1938). The sensitivity to insulin convulsions was increased 24-fold by adrenalectomy, 2-fold by removal of the adrenal medulla, and 7-fold by hypophysectomy. Lack of adrenocortical steroids, therefore, results in increased susceptibility of the nervous system to the convulsant effects of insulin.

3. *Effects on Audiogenic Seizures*

The effect of adrenalectomy on the incidence of audiogenic seizures in wild and domestic rats was studied by Griffiths (1949). Intact and adrenalectomized wild rats, whether maintained on water or on sodium chloride, did not exhibit audiogenic seizures in response to an air blast. In contrast, adrenalectomized domestic rats exhibited an enhanced susceptibility to audiogenic seizures when maintained on water but exhibited a decreased susceptibility to audiogenic seizures when maintained on large doses of sodium chloride. The explanation of these findings lies in the protection afforded by sodium chloride against the increase in brain excitability resulting from adrenalectomy. As discussed above, Davenport (1949) demonstrated that sodium chloride restored the decreased EST of adrenalectomized rats to normal, and D. M. Woodbury (1954) has shown that excessive quantities of sodium chloride will elevate the EST to levels above normal in intact animals and to a greater extent in adrenalectomized animals. Griffiths (1949) also showed that adrenalectomy, whether in wild or domestic rats and whether the rats were treated or not, decreased the spontaneous activity of the animals, probably as a result of the muscle weakness so characteristic of adrenocortical insufficiency.

4. *Effects on Seizure Incidence in Experimental Animals and Man*

It has been observed, almost from the time that Addison's disease was first recognized, that patients in crises due to adrenocortical insufficiency exhibit convulsive episodes (Cleghorn, 1951; Engel and Margolin, 1941; Klippel, 1899). Also in experimental animals, Peiper (1921) noted that adrenalectomy resulted in convulsions. Swingle *et al.* (1937) were able to evoke convulsions in adrenalectomized dogs by giving them large amounts of water. It was observed that the adrenalectomized dogs convulsed after smaller quantities of water than were required in intact dogs. The normal dogs spontaneously recovered from water intoxication if fluid administration was discontinued at the time of onset of convulsions, whereas otherwise healthy and vigorous adrenalectomized dogs subjected to water intoxication did not recover unless injected intravenously with adrenocortical extract or hypertonic sodium chloride solution.

Knobil *et al.* (1953) studied the effects of adrenocortical insufficiency in rhesus monkeys and noted extreme weakness, occasional convulsions, prostration, and coma; such crises invariably occurred after a period of fasting occasioned by removal of food or by anorexia. The crises were associated with a marked decrease in blood sugar concentration; administration of glucose resulted in complete recovery from the crises in 5–60 minutes. The conclusion was reached that hypoglycemia was the immediate cause of death (and presumably of convulsions) in the monkey with adrenocortical insufficiency.

Although most investigators have explained the convulsions on the basis of the hypoglycemia which occurs in adrenal crises, Arnett *et al.* (1942) observed that the frequency of cerebral symptoms in adrenodemedullated and adrenalectomized rats given insulin was unrelated to the blood sugar level. In addition, they found that insulin produced cerebral symptoms (depressed reflexes, coma, convulsions, and delta potentials in the EEG) in 84% of adrenalectomized rats but only in 16% of adrenodemedullated rats, although both groups had a similar degree of hypoglycemia. Thus the adrenalectomized animal is more sensitive than the adrenodemedullated animal to insulin-induced coma, and the convulsions may be due to some other factor(s).

That convulsions are fairly common in Addison's disease has been pointed out by Storrie (1953), who also reported on EEG changes and seizures in four patients with this disease; all four had abnormal EEG's (generally diffuse slow waves), three of the four had grand mal seizures, and all four exhibited cerebral symptoms (confusion, stupor, and paranoid ideas). The fasting blood sugar in these patients was normal, again indicating that the seizures were not hypoglycemic in origin. Therapy with cortisone and deoxycorticosterone improved their conditions and controlled the seizures.

5. *Effects on Electrical Activity of the Brain*

The EEG effects of hypocorticism in man were first reported by Engel and Margolin (1941, 1942) who found a characteristic picture of diffuse, slow activity with frequencies of 2–6 per second and voltages higher than those of alpha waves (up to 75 μV). Hyperventilation induced EEG changes more easily in patients with Addison's disease than in normal subjects, and glucose administration prevented such alterations. Adrenocortical extract but not deoxycorticosterone restored the EEG pattern to normal. A rough correlation was found between the EEG abnormalities and blood sugar level, and the EEG appeared to be improved by factors which improved carbohydrate metabolism, such as adequate replacement therapy in cases of Addison's disease.

The observations of Engel and Margolin in man have been amply confirmed by many investigators (Bricaire *et al.*, 1953; Condon *et al.*, 1954; Forsham, 1951; Forsham *et al.*, 1949; Hoffman *et al.*, 1942; Storrie, 1953; Thorn *et al.*, 1949). Hoffman *et al.* (1942) observed that eighteen of twenty-five patients with Addison's disease exhibited definite abnormalities in the pattern of their resting EEG's. The changes were characterized by (1) oscillations (5–8 per second) slower than the normal alpha rhythm, with a predilection for the frontal area and a relative refractoriness to the usual effect of opening the eyes; (2) an unusual exaggeration of the normal EEG response to voluntary hyperventilation; and (3) a reduction in incidence of low-voltage, high-frequency activity (beta waves). The EEG abnormalities progressed despite deoxycorticosterone therapy; in addition, treatment with adrenocortical extract, vitamin B complex, and a diet high in carbohydrate failed to correct the EEG. Restoration of blood pressure, plasma volume, and electrolyte concentration prevented neither the occurrence of changes in the resting EEG nor the sensitivity to hyperventilation. Gorman and Wortis (1947) also described high-voltage, slow bursts in all leads in the EEG of a patient with Addison's disease; the abnormality was exaggerated by hyperventilation. Thorn *et al.* (1949) and Forsham *et al.* (1949) reported that cortisone abolished the EEG alterations in patients with

Addison's disease; however, "nervousness" was not relieved. Corticosterone has been observed to correct both the EEG abnormalities and the nervousness and excitability of patients with Addison's disease and, like cortisone, to produce a feeling of well-being (Conn *et al.*, 1951). 11-Dehydrocorticosterone appears to produce the same corrective results as corticosterone (Forsham, 1951).

It is of interest that the dominant frequency of the EEG is below normal in adrenalectomized rats as well as in patients with Addison's disease; on the other hand, hypophysectomy in rats does not change the EEG (Bergen, 1951; Bergen *et al.*, 1953; Torda and Wolff, 1952). The normal pattern can be restored by treating adrenalectomized rats with adrenocortical extract and pregnenolone but not with deoxycorticosterone (Bergen, 1951; Bergen *et al.*, 1953).

B. Hyperfunction

1. *Effects on Electrically Induced Seizures*

a. Adult. The effect of deoxycorticosterone on seizure threshold was first tested in rats by Spiegel (1943) and Spiegel and Wycis (1945) who found that this steroid elevated the threshold only at high dose levels; related steroids had only a slight effect.

The effect of chronic administration of adrenocortical steroids and adrenocorticotropic hormone (ACTH) on brain excitability, as measured by changes in electroshock seizure threshold in rats, has been summarized by D. M. Woodbury (1954) who found that deoxycorticosterone increased EST (decreased brain excitability) to the greatest extent. 11-Deoxy-17-hydroxycorticosterone increased EST slightly; corticosterone had no effect in the dose used (2 mg per rat); 11-dehydrocorticosterone slightly decreased EST (increased brain excitability); and cortisol and cortisone markedly decreased EST (D. M. Woodbury, 1952). Adrenocorticotropic hormone slightly increased EST, an observation confirmed by De Salva *et al.*, 1954) and Ercoli and De Salva (1956). The latter workers also noted that rats became tolerant to the effect of chronic ACTH administration. Other steroids such as cholesterol, pregnenolone, and acetoxypregnenolone did not affect brain excitability in rats (D. M. Woodbury, 1954). However, some of the newer synthetic steroids influence EST (Mansor *et al.*, 1956).

The influence of various steroids in combination on brain excitability was also tested (D. M. Woodbury, 1952). The deoxycorticosterone-elevated seizure threshold could be lowered by ACTH, adrenocortical extract, cortisone, cortisol, corticosterone, and dehydrocorticosterone; 11-

deoxy-17-hydroxycorticosterone, cholesterol, pregnenolone, acetoxypregnenolone, and testosterone did not alter the deoxycorticosterone-elevated threshold. On chronic administration, ACTH and cortisone prevented the deoxycorticosterone-induced elevation in seizure threshold; conversely, ACTH and dehydrocorticosterone partially prevented and deoxycorticosterone completely prevented the cortisone-induced decrease in threshold. On acute administration to intact and adrenalectomized rats, corticosterone prevented both the increase in threshold caused by deoxycorticosterone and the decrease in threshold caused by cortisol. The respective effects of deoxycorticosterone, cortisol, and cortisone on threshold were greater in adrenalectomized than in intact rats (D. M. Woodbury, 1954; D. M. Woodbury *et al.*, 1951). Administration of 0.9% sodium chloride solution as drinking water enhanced the EST-elevating effect of deoxycorticosterone in both intact and adrenalectomized rats (D. M. Woodbury *et al.*, 1951). The observation that deoxycorticosterone decreases and cortisone increases susceptibility to seizures evoked by 60-cycle AC in rats has been confirmed in mice by Timiras *et al.* (1954), using both the 60-cycle AC and low-frequency unidirectional current threshold methods.

In addition to their effects on excitable processes in the CNS, the adrenocortical steroids also influence central recovery processes. For example, in patients undergoing insulin shock therapy, cortisone was found to be markedly beneficial in hastening emergence from deep hypoglycemic coma and decreasing postictal depression (Habelmann, 1952). Experimentally, cortisol shortened the duration of the postictal depression that follows electroshock seizures in animals pretreated with insulin (Timiras *et al.*, 1956); the decrease in blood sugar level produced by insulin in these animals was also prevented by cortisol administration.

Chronic treatment of rats with cortisol was found to shorten the recovery time (RT_{50}) from maximal electroshock seizures and to increase the blood sugar concentration. Chronic treatment with deoxycorticosterone, however, did not modify the RT_{50} or the blood sugar concentration (Timiras *et al.*, 1956). The relation of the changes in recovery time to changes in blood sugar is discussed below (Section III,C). The tonic clonic pattern of the maximal electroshock seizure was also modified by cortisone (Timiras *et al.*, 1956). The duration of tonic extension was lengthened. The increase in duration of the tonic extensor component is an indication of increased brain excitability, an observation in agreement with the previously noted decrease in EST produced by cortisone. The effects of ACTH and of steroid hormones other than deoxycorticosterone, cortisone, and cortisol on the recovery process have not been studied.

It is evident that the adrenocortical steroids produce definite changes in brain excitability, as measured by the EST technique. The steroids which predominantly affect electrolyte metabolism (deoxycorticosterone, 11-deoxy-17-hydroxycorticosterone) decrease excitability; those which predominantly affect carbohydrate metabolism (cortisone, cortisol) increase excitability; those with intermediate metabolic effects (corticosterone, 11-dehydrocorticosterone) have intermediate effects on excitability. The relation of the chemical structure of adrenocortical steroids to their effect on brain excitability has been described by D. M. Woodbury (1952, 1954).

The effect of adrenocortical hormones on central excitability as measured by chronaxie in animals has been studied by Chauchard, Lecoq, and their colleagues (see Chauchard, 1952; Lecoq, 1954; Lecoq *et al.*, 1952, 1955). Their results were as follows: deoxycorticosterone and adrenocortical extract increased central excitability; corticosterone increased excitability only after chronic administration. These results are opposite to those reported by investigators using other techniques. Even clinical reports indicate that deoxycorticosterone-like and cortisone-like steroids have effects opposite to those described by the French investigators. It appears likely that the measurement of central chronaxie is not an accurate method for measurement of brain excitability.

In a series of articles, Pasolini (1951, 1952) reported the effects of adrenocortical steroids and ACTH on seizures evoked by electrical stimulation of the cerebral cortex in dogs; the study was undertaken because of the observation of Longo cited by Pasolini (1951) that normal dogs became predisposed to evoked seizures after they were adrenalectomized. In intact and adrenalectomized dogs, injection of deoxycorticosterone increased the threshold for direct stimulation of the cerebral cortex and prevented seizures in some animals. In sharp contrast, cortisone and ACTH decreased the cortical threshold and increased the incidence of evoked convulsions, and cortisone antagonized the effects of deoxycorticosterone. The above-described effects of the adrenocortical steroids on brain excitability as measured by direct cortical stimulation in dogs are in agreement with those obtained by the EST technique in rats and mice, except that ACTH increases brain excitability in dogs but produces little or no change in rats. This single discrepancy can be explained by the fact that ACTH in rats increases the adrenal output of corticosterone, a steroid which does not alter brain excitability, whereas ACTH in dogs enhances adrenal secretion of cortisol, a steroid which increases brain excitability.

b. Young. The field of developmental neuroendocrinology is at present in its experimental stage; the very few reports, however, demonstrate that the endocrine system plays a significant role in the functional development of the CNS. Studies by Millichap (1958), Vernadakis (1961), and Pylkkö and Woodbury (1961) have shown that the seizure pattern induced electrically and chemically in the maturing rat develops in phases which appear in the following sequence: hyperkinesia, clonus, forelimb flexion, forelimb extension, hindlimb flexion, and hindlimb extension. The factors which influence the sequential development of these phases have been discussed by Vernadakis and Woodbury (1963). They also found that the threshold for eliciting the various patterns of developing seizure phases decrease as maturation progresses. The effects of cortisol on the threshold for eliciting various seizure patterns in rats of different ages were also studied by Vernadakis and Woodbury (1963) who found that, when cortisol was administered to rats for a 4-day period during age 8 to 15 days, the electroshock thresholds for all four seizure patterns were lowered as compared to those of the controls. However, cortisol administered to rats during the period between 4 and 7 days after birth either elevated or did not affect the electroshock thresholds for any of the four seizure patterns. This age-dependent effect of cortisol on brain excitability is thought to be related to its influence on myelination of the higher nervous centers. Thus one of the possible mechanisms by which cortisol, given at a critical period of development, may influence brain excitability is by enhancing myelination.

In addition to effects of cortisol on the development and function of higher centers of the CNS, Vernadakis and Woodbury (1964) have also studied the effects of this hormone on the function of lower centers in the spinal cord. The technique of direct spinal cord stimulation described in Section II,B was used. Spinal cord convulsions can be elicited by direct spinal cord stimulation in 1-day-old rats (Vernadakis, 1962). Vernadakis and Woodbury (1964) found that, when cortisol was administered to rats from the eighth to the eleventh day of age, the duration of flexion was significantly decreased as compared to the appropriate controls; the duration of extension did not change. When cortisol was administered to rats for a 4-day period between the first to seventh days of age, the duration of flexion and extension did not differ from those in the appropriate control. The duration of flexion and/or extension is a measure of seizure intensity; thus, the shorter the duration of flexion and/or the longer the duration of extension the more severe is the convulsion and vice versa (Toman *et al.*, 1946; Esplin and Freston, 1960). These results show that the increase in excitability produced by cortisol is present not only in the brain but throughout the entire cerebrospinal axis. The authors suggest that cortisol might facilitate transmission or conduction in the spinal cord.

2. *Effects on Chemically Induced Seizures in Animals*

The effects of ACTH and adrenocortical steroids on the sensitivity of rats to pentylenetetrazol seizures have been studied by several investigators (Leonard *et al.*, 1953; Swinyard *et al.*, 1955; Torda and Wolff, 1951, 1952). Acute administration of ACTH and cortisone increased susceptibility to pentylenetetrazol (Torda and Wolff, 1952); in sharp contrast, chronic administration of ACTH decreased the susceptibility to such seizures (Torda and Wolff, 1952). Leonard *et al.* (1953) found that neither cortisone nor deoxycorticosterone influenced the susceptibility of mice to pentylenetetrazol. However, Swinyard *et al.* (1955) observed that deoxycorticosterone increases susceptibility of mice to intravenously injected pentylenetetrazol, an effect opposite to its influence on electroshock seizures. Deoxycorticosterone was found to protect against seizures induced by cocaine in dogs (Aird, 1944). Methionine sulfoximine has been shown to be the convulsant substance in agene-treated flour (Mellanby, 1946; Reiner *et al.*, 1950). Various steroid hormones have been examined for their influence on seizures induced in dogs by injection of agenized zein. Deoxycorticosterone and progesterone protected against "agene"-induced seizures, whereas ACTH and cortisone exacerbated such seizures, as evidenced by a decrease in their time of onset and an increase in their severity (Costa and Bonnycastle, 1952). Thus, deoxycorticosterone decreases and cortisone increases brain excitability, changes which are similar to those obtained with electrically induced seizures. The increase in seizure susceptibility induced by ACTH in agene-treated dogs can be explained by the fact that ACTH in this species causes the secretion mainly of cortisol; this steroid increases brain excitability.

The effects of large (anesthetic?) doses of steroids on chemically induced seizures in animals appear to be different from smaller doses of such steroids. For example, prednisolone, in small doses exerts an excitatory effect on the nervous system (Mansor *et al.*, 1956), but in large doses (100 mg per kilogram), it is a depressant and raises the convulsive threshold for intravenous strychnine in mice. However, the convulsive threshold for intravenous pentylenetetrazol is not altered (Bonta and Hohensee, 1960).

3. *Effects on Audiogenic Seizures*

A relation between the adrenal cortex and the susceptibility to audiogenic seizures has been postulated by a number of investigators (Colfer, 1947; Ginsberg and Roberts, 1951; Hurder and Sanders, 1953; Vicari *et al.,* 1952). However, the experimental results provide no clear-cut picture of the effects of various adrenal steroids and ACTH on sound-induced seizures. Colfer (1947) found that deoxycorticosterone decreased susceptibility of rats to seizures induced by an air blast; he also noted that brain electrolytes change as a result of deoxycorticosterone treatment. In 30-day-old DBA mice with an allegedly predictable seizure incidence, cortisone raised the incidence of convulsions in females to that characteristic of the males of this strain (Ginsberg and Roberts, 1951). On the other hand, Vicari *et al.* (1952) observed that pregnenolone moderately decreased, and cortisone and adrenocortical extract slightly decreased the incidence of audiogenic seizures in mice and the resulting high mortality as well. Hurder and Sanders (1953) found that ACTH did not influence the susceptibility of rats to audiogenic seizures. The adrenals of their seizure-susceptible group were larger than those of the control nonsusceptible group; whether the large adrenals were the cause or the results of the seizures was not determined.

4. *Effects of Adrenocortical Steroids on Seizure Incidence in Experimental Animals and Man*

Further evidence for a central excitatory effect of the adrenocortical steroids of the cortisone type is provided by the fact that convulsive episodes occasionally occur in experimental animals and in man treated with such steroids. In rabbits, Pincus *et al.* (1951) noted that ACTH treatment often produced convulsions, particularly when the dose was high. When newborn mice and rats were treated for 3 days with cortisone, Hicks (1953) reported that convulsive episodes developed in the second or third week. Pathological changes were also observed in the brains of these animals. Adult animals similarly treated did not exhibit seizures. These results demonstrate the extreme susceptibility of young animals to factors favoring convulsions. The effects of intrathecal administration of soluble cortisol succinate and soluble prednisone-21 phosphate on the CNS of dogs were studied by Oppelt and Rall (1961). They observed that within 5 to 30 minutes after injection of these steroids into the cisterna magna severe tonic clonic seizures were produced; such seizures lasted for 15 minutes or longer and often required pentobarbital sodium for control. The convulsive effect of both steroids was dose dependent and only small amounts were required. Insoluble cortisol suspension in saline had no CNS excitatory effects on intrathecal injection. Thus the cortisol-like steroids have marked direct excitatory effects when placed in the cerebrospinal fluid where they reach the CNS rapidly and in high concentrations.

Many clinical reports attest to the fact that both cortisone and ACTH increase brain excitability in man. In patients with no previous history of seizures, generalized convulsions have occurred during treatment of collagen diseases with ACTH and cortisone (Astwood *et al.*, 1950a,b; Baehr and Soffer, 1950; Bonham, 1953; Dameshek *et al.*, 1950; Elkinton *et al.*, 1949; Geppert *et al.*, 1952; Irons *et al.*, 1951; Lowell *et al.*, 1951; Pine *et al.*, 1951; Wayne, 1954). Status epilepticus has also resulted (Dorfman *et al.*, 1951; Stephen and Noad, 1951). In patients with lupus erythematosus, a disease known to affect the CNS and to cause convulsions, therapy with cortisone and ACTH has resulted in variable effects; precipitation of seizures has been reported, (Baehr and Soffer, 1950), but so has a decrease in seizure frequency (Russell *et al.*, 1951). Adrenocorticotropic hormone stimulates the secretion of cortisol in humans, and of corticosterone in rats (see D. M. Woodbury, 1954). Cortisol increases brain excitability, while corticosterone has little influence on brain excitability, so one would expect ACTH to predispose to seizures in man but not in rats.

Although spontaneous seizures in Cushing's disease are said to be infrequent (Glaser, 1953a), Starr (1952) reported that 4% of his patients had convulsions. There are no reports of spontaneous seizures in cases of adrenogenital syndrome associated with adrenocortical hyperplasia; it is possible that the increased amount of androgens secreted by the adrenals in this disease protects against any increase in brain excitability that would occur from an excessive secretion of cortisone-like steroids. This possibility is supported by the observation of Henneman (1954) that patients with this syndrome are notably resistant to the excitatory effects of cortisone, even when large doses are given.

5. *Effects of Adrenocortical Steroids on Electrical Activity of the Brain*

Electroencephalographic changes induced by adrenocortical steroid hormones and ACTH have been reported by many investigators (Boland and Headley, 1949; Conn *et al.*, 1951; Debré *et al.*, 1952a,b; Forsham, 1951; Friedlander and Rottger, 1951; Friedman and Engel, 1956; Glaser and Merritt, 1952; Glaser *et al.*, 1955; Gottschalk, 1952; Hoefer and Glaser, 1950; Nekhorocheff, 1952; Pine *et al.*, 1951; Ragan *et al.*, 1949; Ransohoff *et al.*, 1951; Streifler and Feldman, 1953; Ulett *et al.*, 1951; Wayne, 1954; Wayne and Boyle, 1953). The first extensive report of the effects of ACTH and cortisone on the EEG in man was that of Hoefer and Glaser (1950) who found that ACTH and particularly cortisone caused the appearance of a significant amount of moderately slow wave activity (4–7 per second), and an increase in sensitivity to hyperventilation; however, the incidence of these changes was variable. In four epileptic patients, Klein and Livingston (1950) observed that ACTH therapy decreased the incidence of seizures and improved the EEG pattern. In contrast, Glaser and Merrit (1952) noted that ACTH and cortisone increased the incidence of abnormalities in the EEG in epileptic patients and did not reduce the frequency of seizures. It is of interest that all but one of the patients treated with ACTH by Klein and Livingston (1950) were on standard anticonvulsant medication; the patient not on an anticonvulsant developed a severe reaction (choreiform movements, and abnormal personality) which necessitated withdrawal of the ACTH. In view of the fact that diphenylhydantoin and phenobarbital protect against cortisone-induced hyperexcitability in rats (Fingl *et al.*, 1952), it seems likely that, in the patients observed by Klein and Livingston, any central excitatory effects of cortisone and ACTH were masked by the concomitant anticonvulsant medication; in the single case in which anticonvulsant medication was not used, excitatory phenomena appeared.

The effects on the EEG produced by intravenous administration of cortisol and ACTH were measured by Glaser *et al.* (1955) who found that both hormones increased the number of waves (5–7 per second) in the EEG. Cortisone seemed to exert this effect more consistently and to a greater degree than did ACTH. The effect was somewhat greater in epileptic subjects with previously abnormal EEG's. In two epileptic patients cortisol increased the incidence of 2–3 per second spike-wave seizure discharge. No correlation between EEG alterations and serum electrolyte changes was found, despite the fact that there was an increase in serum potassium concentration in five of the seven patients given cortisol intravenously.

A tentative hypothesis for the mode of action of cortisone on the EEG has been advanced by Streifler and Feldman (1953), based on the following observations: ACTH and cortisone act on the hypothalamus and thalamus; electrical stimulation of the basal structures of the brain modifies the electrical activity of the cortex in experimental animals; hypothalamic lesions slow cerebral cortical activity. These observations, coupled with those of Castor *et al.* (1951) that cortisone and ACTH cause pathological changes in the hypothalamus and thalamus led Streifler and Feldman (1953) to suggest that the EEG changes induced by these hormones may be due to their direct action on diencephalic structures. The fact that most of the EEG changes induced by the 17-oxysteroids are in the direction of slower activity is compatible with the hypothesis of Streifler and Feldman, and indicates more specifically an effect either to depress the mesencephalic reticular activating system or, more likely, to enhance the recruiting response in the diffuse thalamic projection system (Penfield and Jasper, 1954). The fact that cortisone has general excitatory properties on the nervous system indicates that probably it is acting to enhance the recruiting response in the thalamus, rather than to depress the arousal response from the mesencephalic reticular activating system. It could, however, excite inhibitory pathways in this area and thereby produce the observed effects on the EEG. No evidence for or against this possibility is available. The fact that 17-oxysteroids decrease the low-frequency EST (Timiras *et al.*, 1954) suggests that this steroid does enhance the recruiting response in the diffuse thalamic projection system. Low-frequency seizures appear to originate in this area and then spread to the cerebral cortex. Further research to localize the anatomical sites of cortisone action is needed. It is of interest in this connection that Feldman *et al.* (1961) have demonstrated that the glucocorticoids exert marked effects on the brain stem in cats. They measured the effects of glucocorticoids on potentials in the medial lemniscus, midbrain reticular formation, different regions of the hypothalamus, and intralaminar nuclei of the thalamus evoked by stimulation of the contralateral sciatic nerve. Cortisol and ACTH caused an increase in the negative potentials of the multisynaptic brain stem systems (an excitatory effect), shortly after their administration. However, there was almost no change in the positive evoked potential of the lemniscal response. These experiments of Feldman *et al.* demonstrate that administration of adrenocortical steroids increases excitability in brain centrencephalic structures of cats (reticular formation, hypothalamus, etc.) and provide substantial evidence for the hypothesis of Streifler and Feldman (1953) described above that the glucocorticoids exert a direct effect on diencephalic structures. These subcortical effects could account for the manifold effects of cortisol on electrical activity of the brain, seizure activity, consciousness, and behavior; such effects are regulated by multisynaptic reticular systems in the midbrain and diencephalon.

Corticosterone and 11-dehydrocorticosterone have both been shown to correct the EEG abnormalities in patients with Addison's disease (Conn *et al.*, 1951; Forsham, 1951) but these steroids have not been studied for their EEG effects in patients with collagen diseases or in normal individuals.

Deoxycorticosterone has little influence on the EEG; however, Aird and Gordan (1951) did note a small, but consistent, decrease in the frequency of abnormal waves in six epileptic patients treated with this steroid. Ward *et al.* (1954) found that aldosterone did not alter the EEG pattern of patients with rheumatoid arthritis.

Electroencephalographic changes in Cushing's syndrome are similar to those induced by ACTH and cortisone and need be mentioned only briefly (Glaser, 1953b; Plotz *et al.*, 1952; Soffer, 1946). The main change is a decrease in the frequency of the alpha rhythm to a value of 3–7 per second. This shift appears to be correlated with an enhanced sensitivity to seizures. Two of seven patients in one series developed seizures (Glaser, 1953b).

Relatively few experiments have been performed to test the effects of adrenocortical hormones on the electrical activity of the brain in intact animals, in contrast to animals with adrenocortical insufficiency (Grenell, 1947; Grenell and McCawley, 1947b; Ortiz-Galvan and Morrell, 1956; Prados *et al.*, 1945; Soulairac and Soulairac, 1953; Torda and Wolff, 1952). In cats, adrenocortical extract has been reported to increase the amplitude and the frequency of the EEG and to prevent the flattening of waves associated with the edema resulting from exposure of the brain (Grenell, 1947; Grenell and McCawley, 1947a,b; Prados *et al.*, 1945). Similarly, Torda and Wolff (1952) demonstrated in normal rats that ACTH increased the EEG voltage and produced occasional spiking paroxysmal runs of low-frequency, high-voltage waves. Anoxia-induced disappearance of brain waves in rats was delayed by ACTH administration (Soulairac and Soulairac, 1953). The relation between these reported EEG effects of ACTH and adrenocortical extract and their effects on brain excitability is not clear from the meager data available.

IV. Gonads

A. Hypofunction

1. *Effects on Electrically Induced Seizures*

The effects of castration and ovariectomy on EST and maximal electroshock seizure (MES) patterns have been studied by Woolley and Timiras (1962a,b). The EST was slightly decreased in rats castrated before puberty but did not change in rats castrated after puberty. In postpubertally castrated rats, however, brain excitability decreased, as shown by changes in the MES pattern: the duration of tonic flexion increased whereas the duration of tonic extension decreased. The ratio of tonic flexion to extension is a standard index of seizure intensity; the greater the ratio the less severe is the convulsion. In contrast to postpubertally castrated rats, prepubertally castrated rats did not show any changes in the MES pattern.

The effects of ovariectomy before and after puberty have been described in detail (Woolley and Timiras, 1962b). Rats ovariectomized before puberty demonstrated a decrease in brain excitability as shown by an increase in EST and in flexion to extension ratio. In rats ovariectomized after puberty, brain excitability did not change even though the animals were followed for 3 weeks after the operation.

The effects of sex steroids on central recovery processes have not yet been adequately studied. Woolley and Timiras (1962a) noted that castration lengthens postictal depression, but testosterone treatment of castrated rats did not shorten recovery time to that of the intact controls.

2. *Effects on Audiogenic Seizures*

Although there is little clear-cut evidence showing sex differences in susceptibility to audiogenic seizures, a review by Bevan and Chinn (1956) indicates that the trend is for male rats and mice to be slightly more susceptible to audiogenic seizures than females. However, Werboff and Corcoran (1961) showed that castration had little effect on seizure responses whereas ovariectomy resulted in a decrease in seizure response; testosterone administration resulted in a decrease whereas estradiol and progesterone administration to both castrated and ovariectomized rats resulted in an increased seizure response.

3. *Effects on Electrical Activity of the Brain*

The effects of gonadal insufficiency or gonadectomy on electrical activity of the brain have not been adequately studied.

B. Hyperfunction

1. *Effects on Electrically Induced Seizures*

a. Adult. Early observations by Spiegel and Wycis (1945) showed that deoxycorticosterone, testosterone, and progesterone had slight anticonvulsant effects as measured by an elevation of EST. More extensive studies, however, of the effects of sex steroids on brain excitability as measured by the EST and MES techniques have been performed by Woolley *et al.* (1960) and Woolley and Timiras (1962a,b). The results are summarized as follows. In rats castrated postpubertally, testosterone did not alter the threshold as compared with those of intact, untreated controls. Daily administration of high doses of testosterone to rats castrated before puberty increased the electroshock seizure threshold, whereas low and moderate doses had no effects.

Administration of estradiol to intact mature males and to ovariectomized immature and mature females markedly lowered seizure thresholds. The EST-lowering effect of estradiol was directly proportional to the dose. The minimal effective dose of estradiol on the electroshock threshold lies between 0.25 and 4.0 μg/100 gm body weight; this dose lies in the physiological range. Progesterone rapidly and significantly raised the seizure threshold in female rats but had no immediate effect in males. This anticonvulsant effect of progesterone in females persisted for 10 days. After this time the EST was slightly less than that of the intact female controls. Testosterone and methylandrostenediol significantly lowered the threshold in intact adult male rats; the fall in threshold was less marked than that produced by estradiol. Thus physiological levels of ovarian hormones influence brain excitability in the rat as measured by EST and MES techniques. Mature female rats exhibit a more severe seizure than do prepubertally ovariectomized rats. Since estrogens are the principal ovarian hormones in the mature female rat (Emmens, 1959; Segal, 1958), it is concluded that estrogens exert an excitatory effect on the CNS. That the excitatory effect of estradiol is a direct one and not mediated via stimulation of adenohypophyseal tropic hormones is demonstrated by the fact that it lowers EST even in hypophysectomized rats (Woolley and Timiras, 1962a).

Further evidence for the excitatory effect of estrogens is shown by the changes in threshold and pattern of electroshock seizures during the estrous cycle of the rat (Woolley and Timiras, 1962c). It was observed (1) that the threshold for minimal seizures was highest during diestrus, lower during proestrus, and lowest during estrus; and (2) that the duration of the tonic flexor component was longest during diestrus and shortest during estrus. The increased brain excitability during estrus is probably due to the high level of circulating estradiol during this phase. The effects of testosterone propionate, estradiol benzoate, and progesterone on central excitability as measured by chronaxie in male and female rats have been reported by Chauchard (1947). All three hormones were reported to increase brain excitability in both male and female animals. Again, it appears that results obtained by this method differ from those obtained by more sensitive and accurate techniques.

b. Young. The effects of estradiol on the functional development of the CNS in rats have been studied by Heim and Timiras (1963). They found that when estradiol was administered to rats from the sixth to the sixteenth and from the eighth to the twelfth days of age the duration of flexion was shorter and extension was longer as compared to appropriate controls at various age periods after administration of the hormone. These permanent effects of estradiol on brain excitability in developing rats are probably due to irreversible cellular changes induced by the hormone. Since these effects were not observed when estradiol was administered to rats from the fourth to the eighth, tenth to the fourteenth, or twelfth to the sixteenth days of age, it appears clearly that there is a critical age period during which estradiol is most effective in altering brain function.

Vernadakis and Timiras (1963) studied the effects of estradiol on the function of the developing spinal cord in rats by the use of direct spinal cord stimulation. They found that estradiol significantly decreased the duration of flexion when given in rats from the eighth to the eleventh day of age. It is concluded that estradiol affects the functional development of the central nervous system at all levels of the cerebrospinal axis.

2. *Effects on Chemically Induced Seizures in Animals*

The effects of sex steroids on chemically induced seizures have not been investigated directly. However, Clark and Sarkaris (1958) found that female mice were much more susceptible to acid fuchsin-induced seizures than were male mice. This difference in convulsive susceptibility is probably due to the central excitatory effects of estradiol.

3. *Effects on Audiogenic Seizures*

The effects of sex steroids on audiogenic seizures have not been adequately investigated in intact animals.

4. *Effects on Seizure Incidence in Man*

As early as 1885 Gowers suspected a relationship between epilepsy and menstruation. Since then, several investigators have confirmed this observation and agreed that an exacerbation of epileptic seizures occurs just before or at the time of menstruation (Turner, 1907; Almquist, 1955; Ansell and Clarke, 1956). Progesterone recently has been implicated as a factor governing the occurrence of convulsions during the menstrual cycle. Laidlaw (1956) demonstrated a consistent reduction of seizures in the midluteal period of the cycle and an exacerbation of seizures just prior to menstruation. He suggested from these results that progesterone exerts an anticonvulsant effect when its levels are high during the midluteal phase but as the levels fall abruptly just before menstruation, withdrawal hyperexcitability occurs which leads to an increased incidence of seizures. More recent studies by Logothetis *et al.* (1959) confirm the findings of Laidlaw with respect to the increased seizure incidence prior to menstruation, but these investigators suggest a different cause for the increased susceptibility.

Logothetis *et al.* showed that in twenty-five patients with catamenial epilepsy the seizures occurred primarily during the immediate premenstrual and menstrual periods. In addition, Logothetis *et al.* noted that intravenous injection or topical application of water-soluble estrogenic conjugates (Premarin) on the brain of normal rabbits or on the brain of rabbits with an irritable cortical lesion produced by an ethyl chloride spray resulted in activation of the EEG. They also noted activation of the EEG in epileptics given estrogens. On the basis of these results, Logothetis *et al.* (1959) suggested that the increased incidence of seizures prior to menstruation is due to increased plasma levels of estrogens and not to the sudden decrease in levels of progesterone which occurs during this period, as suggested by Laidlaw. However, the fact that progesterone decreases brain excitability whereas estrogen increases it as discussed above suggests that both effects, i.e., increased plasma estrogen levels and decreased progesterone levels, account for the marked increase in CNS excitability that occurs in the premenstrual-menstrual period.

5. *Effects on Electrical Activity of the Brain*

Dusser de Barenne and Gibbs (1942) studied variations in the EEG during the menstrual cycle and found that sufficient slowing of the EEG occurred in association with menstruation to change a normal EEG to an abnormal one. Gibbs and Reid (1942) demonstrated that in the last weeks of pregnancy (when progesterone levels are high) the electrical activity of the cortex was definitely slow compared to postpartum EEG records. However, the EEG of postmenopausal women was not significantly altered by injections of progesterone or stilbestrol (Cress and Greenblatt, 1945). In contrast to this negative effect of female sex steroids on the EEG of postmenopausal women, Logothetis *et al.* (1959) observed an activating effect of Premarin on the EEG in eleven of sixteen patients with catamenial epilepsy. Thus, further studies are necessary in order to define the effects of female sex steroids on the electrical activity of the brain. The effects of male sex steroids on the EEG have not been described, and no reports on the EEG pattern of patients with adrenogenital syndrome and other diseases of gonadal hyperfunction are available.

Experiments on the effects of sex steroids on the EEG of experimental animals have been mainly confined to studies on the EEG arousal threshold involving the brain stem reticular formation and the hypothalamus and the role of changes in these parameters in sexual behavior and pituitary function. A discussion of the results of such studies is beyond the scope of this chapter. The interested reader should consult Chapters 15 and 22 of this treatise and articles by Kawakami and Sawyer (1959) and Sawyer and Everett (1959) for further information.

V. Thyroid Gland

A. Hypofunction

1. *Effects on Electrically Induced Seizures*

It has been found that both thyroidectomy and propylthiouracil increase EST (decrease brain excitability) in rats, although propylthiouracil was more effective in this respect (D. M. Woodbury *et al.*, 1952). In addition, propylthiouracil caused a significant increase in the duration of the tonic flexor component, so that the total duration of the seizure was significantly increased. In contrast, thyroidectomy produced an opposite effect to that of propylthiouracil on the flexor and extensor components, namely, a marked decrease in the flexor and a marked increase in the extensor component. It is clear from these results that the responses to thyroidectomy and propylthiouracil are not identical, as would be expected if the two procedures affected central nervous function through the common denominator of hypothyroidism. In addition, D. M. Woodbury *et al.* (1952) found that thyroidectomy greatly accelerated recovery from maximal seizures whereas propylthiouracil prolonged recovery time by more than 50%. To explain the contrasting responses of thyroidectomized and propylthiouracil-treated rats, hypocalcemia secondary to parathyroid damage was considered, but the plasma calcium concentrations of the thyroidectomized animals were the same as those of the untreated controls; a direct depressant effect of propylthiouracil on the nervous system independent of its antithyroid action appears to be a more likely explanation. Such a direct effect would account for the higher EST, the prolonged postictal recovery, and the increased duration of the tonic flexor component of the MES pattern. All the changes in seizure properties produced by propylthiouracil are also those which are characteristically produced by anticonvulsant drugs. The effects of thyroidectomy on brain electrolyte concentrations have been investigated by Timiras and Woodbury (1956) and a direct relationship was found between decreased intracellular sodium concentration and decreased brain excitability.

2. *Effects on Audiogenic Seizures*

Vicari (1951) found that propylthiouracil protects against audiogenically induced lethal seizures in mice. This observation is in agreement with the above-described effects of propylthiouracil on MES in rats. Therefore, the available evidence strongly suggests that propylthiouracil has a direct anticonvulsant effect.

3. *Effect on Chemically Induced Seizures*

D. M. Woodbury *et al.* (1952) have reported that both thyroidectomy and propylthiouracil markedly elevate the threshold to pentylenetetrazol in rats. This is further evidence of the anticonvulsant properties of propylthiouracil.

4. *Effects on Electrical Activity of the Brain*

The effects of hypothyroidism on spontaneous electrical activity have not been adequately investigated and contradictory findings have been reported. In hypothyroid individuals, basal metabolic rate and alpha frequency of the electroencephalogram are both decreased (Rubin *et al.*, 1937; Bertrand *et al.*, 1938; Ross and Schwab, 1939). In rats, spontaneous electrical activity was not significantly influenced by thyroidectomy despite a decrease in basal metabolic rate (Lee and Van Buskirk, 1928). However, V. E. Hall and Lindsay (1938) found that thyroidectomy decreased spontaneous activity of rats by 49.5% at the end of a 2-week test period; dinitrophenol, at dose levels of 20 and 30 mg per kilogram per day for 2 weeks, restored the decreased basal metabolic rate to normal but did not restore the spontaneous activity to normal. It was concluded that the thyroid hormone acts on the nervous system independently of its effect on basal metabolic rate. Brody (1941) also found a marked decrease in spontaneous electrical activity of rats thyroidectomized for 60 days, and concluded that the decrease probably resulted from a decreased nervous system irritability.

B. Hyperfunction

1. *Effects on Electrically Induced Seizures*

Chronic administration of thyroxine markedly lowered the electroshock threshold in rabbits and guinea pigs (Tainter *et al.*, 1943; Gerlich, 1949).

It also increased the duration of the tonic phase of the maximal seizure and decreased the clonic phase in guinea pigs (Gerlich, 1949). In addition, the effects of thyroxine and triiodothyronine on seizure thresholds and pattern and on postictal recovery in rats have been reported by D. M. Woodbury *et al.* (1952) and Timiras and Woodbury (1956). Thyroxine did not exert an appreciable effect on the EST until the fourteenth day; the threshold then gradually declined. It also lowered the EST of rats with threshold elevated by thyroidectomy. Triiodothyronine, administered in doses only one-fifth as large as those of thyroxine, produced an effect on EST similar to that of thyroxine. Both thyroxine and triidothyronine significantly prolonged the tonic extensor phase and shortened the tonic flexor and clonic phases. Concomitantly with increased brain excitability, thyroxine and triiodothyronine produced alterations in brain electrolyte metabolism, the most important of which are those concerned with sodium distribution: extracellular sodium concentration decreased, intracellular sodium concentration increased, and the ratio of extacellular to intracellular sodium decreased (Timiras *et al.*, 1955a).

2. *Effects on Chemically Induced Seizures*

The effects of the administration of thyroxine and desiccated thyroid on pentylenetetrazol-induced seizures in guinea pigs have been investigated by Garcia (1943) who found that thyroxine increased the frequency and intensity of pentylenetetrazol convulsions and accelerated the onset. D. M. Woodbury *et al.* (1952) also found that in rats thyroxine significantly reduced the dose of pentylenetetrazol required to elicit seizures. This is, therefore, further evidence that thyroxine increases the level of brain activity.

3. *Effects on Electrical Activity of the Brain*

Administration of thyroxine to normal men and to schizophrenic patients increased the frequency of the alpha rhythm of the EEG (Jasper, 1936; Lindsley and Rubenstein, 1937; Rubin *et al.*, 1937). The increased brain activity which follows thyroxine administration was originally ascribed to an enhanced cerebral metabolism. For example, Lindsley and Rubenstein (1937) found a highly positive correlation between the metabolic rate and the frequency of alpha waves in the EEG of normal adults. However, this interpretation was challenged by V. E. Hall and Lindsay (1938), Brody (1941), and D. M. Woodbury *et al.* (1952), who advocated a direct influence of the thyroid hormones on the central nervous system.

VI. Parathyroid Gland

Since the reported effects of parathyroid hypofunction and hyperfunction on brain activity are mainly concerned with clinical cases, only a brief summary will be presented here.

A. Hypofunction

The occurrence of seizures in hypoparathyroid patients has led to many controversial reports as to whether the convulsions are an incidental disorder or whether they are primarily due to parathyroid deficiency. The subject has been concisely and adequately reviewed by Sugar (1953). The electoencephalogram has been used as a tool to determine the possible relation between hypoparathyroidism and seizures. The seizures usually are associated with paroxysmal abnormalities in the EEG, characterized by slow theta and delta waves, spike-wave discharges varying in frequency from 1.5–4.0 cycles per second, with single and multiple spiking. Usually, treatment of the underlying disorder by the administration of calcium salts, vitamin D, and other phosphaturic agents that elevate plasma calcium relieves the seizure state and improves the EEG. In most cases reported, hypocalcemia is considered to be responsible for the disorders of the central and peripheral nervous system in hypoparathyroidism. It is concluded that low serum calcium as a result of parathyroid hypofunction increases susceptibility to seizures in epileptics. These results agree with observations in experimental animals that administration of calcium salts elevates EST whereas administration of phosphate salts, which lower plasma calcium levels, decreases EST (D. M. Woodbury and Davenport, 1949).

B. Hyperfunction

The effects of hyperparathyroidism on brain excitability are not clear. Various neuropsychiatric and neurological manifestations are observed in patients with primary hyperparathyroidism; in such cases convulsions are not frequently observed (see review by Karpati and Frame, 1964). The various neuropsychiatric manifestations observed in primary hyperparathyroidism are attributed to the high level of serum calcium. Serum calcium levels over 17 mg% are almost always associated with some kind of neurologic or psychiatric abnormality.

VII. Pancreas

A. Pancreatectomy—Diabetes Mellitus

Effects on Electrically Induced Seizures

The effects of pancreatectomy and alloxan on experimental convulsions have been studied in rats by Timiras *et al.* (1955b). In pancreatectomized rats, moderate hyperglycemia was accompanied by a progressive decrease in EST. Alloxan in doses of 30 and 60 mg per kilogram produced a marked hyperglycemia and significantly lowered the EST below normal values. Both pancreatectomy and alloxan significantly increased the duration of the extensor component and shortened the flexor component of the maximal electroshock seizure; they also significantly shortened the duration of postictal depression. The latter results are in agreement with other observations showing that hyperglycemia is accompanied by shortened postictal depression and that hypoglycemia is accompanied by prolonged postictal depression (Timiras *et al.*, 1956).

B. Insulin

1. *Effects on Electrically Induced Seizures*

The effects of insulin on brain function have been the subject of several reports and have been widely utilized in the so-called "shock-therapy" of mental diseases. However, much less is known concerning the influence of diabetes on brain excitability.

The effects of insulin on experimental convulsions have been studied by Timiras *et al.* (1955b). Insulin produced a significant increase in brain excitability. These authors found that the dose of insulin, the degree of hypoglycemia, and the fall in EST appeared to be closely related; the highest dose of insulin produced the most severe hypoglycemia and the most pronounced fall in EST. Insulin did not modify significantly the tonic-clonic convulsions but markedly prolonged the duration of postictal depression. These results appear to add further evidence to the hypothesis that the rapidity with which brain activity is restored after convulsions is dependent on the supply of glucose to the brain (Timiras *et al.*, 1956).

It is concluded from the above-cited studies that both insulin and diabetes enhance brain excitability. These effects cannot be explained on the basis of carbohydrate metabolism, since both hypoglycemia and hyperglycemia enhance brain excitability. The authors suggest that effects of both insulin and diabetes on brain excitability are partly due to changes in brain electrolyte metabolism, especially sodium ions, since they found a direct correlation between intracellular Na^+ concentration and brain excitability.

2. *Effects of Insulin on Electrical Activity of the Brain*

Early in the development of electroencephalography, it was shown in man and animals that insulin-induced hypoglycemia produces changes in cerebral brain potentials that are reversible if glucose is resupplied (Berger, 1937; Hoagland *et al.*, 1937; Himwich *et al.*, 1939; Maddock *et al.*, 1939; Goodwin *et al.*, 1940; Hill, 1948; Heppenstall and Greville, 1950). Both in man and rats, large doses of insulin cause a progressive decline in alpha-wave frequency (Hoagland *et al.*, 1937; D. M. Woodbury and colleagues, unpublished observations).

VIII. Growth Hormone (Somatotropin)

Reports on effects of growth hormone on brain excitability are meager. De Salva and Ercoli (1959) found that in intact growing rats, growth hormone increased the EST without influencing body weight gain. It is difficult, however, to interpret these findings as a direct effect of growth hormone on EST, since the hormone had no effect on the EST-lowering effect of hypophysectomy.

IX. Summary

In this chapter the influence of hormones on the activity of the CNS as assessed by various procedures is discussed. Some of the many methods of measuring CNS activity are described and evaluated.

The steroid hormones of the adrenal cortex profoundly influence the activity of the CNS. Adrenocortical deficiency generally enhances the activity of the nervous system as measured by susceptibility to electrically, chemically, and audiogenically induced seizures. Spontaneous seizures may occur in hypoadrenal crisis. The frequency of electrical activity of the brain is generally slowed in the absence of adrenal steroids. All these changes can be reversed by administration of maintenance doses of adrenal cortical extract, cortisone, corticosterone, or cortisol. Deoxycorticosterone will reverse the changes in excitability but not the changes in electrical activity. Administration of adrenocortical steroids of the mineralocorticoid type (deoxycorticosterone, aldosterone) results in diminished activity of the CNS, whereas those of the glucocorticoid type (cortisol, cortisone) enhance CNS activity. Spontaneous seizures sometimes occur in experimental animals and in humans receiving large doses of cortisone or cortisol. The effects of the mineralocorticoids can be antagonized by the glucocorticoids and vice versa. Corticosterone antagonizes the effects of both deoxycorticosterone and cortisol on CNS activity. Excessive amounts of cortisone and cortisol cause an increase in the amplitude and slowing of the frequency of the waves observed in the EEG. The glucocorticoids are thought to exert excitatory effects at all levels of the CNS.

Cortisol influences the development of the CNS in neonatal animals. It appears to delay development of the brain when given to rats during the fourth to seventh days after birth but accelerates development when given between the eighth and fifteenth days after birth.

Hypofunction of the gonads influences the behavior patterns of animals and man but produces a less profound effect on the activity of the brain than does adrenocortical insufficiency. Castration generally slightly increases whereas ovariectomy usually slightly decreases CNS activity. The male sex steroid, testosterone, decreases CNS activity as measured by most indices. The female sex steroids, estradiol and progesterone, have opposite effects on CNS excitability; estradiol increases whereas progesterone decreases excitability. The excitatory effect of estradiol is apparently a direct one inasmuch as this hormone increases excitability even in hypophysectomized rats. A normal role of the estrogens in regulating CNS excitability is suggested by the observation that during the estrous cycle in the rat the threshold for electrically induced seizures is decreased during diestrus and increased during estrus when the estradiol concentration in plasma is maximal. In humans, CNS activity appears to be increased just prior to or at the time of menstruation. This premenstrual increase in excitability appears to be due to a combination of the increased estrogen levels and decreased progesterone levels in the plasma during the premenstrual-menstrual period.

The thyroid hormones, thyroxine and triiodothyronine, exert marked effects on the CNS. In their absence, CNS activity is decreased as measured by the various indices discussed. The alpha frequency of the EEG is decreased in hypothyroid conditions. A marked increase in CNS activity is induced by excessive quantities of thyroxine or triiodothyronine. Sensitivity to electrically and some chemically induced seizures is increased. The frequency of alpha rhythm of the EEG is increased by thyroxine administration.

Alterations in CNS activity in hypoparathyroidism are a result of the lowered serum calcium level which increases susceptibility to electrically induced seizures. The increased susceptibility to seizures is reduced by administration of calcium salts. In patients with hypoparathyroidism, the

EEG may exhibit paroxysmal abnormalities characterized by slow beta and delta waves and occasionally spike and wave discharges accompanying clinical seizures. These effects can be corrected by calcium salts and vitamin D which elevate plasma calcium level. In hyperparathyroid patients, various neuropsychiatric and neurological manifestations are observed, but usually spontaneous seizures do not occur. The neuropsychiatric and neurological abnormalities are almost always greater when the plasma calcium level exceeds 17 mg%.

In experimental animals with hypoinsulinism or in patients with diabetes mellitus, the activity of the CNS is increased despite the high blood sugar level. However, the duration of convulsions is shortened. Administration of insulin increases the excitability of the CNS, and prolongs convulsions. Thus hyperglycemia is accompanied by shortened depression following increased CNS activity whereas hypoglycemia is accompanied by prolonged depression following increased CNS activity. The enhanced excitability of the CNS in hyperinsulinism and hypoinsulinism cannot be explained by changes in blood sugar but appears to be more closely related to the sodium concentration in brain cells, inasmuch as a direct correlation between intracellular sodium concentration and brain excitability has been observed. A progressive decrease in alpha wave frequency is induced by large doses of insulin.

The effects of growth hormone on CNS activity have not been well characterized.

References

Aird, R. B. (1944). The effect of desoxycorticosterone in epilepsy. *J. Nervous Mental Disease* **99**, 501–502.

Aird, R. B., and Gordan, G. S. (1951). Anticonvulsive properties of desoxycorticosterone. *J. Am. Med. Assoc.* **145**, 715–719.

Almquist, R. (1955). The rhythm of epileptic attacks and its relationships to the menstrual cycle. *Acta Psychiat. Neurol. Scand.* Suppl. **105**, 1–116.

Ansell, B., and Clarke, E. (1956). Epilepsy and menstruation. The role of water retention. *Lancet* **II**, 1232–1235.

Arnett, V., Kessler, M., and Gellhorn, E. (1942). The role of the adrenal cortex in preventing hypoglycemic convulsions. *Am. J. Physiol.* **137**, 653–657.

Astwood, E. B., Cleroux, A. P., Payne, R. W., and Raben, M. S. (1950a). Therapeutic studies on some newer corticotrophic (ACTH) preparations. *Bull. New Engl. Med. Center* **12**, 2–10.

Astwood, E. B., Raben, M. S., Payne, R. W., and Cleroux, A. P. (1950b). Clinical evaluation of crude and highly purified preparations of corticotrophin (ACTH) obtained in good yield by simple laboratory procedures. *J. Clin. Invest.* **29**, 797

Baehr, G., and Soffer, L. J. (1950). Treatment of disseminated lupus erythematosis with cortisone and adrenocorticotropin. *Bull. N.Y. Acad. Med.* **26**, 229–234.

Bergen, J. R. (1951). Rat electrocorticogram in relation to adrenal cortical function. *Am. J. Physiol.* **164**, 16–22.

Bergen, J. R., Hunt, C. A., and Hoagland, H. (1953). Effects of adrenalectomy and replacement therapy on brain circulation, oxygen consumption and the electrocorticogram. *Am. J. Physiol.* **175**, 327–332.

Berger, H. (1937). Über das Elektrenkephalogramm des Menschen. *Arch. Psychiat. Nervenkrankh.* **106**, 165–187.

Bertrand, I., Delay, J., and Guillain, J. (1938). L'electro-encéphalogramme dans le Myxoedéme. *Compt. Rend. Soc. Biol.* **129**, 395–398.

Bevan, W. (1955). Sound-precipitated convulsions: 1947 to 1954. *Psychol. Bull.* **52**, 473–504.

Bevan, W., and Chinn, R. McC. (1956). Audiogenic convulsions in male rats before and after castration and during replacement therapy. *Physiol. Zool.* **29**, 309–314.

Boland, E. W., and Headley, N. E. (1949). Effects of cortisone acetate on rheumatoid arthritis. *J. Am. Med. Assoc.* **141**, 301–308.

Bonham, D. T. (1953). A report on the death of a patient with convulsive seizures during treatment of rheumatoid arthritis with cortisone, ACTH, and post partum plasma. *N.Y. State J. Med.* **53**, 1114–1117.

Bonta, I. L., and Hohensee, F. (1960). Depressant effects of large doses of prednisolone succinate on the central nervous system. *Proc. 1st Intern. Congr. Endocrinol., Copenhagen, 1960* (Session VIIf, No. 417) p. 831.

Brazier, M. A. B. (1958). The development of concepts relating to the electrical activity of the brain. *J. Nervous Mental Disease* **126**, 303–321.

Bricaire, H., Mises, R., Dreyfas-Brisac, C., and Fischgold, H. (1953). Initiation à l'éléctroencéphalographie. EEG d'un cas de maladie d'Addison, *Presse Med.* **61**, 750–751.

Brody, E. B. (1941). The influence of thyroidectomy on the variability of neuromuscular activity in the rat. *Endocrinology* **29**, 916–918.

Castor, C. W., Baker, B. L., Ingle, D. J., and Li, C. H. (1951). Effect of treatment with ACTH or cortisone on anatomy of the brain. *Proc. Soc. Exptl. Biol. Med.* **76**, 353–357.

Chauchard, P. (1947). Hormones sexuelles et système nerveux. *Arch. Intern. Pharmacodyn.* **74**, 286–294.

Chauchard, P. (1952). Hormones et système nerveux. *Rev. Sci. (Paris)* **90**, 120–134.

Cicardo, V. H. (1945). Physiochemical mechanisms in experimental epilepsy. *J. Nervous Mental Disease* **101**, 527–536.

Cicardo, V. H. (1946). Sensibilidad convulsivante de los animales adrenoprivos hipotisoprivose injectados con desoxicorticosterone. *Publ. Centro Invest. Tisiol. (Buenos Aires)* **10**, 233–239.

Clark, G., and Sarkaris, D. S. (1958). Acid fuchsin convulsions and electroshock in the mouse. *J. Neuropathol. Exptl. Neurol.* **17**, 612–619.

Cleghorn, R. A. (1951). Adrenal cortical insufficiency: psychological and neurological observations. *Can. Med. Assoc. J.* **65**, 449–454.

Colfer, H. F. (1947). Studies of the relationship between electrolytes of the cerebral cortex and the mechanism of convulsions. *Res. Publ. Assoc. Research Nervous Mental Disease* **26**, 98–117.

Condon, J. V., Becka, D. R., and Gibbs, F. A. (1954). Electroencephalographic abnormalities in endocrine disease. *New Engl. J. Med.* **251**, 638–641.

Conn, J. W., Fajans, S. S., Louis, L. H., and Johnson, B. (1951). Metabolic and clinical effects of corticosterone (compound B) in man. *Proc. 2nd Clin. ACTH Conf.* **1**, 221–234.

Costa, P. J., and Bonnycastle, D. D. (1952). The effect of DCA, compound E, testosterone, progesterone and ACTH in modifying "agene-induced" convulsions in dogs. *Arch. Intern. Pharmacodyn.* **91,** 330–338.

Cress, C. H., Jr., and Greenblatt, M. (1945). Absence of alteration in the EEG with stilbesterol and progesterone. *Proc. Soc. Exptl. Biol. Med.* **60,** 139.

Dameshek, W., Saunders, R. H., Jr., and Zannas, L. (1950). The use of ACTH in the treatment of acute and subacute leukemia. A preliminary note. *Bull. New Engl. Med. Center* **12,** 11–21.

Davenport, V. D. (1949). Relation between brain and plasma electrolytes and electroshock seizure thresholds in adrenalectomized rats. *Am. J. Physiol.* **156,** 322–327.

Debré, R., Mozziconacci, P., and Nekhorocheff, I. (1952a). Electroencephalograms, corticotropin and cortisone. *J. Am. Med. Assoc.* **150,** 506.

Debré, R., Mozziconacci, P., and Nekhorocheff, I. (1952b). Modifications de l'éléctroencéphalogramme au cours des traitements par l'ACTH et la cortisone. *Presse Med.* **60,** 502.

De Salva, S. J. (1960). Continuous intravenous infusion of strychnine in rats: III. Endocrine influences. *Arch. Intern. Pharmacodyn.* **125,** 355–361.

De Salva, S. J., and Ercoli, N. (1959). Effects of somatotrophin on brain excitability. *Arch. Intern. Pharmacodyn.* **122,** 75–84.

De Salva, S. J., Hendley, C. D., and Ercoli, N. (1954). Acute effects of ACTH and cortisone on brain excitability. *Arch. Intern. Pharmacodyn.* **100,** 35–48.

Dice, L. R. (1935). Inheritance of waltzing and of epilepsy in mice of the genus *Peromyscus. J. Mammal.* **16,** 25–35.

Donaldson, H. H. (1924). "The Rat." Wistar Inst. Anat. and Biol., Philadelphia, Pennsylvania.

Dorfman, A., Apter, N. S., Smull, K., Bergenstal, D. M., and Richter, R. B. (1951). Status epilipticus coincident with use of pituitary adrenocorticotrophic hormones; report of 3 cases. *J. Am. Med. Assoc.* **146,** 25–27.

Dusser de Barrene, D., and Gibbs, F. A. (1942). Variations in electroencephalogram during the menstrual cycle. *Am. J. Obstet. Gynecol.* **44,** 687–690.

Elkinton, J. R., Hunt, A. D., Jr., Godfrey, L., McCrory, W. W., Rogerson, A. C., and Stokes, J., Jr. (1949). Effects of pituitary adrenocorticotropic hormone (ACTH) therapy. *J. Am. Med. Assoc.* **141,** 1273–1279.

Emmens, C. W. (1959). Role of gonadal hormones in reproductive processes. *In* "Reproduction in Domestic Animals" (H. H. Cole and P. T. Cupps, eds.), Vol. 1, pp. 111–154. Academic Press, New York.

Engel, G. L., and Margolin, S. G. (1941). Neuropsychiatric disturbances in Addison's disease and the role of impaired carbohydrate metabolism in production of abnormal cerebral function. *Arch. Neurol. Psychiat.* **45,** 881–884.

Engel, G. L., and Margolin, S. G. (1942). Neuropsychiatric disturbances in internal disease. Metabolic factors and electroencephalographic correlations. *Arch. Internal Med.* **70,** 236–259.

Ercoli, N., and De Salva, S. J. (1956). Relationship between brain excitability, hypophysectomy and prolonged cortisone and ACTH treatment. *Arch. Intern. Pharmacodyn.* **108,** 62–73.

Esplin, D. W., and Freston, J. W. (1960). Physiological and pharmacological analysis of spinal cord convulsions. *J. Pharmacol. Exptl. Therap.* **130,** 68–80.

Esplin, D. W., and Laffan, R. J. (1957). Determinants of flexor and extensor components of maximal seizures in cats. *Arch. Intern. Pharmacodyn.* **113,** 189–202.

Feldman, S., Todt, J. C., and Porter, R. W. (1961). Effect of adrenocortical hormones on evoked potentials in the brain stem. *Neurology* **11**, 109–115.

Fingl, E., Olsen, L. J., Harding, B. W., Cockett, A. T. and Goodman, L. S. (1952). Effect of chronic anticonvulsant administration upon cortisone-induced brain hyperexcitability. *J. Pharmacol. Exptl. Therap.* **105**, 37–45.

Fink, G. B., and Swinyard, E. A. (1959). Modification of maximal audiogenic and electroshock seizures in mice by psychopharmacologic drugs. *J. Pharmacol. Exptl. Therap.* **127**, 318–324.

Forsham, P. H. (1951). In discussion: Conn, J. W., Fajans, S. S., Louis, L. H., and Johnson, B. Metabolic and clinical effects of corticosterone (compound B) in man. *Proc. 2nd Clin. ACTH Conf.* **1**, 233.

Forsham, P. H., Bennett, L. L., Roche, M., Reiss, R. S., Slessor, A., Flink, E. B., and Thorn, G. W. (1949). Clinical and metabolic changes in Addison's disease following the administration of compound E acetate (11-dehydro, 17-hydroxycorticosterone acetate.) *J. Clin. Endocrinol.* **9**, 660–661.

Friedlander, W. J., and Rottger, E. (1951). The effect of cortisone on the electroencephalogram. *EEG Clin. Neurophysiol.* **3**, 311–313.

Friedman, S. B., and Engel, G. L. (1956). Effect of cortisone and adrenocorticotropin on the electroencephalogram of normal adults: qualitative frequency analysis. *J. Clin. Endocrinol.* **16**, 839–847.

Frings, H., Frings, M., and Kivert, A. (1951). Behavior patterns of the laboratory mouse under auditory stress. *J. Mammal.* **32**, 60–76.

Garcia, C. G. (1943). Accion del cardiazol en animales con hipertiroi-dismo experimental. *Rev. Med. Exptl. (Lima)* **2**, 367.

Geppert, L. J., Dietrick, A. C., Johnston, E. H., and Lind, C. J. (1952). Fatal convulsive seizures associated with cortisone therapy. *Am. J. Diseases Children* **84**, 416–420.

Gerlich, N. (1949). Experimental studies on the relations between thyroid gland and nervous irritability. *Arch. Exptl. Pathol. Pharmakol.* **207**, 159–172.

Gibbs, F. A., and Reid, D. E. (1942). Electroencephalogram in pregnancy. *Am. J. Obstet. Gynecol.* **44**, 672–675.

Ginsberg, B. E., and Roberts, E. (1951). Glutamic acid and central nervous system activity. *Anat. Record* **111**, 492–493.

Glaser, G. H. (1953a). On the relationship between adrenal cortical activity and the convulsive state. *Epilepsia* **2**, 7–14.

Glaser, G. H. (1953b). Psychotic reactions induced by corticotropin (ACTH) and cortisone. *Psychosomat. Med.* **15**, 280–291.

Glaser, G. H., and Merritt, H. H. (1952). Effects of corticotropin (ACTH) and cortisone on disorders of the nervous system. *J. Am. Med. Assoc.* **148**, 898–904.

Glaser, G. H., Kornfeld, D. S., and Knight, R. P. (1955). Intravenous hydrocortisone, corticotropin and the electroencephalogram. *Arch. Neurol. Psychiat.* **73**, 338–344.

Goodman, L. S., Toman, J. E. P., and Swinyard, E. A. (1946). The anticonvulsant properties of tridione. Laboratory and clinical investigations. *Am. J. Med.* **1**, 213–228.

Goodwin, J., Kerr, W., and Lawson, F. (1940). Bioelectric responses in metrazol and insulin shock. *Am. J. Psychiat.* **96**, 1389–1405.

Gottschalk, L. A. (1952). Effect of epinephrine on cortical and basal electroencephalograms and the eosinophile count. *Arch. Neurol. Psychiat.* **67**, 522–534.

Greenberg, D. M., and Tufts, E. V. (1935). The effect of a diet low in magnesium on the rat. *J. Biol. Chem.* **109,** 38–39.

Grenell, R. G. (1947). The effects of adrenal cortical extract on the electrical activity of the brain. *Abstr. 17th Intern. Physiol. Congr. IUPS, Oxford, 1947* pp. 296–297.

Grenell, R. G., and McCawley, E. L. (1947a). The effects of adrenal cortical extract on the electroencephalogram. *Federation Proc.* **6,** 116–117.

Grenell, R. G., and McCawley, E. L. (1947b). Central nervous system resistance. III. The effect of adrenal cortical substances on the central nervous system. *J. Neurosurg.* **4,** 508–518.

Griffiths, W. J., Jr. (1949). Effect of adrenalectomy on incidence of audiogenic seizures among domestic and wild rats. *J. Comp. Physiol. Psychol.* **42,** 303–312.

Habelmann, G. (1952). Stoffwechselprobleme der Nebennierenrindenhormonwirkung bei der grossen Insulinkur. *Klin. Wochschr.* **30,** 588–594.

Hall, C. S. (1947). Genetic differences in fatal audiogenic seizures. *J. Heredity* **38,** 2–6.

Hall, V. E., and Lindsay, M. (1938). The relation of the thyroid gland to the spontaneous activity of the rat. *Endocrinology* **22,** 66–72.

Heim, L. M., and Timiras, P. S. (1963). Gonad-brain relationship: Precocious brain maturation after estradiol in rats. *Endocrinology* **72,** 598–606.

Henneman, P. H. (1954). Effects of hormones on brain excitability and electrolytes. *Recent Progr. Hormone Res.* **10,** 65–107.

Heppenstall, M., and Greville, G. (1950). Biochemistry. *In* "Electroencephalography" (D. Hill and G. Parr, eds.), pp. 127–165. Macdonald & Co., London.

Hicks, S. P. (1953). Developmental brain metabolism. Effects of cortisone, anoxia, fluoracetate, radiation, insulin, and other inhibitors on the embryo, newborn, and adult. *Arch. Pathol.* **55,** 302–327.

Hill, D. (1948). The relationship between epilepsy and schizophrenia: E.E.G. studies. *Folia Psychiat. Neurol. Neurochir. Neerl.* **51,** 95–111.

Himwich, H., Frostig, J., Fazekas, J., and Hadidian, Z. (1939). The mechanism of the symptoms of insulin hypoglycaemia. *Am. J. Psychiat.* **96,** 371–385.

Hoagland, H., Rubin, M. A., and Cameron, D. E. (1937). The electrencephalogram of schizophrenics during insulin hypoglycemia and recovery. *Am. J. Physiol.* **120,** 559–570.

Hoefer, P. F., and Glaser, G. H. (1950). Effects of pituitary adrenocorticotropic hormone (ACTH) therapy. Electroencephalographic and neuropsychiatric changes in fifteen patients. *J. Am. Med. Assoc.* **143,** 620–624.

Hoffman, W. C., Lewis, R. A., and Thorn, G. W. (1942). The electroencephalogram in Addison's disease. *Bull. Johns Hopkins Hosp.* **70,** 335–361.

Hurder, W. P., and Sanders, A. F. (1953). Audiogenic seizure and the adrenal cortex. *Science* **117,** 324–326.

Irons, E. N., Ayer, J. P., Brown, R. G., and Armstrong, S. H., Jr. (1951). ACTH and cortisone in diffuse collagen disease and chronic dermatoses. *J. Am. Med. Assoc.* **145,** 861–868.

Jasper, H. H. (1936). Cortical excitatory state and synchronism in the control of bioelectric autonomous rhythms. *Cold Spring Harbor Sym. Quant. Biol.* **4,** 320–338.

Karpati, G., and Frame, B. (1964). Neuropsychiatric disorders in primary hyperparathyroidism. *Arch. Neurol.* **10,** 387–397.

Kawakami, M., and Sawyer, C. H. (1959). Neuroendocrine correlates of changes in brain activity thresholds by sex steroids and pituitary hormones. *Endocrinology* **65**, 652–668.

Klein, R., and Livingston, S. (1950). The effect of adrenocorticotropic hormone in epilepsy. *J. Pediat.* **37**, 733–742.

Klippel (1899). Encéphalopathie addisonnienne. *Rev. Neurol.* **7**, 898–899.

Knobil, E., Hoffmann, F. G., and Greep, R. O. (1953). Nature of adrenal crisis in the rhesus monkey. *Federation Proc.* **12**, 78.

Kruse, H. D., Orent, F. R., and McCollum, E. V. (132). Studies on magnesium deficiency in animals. I. Symptomatology resulting from magnesium deprivation. *J. Biol. Chem.* **96**, 519–539.

Laidlaw, J. (1956). Catamenial epilepsy. *Lancet* **II**, 1235–1237.

Lecoq, R. (1954). Appréciation chronaximetrique du retentissement nerveux des parturbations métaboliques et humorales. *Rev. Pathol. Gen. Comp.* **54**, 529–542.

Lecoq, R., Chauchard, P., and Mazoue, H. (1952). Action de quelques préparations glandulaires et hormonales sur la régulation de l'équilibre acido-basique. *Bull. Soc. Chim. Biol.* **34**, 239–246.

Lecoq, R., Chauchard, P., and Mazoue, H. (1955). Étude comparative de l'aldostérone (hormone cortico-surrénale) et de quelques corticoides de proprietes voisines ou de même origine. *Ann. Pharm. Franc.* **13**, 431–442.

Lee, M. O., and Van Buskirk, E. F. (1928). Studies on vigor. XV. The effect of thyroidectomy on spontaneous activity in the rat, with a consideration of the relation of the basal metabolism to spontaneous activity. *Am. J. Physiol.* **84**, 321–329.

Leonard, C. A., Gorby, C. K., Ambrus, J. L., and Harrisson, J. W. E. (1953). A note on the effect of cortisone and desoxycorticosterone on Metrazol convulsions in mice. *J. Am. Pharm. Assoc., Sci. Ed.* **42**, 444–445.

Lindsley, D. B., and Rubenstein, B. B. (1937). Relationship between brain potentials and some other physiological variables. *Proc. Soc. Exptl. Biol. Med.* **35**, 558–563.

Logothetis, J., Harner, R., Morel, F., and Torres, F. (1959). The role of estrogens in catamenial exacerabation of epilepsy. *Neurology* **9**, 352–360.

Lowell, F. C., Frandlin, W., Beale, H., and Schiller, I. W. (1951). Occurrence of convulsive seizures during treatment of asthma with cortisone acetate. *New Engl. J. Med.* **244**, 49–52.

Maddock, S., Hawkins, J., and Holmes, E. (1939). The inadequacy of substances of the "glucose cycle" for maintenance of normal cortical potentials during hypoglycemia produced by hepatectomy with abdominal evisceration. *Am. J. Physiol.* **125**, 551–565.

Mansor, L. F., Holtkamp, D. E., Heming, A. E., and Christian, H. H. (1956). Effects of prednisone, prednisolone and fludrocortisone acetate on electroshock seizure threshold. *Federation Proc.* **15**, 454.

Mellanby, E. (1946). Diet and canine hysteria: experimental production by treated flour. *Brit. Med. J.* **II**, 885–887.

Millichap, J. G. (1958). Seizure patterns in young animals. Significance of brain carbonic anhydrase. II *Proc. Soc. Exptl. Biol. Med.* **97**, 606–611.

Mirsky, I. A., Elgart, S., and Aring, C. D. (1943). Sonogenic convulsions in rats and mice. I. Control studies. *J. Comp. Psychol.* **35**, 249–253.

Morgan, C. T., and Waldman, H. (1941). "Conflict" and audiogenic seizures. *J. Comp. Psychol.* **31**, 1–11.

Morruzzi, G. (1946). "L'epilessia sperimentale," Monograph. Nicola Zanichelli, Bologna.

Nekhorocheff, I. (1952). L'EEG des enfants traités par l'ACTH ou la cortisone. *EEG Clin. Neurophysiol.* **4,** 248.

Oppelt, W. W., and Rall, D. P. (1961). Production of convulsions in the dog with intrathecal corticosteroids. *Neurology* **11,** 925–927.

Ortiz-Galvan, A., and Morell, F. (1956). Effect of topical hydrocortisone on the electrocorticogram of the cat. *Arch. Neurol. Psychiat.* **75,** 245–250.

Pasolini, F. (1951). Epilessia e ghiandole endocrine. I. Influenza des desossicorticosterone acetate sulla predisposizione all'epilessia riflessa sperimentale nel cane. *Boll. Soc. Ital. Biol. Sper.* **27,** 1624–1626.

Pasolini, F. (1952). Epilessia e ghiandole endocrine. II. Influenza del cortisone sulla predisposizione all'epilessia riflessa sperimentale nel cane. *Boll. Soc. Ital. Biol. Sper.* **28,** 298–300.

Peiper, H. (1921). Die Exstirpation der Nebenniere zur Behandlung epileptischer Krämpfe. *Zentr. Chir.* **48,** 663–664.

Penfield, W., and Jasper, H. (1954). "Epilepsy and the Functional Anatomy of the Human Brain. Little, Brown, Boston, Massachusetts.

Pincus, J. B., Natelson, S., and Lungovoy, J. D. (1951). Effect of epinephrine, ACTH and cortisone on citrate, calcium, glucose and phosphate levels in rabbits. *Proc. Soc. Exptl. Biol. Med.* **78,** 24–27.

Pine, I., Engel, F. L., and Schwartz, T. B. (1951). The electroencephalogram in ACTH and cortisone treated patients. *EEG Clin. Neurophysiol.* **3,** 301–310.

Plotz, C. M., Knowlton, A. I., and Ragan, C. (1952). Natural history of Cushing's syndrome. *Am. J. Med.* **13,** 597–614.

Prados, M., Strowger, B., and Feindel, W. (1945). Studies on cerebral edema. II. Reaction of the brain to exposure; physiologic changes. *Arch. Neurol. Psychiat.* **54,** 290–300.

Ragan, C., Grokoest, A. W., and Boots, R. H. (1949). Effect of adrenocorticotrophic hormone (ACTH) on rheumatoid arthritis. *Am. J. Med.* **7,** 741–750.

Ransohoff, W., Burst, A. A., Reeser, M. F., Mirsky, I. A., and Ferris, E. B. (1951). The effect of sodium and potassium on the metabolic and physiologic responses to ACTH. *Proc. 2nd Clin. ACTH Conf.* **1,** 160–176.

Reiner, L., Misani, F., and Weiss, P. (1950). Studies on nitrogen trichloride-treated prolamines; suppression of development of convulsions with methionine. *Arch. Biochem.* **25,** 447–449.

Ross, D. A., and Schwarb, R. S. (1939). The cortical alpha rhythm in thyroid disorders. *Endocrinology* **25,** 75–79.

Rubin, M. A., Cohen, L. H., and Hoagland, H. (1937). The effect of artificially raised metabolic rate on the electro-encephalogram of schizophrenic patients. *Endocrinology* **21,** 536–540.

Ruch, T. C., and Fulton, J. F., eds. (1960). "Medical Physiology and Biophysics," 18th ed. Saunders, Philadelphia, Pennsylvania.

Russell, P. W., Haserick, J. R., and Zucker, E. M. (1951). Epilepsy in systemic lupus erythematosus. Effect of cortisone and ACTH. *Arch. Internal Med.* **88,** 78–92.

Sawyer, C. H., and Everett, J. W. (1959). Stimulatory and inhibitory effects of progesterone on the release of pituitary ovulating hormone in the rabbit. *Endocrinology* **65,** 644–651.

Segal, S. J. (1958). Comparative aspects of gonadal morphology, physiology, and antigenicity. *In* "Comparative Endocrinology" (A. Gorbman, ed.) pp. 553–567. Wiley, New York.

Soffer, L. J. (1946). "Diseases of the Adrenal." Lea & Febiger, Philadelphia, Pennsylvania.

Soulairac, A., and Soulairac, M. L. (1953). Modifications par la corticostimuline des effets de l'anoxie expérimentale sur l'activité électrique corticale du rat. *J. Physiol. (Paris)* **45**, 521–525.

Spiegel, E. A. (1937). Quantitative determination of the convulsive reactivity by electric stimulation of the brain with the skull intact. *J. Lab. Clin. Med.* **22**, 1274–1276.

Spiegel, E. A. (1943). Anticonvulsant effects of desoxycorticosterone, testosterone, and progesterone. *Federation Proc.* **2**, 47.

Spiegel, E. A., and Wycis, H. (1945). Anticonvulsant effects of steroids. *J. Lab. Clin. Med.* **30**, 947–953.

Starr, A. M. (1952). Personality changes in Cushing's syndrome. *J. Clin. Endocrinol.* **12**, 502–505.

Stephen, E. H. M., and Noad, K. B. (1951). Status epilepticus occurring during cortisone therapy. *Med. J. Australia* **2**, 334–335.

Storrie, V. M. (1953). Convulsions in Addison's disease. *Bull. Tufts New Engl. Med. Center* **1**, 229–237.

Streifler, M., and Feldman, S. (1953). On effect of cortisone on electroencephalogram. *Confinia Neurol.* **13**, 16.

Sugar, O. (1953). Central neurological complications of hypoparathyroidism. *Arch. Neurol. Psychiat.* **70**, 86–107.

Swann, H. G., and Fitzgerald, J. W. (1938). Insulin shock in relation to the components of the adrenals and the hypophysis. *Endocrinology* **22**, 687–692.

Swingle, W. W., Parkins, W. M., Tayler, A. R., and Hays, H. W. (1937). A study of water intoxication in the intact and adrenalectomized dog and the influence of adrenal cortical hormone upon fluid and electrolyte distribution. *Am. J. Physiol.* **119**, 557–566.

Swinyard, E. A., Schiffmann, D. O., and Goodman, L. S. (1955). Effect of variations in extracellular sodium concentration on the susceptibility of mice to pentylenetetrazole (Metrazol)-induced seizures. *J. Pharmacol. Exptl. Therap.* **114**, 160–166.

Tainter, M. L., Tainter, E. G., Lawrence, W. S., Neuru, E. N., Luckey, R. W., Luduena, F. P., Kirtland, H. B., and Gonzalez, R. I. (1943). Influence of various drugs on the threshold for electrical convulsions. *J. Pharmacol. Exptl. Therap.* **79**, 42–54.

Thorn, G. W., Forsham, P. H., Bennett, L. L., Roche, M., Reiss, R. S., Slessor, A., Flink, E. B., and Sommerville, W. (1949). Clinical and metabolic changes in Addison's disease following the administration of compound E acetate (11-dehydro, 17-hydroxycorticosterone acetate). *Trans. Assoc. Am. Physicians* **62**, 233–244.

Timiras, P. S., and Woodbury, D. M. (1956). Effect of thyroid activity on brain function and brain electrolyte distribution in rats. *Endocrinology* **58**, 181–192.

Timiras, P. S., Woodbury, D. M., and Goodman, L. S. (1954). Effect of adrenalectomy, hydrocortisone acetate and desoxycorticosterone acetate on brain excitability and electrolyte distribution in mice. *J. Pharmacol. Exptl. Therap.* **112**, 80–93.

Timiras, P. S., Woodbury, D. M., and Agarwal, S. L. (1955a). Effect of thyroxine and triidothyronine on brain function and electrolyte distribution in intact and adrenalectomized rats. *J. Pharmacol. Exptl. Therap.* **115,** 154–171.

Timiras, P. S., Baker, D. H., and Woodbury, D. M. (1955b). Brain excitability and electrolyte distribution in rats as affected by insulin, alloxan and pancreatectomy. *J. Pharmacol. Exptl. Therap.* **113,** 50.

Timiras, P. S., Woodbury, D. M., and Baker, D. H. (1956). Effect of hydrocortisone acetate, desoxycorticosterone acetate, insulin, glucagon and dextrose, alone or in combination, on experimental convulsions and carbohydrate metabolism. *Arch. Intern. Pharmacodyn.* **105,** 450–467.

Toman, J. E. P., and Goodman, L. S. (1948). Anticonvulsants. *Physiol. Rev.* **28,** 409–432.

Toman, J. E. P., Swinyard, E. A., and Goodman, L. S. (1946). Properties of maximal seizures, and their alteration by anticonvulsant drugs and other agents. *J. Neurophysiol.* **9,** 231–239.

Torda, C., and Wolff, H. G. (1951). Effect of cortisone and ACTH on the threshold of convulsions induced by pentamethylene tetrazol. *Federation Proc.* **10,** 137–138.

Torda, C., and Wolff, H. G. (1952). Effects of various concentrations of adrenocorticotrophic hormone on electrical activity of brain and on sensitivity to convulsion-inducing agents. *Am. J. Physiol.* **168,** 406–413.

Turner, W. A. (1907). "Epilepsy: Study of Idiopathic Disease." Macmillan, New York.

Ulett, G., Trufant, S., and Ronzoni, E. (1951). The EEG with photic stimulation in psychiatric patients receiving ACTH. *EEG Clin. Neurophysiol.* **3,** 79–81.

Vernadakis, A. (1961). Effects of adrenocortical hormones on seizure pattern and brain metabolism during maturation. Ph.D. Thesis, University of Utah.

Vernadakis, A. (1962). Spinal cord convulsions in developing rats. *Science* **137,** 532.

Vernadakis, A., and Timiras, P. S. (1963). Effect of Estradiol on spinal cord convulsions in developing rats. *Nature* **197,** 906.

Vernadakis, A., and Woodbury, D. M. (1963). Effect of cortisol on the electroshock seizure thresholds in developing rats. *J. Pharmacol. Exptl. Therap.* **139,** 110–113.

Vernadakis, A., and Woodbury, D. M. (1964). Effects of cortisol and diphenylhydantoin on spinal cord convulsions in developing rats. *J. Pharmacol. Exptl. Therap.* **144,** 316–320.

Vicari, E. M. (1951). Effect of 6*n*-propylthiouracil on lethal seizures in mice. *Proc. Soc. Exptl. Biol. Med.* **78,** 744–747.

Vicari, E. M., Tracy, A., and Jongblaed, A. (1952). Effect of epinephrine glucose and certain steroids on fatal convulsive seizures in mice. *Proc. Soc. Exptl. Biol. Med.* **80,** 47–50.

Ward, L., Polley, H. F., Slocombe, C. H., Hench, P. S., Mason, H. L., and Mattox, V. R. (1954). Clinical and metabolic effects of aldosterone in rheumatoid arthritis. *J. Lab. Clin. Med.* **44,** 948.

Wayne, H. L. (1954). Convulsive seizures complicating cortisone and ACTH therapy: clinical and electroencephalographic observations. *J. Clin. Endocrinol.* **14,** 1039–1045.

Wayne, H. L., and Boyle, J. (1953). Electroencephalographic observations on patients undergoing cortisone and ACTH therapy. *J. Clin. Endocrinol.* **13,** 1070–1081.

Werboff, J., and Corcoran, J. B. (1961). Effect of sex hormone manipulation on audiogenic seizures. *Am. J. Physiol.* **201**, 830–832.

Woodbury, D. M. (1952). Effect of adrenocortical steroids and adrenocorticotrophic hormone on electroshock seizure threshold. *J. Pharmacol. Exptl. Therap.* **105**, 27–36.

Woodbury, D. M. (1954). Effects of hormones on brain excitability and electrolytes. *Recent Progr. Hormone Res.* **10**, 65–107.

Woodbury, D. M. (1958). Relation between the adrenal cortex and the central nervous system. *Pharmacol. Rev.* **10**, 275–357.

Woodbury, D. M., and Davenport, V. D. (1949). Brain and plasma cations and experimental seizures in normal and desoxycorticosterone treated rats. *Am. J. Physiol.* **157**, 234–240.

Woodbury, D. M., and Esplin, D. W. (1959). Neuropharmacology and neurochemistry of anticonvulsant drugs. *Res. Publ. Assoc. Res. Nervous Mental Disease* **37**, 24–56.

Woodbury, D. M., Emmett, J. W., Hinckley, G. V., Jackson, N. R., Newton, J. D., Bateman, J. H., Goodman, L. S., and Sayers, G. (1951). Antagonism of adrenocortical extract and cortisone to desoxycorticosterone: brain excitability in adrenalectomized rats. *Proc. Soc. Exptl. Biol. Med.* **76**, 65–68.

Woodbury, D. M., Hurley, R. E., Lewis, N. G., McArthur, M. W., Copeland, W. W. Kirschvink, J. F., and Goodman, L. S. (1952). Effect of thyroxine, thyroidectomy and 6-*N*-propyl-2-thiouracil on brain function. *J. Pharmacol. Exptl. Therap.* **106**, 331–340.

Woodbury, L. A., and Davenport, V. D. (1952). Design and use of a new electroshock seizure apparatus, and analysis of factors altering seizure threshold and pattern. *Arch. Intern. Pharmacodyn.* **92**, 97–107.

Woodbury, L. A., and Swinyard, C. A. (1952). Stimulus parameters for electroshock seizures in rats. *Am. J. Physiol.* **170**, 661–667.

Woolley, D. E., and Timiras, P. S. (1962a). The gonad-brain relationship; effects of female sex hormones on electroshock convulsions in the rat. *Endocrinology* **70**, 196–209.

Woolley, D. E., and Timiras, P. S. (1962b). Gonad-brain relationship; effects of castration and testosterone on electroshock convulsions in male rats. *Endocrinology* **71**, 609–617.

Woolley, D. E., and Timiras, P. S. (1962c). Estrous and circadian periodicity and electroshock convulsions in rats. *Am. J. Physiol.* **202**, 379–382.

Woolley, D. E., Timiras, P. S., and Woodbury, D. M. (1960). Some effects of sex steroids on brain excitability and metabolism. *Proc. Western Pharmacol. Soc.* **3**, 11–23.

Wortis, S. B. (1932). Experimental convulsions. *Am. J. Psychiat.* **33**, 611–621.

CHAPTER 27

Effects of Drugs on Neuroendocrine Processes

ERNEST M. GOLD and WILLIAM F. GANONG

I. Introduction

During recent years, the number of reports of drugs affecting endocrine function has multiplied. Gaunt and his associates have called attention to these agents in a thought-provoking review (Gaunt *et al.*, 1961) on endocrine pharmacology. An appreciable number of the drugs exerting endocrine effects act through the nervous system, but the neuroendocrine segment of endocrine pharmacology has not been analyzed in a comprehensive fashion. In this chapter, a catalog of drugs affecting neuroendocrine processes is presented, and selected highlights of the subject are discussed in detail.

The major types of drugs affecting endocrine function are summarized in Table I. Other drugs affect endocrine function indirectly: e.g., mercu-

TABLE I

DRUGS AFFECTING ENDOCRINE FUNCTION

I. Hormone congeners that
   A. Act like naturally occurring hormones
   B. Block the effects of naturally occurring hormones
II. Drugs that act directly on endocrine organs to stimulate or inhibit secretion
III. Drugs that inhibit the actions of hormones on their target organs
IV. Drugs that alter hormone secretion by acting on the nervous system (including drugs that act as stressful stimuli)

rial diuretics cause a diuresis of sodium, which in turn may cause sufficient hypovolemia to stimulate aldosterone secretion. Such agents are not considered in this review. Emphasis has been placed on substances that do not normally occur in the body. There are, of course, many naturally occurring substances, especially neurohumors, that affect endocrine function. Note is made of their effects in several sections of the chapter, but no systematic summary of their actions is presented. Indeed, the effects of naturally occurring substances on endocrine function is in a sense the subject of all the other chapters in this book.

II. Hormone Congeners

Pharmaceutical chemists have synthesized analogs of the naturally occurring estrogens, androgens, glucocorticoids, mineralocorticoids, and posterior pituitary hormones as well as progesterone and thyroxine. Modified insulins and synthetic peptides with some of the actions of hypothalamic releasing factors have also been produced (see below). The structures of these compounds generally resemble those of the parent hormones, although in some instances the differences are marked; for example, the structure of stilbestrol differs markedly from that of any natural estrogen. The congeners receiving the most attention have been those with greater or more prolonged activity than the parent compound. Structural modifications can increase certain activities of the parent molecules while decreasing others; for example, dexamethasone has more than 150 times the anti-inflamatory activity of cortisol (Silber, 1959), but it has very little mineralocorticoid activity (Liddle, 1959). Some hormone congeners—e.g., some of the analogs of thyroxine and triiodothyronine—partially block the actions of the naturally occurring substances, apparently by tying up receptors in the target organs (Barker *et al.*, 1960). However, despite an intensive search, relatively few effective blocking agents have been discovered by studying hormone analogs.

The list of hormone congeners with important neuroendocrine actions includes the synthetic progestational compounds which are currently receiving world-wide attention as oral contraceptive agents. There are many derivatives of progesterone which are active when given by mouth in relatively small doses (Pincus, 1965). One of their actions is production of moderate endometrial hyperplasia, and there has been speculation that they may be contraceptive because the hyperplasia prevents implantation of fertilized ova. However, there is no doubt that their major contraceptive action is inhibition of gonadotropin secretion, with resultant prevention of ovulation.

The mechanism by which the progestational agents inhibit the burst of luteinizing hormone (LH) secretion necessary to produce ovulation has been the subject of much recent study. J. Hilliard and C. H. Sawyer (personal communication, 1965) have failed to produce ovulation by injection of LRF into the pituitary of rabbits treated with a progestational agent, suggesting a direct inhibitory action on the pituitary, but it is possible that this failure was due to technical difficulties. Meanwhile, Sawyer and his colleagues (see C. H. Sawyer, 1963, 1964) have also demonstrated that there are two systems in the brain which affect pituitary secretion of gonadotropins. Activity in one of these, the reticular activating system, seems to be related primarily to sexual activity and mating, while activity in the second, the system responsible for the electroencephalogram (EEG) after-reaction that follows coitus in the rabbit, seems to be related to the ovulation-producing release of LH from the pituitary. Norethynodrel and several other synthetic progestational agents have been shown to selectively raise the threshold for production of the EEG after-reaction without changing the threshold for production of EEG arousal via the reticular activating system (Sawyer, 1963). In addition, implants of norethindrone in the hypothalamus block ovulation (Kanematsu and Sawyer, 1965). Thus, it seems likely that the progestational agents act on the brain to selectively inhibit the mechanisms responsible for triggering the burst of gonadotropin secretion that produces ovulation.

Another topic of neuroendocrine interest is the search for a steroid which inhibits adrenocorticotropic hormone (ACTH) secretion without other actions. In general, the anti-ACTH activity of steroids parallels their glucocorticoid activity (Martini *et al.*, 1962; Ganong, 1963). However, some steroids, including one progestational compound, have considerable ACTH-inhibiting activity with relatively little glucocorticoid activity (Edgren *et al.*, 1959; Martini *et al.*, 1962). This raises the possibility that a steroid with selective ACTH-inhibiting activity may eventually be found.

The reports that certain synthetic polypeptides have corticotropin-releasing factor (CRF) activity (deGarilhe *et al.*, 1960; Kappeler and Schwyzer, 1960; Li *et al.*, 1961) have attracted considerable attention. Some of these compounds were found to be more active than hypothalamic extracts in releasing ACTH. However, Guillemin and Schally (1963) were unable to confirm these results. In addition, the activity was demonstrated by adding the peptides to pituitaries *in vitro.* The specificity of this method of assay has been much debated (Barrett and Sayers, 1958; Guillemin and Schally, 1959), and the peptides have not been reported to have CRF activity *in vivo.*

III. Drugs Acting Directly on Endocrine Organs

There are numerous drugs acting directly on the thyroid gland to inhibit thyroid hormone secretion, and there are also a variety of agents acting on the adrenal cortex and the β-cells of the pancreas. Others act on the adrenal medulla and the posterior pituitary, but these glands are so closely related to the nervous system that they are best considered in the section on the endocrine effects of drugs acting on the nervous system.

Some of the actions of thyrotropin (TSH) on the thyroid, ACTH on the adrenal cortex, and LH on the testis and ovary, as well as the actions of several hormones on their end organs, have been reported to be inhibited by antibiotics. These reports have been summarized by Samuels (1964). In some instances—e.g., the action of aldosterone on sodium transport—it seems clear that the antibiotics act by preventing hormone-induced stimulation of the genetic mechanisms controlling protein synthesis (Edelman *et al.*, 1964), but in others the specificity and the significance of the data remain uncertain. In the case of the adrenal cortex, for example, it has been reported that the increase in steroidogenesis produced by ACTH is inhibited by puromycin (see Samuels, 1964), yet an actinomycin preparation has been reported to increase circulating corticoid levels in the guinea pig (Planelles *et al.*, 1962). Therefore it seems wise to defer conclusions about many of these antibiotic effects until more data are available.

A. Thyroid

The list of drugs inhibiting thyroid hormone secretion is long and varied (see Maloof and Soodak, 1963). Iodide blocks thyroxine formation. The thiocarbamides (thiouracil, propylthiouracil, and related drugs) prevent iodide oxidation in the gland. The aminobenzenes such as sulfonamides and *p*-aminobenzoic acid have a similar action (Astwood *et al.*, 1943; MacKenzie, 1947). A wide variety of drugs with somewhat similar structures have measurable effects on thyroid hormone synthesis, including sulfonylureas, amphenone, and the tranquilizer, amphenidone (Hertz *et al.*, 1950, 1951, 1955, 1956; Arnott and Doniach, 1952; Magliotti *et al.*, 1959; Tranquada *et al.*, 1960; Ingbar, 1961; Pittman and Brown, 1962). An unexplained depression of thyroid function has been reported to be produced by some antihistamines (Magliotti *et al.*, 1959). Certain monovalent ions such as chlorate, hypochlorite, thiocyanate, and perchlorate inhibit iodide transport in the gland, and cobaltous chloride has been reported to depress radioactive iodine uptake by an unknown mechanism (Roche and Layrisse, 1956). There are antithyroid compounds in some plants. A particularly well-studied plant goitrogen is progoitrin, which is found in vegetables of the Brassicaceae family such as rutabagas, turnips, and cabbage (Greer and Deeney, 1959).

None of these substances have any established direct neuroendocrine effects, but by lowering the circulating thyroxine level, they act via the feedback control mechanism to increase TSH secretion. The question of whether thyroxine deficiency increases TSH secretion by an action on the anterior pituitary or the hypothalamus or both is discussed in Chapter 12 (Volume I). Propylthiouracil decreases ACTH secretion, causing adrenal atrophy (Bauman and Marine, 1946; Zarrow *et al.*, 1957; Brown-Grant, 1958; Kowaleski, 1958; Lazo-Wasem, 1960). The cause of this decrease is uncertain, but hypothyroidism is known to decrease the rate at which adrenocortical hormones are metabolized (see Peterson, 1958, 1959). This presumably raises the blood corticoid level, with a resultant inhibition of ACTH secretion.

It has been claimed that when injected in relatively large amounts, vasopressin stimulates thyroid hormone secretion (Harris, 1963). Norepinephrine and epinephrine have been reported both to stimulate and to inhibit thyroxine secretion by a direct action on the gland (see Söderberg, 1958).

B. Adrenal Cortex

The insecticide 1,1,dichloro-2,2-bis(*p*-chlorophenyl)ethane (DDD), a compound related to 1,1,1-trichloro-2,2-bis(*p*-chlorophenyl)ethane (DDT), was the substance first shown to inhibit adrenal cortical hormone synthesis (Brown, 1953; Sheehan *et al.*, 1953; Brown *et al.*, 1955, 1956; Cueto and Brown, 1958a,b; Vilar and Tullner, 1959; Bergenstal *et al.*, 1960; Tullner and Hertz, 1960). The adrenolytic activity of DDD is actually due to its *o,p′*-isomer. Derivatives of DDD were subsequently prepared and studied, including in particular amphenone (Hertz *et al.*, 1950, 1951, 1955, 1956; Larson *et al.*, 1955; Lanthier *et al.*, 1956; Rosenfeld and Bascom, 1956; Thorn *et al.*, 1956; Tullner *et al.*, 1956; Renold *et al.*, 1957; Vogt, 1957; Jenkins *et al.*, 1959). Many other compounds which inhibit adrenal cortical hormone synthesis at one step or another have since been discovered (see Gaunt *et al.*, 1965). Steroidogenesis in the adrenal cortex is summarized in Fig. 1. The inhibitory effect of amphenone is generalized, but in proper doses, its derivative, metyrapone, selectively inhibits 11-β-hydroxylation (Chart *et al.*, 1958; Jenkins *et al.*, 1959; Liddle *et al.*, 1959; Cushman *et al.*, 1963; Gold *et al.*, 1960a, 1961). One can predict the consequences of such a block from Fig. 1; the output of cortisol, corticosterone, and aldosterone decline and there is a compensatory increase in the output of 11-deoxycortisol and 11-deoxycorticosterone. Several other drugs selectively inhibit 17α-hydroxylase (Chart *et al.*, 1962; Kahnt and Neher, 1962). This causes a decrease in the secretion of cortisol and 11-deoxycortisol, and an increase in the secretion of the 11-deoxycorticosterone, corticosterone, and aldo-

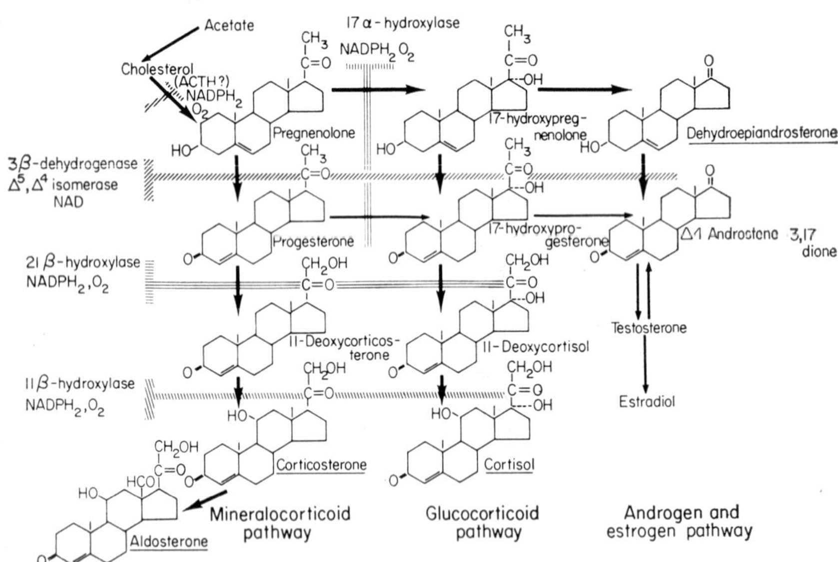

FIG. 1. Outline of major pathways in adrenal cortical hormone biosynthesis. The major secretory products are underlined. The enzymes and cofactors for the reactions progressing down each column are shown on the left and between the first and the second column at the top of the chart. When a particular enzyme is deficient, hormone production is blocked at the points indicated by the shaded bars. (From Ganong, 1965.)

sterone. It is interesting in this regard that the monoamine oxidase inhibitor, tranylcypromine (Parnate) inhibits adrenal cortical secretion, probably by inhibiting 17α-hydroxylase (Johnson *et al.*, 1965). The effect of this compound on 17-hydroxycorticoid secretion in dogs is shown in Fig. 2. An inhibitor of 18-oxidation in the adrenal has been reported (Bledsoe *et al.*, 1964). Other drugs which inhibit adrenal cortical hormone synthesis by a direct action on the gland include triparanol (Gordon *et al.*, 1963), Perthane (Taliaferro and Leone, 1957), Δ^4-cholestenone (Steinberg *et al.*, 1958), ω-methylpantothenic acid (A. D. Goodman, 1960), thiosemicarbazones, streptomycin, a number of triazines, and acetylstrophanthidine (see Gaunt *et al.*, 1961, 1965). Heparin and heparinoids produce a relatively selective inhibition of aldosterone secretion (Schlatmann *et al.*, 1964), and it has been shown that they produce a selective atrophy of the zona glomerulosa in rats (Laidlaw, 1966).

Neuroendocrine effects of drugs inhibiting glucocorticoid secretion, like those of the antithyroid drugs, are exerted primarily via the feedback control of anterior pituitary secretion. DDD damages the adrenal, producing focal necrosis, but in the case of amphenone, the compensatory increase in ACTH secretion leads to adrenal hypertrophy. The increase in ACTH secretion produced by metyrapone can be quantitated

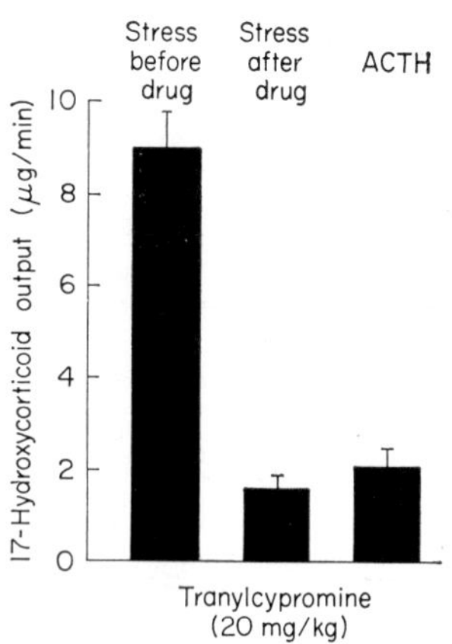

Fig. 2. Effect of tranylcypromine on 17-hydroxycorticoid output in the right adrenal vein of twelve surgically stressed dogs. The dogs were restressed by performing a second laparotomy 25 minutes after intravenous administration of tranylcypromine, and the specimen labeled "stress after drug" was collected starting 30 minutes after administration of the drug. 100–1000 mU of ACTH were then injected and another adrenal venous blood specimen collected starting 4 minutes later. (Data from Johnson *et al.*, 1965.)

by measuring the increment in 11-deoxycortisol secretion that it produces, and this increment is used as an index pituitary function in patients with endocrine diseases (Liddle *et al.*, 1959).

A method for producing a decline in circulating cortisol levels without stimulating afferent nervous pathways or affecting any of the other mechanisms that regulate ACTH secretion would obviously be a valuable tool for investigating the still unsettled question of the locus at which cortisol acts on ACTH secretion (see Chapter 9, in Volume I). Metyrapone has been used for this purpose. Unfortunately, it is a drug which can have stressful side effects, and in dogs, it may increase ACTH secretion in the absence of the adrenals (Ganong and Gold, 1960). However, the possibility that it exerts an ACTH-stimulating action in addition to its direct effect on the adrenal seems to be ruled out in humans (Liddle *et al.*, 1962). Therefore, the fact that the response to metyrapone is depressed in patients with central nervous system disease (Oppenheimer *et al.*, 1961a; see also Chapter 33) is evidence that the corticoid feedback in man is at the brain rather than the anterior pituitary level.

Angiotensin II and ACTH are the primary physiological regulators of adrenal cortical secretion, but certain naturally occurring substances stimulate the release of adrenal cortical hormones when given in large doses. This list includes vasopressin, 5-hydroxytryptamine, melanin-stimulating hormone (α-MSH), cyclic adenosine monophosphate (AMP), and, possibly, thyroxine, acetylcholine, histamine, epinephrine, and norepinephrine. High supraphysiological levels of adrenocortical steroids apparently inhibit steroid formation by a direct action on the adrenal. The subject of agents other than ACTH that affect adrenocortical secretion has been reviewed in detail by Ganong (1963).

C. β-Cells of the Pancreas

Insulin secretion from the β-cells of the pancreatic islets is stimulated by sulfonylureas, and their action appears to be a direct one on the pancreas (Duncan and Baird, 1960). Destruction of the β-cells by alloxan (Dunn *et al.*, 1943; Lukens, 1948) is *par excellence* an example of a drug acting directly on hormone-producing cells. Leucine stimulates insulin secretion under certain conditions (Yalow and Berson, 1960; Weisenfeld and Goldner, 1961), and a compound called styrylquinoline No. 90 has an alloxanlike action (Dunn *et al.*, 1943). Synthalin A and B cause histological changes in the β-cells, but the primary effect of these diguanides on blood sugar is a decrease due to the cellular hypoxia they produce in extrapancreatic tissues (Duncan and Baird, 1960).

It has been claimed that stimulation of the right vagus increases insulin secretion, and that this pathway from the brain to the pancreas is responsible for increased insulin secretion in many patients with functional hypoglycemia (see Williams, 1962). However, the importance of this pathway is uncertain, and agents that stimulate or inhibit parasympathetic discharge do not appear to exert consistent effects on insulin secretion. It has recently been demonstrated that epinephrine inhibits insulin secretion (Karam *et al.*, 1965; Porte *et al.*, 1965).

F. W. Wolff *et al.* (1963) have reported the production of diabetes mellitus in dogs by the combined administration of the hypotensive agent, diazoxide, and the diuretic, trichlormethazide. Diazoxide inhibits insulin secretion (Fajuns *et al.*, 1965). It may also increase catecholamine secretion, but its action on the pancreas appears not to be secondary to increased epinephrine secretion (Seltzer and Crout, 1966).

D. Anterior Pituitary

In view of the multiplicity of drugs acting on other endocrine glands, it is surprising that so few drugs have been reported to act directly on the anterior pituitary. Marks and Vernikos-Danellis (1963) have claimed that ethionine prevents the increase in ACTH secretion produced by stressful stimuli in female rats, and have speculated that it acts directly on the pituitary to inhibit the synthesis of ACTH. However, their results as yet lack confirmation, and an ACTH-inhibiting effect of ethionine cannot be regarded as established.

The drug Enheptin (2-amino-5-nitrathiazole), which is used in the treatment of infections in birds, apparently inhibits gonadotropin secretion in chickens. It may also have this action in rats, but its exact site of action is unknown (Pino and Hudson, 1953; Pino *et al.*, 1954; Snair and Schwinghamer, 1960). Chloramiphene has also been reported to inhibit gonadotropin secretion in rats (Holtkamp *et al.*, 1960).

IV. Drugs Inhibiting the Actions of Hormones on Their Target Organs

Spironolactone and related compounds that block the actions of aldosterone (Liddle, 1958) are probably the best known of the drugs which inhibit the effects of hormones on their end organs. Various antiestrogens and antiandrogens have also been studied (see Gaunt *et al.*, 1961). There is some evidence that estrogens increase uterine blood flow by liberating histamine (Szego, 1959), and this may explain the reported antiestrogen and antiprogesterone effects of antihistamines. It may also explain the antidecidual action of antihistamines (Shelesnyak, 1954b,c, 1957; Kraicer *et al.,* 1963).

The blocking effect of guanethidine and reserpine on the actions of thyroid hormone on the nervous system is of more immediate neuroendocrine interest. In 1956, Brewster *et al.* reported that interrupting sympathetic nervous system outflow by means of paravertebral ganglion block prevented many of the effects of feeding thyroid hormone to dogs. The antiadrenergic agent, guanethidine, was subsequently found to relieve the nervousness, tachycardia, palpitation, tremor, and related symptoms of thyrotoxicosis in man (Lee *et al.,* 1962). It does this without affecting thyroid hormone output. There is excess catecholamine secretion and sympathetic activity in thyrotoxicosis, and the striking effects of sympathetic blockade and guanethidine testify to the importance of this adrenergic hyperactivity in the genesis of the symtoms of the disease. Reserpine also improves the symptoms of thyrotoxicosis (Canary *et al.,* 1957). This it does in part by its tranquilizing action, but also in part by depleting catecholamines, with resultant production of a "chemical sympathectomy."

V. Drugs Altering Hormone Secretion by Acting on the Nervous System

A. Adrenocorticotropic Hormone

The principal and possibly the only control of ACTH secretion is exerted through the nervous system (see Ganong, 1963); impulses in afferent nervous pathways converging on the hypothalamus are major regulators, and the important negative feedback effect of glucocorticoids is also exerted, at least in part, on the brain. Some drugs may eventually be discovered that act directly on the pituitary, but the only present candidate for such a role is ethionine (see Section III,D) and its status is uncertain. Therefore, in a sense, all the agents that affect ACTH secretion act via the nervous system. They include stressors, drugs that alter the circulating glucocorticoid level, and drugs that stimulate or inhibit ACTH secretion by a more direct action on the nervous system.

1. *Stressors*

Many drugs that do not act primarily on the nervous system inrcease ACTH secretion. These agents are usually categorized along with the extremely long and immensely varied list of physiological and pathological stimuli which increase ACTH secretion as "nonspecific stressors."

The term nonspecific is misleading; the drugs and other stimuli obviously ıctivate one or more of the mechanisms which trigger increased libera-ion of CRF from the ventral hypothalamus. Formalin, for instance, is a tandard experimental stress (Aron *et al.*, 1953; Mangili *et al.*, 1965). The pain it produces is probably responsible for the increased ACTH ecretion, since many other painful stimuli have a similar effect (see Ganong, 1963), and trauma increases ACTH secretion only when the ıerves from the traumatized area are intact (Egdahl, 1959b). The sub-ect of stress and stress mechanisms is considered in more detail else-vhere in this treatise (Chapter 9, in Volume I), and in various reviews Ganong and Forsham, 1960; Ganong, 1963). No attempt is made here o catalog all the drugs that are stressors; such a list would include prac-ically any agent capable of making the recipient uncomfortable, hypo-ensive, or sick.

. *Drugs Altering Circulating Glucocorticoid Levels*

It is the free glucocorticoids in the body fluids that exert the nega-ive feedback effect on ACTH secretion. This level of free hormones an be changed by agents which change the rate of adrenocortical ecretion, the degree of binding of circulating glucocorticoids to protein, r the rate at which glucocorticoids are removed from the blood stream. 'he drugs which act directly on the adrenal cortex to inhibit its secre-ion are discussed in Section III,B. Estrogens alter the protein binding f adrenocortical steroids, and various drugs are known to alter the inding of thyroid hormones in the circulation (Section IV,C). Hepatic ıetabolism of adrenocortical steroids is accelerated by thyroxine and ther factors (Peterson, 1958, 1959; Yates and Urquhart, 1962), and ıhibited by thiopental-induced ether anesthesia (Steenburg and Gan-ng, 1955). Changes in this hepatic function may explain the adreno-ortical atrophy said to be produced by administration of propylthioura-il (see Section III,A); the drug decreases thyroxine secretion which in ırn decreases the rate of removal of adrenocortical steroids by the liver, nd this may elevate circulating glucocorticoid levels with resultant in-ibition of ACTH secretion.

. *Drugs Acting Directly on the Nervous System*

a. Stimulators. Drugs acting on the nervous system that have been eported to stimulate ACTH secretion are listed in Table II. It should e emphasized that in this and the other tables in this chapter drugs are ıcluded even when the evidence for an effect on endocrine function is

TABLE II

DRUGS ACTING ON THE NERVOUS SYSTEM THAT STIMULATE ACTH SECRETION[a]

Drugs	Species	References
Anesthetics and central nervous system depressants		
Ether	Rat	Sydnor and Sayers (1954); Royce and Sayers (1958); Casentini *et al.* (1959); Barrett and Stockham (1963); Matsuda *et al.* (1964)
	Dog	Suzuki *et al.* (1959a)
	Man	Siker *et al.* (1956); Virtue *et al.* (1957)
Nitrous oxide	Cat	Kaada *et al.* (1959)
	Man	Bernis and Vanek (1958)
Urethan	Rat	Spriggs and Stockham (1964)
Pentobarbital	Rat	Guillemin *et al.* (1958); Holzbauer and Vogt (1958); Barrett and Stockham (1963)
Hexobarbital	Rat	Lauber *et al.* (1937)
Phenobarbital	Rat	Ashford and Shapero (1962)
Ethanol	Rat	Forbes and Duncan (1951, 1953); J. J-Smith (1951); Rezabeck (1957); San. tisteban (1961); Kalant *et al.* (1963)
	Mouse	Santisteban (1961)
	Guinea pig	Forbes and Duncan (1951, 1953)
Ethanol plus Antabuse	Man	Bliss *et al.* (1954)
Tranquilizers		
Chlorpromazine	Rat	Holzbauer and Vogt (1954); Nasmyth (1955); Olling and De Wied (1956); Mahfouz and Ezz (1958); Reiss (1958); Sapeika (1959); Talwalker *et al.* (1960); Ashford and Shapero (1962); R. L. Smith *et al.* (1963); von Bohus and Endröczi (1964)
	Dog	Egdahl and Richards (1956); Betz and Ganong (1963)
	Monkey	Harwood and Mason (1957)
Promazine	Rat	R. L. Smith *et al.* (1963)
Trifluoperazine	Rat	R. L. Smith *et al.* (1963)
Prochlorperazine	Dog	Cushman and Hilton (1964)
Perphenazine	Rat	Kivalo and Rinne (1960)
Mepazine	Rat	Olling and De Wied (1958)
Reserpine	Rat	Kitay *et al.* (1959); Saffran and Vogt (1960); Brodie *et al.* (1961); Khazan *et al.* (1961); Maickel *et al.* (1961); Gaunt *et al.* (1962); Montanari and Stockham (1962); Ashford and Shapero (1962); Halkerston *et al.* (1964); Giuliani *et al.* (1966)

TOUT 08/15/78

¦SUBJ 38¦ACTIV¦ ¦ ¦
¦PAPER ¦NO SUPP¦Q ¦C, CU ¦

AL DENTAL PRACTICE

967 PHOTOCOPY

TION OF HOSPITAL DENTISTS/DENTISTRY/

I
¦SUBJ 31¦ACTIV¦ ¦ ¦
¦PAPER ¦NO SUPP¦Q ¦C, ST ¦

AL PHARMACY

TRIBUTION--ENGLAND/PHARMACY/

PHARMACISTS, ENGLAND/

C
¦SUBJ 31¦ACTIV¦ ¦ ¦
¦PAPER ¦NO SUPP¦M ¦C, ST ¦

ECOLOGY

N INTERDISCIPLINARY JOURNAL@27895000653D

TABLE II—*Continued*

Drugs	Species	References
	Guinea pig	Khazan *et al.* (1961)
	Dog	Egdahl *et al.* (1956)
	Monkey	Harwood and Mason (1957); Rosenthal and Mason (1961)
	Man	Khazan *et al.* (1961)
Meprobamate	Rat	Mäkelä *et al.* (1959)
Other drugs affecting behavior		
Benzactyzine	Rat	Ashford and Shapero (1962)
RO-1284 (a benzoquinolizine)	Rat	Westermann *et al.* (1962)
Iproniazid	Rat	Sapeika (1959)
Bufotenine	Rat	Costa and Zetler (1958)
Anticonvulsants		
Diphenylhydantoin	Rat	Woodbury (1958)
	Man	Costa *et al.* (1955)
Trimethadione	Rat	Woodbury (1958)
Analgesics		
Morphine	Rat	MacKay and MacKay (1926); Selye (1936); Nasmyth (1954); George and Way (1955); Munson and Briggs (1955); Reynolds and Randall (1957); Tanabe and Cafruny (1958); Oliver and Troop (1963); Paroli and Melchiorri (1961a,b)
	Guinea pig	Sobel *et al.* (1958)
	Dog	Suzuki *et al.* (1959b)
	Man	Bernis and Vanek (1958)
Methadone	Rat	George and Way (1955)
Acetophenetidin	Rat	Feeney *et al.* (1955); Noach *et al.* (1957)
Salicylates	Rat	Blanchard *et al.* (1950); van Cauwenberge (1951); Cronheim and Hyder (1954); George and Way (1957); Wexler (1963); Mangili *et al.* (1965)
	Man	Bayliss and Steinbeck (1954); Done *et al.* (1955)
Phenylbutazone	Rat	Goddijn and Noach (1957); Good and Kelley (1958)
Autonomic drugs		
Amphetamine	Rat	Nasmyth (1950); Ohler and Sevy (1956)
Hydroxyamphetamine (Paredrine)	Rat	Nasmyth (1950); Ohler and Sevy (1952)
Symptol	Rat	Nasmyth (1950)
Arecoline	Rat	Anichkov *et al.* (1962)
Nicotine	Rat	De Wied (1961)
	Dog	Anichkov *et al.* (1962)
Ergot	Rat	Ronzoni and Reichlin (1950)

TABLE II—*Continued*

Drugs	Species	References
Dibenamine	Rat	Ronzoni and Reichlin (1950)
SKF-501	Rat	Guillemin (1955)
Phenoxybenzamine	Rat	Ohler and Sevy (1956)
Methacholine	Rat	Guillemin (1955)
Physostigmine	Rat	Dordoni and Fortier (1950)
	Dog	Harwood and Mason (1956); Suzuki *et al.* (1964)
Atropine	Rat	Dordoni and Fortier (1950); Guillemin (1955)
	Dog	Suzuki *et al.* (1964)
Trasentine	Dog	Anichkov *et al.* (1962)
Tetraethylammonium	Rat	Tepperman and Bogardus (1948)
Convulsants		
Metrazol	Rat	Woodbury (1958)
Bacterial products		
Diphtheria toxin	Guinea pig	Schmid *et al.* (1956)
Typhoid vaccine	Man	Christy *et al.* (1956); Fotherby *et al.* (1959)
Endotoxin	Dog	Egdahl *et al.* (1957); Egdahl (1959a); Melby *et al.* (1960)
Other bacterial pyrogens	Rat	Wexler (1963); Ando *et al.* (1964)
	Man	Bliss *et al.* (1954); McDonald *et al.* (1956); Ferriman and Page (1960); Farmer *et al.* (1961); Brinck-Johnsen *et al.* (1963)
Antihistamines		
Mepyramine maleate	Rat	Nasmyth (1955)
Miscellaneous		
Antifeine	Dog	Anichkov *et al.* (1962)
	Guinea pig	Anichkov *et al.* (1962)

[a] For reviews see Munson and Briggs (1955), Van Brunt and Ganong (1963).

relatively indirect. Drugs are also included when reports about them are unconfirmed or conflicting, in order to make the tables comprehensive. The qualifications and reservations necessary for proper evaluation of the various drug effects are discussed in the text.

Many anesthetic agents stimulate rather than inhibit ACTH secretion. There is evidence that ether acts directly on the hypothalamus to stimulate ACTH secretion in rats (Matsuda *et al.*, 1964). However, the predominant effect of pentobarbital appears to be inhibitory. It has been reported to stimulate ACTH secretion in rats, but in those experiments in which its effects were compared to those of saline, the adrenocortical response to injecting saline was usually greater. Therefore, it appears likely that the response was to the process of injection, not the barbiturate itself.

The presence in Table II of phenothiazine tranquilizers, reserpine, diphenylhydantoin, and morphine also deserves comment; these agents which on acute injection produce increased ACTH secretion have also been reported to inhibit the response to subsequent stress in the rat. The problem of the mechanism of their inhibitory action is discussed below in Section V,A,3,b and in Chapter 9 (Volume I).

Sympathomimetic and parasympathomimetic agents increase ACTH secretion; so do epinephrine, norepinephrine, and acetylcholine, at least in the rat (Casentini *et al.*, 1959). However, it cannot be stated on the basis of this evidence that there are adrenergic and cholinergic synapses in the ACTH-regulating neural paths converging on the ventral hypothalamus because sympathetic and parasympathetic blocking agents also increase ACTH secretion. It is possible that the stimulation by the autonomic blocking agents is secondary to some consequence of the autonomic blockade, or even to the handling of the animals during the administration of the drug, but this could also be true in the case of the sympathomimetic or parasympathomimetic agents.

The various bacterial products listed in Table II are potent stimulators of ACTH secretion. The pyrogens act by liberating a substance from the leukocytes (endogenous pyrogen) which acts directly on the hypothalamus to produce fever (Cooper, 1965). The possibility that this substance also acts directly on the hypothalamus to increase CRF release deserves consideration. Typhoid vaccine and some of the pyrogens have been used to test pituitary-adrenocortical function and they provide a relatively reproducible experimental stress in man (Brinck-Johnson *et al.*, 1963).

b. Inhibitors. Drugs acting on the nervous system which have been reported to inhibit ACTH secretion are cataloged by species in Table III. In the table, they are divided for convenience into those which inhibit basal secretion of ACTH, as indicated by a decline in resting adrenocortical secretion; those which inhibit the response to the "metabolic stress" of the metyrapone test (see Section III,B); and those which inhibit the response to various other stressful stimuli.

Not listed in Table III are drug antagonists which specifically inhibit the stressful effects of particular drugs. For instance, the response to Piromen can be blocked by aspirin, and the response to typhoid vaccine can be blocked by aminopyrine (Christy *et al.*, 1956; McDonald *et al.*, 1956) but neither drug blocks the response to other stresses. Inhibition of the response to pyrogens by antipyretic drugs suggests that the fever triggers the increased ACTH secretion, but the increase in ACTH secre-

TABLE III

Drugs Acting on the Nervous System That Inhibit ACTH Secretion (Excluding Specific Inhibitors of Specific Stressors)[a]

Drugs	Species	References
Drugs inhibiting resting output		
Pentobarbital	Rat	Royce and Sayers (1958); Oliver and Troop (1963)
	Dog	Suzuki *et al.* (1962)
	Monkey	Harwood and Mason (1957)
	Man	Siker *et al.* (1956)
Hexobarbital	Dog	Suzuki *et al.* (1962)
Chlorpromazine	Man	Kinberger *et al.* (1956); Sulman and Winnik (1956b); Co-Tui *et al.* (1956, 1960); Fotherby *et al.* (1959)
Reserpine	Man	Boscott *et al.* (1956)
Diphenylhydantoin	Man	Bray *et al.* (1954); Costa *et al.* (1955)
Morphine	Man	Eisenman *et al.* (1958, 1961)
Normorphine	Man	Fraser *et al.* (1958)
Nialamide	Rat	Jasmin and Richer (1961)
Iproniazid, Imipramine, Metrazol, Amphetamine	Monkey	Harwood and Bigelow (1960)
Ethanol	Man	Krusius *et al.* (1958)
Drugs inhibiting response to metyrapone		
Chlorpromazine, Carisoprodol, Meprobamate, Nialamide	Man	Gold *et al.* (1960b)
Prochlorpromazine	Dog	Cushman and Hilton (1964)
Diphenylhydantoin	Man	Krieger (1962)
Ethinylestradiol	Man	Mestman and Nelson (1963)
Drugs inhibiting response to various stresses		
Pentobarbital	Rat	Ronzoni (1950); Cronheim and Hyder (1954); Munson and Briggs (1955); Rerup and Hedner (1962)
Procaine, etc. (spinal anesthesia)	Man	Virtue *et al.* (1957); Hammond *et al.* (1958)
Chlorpromazine	Rat	Aron *et al.* (1953); Cheymol *et al.* (1954); Hamburger (1955); Olling and De Wied (1956); Sevy *et al.* (1957); Van Peenen and Way (1957); Mahfouz and Ezz (1958); Sapeika (1959); Brodie *et al.* (1961); Klepping *et al.* (1961)

TABLE III—*Continued*

Drugs	Species	References
	Man	Christy *et al.* (1957); Fotherby *et al.* (1959)
Proketazine, Perphenazine	Man	Kothari *et al.* (1961)
Perphenazine	Rat	Kivalo and Rinne (1960)
Mepazine	Rat	Olling and De Wied (1958)
Reserpine	Rat	Wells *et al.* (1956); Van Peenen and Way (1957); Mahfouz and Ezz (1958); Kitay *et al.* (1959); Epstein *et al.* (1960)
	Monkey	Mason and Brady (1956)
Meprobamate	Rat	Mäkelä *et al.* (1959)
α-Ethyltryptamine	Rat	A. V. Schally (personal communication, 1965)
	Dog	Tullner and Hertz (1964); Ganong *et al.* (1965); Lorenzen *et al.* (1965)
Diphenylhydantoin	Rat	Bonnycastle and Bradley (1960); Oliver Troop (1963)
Nialamid	Mice	Staple (1951, 1954)
MO-482 (monoamine oxidase inhibitor)	Man	Kothari *et al.* (1961)
Morphine	Rat	Munson and Briggs (1955); Ohler and Sevy (1956); Oliver and Troop (1963); Slusher and Browning (1961)
Amphetamine, Methamphetamine	Dog	Lorenzen *et al.* (1965)

[a] For reviews see Woodbury (1958), Ganong (1963).

tion produced by Piromen injection precedes the rise in body temperature (McDonald *et al.*, 1956).

Both the stimulatory and the inhibitory actions of morphine on ACTH secretion have been reported to be blocked by the morphine anatagonist, nalorphine. Nalorphine has no action of its own on the pituitary-adrenal system (George and Way, 1955). On acute administration, morphine stimulates ACTH secretion, and this stimulation is prevented when animals are pretreated with morphine (George and Way, 1955). Particularly when given in association with pentobarbital, however, morphine is claimed to block the response to subsequent stressful stimuli in rats, and this blockade does not occur if nalorphine is administered with the morphine (Burdette *et al.*, 1961).

Another interesting antagonism is the blockade of the ACTH-stimulating action of reserpine by monoamine oxidase-inhibiting drugs. Iproniazid and another monoamine oxidase-inhibiting drug have been reported to prevent the increase in ACTH secretion produced by reserpine in rats (Gaunt *et al.*, 1962; Martel *et al.*, 1962; Mizuno *et al.*, 1964) but no inhibition of the response to other stresses in rats has been reported with these drugs and indeed iproniazid is said to stimulate ACTH secretion itself (Sapeika, 1959). The monoamine oxidase inhibitors also prevent the depletion of brain amines and sedation produced by reserpine, but the relation of the brain amines to ACTH secretion is a complex one. The subject is discussed in detail in Chapter 31.

Various antihistamines block the increase in ACTH secretion produced by histamine, but uniformly fail to block the increase produced by other stresses (Fortier and Guillemin, 1953; Guillemin and Fortier, 1953; Nasmyth, 1955); indeed, some of the antihistamines produce mild stimulation of ACTH secretion (Nasmyth, 1955). The serotonin antagonist, lysergic acid diethylamide (LSD), fails to block stress responses (Ganong *et al.*, 1961), but it also fails to block the pituitary-adrenocortical response to serotonin (Milković and Supek, 1956), and there is some doubt that LSD blocks the effects of serotonin in the brain (see Ganong *et al.*, 1961; Ganong, 1963).

Although the adrenergic blocking agents, SKF-501 and phenoxybenzamine, cause increased ACTH secretion when first administered, rats can be "conditioned" to them by repeated injection so that the compounds no longer produce this increase. In such repeatedly injected animals, epinephrine, norepinephrine, and hydroxyamphetamine fail to produce the increase in ACTH they usually produce in this species (Guillemin, 1955; Ohler and Sevy, 1956; Van Peenen and Way, 1957). Somewhat similar results have been reported with Dibenamine and a tetraethylammonium preparation (Tepperman and Bogardus, 1948). Atropine stimulates on initial injection but on repeated injection blocks the response to injections of cholinergic compounds (Guillemin, 1955). However, the blockade of ACTH secretion produced by these sympathetic and parasympathetic blocking agents does not extend to other stressful stimuli such as formalin injections and immobilization. Thus drug studies have not provided any evidence for adrenergic, cholinergic, or "histaminergic" synapses in a final common neural pathway mediating increased ACTH secretion in response to stress.

Interpretation of the data suggesting that drugs inhibit secretion of ACTH in the unstressed state is not always easy. It must be remembered that prolonged inhibition of stress-induced increases in ACTH secretion can probably lead to diminished adrenal responsiveness to ACTH (see Ganong, 1963), and this might explain the decline in basal corticoid output seen with chronic diphenylhydantoin treatment in man. Diminished ACTH responsiveness in patients treated with diphenylhydantoin for long periods has been reported by Bray *et al.* (1954) and Christy and Hofmann (1959).

Another problem is whether or not the controls are unstressed. Boscott *et al.* (1956), for instance, reported that steroid excretion was reduced in schizophrenic patients treated with reserpine. However, it is possible that the predrug levels were somewhat elevated in these patients due to the anxiety and tension associated with their disease. It is pertinent in this regard that Mason and Brady (1956) found that reserpine reduced the high plasma steroid levels seen in monkeys exposed to an anxiety-producing psychological situation. Also, Co-Tui *et al.* (1960) and Gold *et al.* (1960b) failed to observe any effect of reserpine on resting excretion of adrenocortical steroids. Reserpine also failed to alter the response to metyrapone (Gold *et al.*, 1960b). The question of whether or not the controls were truly unstressed also arises in evaluating the decline in glucocorticoid secretion observed in some patients treated with chlorpromazine. Betz and Ganong (1963) found that chlorpromazine failed to diminish the adrenocortical response to the psychic stress of immobilization in the dog, but this does not rule out the possibility that psychic tension in mental patients produces some elevation in steroid output and that relief of this tension leads to a measurable decline in output. No decrease in basal adrenocortical function was observed in the patients treated with chlorpromazine by Gold *et al.* (1960b) and Georges and Cahn (1953).

The same question of the state of the controls arises when considering the reported effects of pentobarbital and other barbiturates on ACTH secretion. The monkeys studied by Harwood and Mason (1957), for instance, were caught, restrained, and bled. Their control corticoid values were certainly not elevated to the level produced by severe stresses, but some elevation due to the capture and bleeding must have been present. The patients studied by Siker *et al.* (1956) were awaiting surgery with, it can be assumed, some apprehension, and the dogs studied by Suzuki *et al.* (1962) did have slightly elevated control steroid outputs in some instances. Therefore, it seems likely that a great variety of minor stressful stimuli act together to produce a moderate level of ACTH secretion, and the ACTH-suppressing action of barbiturates is due to their inhibition of the effect of these minor stimuli (Royce and Sayers, 1958). These stimuli presumably set up impulses which reach the hypothalamus via the reticular system, and barbiturates selectively depress conduction in this system (Magoun, 1963).

Pentobarbital only blocks the responses to relatively mild stresses, and leaves responses to strong stimuli such as surgery intact. In dogs, for instance, the adrenocortical response to surgical stress under pentobarbital anesthesia is maximal, just as it is under ether anesthesia (Van Brunt and Ganong, 1963). In rats, pentobarbital is said to synergize with morphine to block ACTH secretion (see Munson and Briggs, 1955), but pentobarbital alone produces very little inhibition (Ronzoni, 1950; Oliver and Troop, 1963).

The decrease in excretion of adrenocortical steroids in morphine addicts while they are taking morphine or normorphine (Eisenman *et al.*, 1958, 1961; Fraser *et al.*, 1958) is unexplained. So is the reported decrease in plasma corticoid levels in monkeys treated with imipramine, iproniazid, Metrazol, or amphetamine (Harwood and Bigelow, 1960); however, the data in the monkeys have only been reported in abstract form, and they do not appear to have been confirmed.

It should be emphasized that the blockade to various stresses produced by any given drug is relative; some stimuli do not break through the block, but other, presumably more severe, stresses often do. Thus, for instance, Holzbauer and Vogt (1958) found that cannulation of the adrenal vein produced increased ACTH secretion in rats pretreated with pentobarbital and morphine. In addition to relative strengths of inhibitors and stressors, some of the conflicting results in the literature can be explained by the use of different indicators of adrenocortical secretion. For instance, Montanari and Stockham (1962) observed that ether stress induced a significant rise in plasma corticosterone following the administration of reserpine, even though no adrenal ascorbic acid depletion occurred. It seems clear from this and other experiments that some stimuli increase ACTH secretion in rats without producing adrenal ascorbic acid depletion (see Ganong and Forsham, 1960).

It should also be noted that in most of the experiments reporting blockade of the response to stressful stimuli in rats, a drug is injected and then the response to a stress is tested minutes to hours later. Chlorpromazine, mepazine, reserpine, meprobamate, diphenylhydantoin, and morphine are blocking agents when administered in this way (see Table III). However, when first administered, all these drugs cause increased ACTH secretion (see Table II). The fact that the drugs are stresses in themselves raises the question of the specificity of their blocking action. Can any stress inhibit the response of the rat to a second stress—i.e., is there a refractory period after an acute stress in the rat during which the pituitary-adrenal system is unresponsive? Kitay *et al.* (1959) found that epinephrine could act as a stress inhibitor if given before the stress. Maickel and his associates (Brodie *et al.*, 1961; Maickel *et al.*, 1961) found that cold inhibited the response to stressful stimuli, and Itoh and Arimura (1954) found that even vasopressin could block stress responses. Other data documenting the presence of a period of relative stress-nonresponsiveness for several hours after an acute stress in the rat have been reported by Knigge *et al.* (1959) and Henkin and Knigge (1960).

The explanation of the relative stress-nonresponsiveness following initial stress in the rat is unsettled. Kitay *et al.* (1959) and Maickel *et al.* (1961) argued that it was due to temporary depletion of pituitary ACTH, but this view has been challenged on the grounds that other stresses can increase ACTH secretion in the presence of just as marked pituitary ACTH depletion (see Munson, 1963). Obviously, the strength of the stress is an important consideration in such experiments, since blockade is relative rather than absolute. In addition, ACTH depletion is not the only possible explanation of the unresponsiveness, and there is some evidence that a neural inhibitory mechanism is involved (see Ganong, 1963, and Chapter 9, Volume I).

Since the results of inhibition experiments performed in rats are difficult to interpret, conclusions about acute inhibitory effects of drugs must rest primarily on experiments performed in other species. Dogs, unlike rats, respond repeatedly to stress with maximal increases in corticoid secretion (Hume, 1958; Ganong *et al.*, 1961). It is therefore of interest that in dogs, chlorpromazine stimulates ACTH secretion (Egdahl and Richards, 1956; Betz and Ganong, 1963), and fails to block the adrenocortical response to physical stress or the psychic stress of immobilization (Betz and Ganong, 1963).

There are reports that chlorpromazine inhibits the adrenal cortical response to insulin-induced hypoglycemia (Christy *et al.*, 1957), typhoid vaccine (Fotherby *et al.*, 1959), heat stress (Kothari *et al.*, 1961), and metyrapone (Gold *et al.*, 1960b) in humans. There is no evidence for a stress-nonresponsive period in man like that in the rat. However, in the experiments of Gold and his associates, the response to metyrapone plus supramaximal doses of ACTH was reduced as much as the response to metyrapone alone, indicating that the adrenals in their subjects were unresponsive to ACTH. Similarly, Sloane *et al.* (1958) reported data indicating that the sensitivity of the adrenals to ACTH was reduced in patients treated with chlorpromazine. This adrenal unresponsiveness could be due to a direct action of chlorpromazine on the adrenal, or it could be secondary to inhibition for prolonged periods of ACTH secretion in response to minor stressful stimuli, as indicated above in the discussion of the effects of diphenylhydantoin. In dogs, administration of chlorpromazine for 5 days does not impair adrenal responsiveness to ACTH (Betz and Ganong, 1963).

Reserpine decreases the adrenocortical response to an emotional stress in monkeys (Mason and Brady, 1956), but it does not influence the adrenocortical response to a bacterial pyrogen (McDonald *et al.*, 1956) or metyrapone (Gold *et al.*, 1960b) in man.

Administration of morphine to humans has been reported not to produce any immediate change in plasma corticoid levels and to inhibit the rise in corticoid levels produced by intravenous injection of 2 U of vasopressin (McDonald *et al.*, 1959). These observations are interesting, but so far unconfirmed. The mechanism by which estrogens inhibit the response to metyrapone is unknown. Spinal anesthesia presumably inhibits the adrenocortical response to surgery by interrupting the neural pathways that would normally carry impulses to the hypothalamus from the traumatized area (see Ganong, 1963).

The inhibitory effect of α-ethyltryptamine on ACTH secretion has opened up several new avenues of research into ACTH-regulating mechanisms. The transient inhibitory effect of this drug on 17-hydroxycorticoid secretion in a surgically stressed pentobarbital-anesthetized dog is shown in Fig. 3. Exogenous ACTH promptly overcomes the inhibition (Tullner and Hertz, 1964) and α-ethyltryptamine has no acute effect on the response of the adrenal to ACTH in hypophysectomized dogs (W. F. Ganong, unpublished data, 1965), so presumably its entire effect is due to inhibition of ACTH secretion. α-Ethyltryptamine also inhibits the adrenocortical response to insulin hypoglycemia (Ganong, 1964). Unlike most of the compounds reported to inhibit ACTH secretion, α-ethyltryptamine is not a sedative or analgesic. It is an indole with psychic energizer and antidepressant activity, it inhibits monoamine oxidase, and it

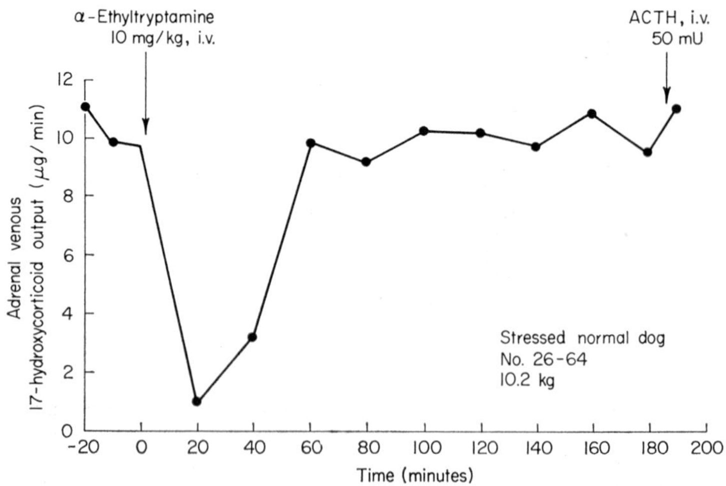

FIG. 3. Effect of α-ethyltryptamine on adrenal cortical secretion in a dog subjected to continuous surgical stress. (Data from Ganong, 1964.)

is a pressor agent. A variety of other indoles, antidepressants, and monoamine oxidase inhibitors fail to inhibit ACTH secretion in the dog, but amphetamine and methamphetamine do (Lorenzen *et al.*, 1965). These compounds have some monoamine oxidase-inhibiting activity but they are potent pressor agents as well and their ACTH-inhibiting activity has been found to correlate with their pressor activity. Furthermore, two other pressor agents, 2-aminoheptane and cyclopentamine (Clopane), have recently been found to produce inhibition of ACTH secretion when administered in amounts sufficient to produce as marked and prolonged a pressor response as α-ethyltryptamine (L. C. Lorenzen, A. T. Boryczka, R. Shackleford, and W. F. Ganong, unpublished data, 1965). In addition, α-ethyltryptamine has no ACTH-inhibiting activity

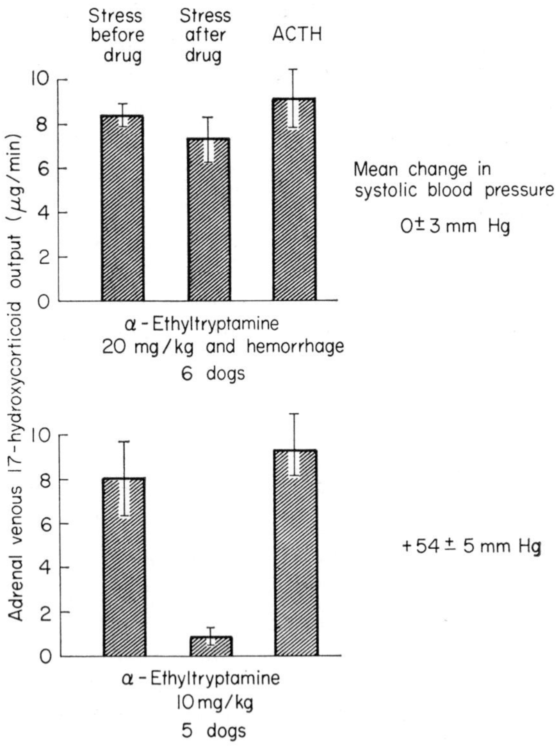

FIG. 4. Effect of preventing the pressor response to α-ethyltryptamine on the ACTH-inhibiting activity of the drug. The animals given 20 mg per kilogram were bled an amount sufficient to prevent any blood pressure rise. Lower bars show the response in dogs receiving 10 mg per kilogram and not subjected to hemorrhage. (From L. C. Lorenzen, A. T. Boryczka, R. Shackleford, and W. F. Ganong, unpublished data, 1965.)

when its pressor response is prevented (Fig. 4). It may be that the pressor response produced by the drug acts on the brain stem to inhibit transmission in pathways concerned with the stimulation of ACTH secretion; experiments with brain stem stimulation have indicated that α-ethyltryptamine does act at this level (Ganong *et al.*, 1965).

The experiments with α-ethyltryptamine in the dog have been performed for the most part in pentobarbital-anesthetized animals, and are open to the criticism that pentobarbital could be responsible in part for the inhibition of ACTH secretion. It is interesting in this regard that α-ethyltryptamine fails to inhibit ACTH secretion in ether-anesthetized surgically stressed dogs (Tullner and Hertz, 1964; and W. F. Ganong, unpublished observations, 1965). However, ether reduces the pressor response produced by α-ethyltryptamine. In addition, α-ethyltryptamine is believed to act on the pathways converging on the median eminence while at least in rats, ether probably stimulates CRF secretion by a direct action on the median eminence (Matsuda *et al.*, 1964). Therefore, ether might be expected to overcome the blocking effect of α-ethyltryptamine. Further research with these and other neurally active drugs should do much to elucidate the neural mechanisms concerned with the control of ACTH secretion.

B. Growth Hormone

Growth hormone secretion has only recently been proved to be under neural control, and relatively few data on the effects of neurohumors, hormones, and drugs on the process have been reported. The secretion of this hormone is a very labile process, and the amounts secreted in adults are as great as those secreted in children (Glick *et al.*, 1965). Hypoglycemia, exercise, and stressful stimuli cause prompt increases in circulating growth hormone levels. Acetylcholine, epinephrine, serotonin, histamine, oxytocin, α- and β-MSH, and glucagon have no effect on growth hormone secretion (Roth *et al.*, 1963; Halasz, 1964). Vasopressin has been claimed to stimulate growth hormone secretion (Del Vecchio *et al.*, 1958), but this report could not be confirmed by Reichlin and Brown (1961). Estrogens (Amesbury *et al.*, 1965) and corticosteroids (Hartog *et al.*, 1964) inhibit growth hormone secretion.

2-Deoxyglucose is a potent stimulator of growth hormone secretion, probably because this analog of glucose inhibits intracellular utilization of glucose and thus produces an intracellular effect similar to that of hypoglycemia (Roth *et al.*, 1963, 1964). Sulman and Winnik (1956a) found that chlorpromazine inhibited growth in rats and this inhibition could be overcome by exogenous growth hormone. Zor *et al.* (1965)

found that a variety of monoamine oxidase-inhibiting drugs decreased the growth of the tibial epiphyseal cartilage in normal rats, and this effect was overcome by administering growth hormone. However, there is some evidence that the inhibition was not due to inhibition of growth hormone secretion. The monoamine oxidase inhibitors which had cartilage growth-inhibiting activity were nialamide, mebanazine, phenelzine, pivhydrazine, pheniprazine, isocarboxazid, tranylcypromine, and pargyline. Iproniazid, 2,5,dichlorophenylhydrazine, α-ethyltryptamine, and amphetamine were inactive. There is some evidence that ethanol inhibits growth hormone secretion (Arky and Freinkel, 1964). General and spinal anesthesia and succinylcholine have been reported to have no effect on plasma growth hormone levels (Glick *et al.*, 1965).

C. Thyrotropin

Thyrotropin secretion is increased by the drop in circulating thyroid hormone levels by the drugs that act directly on the thyroid to inhibit various steps in thyroxine synthesis (see Section III,A). It has been claimed that acetylcholine increases TSH secretion in rabbits when administered intravenously or into the pituitary by microinjection (Harrison, 1961). According to Harrison, injection of epinephrine into the ventral hypothalamus also increases TSH secretion. However, Greer *et al.* (1960) report that in rats, intrahypothalamic injections of acetylcholine, Mecholyl, epinephrine, norepinephrine, histamine, and potassium iodide all failed to increase TSH secretion. They found that potassium iodide, dinitrophenol, and 5-hydroxytryptamine had no effect when injected into the pituitary. No other drugs have been shown to stimulate TSH secretion.

The drugs reported to inhibit TSH secretion are listed in Table IV. Diphenylhydantoin has also been reported to inhibit ACTH, FSH, and LH secretion. However, the inhibitory effect on TSH secretion is apparently not due to a direct action of the drug on the nervous system; instead, the drug displaces thyroxine from binding sites on the thyroxine-binding protein in the circulation (J. Wolff *et al.*, 1961; Oppenheimer and Tavernetti, 1962). This liberates more free thyroxine, with resultant feedback inhibition of TSH secretion. Similar displacement of thyroxine from sites on plasma proteins is produced by salicylates, tetrachlorothyronine, and dinitrophenol, and this probably accounts for the TSH-inhibiting effect of these drugs (Richard *et al.*, 1949; Christensen, 1959; J. Wolff *et al.*, 1961). Salicylates also increase the metabolic rate (Alexander and Johnson, 1956). The bacterial pyrogens probably inhibit TSH secretion by producing fever, since exposure of rats to an elevated am-

TABLE IV

DRUGS ACTING ON THE NERVOUS SYSTEM THAT ALTER TSH SECRETION

Drugs	Species	References
Drugs stimulating TSH secretion:		None
Drugs inhibiting TSH secretion		
Morphine	Rat	Samel (1958)
Chlorpromazine	Rat	Samel (1958); Michel *et al.* (1959)
Reserpine	Rat	Pokorny *et al.* (1957); Moon and Turner (1958, 1959b); Yamazaki *et al.* (1961) [no apparent effect in man: Canary *et al.* (1957); Newman and Fish (1958)]
Iodide	Rat	Richard *et al.* (1949)
Salicylates	Human	Austen *et al.* (1958); J. Wolff *et al.* (1961); L. S. Goodman and Gilman (1965)
Diphenylhydantoin	Human	Oppenheimer *et al.* (1961b); J. Wolff *et al.* (1961); Oppenheimer and Tavernetti (1962)
Tetrachlorothyronine	Rat	Richard *et al.* (1949)
	Human	J. Wolff *et al.* (1961)
Dinitrophenol	Rat	Goldberg *et al.* (1955, 1957)
	Human	Castor and Beierwaltes (1956); J. Wolff *et al.* (1961)
Atropine	Rat	Rose *et al.* (1960)
Bacterial pyrogens	Rabbit	Goldberg *et al.* (1957)

bient temperature also inhibits TSH secretion (Goldberg *et al.*, 1957). The TSH-inhibiting effects of ether, atropine, and morphine deserve further study. Oyama *et al.* (1959) have presented evidence that the effect of ether is due to inhibition of the responsiveness of the thyroid to TSH rather than inhibition of the secretion of TSH. Chlorpromazine and reserpine have been shown to have direct inhibitory effects on thyroid function *in vitro* (Mayer *et al.*, 1956), but apparently these are not seen *in vivo*. The drugs appear to inhibit TSH secretion in rats, but neither appears to have much effect on thyroid function in man (Newman and Fish, 1958; Magliotti *et al.*, 1959). Reserpine does cause marked amelioration of the symptoms of thyrotoxicosis in humans without lowering the output of thyroxine (Canary *et al.*, 1957) because it depletes catecholamines from autonomic nerve endings, thus attenuating the increased adrenergic discharge characteristic of thyrotoxicosis (see Section IV). Yamada (1960a,b; see also Greer *et al.*, 1960) has reported that trypan blue inhibits TSH secretion. This compound has no known effect on the nervous system, and its mechanism of action on TSH secretion is unsettled.

D. Follicle-Stimulating Hormone and Luteinizing Hormone

Clomiphene and its close relative, chlorotrianisene (MER-25) stimulate FSH and LH release. These drugs, along with those which act on the nervous system to inhibit FSH and LH secretion are listed in Table V. It seems clear that clomiphene and chlorotrianisene act by stimulating the release of gonadotropins from the pituitary, but their exact site of action is unsettled. They have weak antiestrogenic activity and it has been postulated that they release the inhibitory effect of circulating estrogens on gonadotropin secretion (see Chapter 15, in Volume I).

In contrast to the list of agents stimulating gonadotropin secretion, the list of agents inhibiting ovulation is a long one. For the most part, the drugs inhibit the sudden release from the pituitary of "ovulating hormone." This is primarily but not necessarily exclusively LH (see Chapter 15, in Volume I). The ovulation-inhibiting drugs fall into four general categories: anesthetics and related CNS depressants, tranquilizers, adrenergic blocking agents and cholinergic blocking agents. The local injection of procaine into the hypothalamus undoubtedly acts to produce a "temporary hypothalamic lesion," and it is not surprising that this blocks ovulation.

The general anesthetics and central nervous system depressants such as morphine presumably inhibit the neural activity necessary to produce the sudden discharge of releasing factor which in turn triggers "ovulating hormone" release. These drugs are active not only in rabbits, which ovulate reflexly in response to copulation, but also in spontaneously ovulating species such as rats, if given at the appropriate time of the estrous cycle. In rats, this time is 2:00 to 4:00 P.M. on the day of proestrus. Injection of barbiturates and other depressant drugs before or after this "critical period" does not block ovulation, so presumably this is the time at which activation of luteinizing hormone releasing factor (LRF) discharge is being initiated. Reserpine also blocks ovulation in the rat and monkey, and chlorpromazine blocks ovulation in the rat and occasionally in the human (see Table V). Like the depressant drugs, they presumably prevent the ovulation-producing burst of gonadotropin secretion from the pituitary.

The demonstration that adrenergic blocking agents (Dibenamine, Dibenzyline, SKF-501) and cholinergic blocking agents (atropine, methantheline, Pathilon) block ovulation led to the conclusion that there were adrenergic and cholinergic synapses in the neural pathways re-

TABLE V

DRUGS ACTING ON THE NERVOUS SYSTEM THAT ALTER FOLLICLE-STIMULATING HORMONE AND LUTEINIZING HORMONE SECRETION[a]

Drugs	Species	References
Drugs that stimulate ovulation (increased FSH and LH secretion)		
Clomiphene	Human	Greenblatt *et al.* (1961); Southam and Janovski (1962); O. W. Smith *et al.* (1963); Somnath *et al.* (1963); Wall *et al.* (1964)
Chlorotrianisene	Human	O. W. Smith *et al.* (1963)
Drugs that inhibit ovulation (decreased FSH and LH secretion)		
Ether	Rat	Everett and Sawyer (1950); Sawyer (1959)
Procaine (in hypothalamus)	Rabbit	Westman and Jacobsohn (1942)
Ethanol	Rat	Sawyer (1963)
	Rabbit	Saul (1959)
Morphine	Human	Menninger-Lerchenthal (1934)
	Rabbit	Saul (1959)
	Rat	Barraclough and Sawyer (1955)
Phenobarbital	Rat	Everett and Sawyer (1950)
Pentobarbital	Rat	Everett and Sawyer (1949b, 1950); Zarrow and Quinn (1963)
	Rabbit	Saul and Sawyer (1957)
Amytal	Rat	Everett and Sawyer (1950)
Dial,	Rat	Everett and Sawyer (1950)
Barbital	Hen[b]	Fraps and Case (1953)
Ipral	Hen[b]	Fraps and Case (1953)
Diphenylhydantoin	Rat	Quinn (1965)
Chlorpromazine	Human	Sulman and Winnik (1956b); Whitelaw (1960)
	Rat	Shibusawa *et al.* (1955); Barraclough and Sawyer (1957); Zarrow and Brown-Grant (1964)
Reserpine	Rat	Gaunt *et al.* (1954); Barraclough and Sawyer (1957)
	Monkey	De Feo and Reynolds (1956)
Iproniazid and other monoamine oxidase inhibitors	Rat	Setnikar *et al.* (1960); Spector (1960, 1961); Bovet-Nitti and Bignami (1963)
Dibenamine	Rat	Everett *et al.* (1949); Everett and Sawyer (1949a); Sawyer *et al.* (1949a); Zarrow and Quinn (1963)
	Rabbit	Sawyer *et al.* (1947, 1949b)
	Hen	van Tienhoven *et al.* (1954)

TABLE V—*Continued*

Drugs	Species	References
Dibenzyline	Rat	Moore (1961)
SKF-501	Rat	Sawyer *et al.* (1950)
	Rabbit	Sawyer *et al.* (1950)
	Hen	Zarrow and Bastian (1953)
Atropine	Rat	Everett *et al.* (1949); Everett and Sawyer (1949a); Zarrow and Quinn (1963)
	Rabbit	Sawyer *et al.* (1949b); Saul and Sawyer (1957)
	Hen	Zarrow and Bastian (1953)
	Cow	Hansel and Trimberger (1951)
Methantheline	Rat	Sawyer (1963)
	Rabbit	Sawyer *et al.* (1951)
Pathilon	Rat	Gitsch and Everett (1958)

[a] For review see Everett (1964).
[b] Premature ovulation produced in the hen.

sponsible for initiating LRF discharge. Timing experiments in rabbits indicated that there was a cholinergic discharge followed by an adrenergic discharge in the sequence of events leading to ovulation (see Sawyer, 1963). The report by Markee *et al.* (1948) that injection of epinephrine into the pituitary produced ovulation led to the hypothesis that LRF might be a catecholamine, but others could not demonstrate that norepinephrine and epinephrine had any LRF activity (see Chapter 31). In addition, SKF-501 failed to block the ovulation produced by electrical stimulation of the hypothalamus or amygdaloid nucleus through implanted electrodes in rabbits (Sawyer, 1963), and LRF is now known to be a polypeptide (see Chapter 8, in Volume I). Therefore, the response to intrapituitary epinephrine is apparently nonspecific, and the adrenergic and cholinergic blocking agents act somewhere in the nervous system proximal to the LRF-secreting neurons. Nicotine does not stimulate LH secretion in rats (McCann, 1963).

Diphenylhydantoin has recently been added to the list of agents producing blockade of ovulation in the rat (Quinn, 1965). This anticonvulsant is also said to inhibit ACTH secretion (see Section V,A,3). Its mechanism of action is uncertain, but it seems reasonable to suspect that it depresses neural thresholds in the hypothalamus and brain stem.

Various monoamine oxidase inhibitors have been reported to interfere with fertility. Interference with LH secretion has been suggested as the cause of this infertility (Setnikar *et al.*, 1960) and it has recently been reported that the potent monoamine oxidase inhibitor, tranylcypromine, blocks ovulation in rats when given before the "critical period" at the time of proestrus (Alleva *et al.*, 1965). As noted above (Section V,A,3), some monoamine oxidase inhibitors have been reported to affect ACTH secretion. Tranylcypromine inhibits 17α-hydroxylase in the adrenal, but does not inhibit ACTH secretion in dogs.

The fact that so many different drugs have the capacity to block ovulation when injected during the critical period in rats raises the possibility that their effects are nonspecific. Timiras (1952) noted that most of the blocking drugs caused increased ACTH secretion, and suggested in effect that anything which increased ACTH secretion decreased gonadotropin secretion. Moore (1961) raised this issue again when he reported that blockade of ovulation correlated positively with the production of adrenal ascorbic acid depletion in rats and noted that although a variety of drugs blocked ovulation on acute administration, they failed to do so when administered chronically. However, a number of stresses and several drugs with far-reaching effects, including dibenzylaminoethanol, the imidazoline adrenergic blocking agents, ganglionic blocking agents, an antihistamine, and intravenously administered procaine, fail to block ovulation in rats (see Sawyer, 1963, 1964). Furthermore, it is not at all certain there is a reciprocal relationship between the rate of ACTH secretion and the rate of FSH and LH secretion; stress appears to have a variable effect on gonadotropin secretion and may in some instances actually increase it (Nowell and Chester-Jones, 1957).

Studies of the effects of various agents injected during the neonatal period show that drugs can exert long-term as well as transient effects on the secretion of FSH and LH. It is now well established that injections of androgens or estrogens in the first few days of life in rats cause profound alterations in gonadotropin secretion and sexual behavior in adulthood. These "inductive" effects of hormones are considered in detail in Chapter 19. Kikuyama (1961, 1962) has demonstrated that the effects of injecting androgens in early life are prevented if chlorpromazine or reserpine is injected at the same time. Recently, Carraro *et al.* (1964, 1965) have shown that a single injection of reserpine on the fourth day of life in female rats delays the onset of puberty and causes prolonged periods of diestrus in adulthood.

E. Prolactin

Drugs acting on the nervous system that are believed to affect prolactin secretion are listed in Table VI. There is no generally available assay for prolactin in body fluids, and indirect indices of prolactin secretion have been used in experiments indicating stimulation or inhibi-

TABLE VI

DRUGS ACTING ON THE NERVOUS SYSTEM THAT ALTER PROLACTIN (LTH) SECRETION[a]

Drugs	Species	Indices used	References
Drugs producing stimulation			
Chloroform	Rat	Pseudopregnancy	Swingle *et al.* (1951b)
Ether	Rat	Pseudopregnancy	Fraschini *et al.* (1961)
Morphine	Rat	Lactation	Meites *et al.* (1960)
Metrazol	Rat	Pseudopregnancy	Swingle *et al.* (1951a)
Chlorpromazine	Rat	Pseudopregnancy	Barraclough and Sawyer (1959)
	Rat	Lactation	Grönroos *et al.* (1959); Meites *et al.* (1960); Talwalker *et al.* (1960)
	Human	Lactation	Winnik and Tennenbaum (1955); Polishuk and Kulckar (1956)
Reserpine	Rat	Increased LTH secretion	Meites *et al.* (1963); Moon and Turner (1959a)
	Rabbit	Increased LTH secretion	Kanematsu *et al.* (1961)
	Rat	Pseudopregnancy	Benson (1958); Barraclough and Sawyer (1959)
	Rat	Lactation	Desclin (1960)
	Rabbit	Lactation	Meites (1957); Sawyer (1957)
Meprobamate	Rat	Lactation	Meites *et al.* (1960)
Amphetamine	Rat	Lactation	Meites *et al.* (1960)
Pilocarpine	Rat	Lactation	Meites *et al.* (1960)
Physostigmine	Rat	Lactation	Meites *et al.* (1960)
Atropine (large dose)	Rat	Lactation	Meites *et al.* (1960)
Pathilon	Rat	Pseudopregnancy	Gitsch and Everett (1958)
Salicylates	Rat	Pseudopregnancy	Fraschini *et al.* (1961); Gavazzi *et al.* (1961)
Drugs producing inhibition			
Ether	Rat	Pseudopregnancy	Jacobson *et al.* (1950)
Pentobarbital	Rat	Pseudopregnancy	Jacobson *et al.* (1950)
Ergotoxine	Rat	Pseudopregnancy	Shelesnyak (1954a, 1955)
Ergocornine methane sulfonate	Mouse	Termination of pregnancy	Carlsen *et al.* (1961)
Dibenamine	Rat	Lactation	Grosvenor and Turner (1958)
Atropine (low dose)	Rat	Pseudopregnancy	Jacobson *et al.* (1950)
	Rat	Lactation	Grosvenor and Turner (1958)
Iproniazid	Rat	Lactation	Mizuno *et al.* (1964)

[a] For review see Meites *et al.* (1963).

tion of prolactin secretion by drugs acting on the nervous system. Lactation is one such index; many hormones are involved in this process, although variations in the rate of prolactin secretion certainly exert an important effect if the other hormones are present in adequate amounts (see Chapter 16, in Volume I). Pseudopregnancy is another index; this condition can be produced in rats by transplantation of the pituitary to a site distant from the median eminence (Everett, 1964), a procedure which produces a marked increase in prolactin secretion. Therefore, the occurrence of pseudopregnancy indicates an increase in prolactin secretion and inhibition of the production of pseudopregnancy indicates inhibition of the secretion of this hormone.

In lactation and pseudopregnancy, there is a concomitant decline in FSH and LH secretion; indeed the secretion of prolactin seems generally to vary inversely with that of FSH and LH (see Chapter 15, in Volume I). It has even been suggested that LRF and prolactin-inhibiting factor (PIF) are the same substance, although there is now evidence that they are probably separate entities (Schally *et al.*, 1964; see also Chapter 8, in Volume I). Meites has pointed out that there is a parallelism between the secretion of prolactin and ACTH, and many stresses that increase ACTH secretion also increase prolactin secretion (see Chapter 16, in Volume I). These reciprocal relations appear to hold true in the case of chlorpromazine and reserpine (Table VI). Both of these drugs produce pseudopregnancy and lactation in rats, and chlorpromazine produces lactation in humans; both drugs stimulate ACTH secretion and block ovulation. Morphine also inhibits ovulation, stimulates lactation, and increases ACTH secretion. The irritant formaldehyde and three different carcinogens have been reported to increase the secretion of prolactin and ACTH (Meites *et al.*, 1963). However, barbiturates block ovulation while inhibiting prolactin and ACTH secretion. As noted above, cholinergic blocking agents and adrenergic blocking agents inhibit FSH and LH secretion. Cholinergic agents (such as pilocarpine, physotigmine, and Pathilon) and adrenergic agents (such as amphetamine) stimulate prolactin secretion, as do acetylcholine and the catecholamines (Meites *et al.*, 1963); atropine in small doses and the adrenergic blocking agents ergotoxine and Dibenamine exert effects which suggest that they decrease prolactin secretion. In mice, the ergot derivative, ergocornine inhibits deciduoma formation, a process which depends on prolactin secretion (Carlsen *et al.*, 1961). However, large doses of atropine have been reported to stimulate lactation and the whole problem needs a more thorough investigation with a more direct index of prolactin secretion before any firm conclusions can be drawn.

The monoamine oxidase inhibitor, iproniazid, is of special interest because it inhibits the lactational response to electrical stimulation of the uterine cervix but does not inhibit the increase in prolactin secretion produced by reserpine (Mizuno *et al.*, 1964) even though it reduces or blocks the increase in ACTH secretion produced by this drug (see Section V,A,3).

F. Vasopressin

There is evidence that the anesthetics pentobarbital, phenobarbital, Amytal, urethan, and ether and the analgesics morphine and meperidine all stimulate vasopressin secretion (Table VII). The mechanisms by which they produce this stimulation are unknown. Chloralose may be unique among the anesthetics in that, in rats, it does not stimulate vasopressin secretion (Heller, 1960). However, Moran *et al.* (1964) have reported that anesthesia with halothane, thiopental, methoxyflurane, or nitrous oxide does act to elevate blood vasopressin levels in humans. There is considerable uncertainty whether the supraoptic neurons themselves are cholinergic, but there is a good deal of evidence that cholinergic fibers activate the supraoptic neurons (see Chapters 6, in Volume I, and 31). Therefore, it is not surprising that not only acetylcholine but eserine, nicotine, and lobeline stimulate vasopressin secretion. However, there is some evidence that atropine and hexamethonium also increase vasopressin secretion. Aminopyrine decreases urine volume and increases urine osmolality. Strom and Zemek (1964) have reported that this drug is more effective on intracarotid than on systemic injection in dogs, so it is included in Table VII as an agent which may stimulate vasopressin secretion. It has an antidiuretic action in patients with diabetes insipidus, but this could be due to the release of vasopressin from remaining supraoptic neurons.

It is well established that ethyl alcohol inhibits vasopressin secretion, but alcohol may not be unique in this respect. Moses (1964) has claimed that reserpine and chlorpromazine both inhibit vasopressin secretion. Chlorpromazine does produce a diuresis, but the mechanism of this diuresis is disputed (Parrish and Levine, 1956; W. P. Smith *et al.*, 1958). Choral hydrate causes an increase in urine volume in humans which is suggestive of decreased vasopressin secretion (Hill *et al.*, 1958).

Mills and Wang (1964a,b; see also Chapter 6, in Volume I) have recently reported interesting experiments in which the effects of drugs on the release of vasopressin produced by stimulation of the vagus nerve or the ulnar nerve were tested in dogs. The vagi carry fibers that mediate changes in vasopressin secretion in response to changes in central venous pressure, while stimulation of pain fibers in the ulnar or any

TABLE VII

DRUGS ACTING ON THE NERVOUS SYSTEM THAT ALTER VASOPRESSIN SECRETION[a]

Drugs	Species	References
Drugs that stimulate vasopressin secretion		
Ether	Rat	Heller (1960)
	Dog	Craig *et al.* (1945)
	Man	Burnett *et al.* (1949)
Urethan	Rat	Heller (1960)
Pentobarbital, Phenobarbital, Amytal	Dog	deBodo and Prescott (1945)
Barbiturates	Man	Papper and Papper (1964)
Hydroxyzine	Dog	Blackmore (1960)
Morphine	Rat	Giarman *et al.* (1953); Giarman and Condouris (1954); Winter *et al.* (1954); Heller (1960)
	Dog	Lipschitz and Stokey (1947)
	Man	Walker (1949); Papper and Papper (1964)
Meperidine	Man	Papper and Papper (1964)
Hexamethonium	Rat	Bisset and Walker (1957)
Eserine	Dog	Duke and Pickford (1951)
Nicotine	Rat	Bisset and Walker (1957)
	Man	Cates and Garrod (1951); Walker (1949)
Lobeline	Rat	Grewal *et al.* (1960)
Atropine	Dog	Lasagna and Dearborn (1952)
Physostigmine	Dog	Lasagna and Dearborn (1952)
Aminopyrine	Dog	Strom and Zemek (1964)
	Man	Brings (1931); Scherf (1931); Culligan and Prendergast (1933); Canelo and Lisser (1935); Balsam and Katz (1961)
Drugs that inhibit vasopressin secretion		
Ethyl alcohol	Rat	Bisset and Walker (1957)
	Dog	Van Dyke and Ames (1951)
	Man	Eggleton (1942); Eggleton and Smith (1946)
Chloral hydrate	Man	Hill *et al.* (1958)
Chlorpromazine	Man	Parrish and Levine (1956) [but see W. P. Smith *et al.* (1958)]
Reserpine	Rat	Moses (1964)

[a] For reviews see W. H. Sawyer (1961) and Chapters 6 and 7 (in Volume I).

other nerve increases vasopressin secretion. In the studies of Mills and Wang, morphine and meperidine produced an antidiuresis that apparently was not due to vasopressin secretion, and both drugs blocked the increase in vasopressin secretion produced by ulnar nerve stimulation, but not that produced by vagal stimulation. In small doses, the adrenergic blocking agents Hydergine, phenoxybenzamine, and phentolamine inhibited the response to ulnar stimulation but in large doses they inhibited the vagal response as well. The cholinergic blocking agents atropine and ethybenztropine blocked neither response. These investigators reviewed the data of others indicating that adrenergic neurons end on the supraoptic neurons (Carlsson *et al.*, 1962), as well as the evidence indicating a relation between the supraoptic nuclei and acetylcholine. Catecholamines have been reported to inhibit vasopressin secretion, but there is also evidence that they may stimulate it (see Chapter 6, in Volume I). Therefore, the interesting possibility exists that the neurons mediating the response to noxious stimuli and the vagal fibers passing to the supraoptic nuclei resemble the neurons in the peripheral autonomic nervous system described by Burn and associates (see Burn, 1963; Burn and Froede, 1963). According to Burn, the endings of these peripheral neurons first release acetylcholine, which in turn liberates norepinephrine. At these sites, as in the supraoptic nuclei, atropine fails to exert a blocking effect.

G. Oxytocin

The drugs influencing oxytocin secretion have not received as much attention as those affecting vasopressin secretion. Many of those which release vasopressin also liberate oxytocin: e.g., nicotine and anesthetics in animals and nicotine in man (Bisset and Walker, 1957; Chaudhury and Walker, 1958). Alcohol inhibits the secretion of oxytocin as well as that of vasopressin (Fuchs and Wagner, 1963). The problem of physiological factors controlling oxytocin secretion and the question of secretion of oxytocin without concomitant vasopressin secretion is discussed in detail in Chapter 7 (in Volume I).

H. Adrenal Medulla

The physiology of the adrenal medulla and the effects of some drugs on its secretion are discussed in Chapter 25. This gland is in an important sense a sympathetic ganglion in which the postganglionic neurons have lost their axons and become specialized instead for the secretion of norepinephrine and epinephrine into the blood stream. The gland is thus controlled for the most part via the nervous system, and if its nerve supply is cut, adrenal medullary secretion drops to very low levels. However, its nerve supply is cholinergic, like all preganglionic neurons in the body, and the adrenal medullary cells respond like sympathetic ganglia to nicotine and nicotinic drugs. Thus, cholinergic agents such as carbaminoylcholine (Feldberg, 1932), choline (Glaubach and Pick, 1925; Feldberg and Vartiainen, 1935), and pilocarpine (Dale and Laidlaw, 1912), as well as nicotine (Eichholtz, 1923; Houssay and Molinelli, 1926) and α-lobeline (Houssay and Molinelli, 1925; Konzett, 1951) stimulate adrenal medullary secretion by a direct action on the gland. Tetramethylammonium chloride stimulates medullary cells directly (Stone *et al.*, 1951). Other drugs affecting secretion are discussed in detail by Sataké (1954, 1955).

Reserpine acts on catecholamine-secreting cells to inhibit the active transport of the catecholamines into storage sites. Its administration is therefore followed by a transient outflow of norepinephrine and epinephrine from the adrenal medulla, although the main long-term action of reserpine is, of course, a marked inhibition of adrenal medullary secretion (Carlsson and Hillarp, 1956; Burger, 1957; Hertting *et al.*, 1961). Tyramine, amphetamine, cocaine, chlorpromazine, imipramine, guanethidine, and phenoxybenzamine have also been reported to produce a transient rise in circulating norepinephrine (Hertting *et al.*, 1961), presumably by liberating catecholamines from the adrenal medulla as well as other sympathetic postganglionic neurons. However, guanethidine and several of the other drugs listed above, like reserpine, are long-term inhibitors of adrenergic discharge.

It is not possible to consider drugs affecting the adrenal medulla directly in greater detail without considering the broader problem of adrenergic stimulation and inhibition, and this immensely complex field is outside the scope of this chapter. The interested reader is therefore referred to texts and recent review articles for further information (Comroe, 1963; L. S. Goodman and Gilman, 1965; Wurtman, 1965).

Other drugs which increase adrenal medullary secretion, presumably by an action on the central nervous system rather than directly on the gland, include the anesthetics ether, chloroform, urethan, and chloralose (Elliott, 1912; Emmelin and Stromblad, 1951; Brewster *et al.*, 1952; Sataké, 1954, 1955; Ganong, 1959; Wise *et al.*, 1960). Morphine has a similar effect (deBodo *et al.*, 1937; Hebb and Konzett, 1949; Houssay *et al.*, 1950). Carbon tetrachloride and β-tetrahydronaphthylamine increase secretion by a central action (see Chapter 25). Dimercaprol (British anti-Lewisite, BAL), thallium, diphtheria toxin, *Salmonella* endotoxin, ethanol, prenylamine, acetaldehyde, and decaborane cause increased catecholamine secretion but whether they act on the nervous system or directly on the gland is uncertain (Kimura, 1927; Tillman, 1952; Prout *et al.*, 1958; Perman, 1958a,b; Schöne and Lindner, 1962; Serafimov, 1962; Merrit *et al.*, 1964). Pentobarbital inhibits epinephrine secretion (Ronzoni, 1950).

I. Hormones of the Intermediate Lobe of the Pituitary

In Chapters 23 and 24 α- and β-MSH and the mechanisms regulating their secretion are discussed. The effects of neurohumors on the secretion of the intermediate lobe of the pituitary are discussed in Chapter 31. In some species of amphibians and fish, the melanophores are affected by nerve fibers as well as circulating MSH's and melatonin, and in these and other species, a wide variety of drugs have been found to act on the pigment cells. These drugs may produce aggregation or dispersion of the melanin granules; the list of active agents includes acetylcholine and related compounds, epinephrine, norepinephrine, tyramine, tryptamine, caffeine, diethyl ether, ethanol, dinitrophenol, hydroxyquinone, Mesantoin, compounds that inhibit sulfhydryl groups, and antiadrenergic compounds, including ergot derivatives (Lerner and Fitzpatrick, 1950; Lerner *et al.*, 1954; Lerner, 1955; Wright, 1955; Lerner and Takahashi, 1956; Davey, 1960; Fujii, 1960, 1961; Watanabe 1960; Scheline, 1963). However, all these agents act directly on the end organ, the pigment cell, rather than by way of alterations in the secretion of the intermediate lobe of the pituitary. The only drugs claimed to act directly on intermediate lobe secretion are LSD, which is said to inhibit secretion in toads (Burgers *et al.*, 1958), and some of the phenothiazine tranquilizers, which are said to stimulate secretion in frogs (Scott and Nading, 1961).

VI. Conclusions

Drugs affecting endocrine secretion include hormone congeners, drugs acting directly on endocrine glands to inhibit or stimulate their secretion, drugs blocking the actions of hormones on their target organs, and drugs affecting endocrine function by an action upon the nervous system. The last group includes drugs usually categorized as "nonspecific stressors" which bring about various changes leading secondarily to activation of the neural mechanisms controlling ACTH secretion.

Hormone congeners of neuroendocrine interest include the synthetic progesterone derivatives used as oral contraceptives. These compounds appear to inhibit gonadotropin secretion by an action on the hypothalamus.

Drugs inhibiting thyroid and adrenocortical function cause increased TSH and ACTH secretion via the negative feedback mechanisms controlling secretion of these two hormones, but aside from such actions, these and other drugs acting directly on endocrine glands generally lack neuroendocrine effects.

Drugs of neuroendocrine interest which block the effects of hormones on their target organs include reserpine and guanethidine, which prevent some of the effects of thyroid hormone on the nervous system.

There are drugs acting on the nervous system which alter the secretion of all of the known hormones of the anterior, intermediate, and posterior lobes of the pituitary gland and the adrenal medulla. These include particularly anesthetics, tranquilizers, some monoamine oxidase inhibitors, and analgesics, but striking effects are also produced in many instances by autonomic drugs. Research with these drugs has provided valuable insights into the ways the pituitary regulatory mechanisms work; for instance, it has been demonstrated that the increase in pituitary gonadotropin secretion that triggers ovulation depends on a cholinergic followed by an adrenergic neural discharge. Further study of the endocrine effects of drugs acting on the nervous system should be very fruitful not only for pharmacologists but for physiologists studying the fundamental aspects of neuroendocrinology.

References

Alexander, W. D., and Johnson, W. K. M. (1956). A comparison of the effects of acetylsalicylic acid and di-triiodothyronine in patients with myxoedema. *Clin. Sci.* **15,** 593–601.

Alleva, J. J., Overpeck, J. G., and Umberger, E. J. (1965). Inhibition of ovulation in rats by tranylcypromine. *Federation Proc.* **24,** 129 (Abstract).

Amesbury, O. F., Contopoulos, A. N., and Koneff, A. F. (1965). Effects of estrogen on pituitary function in the thyroidectomized rat. *Acta Endocrinol.* **48,** 355–368.

Ando, S., Guze, L. B., and Gold, E. M. (1964). ACTH release *in vivo* and *in vitro:* Extrapituitary mediation during *Esch. coli* bacteremia. *Endocrinology* **74,** 894–901.

Anichkov, S. V., Poskalenko, A. N., and Ryzhenkov, V. E. (1962). Action of neurotropic drugs upon ACTH secretion. *Proc. 1st Intern. Pharmacol. Meeting, Stockholm, 1961* Vol. 1, pp. 1–8. Pergamon Press, Oxford.

Arky, R. A., and Freinkel, N. (1964). The response of plasma human growth hormone to insulin and ethanol-induced hypoglycemia in two patients with "isolated adrenocorticotropic defect." *Metab., Clin. Exptl.* **13,** 547–550.

Arnott, D. G., and Doniach, I. (1952). The effect of compounds allied to resorcinol upon the uptake of radioactive iodine (I^{131}) by the thyroid of the rat. *Biochem. J.* **50,** 473–479.

Aron, E., Chambon, Y., and Voisin, A. (1953). Action d'un végétatiovolytique sur la réaction hypophysosurrénalienne du rat blanc. Application au dosage pratique des substances corticotropes. *Bull. Acad. Natl. Med.* (*Paris*) [3] **137,** 417–420.

Ashford, A., and Shapero, M. (1962). Effect of chlorpromazine, reserpine, benactyzine and phenobartone on the release of corticotrophin in the rat. *Brit. J. Pharmacol.* **19**, 458–463.

Astwood, E. B., Sullivan, J., Bissell, A., and Tyslowitz, R. (1943). Action of certain sulfonamides and of thiourea upon the function of the thyroid gland of the rat. *Endocrinology* **32**, 210–225.

Austen, F. K., Rubini, M. E., Meroney, W. H., and Wolff, J. (1958). Salicylates and thyroid function. 1. Depression of thyroid function. *J. Clin. Invest.* **37**, 1131–1143.

Balsam, T., and Katz, H. M. (1961). Diabetes insipidus successfully treated with oral aminopyrine. *J. Am. Med. Assoc.* **176**, 1112–1114.

Barker, S. B., Pittman, C. S., Pittman, J. A., Jr., and Hill, S. R., Jr. (1960). Thyroxine antagonism by partially iodinated thyronines and analogues. *Ann. N.Y. Acad. Sci.* **86**, 545–562.

Barraclough, C. A., and Sawyer, C. H. (1955). Inhibition of the release of pituitary ovulatory hormone in the rat by morphine. *Endocrinology* **57**, 329–337.

Barraclough, C. A., and Sawyer, C. H. (1957). Blockade of the release of pituitary ovulating hormone in the rat by chlorpromazine and reserpine: possible mechanisms of action. *Endocrinology* **61**, 341–351.

Barraclough, C. A., and Sawyer, C. H. (1959). Induction of pseudopregnancy in the rat by reserpine and chlorpromazine. *Endocrinology* **65**, 563–571.

Barrett, A. M., and Sayers, G. (1958). Loss of ACTH activity following incubation of pituitary tissues: inhibition by glucagon and pitressin. *Endocrinology* **62**, 637–645.

Barrett, A. M., and Stockham, M. A. (1963). The effect of housing conditions and simple experimental procedures upon the corticosterone level in the plasma of rats. *J. Endocrinol.* **26**, 97–105.

Baumann, E. T., and Marine, D. (1946). Involution of adrenal cortex in rats fed thiouracil. *Endocrinology* **36**, 400–405.

Bayliss, R. I. S., and Steinbeck, A. W. (1954). Salicylates and the plasma level of adrenal steroids. *Lancet* **I**, 1010–1011.

Benson, G. K. (1958). Effect of reserpine on mammary gland involution and on other organs in the rat. *Proc. Soc. Exptl. Biol. Med.* **99**, 550–553.

Bergenstal, D. M., Hertz, R., Lipsett, M. B., and Moy, R. H. (1960). Chemotherapy of adrenocortical cancer with *o,p'*DDD. *Ann. Internal Med.* **53**, 672–682.

Bernis, R., and Vanek, R. (1958). L'élimination des corticoids urinaires réducteurs "totaux" dans le stress chirugical. *Acta Anesthesiol. Belg.* **9**, 116–138.

Betz, D., and Ganong, W. F. (1963). Effect of chlorpromazine on pituitary-adrenal function in the dog. *Acta Endocrinol.* **43**, 264–270.

Bisset, G. W., and Walker, J. M. (1957). The effect of nicotine, hexamethonium and ethanol on the secretion of antidiuretic and oxytocic hormones of the rat. *Brit. J. Pharmacol.* **12**, 461–467.

Blackmore, W. P. (1960). Effect of hydroxyzine on urine flow in the dog. *Proc. Soc. Exptl. Biol. Med.* **103**, 518–520.

Blanchard, K. C., Dearborn, E. H., Maren, T. H., Marshall, E. K., Jr. (1950). Stimulation of the anterior pituitary by certain cinchoninic acid derivatives. *Bull. Johns Hopkins Hosp.* **86**, 83–88.

Bledsoe, T., Island, D. P., Riondel, A. M., and Liddle, G. W. (1964). Modification of aldosterone secretion and electrolyte excretion in man by a chemical inhibitor of 18-oxidation. *J. Clin. Endocrinol. Metab.* **24**, 740–746.

Bliss, E. L., Migeon, C. J., Eik-Nes, K., Sandberg, A. A., and Samuels, L. T. (1954). The effects of insulin, histamine, bacterial pyrogen, and the antabuse-alcohol reaction upon the levels of 17-hydroxycorticosteroids in the peripheral blood of man. *Metab., Clin. Exptl.* **3**, 493–501.

Bonnycastle, D. D., and Bradley, A. J. (1960). Diphenylhydantoin and the release of adrenocorticotropic hormone in the albino rat. *Endocrinology* **66**, 355–361.

Boscott, R. J., Jeavons, M., and Kar, A. B. (1956). Preliminary investigations on the influence of reserpine therapy on adrenocortical function in schizophrenia. *Experientia* **12**, 271.

Bovet-Nitti, F., and Bignami, G. (1963). Action of certain derivatives of 2-aminomethyl-benzodioxan on the hormonal equilibrium of the reproductive cycle, pseudopregnancy and pregnancy in the rat. *Proc. 1st Intern. Pharmacol. Meeting, Stockholm, 1961* Vol. 10, p. 3. Pergamon Press, Oxford (Abstract).

Bray, P. F., Ely, R. S., and Kelley, V. C. (1954). Studies of 17-hydroxycorticosteroids. VIII. Adrenocortical function in patients with convulsive disorder. *AMA Arch. Neurol. Psychiat.* **72**, 583–590.

Brewster, W. R., Jr., Bunker, J. P., and Beecher, H. K. (1952). Metabolic effects of anesthesia. VI. Mechanism of metabolic acidosis and hyperglycemia during ether anesthesia in the dog. *Am. J. Physiol.* **171**, 37–47.

Brewster, W. R., Jr., Isaacs, J. P., Osgood, P. F., and King, T. L. (1956). The hemodynamic and metabolic interrelationships in the activity of epinephrine, norepinephrine and the thyroid hormones. *Circulation* **13**, 1–20.

Brinck-Johnsen, T., Solem, J. H., Brinck-Johnsen, K., and Ingvaldsen, P. (1963). The 17-hydroxycorticosteroid response to corticotrophin, metopiron and bacterial pyrogen. *Acta Med. Scand.* **173**, 129–140.

Brings, L. (1931). Über die Wirkung von Pyramidon auf die Diurèse von Thalamus and Vierhügelkaninchen. *Arch. Exptl. Pathol. Pharmakol.* **162**, 515–520.

Brodie, B. B., Maickel, R. P., and Westermann, E. O. (1961). Action of reserpine on pituitary-adrenocortical system through possible action on hypothalamus. *Proc. 4th Intern. Neurochem. Symp., Varenna, 1960* pp. 351–361. Pergamon Press, Oxford.

Brown, J. H. U. (1953). Influence of the drug DDD on adrenal cortical function in adult rats. *Proc. Soc. Exptl. Biol. Med.* **83**, 59–62.

Brown, J. H. U., Griffin, J. B., and Smith, R. B., III (1955). Excretion of urinary 17-hydroxycorticoids in dogs fed DDD. *Metab., Clin. Exptl.* **4**, 542–544.

Brown, J. H. U., Griffin, J. B., Smith, R. B., III, and Anason, A. (1956). Physiologic activity of an adrenocorticolytic drug in the adult dog. *Metab., Clin. Exptl.* **5**, 594–600.

Brown-Grant, K. (1958). Thyroid function and adrenal weight in the rabbit. *J. Endocrinol.* **17**, 197–200.

Burdette, B. H., Leeman, S., and Munson, P. L. (1961). The reversal by nalorphine of the inhibitory effect of morphine on the secretion of adrenocorticotrophic hormones in stress. *J. Pharmacol. Exptl. Therap.* **132**, 323–328.

Burger, M. (1957). Verandrungen der Adrenalin- und Noradrenalinkonzentrationene im menschlichen Blutplasma unter Reserpin. *Arch. Exptl. Pathol. Pharmakol.* **230**, 489–498.

Burgers, A. C. J., Leemreis, W., Dominiczak, T., and van Oordt, G. J. (1958). Inhibition of the secretion of intermedine by D-lysergic acid diethylamide (LSD-25) in the toad, *Xenopus laevis.* *Acta Endocrinol.* **29**, 191–200.

Burn, J. H. (1963). The liberation of norepinephrine. *Physiol. Physicians* **1,** October, 1–4.

Burn, J. H., and Froede, H. (1963). The action of substances which block sympathetic postganglionic nervous transmission. *Brit. J. Pharmacol.* **20,** 378–387.

Burnett, C. H., Bloomberg, E. L., Shortz, G., Compton, D. W., and Beecher, H. K. (1949). A comparison of the effects of ether and cyclopropane anesthesia on the renal function of man. *J. Pharmacol. Exptl. Therap.* **96,** 380–387.

Canary, J. J., Schaaf, M., Duffy, B. J., Jr., and Kyle, L. H. (1957). Effects of oral and intramuscular administration of reserpine in thyrotoxicosis. *New Engl. J. Med.* **257,** 435–442.

Canelo, C. K., and Lisser, H. (1935). A case of diabetes insipidus controlled with powdered pituitary posterior lobe extract applied intranasally as snuff. *Calif. Med.* **42,** 178–180.

Carlsen, R. A., Zielmaker, G. H., and Shelesnyak, M. C. (1961). Termination of early (pre-nidation) pregnancy in the mouse by single injection of ergocornine methanesulphonate. *J. Reprod. Fertility* **2,** 369–373.

Carlsson, A., and Hillarp, N. Å. (1956). Release of adrenaline from the adrenal medulla of rabbits produced by reserpine. *Kgl. Fysiograf. Sallskap. Lund., Forh.* **26,** No. 8, 90–91.

Carlsson, A., Falck, B., and Hillarp, N. Å. (1962). Cellular localization of brain monoamines. *Acta Physiol. Scand.* Suppl. 196, 1–28.

Carraro, A., Fraschini, F., Giuliani, G., Martini, L., and Pecile, A. (1964). Centrally acting drugs and anterior pituitary function. Proc. 2nd Intern. Congr. Endocrinol., London, 1964. *Excerpta Med., Intern. Congr. Ser.* **83,** pp. 617–623.

Carraro, A., Corbin, A., Fraschini, F., and Martini, L. (1965). The effect of prepuberal treatment with reserpine on puberty, pituitary luteinizing hormone and the oestrus cycle of the rat. *J. Endocrinol.* **32,** 387–393.

Casentini, S., De Poli, A., Hukovic, S., and Martini, L. (1959). Studies on control of corticotrophin release. *Endocrinology* **64,** 483–493.

Castor, C. W., and Beirwaltes, W. (1956). Effect of 2,4-dinitrophenol on thyroid function in man. *J. Clin. Endocrinol. Metab.* **16,** 1026–1031.

Cates, J. E., and Garrod, O. (1951). The effect of nicotine on urinary flow in diabetes insipidus. *Clin. Sci.* **10,** 145–160.

Chart, J. J., Sheppard, H., Allen, M. J., Bencze, W. F., and Gaunt, R. (1958). New amphenone analogues as adrenocortical inhibitors. *Experientia* **14,** 151–152.

Chart, J. J., Sheppard, H., Mowles, T., and Howie, N. (1962). Inhibitors of adrenal corticosteroid 17α-hydroxylation. *Endocrinology* **71,** 479–486.

Chaudhury, R. R., and Walker, J. M. (1958). The release of neurohypophysial hormones in the rabbit by anesthetics and by haemorrhage. *J. Physiol.* (*London*) **143,** 16P (Abstract).

Cheymol, J., de Leeuw, J., and Oger, J. (1954). Que faut-il penser de l'hypophysectomie pharmacodynamique par las chlorpromazine? *Compt. Rend. Soc. Biol.* **148,** 1213–1216.

Christensen, L. K. (1959). Thyroxine-releasing effect of salicylate and of 2,4-dinitrophenol. *Nature* **183,** 1189–1190.

Christy, N. P., and Hofmann, A. D. (1959). Effects of diphenylhydantoin upon adrenal cortical function in man. *Neurology* **9,** 245–248.

Christy, N. P., Donn, A., and Jailer, J. W. (1956). Inhibition by aminopyrine of adrenocortical activation caused by pyrogenic reaction. *Proc. Soc. Exptl. Biol. Med.* **91,** 453–456.

Christy, N. P., Longson, D., Horwitz, W. A., and Knight, M. M. (1957). Inhibitory effect of chlorpromazine upon the adrenal cortical response to insulin hypoglycemia in man. *J. Clin. Invest.* **36,** 543–549.

Comroe, J. H., Jr. (1963). The mechanism of action of some drugs on the sympathetic nervous system. *Physiol. Physicians* **1,** October, 5–8.

Cooper, K. E. (1965). The role of the hypothalamus in the genesis of fever. *Proc. Roy. Soc. Med.* **58,** 740.

Costa, E., and Zetler, G. (1958). Effect of epinephrine on adrenal ascorbic acid following premedication with LSD or 5-OH-indolalkylamines. *Proc. Soc. Exptl. Biol. Med.* **98,** 249–252.

Costa, P. J., Glaser, G. H., and Bonnycastle, D. D. (1955). Effects of diphenylhydantoin (Dilantin) on adrenal cortical function. *AMA Arch. Neurol. Psychiat.* **74,** 88–91.

Co-Tui, F. W., Riley, E., and Orr, A. (1956). 17-Hydroxycorticosteroid levels in the peripheral blood of psychotic patients under treatment with chlorpromazine and reserpine. *J. Clin. Exptl. Psychopathol. & Quart. Rev. Psychiat. Neurol.* **17,** 142–146.

Co-Tui, F. W., Brinitzer, W., Orr, A., and Orr, E. (1960). Effect of chlorpromazine and of reserpine on adrenocortical function. *Psychiat. Quart.* **34,** 47–61.

Craig, F. N., Visscher, F. E., and Houck, C. R. (1945). Renal function in dogs under ether or cyclopropane anesthesia. *Am. J. Physiol.* **143,** 108–118.

Cronheim, G., and Hyder, N. (1954). Effect of salicylic acid on adrenal-pituitary system. III. Studies on mechanism of this effect. *Proc. Soc. Exptl. Biol. Med.* **86,** 409–413.

Cueto, C., and Brown, J. H. U. (1958a). The chemical fractionation of an adrenocorticolytic drug. *Endocrinology* **62,** 326–333.

Cueto, C., and Brown, J. H. U. (1958b). Biological studies on an adrenocorticolytic agent and the isolation of the active components. *Endocrinology* **62,** 334–339.

Culligan, J. M., and Prendergast, H. J. (1933). Amidopyrine in diabetes insipidus. *Minn. Med.* **16,** 635–641.

Cushman, P., Jr., and Hilton, J. G. (1964). Pituitary-adrenal function during acute prochlorperazine administration in the dog. *Am. J. Physiol.* **207,** 1374–1378.

Cushman, P., Jr., Westermann, C. D., Athos, W. J., and Hilton, J. G. (1963). Increased plasma ACTH-like activity following methopyrapone administration in the dog. *Endocrinology* **73,** 524–534.

Dale, H. H., and Laidlaw, P. P. (1912). The significance of the suprarenal capsules in the action of certain alkaloids. *J. Physiol.* (*London*) **45,** 1–26.

Davey, K. G. (1960). Intermedin and change of color in frogs: A new hypothesis. *Can. J. Zool.* **38,** 715–721.

deBodo, R. C., and Prescott, K. F. (1945). The antidiuretic action of barbiturates (phenobarbital, amytol, pentobarbital) and the mechanism involved in this action. *J. Pharmacol. Exptl. Therap.* **85,** 222–233.

deBodo, R. C., Co-Tui, F. W., and Benagila, A. E. (1937). Studies on the mechanism of morphine hyperglycemia. The role of the adrenal glands. *J. Pharmacol. Exptl. Therap.* **61,** 48–57.

De Feo, V. J., and Reynolds, S. R. M. (1956). Modification of menstrual cycle in rhesus monkeys by reserpine. *Science* **124,** 726–727.

deGarilhe, M. P., Gros, C., Porath, J., and Lindner, E. B. (1960). Further studies on corticotrophin-releasing factor (CRF); corticotropin releasing activity of synthetic peptides. *Experientia* **16,** 414–415.

Del Vecchio, A., Genovese, B., and Martini, L. (1958). Hypothalamus and somatotrophic hormone release. *Proc. Soc. Exptl. Biol. Med.* **98**, 641–645.

Desclin, L. (1960). Influence of reserpine, oxytocin and adrenaline on the structure, secretory activity and involution of mammary glands in virgin and postpartum rats. *Anat. Record* **136**, 182.

De Wied, D. (1961). The significance of the antidiuretic hormone in the release mechanism of corticotrophin. *Endocrinology* **68**, 956–970.

Done, A. K., Ely, R. S., and Kelley, V. C. (1955). Response of plasma 17-hydroxycorticoid to salicylate administration in normal human subjects. *Metab., Clin. Exptl.* **4**, 129–142.

Dordoni, F., and Fortier, C. (1950). Effect of eserine and atropine on ACTH release. *Proc. Soc. Exptl. Biol. Med.* **75**, 815–816.

Duke, H. N., and Pickford, M. (1951). Observations on the action of acetylcholine and adrenaline on the hypothalamus. *J. Physiol.* (*London*) **114**, 325–332.

Duncan, L. J. P., and Baird, J. D. (1960). Compounds administered orally in the treatment of diabetes mellitus. *Pharmacol. Rev.* **12**, 91–158.

Dunn, J. S., Sheehan, H. L., and McLetchie, N. G. B. (1943). Necrosis of islets of Langerhans produced experimentally. *Lancet* **I**, 484–487.

Edgren, R. A., Hamburger, W. F., and Calhoun, D. W. (1959). Production of adrenal atrophy by 6-methyl-17-acetoxy progesterone, with remarks on the adrenal effects of other progestational agents. *Endocrinology* **65**, 505–507.

Edelman, I. S., Bogoroch, R., and Porter, G. A. (1964). Specific action of aldosterone on RNA synthesis. *Trans. Assoc. Am. Physicians* **77**, 307–316.

Egdahl, R. H. (1959a). The differential response of the adrenal cortex and medulla to bacterial endotoxin. *J. Clin. Invest.* **38**, 1120–1125.

Egdahl, R. H. (1959b). Pituitary-adrenal response following trauma to the isolated leg. *Surgery* **46**, 9–21.

Egdahl, R. H., and Richards, J. B. (1956). Effect of chlorpromazine on pituitary ACTH secretion in the dog. *Am. J. Physiol.* **185**, 235–238.

Egdahl, R. H., Richards, J. B., and Hume, D. B. (1956). Effect of reserpine on adrenocortical function in unanesthetized dogs. *Science* **123**, 418 (Abstract).

Egdahl, R. H., Melby, J. C., and Spink, W. W. (1957). Adrenal cortical and body temperature response to repeated endotoxin administration. *Proc. Soc. Exptl. Biol. Med.* **101**, 369–372.

Eggleton, M. G. (1942). The diuretic action of alcohol in man. *J. Physiol.* (*London*) **101**, 172–191.

Eggleton, M. G., and Smith, I. G. (1946). The effect of ethyl alcohol and some other diuretics on chloride excretion in man. *J. Physiol.* (*London*) **104**, 435–442.

Eichholtz, F. (1923). Über den Einfluss von Nikotin und nikotinartig wirkenden Substanzen auf die Adrenalinsekretion. *Arch. Exptl. Pathol. Pharmakol.* **99**, 172–184.

Eisenman, A. J., Fraser, H. F., Sloan, J., and Isbell, H. (1958). Urinary 17-ketosteroid excretion during a cycle of addiction to morphine. *J. Pharmacol. Exptl. Therap.* **124**, 305–311.

Eisenman, A. J., Fraser, H. F., and Brooks, J. W. (1961). Urinary excretion and plasma levels of 17-hydroxycorticosteroids during a cycle of addiction to morphine. *J. Pharmacol. Exptl. Therap.* **132**, 226–231.

Elliott, T. R. (1912). The control of the suprarenal glands by the splanchnic nerves. *J. Physiol* (*London*) **44**, 374–409.

Emmelin, N., and Stromblad, R. (1951). Adrenaline and noradrenaline content of the suprarenals of cats in chloralose and morphine-ether anesthesia. *Acta Physiol. Scand.* **24,** 261–266.

Epstein, R., Erikson, L. B., and Reynolds, S. R. M. (1960). Reserpine and the chronic stress of reduced barometric pressure in female rats. Observations on body weight, adrenal weight and histology and hematocrit values. *Endocrinology* **66,** 167–174.

Everett, J. W. (1964). Central neural control of reproductive functions of the adenohypophysis. *Physiol. Rev.* **44,** 373–431.

Everett, J. W., and Sawyer, C. H. (1949a). A neural timing factor in the mechanism by which progesterone advances ovulation in the cyclic rat. *Endocrinology* **45,** 581–595.

Everett, J. W., and Sawyer, C. H. (1949b). The blocking effect of nembutal on the ovulatory discharge of gonadotropin in the cyclic rat. *Proc. Soc. Exptl. Biol. Med.* **71,** 696–698.

Everett, J. W., and Sawyer, C. H. (1950). A 24-hour periodicity in the "LH release apparatus" of female rats, disclosed by barbiturate sedation. *Endocrinology* **47,** 198–218.

Everett, J. W., Sawyer, C. H., and Markee, J. E. (1949). A neurogenic timing factor in control of the ovulatory discharge of luteinizing hormone in the cyclic rat *Endocrinology* **44,** 234–250.

Fajans, S. S., Floyd, J. C., Jr., Knopf, R. F., Rull, J., Guntsche, E., and Conn, J. W. (1965). Evidence that decreased insulin secretion contributes to benzothiadiazine-induced hyperglycemia. *Progr. 47th Meeting Endocrine Soc., New York,* p. 66 (Abstract).

Farmer, T. A., Jr., Hill, S. R., Jr., Pittman, J. A., Jr., and Herod, J. W., Jr. (1961). The plasma 17-hydroxycorticosteroid response to corticotropin, SU-4885, and lipopolysaccharide pyrogen. *J. Clin. Endocrinol. Metab.* **21,** 433–455.

Feeney, G. C., Carlo, P.-E., and Smith, P. K. (1955). Action of salicylates and related compounds on carbohydrate metabolism and on adrenal ascorbic acid and cholesterol concentrations. *J. Pharmacol. Exptl. Therap.* **114,** 299–305.

Feldberg, W. (1932). Die Wirkung von Lentin (Cabaminoylcholinchlorid) auf die Nebennieren der Katze. *Arch. Exptl. Pathol. Pharmakol.* **168,** 287–291.

Feldberg, W., and Vartiainen, A. (1935). Further observations on the physiology and pharmacology of a sympathetic ganglion. *J. Physiol.* (*London*) **83,** 103–128.

Ferriman, D., and Page, B. (1960). Pituitary responsiveness to stress after corticoid therapy. *Lancet* **II,** 410–411.

Forbes, J. C., and Duncan, G. M. (1951). The effect of acute alcohol intoxication of the adrenal glands of rats and guinea pigs. *Quart. J. Studies Alc.* **12,** 355–359.

Forbes, J. C., and Duncan, G. M. (1953). Effect of intraperitoneal administration of alcohol on the adrenal levels of cholesterol and ascorbic acid in rats and guinea pigs. *Quart. J. Studies Alc.* **14,** 19–21.

Fortier, C., and Guillemin, R. (1953). Étude du mecanisme histaminergique de la stimulation de l'axe hypophyso-surrénalien par le stress. *Ann. Endocrinol.* (*Paris*) **14,** 42–45.

Fotherby, K., Forrest, A. D., and Laverty, S. G. (1959). The effect of chlorpromazine on adrenocortical function. *Acta Endocrinol.* **32,** 425–436.

Fraps, R. M., and Case, J. F. (1953). Premature ovulation in domestic fowl following administration of certain barbiturates. *Proc. Soc. Exptl. Biol. Med.* **82,** 167–171.

Fraschini, F., Martini, L., Motta, M., and Pecile, A. (1961). Studies on mechanisms controlling luteotrophic hormone release. *Biochem. Pharmacol.* **8**, 103 (Abstract).

Fraser, H. F., Wikler, A., Van Horn, G. D., Eisenman, A. J., and Isbell, H. (1958). Human pharmacology and addiction liability of normorphine. *J. Pharmacol. Exptl. Therap.* **122**, 359–369.

Fuchs, A.-R., and Wagner, G. (1963). The effect of ethyl alcohol on the release of oxytocin in rabbits. *Acta Endocrinol.* **44**, 593–605.

Fujii, R. (1960). The seat of atropine action in the melanophore-dispersing system of fish. *J. Fac. Sci. Univ. Tokyo, Sect. IV* **8** (Pt. 4), 643–657.

Fujii, R. (1961). Demonstration of the adrenergic nature of transmission at the junction between melanophore-concentrating nerve and melanophore in bony fish. *J. Fac. Sci. Univ. Tokyo, Sect. IV* **9** (Pt. 2), 171–196.

Ganong, W. F. (1959). Adrenal-hypophyseal interrelations. *In* "Comparative Endocrinology" (A. Gorbman, ed.), pp. 187–201. Wiley, New York.

Ganong, W. F. (1963). The central nervous system and the synthesis and release of adrenocorticotropic hormone. *In* "Advances in Neuroendocrinology" (A. V. Nalbandov, ed.), pp. 92–149. Univ. of Illinois Press, Urbana, Illinois.

Ganong, W. F. (1964). The effect of chlorpromazine and related drugs on ACTH release. Proc. 2nd Intern. Congr. Endocrinol., London, 1964. *Excerpta Med., Intern. Congr. Ser.* **83**, 624–628.

Ganong, W. F. (1965). "Review of Medical Physiology," 2nd ed., 610 pp. Lange Med. Publ., Los Altos, California.

Ganong, W. F., and Forsham, P. H. (1960). Adenohypophysis and adrenal cortex. *Ann. Rev. Physiol.* **22**, 579–614.

Ganong, W. F., and Gold, E. M. (1960). Changes in blood ACTH levels following administration of SU-4885 to adrenalectomized dogs. *Physiologist* **3**, 21 (Abstract).

Ganong, W. F., Goldfien, A., Halevy, A., Davidson, J. M., and Boryczka, A. T. (1961). Effect of lysergic acid diethylamide on adrenocortical and adrenal medullary function in the dog. *Acta Endocrinol.* **37**, 583–588.

Ganong, W. F., Wise, B. L., Shackleford, R., Boryczka, A. T., and Zipf, B. (1965). Site at which α-ethyltryptamine acts to inhibit the secretion of ACTH. *Endocrinology* **76**, 526–530.

Gaunt, R., Renzi, A. A., Antonchak, N., Miller, G. J., and Gilman, M. (1954). Endocrine aspects of the pharmacology of reserpine. *Ann. N.Y. Acad. Sci.* **59**, 22–35.

Gaunt, R., Chart, J. J., and Renzi, A. A. (1961). Endocrine pharmacology. *Science* **133**, 613–621.

Gaunt, R., Renzi, A. A., and Chart, J. J. (1962). Endocrine pharmacology of methyl reserpate derivatives. *Endocrinology* **71**, 527–535.

Gaunt, R., Chart, J. J., and Renzi, A. A. (1965). Inhibitors of adrenal cortical function. *Ergeb. Physiol. Biol. Chem. Exptl. Pharmakol.* **56**, 114–172.

Gavazzi, G., Giuliani, G., Martini, L., and Pecile, A. (1961). Action de plusieurs stress sur la libération de prolactine (hormone lutéotrophique-LTH). *Ann. Endocrinol. (Paris)* **22**, 788–791.

George, R., and Way, E. L. (1955). Studies on the mechanism of pituitary-adrenal activation by morphine. *Brit. J. Pharmacol.* **10**, 260–264.

George, R., and Way, E. L. (1957). The hypothalamus as an intermediary for pituitary-adrenal activation by aspirin. *J. Pharmacol. Exptl. Therap.* **119**, 310–316.

Georges, G., and Cahn, J. (1953). Couple hypophyso-surrénalien et hibernation. *Anesthesie Analgesie* **10**, 409–419.

Giarman, N. J., and Condouris, G. A. (1954). The antidiuretic action of morphine and some of its analogs. *Arch. Intern. Pharmacodyn.* **97,** 28–33.

Giarman, N. J., Mattie, L. R., and Stephenson, W. F. (1953). Studies on the antidiuretic action of morphine. *Science* **117,** 225–226.

Gitsch, E., and Everett, J. W. (1958). Influence of the anticholinergic drug, Pathilon, on the reproductive cycle of the female rat. *Endocrinology* **62,** 400–409.

Giuliani, G., Motta, M., and Martini, L. (1966). Reserpine and adrenocorticotropin secretion. *Acta Endocrinol.* **51,** 203–209.

Glaubach, S., and Pick, E. P. (1925). Über die Einwirkung des Cholins und eines Cholinesters auf den Blutdruck nach Nebennierenausschaltung. *Arch. Exptl. Pathol. Pharmakol.* **110,** 212–224.

Glick, S. M., Roth, J., Yalow, R. S., and Berson, S. A. (1965). The regulation of growth hormone secretion. *Recent Progr. Hormone Res.* **21,** 241–283.

Goddijn, J. P., and Noach, E. L. (1957). Effects of phenylbutazone on the adrenal glands. *Arch. Intern. Pharmacodyn.* **109,** 121–126.

Gold, E. M., DiRaimondo, V. C., and Forsham, P. H. (1960a). Quantitation of pituitary corticotropin reserve in man by use of an adrenocortical 11-beta hydroxylase inhibitor (SU-4885). *Metab., Clin. Exptl.* **9,** 3–20.

Gold, E. M., DiRaimondo, V. C., Kent, J. R., and Forsham, P. H. (1960b). Comparative effects of certain nonnarcotic central nervous system analgesics and muscle relaxants on the pituitary-adrenocortical system. *Ann. N.Y. Acad. Sci.* **86,** 178–190.

Gold, E. M., Kent, J. R., and Forsham, P. H. (1961). Clinical use of a new diagnostic agent, methopyrapone (SU-4885), in pituitary and adrenocortical disorders. *Ann. Internal Med.* **54,** 175–188.

Goldberg, R. C., Wolff, J., and Greep, R. O. (1955). The mechanism of depression of plasma protein bound iodine by 2,4-dinitrophenol. *Endocrinology* **56,** 560–566.

Goldberg, R. C., Wolff, J., and Greep, R. O. (1957). Studies on the nature of the thyroid-pituitary interrelationship. *Endocrinology* **60,** 38–52.

Good, T. A., and Kelley, V. C. (1958). Studies concerning the relationship of phenylbutazone to pituitary-adrenal cortical function and metabolism of 17-hydroxycorticosteroids. *Arthritis Rheumat.* **1,** 435–453.

Goodman, A. D. (1960). Studies on the effect of omega-methyl-pantothenic acid on corticosterone secretion in the rat. *Endocrinology* **66,** 420–427.

Goodman, L. S., and Gilman, A. (1965). "The Pharmacologic Basis of Therapeutics," 3rd ed., 1785 pp. Macmillan, New York.

Gordon, S., Mauer, S., Cekleniak, W. P., and Partridge, R. (1963). Mechanism of triparanol-induced adrenal hypertrophy and reduced adrenal function. *Endocrinology* **72,** 643–648.

Greenblatt, R. B., Barfield, W. E., Jungck, E. C., and Ray, A. W. (1961). Induction of ovulation with MRL/41. *J. Am. Med. Assoc.* **178,** 101–104.

Greer, M. A., and Deeney, J. M. (1959). Antithyroid activity elicited by the ingestion of pure progoitrin, a naturally occurring thioglycoside of the turnip family. *J. Clin. Invest.* **38,** 1465–1474.

Greer, M. A., Yamada, T., and Iino, S. (1960). The participation of the nervous system in the control of thyroid function. *Ann. N.Y. Acad. Sci.* **86,** 667–675.

Grewal, R. S., Lu, F. C., and Allmark, M. G. (1960). Release of posterior pituitary hormone in rats by nicotine and lobeline. *Federation Proc.* **19,** 167 (Abstract)

Grönroos, M., Kalliomäki, J. L., Keyriläinen, T. O., and Marjanen, P. (1959). Effects of reserpine and chlorpromazine on mammary glands of the rat. *Acta Endocrinol.* **31**, 154–160.

Grosvenor, C. E., and Turner, C. W. (1958). Effects of oxytocin and blocking agents upon pituitary lactogen discharge in lactating rats. *Proc. Soc. Exptl. Biol. Med.* **97**, 463–465.

Guillemin, R. (1955). A re-evaluation of acetylcholine, adrenaline, nor-adrenaline and histamine as possible mediators of the pituitary adrenocorticotrophic activation by stress. *Endocrinology* **56**, 248–255.

Guillemin, R., and Fortier, C. (1953). Adaptation à l'effet adrenocorticotrophique d'un antihistaminique de synthèse. *Ann. Endocrinol. (Paris)* **14**, 38–41.

Guillemin, R., and Schally, A. V. (1959). Reevaluation of a technique of pituitary incubation *in vitro* as an assay for corticotropin releasing factor. *Endocrinology* **65**, 555–562.

Guillemin, R., and Schally, A. V. (1963). Recent advances in the chemistry of neuroendocrine mediators originating in the central nervous system. *In* "Advances in Neuroendocrinology" (A. V. Nalbandov, ed.), pp. 314–328. Univ. of Illinois Press, Urbana, Illinois.

Guillemin, R., Clayton, G. W., Smith, J. D., and Lipscomb, H. S. (1958). Measurement of free corticosterone in rat plasma: Physiological validation of a method. *Endocrinology* **63**, 349–358.

Halasz, B. (1964). Neural control of growth hormone secretion. Proc. 2nd Intern. Congr. Endocrinol., London, 1964. *Excerpta Med., Intern. Congr. Ser.* **83**, 517–521.

Halkerston, I. D. K., Feinstein, M., and Hechter, O. (1964). Increased responsivity of adrenals from reserpine-treated or stressed rats to steroidogenic activity of ACTH. (28894) *Proc. Soc. Exptl. Biol. Med.* **115**, 292–295.

Hamburger, C. (1955). Substitution of hypophysectomy by the administration of chlorpromazine in the assay of corticotrophin. *Acta Endocrinol.* **20**, 383–390.

Hammond, W. G., Vandam, L. D., Davis, J. M., Carter, R. D., Ball, M. R., and Moore, F. D. (1958). Studies in surgical endocrinology. IV. Anesthetic agents as stimuli to changes in corticosteroids and metabolism. *Ann. Surg.* **148**, 199–211.

Hansel, W., and Trimberger, G. W. (1951). Atropine blockage of ovulation in the cow and its possible significance. *J. Animal Sci.* **10**, 719–732.

Harris, G. W. (1963). Discussion of D'Angelo, S. A.: Central nervous regulation of the secretion and release of thyroid stimulating hormone. *In* "Advances in Neuroendocrinology" (A. V. Nalbandov, ed.), pp. 205–208. Univ. of Illinois Press, Urbana, Illinois.

Harrison, T. S. (1961). Some factors influencing thyrotropin release in the rabbit. *Endocrinology* **68**, 466–478.

Hartog, M., Gaafar, M. A., and Fraser, R. (1964). Effect of corticosteroids on serum growth hormone. *Lancet* **II**, 376–378.

Harwood, C. T., and Bigelow, W. M. (1960). Endocrine effects of psychic energizers and CNS stimulants. *Pharmacologist* **2**, 93 (Abstract).

Harwood, C. T., and Mason, J. W. (1956). Effects of intravenous infusion of autonomic agents on peripheral blood 17-hydroxycorticosteroid levels in the dog. *Am. J. Physiol.* **186**, 445–452.

Harwood, C. T., and Mason, J. W. (1957). Acute effects of tranquilizing drugs on the anterior pituitary-ACTH mechanism. *Endocrinology* **60**, 239–246.

Hebb, C. O., and Konzett, H. (1949). The effect of certain analgesic drugs on synaptic transmission as observed in the perfused superior cervical ganglion of the cat. *Quart. J. Exptl. Physiol.* **35,** 213–217.

Heller, J. (1960). The physiology of the antidiuretic hormone. IV. The effect of certain anesthetics on the antidiuretic activity of rat blood plasma. *Physiol. Bohemoslov.* **9,** 283–288.

Henkin, R. I., and Knigge, K. M. (1960). The effects of sound on the hypothalamic-pituitary-adrenal axis. *Acta Endocrinol.* Suppl. 51, 39.

Hertting, G., Axelrod, J., and Whitby, L. G. (1961). Effect of drugs on the uptake and metabolism of H^3-norepinephrine. *J. Pharmacol. Exptl. Therap.* **134,** 146–153.

Hertz, R., Allen, M. J., and Tullner, W. W. (1950). Effects of amphenone "B" on thyroid, adrenals, and genital tract of female rat. *Proc. Soc. Exptl. Biol. Med.* **75,** 627–630.

Hertz, R., Tullner, W. W., Schricker, J. A., Dhyse, F. G., and Hallman, T. F. (1955). Studies on amphenone and related compounds. *Recent Progr. Hormone Res.* **11,** 119–147.

Hertz, R., Pittman, J. A., Jr., and Graff, M. M. (1956). Amphenone: Toxicity and effects on adrenal and thyroid function in man. *J. Clin. Endocrinol. Metab.* **16,** 705–723.

Hertz, R., Tullner, W. W., and Allen, M. J. (1951). Selective inhibition of adrenal and thyroid stimulating effect of amphenone B by cortisone and thyroxine. *Proc. Soc. Exptl. Biol. Med.* **77,** 480–481.

Hill, L. L., Daeschner, C. W., Jr., and Moyer, J. H. (1958). The influence of sedative agents upon renal hemodynamics. *J. Lab. Clin. Med.* **52,** 125–128.

Holtkamp, D. E., Greslin, J. G., Root, C. A., and Lerner, L. J. (1960). Gonado-trophin inhibiting and anti-fecundity effects of chloramiphene. *Proc. Soc. Exptl. Biol. Med.* **105,** 197–201.

Holzbauer, M., and Vogt, M. (1954). The action of chlorpromazine on diencephalic sympathetic activity and on the release of adrenocorticotropic hormone (ACTH). *Brit. J. Pharmacol.* **9,** 402–407.

Holzbauer, M., and Vogt, M. (1958). Release of corticotropin during severe stress in the rat treated with pentobarbital and morphine. *Acta Endocrinol.* **29,** 231–237.

Houssay, B. A., and Molinelli, E. A. (1925). Action de la nicotine, de la cystine, de la lobeline, de la coniine, de la piperidine et de diverses bases d'ammonium sur la sécrétion de l'adrenaline. *Compt. Rend. Soc. Biol.* **93,** 1124–1126.

Houssay, B. A., and Molinelli, E. A. (1926). Effect of nicotin, cystosin, lobelin, coniin, piperidin, and quaternary ammonias on adrenal secretion. *Am. J. Physiol.* **76,** 551–576.

Houssay, B. A., Gerschman, R., and Rapela, C. E. (1950). Études sur l'hyper-glycémie consécutive a l'injection de morphine. Rôle des surrénales. *Compt. Rend. Soc. Biol.* **99,** 1408–1410.

Hume, D. M. (1958). The secretion of epinephrine and corticosteroids in the ad-renal venous blood of the dog following single and repeated trauma. *Surg. Forum* **8,** 111–115.

Ingbar, S. H. (1961). The action of 1,1,3-tricyano-2-amino-1-propene (U-9189) on the thyroid gland of the rat and its effects in human thyrotoxicosis. *J. Clin. Endocrinol. Metab.* **21,** 128–139.

Itoh, S., and Arimura, A. (1954). The effect of posterior pituitary hormone on the release of adrenocorticotropic hormone. *Nature* **174,** 37.

Jacobson, A., Salhanick, H. A., and Zarrow, M. X. (1950). Induction of pseudopregnancy and its inhibition by various drugs. *Am. J. Physiol.* **161**, 522–527.

Jasmin, G., and Richer, G. L. (1961). Effect of nialamide on plasma and adrenal corticosterone in rats. *Program 43rd Meeting Endocrine Soc., New York* pp. 70–71 (Abstract).

Jenkins, J. S., Meakin, J. W., and Nelson, D. H. (1959). A comparison of the inhibitory effects of 2-methyl-1,2-bis(30 pyridyl)-1-propanone and amphenone B on adrenal cortical secretion in the dog. *Endocrinology* **64**, 572–578.

Johnson, P. C., Lorenzen, L. C., Biglieri, E. G., and Ganong, W. F. (1965). The effect of the monoamine oxidase inhibitor, tranylcypromine, on adrenocortical secretion in dogs. *Am. Zoologist* **5**, 689 (Abstract).

Kaada, B. R., Setekleiv, J., and Skaug, O. E. (1959). Effects of barbiturates and nitrous oxide on level of 17-OH-steroids and eosinophil cells in cat. *Acta Pharmacol.* **16**, 87–96.

Kahnt, F. W., and Neher, R. (1962). On the specific inhibition of adrenal steroid biosynthesis. *Experientia* **18**, 499–501.

Kalant, H., Hawkins, R. D., and Czaja, C. (1963). Effect of acute alcohol intoxication on steroid output of rat adrenals *in vitro*. *Am. J. Physiol.* **204**, 849–855.

Kanematsu, S., and Sawyer, C. H. (1965). Blockade of ovulation in rabbits by hypothalamic implants of norethindrone. *Endocrinology* **76**, 691–699.

Kanematsu, S., Hilliard, J., and Sawyer, C. H. (1961). Effects of reserpine and hypothalamic lesions on pituitary lactogen content in the rabbit. *Program 43rd Meeting Endocrine Soc., New York* p. 3 (Abstract).

Kappeler, H., and Schwyzer, R. (1960). Synthetic peptides related to the corticotropins (ACTH) and the melanophore-stimulating hormones (MSH) possessing corticotropin releasing activity (CRF-activity). *Experientia* **16**, 415–417.

Karam, J. H., Grasso, S. G., Wegienka, L. C., Grodsky, G. M., and Forsham, P. H. (1965). Studies on the mechanism of insulin secretion in man. *Diabetes* **14**, 444 (Abstract).

Khazan, M., Sulman, F. G., and Winnik, H. Z. (1961). Activity of pituitary-adrenal cortex axis during acute and chronic reserpine treatment. *Proc. Soc. Exptl. Biol. Med.* **106**, 579–581.

Kikuyama, S. (1961). Inhibitory effect of reserpine on the induction of persistent estrus by sex steroids in the rat. *Annotationes Zool. Japon.* **34**, 111–116.

Kikuyama, S. (1962). Inhibition of induction of persistent estrus by chlorpromazine in the rat. *Annotationes Zool Japon.* **35**, 6–11.

Kimura, S. (1927). Zur Kenntnis der Wirkung des Tetrodongiftes. *Tohoku J. Exptl. Med.* **9**, 41–65.

Kinberger, B., Lassesnius, R., and Osterman, E. (1956). Chlorpromazine verkan pa hypofyshinjurebark-systenet hos manniska. *Nord. Med.* **55**, 723–727.

Kitay, J. I., Holub, D. A., and Jailer, J. W. (1959). "Inhibition" of pituitary ACTH release after administration of reserpine or epinephrine. *Endocrinology* **65**, 548–554.

Kivalo, E., and Rinne, U. K. (1960). Effect of perphenazine on the ACTH release induced by neurotropic stress. *Psychopharmacologia* **1**, 288–293.

Klepping, J., Michel, R., Truchot, R., Boucquemont, J., and Tron-Loisel, H. (1961). Influence de l'adrenaline et de divers sympathomimétiques sur l'ascorbic et le cholesterol surrénaliens du rat. *Compt. Rend. Soc. Biol.* **155**, 57–61.

Knigge, K. M., Penrod, C. H., and Schindler, W. J. (1959). *In vitro* and *in vivo* adrenal corticosteroid secretion following stress. *Am. J. Physiol.* **196**, 579–582.

Konzett, H. (1951). Zur Pharmakologie von Lobelin. *Arch. Intern. Pharmacodyn.* **85,** 446–450.

Kothari, N. J., Saunders, J. C., and Kline, N. S. (1961). Effect of phenothiazines and hydrazines on pituitary-adrenal-cortical response. *Psychopharmacologia* **2,** 22–26.

Kowaleski, K. (1958). Effect of corticotropin on the plasma 17-hydroxycorticosteroids in normal and thiouracil treated guinea pigs. *Acta Endocrinol.* **27,** 257–261.

Kraicer, P. F., Marcus, G. J., and Shelesnyak, M. C. (1963). Studies on the mechanisms of decidualization. III. Decidualization in the histamine-depleted rat. *J. Reprod. Fertility* **5,** 417–421.

Krieger, D. T. (1962). Effect of diphenylhydantoin on pituitary-adrenal interrelations. *J. Clin. Endocrinol. Metab.* **22,** 490–493.

Krusius, F. E., Vartia, K. O., and Forsander, O. (1958). Biological action of alcohol. II. Adrenocortical function. *Ann. Med. Exptl. Biol. Fenniae (Helsinki)* **36,** 424–433.

Laidlaw, J. C. (1966). Discussion of paper by Ganong, W. F., Biglieri, E. G., and Mulrow, P. J. *Recent Progr. Hormone Res.* **22** (in press).

Lanthier, A., Saint-Marc, J., and Reddy, W. J. (1956). The effect of amphenone on urinary 17-ketosteroid excretion. *J. Clin. Endocrinol. Metab.* **16,** 954–955.

Larson, P. S., Henniger, G. R., Finnegan, J. K., Smith, R. B., and Haag, H. B. (1955). Observations on the relation of chemical structure to the production of adrenal cortical atrophy or hypertrophy in dog by derivatives of 2,2-bis(*p*-chlorophenyl)-1,1-dichloroethane (DDD, TDE). *J. Pharmacol. Exptl. Therap.* **115,** 408–412.

Lasagna, L., and Dearborn, E. H. (1952). Antidiuretic effects of physostigmine and atropine in the dog. *Proc. Soc. Exptl. Biol. Med.* **80,** 430–431.

Lauber, H. J., Dumke, H., and Patzschke, A. (1937). Histologische Intersuchungen uber die Beeinflussung des Vitamin C-Gehaltes in Verschiedenen Organen durch Narkosen. *Z. Ges. Exptl. Med.* **102,** 1–7.

Lazo-Wasem, E. A. (1960). Pituitary ACTH levels during adrenal involution following thiouracil. *Proc. Soc. Exptl. Biol. Med.* **103,** 300–302.

Lee, W. Y., Bronsky, D., and Waldstein, S. S. (1962). Studies of thyroid and sympathetic nervous system interrelationships. II. Effects of guanethidine on manifestations of hyperthyroidism. *J. Clin. Endocrinol. Metab.* **22,** 879–885.

Lerner, A. B. (1955). Melanin pigmentation. *Am. J. Med.* **19,** 902–924.

Lerner, A. B., and Fitzpatrick, T. B. (1950). Biochemistry of melanin formation. *Physiol. Rev.* **30,** 91–126.

Lerner, A. B., and Takahashi, Y. (1956). Hormonal control of melanin pigmentation. *Recent Progr. Hormone Res.* **12,** 303–313.

Lerner, A. B., Shizume, K., and Bunding, I. (1954). The mechanism of endocrine control of melanin pigmentation. *J. Clin. Endocrinol. Metab.* **14,** 1463–1490.

Li, C. H., Schnabel, E., Chung, D., and Lo, T. (1961). Synthesis of L-methionyl-L-glutamyl-L-histidyl-L-phenylalanyl-L-arginyl-L-tryptophyl-glycine and its melanocyte-stimulating and corticotropin-releasing activity. *Nature* **189,** 143.

Liddle, G. W. (1958). Aldosterone antagonists. *AMA Arch. Internal Med.* **102,** 998–1004.

Liddle, G. W. (1959). Effects of anti-inflammatory steroids on electrolyte metabolism. *Ann. N.Y. Acad. Sci.* **82,** 854–866.

Liddle, G. W., Estep, H. L., Kendall, J. W., Jr., Williams, W. C., Jr., and Townes, A. W. (1959). Clinical application of a new test of pituitary reserve. *J. Clin. Endocrinol. Metab.* **19,** 875–894.

Liddle, G. W., Island, D. P., and Meader, C. (1962). Normal and abnormal regulation of corticotropin secretion in man. *Recent Progr. Hormone Res.* **18,** 125–166.

Lipschitz, W. L., and Stokey, E. (1947). Mechanisms of antidiuresis in the dog and in the rat. *Am. J. Physiol.* **148,** 259–268.

Lorenzen, L. C., Wise, B. L., and Ganong, W. F. (1965). ACTH-inhibiting activity of drugs related to α-ethyltryptamine: relation to pressor activity. *Federation Proc.* **24,** 128 (Abstract).

Lukens, F. D. W. (1948). Alloxan diabetes. *Physiol. Rev.* **28,** 304–330.

MacKay, E. M., and MacKay, L. L. (1926). Resistance to morphine in experimental uremia. *Proc. Soc. Exptl. Biol. Med.* **24,** 129.

MacKenzie, C. G. (1947). Differentiation of the antithyroid action of thiouracil, thiourea and PABA from sulfonamides by iodide administration. *Endocrinology* **40,** 137–153.

Mäkelä, S., Näätänen, E., and Riine, U. K. (1959). The response of the adrenal cortex to psychic stress after meprobamate treatment. *Acta Endocrinol.* **32,** 1–7.

Magliotti, M. F., Hummon, I. F., and Hierschbiel, E. (1959). The effect of disease and drugs on the twenty-four hour I^{131} thyroid uptake. *Am. J. Roentgenol., Radium Therapy, Nucl. Med.* **81,** 47–64.

Magoun, W. H. (1963). "The Waking Brain," 2nd ed., 188 pp. Thomas, Springfield, Illinois.

Mahfouz, M., and Ezz, E. A. (1958). Effect of reserpine and of chlorpromazine on the response of the rat to acute stress. *J. Pharmacol. Exp. Therap.* **123,** 39–42.

Maickel, R. P., Westermann, E. O., and Brodie, B. B. (1961). Effects of reserpine and cold-exposure on pituitary adrenocortical function in rats. *J. Pharmacol. Exp. Therap.* **134,** 167–175.

Maloof, F., and Soodak, M. (1963). Intermediary metabolism of thyroid tissue and the action of drugs. *Pharmacol. Rev.* **15,** 43–95.

Mangili, G., Motta, M., Muciaccia, W., and Martini, L. (1965). Midbrain stress and ACTH secretion. *Eur. Rev. Endocrinol.* **1,** 247–253.

Markee, J. E., Sawyer, C. H., and Hollinshead, W. H. (1948). Adrenergic control of the release of luteinizing hormone from the hypophysis of the rabbit. *Recent Progr. Hormone Res.* **2,** 117–131.

Marks, B. H., and Vernikos-Danellis, J. (1963). Effect of acute stress on the pituitary gland; action of ethionine on stress-induced ACTH release. *Endocrinology* **72,** 582–587.

Martel, R. R., Westermann, E. O., and Maickel, R. P. (1962). Dissociation of reserpine-induced sedation and ACTH hypersecretion. *Life Sciences* **4,** 151–155.

Martini, L., Fochi, F., Gavazzi, G., and Pecile, A. (1962). Inhibitory action of steroids on the release of corticotrophin. *Arch. Intern. Pharmacodyn.* **140,** 156–163.

Mason, J. W., and Brady, J. V. (1956). Plasma 17-hydroxycorticosteroid changes related to reserpine effects on emotional behaviour. *Science* **124,** 983–984.

Matsuda, K., Duyck, C., Kendall, J. W., Jr., and Greer, M. A. (1964). Pathways by which traumatic stress and ether induce increased ACTH release in the rat. *Endocrinology* **74,** 981–985.

Mayer, S. W., Kelly, F. H., and Morton, M. E. (1956). The direct antithyroid action of reserpine, chlorpromazine and other drugs. *J. Pharmacol. Exptl. Therap.* **117,** 197–201.

McCann, S. M. (1963). Recent studies on the regulation of hypophysial luteinizing hormone secretion. *Am. J. Med.* **34,** 379–393.

McDonald, R. K., Weise, V. K., and Peterson, R. E. (1956). Effect of aspirin and reserpine on adrenocortical response to Piromen in man. *Proc. Soc. Exptl. Biol. Med.* **93,** 343–348.

McDonald, R. K., Evans, F. T., Weise, V. K., and Patrick, R. W. (1959). Effect of morphine and nalorphine on plasma hydrocortisone levels in man. *J. Pharmacol. Exptl. Therap.* **125,** 241–247.

Meites, J. (1957). Induction of lactation in rabbits with reserpine. *Proc. Soc. Exptl. Biol. Med.* **96,** 728–730.

Meites, J., Nicoll, C. S., Talwalker, P. K., and Hopkins, T. F. (1960). Induction and maintenance of mammary growth and lactation by neurohormones, drugs, non-specific stresses and hypothalamic tissue. *Acta Endocrinol.* Suppl. 51, 1137 (Abstract).

Meites, J., Nicoll, C. S., and Talwalker, P. K. (1963). The central nervous system and the secretion and release of prolactin. *In* "Advances in Neuroencocrinology" (A. V. Nalbandov, ed.), pp. 238–277. Univ. of Illinois Press, Urbana, Illinois.

Melby, J. C., Egdahl, R. H., and Spink, W. W. (1960). Secretion and metabolism of cortisol after injection of endotoxin. *J. Lab. Clin. Med.* **56,** 50–62.

Menninger-Lerchenthal, E. (1934). Schwangerschaft und Geburt morphinitischer Frauen. *Zentr. Gynaekol.* **58,** 1044–1051.

Merrit, J. H., Schultz, E. J., and Wykes, A. A. (1964). Effect of decaborane on the norepinephrine content of rat brain. *Biochem. Pharmacol.* **13,** 1364–1366.

Mestman, J. H., and Nelson, D. H. (1963). Inhibition by estrogen administration of adrenal-pituitary response to methopyrapone. *J. Clin. Invest.* **42,** 1529–1534.

Michel, R., Tron-Loisel, H., and Truchot, R. (1959). Influence de l'activité thyroïdienne sur la sécrétion de la corticotrophine hypophysaire et de la chlorpromazine sur celle de la thyréostimuline. *Compt. Rend. Soc. Biol.* **153,** 569–572.

Milković, S., and Supek, Z. (1956). Über die Wirkung von 5-Oxytryptanin (Serotonin) und Lysergsäurediathylamid (LSD) auf das Hypophysen-Nebennierenrinde-System. *Arch. Exptl. Pathol. Pharmakol.* **228,** 146.

Mills, E., and Wang, S. C. (1964a). Liberation of antidiuretic hormone: location of ascending pathways. *Am. J. Physiol.* **207,** 1399–1404.

Mills, E., and Wang, S. C. (1964b). Liberation of antidiuretic hormone: pharmacologic blockade of ascending pathways. *Am. J. Physiol.* **207,** 1405–1410.

Mizuno, H., Talwalker, P. K., and Meites, J. (1964). Inhibition of mammary secretion in rats by iproniazid. *Proc. Soc. Exptl. Biol. Med.* **115,** 604–607.

Montanari, R., and Stockham, M. A. (1962). Effects of single and repeated doses of reserpine on the secretion of adrenocorticotrophic hormone. *Brit. J. Pharmacol.* **18,** 337–345.

Moon, R. C., and Turner, C. W. (1958). Effect of reserpine on thyroid activity in rats. *Proc. Soc. Exptl. Biol. Med.* **100,** 679–681.

Moon, R. C., and Turner, C. W. (1959a). Effect of reserpine on oxytocin and lactogen discharge in lactating rats. *Proc. Soc. Exptl. Biol. Med.* **101,** 332–335.

Moon, R. C., and Turner, C. W. (1959b). A mode of action for thyroid inhibition by reserpine. *Proc. Soc. Exptl. Biol. Med.* **102,** 134–136.

Moore, W. W. (1961). Failure of adrenergic and cholinergic blocking agents to block ovulation in the rat. *Am. J. Physiol.* **200,** 1293–1295.

Moran, W. H., Jr., Miltenberger, W., Shuayb, W. A., and Zimmermann, B. (1964). The relationship of antidiuretic hormone secretion to surgical stress. *Surgery* **56,** 99–108.

Moses, A. M. (1964). Inhibition of vasopressin release in rats by chlorpromazine and reserpine. *Endocrinology* **74,** 889–893.

Munson, P. L. (1963). Pharmacology of neuroendocrine blocking agents. *In* "Advances in Neuroendocrinology" (A. V. Nalbandov, ed.), pp. 427–444. Univ. of Illinois Press, Urbana, Illinois.

Munson, P. L., and Briggs, F. N. (1955). The mechanism of stimulation of ACTH secretion. *Recent Progr. Hormone Res.* **11,** 83–117.

Nasmyth, P. A. (1950). The effect of some sympathomimetic amines on the ascorbic acid content of rats' adrenal glands. *J. Physiol.* (*London*) **110,** 294–300.

Nasmyth, P. A. (1954). Factors influencing the effect of morphine sulfate on the ascorbic acid content of rats' adrenal glands. *Brit. J. Pharmacol.* **9,** 95–99.

Nasmyth, P. A. (1955). The effect of chlorpromazine on adrenocortical activity in stress. *Brit. J. Pharmacol.* **10,** 336–339.

Newman, S., and Fish, V. J. (1958). The influence of tranquilizing drugs on results of thyroid function studies. *J. Clin. Endocrinol. Metab.* **18,** 1296–1301.

Noach, E. L., Kuipers, E., and de Jongh, S. E. (1957). Interactions between antipyretics and adrenal cortex. *Acta Physiol. Pharmacol. Neerl.* **6,** 165–178.

Nowell, N. W., and Chester-Jones, I. (1957). Some aspects of the storage and secretion of corticotrophin and gonadotropins. *Acta Endocrinol.* **26,** 273–285.

Ohler, E. A., and Sevy, R. W. (1952). Effect of Paredrine and adrenergic blockade on ACTH discharge. *Am. J. Physiol.* **171,** 753–754.

Ohler, E. A., and Sevy, R. W. (1956). Inhibition of stress induced adrenal ascorbic acid depletion by morphine, dibenzyline and adrenal cortex extract. *Endocrinology* **59,** 347–355.

Oliver, J. T., and Troop, R. C. (1963). Plasma corticosterone levels in stressed rats following the administration of pentobarbital, morphine and diphenylhydantoin. *Steroids* **1,** 670–677.

Olling, C. C. J., and De Wied, D. (1956). Inhibition of the release of corticotrophin from the hypophysis by chlorpromazine. *Acta Endocrinol.* **22,** 283–292.

Olling, C. C. J., and De Wied, D. (1958). Influence of pacatal on the corticotrophin-releasing activity of the hypophysis. *Acta Endocrinol.* **28,** 428–434.

Oppenheimer, J. H., and Tavernetti, R. R. (1962). Studies on the thyroxine-diphenylhydantoin interaction: effect of 5,5′-diphenylhydantoin on the displacement of L-thyroxine from thyroxine-binding globulen (TBG). *Endocrinology* **71,** 496–504.

Oppenheimer, J. H., Fisher, L. V., and Jailer, J. W. (1961a). Disturbance of the pituitary-adrenal interrelationship in diseases of the central nervous system. *J. Clin. Endocrinol. Metab.* **21,** 1023–1036.

Oppenheimer, J. H., Fisher, L. V., Nelson, K. M., and Jailer, J. W. (1961b). Depression of the serum protein-bound iodine level by diphenylhydantoin. *J. Clin. Endocrinol. Metab.* **21,** 252–262.

Oyama, T., Potsaid, M. S., and Slingerland, D. W. (1959). Effect of di-ethyl ether anesthesia on thyroid function of rats: pituitary, adrenal and thyroid relationship. *Endocrinology* **65,** 459–464.

Papper, S., and Papper, E. M. (1964). The effects of preanesthetic, anesthetic, and postoperative drugs on renal function. *Clin. Pharmacol. Therap.* **5,** 205–215.

Parrish, A. E., and Levine, E. H. (1956). Chlorpromazine-induced diuresis. *J. Lab. Clin. Med.* **48,** 264–269.

Paroli, E., and Melchiorri, P. (1961a). Inhibitory effects of morphine on metabolism of adrenal and testicular steroids. *Biochem. Pharmacol.* **6,** 18–20.

Paroli, E., and Melchiorri, P. (1961b). Urinary excretion of hydroxysteroids, 17-ketosteroids and aldosterone in rats during a cycle of treatment with morphine. *Biochem. Pharmacol.* **6**, 1–17.

Perman, E. S. (1958a). The effect of acetaldehyde on the secretion of adrenaline and noradrenaline from the suprarenal gland of the cat. *Acta Physiol. Scand.* **43**, 71–76.

Perman, E. S. (1958b). The effect of ethyl alcohol on the secretion from the adrenal medulla in man. *Acta Physiol. Scand.* **44**, 241–247.

Peterson, R. E. (1958). The influence of the thyroid on adrenal cortical function. *J. Clin. Invest.* **37**, 736–743.

Peterson, R. E. (1959). The miscible pool and turnover rate of adrenocortical steroids in man. *Recent Progr. Hormone Res.* **15**, 231–274.

Pincus, G. (1965). "The Control of Fertility," 360 pp. Academic Press, New York.

Pino, J. A., and Hudson, C. B. (1953). Duration of sexual retardation in S.C. white leghorn pullets and cockerels following enheptin (2-amino,5-nitrothiazole) feeding. *Poultry Sci.* **32**, 650–655.

Pino, J. A., Rosenblatt, L. S., and Hudson, C. B. (1954). Inhibition of pituitary gonadotrophin secretion in domestic fowl by enheptin (2-amino,5-nitrothiazole). *Proc. Soc. Exptl. Biol. Med.* **87**, 201–207.

Pittman, J. A., Jr., and Brown, R. W. (1962). Antithyroid activity of amphenizone. *J. Clin. Endocrinol. Metab.* **22**, 100–102.

Planelles, J., Ozeretskovsky, N., and Djeksenbsaev, O. (1962). Influence of actinomycins on the content of 17-hydroxycorticosteroids in guinea pig plasma. *Nature* **195**, 713–714.

Pokorny, C., Wilkinson, P. N., McCusker, E. N., and Hellwig, C. A. (1957). An effect of Rauwolfia alkaloids on the thyroid. *Growth* **2**, 89–93.

Polishuk, W. S., and Kulckar, S. (1956). Effects of chlorpromazine on pituitary function. *J. Clin. Endocrinol. Metab.* **16**, 292–293.

Porte, D., Jr., Graber, A., Kuzuya, T., and Williams, R. H. (1965). Epinephrine inhibition of insulin release. *J. Clin. Invest.* **44**, 1087 (Abstract).

Prout, T. E., Weaver, J. A., Scott, G. W., and Asper, S. P., Jr. (1958). Effect of dimercaprol (BAL) on carbohydrate metabolism. *Metab. Clin. Exptl.* **7**, 240–254.

Quinn, D. L. (1965). Influence of diphenylhydantoin on spontaneous release of ovulating hormone in the adult rat. *Proc. Soc. Exptl. Biol. Med.* **119**, 982–985.

Reichlin, S., and Brown, J. D. (1961). Failure to confirm reports that pitressin has growth stimulating effect. *Endocrinology* **69**, 394–396.

Reiss, M. (1958). Influence of chlorpromazine on endocrine function. *In* "Psychoendocrinology" (M. Reiss, ed.), pp. 182–197. Grune & Stratton, New York.

Renold, A. E., Crabbe, J., Hernando-Avendano, L., Nelson, D. H., Ross, E. J., Emerson, K., Jr., and Thorn, G. W. (1957). Inhibition of aldosterone secretion by amphenone in man. *New Engl. J. Med.* **256**, 16–21.

Rerup, C., and Hedner, P. (1962). The effect of pentobarbital (Nembutal, Mebumal NFN) on corticotrophin release in the rat. *Acta Endocrinol.* **39**, 518–526.

Reynolds, A. K., and Randall, L. O. (1957). "Morphine and Allied Drugs," 393 pp. Univ. of Toronto Press, Toronto, Ontario.

Rezabek, K. (1957). The effect of ethyl alcohol on secretion of the adrenocorticotrophic hormone of the pituitary gland in rats. Notes on the mechanism of control of the secretion of ACTH. *Physiol. Bohemoslov.* **6**, 516–522.

Richard, C. E., Brady, R. O., and Riggs, D. S. (1949). Thyroid hormone-like properties of tetrabromthyronine and tetrachlorthyronine. *J. Clin. Endocrinol. Metab* **9**, 1107–1121.

Roche, M., and Layrisse, M. (1956). Effect of cobalt on thyroidal uptake of I^{131}. *J. Clin. Endocrinol. Metab.* **16**, 831–833.

Ronzoni, E. (1950). Sodium pentobarbital anesthesia and the response of the adrenal cortex to stress. *Am. J. Physiol.* **160**, 499–505.

Ronzoni, E., and Reichlin, S. (1950). Adrenergic agents and the adrenocorticotrophic activity of the anterior pituitary. *Am. J. Physiol.* **160**, 490–498.

Rose, S., Nelson, J., and Bradley, T. R. (1960). Regulation of TSH release. *Ann. N.Y. Acad. Sci.* **86**, 647–666.

Rosenfeld, G., and Bascom, W. D. (1956). The inhibition of steroidogenesis by amphenone B; studies *in vitro* with the perfused calf adrenal. *J. Biol. Chem.* **222**, 565–580.

Rosenthal, N. R., and Mason, J. W. (1961). Alterations in urinary 17α-hydroxycorticosteroid excretion associated with administration of reserpine in the rhesus monkey. *Psychopharmacologia* **2**, 555–562.

Roth, J., Glick, S. M., Yalow, R. S., and Berson, S. A. (1963). Secretion of human growth hormone: physiologic and experimental modification. *Metab., Clin. Exptl.* **12**, 577–579.

Roth, J., Glick, S. M., Yalow, R. S., and Berson, S. A. (1964). The influence of blood glucose on the plasma concentration of growth hormone. *Diabetes* **13**, 355–361.

Royce, R. C., and Sayers, G. (1958). Blood ACTH: Effects of ether, pentobarbital, epinephrine and pain. *Endocrinology* **63**, 794–800.

Saffran, M., and Vogt, M. (1960). Depletion of pituitary corticotropin by reserpine and by a nitrogen mustard. *Brit. J. Pharmacol.* **15**, 165–169.

Samel, M. (1958). Blocking of the thyrotrophic hormone secretion by morphine and chlorpromazine in rats. *Arch. Intern. Pharmacodyn.* **117**, 151–157.

Samuels, L. D. (1964). Actinomycin and its effects: influence on an effector pathway for hormonal control. *New Engl. J. Med.* **271**, 1252–1258 and 1301–1306.

Santisteban, G. A. (1961). The response of the thymolymphatic system to graded doses of ethyl alcohol and its relationship to adrenocortical activity. *Quart. J. Studies Alc.* **22**, 1–13.

Sapeika, N. (1959). The effect of chlorpromazine, iproniazid, and chloroquine on adrenal ascorbic acid in the rat. *Arch. Intern. Pharmacodyn.* **122**, 196–200.

Sataké, Y. (1954). Secretion of adrenaline and sympathins. *Tohoku J. Exptl. Med.* **60**, Suppl. 2.

Sataké, Y. (1955). "Secretion of Adrenaline and Sympathin," 158 pp. Nanzando Co., Tokyo.

Saul, G. D. (1959). Blockade of ovulation in the rabbit by intoxicating doses of ethyl alcohol. *Anat. Record* **122**, 332.

Saul, G. D., and Sawyer, C. H. (1957). Atropine blockade of electrically induced hypothalamic activation of the rabbit adenohypophysis. *Federation Proc.* **16**, Suppl. 1, 112.

Sawyer, C. H. (1957). Induction of lactation in the rabbit with reserpine. *Anat. Record* **127**, 362–363.

Sawyer, C. H. (1959). Nervous control of ovulation. *In* "Recent Progress in the Endocrinology of Reproduction" (C. W. Lloyd, ed.), pp. 1–20. Academic Press, New York.

Sawyer, C. H. (1963). Discussion of paper by Munson, P. L. Pharmacology of neuroendocrine blocking agents. *In* "Advances in Neuroendocrinology" (A. V. Nalbandov, ed.), pp. 444–459. Univ. of Illinois Press, Urbana, Illinois.

Sawyer, C. H. (1964). Blockade of the release of gonadotrophic hormones by pharmacologic agents. Proc. 2nd Intern. Congr. Endocrinol., London, 1964. *Excerpta Med., Intern. Congr. Ser.* **83,** 629–634.

Sawyer, C. H., Markee, J. E., and Hollinshead, W. H. (1947). Inhibition of ovulation in the rabbit by the adrenergic-blocking agent dibenamine. *Endocrinology* **41,** 395–402.

Sawyer, C. H., Everett, J. H., and Markee, J. E. (1949a). A neural factor in the mechanism by which estrogen induces the release of luteinizing hormone in the rat. *Endocrinology* **44,** 218–233.

Sawyer, C. H., Markee, J. E., and Townsend, B. F. (1949b). Cholinergic and adrenergic components in the neurohumoral control of the release of LH in the rabbit. *Endocrinology* **44,** 18–37.

Sawyer, C. H., Markee, J. E., and Everett, J. W. (1950). Further experiments on blocking pituitary activation in the rabbit and rat. *J. Exptl. Zool.* **113,** 659–682.

Sawyer, C. H., Markee, J. E., and Everett, J. W. (1951). Blockade of neurogenic stimulation of the rabbit adenohypophysis by banthine. *Am. J. Physiol.* **166,** 223–228.

Sawyer, W. H. (1961). Neurohypophysial hormones. *Pharmacol. Rev.* **13,** 225–277.

Schally, A. V., Meites, J., Bowers, C. Y., and Ratner, A. (1964). Identity of prolactin inhibiting factor (PIF) and luteinizing hormone-releasing factor (LRF). *Proc. Soc. Exptl. Biol. Med.* **117,** 252–254.

Scheline, R. R. (1963). Adrenergic mechanisms in fish: chromatophore pigment concentration in the cucoo wrasse, *Labrus ossifagus. Comp. Biochem. Physiol.* **9,** 215–227.

Scherf, D. (1931). Pyramidon deim Diabetes Insipidus. *Wien. Arch. Inn. Med.* **22,** 457–472.

Schlatmann, R. J. A. F. M., Jansen, A. P., Prenen, H., van der Korst, J. K., and Majoor, C. L. H. (1964). The natriuretic and aldosterone-suppressive action of heparin and some related polysulfated polysaccharides. *J. Clin. Endocrinol. Metab.* **24,** 35–47.

Schmid, R., Gonzalo, L., Blobel, R., Muschke, E., and Tonutti, E. (1956). Zur hypothalamischen Steuerung der ACTH-Abgabe aus der Hypophyse. *Naturwiss.* **43,** 424–425.

Schöne, H.-H., and Lindner, E. (1962). Über die Wirkung von *N*-(3′-phenyl-propyl-(2′)-1,1-diphenyl-propyl-(3)-amin auf den Katecholamin-Stoffwechsel. *Klin. Wochschr.* **40,** 1196–1200.

Scott, G. T., and Nading, L. K. (1961). Relative effectiveness of phenothiazine tranquilizing drugs causing release of MSH. *Proc. Soc. Exptl. Biol. Med.* **106,** 88–90.

Seltzer, H. S., and Crout, J. R. (1966). Effects of different benzothiadiazines and catecholamines on insulin secretion. *Progr. 48th Meeting Endocrine Soc., Chicago,* p. 78 (Abstract).

Selye, H. (1936). Thymus and adrenals in the response of the organism to injuries and intoxications. *Brit. J. Exptl. Pathol.* **17,** 234–248.

Serafimov, N. (1962). Urinary excretion of catecholamines in endotoxin-induced fever in rabbits. *Acta Physiol. Scand.* **54,** 354–358.

Setnikar, I., Murmann, W., and Magistretti, M. J. (1960). Retardation of sexual development in female rats due to iproniazide treatment. *Endocrinology* **67,** 511–520.

Sevy, R. W., Ohler, E. A., and Weiner, E. (1957). Effect of chlorpromazine on stress induced adrenal ascorbic acid depletion. *Endocrinology* **61**, 45–51.

Sheehan, H. L., Summers, V. K., and Nichols, J. (1953). DDD therapy in Cushing's syndrome. *Lancet* **I**, 312–314.

Shelesnyak, M. C. (1954a). Ergotoxine inhibition of deciduoma formation and its reversal by progesterone. *Am. J. Physiol.* **179**, 301–304.

Shelesnyak, M. C. (1954b). Comparative effectiveness of antihistamines in suppression of the decidual cell reaction in the pseudopregnant rat. *Endocrinology* **54**, 396–401.

Shelesnyak, M. C. (1954c). The action of selected drugs on deciduoma formation. *Endocrinology* **55**, 85–89.

Shelesnyak, M. C. (1955). Disturbance of hormone balance in the female rat by a single injection of ergotoxine ethanesulphonate. *Am. J. Physiol.* **180**, 47–49.

Shelesnyak, M. C. (1957). Some experimental studies on the mechanism of ova-implantation in the rat. *Recent Progr. Hormone Res.* **13**, 269–322.

Shibusawa, K., Saito, S., Fukuda, M., Kawai, T., Yamada, H., and Tomizawa, K. (1955). Inhibition of the hypothalamo-neurohypophyseal neurosecretion by chlorpromazine. *Endocrinol. Japon.* **2**, 189–194.

Siker, E. S., Lipschitz, E., and Klein, R. (1956). The effect of preanesthetic medications on the blood level of 17-hydroxycorticosteroids. *Ann. Surg.* **143**, 88–91.

Silber, R. H. (1959). The biology of anti-inflammatory steroids. *Ann. N.Y. Acad. Sci.* **82**, 821–828.

Sloane, R. B., Saffran, M., and Clegharn, R. A. (1958). Steroid response to ACTH and the effect of ataractic drugs. *In* "Psychoendocrinology" (M. Reiss, ed.), pp. 198–203. Grune & Stratton, New York.

Slusher, M. A., and Browning, B. (1961). Morphine inhibition of plasma corticosteroid levels in chronic venous-catheterized rats. *Am. J. Physiol.* **200**, 1032–1034.

Smith, J. J. (1951). The effect of alcohol on the adrenal ascorbic acid and cholesterol of the rat. *J. Clin. Endocrinol.* **11**, 792.

Smith, O. W., Smith, G. V., and Kistner, R. W. (1963). Action of MER-25 and clomiphene on the human ovary. *J. Am. Med. Assoc.* **184**, 878–886.

Smith, R. L., Maickel, R. P., and Brodie, B. B. (1963). ACTH-hypersecretion induced by phenothiazine tranquilizers. *J. Pharmacol. Exptl. Therap.* **138**, 185–190.

Smith, W. P., Papper, S., and Rosenbaum, J. D. (1958). Inhibition of antidiuretic hormone activity as the mechanism of promazine-induced diuresis. *Clin. Res.* **6**, 289.

Snair, D. W., and Schwinghamer, L. A. (1960). The effect of 2-amino-5-nitrothiazole (Enheptin) on fertility, organ weight, body weight, estrous cycle and pituitary hormones in the rat. *Toxicol. Appl. Pharmacol.* **2**, 418–429.

Sobel, H., Schapiro, S., and Marmorston, J. (1958). Influence of morphine on urinary corticoid excretion by guinea pigs following exposure to cold and administration of pitressin. *Am. J. Physiol.* **195**, 147–149.

Söderberg, U. (1958). Short term reactions in the thyroid gland revealed by continuous measurement of blood flow rate, uptake of radioactive iodine and rate of release of labelled hormones. *Acta Physiol. Scand.* Suppl. 147, 1–113.

Somnath, R., Greenblatt, R. B., Mahesh, V. B., and Jungck, E. C. (1963). Clomiphene citrate: further observations on its use in induction of ovulation in the human and on its mode of action. *Fertility Sterility* **14**, 575–595.

Southam, A. L., and Janovski, M. A. (1962). Massive ovarian hyperstimulation with clomiphene citrate. *J. Am. Med. Assoc.* **181**, 443–445.

Spector, W. G. (1960). Anti-fertility action of a monoamine oxidase inhibitor. *Nature* **187,** 514–515.

Spector, W. G. (1961). Suppression of fertility in rats by an inhibitor of monoamine oxidase. *J. Reprod. Fertility* **2,** 362–368.

Spriggs, T. L. B., and Stockham, M. A. (1964). Urethane anesthesia and pituitary-adrenal function in the rat. *J. Pharm. Pharmacol.* **16,** 603–610.

Staple, P. H. (1951). Action of diphenylhydantoin sodium on the adrenal gland. *Lancet* **I,** 1074.

Staple, P. H. (1954). The effects of continued administration of 5 : 5 diphenylhydantoin (Dilantin) sodium on the adrenal glands in mice. *J. Roy. Microscop. Soc.* **74,** 10–21.

Steenburg, R. W., and Ganong, W. F. (1955). Observations on the influence of extra-adrenal factors on circulating 17-hydroxycorticoids in the surgically stressed, adrenalectomized animal. *Surgery* **38,** 92–104.

Steinberg, D., Frederickson, D. S., and Avigan, J. (1958). Effects of Δ^4-cholestenone in animals and in man. *Proc. Soc. Exptl. Biol. Med.* **97,** 784–790.

Stone, C. A., Entwisle, G. E., and Loew, E. R. (1951). Effect of tetraethylammonium chloride on the adrenal medulla of cats. *J. Pharmacol. Exptl. Therap.* **101,** 34.

Strom, L., and Zemek, L. (1964). Studies on the antidiuretic action of aminopyrine. *Metab., Clin. Exptl.* **13,** 365–372.

Sulman, F. G., and Winnik, H. Z. (1956a). Hormonal depression due to treatment of animals with chlorpromazine. *Nature* **178,** 365.

Sulman, F. G., and Winnik, H. Z. (1956b). Hormonal effects of chlorpromazine. *Lancet* **I,** 161–162.

Suzuki, T., Yamashita, K., and Mitamura, T. (1959a). Effect of ether anesthesia on 17-hydroxycorticosteroid secretion in dogs. *Am. J. Physiol.* **197,** 1261–1262.

Suzuki, T., Yamashita, K., Zinnouchi, S., and Mitamura, T. (1959b). Effect of morphine upon the adrenal 17-hydroxycorticosteroid secretion in the dog. *Nature* **183,** 825.

Suzuki, T., Yamashita, K., Kamo, M., and Hirai, K. (1962). Effect of sodium pentobarbital and sodium hexobarbital anesthesia on the adrenal 17-hydroxycorticosteroid secretion rate in the dog. *Endocrinology* **70,** 71–74.

Suzuki, T., Hirai, K., Yoshio, H., Kurouji, K.-I., and Hirose, T. (1964). Effect of eserine and atropine on adrenocortical hormone secretion in unanaesthetized dogs. *J. Endocrinol.* **31,** 81–82.

Swingle, W. W., Fedor, E. J., Barlow, G., Jr., Collins, F. J., and Perlmutt, J. (1951a). Induction of pseudopregnancy in rat following adrenal removal. *Am. J. Physiol.* **167,** 593–598.

Swingle, W. W., Seay, P., Perlmutt, J., Collins, E. J., Barlow, G., Jr., and Fedor, E. J. (1951b). An experimental study of pseudopregnancy in the rat. *Am. J. Physiol.* **167,** 586–592.

Sydnor, K. L., and Sayers, G. (1954). Blood and pituitary ACTH in intact and adrenalectomized rats after stress. *Endocrinology* **55,** 621–636.

Szego, C. (1959). Discussion of Hagerman, D. D., and Villee, C. A.: Metabolic studies of the mechanism of action of estrogens. *In* "Recent Progress in Endocrinology of Reproduction" (C. W. Lloyd, ed.), pp. 332–333. Academic Press, New York.

Taliaferro, I., and Leone, L. (1957). Inhibitory effect of Perthane (2,2-bis-(para-ethylphenyl)-1,1-dichloroethane) on adrenocortical function in human subjects. *New Engl. J. Med.* **257,** 855–860.

Talwalker, P. K., Meites, J., Nicoll, C. S., and Hopkins, T. F. (1960). Effects of chlorpromazine on mammary glands of rats. *Am. J. Physiol.* **199,** 1073–1076.

Tanabe, T., and Cafruny, E. J. (1958). Adrenal hypertrophy in rats treated chronically with morphine. *J. Pharmacol. Exptl. Therap.* **122,** 148–153.

Tepperman, J., and Bogardus, J. S. (1948). Attempts at pharmacologic blockade of the secretion of adrenocorticotrophin. *Endocrinology* **43,** 448–450.

Thorn, G. W., Renold, A. E., Goldfien, A., Nelson, D. H., Reddy, W. J., and Hertz, R. (1956). Inhibition of corticosteroid secretion by amphenone in a patient with adrenocortical carcinoma. *New Engl. J. Med.* **254,** 547–551.

Tillman, S. (1952). Noradrenalinstegring vid thalliumforgiftuing. *Svenska Lakartion.* **49,** 1523–1525.

Timiras, P. S. (1952). Discussion of Everett, J. W.: Presumptive hypothalamic control of spontaneous ovulation. *Ciba Found. Colloq. Endocrinol.* **4,** 177–178.

Tranquada, R. D., Solomon, D. H., Brown, J., and Green, R. (1960). The effect of oral hypoglycemic agents on thyroid function in the rat. *Endocrinology* **67,** 293–297.

Tullner, W. W., and Hertz, R. (1960). Effect of intravenous *o,p'*-DDD on plasma 17-hydroxycorticoid secretion in the dog. *Endocrinology* **66,** 494–496.

Tullner, W. W., and Hertz, R. (1964). Suppression of corticosteroid production in the dog by monase. *Proc. Soc. Exptl. Biol. Med.* **116,** 837–840.

Tullner, W. W., Graff, M. M., and Hertz, R. (1956). Amphenone inhibition of adrenal corticosteroid output in the hypophysectomized dog. *Endocrinology* **58,** 802–807.

Van Brunt, E. E., and Ganong, W. F. (1963). The effects of preanesthetic medication, anesthesia and hypothermia on the endocrine response to injury. *Anesthesiology* **24,** 500–514.

van Cauwenberge, H. (1951). Relation of salicylate action to pituitary gland: Observations in rats. *Lancet* **II,** 374–375.

Van Dyke, H. B., and Ames, R. G. (1951). Alcohol diuresis. *Acta Endocrinol.* **7,** 110–121.

Van Peenen, P. F. D., and Way, E. L. (1957). Effect of certain central nervous system depressants on pituitary-adrenal activating agents. *J. Pharmacol. Exptl. Therap.* **120,** 261–267.

van Tienhoven, A., Nalbandov, A. V., and Norton, H. W. (1954). Effect of dibenamine on progesterone-induced and "spontaneous" ovulation in the hen. *Endocrinology* **54,** 605–611.

Vilar, O., and Tullner, W. W. (1959). Effects of *o,p'*-DDD on histology and 17-hydroxycorticosteroid output of the dog adrenal cortex. *Endocrinology* **65,** 80–86.

Virtue, R. W., Helmreich, M. L., and Gainza, E. (1957). The adrenocortical response to surgery. I. The effect of anesthesia on plasma 17-hydroxycorticosteroid levels. *Surgery* **41,** 549–566.

Vogt, M. (1957). The effects of hexestrol and of "amphenone B" on morphology and function of the rat adrenal cortex. *Yale J. Biol. Med.* **29,** 469–479.

von Bohus, B., and Endröczi, E. (1964). Untersuchungen über die Wirkung von Chlorpromazin auf das Hypophysen-Nebennierenrinden-System bei Ratten. *Endokrinologie* **46,** 126–133.

Walker, J. M. (1949). The effects of smoking on water diuresis in man. *Quart. J. Med.* **18,** 51–55.

Wall, J. A., Franklin, R. R., and Kaufman, R. H. (1964). Reversal of benign and malignant endometrial changes with clomiphene. *Am. J. Obstet. Gynecol.* **88,** 1072–1085.

Watanabe, M. (1960). The mode of action of atropine on melanophores in the isolated scale of a crucian carp. *Biol. J. Okayama Univ.* **6**, 114–123.

Weisenfeld, S., and Goldner, M. G. (1961). Hyperinsulinemia in L-leucine-sensitive hyperglycemia in an adult. *Am. J. Med.* **31**, 659–664.

Wells, H., Briggs, F. N., and Munson, P. L. (1956). The inhibitory effect of reserpine on ACTH secretion in response to stressful stimuli. *Endocrinology* **59**, 571–579.

Westermann, E. O., Maickel, R. P., and Brodie, B. B. (1962). On the mechanism of pituitary-adrenal stimulation by reserpine. *J. Pharmacol. Exptl. Therap.* **138**, 208–217.

Westman, A., and Jacobsohn, D. (1942). Die Wirkung transorbital an das Tuber Cinereum injizierten Novocains auf die Ovulation. *Acta Obstet. Gynecol. Scand.* **22**, 16–23.

Wexler, B. C. (1963). Effects of a bacterial polysaccharide (Piromen) on the pituitary-adrenal axis: modification of ACTH release by morphine and salicylate. *Metab., Clin. Exptl.* **12**, 49–56.

Whitelaw, M. J. (1960). Chlorpromazine (thorazine) in the infertile female. *Intern. J. Fertility* **5**, 175–177.

Williams, R. H. (1962). Hypoglycemia and hypoglycemoses. *In* "Textbook of Endocrinology" (R. H. Williams, ed.), 2nd ed., pp. 714–730. Saunders, Philadelphia, Pennsylvania.

Winnik, H. Z., and Tennenbaum, L. (1955). Apparition de glactorrhee au cours du traitement de largatil. *Presse Med.* **63**, 1092.

Winter, C. A., Gaffney, C. E., and Flataker, L. (1954). The effect of *N*-allyinormorphine upon the antidiuretic action of morphine. *J. Pharmacol. Exptl. Therap.* **111**, 360–364.

Wise, B. L., Goldfien, A., and Ganong, W. F. (1960). Endocrine function in dogs after ablation of the area postrema. *Acta Neurovegat.* **22**, 1–13.

Wolff, F. W., Langdon, R. G., Ruebuer, B. H., Hollander, C., and Skoglund, R. D. (1963). A new form of experimental diabetes. *Diabetes* **12**, 335–338.

Wolff, J., Standaert, M. E., and Rall, J. E. (1961). Thyroxine displacement from serum proteins and depression of serum protein-bound iodine by certain drugs. *J. Clin. Invest.* **40**, 1373–1379.

Woodbury, D. M. (1958). Relation between the adrenal cortex and the central nervous system. *Pharmacol. Rev.* **10**, 275–357.

Wright, P. A. (1955). Physiological responses of frog melanophores *in vitro. Physiol. Zool.* **28**, 204–218.

Wurtman, R. J. (1965). Catecholamines. *New Engl. J. Med.* **273**, 637–646, 693–709, and 746–753.

Yalow, R. S., and Berson, S. A. (1960). Immunoassay of endogenous plasma insulin in man. *J. Clin. Invest.* **39**, 1157–1175.

Yamada, T. (1960a). The effect of trypan blue on thyroid function in the rat. *Endocrinology* **67**, 204–211.

Yamada, T. (1960b). Mechanism of action of trypan blue in suppressing thyroid function. *Endocrinology* **67**, 212–221.

Yamazaki, E., Slingerland, D. W., and Noguchi, A. (1961). The effect of reserpine on thyroxine degradation and thyrotropin secretion. *Acta Endocrinol.* **36**, 319–326.

Yates, F. E., and Urquhart, J. (1962). Control of plasma concentrations of adrenocortical hormones. *Physiol. Rev.* **42**, 359–443.

Zarrow, M. X., and Bastian, J. W. (1953). Blockade of ovulation in the hen with adrenolytic and parasympatholytic drugs. *Proc. Soc. Exptl. Biol. Med.* **84**, 457–459.

Zarrow, M. X., and Brown-Grant, K. (1964). Inhibition of ovulation in the gonadotrophin-treated immature rat by chlorpromazine. *J. Endocrinol.* **30**, 87–95.

Zarrow, M. X., Horger, L. M., and McCarthy, J. L. (1957). Atrophy of adrenal gland following thiouracil and Vit. B 12. *Proc. Soc. Exptl. Biol. Med.* **94**, 348–349.

Zarrow, M. X., and Quinn, D. L. (1963). Superovulation in the immature rat following treatment with PMS alone and inhibition of PMS-induced ovulation. *J. Endocrinol.* **26**, 181–188.

Zor, U., Dikstein, S., and Sulman, F. G. (1965). The effect of monoamine oxidase inhibitors on growth and the rat tibia test. *J. Endocrinol.* **32**, 35–43.

CHAPTER 28

Neuroendocrine Mechanisms in Invertebrates

IRVINE R. HAGADORN

I. Introduction

The field of neuroendocrinology in the invertebrates is a broad, and for the most part, a loosely related one; what little we know of neuroendocrinology in many of the lower groups rests mainly upon the demonstration of neurosecretory cells in their nervous system. Neurosecretion is nearly ubiquitous in the animal kingdom; no major metazoan phylum lacks histological evidence for the phenomenon. Due to the key position of neurosecretory cells in neuroendocrine correlation, if one accepts the view that the histological manifestations observed imply an accompanying hormone production by these neurons, one must conclude that neuroendocrine correlation is equally widespread. However, if the requirement of fulfillment of all—or even a majority—of the accepted criteria for proof of hormonal function commonly used in mammalian studies (excision, replacement, isolation of active principle, etc.) is rigorously applied, the field is with few exceptions narrowed to a consideration of the Crustacea and Insecta. The main objective of this chapter is to indicate to the student of vertebrate neuroendocrinology not only the well-established facets of (primarily) arthropod neuroendocrinology, but also those areas where more or less incomplete data holds promise of valuable advances in the near future. The bibliography contains only reviews and selected papers; Bern and Hagadorn (1965) give a thorough treatment of neurosecretion in the invertebrates and include a comprehensive bibliography for most groups.

A. Processes Controlled by Neuroendocrine Mechanisms in Invertebrates

The mechanisms under neuroendocrine control in the invertebrates are of the same nature as those found in the vertebrates: relatively long-term processes which require a certain degree of freedom from the brief random fluctuations of the environment, but which at the same time depend on the ability of the nervous system to integrate diverse external and internal stimuli in order to maintain the animal in harmony with environmental events. These mechanisms fall naturally into four categories (modified from Scharrer and Scharrer, 1963):

1. Growth, maturation, and regeneration. This class includes such phenomena as the growth by addition of segments as seen in polychaetes, the complex processes of molting and metamorphosis observed in the arthropods, and the often highly developed regenerative abilities possessed by such diverse groups as the annelids and crustaceans. Diapause may also be considered here, since it is a normal stage in the development of many forms.

2. Reproduction. Within this category has been grouped control of gametogenesis, development and maintenance of sex ducts and secondary sex characters, release of sexual behavior and initiation of spawning and oviposition.

3. Metabolism and homeostasis. Herein are included processes controlling the varied functions of intermediary metabolism and the maintenance of the stability of the internal environment: ionic and osmotic regulation, anabolism and catabolism, control of cardiac output, etc.

4. Adaptation to external factors. This group includes processes adapting the animal to specific environmental factors, principally control of physiological color change, cryptic coloration, and visual adaptation to light intensity.

B. Patterns of Neuroendocrine Control in Invertebrates

1. *Generalized Pattern of Neuroendocrine Mechanisms in Invertebrates*

The alternative pathways available are represented in Fig. 1, and consist of the following components: (a) the central nervous system, constituting the primary integration and command center; (b) the efferent loop, which may be composed of the following links operating either in series or in parallel: *neural outflow, neurosecretory output,* and *non-neural endocrine organs;* (c) the target organs; (d) the afferent feedback, either of neural or humoral nature; and (e) sensory cues, either internal or external.

In no one case are all of the alternates utilized, although most of them are brought into play in some situation by one group or another. This scheme, when fully developed, portrays a balanced system which tends to seek a stable level when left to its own devices. The imbalance required to produce the cyclic phenomena so prevalent in many phases of animal physiology is usually injected by appropriate sensory inputs; these trigger a cycle which often may proceed to completion even

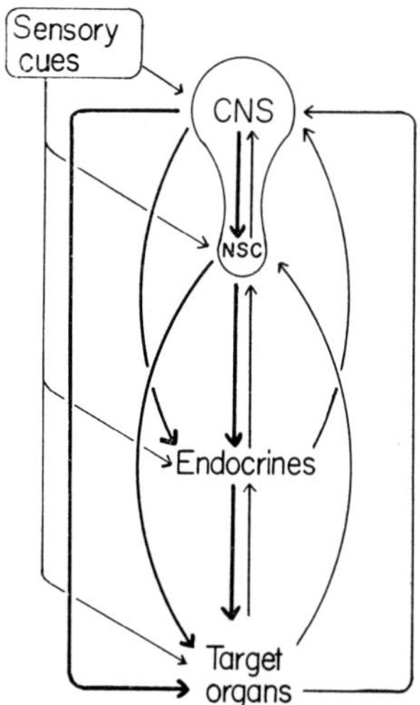

FIG. 1. Diagram showing the possible paths of interaction available for neuroendocrine control patterns. No one species utilizes all available paths. Efferent pathways indicated in heavy arrows, afferent pathways in light arrows. Due to the seeming rarity of third-order neuroendocrine reflexes in invertebrates, the third-order pathways are not included (see text). CNS, central nervous system; NSC, neurosecretory cells.

after removal of the adequate stimulus. In some cases this imbalance may also be produced by utilization of positive feedback in the system (for example, in the control of protease production in the gut of the blowfly *Calliphora;* see Table I).

2. *Complexity Attained*

In the lowest groups, neuroendocrine reflexes are simple; the peripheral targets remain under direct control of the central nervous system through the intervention of neurosecretory cells. Although this uncomplicated mechanism is retained into the highest groups, there have also been developed more complex systems in which one or, rarely, more non-neuronal endocrine organs are intercalated between the central nervous system and the ultimate target structure. This increasing complexity of the afferent loop in evolution has been discussed by Rothballer (1957). He proposed the following terminology, which has been adopted for the purposes of this discussion:

a. First-Order Neuroendocrine Reflexes. The first-order reflexes include those cases where hormones produced by the central nervous system itself act directly upon the peripheral targets. This is usually accomplished by neurosecretory cells; a familiar example to the vertebrate endocrinologist is the suckling reflex (see Chapter 6). A comparable system in the invertebrates is that controlling the position of the light-adaptive distal retinal pigments in the crustacean eye. Those instances in which the activity of a non-neuronal endocrine organ is under the control of a direct secretomotor or inhibitory innervation (for example, the optic gland of cephalopods) would presumably be special cases of the first-order reflex, since here too the nervous system retains direct control over the secretion of the peripherally active principle.

b. Second-Order Neuroendocrine Reflexes. The second-order reflexes consist of systems in which one non-neuronal endocrine organ has been added as a link between the neurosecretory cell and the target structure. Control of the initiation of molting in insects by the ecdysial gland under stimulation of neurosecretion from the brain is a case in point.

c. Third-Order Neuroendocrine Reflexes. The third-order reflexes include those situations in which two epithelial endocrine organs in series separate the target structures from their ultimate neural control. Such complex systems seem rare in the invertebrates; a possible example is the hormonal control of heart rate in certain insects.

Along with this increasing complexity of the efferent loop in the invertebrate phyla, the appearance of the afferent feedback mechanism may be noted. Evidence suggestive of both humoral and neural feedbacks is available in the arthropods; however, information concerning such mechanisms is scarce in the lower groups. Although intuitively one feels that feedback, particularly of the negative variety, must be involved in the control of some physiological activities even in the more primitive groups, in other cases there seems to be little need to suppose that this aspect of regulation is in operation.

II. The Components of Invertebrate Neuroendocrine Control

The various links in the chain of neuroendocrine control are discussed individually in this and succeeding sections. Their interrelationships are set forth in Section III,A and Table I.

A. The Nervous System

1. *Generalized Anatomy*

The form of the nervous system in higher invertebrates (particularly of the annelid-arthropod line) can be derived in principle from the "ladder" configuration first seen in certain of the flatworms (see Bullock and Horridge, 1965). In these animals the nervous system consists of two principal ventral nerve cords, composed of a central area of fiber tracts which arise from a superficial cortex of cell bodies scattered along the length of the cords. These cords are joined at the anterior end by an enlarged ganglionic mass, the cerebral ganglion, and at irregular intervals along their length by cross-connections similar in character to the longitudinal cords. Modification of this basic plan in the higher phyla occurs by loss of secondary longitudinal cords, partial fusion of the two principal cords in the midventral line, and concentration of the cell bodies into nerve ganglia (primitively one per segment in segmented forms); the neuron perikarya become partially or entirely excluded from the interganglionic connectives. Further modification commonly occurs by fusion of adjacent ganglia; this may occur at any point along the cords, but especially at the anterior end. These changes give rise to the typical annelid-arthropod type of nervous system of which the brain of the leech may be taken as a simple example (Fig. 2). The nervous system in the head consists of the supraesophageal ganglion (composed of two fused segmental ganglia in the leech), the circumesophageal connectives, the subesophageal ganglion (formed by the fusion of four segmental ganglia in the leech) and the paired ventral nerve cord which expands into a ganglion in each segment. The arthropod nervous system

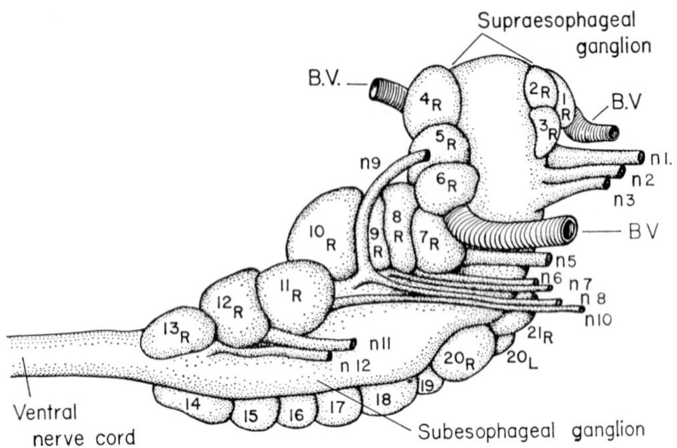

FIG. 2. Diagrammatic view of the brain of a leech. Anterior is toward the right. The leech brain, with its division into supra- and subesophageal areas, its centrally located fiber tracts and neuropil, and its peripherally located cell bodies, is typical of the nervous system found in the annelid–arthropod–mollusk line of evolution. BV, blood vessel; n1–n12, cephalic nerves 1–12; 1_R–21_R, cell compartments 1–21 of the right side (all except 14–19 are bilateral). Part of compartment 20_L is also shown. (From Hagadorn, 1958.)

differs primarily in having an increased number of ganglia incorporated into the brain and by the appearance of additional ganglionic fusions, giving rise to compound thoracic and/or abdominal ganglia in many forms. In the unsegmented mollusks, there is a somewhat different plan; there are a series of ganglia which commonly include paired cerebral, pleural, pedal, and visceral ganglia, interrelated by connectives. As with the annelids and arthropods, these ganglia may show a high degree of fusion.

2. *Function*

a. Neural Integration. The cerebral ganglia enjoy a central role in the coordination of neuroendocrine reflexes in most invertebrates. This is due to at least two factors. The first of these is the wealth of sensory information received by the brain. Especially important in many cases is the almost universal association of the eyes with the supraesophageal ganglion. Second is the suprasegmental nature of many of the activities of the supra- and subesophageal ganglia. It is commonly the case that each segmental ganglion is autonomous in its ability to integrate essentially normal motor responses to sensory stimuli occurring within its own segment; adjacent ganglia, if their interconnections are preserved, can carry out complex activities such as walking or flying in insects, in the absence of the cerebral ganglia. However, although such movements may be called forth in response to appropriate strong stimuli, they are usually not initiated spontaneously. The brain appears to play the part of an on-off switch, perhaps by setting the threshold level to stimuli. In this role of overseer it is not surprising that the brain should make use of hormonal outputs where appropriate, as well as conventional neural efferents.

Although the ganglia essential to one or another neuroendocrine reflex and the interganglionic nerve routes involved have been elucidated in many groups by isolation and extirpation experiments, the intraganglionic neural paths are very poorly known. The terminal step in the central nervous pathways, if it is a neurosecretory cell, is often readily identifiable due to its peculiar staining properties, but there is little or no information available concerning the conventional neuronal links immediately preceding. In the case where the output of the brain is in the form of a direct innervation of non-neuronal endocrine organs, some information is at hand: in the cephalopods, lesion experiments have allowed the localization of the origin of the inhibitory innervation of the optic glands (see Section II,A,4, and Table I) to a particular area of the supraesophageal ganglion. Similar experiments in insects have led to the conclusion that the inhibitory innervation to the corpora allata arises in part from the protocerebrum (see Section II,B,4,a).

b. Neurosecretion. The neurosecretory cell, in addition to possessing typically neuronal features, shows a characteristic attribute of its own: the ability to produce hormonal substances, commonly polypeptides of low molecular weight. This ability is generally reflected at the level of the light microscope by the presence of quantities of stainable secretory material in the perikaryon and cell processes, and by the termination of the axon in close relation to the vascular or coelomic systems rather than directly upon its target structure. The axon endings are usually swollen, serving the role of a storage-release site for the secretions. These axons may end diffusely at the surface of the nervous system, but especially in the higher phyla, the axons of neurosecretory cells tend to be grouped together into more or less highly developed structures termed neurohemal organs. At their simplest these organs are little more than a loose association of axon endings on the walls of capillaries or other vascular spaces. In their most elaborate form they are highly compact structures, well adapted to facilitate the storage and release of the secretions they contain; they frequently are associated with non-neuronal glandular structures of known or suspected endocrine significance. By its very character, possessing as it does both neuronal and endocrine abilities, the neurosecretory cell is a miniature neuroendocrine correlation system within a single cell.

The distribution of neurosecretory cells within the nervous system is broad; when judged on purely histological criteria, presumptive neurosecretory cells may be observed in one or another animal group in almost any portion of the nervous system, including the stomatogastric and peripheral divisions. However, without exception the cephalic neurosecretory systems are the best studied and understood from the physiological point of view.

The anatomy of neurosecretory systems in the major phyla. In the more primitive groups the neurohemal structure is either simple or completely lacking as a discrete organ. Although neurosecretory cells may be observed in the brain and nerve cords of flatworms (Lender and Klein, 1961) and nemertineans (Lechenault, 1962), definite information is lacking concerning the site of their axonal terminations. It is quite possible that the endings are diffuse. The neurohemal organ of the cerebral neurosecretory system of annelids is a loose aggregation of axon endings on cerebral capillaries (oligochaetes, see Herlant-Meewis, 1956) or on the surface of the brain (polychaetes and leeches, see Bobin and Durchon, 1952; Hagadorn, *et al.*, 1963). Structural specializations appear lacking or rather subtle; in the leech the only obvious feature is the absence of the glial barrier between axon endings and perineurium, which is present in most other areas of the brain. In the nereid polychaetes, the neurohemal area at the base of the brain is specialized to the extent of possessing a differentiation of the mesothelial cells which separate the brain capsule from the underlying infracerebral artery. The significance of this elaboration is unknown.

Although histological indications of neurosecretion have been reported in all classes of the Mollusca with the exception of the Amphineura, only in the gastropods is there good evidence for its endocrine role. Within the three classes in which the neuroendocrine system has been studied (the Lamellibranchia, Gastropoda, and Cephalopoda) there is gradation in complexity of the nervous system. The lamellibranchs have a reduced nervous system associated with their sedentary mode of life, while the gastropods and especially the cephalopods have a complex brain and associated ganglia. The neurosecretory system of the bivalves consists of scattered neurosecretory neurons in the cerebral, visceral, and pedal ganglia (Antheunisse, 1963). No information concerning the site of termination of their axons is available. In the gastropods, neurons showing the histological characteristics of neurosecretory cells are found in most ganglia of the nervous system. Many of these putative neurosecretory cells show rather peculiar features, being observed to innervate muscle cells, unicellular glands, etc. These histological observations have led to the suggestion (Lemche, 1955) that neurosecretion in these forms may play a more direct role in the innervation of effector organs; however, due to the frequent presence of stainable pigments in gastropod neurons such reports are difficult to evaluate. Neurosecretory cells of more conventional appearance are also seen, especially in the cerebral and rhinophore ganglia. These cells form neurohemal organs which are often associated with quasiglandular or neurosensory structures (Tuzet *et al.*, 1957). No physiological information is available concerning possible neurosecretion in cephalopods.

In the present state of our knowledge, the peak of complexity of the neuroendocrine system is attained in the arthropods. Although the most elaborate mechanisms are seen in the Crustacea and Insecta, the basic design seems to have been laid down early in the evolution of the phylum. In general, the other groups of arthropods, including most of the arachnids and myriopods, show variations of a common plan (see Bern and Hagadorn, 1965). Neurosecretory cells are consistently present in the protocerebral portion of the supraesophageal ganglion; they are generally found in the tritocerebrum, subesophageal ganglion, and other parts of the nervous system as well. The axons from the protocerebral neurosecretory cell groups, and in some classes from cell groups of other areas, form tracts which terminate in organs lying outside the brain, generally in a retrocerebral location. While these organs are given a variety of names in the various classes and orders (Schneider's organs in the araneids, cerebral glands in chilopods and diplopods, organs of Police in the Scorpionida, etc.), they all show a similar structure: that of a neurohemal organ in which the axon endings of the neurosecretory cells are usually intermingled with epithelioid cells of a glandular appearance. Although the comparative anatomy of this system suggests a common function in all of these groups, its physiological significance has been put to the test only in the Chilopoda, in which it has been found to play a role in molting (Joly, 1966).

The insect neurosecretory system (Fig. 3) is an elaboration of the above; that of the cockroach may be taken as an example. One or more paired groups of neurosecretory cells occur in the pars intercerebralis of the protocerebrum. Axons from these cells in company with axons from non-neurosecretory neurons leave the brain, many after decussation, via the nervi corpora cardiaci. The axons terminate in the retrocerebral complex, which in the cockroach consists of the corpora cardiaca and corpora allata. Most of the neurosecretion-bearing axons end in the corpora cardiaca; however, some may be observed to leave the corpora

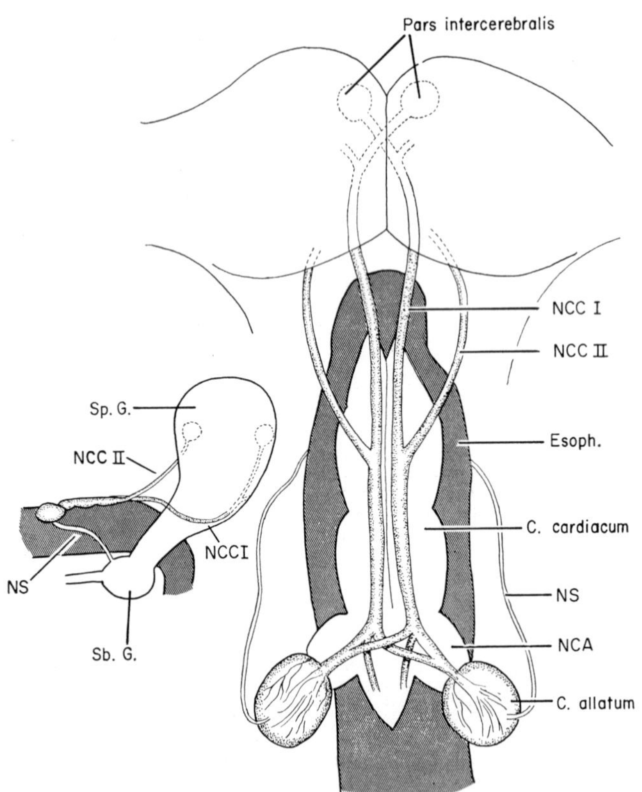

FIG. 3. Diagrammatic view of the brain and retrocerebral complex of *Periplaneta* (cockroach) as seen from above. The continuations of the nervi corporis cardiaci are shown traversing the corpus cardiacum en route to the corpora allata. C. allatum, corpus allatum; C. cardiacum, corpus cardiacum; Esoph., esophagus; NCA, nervus corporis allati; NCC I and II, nervi corporis cardiaci I and II; NS, nervus allato-subesophagealis. *Inset:* View of brain and retrocerebral complex from right side. Anterior toward right. Sp. G., supraesophageal ganglion; Sb. G., subesophageal ganglion. (Modified from Engelmann, 1957.)

cardiaca and enter the corpora allata via the nervi corpora allati, which are also mixed nerves. The corpora allata are also connected by the nervi allato-subesophageali to the subesophageal ganglion. Both the corpora cardiaca and corpora allata contain intrinsic glandular cells as well as nerve fiber terminations; these cells have endocrine significance of their own. The corpora cardiaca are viewed as being the major storage-release site for protocerebral neurosecretions. In addition, it is quite possible that these secretions also influence the glandular activity of the intrinsic cardiacum cells. The corpora allata, on the other hand, are considered to be primarily a target organ for the neurosecretions which reach them via the allatal nerves and possibly also by way of the hemolymph after release from the corpora cardiaca. The corpora cardiaca and corpora allata are partially or completely fused in many groups. In some a third endocrine organ, the ecdysial (prothoracic) gland, also forms a portion of the retrocerebral complex. This endocrine system has been implicated in the control of molting and a variety of other processes (Gilbert, 1963; L'Helias, 1964).

In addition to the pars intercerebralis-corpus cardiacum-corpus allatum system, there are other physiologically defined areas of glandular activity in the insect nervous system. Neurosecretory cells are found in the tritocerebrum (Raabe, 1964). The subesophageal ganglion is also a site of neurosecretory activity (B. Scharrer, 1941) as are the segmental ganglia of the thoracic region. Neurosecretory cells may be observed in abdominal and other ganglia (Bareth, 1963), but their physiology has not been tested. The insect neuroendocrine system is thus a well-developed one, containing endocrine organs (Section II,B,3) as well as neurosecretory components.

In the Crustacea (Fig. 4), a number of neurosecretory systems have been established experimentally (see Carlisle and Knowles, 1959). These include (1) the sinus gland system, consisting of neurosecretory cells of the optic ganglia, brain and possibly other centers, whose axons terminate in the sinus gland, a neurohemal structure located in the eyestalk (higher crustaceans) or brain (eyestalkless forms); (2) the postcommissural organs, neurohemal structures located behind the tritocerebral commissure, which consists of secretion-bearing axons from neurons located (probably) in the tritocerebrum of the brain; (3) the pericardial organs, neurohemal structures located in the pericardium, consisting of axonal terminations from neurosecretory cells of the ventral segmental ganglia, and (4) possibly the sensory pore X-organ (pars distalis X-organ) system, consisting of neurosecretory cells of the ganglionic X-organ and brain, whose axons terminate in the sensory pore X-organ located in the eyestalk of certain higher crustaceans. Of the neurohemal organs involved in these four systems, only the sensory pore X-organ clearly contains intrinsic glandlike cells (of unknown significance); the sinus gland and pericardial organs may contain a few intrinsic cells, but their glandular nature is debatable. The sinus gland system has been associated with control of a variety of physiological functions, including molting and reproduction; the postcommissural organs are concerned with physiological color change; and the pericardial organs are involved with the control of cardiac output. The sensory pore X-organ system has been suggested to play a role in the control of molting.

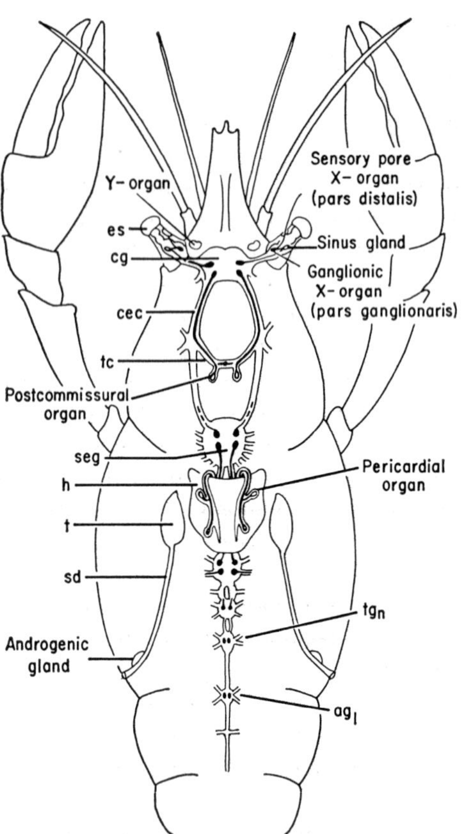

FIG. 4. The endocrine system of a generalized male crustacean. Neurosecretory cells are found throughout the nervous system. Neurosecretory cell groups are indicated as dark circles, their axonal terminations as open circles. es, eyestalk; cg, cerebral ganglia; cec, circumesophageal connectives; tc, tritocerebral commissure; seg, subesophageal ganglion; h, heart; t, testis; sd, sperm duct; ag_1, first abdominal ganglion; tg_n, last thoracic ganglion. (From Gorbman and Bern, 1962.)

Relatively little is known concerning the neuroendocrine system of the invertebrate members of the echinoderm-chordate line. In the ophiuroids and asteroids, neurosecretory cells may be observed in the circumoral nerve ring and radial nerves; extracts of the radial nerves have effects upon gametogenesis, spawning, and water balance (Fontaine, 1962; Unger, 1962; Kanatani, 1964). In the urochordates, the neural complex consists of the cerebral ganglion, neural gland and ciliated funnel; neurosecretory cells are present in the cerebral ganglion. Attempts have been made to homologize this complex to the vertebrate pituitary; however, the comparison is doubtful (see Dodd, 1955; Hisaw *et al.*, 1962).

B. The Efferent Loop

1. *Neurosecretion as a Final Path*

The first-order neuroendocrine reflex appears the general rule in the lower groups of invertebrates. In these forms, which include the flatworms, nemertineans, annelids, and echinoderms, there is little evidence for the presence of epithelial endocrine organs, and none whatsoever for their intervention in the efferent loop. In the case of reproduction in the polychaete annelids, the first-order status of the control mechanisms seems probable. Certain polychaetes undergo dramatic morphological changes [the heteronereid transformation (Clark, 1961)] at the time of sexual maturity. These changes, as well as the maturation of the gametes, are under inhibitory control by neurosecretions from the brain. It has been found that the heteronereid change will occur in parapodia isolated in organ culture; the gametes in the coelom will also mature. Explantation of the prostomium along with the parapodium will prevent maturation of both parapodium and gametes, suggesting a direct effect of the brain upon these target structures (Durchon and Schaller, 1964). However, these experiments do not eliminate the possibility of involvement of other, as yet undescribed, prostomial endocrine structures in the control sequence.

In the mollusks and arthropods, non-neuronal endocrine organs make their appearance and in the arthropods supplant the neurosecretory cell as the final efferent path in many areas of regulation. However, the first-order reflex is retained in these groups in the control of a number of processes, particularly those in which relative rapidity of response is desirable; examples include physiological color change in crustaceans and insects, and control of heart rate by the pericardial organs in crustaceans (see Carlisle and Knowles, 1959; Joly, 1962).

2. *Epithelial Endocrines of Neuronal Origin*

As is the case with the mammalian adrenal medulla, certain invertebrate endocrine organs are apparently of neuronal origin, but have developed their glandular attributes to the partial or complete loss of their neuronal features. Such an organ is the corpus cardiacum of insects. First described as a sympathetic ganglion, it has since been recognized to be a complex structure which contains at least three components in its make-up (cf. Bern and Hagadorn, 1965): (1) neurons, occasionally described as neurosecretory, (2) intrinsic glandular cells, which the electron microscope portrays as possessing many neuronal features (B. Scharrer, 1963), and (3) in its role as a major neurohemal organ, the secretion-filled end bulbs of axons from neurosecretory cells of the brain.

The exact functions of the corpus cardiacum have proved elusive, in part because of its structural variability in different groups of insects and in part because of the nature of its connections with the brain and with the corpora allata. The structure of the cardiacum is in fact quite changeable; the three components mentioned above vary considerably in the degree of importance of their contribution to the organ in various groups. In some, the neurosecretion-laden fiber endings are lacking; the neurohemal structure is elsewhere, associated with the wall of the aorta. In others the glandular or neuronal components are said to be absent, while in still others all three components are prominently present. Finally, the fact that the cardiacum generally receives both neurosecretory and conventional nerve fibers from the brain, and is also traversed by similar fibers running from the brain to the corpora allata, renders the interpretation of both extraction and excision experiments treacherous. Active principles demonstrable in corpus cardiacum extracts need not have originated in the cardiacum; the effects of excision may only indicate disturbances in corpus allatum function in response to the interruption of the allatal innervation. Despite these difficulties, a number of active principles have been suggested to be intrinsic secretions of the corpora cardiaca, including myotropic factors and a factor causing release of a cardioaccelerator by the pericardial cells (Davey, 1963).

As noted above, retrocerebral organs showing a relationship to the protocerebral neurosecretory cell groups like that of the corpora cardiaca are seen in many of the lower arthropod groups. Of these, Schneider's organs of the araneids are particularly reminiscent of the corpora cardiaca, since they too possess the same three structural components: nerve cells, intrinsic glandular cells, and neurosecretion-bearing axon endings (Kühne, 1959; Legendre, 1959). It is not known whether this similarity of constitution reflects physiological similarities.

3. *The Non-neuronal Endocrine Organs*

The arthropods are well endowed with epithelial endocrine glands; by contrast, only four have been described in nonarthropod groups. These include (1) the gastropod gonad, governing the glandular activity of the genital tract in certain pulmonates (Laviolette, 1954); (2) the maturing ova in nereid polychaetes, suggested to exert a negative feedback in the control of reproductive maturity (Durchon, 1952); (3) the posterior salivary glands in *Octopus*, reported to play a role in the tonic control of the chromatophores (Sereni, 1930; Kahr, 1959); and (4) the optic glands of cephalopods, implicated in the control of sexual maturity. However, the optic glands may be of neural origin

(Wells, 1960). Of these four only the pulmonate gonad, and to a lesser extent, the optic gland may be said to have their endocrine function established on a reasonably firm experimental basis. The seeming rarity of epithelial endocrine organs in the nonarthropod invertebrates may be due in part to the fact that until recently few workers were interested in these groups; our knowledge is very incomplete. However, non-neuronal glands may actually play a less prominent role in lower groups. This is suggested by the demonstration in nereids of a probable first-order control of reproductive maturation, a process in which epithelial endocrine glands figure importantly in higher groups. In addition, three of the four organs mentioned above are found in the gastropod or cephalopod mollusks, animals which can scarcely be said to be less complex than the arthropods.

The arthropods possess a number of known or suspected epithelial endocrine organs. In the insects (Gilbert, 1963; de Wilde, 1964) these include the corpus allatum, the ecdysial gland, the pericardial cells (Davey, 1963), the ovary and the hindgut (Beck and Alexander, 1964) (the last two named are not part of the efferent loop). Of these structures, the corpus allatum and the ecdysial gland are the best studied of the invertebrate endocrines; they have been subjected to all of the usual tests of endocrine function. The probable structure of ecdysone, the presumed product of the ecdysial gland, is known (Karlson, 1963; Karlson *et al.*, 1965); it is a derivative of cholesterol containing the cyclopentanoperhydrophenanthrene nucleus found in steroid hormones in vertebrates. In the Crustacea, three well-established non-neuronal endocrine structures are found: the Y-organ, the androgenic gland, and the ovaries (Carlisle and Knowles, 1959).

The arthropod endocrine organs have a wide variety of physiological functions. The insect ecdysial gland and the crustacean Y-organs are concerned with the inception of the molting process. In insects the effects of ecdysone upon the target structures are modulated in the larval stages by juvenile hormone (neotenin), the hormone of the corpus allatum. Whether any analogous organ operates during the early phase of crustacean development is unknown. The corpus allatum is also responsible in most insects for the completion of oogenesis and the development of the female sex glands (Section III,B,2), as well as having diverse effects upon metabolism (L'Helias, 1964). The control of reproductive function is different in the crustaceans: the development of the ovary is apparently under the control of an inhibitory first-order reflex mediated by neurosecretory cells of the eyestalk or brain, while the secondary female characteristics are under the control of the ovary. The androgenic gland of the male crustacean is responsible for the development and maturation of the testes and of the male sex ducts and accessories. As yet, no analogous structure has been reported in the insects.

Hormonal regulation of the heart rate in insects is under the control of a factor from the pericardial cells, which either lie scattered or are found in groups in or around the heart, pericardial septum, and alary muscles. Although these cells are often viewed as being excretory in nature, it has been reported recently that they in fact play a role analogous to the neurosecretory pericardial organs of the crustaceans, releasing a cardioaccelerator in response to materials carried via the hemolymph from the corpora cardiaca.

4. *Control of Endocrine Function*

Insofar as it is known, the regulation of the activity level of the epithelial endocrine organs of invertebrates is under the immediate control of the central nervous system, either via direct innervation of the gland or by means of neurosecretory cells. Only in the insects is there indication of possible third-order reflexes, involving the interposition of a second endocrine structure between the nervous system and the final gland in the control sequence (Davey, 1963).

a. Direct Innervation. The innervation of gland cells by stimulatory or inhibitory nerves has been reported in several cases. The innervated glands are mainly concerned with the control of reproductive activity. In the case of both the cephalopod optic gland (Wells, 1960) and of the corpora allata of female insects (Engelmann, 1957), secretion of a gonadotropic hormone is prevented by inhibitory innervation. Whether or not this same innervation aids in the timing of corpus allatum secretion during the molting stages is not known. Despite these accepted cases, the presence of secretomotor fibers to the endocrine glands seems no more widespread than it is in the vertebrates; the common mode of control is via the secretions of neurosecretory cells.

b. Regulation by Neurosecretory Cells. The ability of the neurosecretory cell to receive a varied neural input and to translate this input into an increased or decreased rate of discharge of its secretory products gives it a central role in the liaison between nervous system and endocrine glands. The possibility of intimate synaptic contacts with a variety of nerve centers allows for an integrated response to a variety of stimuli, both internal and external, while the hormone-like nature of its output confers the more smoothly modulated long-term control of its target which is a prime feature of endocrine regulation. The neurosecretory cell can thus act as an impedance-matching device, serving to link with the greatest possible efficiency the rapid phasic activity of the nervous system to the slow, smooth responses of many target organs. Usually the neurosecretory cell acts as a true endocrine gland cell, discharging its secretions into the blood-vascular system or coelom; in the vast majority of cases a more or less extensive vascular discontinuity exists between the site of release of secretions by the neurosecretory cell and the target affected. In a few instances, this gap is not apparent and the neurosecretory cells are in close contact with their targets. Such a case is the control of the corpus allatum, in which, as previously noted, some of the axons of the pars intercerebralis neurosecretory cells pass through the corpora cardiaca and enter the corpora allata, where they presumably make direct contact with their target cells. It is not clear to what degree this contact is necessary, however, since there are reports that the corpora allata can become activated and function when severed from their neural connections (Englemann, 1960). The uncertainty arises over the question of whether the stimulation in this case comes from neurosecretory materials released from the corpora cardiaca, or from neurosecretion already present in the allatum at the time of its denervation. Recently, Knowles and Bern (see Chapter 5, Volume I) have suggested that the essential feature of neurosecretory cells in their role of intermediary between nervous and endocrine systems is the production of long-acting, slowly degradable secretions; whether these secretions reach their targets as true hormones carried via the vascular system or by direct contact of the neurosecretory fiber ending with its target is, in Knowles' and Bern's view, secondary. This view has the advantage of emphasizing the role of neurosecretory cells as the final common pathway for neuroendocrine correlation and would resolve the seeming paradoxes raised by cases such as the insect corpus allatum and the pars intermedia of vertebrates.

C. Target Organs

1. *The Nature of the Target Organs*

The target structures of the efferent loop are varied in their nature. They include peripheral targets such as the crustacean chromatophore, the epidermal cell and fat body cell of insects and annelid gametes; but they also include intermediate target structures—other endocrine organs—and the central nervous system itself. Just as the insect epidermal cell is the target for the ecdysial gland, so the ecdysial gland is itself the target for the protocerebral neurosecretory cells. This cascading of two or more endocrine structures in series has been likened to a biological amplifier serving to intensify the signal (Rothballer, 1957). It also allows increased opportunities for integration by virtue of the differing response characteristics and inputs of the various stages.

2. *Effects of the Central Nervous System on Target Response.*

Not uncommonly, the nervous system interacts with the endocrines at levels other than that of the first-order reflex, either by modifying the response of the target organs to their hormonal control, or by exerting a parallel control with the endocrines over the peripheral structures. One of the best examples of parallel control is seen in the crustaceans, in the control of heart rate. The decapod heart is neurogenic, the stimulus to contract arising in neurons of the cardiac ganglion, which lies imbedded in the dorsal wall of the heart. Although this stimulus is intrinsic to the ganglion, the beat frequency may be modified by two means: by cardioaccelerator and cardioinhibitor nerve fibers from the ventral nerve cord, and also by the predominently cardioacceleratory secretions from the pericardial organs (Alexandrowicz and Carlisle, 1953). In addition to long-term fluctuations, the heart rate can be observed to show rapid and relatively short-term reflex responses to a variety of chemical, tactile, and visual stimuli (Larimer, 1964). Although the precise interactions of these various factors in the intact animal remain to be determined, it would appear that in this case both mechanisms act in parallel upon the cardiac ganglion; the hormonal control sets the basal level of activity (Brown, 1964), while the neural control is responsible for the phasic reflex responses.

A somewhat similar, although apparently more complex, situation is seen in the control of the chromatophores in cephalopods (Sereni, 1930; Kahr, 1959). These chromatophores consist of a central pigmented cell, to the periphery of which are attached radially oriented muscle fibers. The pigment cell is caused to dilate by the contraction of the radial musculature; it contracts by its own elasticity upon the relaxation of the muscle fibers. This system is under the control of nerve fibers from centers in the brain of the animals. However, it was long ago shown that there are factors in the blood (apparently serotonin, tyramine, and betaine) which can cause dilatation or contraction of the chromatophores. These substances originate in the posterior salivary glands, and are reported to affect the chromatophores primarily by influencing the activity of the motor and inhibitory centers controlling the chromatophore musculature, but also by direct effects upon the chromatophores themselves. Here again it would appear that the nervous system is responsible for phasic fluctuations about a base line set by the humoral mechanisms; in this case, however, the target acted upon is not a peripheral motor ganglion but rather, antagonistic centers located within the central nervous system. In addition, the substances acting upon the nerve centers in *Octopus* are also capable of acting upon the chromatophore muscles directly. It has recently been suggested (Brown, 1964) that in the Crustacea, the same is true of the pericardial organ extracts; in Brown's view, these may act not only upon the cardiac ganglion (see above), but directly on the myocardium.

In other situations the role of the nervous system is more obscure. The participation of hormones in the control of regeneration has been demonstrated in groups as diverse as the polychaetes and the crustaceans (Clark and Bonney, 1960; Passano and Jyssum, 1963). However, components of the nervous system must generally be present at the site for regeneration to proceed normally. The exact contribution of the nervous tissue is uncertain, but has been suggested in the Crustacea to be that of inducing a basal growth of the regenerating tissue upon which the endocrine system can act prior to and during the molt (Bliss, 1960). Again, it has been reported that denervation affects the mechanical properties of the cuticle in insects, the tanning of which is under endocrine control (Fraenkel and Hsiao, 1963; Núñez, 1963). Here too, there seems to be interaction of nervous and endocrine control mechanisms.

3. *Direct Effects of the Environment upon Target Organ Responses*

Environmental factors can modify directly the response of the effectors to a hormonal stimulus, light and temperature being particularly effective in this respect. In the decapod compound eye for example, the movement of the distal retinal shielding pigment from the dark to the light-adapted position is under the control of a light-adapting hormone released from the sinus gland (see Carlisle and Knowles, 1959). This response of the distal pigment cells to the neurohormone is potentiated by light. If one half of the compound eye is covered, preventing light from reaching the ommatidia on that side, and the eye is illuminated, only the pigment in the uncovered half will reach full light adaptation (Knowles, 1948). It would appear that the distal pigment cells are sensitized to the light-adapting hormone by the presence of light. Similar effects of light upon the chromatophores of the general body surface have also been reported.

D. The Afferent Feedback

Although in many cases it is reasonable to infer that feedback circuits are in operation in the processes controlled by neuroendocrine paths, direct experimental evidence on this aspect of the control system in invertebrates is relatively rare and for the most part, related to control of reproduction. In the polychaetes, two reports of feedback exist. One of these indicates that the presence of maturing gametes in the coelom of *Arenicola* inhibits the release or action of the maturation hormone (Howie and McClenaghan, 1965; see Table I), thus terminating further gametogenesis. Whether this effect of the maturing gametes is due to a hormone or to accumulation of some metabolite is uncertain. The other case suggests that maturing ova in the coelom of the nereid polychaetes inhibits the production of the juvenile hormone by the cerebral ganglion, thus actually speeding maturation of the gametes and the heteronereid change (Durchon, 1952). The net effect of this particular feedback link would be positive, by inhibition of the inhibitor of the process in question.

In the insects, a number of feedbacks have been reported, some positive in nature, some negative. The corpora allata of adult *Calliphora* (Diptera) have been shown to exert a positive feedback upon the median neurosecretory cells which stimulate not only the corpora allata themselves but protein metabolism, particularly protease production by the gut (Lea and Thomsen, 1962; Thomsen and Møller, 1963). The effect of this feedback is to speed the digestion and utilization of protein following the meat meal required for reproduction in these flies. Other cases of feedback in the Insecta include the inhibition, apparently involving both neural and humoral pathways, which is exerted by developing embryos in the brood sac of ovoviviparous roaches upon gonadotropin production by the corpus allatum; this serves to prevent a new cycle of maturation during pregnancy (Englemann, 1960, 1964). In a similar manner, the maturing eggs of oviparous forms are reported to produce a humoral factor causing a negative feedback upon the brain and corpus allatum which inhibits maturation of further ovules. It may be this same factor which stimulates release of neurosecretory material from the corpus cardiacum, initiating the process of oviposition (see Section III,B,6).

It would thus appear that both negative and positive feedbacks are utilized in invertebrate control systems—negative feedback to limit or terminate fully developed processes, positive feedback to initiate new phases of physiological activity or to speed them to completion.

Apart from a few cases such as the above, in which some direct evidence is available, there are many tantalizing hints of feedback mechanisms in operation. For example, a hormonal factor from the brain controls gametogenesis in the earthworms (Herlant-Meewis, 1959). It has been reported that castration results in drastic cytological changes in one of the neurosecretory cell types in the brain (Hubl, 1953), suggesting the presence of a feedback between gonads and brain neurosecretory cells. In many other situations, particularly in the area of metabolic control, feedback seems a logical necessity. It is to be presumed that as our knowledge of these areas increases many more cases of feedback will come to light.

E. Sensory Cues

The neuroendocrine system of any animal performs a number of functions. In the first place it directs the homeostatic processes tending to maintain the stability of the internal environment. Secondly, it initiates and ensures the orderly sequential progression of such discontinuous physiological processes as reproduction and molting. Lastly, it accomplishes the above in the fashion best calculated to allow the animal to survive and reproduce in a changeable external environment. This requires a variety of sensory information concerning both the internal and external environments. For example, in the timing of the completion of oogenesis in many insects, the state of internal readiness (particularly in terms of nutritional reserves) must be ascertained and the presence of the proper combination of factors in the external environment determined. As a result of the coincidence of the proper internal and external conditions, the reproductive sequence is begun. At this point, further sensory information is required to ensure the proper succession of steps leading to egg maturation and finally oviposition or pregnancy and birth.

The nature of the sensory cues used is as varied as the processes controlled and the animals using them. Some are specific measures of the parameter they are being used to evaluate; others are only general correlates. Both oogenesis and molting, for example, are strenuous processes requiring adequate food reserves. During oogenesis, many insects require a high protein diet to support yolk formation; in some cases (e.g., the blowfly *Calliphora*) a high-protein meal is required to activate the endocrine system and initiate egg maturation. Here the specific nature of the meal is apparently considered, since a carbohydrate meal will not do (see Thomsen and Møller, 1963). On the other hand, the process of molting in *Rhodnius* (an assasin bug) is also triggered by feeding. *Rhodnius* feeds only on blood; a single full meal is sufficient to precipitate the next molt. In this case the character of the meal is predetermined, and the significant feature is its presence or absence. *Rhodnius* utilizes a normal correlate of feeding–abdominal distention–as the cue to proceed. This operates via stretch receptors in the abdomen. Artificial distension of the abdomen with saline will initiate molting although it is nutritionally inadequate, while a series of small blood meals which fail to distend the abdomen enough to activate the sensory endings fail to evoke the molt even though they are, in sum, nutritionally sufficient.

Of the various external sensory cues, the most commonly used are light (especially photoperiod), temperature, and a variety of stimuli which may be classified as social contacts in the broad sense. With respect to light, at least two aspects of the light-dark cycle are used as cues by various groups: the time of "lights-on" or "lights-off" is used in setting the phases of many circadian rhythms of activity (see Harker, 1964), while the use of the photoperiod as a means of coordinating annually occurring events such as reproduction or diapause is widespread. The increasing photoperiods of spring are used by groups from the annelids to the vertebrates to initiate reproduction, while short photoperiods such as encountered in fall and winter induce and maintain diapause in many insects (see de Wilde, 1961). Although blinding seems effective in activating the optic glands in *Octopus* (Wells, 1960), the receptors for the light stimuli are not always the obvious. In insects for example, painting over the compound eyes of *Leptinotarsa* (the Colorado beetle) has no effect upon the influence of photoperiod in diapause induction (see de Wilde, 1961). Furthermore, there is evidence that photoperiodic effects on the method of reproduction in aphids are mediated by the direct effects of light upon the protocerebrum of these animals, possibly by acting upon the neurosecretory cells themselves (Lees, 1964).

Temperature itself has effects upon certain of these processes, apparently apart from its generalized metabolic effects upon poikilotherms. Temperature increases oppose the effect of short photoperiod in diapause induction in adult *Leptinotarsa* and a number of other insects (see de Wilde, 1961); the effect of chilling on the termination of pupal diapause in the *Cecropia* moth is also well known (see Gilbert, 1963).

Social contacts include a wide variety of stimuli, many of them involved in the control of reproduction. The roles of these factors are best known in the Insecta, where they are especially important in the social insects. Some of the stimuli included in this category are the visual stimuli, various tactile stimuli and, in some cases, copulation. The stimuli are required in various groups for the initiation of the train of events leading to egg maturation. One of the most important modes of social interaction is via chemical means, particularly by the pheromones. These substances, which are released into the environment by an individual and affect other members of the same species, are present in such diverse groups as annelids, echiuroids, and lamellibranchs. Their effects are best known and most dramatically illustrated in the control of reproduction and the determination of social structure in the insects (see Butler, 1964). In many moths and roaches, the female secretes a pheromone which serves both to attract males, in some cases from distances of several miles, and to initiate male sexual behavior. In the desert locust, a male pheromone stimulates egg production by the female. In contrast to these agents, which work via the olfactory senses, the pheromones influencing the social organization of the bees and termites are passed by mouth. The queen substance of bees has the effect of suppressing the reproductive tract of the workers, and of preventing development of additional queens. In termite colonies (Lüscher, 1961), pheromones from the active king and queen inhibit the development of supplementary reproductives. It is also reported that the functional male produces a substance favoring development of additional female reproductives. The chemistry of the queen substance and of several of the sex attractants has been determined (Karlson, 1963); most of them share in common the feature of being low molecular weight fatty acid derivatives. Queen substance (I), for example, is 9-oxydec-2-enolic acid, while the female

$$H_3C{-}CO{-}(CH_2)_5{-}CH{=}CH{-}COOH$$

(I)

sex attractants of *Bombyx* ("Bombykol") and of the gypsy moth are closely related molecules containing an unsaturated, 16-carbon chain and a primary alcohol group.

III. Brief Survey of Neuroendocrine Mechanisms in the Invertebrates

A. Table I

Table I includes information concerning many of the processes known to be controlled by neuroendocrine mechanisms in the various phyla. It is divided into four sections according to the processes controlled (see Section I,A); within these sections the division is phylogenetic. For each process the control pattern is in the form of a flow diagram in which each column corresponds to a component of the neuroendocrine control sequence (see Section I,B,1). Arrows extend from the controlling struc-

TABLE IA
GROWTH, MATURATION AND REGENERATION[a]

Phylum	Aspect controlled	Sensory cues	Central pathways	Efferent Loop: Neurosecretory	Efferent Loop: Endocrine	Targets	References
Platyhelminthes	Regeneration	Injury to eyespots →	Central integration →	Cerebral NSC →		Eyespot regeneration	Stephan-Dubois and Lender, 1956
Annelida Polychaeta	Growth	? →	Central integration →	Supraesophageal NSC (young animals) →		Segment proliferation	Clark and Scully, 1964
	Regeneration	Damage to nerve cord? →	Central integration →	Supraesophageal NSC →		Potentiation of regenerative abilities	Clark and Ruston, 1963; Golding, 1963
Arthropoda Insecta	Initiation of molt and development of adult characteristics	Photoperiod, abdominal distention, etc. →	Central integration →	Pars intercerebralis NSC (ecdysiotropin) →	Ecdysial gland (ecdysone) → ↑ ?	Imaginal discs, epidermal cells, etc. (promotes molt and metamorphosis)	Cf. Gilbert, 1964; Schneiderman and Gilbert, 1964
	Retention of larval attributes at molt	? →	Central integration (especially supraesophageal and subesophageal) →	Medial NSC →	Corpus allatum (juvenile hormone) →	Retention of larval traits in proportion to juvenile hormone: ecdysone ratio	
	Larval diapause, pupal diapause	Photoperiod, temperature →	Central integration (inhibitory) →	Pars intercerebralis NSC (ecdysiotropin inhibited)			Cf. Gilbert, 1964
	Larval diapause development (*Ostrinia*)	Photoperiod →	Central integration →	? →	Anterior hindgut (proctodone) ? →	Acts on or with pars intercerebralis NSC to initiate diapause development ?	Beck and Alexander, 1964

	Adult diapause	Photoperiod, nutrition, temperature →	Central integration (inhibitory) →		Corpus allatum (inhibited) →	Promotion of diapause	Cf. de Wilde, 1964
	Embryonic (egg) diapause (*Bombyx*)	Temperature, photoperiod →	Central integration (adult female) →	Subesophageal NSC →		Ovary (promotes production of diapause eggs)	Cf. Gilbert, 1964
	Cuticular tanning	Neural via ventral nerve cord →	Central integration →	Median NSC; thoracic ganglia →		Cuticle (promotes tanning)	Fraenkel and Hsiao, 1963
	Mechanical properties of cuticle (*Rhodnius*)	? →	Mesothoracic ganglion →			Cuticle (determines "tonus" of abdominal cuticle)	Núñez, 1963
Crustacea	Molt (initiation of proecdysis)	Light, temperature, humidity, etc. →	Central integration (inhibitory) →	Medulla terminalis NSC (molt-inhibiting hormone inhibited) →	Y-organ (molting hormone) →	Epidermal cells, metabolic activity, etc. (promotes entry to premolt phase)	Cf. Carlisle and Knowles, 1959; Bliss and Boyer, 1964
		? →	Central integration →	Medulla terminalis and brain NSC (molt-accelerating hormone) ? → (? to Y-organ; ? to epidermal cells)			
	Regeneration of limbs	Light, temperature, humidity, etc. →	Central integration →	Medulla terminalis NSC →	Y-organ (molting hormone) →	Premolt limb growth	Cf. Bliss, 1960; Passano and Jyssum, 1963
			↓ local nerve supply →	(Medulla terminalis NSC ? →)		basal limb growth ?	
Myriapoda Chilopoda	Molt	? →	Central integration →	Protocerebral NSC (inhibitory) →	? →	Molt (inhibited)	Joly, 1966

[a] Pathways stimulatory except where noted. NSC = neurosecretory cells.

TABLE IB

REPRODUCTION[a]

Phylum	Aspect controlled	Sensory cues	Central pathways	Efferent Loop: Neurosecretory	Efferent Loop: Endocrine	Targets	References
Nemertinea	Oogenesis	?	Central integration	Brain NSC (inhibitory)		Developing ova (inhibited)	Gontcharoff and Lechenault, 1958
Annelida							
Polychaeta Errantia (Nereidae, Nephtyidae)	Gametogenesis, epitoky	Photoperiod, etc.	Central integration	Supraesophageal NSC (juvenile hormone—inhibitory)		Developing gametes, musculature, sensory organs, etc. (genital maturation and epitoky inhibited)	Cf. Durchon, 1960
Sedentaria (*Arenicola*)	Gametogenesis	Temperature, etc.	Central integration	Supraesophageal NSC (maturation hormone)		Developing gametes	Howie, 1963
Oligochaeta	Gametogenesis	Temperature, etc.	Central integration	Supraesophageal NSC		Maturation of gametes (promotes meiosis)	Herlant-Meewis, 1956, 1959
	Secondary sex characters			Supraesophageal NSC		Development and function of clitellum, etc.	
Hirudinea	Gametogenesis	?	Central integration	Brain NSC		Developing gametes	Hagadorn, 1962
Mollusca							
Gastropoda	Gametogenesis	Temperature, photoperiod	Central integration	NSC of tentacular and cerebral ganglia		Developing gametes	Pelluet, 1964
					Gonads	Development, function of sex ducts and glands	Laviolette, 1954
Cephalopoda	Gametogenesis	Visual: photoperiod?	Subpeduncular and/or dorsal basal lobes (inhibitory)		Optic gland (gonadotropin inhibited)	Developing gametes	Wells, 1960

		nutrition, temperature, etc., male pheromone (some), copulation (some)	tion		(gonadotropin)	cells and ova (promotes yolk formation); production of ovarian hormone?	
	Development and function of female accessory glands	Photoperiod, nutrition, temperature, etc. →	Central integration →	Medial NSC →	Corpus allatum →	Female accessory glands (promotes development and function)	
	Production of male and female sex pheromones (some)	Photoperiod, nutrition, temperature, etc. →	Central integration →	Medial NSC →	Corpus allatum →	Stimulates production of sex pheromones	
	Oogenesis (termination)	Hormone from active ovary?; developing embryos in brood sac (ovoviviparous forms) etc. →	Neurons of supraesophageal and subesophageal (inhibitory) →		Corpus allatum (inhibited) →	Suppression of ovule maturation	
	Oviposition	Hormone from active ovary? →	Central integration →	Supraesophageal NSC →		Promotes oviposition (inhibits subesophageal centers inhibitory to oviposition movements?)	
	Male sex behavior (some species)	Female sex pheromone →	Central integration →	Medial NSC? →		Release of male sex behavior (suppression of subesophageal inhibitory centers?)	
Crustacea	Differentiation and maturation of male structures	? →	Central integration →	? (Testis inhibiting hormone in crabs) →	Androgenic gland →	Primary and secondary male sex characters	Charniaux-Cotton, 1962
	Reproduction in female	Photoperiod, etc. →	Central integration →	Medulla terminalis NSC (ovarian inhibiting hormone) →		Oogenesis	Cf. Carlisle and Knowles, 1959
				→	Ovary (ovarian hormone) →	Secondary female sex characters	

TABLE IB—*Continued*

Phylum	Aspect controlled	Sensory cues	Central pathways	Efferent Loop: Neurosecretory	Efferent Loop: Endocrine	Targets	References
Echinodermata	Gametogenesis and spawning (Asteroidea)	Temperature, sex products of other individuals, etc. →	Central integration →	NSC of radial nerves? (shedding substance) →	→	Meiosis and spawning	Unger, 1962; Chaet, 1964; Noumura and Kanatani, 1962; Kanatani, 1964
			→	NSC of radial nerves? ("shedhibin") →	→	Spawning (inhibition)	

[a] Pathways stimulatory except where noted. NSC = neurosecretory cells.

ture to the structure or process controlled; unless otherwise indicated, the influence is a stimulatory one. Since established instances of feedback control are uncommon, this part of the control pattern has not been included in Table I; it is discussed in Section II,D. Table I may be used to compare patterns of control of similar processes in different groups and to trace the appearance of the several components of control in the phylogenetic sequence, as well as to determine what is known of the control of a process in a given animal group. References are included if not cited in the text.

B. Control of Reproduction in the Female Insect

The control of egg maturation and reproductive activity in the female insect may be taken as an example illustrating both the complexity that neuroendocrine control has achieved in invertebrates and the major uncertainties which abound even in an area such as this, which has attracted the continuing interest of investigators since the first experimental work was done thirty years ago.

1. *Oogenesis as a Process*

Insects are for the most part oviparous animals, although both ovoviviparous and viviparous forms are known (Wigglesworth, 1950). The ovaries are paired; each is composed of one to many ovarioles, tubular structures within which the ova develop (Fig. 5). Oogonia are present at the apex of the ovarioles; as they mature they become surrounded by a layer of follicle cells and are moved progressively further down into the midportion of the ovariole. During this period the ova increase greatly in size and yolk formation occurs. This vitellogenesis is carried out by the egg with the assistance of the follicle cells and, in many insects, of auxiliary nurse cells as well. In the initial stage a primarily lipoid yolk is formed, protein yolk being synthesized in the later phases. Finally, the follicle secretes a cuticular covering or chorion over the egg which is then discharged into the lateral oviduct. The ovum passes through the lateral and median oviducts and is fertilized in the genital chamber by sperm stored in the spermatheca since copulation. Oviposition may then occur, or in the case of ovoviviparous and viviparous forms, the eggs may be retained in a brood sac to develop.

2. *Role of the Corpora Allata and Their Control by the Brain*

Oogenesis is a nutritionally demanding process; the phase of protein yolk formation appears to be a particularly crucial period. In many

TABLE IC

METABOLISM AND HOMEOSTASIS[a]

Phylum	Aspect controlled	Sensory cues	Central pathways	Efferent Loop: Neurosecretory	Efferent Loop: Endocrine	Targets	References
Annelida Oligochaeta	Protein, oxygen metabolism	Temperature →	Central integration →	Supraesophageal NSC →		Protein synthesis, oxygen consumption	Rao, 1962
	Osmotic and ionic regulation	? →	Central integration →	Supraesophageal NSC →		Water and Na^+ balance	Kamemoto, 1964
Mollusca Gastropoda	Osmotic balance	? →	Central integration →	Pleural ganglion NSC →		Water balance; (loss in fresh-water forms; gain in marine forms)	Lever *et al.*, 1961; Vicente, 1963
Arthropoda Insecta	Osmotic balance (*Rhodnius*)	Distention of abdomen →	Thoracic ganglia →	Mesothoracic ganglion NSC (diuretic hormone) →		Malpighian tubules	Madrell, 1964
	Osmotic balance (*Periplaneta*)	? →	Central integration →	Supraesophageal NSC (anti-diuretic hormone) →	Corpora allata? →	Malpighian tubules	Wall and Ralph, 1964
	Carbohydrate metabolism (trehalose, etc.)	? —	? —	? →	Corpus cardiacum (hyperglycemic hormone) →	Fat body (activates phosphorylase)	Steele, 1963
	Protein metabolism (plasma protein level, gut protease activity, etc.)	Protein content of meal, etc. →	Central integration →	Medial NSC (supraesophageal) →		Amino acid incorporation; gut protease production, etc.	Hill, 1962; Thomsen and Møller, 1963
				(Medial NSC) →	Corpus allatum →	Medial NSC (positive feedback link)	

	Lipid metabolism, oxygen consumption, oxidative phosphorylation, etc.	? →	? →	Medial NSC? →	Corpus allatum →	Lipid turnover (fat body), oxygen consumption, phosphorylation	Orr, 1964; de Wilde, 1964; Sláma, 1964
	Heart rate	Enforced activity, etc. →	Central integration →	? →	Corpus cardiacum →	Pericardial cells (release of cardioaccelerator amine)	Davey, 1963
	Cyclic motor activity (roach)	Light-dark cycle →	Central integration →	Subesophageal NSC →		Motor activity level	Harker, 1956, 1964
Crustacea	Cardiac output; amplitude, rate	? →	Central integration →	Thoracic ganglion NSC (endings in pericardial organs) →		Cardiac ganglion (stimulates firing rhythm of cardiac ganglion cells)	Brown, 1964; cf. Carlisle and Knowles, 1959
		Visual, chemosensory, etc. →	Central integration (stimulatory and inhibitory) →			Cardiac ganglion cells	Larimer, 1964
	Carbohydrate metabolism	"Stress" →	Central integration →	Eyestalk NSC (hyperglycemic factor) →		Blood sugar level (increase)	Scheer, 1960
		? →	Central integration →	Eyestalk NSC →		Hepatopancreas (favor hexosemonophosphate shunt in intermolt animals; Embden-Meyerhof path in premolt animals)	McWhinnie and Chua, 1964
	Ca^{2+} metabolism	Various →	Central integration (inhibitory) →	Eyestalk NSC (molt-inhibiting hormone inhibited) →	Y-organ (molting hormone) →	Hepatopancreas (depletion, with rise in blood Ca^{2+})	Cf. Passano, 1960

[a] Pathways stimulatory except where noted. NSC = neurosecretory cells.

TABLE ID

ADAPTATION TO EXTERNAL FACTORS[a]

Phylum	Aspect controlled	Sensory cues	Central pathways	Efferent Loop: Neurosecretory	Efferent Loop: Endocrine	Targets	References
Annelida Hirudinea	Physiological color change	Light →	Central integration →	Brain NSC →		Chromatophores (dispersion)	Smith, 1942; Gersch and Richter, 1961
		Light → ? Direct sensitization ? → Chromatophores					
Mollusca Cephalopoda	Physiological color change	Visual, tactile, etc. →	Motor and inhibitory centers in brain → (← from Posterior salivary glands)			Chromatophore muscles	
		Visual, tactile, etc. →	Central integration →		Posterior salivary glands (5-hydroxytryptamine, tyramine) →	Chromatophore muscles	
Arthropoda Insecta	Physiological color change (Phasmids)	Light, temperature, humidity →	Central integration →	Tritocerebral NSC →		Hypodermal pigment cells (dispersion)	Raabe, 1964
	Physiological color change (*Corethra* larva)	Light →	Central integration →	Supraesophageal NSC →		Chromatophores of larval tracheae (dispersion)	Cf. Fingerman, 1963
	Morphological color change (Phasmids, locust, etc.)	Pheromones, etc. →	Central integration →	? →	Corpus allatum →	Hypodermal pigment formation	Raabe, 1964
Crustacea	Physiological color change	Visual, etc. →	Central integration →	NSC of eyestalk, brain, and ventral nerve cord (Chromatophorotropins) →		Chromatophores (dispersion and/or concentration)	Cf. Carlisle and Knowles, 1959; Fingerman, 1963
		Visual, etc. → Direct effects of light, etc. → Chromatophores					

Visual adaptation to light intensity	Light (high intensity) →	Central integration →	Brain and eyestalk NSC (light-adapting hormone) →	Distal retinal pigment (causes light adaptation)	Cf. Carlisle and Knowles, 1959
	Light (high intensity) → Direct sensitization →			Distal retinal pigment (causes light adaptation)	
	Light (low intensity) →	Central integration →	Brain and eyestalk NSC (dark-adapting hormone) →	Distal retinal pigment (causes dark adaptation)	

[a] Pathways stimulatory except where noted. NSC = neurosecretory cells.

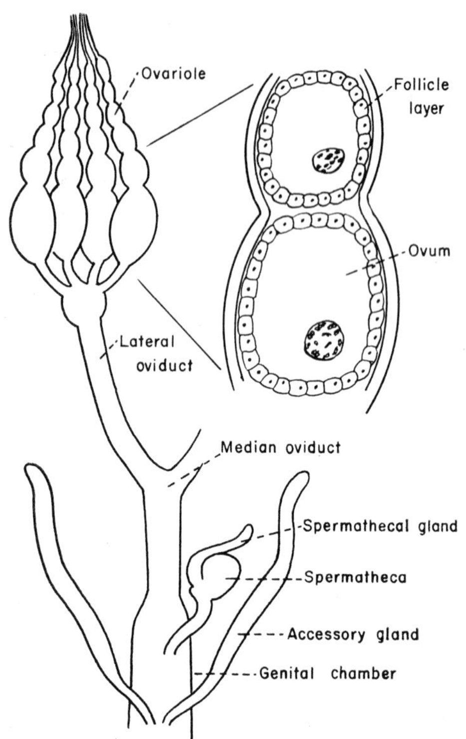

FIG. 5. The reproductive tract of a generalized female insect. *Inset:* An enlarged sectional view of a portion of one ovariole, from the area indicated. (Modified from DuPorte, 1959.)

forms the process is under the endocrine control of the corpora allata, which are in turn regulated by both neurosecretory and conventional innervation from the brain. The following pertinent experimental evidence may be cited: (1) Excision of the corpora allata results in failure of oogenesis at the stage of protein yolk formation, followed by degeneration of the developing ova. This deficiency can be remedied by implantation of active corpora allata, or by parabiotic union with an animal possessing active corpora allata (Wigglesworth, 1936). (2) Section of the nervi corpora allati, or lesions in certain parts of the protocerebrum (*not* involving the median neurosecretory cell groups) results in hypertrophy, and at least in certain cases, hyperactivity of the corpora allata (Engelmann, 1957). (3) Destruction of the median neurosecretory cell groups of the protocerebrum results in inactivity of the corpora allata (Thomsen, 1952; Highnam, 1962a). (4) Destruction of the median neurosecretory cells also results in disturbances of protein metabolism resulting in depressed incorporation of amino acids into protein; this deficiency is not fully remedied by implantation of active corpora allata (Thomsen and Møller, 1963). These observations are interpreted as indicating that (1) the corpora allata produce a gonadotropic hormone which acts upon the ova and follicle cells to promote formation of protein yolk, (2) the development and activity of the corpora allata are stimulated by the secretions of the median neurosecretory cells and inhibited by conventional innervation from other areas of the protocerebrum, and (3) the median neurosecretory cells, apart from their allatotropic effect, may influence vitellogenesis by virtue of their effects upon protein metabolism.

3. *Initiation of the Reproductive Sequence*

The stimulus which results in the activation of the corpora allata varies from group to group. In some cases it is nutritional: oogenesis in *Rhodnius* is normally initiated by the taking of a blood meal (Wigglesworth, 1936), while in the blowfly, activation of the median neurosecretory cells—and hence of the corpora allata—results from high protein content in the diet (Lea and Thomsen, 1962; Strangways-Dixon, 1962). In other groups, the presence of males results in activation, probably by means of pheromones (Highnam, 1962b). In still others copulation itself is the required stimulus (Engelmann, 1960). Whatever the adequate stimulus, the effect is presumably to inactivate the inhibitory innervation to the corpora allata, allowing release of their gonadotropin.

4. *Control of Secondary Sex Characters*

In addition to their role as a gonadotropin source, the corpora allata have been found to be responsible for the maintenance and function of certain of the sex accessory glands (Wigglesworth, 1936). The accessory glands of the reproductive tract have a number of functions. These include secretion of a variety of cements and egg coverings in the female, and formation of the seminal fluid in the male. Removal of the corpora allata renders them inactive, and replacement, for example by parabiosis with a normal animal, reactivates them. Similarly, the glands producing the male and female sex pheromones in locusts (Loher, 1961) and roaches (Barth, 1961) have been shown to be dependent on the corpora allata. It is assumed but not proved that the hormone involved is identical with the gonadotropic hormone.

5. *Termination of the Cycle*

Of equal interest to activation of the corpora allata is the method of their inactivation. In many insects egg development is cyclical; the presence of numbers of eggs in an advanced stage of oogenesis in the ovary prevents the further development of the younger stages. The observation that ovariectomy often results in hypertrophy of the corpora allata (von Harnack and Scharrer, 1956) has raised the possibility of a negative feedback mechanism. It has also been reported that injection of extracts of ripe ovaries results in inactivation of the corpus allatum (Nayar, 1958). In the viviparous roaches, the corpora allata are inhibited during the period when the egg case is present in the brood sac (Engelmann, 1960), presumably by re-establishment of the dominance of the inhibitory innervation to the corpora allata. This inhibition works via the ventral nerve cord.

6. *Induction of Oviposition*

The culmination of the reproductive process in oviparous forms is the act of oviposition. Although the events precipitating oviposition are poorly understood, there are a number of factors suggesting the involvement of neuroendocrine regulatory mechanisms. Ovipositional movements are under the control of centers in the last abdominal ganglia; these in turn are normally inhibited by centers in the subesophageal ganglion. Severing the ventral nerve cord between the subesophageal and abdominal ganglia removes this inhibition and results in ovipositional movements, even leading to premature deposition of abnormal egg cases in some forms (Roeder, 1963). Extracts of corpora cardiaca and of brain have been reported to increase motility of the oviducts, leading to oviposition. In addition, corpus cardiacum extracts release neural activity in the nerves leading from the abdominal ganglia to the genitalia, mimicking the releasing effect of cutting the ventral nerve cord (Milburn *et al.*, 1960). It is suggested that the extracts act by removing the inhibitory control exerted by the subesophageal ganglion upon the abdominal ganglia. Since cutting the nervi corporis cardiaci results in a drop in the potency of cardiacum extracts, it has been assumed that the activity is due to the neurosecretory material normally stored in the corpus cardiacum (Hodgson, 1962). A possible connecting link between these observations and the events controlling egg maturation is furnished by a report that the same extract of ripe ovaries that causes allatal inhibition in the bug *Iphita* promotes release of neurosecretory material from the corpora cardiaca (Nayar, 1958).

Observations such as the above can be used to construct the following hypothetical sequence of events (see also Table I).

a. In response to the appropriate stimuli, the median neurosecretory cells are activated and the inhibitory innervation to the corpora allata is suppressed. As a result, the corpora allata are induced to release their hormone. Protein metabolism is also stimulated.

b. Gonadotropin from the corpora allata promotes yolk formation in the ova and stimulates the sex accessory glands.

c. "Ovarian hormone" is released from the ovary containing maturing eggs. This inhibits further gonadotropin release from the corpora allata and favors the release of neurosecretory material from the corpora cardiaca.

d. The neurosecretory materials promote oviposition, possibly by acting upon the central nervous system to remove neural inhibition of the centers controlling ovipositional movements.

e. Oviposition terminates the cycle, leaving the animal free to initiate the sequence again.

This scheme seems to be followed at least in part in many groups, and especially in those such as roaches which have an extended reproductive period in which oogenesis is completed after the final molt. However, steps c and d are not firmly established, and there are many variations on the entire pattern, some major. For example, injection of extracts of "mature" ovaries does not inhibit the corpora allata in all groups (Highnam and O. Lusis, 1963; cited in Highnam, 1964). In forms of Lepidoptera such as *Bombyx*, the corpora allata seem completely unneccessary for gonadal maturation (Gilbert, 1963). Removal of the corpora allata in larval stages results in premature metamorphosis and the development of diminutive but reproductively mature adults. Since corpus allatum hormone is absent or in low titer under these conditions, it is assumed that in this case ecdysone is the responsible gonadotropic factor. Ecdysone is presumably required for the initial development of the ovary in all groups, and possibly in these animals, it has taken over the whole process. An intermediate condition is seen in the cabbage butterfly (*Pieris*) in which allatectomy blocks egg production if done in the last larval instar (Karlinsky, 1962). It seems possible that the same basic mechanism underlies the control of oogenesis in all forms with the overt differences being the result of varying emphasis on the several endocrine mechanisms involved (median neurosecretory cells, corpus allatum, ecdysial gland), different target tissue sensitivities, variations in critical periods, and the like. Whether this is the case, or whether the insects have in fact developed several differing means of control remains to be determined.

IV. General Comments and Conclusions

A. Trends in the Development of Complexity

The apparently universal presence of neurosecretory cells in all forms possessing a nervous system and the later appearance of epithelial endocrine organs in phylogeny is the most obvious feature of the evolution of neuroendocrine correlation. Neurosecretion has been reported in coelenterates (Burnett *et al.*, 1964) and flatworms (Lender and Klein, 1961), the most primitive phyla known to possess nervous systems. Neurosecretory cells are the only known source of hormones in the lower groups through the annelids on the protostome line and the echinoderms among the deuterostomes. The intimate interrelationship of the nervous and endocrine systems is thus an exceedingly ancient one, as is the ability of the nervous system itself to secrete chemical substances. Clear evidence for the presence of non-neural endocrines is not available until the high degree of structural and functional complexity characteristic of the arthropods and certain mollusks is achieved. Although there have been suggestions that epithelial endocrine structures are present in lower groups, the evidence is circumstantial (for example, see Kenk, 1941). Although there are a number of evidences of feedback mechanisms in operation between brain and gonad in annelid reproduction (Section II,D), there is no particular need to assume that gonadal hormones are involved; changes in brain function as a result of accumulation or depletion of metabolites could also explain the observations. Definite evidence for non-neuronal sources of hormones that feed back to control secretion is available only in animals well up the phylogenetic tree. Although it is likely that other epithelial endocrine organs will be discovered in the future, it seems fairly clear that hormone production by the nervous system is phylogenetically very old, and that extraneural hormone sources are in all probability a more recent development.

B. Present Trends in Research

The increase in interest in invertebrate endocrinology and the application of modern techniques to its problems has resulted in a burgeoning of the amount and variety of information available. The extension of the conventional techniques of endocrinology to the nonarthropod phyla is opening the way to a comparative study of the patterns of control utilized by various groups, while the better-known insect and crustacean systems are being subjected to more detailed analyses in terms of interactions of endocrine organs and hormone effects at the cellular level. Histochemistry and cytochemistry are being used to characterize the enzyme complements of neurosecretory cells and the chemistry of their secretory products, while the electron microscope is being used to study the ultrastructural characteristics of neurosecretion as a process. A particularly important advance has been the purification and chemical characterization of ecdysone, the insect molting hormone. This has stimulated research on the mode of action of ecdysone and study of the effects of purified ecdysone upon puffing in the salivary chromosomes of dipterans has produced results of great interest to developmental biologists (e.g. Clever, 1962; Kroeger, 1963). The job of purification of ecdysone was rendered truly heroic by the small size of the endocrine organs involved and the rather low titer of hormone present in the tissue extracted. The first 25-mg sample of crystalline hormone was extracted from 500 *kg* of whole *Bombyx* pupae, which is roughly analogous to being forced to extract adrenocortical hormones from whole cows, rather than from isolated adrenals.

The small size of invertebrate endocrine structures has also created difficulties for the endocrinologist. These organs are generally hard to locate. Even when a putative endocrine organ is identified, surgical intervention is often difficult to achieve without damage to neighboring structures. As a result, it is quite possible for the intercalation of a second endocrine structure between a neurosecretory cell and the ultimate target to escape notice for extended periods. For example, the brain of *Rhodnius* was assumed to be the immediate source of the molting hormone for more than a decade; it was not until after the demonstration of the function of the ecdysial gland in the Lepidoptera that the second-order status of control of molt was shown to obtain in *Rhodnius* as well. The recent perfection of organ culture techniques for invertebrates offers a tool which should be of considerable value in this context. It has already been used by Durchon and Schaller (1964) to test the status of the control of reproduction in polychaete annelids as a first-order neuroendocrine reflex; similar techniques are being applied to studies on tissues of tunicates (Sengel and Kieny, 1962) and crustaceans (Berreur-Bonnenfant, 1963).

A last trend that may be noted is the appearance in the past several years of papers of a truly neuroendocrine nature. These are reports of experiments studying the interrelationship of the invertebrate nervous and endocrine systems in a variety of ways: by the application of neurophysiological techniques to the study of the neuronal properties of neurosecretory cells (Yagi *et al.*, 1963), by production of localized lesions in the central nervous system (Engelmann, 1957), and by the examination of the effects of hormones upon the electrical activity of the nervous system as well as upon the behavior of the animals (Hodgson, 1962).

There are still large gaps in our understanding of neuroendocrine control pathways in all groups, but especially in the nonarthropod phyla. The precise sensory cues used to initiate and control the various processes, the central nervous and feedback pathways involved, and the effects at the molecular level of the hormones involved are all aspects which require more study. However, significant progress has been made in all of these areas, especially within the past 10 years, and the current interest in invertebrate neuroendocrinology should make the next decade a most fruitful one.

References

Alexandrowicz, J. S., and Carlisle, D. B. (1953). Some experiments on the function of the pericardial organs in Crustacea. *J. Marine Biol. Assoc. U.K.* **32**, 175–192.

Antheunisse, L. J. (1963). Neurosecretory phenomena in the zebra mussel *Dreissena polymorpha* Pallas. *Arch. Neerl. Zool.* **15**, 237–314.

Bareth, C. (1963). Mise en évidence de cellules neurosécrétrices dans le ganglion sous-esophagien, les ganglions thoraciques et abdominaux chez *Campodea* (C.) *remyi* Denis (Diploures, Campodéidés). *Compt. Rend.* **256**, 785–786.

Barth, R. H., Jr. (1961). Hormonal control of sex attractant production in the Cuban cockroach. *Science* **133**, 1598–1599.

Beck, S. D., and Alexander, N. (1964). Proctodone, an insect developmental hormone. *Biol. Bull.* **126**, 185–198.

Bern, H. A., and Hagadorn, I. R. (1965). Neurosecretion. *In* "Structure and Function in the Nervous System of Invertebrates" (by T. H. Bullock and G. A. Horridge) Vol. I, pp. 353–429. Freeman, San Francisco, California.

Berreur-Bonnenfant, J. (1963). Survie et activité des gonades et de la glande androgène des mâles d'*Orchestia gammarella* en culture organotypique. *Compt. Rend.* **256**, 2244–2246.

Bliss, D. E. (1960). Autotomy and regeneration. *In* "Physiology of Crustacea" (T. H. Waterman, ed.), Vol. I, pp. 561–589. Academic Press, New York.

Bliss, D. E., and Boyer, J. R. (1964). Environmental regulation of growth in the decapod crustacean *Gecarcinus lateralis*. *Gen. Comp. Endocrinol.* **4**, 15–41.

Bobin, G., and Durchon, M. (1952). Étude histologique du cerveau de *Perinereis cultrifera* Grube (Annélide Polychète). Mise en évidence d'un complex cérébrovasculaire. *Arch. Anat. Microscop.* **41**, 25–40.

Brown, H. F. (1964). Electrophysiological investigations of the heart of *Squilla mantis*. III. The mode of action of pericardial organ extract on the heart. *J. Exptl. Biol.* **41**, 723–734.

Bullock, T. H., and Horridge, G. A. (1965). "Structure and Function in the Nervous System of Invertebrates," 2 vols. Freeman, San Francisco, California.

Burnett, A. L., Diehl, N. A., and Diehl, F. (1964). The nervous system of *Hydra*. II. Control of growth and regeneration by neurosecretory cells. *J. Exptl. Zool.* **157**, 227–236.

Butler, C. G. (1964). Pheromones in sexual processes in insects. *In* "Insect Reproduction," 2nd Symp. R.E.S. (K. C. Highnam, ed.), pp. 66–77. Roy. Entomol. Soc., London.

Carlisle, D. B., and Knowles, F. (1959). "Endocrine Control in Crustaceans." Cambridge Univ. Press, London and New York.

Chaet, A. B. (1964). A mechanism for obtaining mature gametes from starfish. *Biol. Bull.* **126**, 8–13.

Charniaux-Cotton, H. (1962). Androgenic gland of crustaceans. *Gen. Comp. Endocrinol.* Suppl. 1, 241–247.

Clark, R. B. (1961). The origin and formation of the heteronereis. *Biol. Rev.* **36**, 199–236.

Clark, R. B., and Bonney, D. G. (1960). Influence of the supraoesophageal ganglion on posterior regeneration in *Nereis diversicolor. J. Embryol. Exptl. Morphol.* **8**, 112–118.

Clark, R. B., and Ruston, R. J. G. (1963). Time of release and action of a hormone influencing regeneration in the polychaete *Nereis diversicolor. Gen. Comp. Endocrinol.* **3**, 542–553.

Clark, R. B., and Scully, U. (1964). Hormonal control of growth in *Nereis diversicolor. Gen. Comp. Endocrinol.* **4**, 82–90.

Clever, U. (1962). Über das Reaktionssystem einer hormonalen Induktion. Untersuchungen an *Chironomus tentans. Zool. Anz. Suppl.* **25**, 75–92.

Davey, K. G. (1963). The release by enforced activity of the cardiac accelerator from the corpus cardiacum of *Periplaneta americana. J. Insect. Physiol.* **9**, 375–381.

de Wilde, J. (1961). Extrinsic control of endocrine functions in insects. *Bull. Res. Council Israel* **10B**, 36–52.

de Wilde, J. (1964). Reproduction—endocrine control. *In* "The Physiology of Insecta" (M. Rockstein, ed.), Vol. I, pp. 59–90. Academic Press, New York.

Dodd, J. M. (1955). The hormones of sex and reproduction and their effects in fish and lower chordates. *Mem. Soc. Endocrinol.* **4**, 166–187.

DuPorte, E. M. (1959). "Manual of Insect Morphology." Reinhold, New York.

Durchon, M. (1952). Recherches expérimentales sur deux aspects de la reproduction chez les annélides polychètes: l'épitoquie et la stolonisation. *Ann. Sci. Nat. Zool.* **14**, 117–206.

Durchon, M. (1960). L'Endocrinologie chez les Annélides Polychètes. *Bull. Soc. Zool. France* **85**, 275–301.

Durchon, M., and Schaller, F. (1964). Recherches endocrinologiques en culture organotypique chez les annélides polychètes. *Gen. Comp. Endocrinol.* **4**, 427–432.

Engelmann, F. (1957). Die Steuerung der Ovarfunktion bei der ovoviviparen Schabe *Leucophaea maderae* (Fabr.). *J. Insect Physiol.* **1**, 257–278.

Engelmann, F. (1960). Mechanisms controlling reproduction in two viviparous cockroaches (Blattaria). *In* "Aspects of Insect Endocrinology" (D. Bodenstein, ed.). *Ann. N.Y. Acad. Sci.* **89**, 516–536.

Engelmann, F. (1964). Inhibition of egg maturation in a pregnant viviparous cockroach. *Nature* **202**, 724–725.

Fingerman, M. (1963). "The Control of Chromatophores." Macmillan, New York.

Fontaine, A. R. (1962). Neurosecretion in the ophiuroid *Ophiopholis aculeata. Science* **138**, 908–909.

Fraenkel, G., and Hsiao, C. (1963). Tanning in the adult fly: a new function of neurosecretion in the brain. *Science* **141**, 1057–1058.

Gersch, M., and Richter, K. (1961). Experimentelle Untersuchungen des physiologischen Farbwechsels von *Pisicola geometra* (Hirudinea). *Zool. Jahrb., Abt. Allgem. Zool. Physiol. Tiere* **69,** 273–284.

Gilbert, L. I. (1963). Hormones controlling reproduction and molting in invertebrates. *In* "Comparative Endocrinology" (U. S. von Euler and H. Heller, eds.), Vol. II, pp. 1–46. Academic Press, New York.

Gilbert, L. I. (1964). Physiology of growth and development: endocrine aspects. *In* "The Physiology of Insecta" (M. Rockstein, ed.), Vol. I, pp. 149–225. Academic Press, New York.

Golding, D. W. (1963). Activation of the supra-esophageal ganglion of *Nereis diversicolor*, for the production of hormones relating to regeneration. *Gen. Comp. Endocrinol.* **3,** 703–704.

Gontcharoff, M., and Lechenault, H. (1958). Sur la déterminatisme de la ponte chez *Lineus lacteus*. *Compt. Rend.* **246,** 1929–1930.

Gorbman, A., and Bern, H. A. (1962). "A Textbook of Comparative Endocrinology." Wiley, New York.

Hagadorn, I. R. (1958). Neurosecretion and the brain of the rhynchobdellid leech, *Theromyzon rude* (Baird, 1869). *J. Morphol.* **102,** 55–90.

Hagadorn, I. R. (1962). Functional correlates of neurosecretion in the rhynchobdellid leech, *Theromyzon rude*. *Gen. Comp. Endocrinol.* **2,** 516–540.

Hagadorn, I. R., Bern, H. A., and Nishioka, R. S. (1963). The fine structure of the supraesophageal ganglion of the rhynchobdellid leech, *Theromyzon rude*, with special reference to neurosecretion. *Z. Zellforsch.* **58,** 714–758.

Harker, J. E. (1956). Factors controlling the diurnal rhythm of activity of *Periplaneta americana* L. *J. Exptl. Biol.* **33,** 224–234.

Harker, J. E. (1964). "The Physiology of Diurnal Rhythms." Cambridge Univ. Press, London and New York.

Herlant-Meewis, H. (1956). Reproduction et neurosécrétion chez *Eisenia foetida* (Sav.). *Ann. Roy. Soc. Zool. Belg.* **87,** 151–185.

Herlant-Meewis, H. (1959). Phénomènes neuro-sécrétoires et sexualité chez *Eisenia foetida*. *Compt. Rend.* **248,** 1405–1406.

Highnam, K. C. (1962a). Neurosecretory control of ovarian development in *Schistocerca gregaria*. *Quart. J. Microscop. Sci.* **103,** 57–72.

Highnam, K. C. (1962b). Neurosecretory control of ovarian development in *Schistocerca gregaria*, and its relation to phase differences. *Coll. Intern. CNRS (Paris)* **114,** 1–10.

Highnam, K. C. (1964). Endocrine relationships in insect reproduction. *In* "Insect Reproduction," 2nd Symp. R.E.S. (K. C. Highnam, ed.), pp. 26–42. *Roy. Entomol. Soc. London.*

Hill, L. (1962). Neurosecretory control of haemolymph protein concentration during ovarian development in the desert locust. *J. Insect Physiol.* **8,** 609–619.

Hisaw, F. L., Jr., Botticelli, C. R., and Hisaw, F. L. (1962). The relation of the cerebral ganglion-sub-neural gland complex to reproduction in the ascidian, *Chelyosoma productum*. *Am. Zoologist* **2,** 415 (abs.).

Hodgson, E. S. (1962). Neurosecretion and behavior in arthropods. *Gen. Comp. Endocrinol.* Suppl. 1, 180–187.

Howie, D. I. D. (1963). Experimental evidence for the humoral stimulation of ripening of the gametes and spawning in the Polychaete *Arenicola marina* (L.). *Gen. Comp. Endocrinol.* **3,** 660–668.

Howie, D. I. D., and McClenaghan, C. M. (1965). Evidence for a feedback mechanism influencing spermatogonial division in the lugworm (*Arenicola marina* L.). *Gen. Comp. Endocrinol.* **5**, 40–44.

Hubl, H. (1953). Die inkretorischen Zellelemente im Gehirn der Lumbriciden. *Arch. Entwicklungsmech. Organ.* **146**, 421–432.

Joly, P. (1962). Chromatic adaptation in insects. *Gen. Comp. Endocrinol.* Suppl. 1, 94–98.

Joly, R. (1966). Etude expérimentale du cycle de mue et de sa régulation endocrine chez les Myriopodes Chilopodes. *Gen. Comp. Endocrinol.* **6**, 519–533.

Kahr, H. (1959). Zur Endokrinen Steuerung der Melanophoren-Reaktion bei *Octopus vulgaris. Z. Vergleich. Physiol.* **41**, 435–448.

Kamemoto, F. I. (1964). The influence of the brain on osmotic and ionic regulation in earthworms. *Gen. Comp. Endocrinol.* **4**, 420–426.

Kanatani, H. (1964). Spawning of starfish: action of gamete-shedding substance obtained from radial nerves. *Science* **146**, 1177–1179.

Karlinsky, A. (1962). Effets de l'ablation des corpora allata larvaires sur le développement ovarien de *Pieris brassicae* L. (Lépidoptère). *Compt. Rend.* **255**, 191–193.

Karlson, P. (1963). Insect hormones. *In* "Comprehensive Biochemistry," (M. Florkin and E. H. Stotz, eds.), Vol. 11, pp. 168–180. Am. Elsevier New York.

Karlson, P., Hoffmeister, H., Hummel, H., Hocks, P., and Spiteller, G. (1965). Reaktionen des Ecdysonmoleküls. *Chem. Ber. Sonderdruck* **98**, 2394–2402.

Kenk, R. (1941). Induction of sexuality in the asexual form of *Dugesia tigrina* (Girard). *J. Exptl. Zool.* **87**, 55–69.

Knowles, F. G. W. (1949). The problem of the number hormones concerned in the pigment movements of crustaceans. In "Endocrinologie des Arthropodes." *Colloq. Intern. CNRS (Paris)* **4**, 149–159.

Kroeger, H. (1963). Chemical nature of the system controlling gene activities in insect cells. *Nature* **200**, 1234–1235.

Kühne, H. (1959). Die neurosekretorischen Zellen und der retrocerebrale neuroendokrine Komplex von Spinnen (Araneae, Labidognatha) unter Berücksichtigung einiger histologische erkennbarer Veränderungen während des postembryonalen Lebensablaufes. *Zool. Jahrb., Abt. Anat. Ontog. Tiere* **77**, 527–600.

Larimer, J. L. (1964). Sensory-induced modifications of ventilation and heart rate in crayfish. *Comp. Biochem. Physiol.* **12**, 25–36.

Laviolette, P. (1954). Rôle de la gonade dans le déterminisme humoral de la maturité glandulaire du tractus génital chez quelques gastéropodes Arionidae et Limacidae. *Bull. Biol.* **88**, 310–332.

Lea, A. O., and Thomsen, E. (1962). Cycles in the synthetic activity of the medial neurosecretory cells of *Calliphora erythrocephala* and their regulation. *In* "Neurosecretion" (H. Heller and R. B. Clark, eds.). *Mem. Soc. Endocrinol.* **12**, 345–347.

Lechenault, H. (1962). Sur l'existence de cellules neurosécrétrices dans les ganglions cérébroïdes des *Lineidae* (Hétéronémertes). *Compt. Rend.* **255**, 194–196.

Lees, A. D. (1964). The location of the photoperiodic receptors in the aphid *Megoura viciae* Buckton. *J. Exptl. Biol.* **41**, 119–133.

Legendre, R. (1959). Contribution à l'étude du système nerveux des Aranéides. *Ann. Sci. Nat., Zool. Biol. Animale* [12] **1**, 339–473.

Lemche, H. (1955). Neurosecretion and incretory glands in a tectibranch mollusc. *Experientia* **11**, 320–322.

Lender, T., and Klein, N. (1961). Mise en évidence de cellules sécrétrices dans le cerveau de la Planaire *Polycelis nigra.* Variation de leur nombre au cours de la régénération postérieure. *Compt. Rend.* **253,** 331–333.

Lever, J., Jansen, J., and De Vlieger, T. A. (1961). Pleural ganglia and water balance in the fresh water pulmonate *Limnaea stagnalis. Proc. Koninkl. Ned. Akad. Wetenschap.* **C64,** 531–542.

L'Helias, C. (1964). Aspects chimiques des mécanismes endocriniens chez les insectes. *Annee Biol.* **3,** 1–31.

Loher, W. (1961). The chemical acceleration of the maturation process and its hormonal control in the male of the desert locust. *Proc. Roy. Soc.* **B153,** 380–397.

Lüscher, M. (1961). Social control of polymorphism in termites. *In* "Insect Polymorphism," 1st Symp. R.E.S. (J. S. Kennedy, ed.), pp. 57–67. Roy. Entomol. Soc. London.

McWhinnie, M. A., and Chua, A. S. (1964). Hormonal regulation of crustacean tissue metabolism. *Gen. Comp. Endocrinol.* **4,** 624–633.

Maddrell, S. H. P. (1964). Excretion in the blood-sucking bug, *Rhodnius prolixus* Stål. III. The control of the release of the diuretic hormone. *J. Exptl. Biol.* **41,** 459–472.

Milburn, N., Weiant, E. A., and Roeder, K. D. (1960). The release of efferent nerve activity in the roach, *Periplaneta americana,* by extracts of the corpus cardiacum. *Biol. Bull.* **118,** 111–119.

Nayar, K. K. (1958). Probable endocrine mechanism controlling oviposition in the insect *Iphita limbata* Stal. *Proc. 2nd Intern. Symp. Neurosecretion, Lund, 1958* pp. 102–104. Springer, Berlin.

Noumura, T., and Kanatani, H. (1962). Induction of spawning by radial nerve extracts in some starfishes. *J. Fac. Sci. Univ. Tokyo, Sect. IV* **9,** 397–402.

Núñez, J. A. (1963). Central nervous control of the mechanical properties of the cuticle in *Rhodnius prolixus. Nature* **199,** 621–622.

Orr, C. W. M. (1964). The influence of nutritional and hormonal factors on the chemistry of the fat body, blood, and ovaries of the blowfly *Phormia regina* Meig. *J. Insect Physiol.* **10,** 103–119.

Passano, L. M. (1960). Molting and its control. *In* "Physiology of Crustacea" (T. H. Waterman, ed.), Vol. I, pp. 473–536. Academic Press, New York.

Passano, L. M., and Jyssum, S. (1963). The role of the Y-organ in crab proecdysis and limb regeneration. *Comp. Biochem. Physiol.* **9,** 195–213.

Pelluet, D. (1964). On the hormonal control of cell differentiation in the ovotestis of slugs (Gastropoda: Pulmonata). *Can. J. Zool.* **42,** 195–199.

Raabe, M. (1964). Nouvelles recherches sur la neurosécrétion chez les insectes. *Ann. Endocrinol. (Paris)* **25,** 107–112.

Rao, K. P. (1962). Physiology of acclimation to low temperature in poikilotherms. *Science* **137,** 682–683.

Roeder, K. D. (1963). "Nerve Cells and Insect Behavior," pp. 129–147. Harvard Univ. Press, Cambridge, Massachusetts.

Rothballer, A. B. (1957). Neuroendocrinology. *Excerpta. Med., Sect. III* **11,** 3–7.

Scharrer, B. (1941). Neurosecretion. II. Neurosecretory cells in the central nervous system of cockroaches. *J. Comp. Neurol.* **74,** 93–108.

Scharrer, B. (1963). Neurosecretion. XIII. The ultrastructure of the corpus cardiacum of the insect *Leucophaea maderae. Z. Zellforsch. Mikroskop. Anat.* **60,** 761–796.

Scharrer, E., and Scharrer, B. (1963). "Neuroendocrinology." Columbia Univ. Press, New York.

Scheer, B. T. (1960). Aspects of the intermoult cycle in natantians. *Comp. Biochem. Physiol.* **1**, 3–18.

Schneiderman, H. A., and Gilbert, L. I. (1964). Control of growth and development in insects. *Science* **143**, 325–333.

Sengel, P., and Kieny, M. (1962). Rôle du complex formé par la glande neurale, le ganglion nerveux et l'organe vibritile sur la différentiation sexuelle des gonades de *Molgula manhattensis* (Tunicier ascidiacé). *Bull. Soc. Zool. France* **87**, 615–628.

Sereni, E. (1930). The chromatophores of the cephalopods. *Biol. Bull.* **59**, 247–268.

Sláma, K. (1964). Hormonal control of respiratory metabolism during growth, reproduction, and diapause in female adults of *Pyrrhocoris apterus* L. (Hemiptera). *J. Insect Physiol.* **10**, 283–303.

Smith, R. I. (1942). Nervous control of chromatophores in the leech *Placobdella parasitica. Physiol. Zool.* **15**, 410–417.

Steele, J. E. (1963). The site of action of insect hyperglycemic hormone. *Gen. Comp. Endocrinol.* **3**, 46–52.

Stephan-Dubois, F., and Lender, T. (1956). Corrélations humorales dans la régénération des Planaires paludicoles. *Ann. Sci. Nat., Zool. Biol. Animale* [11] **18**, 223–230.

Strangways-Dixon, J. (1962). The relationship between nutrition, hormones, and reproduction in the blowfly *Calliphora erythrocephala* (Meig.). III. The corpus allatum in relation to nutrition, the ovaries, innervation and the corpus cardiacum. *J. Exptl. Biol.* **39**, 293–306.

Thomsen, E. (1952). Functional significance of the neurosecretory brain cells and the corpus cardiacum in the female blowfly, *Calliphora erythrocephala* Meig. *J. Exptl. Biol.* **29**, 137–172.

Thomsen, E., and Møller, I. (1963). Influence of neurosecretory cells and of corpus allatum on intestinal protease activity in the adult *Calliphora erythrocephala* Meig. *J. Exptl. Biol.* **40**, 301–321.

Tuzet, O., Sanchez, S., and Pavans de Ceccatty, M. (1957). Donneés histologiques sur l'organisation neuroendocrine de quelques Mollusques Gastéropodes. *Compt. Rend.* **224**, 2962–2964.

Unger, H. (1962). Experimentelle und histologische Untersuchungen über Wirkfaktoren aus dem Nervensystem von *Asterias* (*Marthasterias*) *glacialis* (Asteroidea; Echinodermata). *Zool. Jahrb., Abt. Allgem. Zool. Physiol. Tiere* **69**, 481–536.

Vicente, N. (1963). Ablation de ganglions nerveux et osmorégulation chez *Aplysia rosea* (Rathke) (Gastéropode Opisthobranche). *Compt. Rend.* **256**, 2928–2930.

von Harnack, M., and Scharrer, B. (1956). A study of the corpora allata of gonadectomized *Leucophaea maderae* (Blattaria). *Anat. Record* **125**, 558 (Abstract).

Wall, B. J., and Ralph, C. L. (1964). Evidence for hormonal regulation of malpighian tubule excretion in the insect, *Periplaneta americana* L. *Gen. Comp. Endocrinol.* **4**, 452–456.

Wells, M. J. (1960). Optic glands and the ovary of *Octopus. Symp. Zool. Soc. London* **2**, 87–107.

Wigglesworth, V. B. (1936). The function of the corpus allatum in the growth and reproduction of *Rhodnius prolixus* (Hemiptera). *Quart. J. Microscop. Sci.* **79**, 91–121.

Wigglesworth, V. B. (1950). "The Principles of Insect Physiology," Chapter 15. Methuen, London.
Wigglesworth, V. B. (1954). "The Physiology of Insect Metamorphosis." Cambridge Univ. Press, London and New York.
Yagi, K., Bern, H. A., and Hagadorn, I. R. (1963). Action potentials of neurosecretory neurons in the leech *Theromyzon rude*. *Gen. Comp. Endocrinol.* 3, 490–495.

CHAPTER 29

Neuroendocrine Mechanisms in Lower Vertebrates

C. BARKER JØRGENSEN and LIS OLESEN LARSEN

I. Introduction

This chapter is concerned mainly with the identity and nature of the hypothalamic structures by which the central nervous system may control adenohypophyseal functions in cyclostomes, fishes, and amphibians. The reptiles have been omitted because so little is known about the functional relation between the hypothalamus and the hypophysis in this class.

Chemically related, or even identical, hormones have been demonstrated in or isolated from the hypophysis in all vertebrate classes. In amphibians, the adenohypophysis seems to be controlled by the central nervous system in a way similar to that in mammals. At least some of the adenohypophyseal functions appear to be under central nervous control in fishes, and possibly even in the most primitive vertebrates, the cyclostomes. The hypothalamic-hypophyseal neuroendocrine mechanisms in the mammals therefore appear to have a long ancestry in the vertebrates, and it becomes of interest to compare the mechanisms by which central nervous control of hypophyseal functions is exerted in the various vertebrate classes.

The hypophyseal region in amphibians is of the general tetrapod type, but in most fishes and the cyclostomes the morphology of the region, and especially the structural relations between hypothalamus and adenohypophysis differ significantly from those in the tetrapods.

Little is definitely known about the functional relations between the hypothalamus and adenohypophysis in cyclostomes and fishes, although the structural relations have been described in detail in many species. Detailed knowledge of the structural relationships between the central nervous system and the hypophysis and especially the elucidation of the neural and vascular connections between the hypothalamus and the hypophysis (Chapters 2, in Volume 1, and 30) have been important in understanding the mechanisms by which the central nervous control of adenohypophyseal functions is exerted in the tetrapods. Special attention has therefore been paid in the lower vertebrates to the way in which nerve tracts may terminate within the hypophysis and to the vascularization and circulation of blood in the hypophyseal region, with special reference to the existence of portal connections between hypothalamus and hypophysis. On the basis of these studies and on analogies with the conditions in better known higher vertebrates, theories for the mechanism and nature of the neuroendocrine control of adenohypophyseal functions have been developed. However, the available data do not permit firm conclusions, and the identity and nature of the possible hypothalamic mediators of central nervous control of adenohypophyseal functions in the fishes still remain largely unknown. The identification of the structures that may mediate central nervous control of adenohypophyseal functions in cyclostomes and fishes has been made difficult because the neurohypophysis can be expected not only to act as mediator of central nervous control, but also to have functions outside the hypophysis.

A Note on the Term Neurosecretion

In the literature dealing with hypothalamic-hypophyseal relations, the concept of neurosecretion occupies a dominant position. The subject is treated in detail in Chapter 5 (Volume I). However, it is necessary to discuss the use of the term neurosecretion briefly in order to explain why we have avoided using it in the present chapter.

Since the first descriptions by C. C. Speidel and by Ernst Scharrer (see Scharrer, 1954), more than 40 years ago, of what appeared to be special, secretory neurons within the vertebrate central nervous system, the concept of neurosecretion has undergone several modifications and extensions, and the use of the term has changed correspondingly. Originally, neurosecretory neurons were identified by the affinity to certain stains displayed by their secretory products. In many instances, both in vertebrates and invertebrates, these products were believed to be produced in the perikaryon, transported along the axons, and stored and eventually released from the nerve terminals (Scharrer, 1954). Later, neurosecretory neurons were defined not only by their cytological properties, but also as neurons which liberated active principles into the blood circulation in specialized neurohemal organs (Knowles, 1958). The neurosecretory neurons of the magnocellular nuclei in the anterior hypothalamus, which in higher vertebrates typically terminate in close proximity to the blood vessels within the pars nervosa, may in fishes ramify within the adenohypophysis, especially its pars intermedia. Knowles (1963, 1964) therefore extended the concept of neurosecretion to include also direct innervation of the cells of endocrine glands. However, the target cells need not necessarily be endocrine cells, as in the vertebrate hypophysis. In insects, neurosecretory neurons may innervate nonendocrine target organs such as muscles (Thomsen, 1954; Johnson and Bowers, 1963; Whitten, 1964).

Obviously, it is becoming increasingly difficult to delimit "neurosecretory" from "ordinary" neurons. Formation of secretory products centrally and their transport along the axons were once thought to be characteristic of neurosecretory neurons. However, synthesis may not always be localized exclusively to the perikaryon. De Robertis (1964) found that the size of the secretory granules increases en route from the perikaryon to the nerve terminals in neurosecretory neurons arising in the magnocellular nuclei in the anterior hypothalamus. He therefore assumes that synthesis also takes place along the axons. Sachs (1959) has provided evidence for a considerable synthesis of vasopressin in the peripheral parts of the neurons. Moreover, "ordinary" adrenergic and cholinergic neurons seem to produce their transmitter substances in various parts of the neurons. Synthesis seems to occur in the perikaryon and other parts of the neuron, although synthesis presumably takes place predominantly in the nerve terminals (von Euler, 1963; Eccles, 1964; De Robertis, 1964). Synthesis of protein storage granules for the transmitters in ordinary neurons may only take place centrally. The concept of neurosecretion may therefore be said to encompass all neurons, including ordinary ones (von Euler, 1963; De Robertis, 1964).

The term neurosecretion has also been applied to secretion by cells that are not neurons, for instance, the secretory cells of the pineal gland and adrenal medulla (De Robertis, 1964). Olsson (1963) argues that a clear-cut definition of neurosecretory cells cannot be given, but he suggests that a definition should not include neurons or neuroglial cells.

This brief survey shows that the term "neurosecretory neurons" may have different meanings when used by different authors and at different times. In order to prevent ambiguities we have therefore avoided using the term in this chapter. Neuronal types are characterized here by the chemical nature of their secretions and by the mode by which the secretions are carried to their target cells. Neurons that affect their target cells within the adenohypophysis by means of nerve terminals ending on or between the cells are termed "ordinary neurons," since most neurons act in this way. If they act via the blood circulation, for instance by releasing substances in the median eminence which are carried to the pars distalis in the portal vessels, they are termed "endocrine neurons."

II. Comparative Anatomy of the Hypophyseal Region

The comparative anatomy of the vertebrate hypophysis has recently been thoroughly discussed by Wingstrand (1966). The following survey draws extensively from his account and conclusions. The vertebrate hypophysis consists typically of an adenohypophysis in intimate contact with a neurohypophysis.

A. Hypophysis

1. *Cyclostomes*

In the lamprey adenohypophysis, three parts, the pro-, the meso-, and the meta-adenohypophysis are easily distinguished (Fig. 1), whereas no

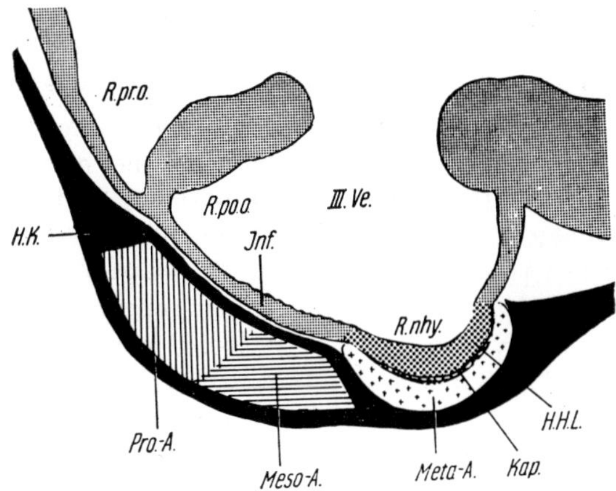

FIG. 1. Median section through the hypothalamic-hypophyseal region of the lamprey *Lampetra fluviatilis;* semidiagrammatically. R.pr.o., recessus praeopticus; R.po.o., recessus postopticus; III.Ve., third ventricle; R.nhy., recessus neurohypophyseus; H.K., connective tissue capsule enclosing the brain; Pro-A., proadenohypophysis; Meso-A., mesoadenohypophysis; Meta-A., meta-adenohypophysis; Kap., capillaries; H.H.L., neurohypophysis; Inf., infundibulum. (From Adam, 1959.)

such differentiation is apparent in the adenohypophysis of the hagfish (Fig. 2).

The neurohypophysis constitutes a little-differentiated part of the hypothalamic floor posterior to the optic chiasm. In the lampreys the neuro-

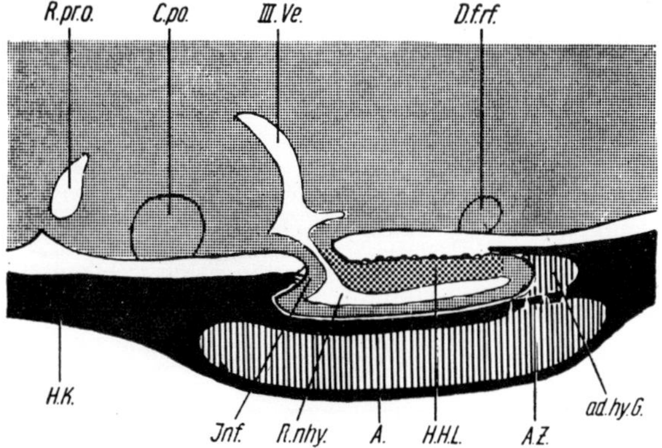

FIG. 2. Median section through the hypothalamic-hypophyseal region of the hagfish *Myxine glutinosa;* semidiagrammatically. C.po., commissura postoptica; D.f.rf., decussatio fasciculi retroflexi; A., adenohypophysis; A.Z., "Auflockerungszone"; ad.hy.G., adenohypophyseal tissue caudal to the neurohypophysis. Other abbreviations identical to those used in Fig. 1. (From Adam, 1959.)

hypophysis is in contact with the meta-adenohypophysis (Fig. 1). A distinct median eminence has not been described. The hagfish neurohypophysis is stated by most authors to be completely separated from the adenohypophysis by a connective tissue membrane. However, in older stages of the hagfish *Myxine glutinosa*, the membrane between the posterior parts of the neurohypophysis and the adenohypophysis is partly lost, and direct contact is established between the two parts of the hypophysis (Adam, 1959, 1960–1961; Matty, 1960). Olsson (1959) has described a median eminence-like structure in *Myxine glutinosa* (Fig. 2).

2. *Selachians*

The selachian adenohypophysis is characterized by a ventral lobe which is not in direct contact with the hypothalamus (Fig. 3). In the remaining part of the adenohypophysis, a pars intermedia, or meta-adenohypophysis, and an anterior lobe with distinct rostral and caudal parts can be distinguished.

The neurohypophysis and its relations to the pars intermedia of the adenohypophysis vary with the species. Meurling (1962) distinguishes between primitive and more advanced types of relations between the two parts of the hypophysis (Fig. 4). The "*Squalus* type" has been studied in detail in *Squalus acanthias*. It has also been found in the primitive hexanchoids and outside the selachians, in such primitive osteichtyans as *Acipencer* and *Lepisosteus*. In this type the neurohy-

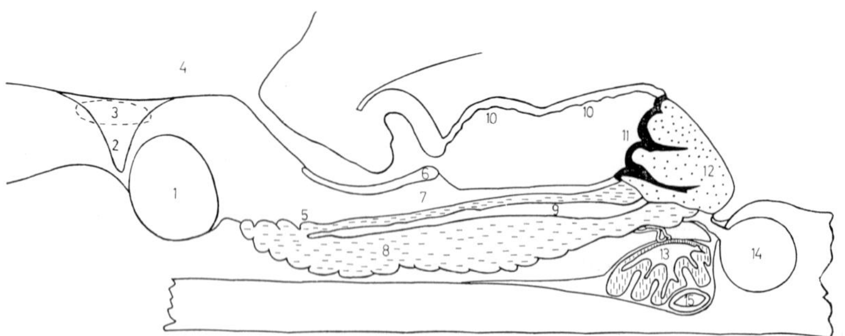

FIG. 3. Median section through the hypothalamic-hypophyseal region of the dogfish *Scyliorhinus caniculus;* semidiagrammatically. 1, optic chiasm; 2, preoptic recess; 3, preoptic nucleus; 4, third ventricle; 5, anterior median eminence; 6, nucleus tuberis; 7, posterior median eminence; 8, anterior lobe; 9, cavity in anterior lobe; 10, saccus vasculosus; 11, pars nervosa; 12, pars intermedia; 13, ventral lobe; 14, hypophyseal vein; 15, carotid branch. (After Mellinger, 1963b, simplified.)

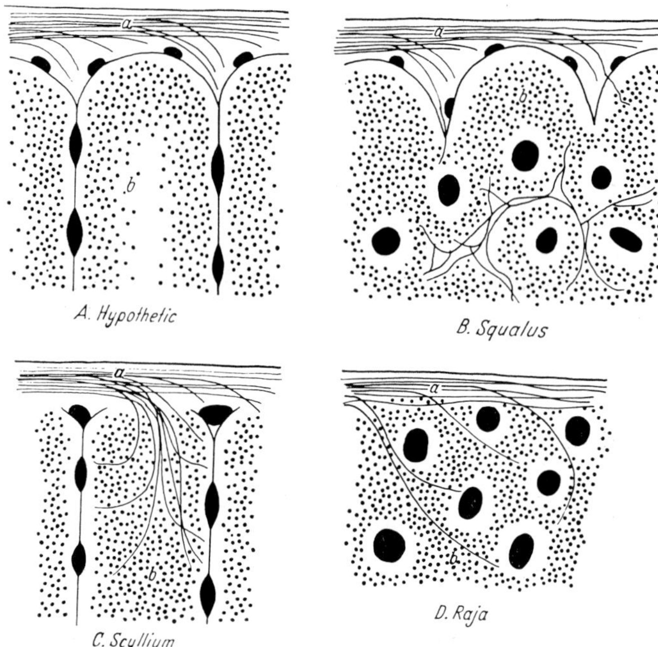

FIG. 4. Diagram of neurointermediate relations in elasmobranchs. A represents hypothetical common stage in evolution of neurointermediate relations. a, neural lobe; b, intermediate lobe; thick lines = connective tissue membranes and ependymal layer bordering ventricle; thin lines = nerves; in B they also represent reticular fibers in the intermediate lobe. (From Meurling, 1962.)

pophysis remains a distinct part of the brain, in most places separated from the pars intermedia by a membrane of connective tissue. This type is considered primitive. In the "*Scyllium* type" broad nerve bundles penetrate the pars intermedia and split up into individual fibers within the pars intermedia. The membrane between the lobes may be absent. To this type belong the hypophyses of *Raja*, *Torpedo*, and *Pristurus*, as well as many teleosts (Bargmann, 1953).

A median eminence in vascular contact with the adenohypophysis has been described in the selachians by Meurling (1960) and Mellinger (1960a,b, 1963b). It is discussed below in the section on the vascular connections between the brain and the hypophysis.

3. *Teleosts*

The teleost adenohypophysis is usually subdivided into three lobes termed the pro-, the meso-, and the meta-adenohypophysis, as in the

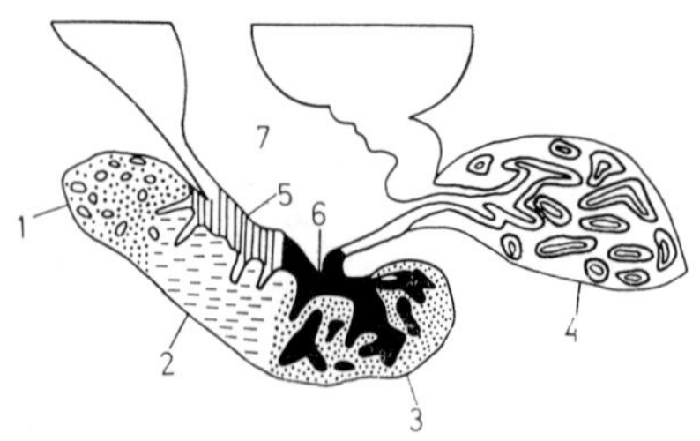

FIG. 5. Median section through the hypothalamic-hypophyseal region of the eel *Anguilla anguilla;* semidiagrammatically. 1, proadenohypophysis; 2, mesoadenohypophysis; 3, meta-adenohypophysis; 4, saccus vasculosus; 5, anterior part of neurohypophysis; 6, posterior part of neurohypophysis; 7, third ventricle. (From Wingstrand, 1966.)

lampreys (Fig. 5). However, in some fishes only two, in others more than three lobes or regions have been distinguished (e.g., in *Lepidogobius lepidus,* see Kobayashi *et al.,* 1959).

The neurohypophysis typically branches into all three parts of the adenohypophysis. However, the interdigitation of neurohypophyseal and adenohypophyseal tissue is most pronounced in the region of the meta-adenohypophysis (Fig. 5) (Bargmann, 1953; Dodd and Kerr, 1963). The part of the neurohypophysis in contact with the pro- and mesoadenohypophysis has been compared with the median eminence, and the part in contact with the meta-adenohypophysis with the pars nervosa of the tetrapod neurohypophysis (Diepen, 1953; Legait, 1957).

4. *Amphibians*

In amphibians, the adenohypophysis is of the type that is found in the higher vertebrates, consisting of a pars intermedia and a pars distalis (Fig. 6). A pars tuberalis, which is typical of mammals and birds, has been recognized in amphibians in the form of cell cords (urodeles) or islands of tissue isolated from the rest of the adenohypophysis (anurans).

The amphibian neurohypophysis is of the tetrapod type, consisting of a pars nervosa closely associated with a pars intermedia and a median eminence at the anterior end of the pars distalis (Fig. 6). The pars nervosa and the median eminence are generally larger and better differentiated in the anurans than in the urodeles.

B. Comparison between the Hypophyses in Cyclostomes, Fishes, and Tetrapods

In his studies on the comparative anatomy of the vertebrate hypophysis, Wingstrand (1966) has used embryological criteria as basis for de-

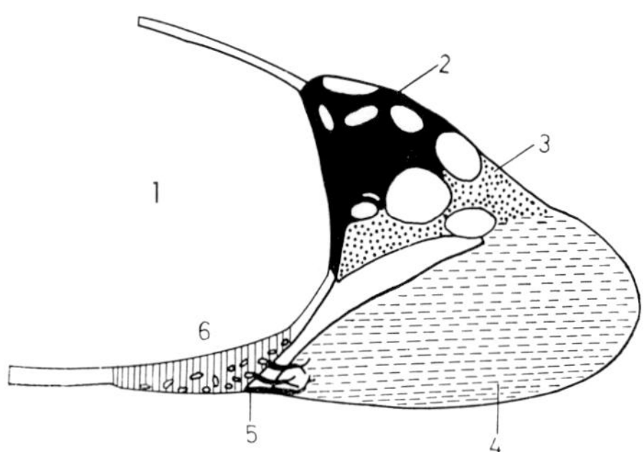

FIG. 6. Median section through the hypophysis of the toad *Bufo bufo;* semi-diagrammatically. 1, third ventricle; 2, pars nervosa; 3, pars intermedia; 4, pars distalis; 5, portal vessels; 6, median eminence. (From Wingstrand, 1966.)

ciding homologies. These criteria are not so much subject to adaptive variations as are cytological features, which are directly associated with function.

It is generally agreed that the meta-adenohypophyses of the lampreys and the fishes are homologous with the tetrapod pars intermedia. All are formed from the same part of Rathke's pouch, the aboral lobe. The pars tuberalis derives from the lateral lobes of Rathke's pouch, but the differentiated structure is found in contact with the brain in most vertebrates, while it becomes the ventral lobe in the selachians. A pars tuberalis is absent in the cyclostomes and in teleosts.

The pars distalis of the tetrapod hypophysis, the pro- and mesoadenohypophysis of teleosts and cyclostomes, and the anterior lobe of the selachian hypophysis are probably homologous structures (Wingstrand, 1966). Olivereau and Ball (1964) have recently provided further evidence for the homology between the teleost pro- and mesoadenohypophysis and the pars distalis of higher vertebrates.

The neurohypophysis always develops in close proximity to the adenohypophysis. It is generally possible to distinguish two regions in the vertebrate neurohypophysis: (1) the pars nervosa which develops in contact with the posterior part of the adenohypophysis and within which terminates the greater part of the neurons that originate in the magnocellular nuclei in the anterior hypothalamus; and (2) the median eminence which develops at the anterior end of the adenohypophysis with which it establishes vascular contact.

The neurohypophyseal region of all vertebrates is differentiated in an almost identical way in the young embryos, from the floor of the postoptic hypothalamus. The posterior part of the floor is evaginated to form an unpaired process, the saccus infundibuli. Typically, the pars nervosa of the neurohypophysis differentiates within the saccus infundibuli, and the median eminence in front of this structure. Only in the teleosts does the entire neurohypophysis differentiate in front of the saccus infundibuli (Wingstrand, 1966).

C. Hypothalamic-Neurohypophyseal Nerve Tracts

The most conspicuous nerve tracts terminating within the neurohypophysis of amphibians, fishes, and cyclostomes are those arising from the magnocellular parts of the preoptic nuclei in the anterior hypothalamus. These neurons are known to produce octapeptide hormones in the perikaryon and to store the hormones, often in large amounts, in the nerve terminals within the neurohypophysis.

Because they are easily stained with the Gomori technique, the nerve tracts from the magnocellular nuclei in the anterior hypothalamus have been studied the most in the different groups, but other nerve tracts terminate in the neurohypophysis. Thus, in several teleosts and the selachian *Scyllium canicula,* neurons whose secretory products do not stain with the Gomori technique have been found to arise in the nucleus lateralis tuberis. Other lesser known fiber systems also terminate in the neurohypophysis (Billenstien, 1963; Mellinger, 1964; Follenius, 1965a,b).

Direct Innervation of the Adenohypophysis by Hypothalamic-Neurohypophyseal Nerves

In order to elucidate possible neuroendocrine relations between the neurohypophysis and the various parts of the adenohypophysis and to decide whether the nerves terminating in the neurohypophysis act on intra- or extrahypophyseal target structures, it is of interest to know whether the nerve endings are associated with blood capillaries or with gland cells within the hypophysis. Meurling (1963) studied the penetration of nervous elements from the neurohypophysis into the pars intermedia in *Etmopterus spinax,* which belongs to the *Squalus* type of selachians (Section II,B,2). He found in this species little intermingling between neurohypophyseal and pars intermedia tissue. Gomori-positive neurons entered the pars intermedia and terminated between some of its cells, but the largest fraction of the Gomori-positive fibers terminated on blood vessels in the neurohypophysis. Thus, in *Etmopterus* only a small part of the pars intermedia cells have direct contact with Gomori-positive fibers. Other fibers were found to penetrate the pars intermedia, and in contrast to the Gomori-positive fibers, they reached the cells of the whole intermediate lobe. In *Scyllium canicula* in which the neurohypophysis intermingles profusely with pars intermedia tissue, Mellinger (1962, 1963b) found by means of the electron microscope that the nerve fibers generally terminate in contact with the glandular cells of the pars intermedia; synaptic structures on the cells could be observed. The fibers all seemed to belong to one type containing large granules about 1800 Å in diameter. They presumably correspond to the Gomori-positive neurons originating in the preoptic nuclei. However, in the same species, Knowles (1963, 1965) described a double innervation of the pars intermedia cells. He reported that "A type" fibers innervated the pole of the cell in which synthesis occurs, and that "B type" innervated the storage and release pole. Both types contained secretory granules. In the "A type" the granules were 1800 Å in diameter, and these fibers presumably correspond to the fibers described by Mellinger. In the "B type" the granules were 700 Å in diameter, and the fibers may correspond to the Gomori-negative fibers described by Meurling in *Etmopterus*.

In the meta-adenohypophysis of teleosts, variation in the relations between neurohypophyseal terminals and adenohypophyseal tissue has also been described. In *Gadus morrhua,* Bargmann and Knoop (1960) observed fibers containing 700–1800 Å granules terminating in synaptic structures on meta-adenohypophyseal cells. However, fibers of the same type were also seen to end on the blood capillaries in the meta-adenohypophysis. Close relations between nerve terminals of the neurohypophysis and gland cells of the meta-adenohypophysis were also found by Follenius (1962b) in *Phoxinus* and *Lebistes,* whereas in *Perca* and the trout, the membrane between the neurohypophyseal digitations and adenohypophyseal tissue was mostly intact. Most of the fibers terminated on the membrane or on the blood capillaries, and few penetrated the membrane. According to Follenius (1962b, 1965a), the nerve fibers in the digitations of the neurohypophysis generally do not penetrate the basal membrane between the neurohypophysis and the adenohypophyseal tissue to enter the teleost pro- and mesoadenohypophysis and thus do not innervate the gland cells directly.

The nerve tracts terminating in the part of the neurohypophysis in contact with the pro- and mesoadenohypophysis seem to be of partly different origin from those terminating in contact with the meta-adenohypophysis. They contain fewer Gomori-positive fibers, and many of the fibers apparently arise in the nucleus lateralis tuberis. They can be distinguished from those arising in the preoptic nucleus by the smaller average size of their secretory granules, viz., 1045 Å against 1475 Å in the fibers from the preoptic nucleus. In the perch and trout, Follenius (1962b) found fibers terminating at the level of the proadenohypophysis which presumably did not belong to the tractus tuberohypophyseus because they contained small-size secretory granules about 700 Å in diameter. The origin of these fibers is not known (Follenius, 1965a).

In the tetrapods, including amphibians, the pars nervosa of the neurohypophysis is distinctly separated from the pars intermedia; however, penetrating Gomori-positive fibers have been described as terminating between the pars intermedia cells of the frog, *Rana pipiens* (Dawson, 1953) and the newt, *Triturus cristatus* (Mazzi, 1954), although not in the tree frog, *Hyla regilla* (Wilson *et al.*, 1957). Recent electron-microscopic studies of Iturriza (1964) on the pars intermedia of the toad *Bufo arenarum* revealed nerve fibers that terminate in close contact with pars intermedia cells. The nerve endings were found to contain synaptic vesicles, but not the secretory granules that are characteristic of the nerve fibers terminating in the pars nervosa.

D. Vascularization and Blood Circulation in the Hypothalamic-Hypophyseal Region

Until recently, it was believed that a true hypophyseal portal system was found only in the tetrapods and lungfishes, in which the neurohypophysis is differentiated into a pars nervosa and a median eminence, the latter containing the primary plexus of the portal system. However, more or less typical portal systems have now been described in cyclostomes, elasmobranchs, and teleosts, as well as in other groups of fishes (Wingstrand, 1966).

1. *Cyclostomes*

In *Polistotrema stoutii*, Gorbman *et al.* (1963) have described a portal system between the anterior diencephalic floor (at the level of the preoptic nuclei) and the neurohypophysis (Fig. 7). However, it is not certain that this is a portal circulation analogous with the hypophyseal portal vessels of tetrapods which transport substances released into the primary plexus to act on the tissue vascularized by the secondary plexus.

2. *Selachians*

In selachians, a well-developed portal system connecting the hypothalamus and the adenohypophysis was described independently by Meurling (1960) and Mellinger (1960a,b, 1963b) (Fig. 8). The primary plexus is situated in the posterior part of the structure termed the median eminence (Section II,B,2) whereas the localization of the secondary

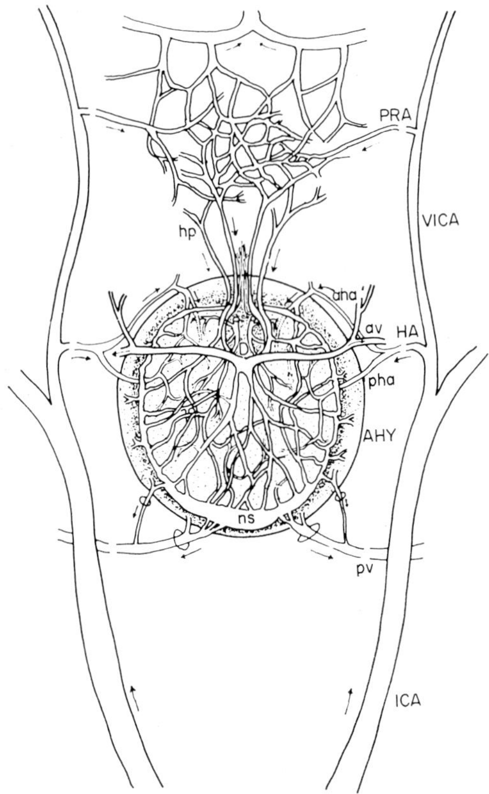

FIG. 7. Semidiagrammatic representation of vascular connections in the hypophyseal region of the hagfish *Polistotrema stoutii*, dorsal view. The neurohypophysis, lightly stippled, is shown above, and the adenohypophysis beneath it. aha, anterior hypophyseal artery; AHY, adenohypophysis; av, anterior hypophyseal vein; D, descending artery from hypothalamus to neurohypophyseal plexus; HA, hypophyseal artery; hp, hypophyseal portal veins; ICA, internal carotid artery; ns, neurohypophyseal sinus; pha, posterior hypophyseal artery; PRA, prehypophyseal artery leading into the prehypophyseal plexus; pv, posterior hypophyseal vein; VICA, ventral internal carotid artery. (From Gorbman *et al.*, 1963.)

plexus varies with the species. In *Scyllium caniculi,* Mellinger (1960a,b) found the secondary plexus in the caudal part of the anterior lobe, whereas according to Meurling (1960, and personal communication, 1965) there is also a significant supply of portal vessels to the neurointermediate lobe. In *Squalus acanthias,* Meurling found the primary plexus to be less distinct than in *Scyllium* and most of the portal vessels entered the anterior lobe, whereas in *Raja batis* and *Raja radiata* the highly developed portal system was found to constitute the main supply of the neurointermediate lobe. The parts of the adenohypophysis that are

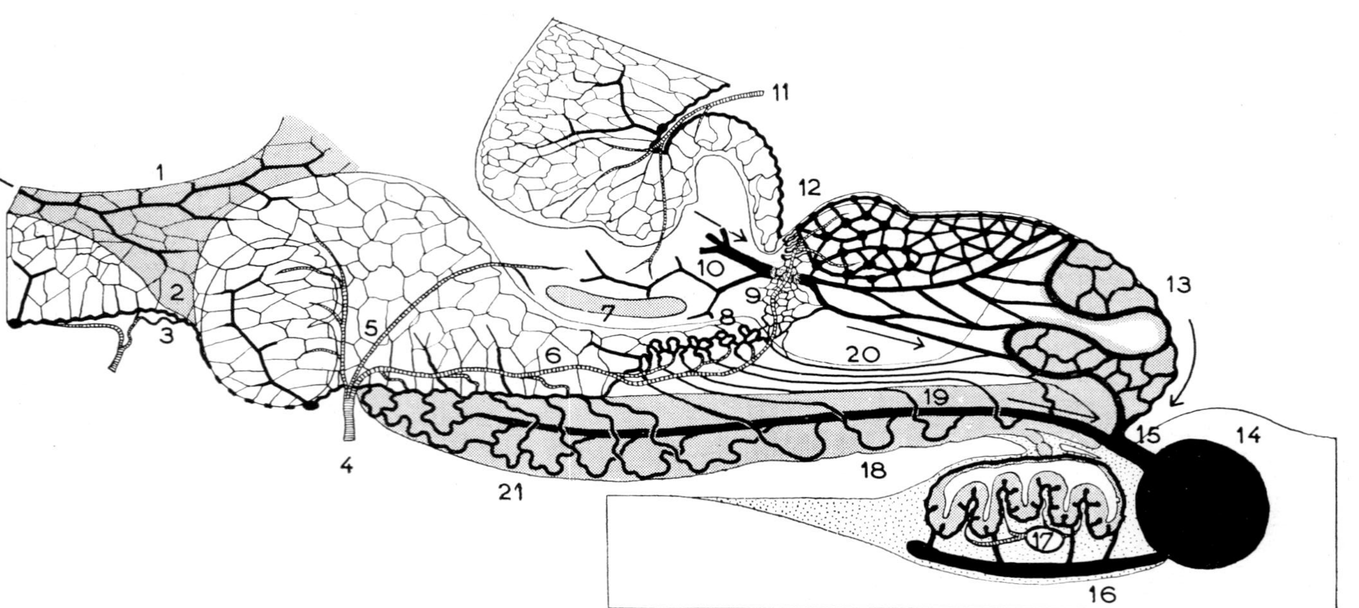

FIG. 8. Semidiagrammatic representation of the hypothalamo-hypophyseal vascular connections in the dogfish *Scyliorhinus caniculus*. 1, preoptic region; 2, preoptic recess; 3, superficial plexus; 4, inferior hypothalamic artery; 5, arteries of the hypothalamic inferior lobes; 6, anterior median eminence; 7, orifice to inferior lobes; 8, primary plexus in posterior median eminence; 9, reticular zone of perineural plexus; 10, lateral veins to neurointermediate lobe; 11, superior hypothalamic artery; 12, saccus vasculosus, with primary plexus; 13, neurointermediate lobe, with secondary plexus; 14, hypophyseal vein; 15, vein of hypophyseal ligament; 16, ventral lobe veins; 17, ventral lobe arterioles; 18, anterior lobe, caudal part, with secondary plexus; 19, central vein in anterior lobe; 20, portal vessels; 21, anterior lobe, cranial part, with capillary plexus. Note separate vascular supply of ventral lobe. (From Mellinger, 1963b.)

supplied by the blood from the portal vessels therefore seem to vary with the species.

In *Scyllium* and some other selachians, another portal system supplies the neurointermediate lobe through the lateral afferent veins (Fig. 8). The primary plexus of this system is not well-defined, the blood entering the lateral afferent veins coming from a relatively large region of the brain. This portal system, which resembles the system described by Cruz in the frog (see below), seems to be absent in *Raja batis* and *Raja radiata* (Meurling, 1960).

3. *Teleosts*

In cypriniform teleosts, a vascularization of the infundibular region reminiscent of the primary plexus of a median eminence has been described (Bretschneider and de Wit, 1947; Barrington, 1960; Follenius, 1961, 1965b). According to Follenius (1961), however, it is doubtful if a portal circulation of the tetrapod type is present, and he suggests that the capillary plexus in cyprinids may represent a vestigial portal system. The infundibular capillary net is absent in the other groups of teleosts investigated (Follenius, 1961, 1962a). Of course, vascular links that are less differentiated than portal systems might be capable of establishing humoral connections between the hypothalamus and hypophysis. Thus, in selachians, Mellinger (1964) describes simple capillary connections between the anterior part of the "median eminence" and the cranial part of the anterior lobe of the adenohypophysis (Fig. 8).

In teleosts, the capillary plexus of the neurohypophysis which to a large extent drains through adenohypophyseal tissue has been assumed to play a role similar to that of the primary plexus in tetrapods (Green, 1951; Bugnon and Lenys, 1960–1961; Follenius, 1962a, 1965a,b).

In contrast to the conditions in fishes, vascular connections between the neurohypophysis and adenohypophysis are poorly developed in the cyclostomes, both hagfish and lampreys. Vascular connections may even be lacking between the neurohypophysis and the anterior parts of the adenohypophysis (Gorbman *et al.*, 1963; Gorbman, 1965).

4. *Amphibians*

The vascularization of the amphibian hypophysis is of the typical tetrapod type. The pars distalis receives blood mainly from the portal vessels arising from the primary plexus in the median eminence (Fig. 9). The hypophyseal portal system is better differentiated in anurans than in urodeles. The pars nervosa receives an independent circulation, and the blood from the gland drains into the systemic circulation.

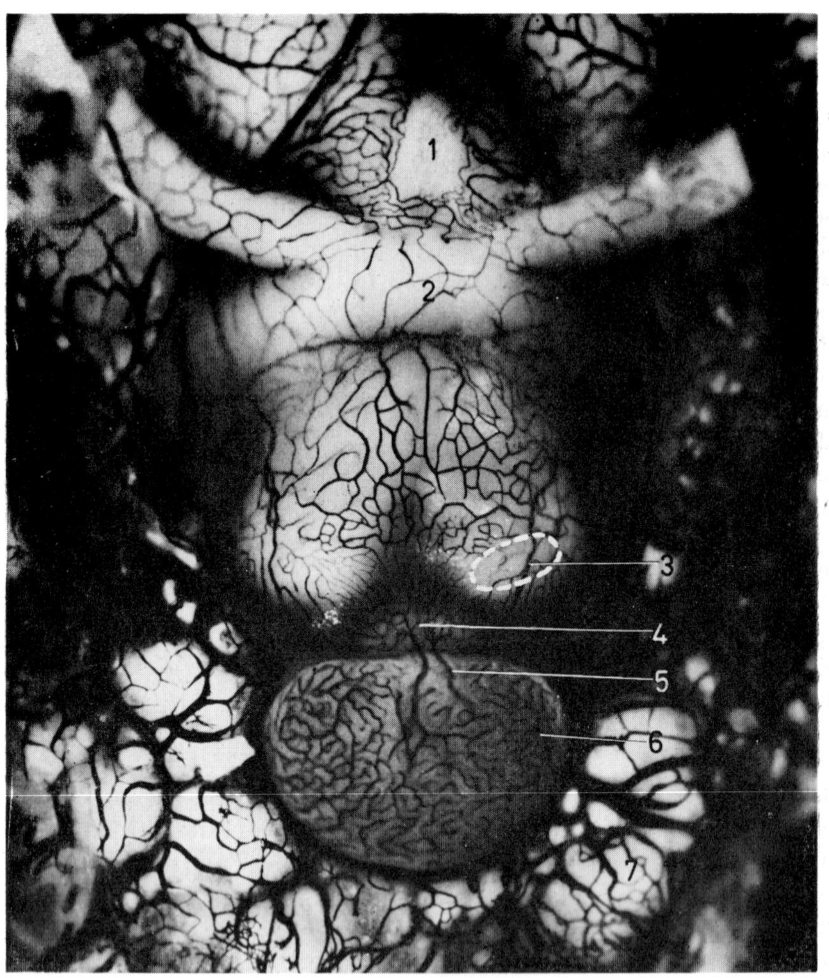

FIG. 9. Hypothalamus and hypophysis of the toad *Bufo bufo* in ventral view; the blood vessels have been injected with an India ink gelatin suspension. 1, preoptic recess; 2, optic chiasm; 3, pars tuberalis; 4, primary plexus of median eminence; 5, portal vessel; 6, pars distalis; 7, endolymphatic sacs. (From Wingstrand, 1966.)

III. Functional Hypothalamic-Adenohypophyseal Relationships

A. Amphibians

In dealing with the functional relationships between hypothalamus and adenohypophysis in the lower vertebrates, it is convenient to begin with the amphibians because this class has been most extensively studied.

1. *Pars Distalis*

a. Demonstration of Dependency of Pars Distalis Functions upon Central Nervous Control. There is good evidence that in the amphibians a number of pars distalis functions are influenced by the central nervous system. This evidence has been obtained by studying the effects of stalk section, hypothalamic lesions, and ectopic transplantation of the pars distalis. In the toad *Bufo bufo,* transplantation experiments indicate that with respect to corticotropic function, the pars distalis is wholly dependent upon normal central nervous contact. After transplantation of the pars distalis to an eye muscle, only insignificant amounts of adrenocorticotropic hormone (ACTH) are released from the gland (Jacobsohn and Jørgensen, 1956; Jørgensen and Larsen, 1963c; van Dongen *et al.*, 1966). However, in metamorphosed *Ambystoma mexicanum,* the ectopically transplanted hypophysis appears to secrete normal amounts of ACTH as judged from the normal survival of the graft-bearing animals (Jørgensen and Larsen, 1963a, and Table I). In the urodeles *Pleurodeles waltlii* (Pasteels, 1960) and *Triturus hongkongensis* (L. O. Larsen and P. Rosenkilde, unpublished, 1964) the transplanted hypophysis maintains apparently normal corticotropic activity. The high corticotropic activity of the transplanted hypophysis in the urodeles investigated of course does not exclude central nervous control of ACTH release.

Thyrotropic (TSH) activity of the transplanted hypophysis was maintained at a high level in metamorphosed *Ambystoma mexicanum* (P. Rosenkilde, see Jørgensen and Larsen, 1963a) and adult *Triturus hongkongensis* (L. O. Larsen and P. Rosenkilde, unpublished, 1964). However, the thyrotropic activity may be reduced compared to normal thyrotropic activity (Pasteels, 1960; Etkin and Sussman, 1961; Mazzi and Peyrot, 1962–1963). In the anurans investigated, transplantation of the pars distalis seems to reduce thyrotropic activity more than in urodeles (Vivien, 1959; Pehlemann, 1962; Hanaoka, 1963; Rosenkilde, 1963).

Gonadotropic function has been found to be reduced or absent in ectopically transplanted hypophyses, both in anurans and urodeles (Vivien, 1959; Schott, 1960; Jørgensen and Larsen, 1963a; Mazzi and Peyrot, 1962–1963; Dierickx, 1964; van Dongen *et al.*, 1966). However, in *Bufo bufo* females the dependency of gonadotropic function on central nervous control seems to vary seasonally; it is slight or absent immediately after the breeding season (van Dongen *et al.*, 1966).

Growth hormone secretion seems to be little affected by transplantation of the hypophysis to sites remote from the hypothalamus in urodeles and anuran larvae, as judged from the normal rate of growth ex-

TABLE I

EFFECT OF AUTOTRANSPLANTATION OF HYPOPHYSIS ON SURVIVAL IN METAMORPHOSED *Ambystoma mexicanum*

Type of operation	Series	Survival in days[a]
Hypophysectomized controls	1959–1960	13, 28, >28, 36, 38, 41, 46
	1961	11, 31, 43, 43, 44, >44, 45
Hypophysis retransplanted under hypothalamus	1959–1960	>28, >28, >51, >52, >73
	1961	3, 28, 34, 47, 54, >71, >71, >71, >71, >72, >72, >73, >75, >75, >76, >76
Hypophysis transplanted under palate mucosa	1959–1960	20, 46, 48, >50, >51, >51, >53, >72
	1961	11, >21, 25, 42, 57, 66, >71, >71, 72, >73, >73, >73, >74, >75, >76

[a] All minimum values are for animals that were in good health when killed.

hibited by the operated animals (Etkin and Lehrer, 1960; Pasteels, 1960; Pehlemann, 1962; Hanaoka, 1963).

The secretion of luteotropic hormone (LTH) has been found to be under inhibitory control by the central nervous system in the urodele *Diemictylus viridescens* (Masur, 1962). The control mechanism for this hormone therefore appears to be similar to that found in mammals.

b. Mechanisms of Control. The nature of the hypothalamic control of pars distalis functions in amphibians is probably similar to that in birds and mammals (Chapters 8, in Volume I, and 30). The control seems to be exclusively by means of hormones liberated into the blood vessels of the primary plexus in the median eminence and transported to the pars distalis by the portal vessels.

Little is known about the chemical nature and origin of the factors mediating the hypothalamic control of the release of the various pars distalis hormones. However, corticotropin-releasing factor (CRF) appears to be closely related to the octapeptide neurohypophyseal hormones in the amphibians, as it is in mammals (see Chapter 8, in Volume I) because both arginine and lysine vasopressin are highly active in causing release of ACTH from the pars distalis in the toad *Bufo bufo* (Jørgensen and Larsen, 1963a). The ACTH-releasing activity of vasopressin can be demonstrated in toads with the pars distalis transplanted to an eye muscle. Molting is inhibited in such toads, but a normal molt can be produced by injection of vasopressin, ACTH, or a corticosteroid. In hypophysectomized toads, injection of ACTH or corticosteroids, but not vasopressin, causes molting. In the graft-bearing toads, vasopressin therefore appears to cause molting indirectly by stimulating ACTH release from the pars distalis. This conclusion is further substantiated by the finding that longer time intervals generally elapse between injection and molting after injection of vasopressin than after injection of ACTH or corticosteroids. From Table II it can be seen that at room

TABLE II

INTERVAL IN HOURS BETWEEN INJECTION OF ALDOSTERONE, ACTH, OR LYSINE VASOPRESSIN AND SUBSEQUENT MOLTING IN TOADS (*Bufo bufo*) WITH THE PARS DISTALIS TRANSPLANTED TO AN EYE MUSCLE

	Aldosterone (5 μg)	ACTH (10 mU)	Vasopressin (0.4 IU)
	6.5	7.25	<7.75
	6.5	<7.75	8
	6.5	<7.75	8.75
	<7.25	8	9.25
	7.25	8.25	9.25
	7.5	<8.5	9.50
	7.5		<10
			10
Average	ca. 7 hours	ca. 8 hours	ca. 9 hours

temperature the toads molted, on the average, 7 hours after the injection of aldosterone, 8 hours after injection of ACTH, and 9 hours after injection of lysine vasopressin. It is therefore indicated that vasopressin acted on the pars distalis for about 1 hour to cause release of ACTH in amounts sufficient to precipitate a molt, and that ACTH acted on the adrenals for about 1 hour before enough corticosteroid was secreted for a molt to occur.

The amphibian hypophysis does not contain vasopressin, but vasotocin. This peptide is found instead of the mammalian vasopressins in nonmammalian vertebrates (see below). Vasotocin also possesses CRF activity in toads, but it is less potent than the vasopressins (Jørgensen and Larsen, 1963a).

In order to see whether, apart from causing release of ACTH from the pars distalis, vasopressin can also stimulate synthesis of ACTH, the effects of long-term treatment with vasopressin on molting and survival were studied in toads (*Bufo bufo*) with the pars distalis transplanted to an eye muscle. Toads with the pars distalis ectopically transplanted do not survive longer than toads with the pars distalis extirpated (Jacobsohn and Jørgensen, 1956). Death appears to be caused by the lack of corticotropic function (Jørgensen and Larsen, 1963a,b). The rapid death of the toads bearing ectopic transplants of the pars distalis therefore seems to indicate the absence of secretion of ACTH. With no corticotropic activity, toads survive only about 3 weeks at room temperature (20°–22°C), but daily injections of lysine vasopressin almost doubled the average length of survival of toads with the transplanted pars distalis (Table III). Moreover, the toads continued to molt and to shed the

TABLE III

EFFECT OF DAILY INJECTIONS OF LYSINE VASOPRESSIN ON SURVIVAL IN NORMAL TOADS AND IN TOADS WITH THE PARS DISTALIS TRANSPLANTED TO AN EYE MUSCLE[a]

	Survival after first injection (days)[b]	
	Normals[c]	Pars distalis transplanted[d]
Average	38.0	40.4
Range	21–55	5–63

[a] Temperature, 20°–22°C.

[b] Lysine vasopressin (1 IU, Sandoz) injected daily, 6 times a week. During the first 2 weeks of the experiment the group with the transplanted pars distalis received only 0.1 IU lysine vasopressin daily.

[c] Eight adult males.

[d] Fifteen adult males.

sloughs until they died. The secretion of ACTH therefore seems to have been maintained throughout the period of survival, which in some cases was up to 2 months. It is noteworthy that normal toads treated with lysine vasopressin did not survive better than did the toads with the pars distalis transplanted. Therefore, apart from stimulating ACTH secretion, the treatment with lysine vasopressin had deleterious side effects. It seems likely that the toads with the ectopic pars distalis did not die because of lack of corticotropic activity, but because of the same side effects of the treatment. The finding that vasopressin may stimulate both release and synthesis of ACTH in the pars distalis in the toad provides additional support for the theory that the amphibian CRF is chemically and structurally closely related to the octapeptide neurohypophyseal hormones. It also suggests that the CRF-secreting neurons terminating in the median eminence of the toad are related to the octapeptide hormone-secreting neurons terminating in the pars nervosa of the neurohypophysis.

The origin of the neurons that mediate the hypothalamic control of functions of the tetrapod pars distalis has attracted much interest. An extensive literature deals with the possible functional relationships between the pars distalis and the Gomori-positive neurons of the magnocellular nuclei in the anterior hypothalamus in various vertebrate groups (see Jørgensen, 1965).

In the amphibians, Dawson (1957) and Dierickx and co-workers (see Dierickx and van den Abeele, 1959; Dierickx *et al.*, 1960) have suggested that the control of pars distalis functions is exerted by Gomori-positive neurons arising in the preoptic nucleus. Control of ACTH release was suggested by Tuurala (1959), but the possible role of the neurons from the preoptic nucleus as the mediators of the hypothalamic control of TSH release has received the most attention (Scharrer, 1959; Etkin, 1963; Voitkevich, 1961).

Voitkevich (1962, 1964) and Voitkevich and Ovchinnikova (1964) conclude that thyrotropic function is stimulated by principles secreted by the neurons of the preoptic nucleus, since extirpation of this nucleus prevents metamorphosis of tadpoles, and TSH is responsible for normal metamorphosis in anurans. In some of the experiments the preoptic nucleus was extirpated by removal of the diencephalon and telencephalon; in other experiments it is not clear exactly how much brain outside the preoptic nucleus was removed. Etkin (1963) has further developed the theory of the functional relationships between the preoptic nucleus, the thyrotropic cells of the pars distalis, and the thyroid in amphibians. However, conclusive evidence that the preoptic nucleus is responsible for the control of thyrotropic function is lacking (Jørgensen, 1965).

Stutinsky and Befort (1964) observed that electric stimulation of the region between the optic chiasm and the hypophysis, but not the region of the preoptic nucleus, resulted in spermiation in the frog *Rana esculanta*. This suggests that in the frog, neurons of the preoptic nucleus are not the hypothalamic mediators of central nervous control of gonadotropin secretion. Recent experiments of Dierickx (1965) showed that hypothalamic control of gonadotropic function in males and females of the frog *Rana temporaria* was maintained after isolation of the pars ventralis of the tuber cinereum from the rest of the brain by sectioning of the nerve tracts. Thus, the nervous structures that mediate the gonadotropic control must be located close to the median eminence.

2. *Pars Intermedia*

The control of secretion of melanophore-stimulating hormone (MSH) from the pars intermedia is the subject of Chapter 24. Discussion in the present chapter is limited to the nature of the nerves by which this control is exerted. Nerve cutting and transplantation experiments indicate that the central nervous control of MSH secretion is mediated by direct innervation of the pars intermedia tissue, and not by blood-borne principles, as in the control of secretion of the pars distalis hormones (Jørgensen and Larsen, 1963c). However, the nature and origin of the nerves controlling the pars intermedia are unsettled. It has been suggested that the nerves originate in the magnocellular portion of the preoptic nucleus, thus being closely related to the nerves that terminate in the pars nervosa (Etkin, 1962; Legait and Legait, 1962; Voitkevich, 1963). However, Gomori-positive nerve fibers from the preoptic nucleus do not seem to penetrate into the pars intermedia in all species of amphibians. Moreover, in *Bufo arenarum,* pars intermedia cells have been observed to be innervated by nerve fibers that do not contain the secretory granules that are typical of the nerve endings in the pars nervosa (Section II,C,1). In the frog *Rana temporaria,* Enemar and Falck (1965) have recently observed that every cell of the pars intermedia is enclosed by nerve fibers that stain with a sensitive fluorescent technique that is highly specific for certain catecholamines and tryptamines.

In order to elucidate the nature of the nerves that control pars intermedia function in amphibians, the effect of various hormones and drugs on MSH release from the pars intermedia has been studied in frogs (Ingrid Spies, preliminary unpublished experiments, 1964). The substances selected were representatives of the pars nervosa octapeptide hormones and more or less well-established nervous transmitters. The experiments were performed on frogs (*Rana temporaria* and *Rana esculanta*) in which the pars distalis had been extirpated in order to expose the pars intermedia and the pars intermedia had been denervated by sectioning of the hypothalamic nerve tracts to the neurointermediate lobe. After the operation, the toads turned dark because of the uncontrolled secretion of MSH from the pars intermedia due to sectioning of inhibitory nerves to the gland.

The effect of the various drugs on MSH secretion was tested by applying a solution of the drug directly on the exposed surface of the pars intermedia. It was assumed that because of the thinness of the pars intermedia, substances placed on its surface would rapidly reach all parts of the gland by diffusion. Consequently, if the drug was capable of inhibiting MSH secretion by acting directly on the pars intermedia cells, inhibition should result by placing a small drop of a sufficiently concentrated solution of the drug on the surface of the gland. The secretory state of the pars intermedia was evaluated by recording the state of the melanophores in the web of a hind leg of the frog, which was immobilized by curarization.

Table IV shows the results. It can be seen that the solutions of the octapeptide hormones, vasotocin, lysine-8-vasopressin, and oxytocin had no significant effect on MSH release. The same was true for 5-hydroxytryptamine (serotonin) and acetylcholine, even in high concentrations. Melanophore reactions did follow the application of γ-aminobutyric acid in three out of seven experiments, whereas the same amount of the drug had no effect on the melanophores when injected systemically. However, it does not necessarily follow that in the positive cases, γ-aminobutyric acid caused a specific inhibition of MSH release from the pars intermedia cells. Melanin concentration in the melanophores may have occurred independently of the applied drug, and be due, for instance, to a decrease in blood circulation in the pars intermedia or in the capillaries in the region of the web where the reading of the melanophore index took place. Even though the results recorded in Table IV are all from experi-

TABLE IV

EFFECT OF VARIOUS HORMONES OR DRUGS ON THE RELEASE OF MSH FROM DENERVATED PARS INTERMEDIA IN FROGS

Hormone or drug	Concentration	Mode of application[a]	Number of experiments in which a significant effect[b] Was observed	Was not observed
Oxytocin (Syntocinon)	10 IU per milliliter	D	0	2
Lysine-8-vasopressin	10 IU per milliliter	D	1	6
Vasotocin	0.7 IU per milliliter	D	0	4
Serotonin[c]	10^{-3}–10^{-2}	D	0	8
Acetylcholine[c]	10^{-2}	D	0	4
γ-aminobutyric acid[c]	10^{-2}	D	3	4
		I	0	7
Epinephrine[c]	10^{-3}	D	7	11
		I	9	4
Norepinephrine[c]	10^{-3}	D	2	2
		I	1	2

[a] Mode of application: D, the solution was dropped directly on the exposed surface of pars intermedia; I, the same amount of the solution was injected subcutaneously.

[b] The melanophore index decreased one or more units.

[c] Concentration given in weight percent; e.g., 10^{-3} = 1 gm substance per kilogram (liter) of water.

ments in which the blood flow in the pars intermedia and web was judged to be unrestricted, a few positive results cannot be considered convincing evidence for a direct effect of the drug on the secretion of MSH. More consistent results were obtained with epinephrine. However, the dose which was effective when applied locally on the pars intermedia was also effective when injected in a lymph sac. Most probably, therefore, epinephrine did not cause melanin concentration by inhibiting MSH release from the pars intermedia, but by acting directly on the melanophores. It is well known that epinephrine causes melanin concentration within the melanophores of cold-blooded vertebrates (Waring, 1963). In the few experiments with norepinephrine, the results were similar to those obtained with epinephrine. Therefore, these experiments do not provide evidence that any of the substances tested so far is the normal transmitter of nervous inhibition of MSH release from the pars intermedia cells.

B. Teleosts

1. *Dependency of Adenohypophyseal Functions upon Central Nervous Control*

a. Pro- and Mesoadenohypophyseal Functions. The functions of the tetrapod pars distalis are exerted by the pro- and mesoadenohypophysis in teleosts. The fact that gonadal function is seasonal in many teleosts indicates that gonadotropic activity is regulated by environmental factors which presumably act on the hypophysis via the central nervous system (Pickford and Atz, 1957, 1964; Hoar, 1962; Henderson, 1963). However, stimulation by external factors does not necessarily provide conclusive evidence for central nervous control of gonadotropin secretion from the adenohypophysis. Thus, in *Oryzias* females, oviposition induced by the presence of the male appears to occur through direct action of neurohypophyseal hormone on peripheral effector organs (Egami and Nambu, 1961). Central nervous control of thyrotropin function is indicated by Baggerman's demonstration (1957) that increase in day length stimulates thyrotropin secretion.

Few attempts have been made directly to demonstrate the possible role of the central nervous system in regulating adenohypophyseal functions. Ball and Kallman (1962) observed that growth in the cyprinodont *Poecilia formosa* with a hypophyseal homotransplant in the musculature of the tail was superior to that of hypophysectomized fish, but inferior to that of normal controls. This suggests that the hypophyseal hormones responsible for normal growth are secreted in subnormal amounts in the absence of hypothalamic contact. Ball *et al.* (1963) showed that TSH secretion was at least as high as normal from the transplanted hypophysis in these fish. In many of the graft-bearing hypophysectomized fish, the thyroids showed hypertrophy compared with intact controls. This suggests that the hypothalamus normally exerts an inhibitory action on TSH secretion from the adenohypophysis. It has further been found that the ectopic hypophysis secretes no gonadotropin, and ACTH only at reduced rates (Ball *et al.*, 1965). Luteotropic hormone secretion from the ectopic tissue has been demonstrated in both *Poecilia* (Ball *et al.*, 1965) and *Xiphophorus* (Schreibman and Kallman, 1964) by the ability of the graft-bearing fish to survive in fresh water. It is unsettled whether LTH secretion is under central nervous system control.

b. Meta-adenohypophysis. The meta-adenohypophysis in teleosts is apparently homologous with the tetrapod pars intermedia and produces MSH-like principles. The effect of the principles upon the intracellular movement of melanin varies with the species (Waring, 1963; Kent, 1961). In some species they apparently play a role similar to that in amphibians and cause melanin dispersion within the melanophores; in other species, they seem to produce melanin concentration. In still other teleosts, the melanophores do not respond to MSH, but seem to be exclusively under direct nervous control. Control by innervation of the melanophores also plays a role in the species where melanophores respond to MSH. In those teleosts in which MSH participates in color responses, the central nervous system presumably controls the secretory activity of the meta-adenohypophysis.

2. *Mechanisms of Control*

The evidence summarized above indicates that in the teleosts there is some evidence for a central nervous control of secretion of MSH, gonadotropin, ACTH, TSH, and growth hormone, whereas it is left undecided whether the secretion of LTH is under central nervous control. Little that is definite can be said about the mechanisms by which the central nervous control of the various hormones is exerted.

The anatomy and fine structure of the hypophyseal region in teleosts suggest that hypothalamic control of adenohypophyseal functions may be mediated by means of direct innervation of the individual cells, by principles from nerves that diffuse intercellularly, or by principles carried by the blood stream in capillaries constituting vascular links between neurohypophyseal and adenohypophyseal tissues. Direct innervation seems to be much more common in the meta-adenohypophysis than in the other regions of the adenohypophysis. It is of special interest that the same type of neurons appear to be able to establish direct contact with adenohypophyseal cells and with blood vessels within the gland, the relative prominence of the two types of termination of the neurons varying with the species.

The neurohypophyseal axons that arise in the nucleus preopticus and the nucleus lateralis tuberis have attracted special interest in attempts to elucidate the possible role of the neurohypophysis as a mediator of hypothalamic control of adenohypophyseal functions. Several studies have been made in the teleosts of possible correlations between adenohypophyseal functions, especially cyclical gonadotropic and thyrotropic activities, and the state of the preoptic nucleus. Correlations have been reported in the salmon (*Salmo salar*, see Barannikova, 1961), and also in some chondrosteans (e.g., *Acipenser güldenstädti*, see Barannikova and Polenov, 1960). However, no correlation between reproductive cycles and seasonal variations in the cytology and histology of the preoptic-hypophyseal tract was observed in several species of teleosts (*Tinca vulgaris*, see Schiebler and von Brehm, 1958; Schiebler and Hartmann, 1963; *Platypoecilus maculatus*, see Öztan, 1963; various teleosts, see Stahl and Leray, 1962). By contrast, the cytology of the nucleus lateralis tuberis has been found to vary with the reproductive cycles. The nucleus lateralis tuberis has therefore been ascribed a role in the regulation of the gonadotropic function of the adenohypophysis in teleosts (Stahl, 1953; Zaitsev, 1955; Schiebler and von Brehm, 1958; Billenstien, 1962; Stahl and Leray, 1962; Öztan, 1963). An exception is *Morene labrax*, in which Stahl and Leray (1962) found no correlation between sexual maturation and activity of the nucleus lateralis tuberis; however, they reported that a single cell in the preoptic nucleus showed cyclical modifications. It does not seem possible to draw definite conclusions concerning the functional significance of any of these correlations.

C. Selachians

1. *Dependency of Adenohypophyseal Functions upon Central Nervous Control*

Knowledge about which hormones are produced by the adenohypophysis and their functions is less complete in the selachians than in the teleosts. However, it has been demonstrated that the pars intermedia produces MSH which controls the activity of the melanophores (Mellinger, 1963), and the ventral lobe produces gonadotropin(s), without which normal gonadal development and reproduction is not possible

(Dodd *et al.*, 1960). There is also evidence that TSH is secreted by the ventral lobe (Dodd *et al.*, 1960), and that ACTH and growth hormone are produced in the selachian adenohypophysis (Bern and Nandi, 1964). Therefore, it seems reasonable to expect that most or all of the hormones that have been isolated from the mammalian adenohypophysis are produced in the selachians.

Central nervous control of MSH secretion has been demonstrated. The secretion is normally under central nervous inhibition, since lesions that interrupt the hypothalamic hypophyseal nerve fibers cause increased MSH secretion and hyperplasia of the meta-adenohypophysis (Mellinger, 1963a).

Knowledge about the central nervous control of the anterior and ventral lobes of the selachian adenohypophysis is meager. Only the gonadotropic function has been studied, and this function appears to be highly autonomous. In *Scyliorhinus caniculus*, extirpation of the ventral lobe results in degeneration of the gonads in both sexes, whereas extirpation of the rostral and neurointermediate lobes has no effect on ovulation and egg deposition in mature females (Dodd *et al.*, 1960). The ventral lobe seems to be without nervous or vascular contact with the brain.

2. *Mechanisms of Control*

Although a dependency of adenohypophyseal functions upon central nervous control remains to be demonstrated, a number of structures have been described in the hypophyseal region of the brain of various selachians that might serve the purpose of mediating such control. Several types of nerve fibers have been found to terminate in the hypophysis, and several vascular systems have been found to connect regions of the brain with regions of the adenohypophysis (see above). Mellinger (1963b) speculates that these vascular systems function as mediators of central nervous control of hypophyseal functions. However, Meurling (1960) has pointed out that in the selachians, the systems do not constitute constant vascular links between definite regions of the brain and the hypophysis (Section II,D).

Pars intermedia cells have been found to be innervated, but the type of innervation varies between species. One or two types of neurons may be involved. It has been suggested that one of the types of neurons that innervate the pars intermedia cells in *Scyliorhinus caniculus* originates in the nucleus preopticus and that this nucleus should therefore mediate central nervous control of MSH secretion in this species (Mellinger, 1963a). However, neurons from this nucleus do not generally terminate in close contact with pars intermedia cells in other species.

D. Cyclostomes

Structural details and knowledge about hypophyseal function differ in the two orders of cyclostomes, the hagfishes and the lampreys, so separate discussion of them is advisable.

1. *Lampreys*

a. Dependency of Adenohypophyseal Functions upon Central Nervous Control. The meta-adenohypophysis has been shown to contain an MSH-like principle (Lanzing, 1954) and to be responsible for the dark color normally maintained in *Lampetra fluviatilis* (Young, 1935; Larsen, 1965). These animals do not change their color according to background. However, *Lampetra planeri* reacts to light and darkness and shows a diurnal rhythm, being somewhat lighter in the day than at night, thus suggesting a central nervous control of MSH secretion.

Gonadotropic activity has been demonstrated in hypophyseal extracts of *Lampetra fluviatilis* (Strahan, 1959). Gonadotropic function has been evaluated by Dodd *et al.* (1960), by Evennett and Dodd (1963a,b), and by Larsen (1965). Larsen concluded that the part of the gonadotropic activity which stimulates spermatogenesis and growth of eggs is weak or absent, whereas that part which is responsible for ovulation and release of sperm into the body cavity is marked. These latter functions are probably under central nervous system control because they are the keys to spawning, and spawning is seasonal in this species.

Thyrotropic activity (Dodd, 1961) and adrenocorticotropic activity (Strahan, 1959) have been demonstrated in hypophyseal extracts of *Lampetra fluviatilis*. Mammalian TSH has been shown to have an effect on I^{131} metabolism in ammocoetes (Leloup and Fontaine, 1960; Clements-Merlini, 1962). Mammalian ACTH causes sodium retention in *Lampetra fluviatilis* (Bentley and Follett, 1962). However, hypophysectomized adult lampreys survive well in fresh water, and live even longer than normal lampreys, which die within a few weeks after spawning. Indeed, it has been suggested that natural death is caused by a hypersecretion of ACTH (Larsen, 1965). The corticotropin-adrenal cortex system may also be involved in metamorphosis in ammocoetes (Sterba, 1955).

Transplantation of the lamprey hypophysis has been performed by L. O. Larsen (unpublished preliminary experiments, 1963). That part of the pro- and mesoadenohypophyseal tissue which could be removed in one piece was transplanted to a muscle in the pharynx. The remaining pro- and mesoadenohypophyseal tissue was sucked out or destroyed by electrocautery. These transplantation experiments were performed at the same time as a series of hypophysectomies, of which a full account has been given (Larsen, 1965). The results are summarized in Table V, which shows that pro- and mesoadenohypophyseal tissue transplanted to a muscle was able to maintain release of sperm into the body cavity in four of five males, but able to produce ovulation in only one of five females. The experiments suggest that at least in males, there is autonomous secretion of gonadotropin from the adenohypophysis.

b. Mechanisms of Control. There is no information on mechanisms of possible central nervous control of adenohypophyseal functions. Gorbman (1965) found no portal system in the hypophyseal region of *Petromyzon marinus* and *Lampetra planeri,* although Roth (1956) described capillaries with which chrom-alum-hematoxylin- and aldehyde-fuchsin-positive axons establish contact in *Petromyzon marinus.*

2. *Hagfishes*

As mentioned above, the adenohypophysis of the hagfishes seems not to be differentiated into separate regions. Strahan (1962) found weak gonadotropic and adrenocorticotropic activity in *Myxine* hypophyseal extracts, and R. Olsson and his co-workers (see Olsson *et al.*, 1965) found cytological evidence for ACTH and gonadotropin-secreting cells in experiments involving gonadectomy and the injection of various hormones and drugs. D. B. Carlisle and R. Olsson (unpublished results, 1964) furthermore demonstrated that the posterior part of the adenohypophysis contains strong MSH-like activity, whereas the anterior part has only weak activity. The color changes in hagfishes seem to depend

TABLE V

EFFECT OF AUTOTRANSPLANTATION OF THE HYPOPHYSIS ON GONADOTROPIC ACTIVITY IN *Lampetra Fluviatilis*

		Liberation of gonadal products into the body cavity	
		Present	Absent
Pro- and mesoadenohypophysis extirpated	Males	0	3
	Females	0	4
Pro- and mesoadenohypophysis transplanted to muscle	Males	4	1
	Females	1	4

upon disappearance and resynthesis of pigment and not upon pigment migration within melanophores (Coonfield, 1940). It is unknown whether the color change depends upon central nervous system-regulated MSH secretion. The hagfishes seem to breed at all seasons of the year (Nikolski, 1957; Walvig, 1963). Gonadotropin secretion may therefore be more or less independent of environmental stimuli, and thus not necessarily be under central nervous system control. The poorly developed or absent nervous and vascular connections between the hypothalamus and adenohypophysis (Sections II,A and II,D) also suggest a lack of central nervous system control.

IV. Extrahypophyseal Functions of the Neurohypophyseal Hormones in Lower Vertebrates

The neurons of the magnocellular nuclei in the anterior hypothalamus have been found to produce octapeptide hormones that are chemically closely related in all vertebrate groups. Several hormones have now been identified and some have been found to be widely distributed, especially arginine vasotocin which has been demonstrated in the neurohypophysis of cyclostomes, selachians, teleosts, lungfishes, amphibians, reptiles, and birds (Sawyer, 1961, 1965; Acher, 1963; Follett and Heller, 1964a,b; Heller, 1963). Vasotocin thus has a long ancestry in vertebrate evolution.

It is well known that in the tetrapods, vasotocin and other neurohypophyseal hormones act on target organs outside the hypophysis, such as the kidney of most groups, the urinary bladder and skin of amphibians, and the uterus and mammary glands of mammals. Far less is known about the functions of the octapeptide neurohypophyseal hormones in the fishes and cyclostomes (Maetz and Morel, 1965). In the cyclostome *Lampetra fluviatilis*, Bentley and Follett (1962, 1963) found no effect of vasotocin on urine flow. Vasotocin is the only identified neurohypophyseal hormone in the cyclostomes. The hormone did increase renal sodium excretion but this effect was considered to be of doubtful physiological significance. Nothing seems to be known about functions of the neurohypophysis in selachians (Heller and Bentley, 1963).

In teleosts, the neurohypophyseal hormones, vasotocin and isotocin, have been found to enhance sodium uptake in the gills of a fresh-water fish, the goldfish, and sodium excretion in the gills of the flounder in sea water (Maetz, 1963; Motais and Maetz, 1964). Vasotocin but not isotocin enhances the renal excretion of electrolytes and water in the goldfish (Maetz *et al.*, 1964). The differing effects of neurohypophyseal hormones on a fresh-water and a marine fish may be physiological in both species. Also in amphibians, the varying effects of neurohypophyseal hormones on the salt and water metabolism are closely related to the ecology of the species (Maetz, 1963; Bentley and Heller, 1964; Heller, 1965).

The teleost neurohypophysis may also possess extrahypophyseal functions concerned with spawning or oviposition (Egami and Ishii, 1962; Sawyer and Pickford, 1963) (see also Section III,B,1). This indicates that even in the teleosts, in which nerve fibers arising in the preoptic nucleus end in the adenohypophysis, the nerve fibers may control target organs outside the hypophysis.

V. Discussion and Conclusions

Part of the literature dealing with the identity and nature of the neurons by which central nervous control of adenohypophyseal functions are exerted assumes that the control is mediated by means of neurons that arise in the magnocellular parts of the preoptic nucleus in the lower vertebrates, or in the homologous nuclei in higher vertebrates. The terminals of the nerve fibers from these nuclei are normally greatly distended by the secretory products which are easily made visible by the Gomori or related staining techniques. However, other types of nerves innervate adenohypophyseal tissue directly, especially the pars intermedia, or terminate in close proximity to blood vessels in the median eminence of tetrapods. There are similar endings on blood vessels in structures in lower vertebrates that resemble the tetrapod median eminence. There are therefore several types of neurons which are possible candidates for the roles of the ultimate mediators of central nervous control of adenohypophyseal functions.

A. The Role of the Magnocellular Nuclei in the Anterior Hypothalamus as Mediators of Central Nervous Control of Adenohypophyseal Functions in Lower Vertebrates

In the amphibians and other tetrapods, support for the assumption that neurons from the magnocellular nuclei in the anterior hypothalamus mediate central nervous control of adenohypophyseal function has been found in the observed correlations in functional states of the pars distalis and the neurons originating in the magnocellular nuclei. However, more direct evidence strongly suggests that other neurons than those arising in the magnocellular nuclei mediate the central nervous control of pars distalis functions in mammals (Chapters 9, 12, 14, 15, in Volume I). Therefore, the correlations in functional states that can be observed under certain conditions in these animals seem to be coincidental (see also Jørgensen, 1965). Consequently, little weight can be placed on similar correlations when observed in lower vertebrates, as long as they remain unsupported by direct evidence.

In teleosts and selachians, the intimate contact which has often been described between neurohypophysis, especially its posterior part, and the adenohypophysis, especially the meta-adenohypophysis, has quite understandably led to theories which suggest that in these vertebrate groups, neurons from the magnocellular parts of the preoptic nucleus mediate the central nervous control of adenohypophyseal functions. It has been argued that the striking variation in the structural relations between the elements of the preoptic-hypophyseal nerve tract and adenohypophyseal tissue indicates that the mode of control may vary between direct nervous and indirect humoral regulation. However, an equally justified conclusion is that the preoptic-hypophyseal nerve tract is not mediating control of adenohypophyseal functions. The intimate intermingling of adenohypophyseal with neurohypophyseal tissue in selachians and teleosts may therefore have another unknown functional significance. It may be appropriate to compare the branching of neurohypophyseal elements within the meta-adenohypophysis with the intimate mixing of cortical and medullary tissue in the adrenal gland of birds.

In amphibians and higher vertebrates, neurons from the magnocellular nuclei in the anterior hypothalamus apparently innervate the pars intermedia. However, there is no functional evidence that central nervous control of pars intermedia function is mediated by neurons of the preoptic magnocellular nuclei.

B. The Relationships between the Neurohypophyseal Neurons with Intrahypophyseal and with Extrahypophyseal Functions

In preceding sections, evidence has been presented that neurons in the magnocellular nuclei in the anterior hypothalamus are not the hypothalamic mediators of central nervous control of adenohypophyseal functions in the various vertebrate classes, but do have extrahypophyseal functions. These functions are well established in the tetrapods. They are probable in teleosts, and even in the phylogenetically oldest vertebrates, the cyclostomes, effects on salt metabolism have been observed. Therefore, it is suggested that the functional evolution of the preoptic-neurohypophyseal tract has proceeded independently of those hypothalamic-neurohypophyseal nerve tracts that serve as hypothalamic mediators of central nervous control of adenohypophyseal functions.

This of course does not necessarily imply that the hypothalamic mediator neurons are not related to the neurons of the preoptic-neurohypophyseal and homologous tracts. In fact, there is evidence that in mammals one of the hypothalamic factors that presumably mediates control of ACTH secretion from the pars distalis, β-CRF, is chemically related to the octapeptide hormones of the magnocellular nuclei (Guillemin, 1964; Schally *et al.*, 1964). This close chemical relationship between the secretory products of the neurons producing the pars nervosa hormones and the CRF's suggests that the neurons secreting them have a common embryological origin.

In mammals, the other hypothalamic CRF's (α_1- and α_2-CRF) which have been isolated by Guillemin (1964) are chemically related to MSH. However, the relations of the various putative CRF's to the factors normally mediating the central nervous control of ACTH secretion from the pars distalis are still unsettled.

The chemistry of the other hypothalamic mediators is discussed in Chapter 8 (Volume I). Thyrotropin releasing factor and LRF in mammals appear to be small polypeptides (Guillemin, 1964; McCann and Ramirez, 1964; Schally and Bowers, 1964; Schreiber, 1964) which seem to be structurally unrelated to the chemically identified octapeptide neurohypophyseal hormones (Ramirez *et al.*, 1964; Schally and Bowers, 1964; Schreiber, 1964). The chemistry of follicle-stimulating hormone releasing factor, growth hormone releasing factor and prolactin inhibiting factor is unsettled. In several mammals, Carlson *et al.* (1962), Falck (1964) and Fuxe (1964) have demonstrated monoamine-containing nerve fibers that terminate in close proximity to the capillaries of the primary plexus in the median eminence. These fibers appear to originate in hypothalamic nuclei and they have been assumed to act as mediators of central nervous control of pars distalis function. Monoamines have recently also been demonstrated in large amounts in the median eminence of the frog *Rana temporaria* (Enemar and Falck, 1965).

C. The Significance of the Differentiation of the Neurohypophysis into a Pars Nervosa and a Median Eminence

The differentiation of a pars nervosa within the neurohypophysis is closely related to the adaptation to terrestrial habitats (Green, 1951; Wingstrand, 1959). This development may be causally related to the increased need of neurohypophyseal hormones serving water conservation which followed the transition from aquatic to terrestrial environments in vertebrate evolution. It is of interest in this regard that the main water-conserving hormone in the amphibians, vasotocin, is also a CRF. The minimal ACTH-releasing dose of vasotocin in the toad *Bufo bufo* has been found to be about 40 times greater than the dose needed to enhance water uptake through the skin (Jørgensen and Larsen, 1963a). However, the hormone was injected subcutaneously, and it seems likely that the dose needed to stimulate the release of ACTH would be much smaller if applied directly to the pars distalis. The normal secretion of large amounts of vasotocin from the pars nervosa might have unwanted side effects on ACTH secretion if the blood from the pars nervosa did not drain into the systemic circulation, but through the adenohypophyseal tissue, as is mainly the case in fishes with an undifferentiated neurohypophysis.

Jørgensen and Larsen (1963a) extirpated or denervated the pars nervosa in *Bufo bufo*. The immediate result of the operations was an accumulation of the pars nervosa hormones within the median eminence. The blood in the vessels of the median eminence drains through the pars distalis, so the greater part of the pars nervosa hormones which accumulated in the median eminence were probably carried to the pars distalis. Many of the experimental toads showed disturbed ACTH function; in extreme cases the animals died with symptoms of adrenocortical hypofunction. The cortical hypofunction which seemed to develop in many of the operated toads may be due to exhaustion of the adrenocortical cells or of the ACTH-producing cells of the pars distalis caused by overstimulation by the pars nervosa hormones draining through the pars distalis. In a previous paper (Jørgensen and Larsen, 1963a) this possibility was dismissed because it was found that the toads showing severe symptoms of adrenocortical insufficiency did not respond with molting to large doses of ACTH or corticosteroids. Molting is inhibited in hypophysectomized toads, but is restored by injection of small amounts of ACTH or corticosteroids such as aldosterone or corticosterone. However, ACTH or corticosteroids never cause molting in toads with functioning adrenals (Jørgensen and Larsen, 1964). Therefore, the inability of ACTH and corticosteroids to produce molting in the toads with abnormal molting may have been due to the secretion of corticosteroids still being high enough to prevent the molt-provoking activity of injections of ACTH or corticosteroids. There was no significant effect of the operation on gonadotropic and thyrotropic functions (Jørgensen, Larsen and Rosenkilde, unpublished results, 1964).

D. The Evolution of Hypothalamic Mediation of Central Nervous Control of Adenohypophyseal Functions

Nothing definite can be said about the evolutionary history of central nervous system control of adenohypophyseal functions. We do not know whether control was established early in the vertebrate evolution, whether one or more of the adenohypophyseal functions came under central nervous control late in the history of the vertebrates, or whether previously established control was lost, then secondarily regained. If both types of CRF's that have been isolated from hypothalamic extracts turn out to be natural mediators, this would indicate that central nervous control of ACTH release from the pars distalis has been established twice by at least partly independent central nervous structures, each controlling secretion of ACTH by its specific hypothalamic mediator.

E. Significance of Hypophyseal Portal Circulation in the Lower Vertebrates

It is characteristic of the hypothalamic-hypophyseal relationships in tetrapods that hypothalamic mediators exert their action on the pars distalis humorally, via the portal circulation, whereas the action on the pars intermedia appears to be by direct innervation. This clear distinction is less pronounced in groups of the fishes, and may be missing in teleosts. In the selachians, vascular structures have been interpreted to be portal-like vessels that serve to transport hypothalamic mediators to the target cells in the adenohypophysis, but such structures are not present in all fish. However, the tendency to form portal-like vascular systems can be imagined to have been of preadaptive significance in the development of functioning portal systems of the type which has been demonstrated in tetrapods. It is noteworthy that even in the anurans portal circulations of no known function have been described between brain and hypophysis (Cruz, 1956, 1959).

F. Has There Been a Free Choice of Hypothalamic Neurons as Mediators in the Evolution of Central Nervous Control of Adenohypophyseal Functions?

The comparative morphological studies of hypothalamic-adenohypophyseal relations in the vertebrates, especially in the various groups of fishes, have been interpreted as indicating (1) that different types of neurons have been incorporated as hypothalamic mediators of central nervous control of the same adenohypophyseal functions, and (2) that a given type of neuron may exert its function humorally, as an endocrine neuron, in one species and by direct innervation of the effector cell in another. It is questionable whether these interpretations of the morphological data are justified. All blood-borne mediators whose chemical nature has been determined so far appear to be polypeptides. This suggests that in establishing central nervous control of an adenohypophyseal function via the blood circulation, polypeptide-secreting neurons have been preferentially or even exclusively selected, whereas directly innervating neurons may be of another type. More information on the nature of the mediator neurons may help in answering the question of why control of the pars intermedia (or homologous parts of the adenohypophysis in the fishes) generally seems to be nervous, while control of the remaining parts of the adenohypophysis is hormonal.

VI. Summary

The hypothalamic-neurohypophyseal structures by which central nervous control of adenohypophyseal functions may be mediated have been described and compared in amphibians, fishes, and cyclostomes.

In the amphibians, as in other tetrapods, there is good evidence that secretion of pars distalis hormones is ultimately controlled by endocrine neurons terminating in the median eminence of the neurohypophysis and acting on the pars distalis cells by means of hormones that are released into the hypophyseal portal circulation. Central nervous control of the function of the pars intermedia appears to be exerted by neurons which directly innervate the pars intermedia tissue.

In teleost fishes, structural relationships between the neurohypophysis and adenohypophysis have been interpreted by some investigators as indicating that mediation of central nervous control of adenohypophyseal functions may be exerted partly by neurons that innervate adenohypophyseal tissue directly and partly by neurons that release factors that are carried by capillary circulation from the neurohypophysis to the adenohypophysis. The morphological evidence suggests that the relative importance of the ordinary and hormonal nervous action on the adenohypophyseal cells varies between species, and that the same type of neuron can function as an ordinary or endocrine neuron. However, functional evidence in support of such theories is lacking.

Hypothalamic-hypophyseal portal systems are widely distributed within the various groups of fishes, down to the hagfish; but they are typically absent in the teleosts. In selachians, especially well-developed portal systems connect the hypothalamus and other regions of the brain with various parts of the adenohypophysis. It has been suggested that these systems have functions like the hypophyseal portal system in tetrapods, but the great species variability in the systems speaks against this hypothesis. The tendency to form portal-like vascular systems in the lower vertebrates may have been of preadaptive significance in the development of portal systems that mediate central nervous control of adenohypophyseal functions.

The neurohypophyses of amphibians, fishes, and cyclostomes contain hormones that are chemically closely related to the octapeptide hormones of the pars nervosa of the hypophysis in mammals. The hormones apparently serve extrahypophyseal functions in amphibians, and perhaps also in fishes and cyclostomes.

The factor which mediates the central nervous control of ACTH release in the toad *Bufo bufo* appears to be structurally related to the octapeptide hormones that are produced by neurons of the magnocellular parts of the preoptic nucleus, but the relationships between these neurons and those producing CRF's are not known.

In fishes and cyclostomes the chemical nature of the possible mediators of central nervous control of adenohypophyseal functions and the relationships between the hypothalamic neurons that have intra- and extrahypophyseal functions are unknown.

References

Acher, R. (1963). The comparative chemistry of neurohypophysial hormones. *Symp. Zool. Soc. London* **9**, 83–92.

Adam, H. (1959). Hypophyse und hypothalamo-neurohypophysäres Neurosekretsystem bei den Cyclostomen *Myxine glutinosa* und *Bdellostoma stouti*. *Verhandl. Deut. Zool. Ges.* pp. 158–171.

Adam, H. (1960–1961). Zur Kenntnis des Baues der Hypophyse von *Myxine glutinosa* L. (Cyclostomata). *Anat. Anz.* **109**, Suppl., 479–491.

Baggerman, B. (1957). An experimental study of the timing of breeding and migration in the three-spined stickleback (*Gasterosteus aculeatus* L.) *Arch. Neerl. Zool.* **12**, 105–318.

Ball, J. N., and Kallman, K. D. (1962). Functional pituitary transplants in the all-female, gynogenetic teleost, *Mollienesia formosa* (Girard). *Am. Zoologist* **2**, 264.

Ball, J. N., Olivereau, M., and Kallman, K. D. (1963). Secretion of thyrotrophic hormone by pituitary transplants in a teleost fish. *Nature* **199**, 618–620.

Ball, J. N., Olivereau, M., Slicher, A. M., and Kallman, K. D. (1965). Functional capacity of ectopic pituitary transplants in the teleost *Poecilia formosa*, with a comparative discussion on the transplanted pituitary. *Phil. Trans.* **B249**, 69–99.

Barannikova, I. A. (1961). The functional morphology of the hypothalamo-hypophysial neurosecretory system in salmon at different stages of the life cycle. *Dokl.–Biol. Sci. Sect.* (*Engl. Transl.*) **136**, 133–136.

Barannikova, I. A., and Polenov, A. L. (1960). An ecological and histophysiological analysis of the preoptic-pituitary neurosecretory system in the Acipenseridae. *Dokl. –Biol. Sci. Sect.* (*Engl. Transl.*) **133**, 611–614.

Bargmann, W. (1953). Zwischenhirn-Hypophysensystem von Fischen. *Z. Zellforsch. Mikroskop. Anat.* **38**, 275–298.

Bargmann, W., and Knoop, A. (1960). Über die morphologischen Beziehungen des neurosekretorischen Zwischenhirnsystems zum Zwischenlappen der Hypophyse (Licht- und Elektronenmikroskopische Untersuchungen). *Z. Zellforsch. Mikroskop. Anat.* **52**, 256–277.

Barrington, E. J. W. (1960). Some features of the vascularization of the hypothalamus and pituitary stalk in the minnow *Phoxinus phoxinus* L. *Proc. Zool. Soc. London* **135**, 551–558.

Bentley, P. J., and Follett, B. K. (1962). The action of neurohypophysial and adrenocortical hormones on sodium balance in the cyclostome, *Lampetra fluviatilis. Gen. Comp. Endocrinol.* **2**, 329–335.

Bentley, P. J., and Follett, B. K. (1963). Kidney function in a primitive vertebrate, the cyclostome *Lampetra fluviatilis. J. Physiol.* (*London*) **169**, 902–918.

Bentley, P. J., and Heller, H. (1964). The action of neurohypophysial hormones on the water and sodium metabolism of urodele amphibians. *J. Physiol.* (*London*) **171**, 434–453.

Bern, H. A., and Nandi, J. (1964). Endocrinology of poikilothermic vertebrates. *In* "The Hormones" (G. Pincus *et al.*, eds.), Vol. 4, pp. 199–298. Academic Press, New York.

Billenstien, D. C. (1962). The seasonal secretory cycle of the nucleus lateralis tuberis of the hypothalamus and its relation to reproduction in the eastern brook trout, *Salvelinus fontinalis. Gen. Comp. Endocrinol.* **2**, 111–112.

Billenstien, D. C. (1963). Neurosecretory material from the nucleus lateralis tuberis in the hypophysis of the eastern brook trout, *Salvelinus fontinalis. Z. Zellforsch. Mikroskop. Anat.* **59**, 507–512.

Bretschneider, L. H., and de Wit, J. J. D. (1947). "Sexual Endocrinology of Nonmammalian Vertebrates." Elsevier, Amsterdam.

Bugnon, C., and Lenys, D. (1960–1961). Recherches sur les relations hypothalamo-hypophysaires chez diverses espèces de poissons. *Anat. Anz.* **109**, Suppl., 520–529.

Carlsson, A., Falck, B., and Hillarp, N. Å. (1962). Cellular localization of brain monoamines. *Acta Physiol. Scand.* **56**, Suppl. 196, 1–28.

Clements-Merlini, M. (1962). Altered metabolism of I^{131} by the endostyle and notochord of ammocoetes larvae I. Effects of treatment with thyrotropic stimulating hormone. *Gen. Comp. Endocrinol.* **2**, 354–360.

Coonfield, B. R. (1940). The pigment in the skin of *Myxine glutinosa* Linn. *Trans. Am. Microscop. Soc.* **59**, 398.

Cruz, A. R. (1956). Sur l'existence de deux systèmes porte dans l'hypophyse des Amphibiens anoures. *Compt. Rend.* **242**, 189–190.

Cruz, A. R. (1959). Sur l'existence d'un système porte dans la neuro-hypophyse des Amphibiens anoures. *Acta Anat.* **36**, 153–168.

Dawson, A. B. (1953). Evidence for the termination of neurosecretory fibres within the pars intermedia of the frog (*Rana pipiens*). *Anat. Record* **115**, 63–69.

Dawson, A. B. (1957). Morphological evidence of a possible functional interrelationship between the median eminence and the pars distalis of the anuran hypophysis. *Anat. Record* **128**, 77–90.

De Robertis, E. D. P. (1964). "Histophysiology of Synapses and Neurosecretion." Pergamon Press, Oxford.

Diepen, R. (1953). Über das Hypophysen-Hypothalamussystem bei Knochenfischen (eine vergleichend-anatomische Betrachtung). *Verhandl. Anat. Ges., 51. Versamml.* pp. 111–122.

Dierickx, K. (1964). On the regeneration of the hypophysis after partial resection in *Rana temporaria*. *Naturwiss.* **51**, 292.

Dierickx, K. (1965). The origin of the aldehyde-fuchsin-negative nerve fibres of the median eminence of the hypophysis: a gonadotropic centre. *Z. Zellforsch. Mikroskop. Anat.* **66**, 504–518.

Dierickx, K., and van den Abeele, A. (1959). On the relations between the hypothalamus and the anterior pituitary in *Rana temporaria*. *Z. Zellforsch. Mikroskop. Anat.* **51**, 78–87.

Dierickx, K., van den Abeele, A., and Rysenaer, M. (1960). Phénomènes d'activité cycliques dans le système hypothalamo-hypophysaire de *Rana temporaria*. Données nouvelles. *Arch. Anat. Microscop. Morphol. Exptl.* **49**, 73–88.

Dodd, J. M. (1961). Adenohypophyseal hormones of fishes. *Abstr. 10th Pacific Sci. Congr., Honolulu, 1961*, p. 167. Published by Tenth Pacific Science Congress, Honolulu, Hawaii.

Dodd, J. M., and Kerr, T. (1963). Comparative morphology and histology of the hypothalamo-neurohypophysial system. *Symp. Zool. Soc. London* **9**, 5–27.

Dodd, J. M., Evennett, P. J., and Goddard, C. K. (1960). Reproductive endocrinology in cyclostomes and elasmobranchs. *Symp. Zool. Soc. London* **1**, 77–103.

Eccles, J. C. (1964). "The Physiology of Synapses." Springer, Berlin.

Egami, N., and Ishii, S. (1962). Hypophyseal control of reproductive functions in teleost fishes. *Gen. Comp. Endocrinol.* Suppl. 1, 248–253.

Egami, N., and Nambu, M. (1961). Factors initiating mating behavior and oviposition in the fish, *Oryzias latipes*. *J. Fac. Sci. Univ. Tokyo, Sect. 4* **9**, 263–278.

Enemar, A., and Falck, B. (1965). On the presence of adrenergic nerves in the pars intermedia of the frog, *Rana temporaria*. *Gen. Comp. Endocrinol.* **5**, 577–583.

Etkin, W. (1962). Hypothalamic inhibition of pars intermedia activity in the frog. *Gen. Comp. Endocrinol.* Suppl. 1, 148–159.

Etkin, W. (1963). Maturation of the hypothalamic neurosecretory mechanism by thyroid feedback in the frog. *Life Sciences* **2**, 125–128.

Etkin, W., and Lehrer, R. (1960). Excess growth in tadpoles after transplantation of the adenohypophysis. *Endocrinology* **67**, 457–466.

Etkin, W., and Sussman, W. (1961). Hypothalamo-pituitary relations in metamorphosis of *Ambystoma*. *Gen. Comp. Endocrinol.* **1**, 70–79.

Evennett, P. J., and Dodd, J. M. (1963a). The pituitary gland and reproduction in the lamprey (*Lampetra fluviatilis* L.). *J. Endocrinol.* **26**, xiv–xv.

Evennett, P. J., and Dodd, J. M. (1963b). Endocrinology of reproduction in the river lamprey. *Nature* **197**, 715–716.

Falck, B. (1964). Cellular localization of monoamines. *Progr. Brain Res.* **8**, 28–44.

Follenius, E. (1961). Comparaison des relations vasculaires hypothalamo-hypophysaires chez quelques espèces de Téléostéens. *Compt. Rend.* **253**, 1015–1017.

Follenius, E. (1962a). La vascularisation de l'hypophyse chez quelques Cyprinodontes. *Anat. Anz.* **109**, Suppl., 530–538.

Follenius, E. (1962b). Rapports neurovasculaires et neuroglandulaires dans l'hypophyse de quelques poissons. Étude au microscope électronique. *Compt. Rend.* **255**, 3474–3476.

Follenius, E. (1965a). Bases structurales et ultrastructurales des correlations diencéphalo-hypophysaires chez les Sélaciens et les Téléostéens. *Arch. Anat. Microscop. Morphol. Exptl.* **54**, 195–216.

Follenius, E. (1965b). Bases structurales et ultrastructurales des corrélations hypothalamo-hypophysaires chez quelques espèces de poissons téléostéens. *Ann. Sci. Nat. Zool. Paris* **7**, 1–150.

Follett, B. K., and Heller, H. (1964a). The neurohypophysial hormones of bony fishes and cyclostomes. *J. Physiol.* (*London*) **172**, 74–91.

Follett, B. K., and Heller, H. (1964b). The neurohypophysial hormones of lungfishes and amphibians. *J. Physiol.* (*London*) **172**, 92–106.

Fuxe, K. (1964). Cellular localization of monoamines in the median eminence and the infundibular stem of some mammals. *Z. Zellforsch. Mikroskop. Anat.* **61**, 710–724.

Gorbman, A. (1965). Vascular relations between the neurohypophysis and adenohypophysis of cyclostomes and the problem of evolution of hypothalamic neuroendocrine regulation. *Arch. Anat. Microscop. Morphol. Exptl.* **54**, 163–194.

Gorbman, A., Kobayashi, H., and Uemura, H. (1963). The vascularisation of the hypophysial structures of the hagfish. *Gen. Comp. Endocrinol.* **3**, 505–514.

Green, J. D. (1951). The comparative anatomy of the hypophysis, with special reference to its blood supply and innervation. *Am. J. Anat.* **88**, 225–311.

Guillemin, R. (1964). Hypothalamic factors releasing pituitary hormones. *Recent Progr. Hormone Res.* **20**, 89–130.

Hanaoka, Y. (1963). The effect of hypothalectomy at open neurula embryos in *Rana pipiens*. *Am. Zoologist* **3**, No. 140 (Abstract).

Heller, H. (1963). Pharmacology and distribution of neurohypophysial hormones. *Symp. Zool. Soc. London* **9**, 93–106.

Heller, H. (1965). Osmoregulation in Amphibia. *Arch. Anat. Microscop. Morphol. Exptl.* **54**, 471–490.

Heller, H., and Bentley, P. J. (1963). Comparative aspects of the action of neurohypophysial hormones on water and sodium metabolism. *Mem. Soc. Endocrinol.* **13**, 59–65.

Henderson, N. E. (1963). Influence of light and temperature on the reproductive cycle of the eastern brook trout *Salvelinus fontinalis* (Mitchill). *J. Fish. Res. Bd. Can.* **20**, 859–897.

Hoar, W. S. (1962). Reproductive behavior of fish. *Gen. Comp. Endocrinol.* Suppl. 1, 206–216.

Iturriza, F. C. (1964). Electron-microscopic study of the pars intermedia of the pituitary of the toad, *Bufo arenarum*. *Gen. Comp. Endocrinol.* **4**, 492–502.

Jacobsohn, D., and Jørgensen, C. B. (1956). Survival and function af auto- and homografts of adenohypophysial tissue in the toad, *Bufo bufo* (L.). *Acta Physiol. Scand.* **36**, 1–12.

Johnson, B., and Bowers, B. (1963). Transport of neurohormones from the corpora cardiaca in insects. *Science* **141**, 264–266.

Jørgensen, C. B. (1965). Brain pituitary relationships in amphibians, birds and mammals. *Arch. Anat. Microscop. Morphol. Exptl.* **54**, 261–276.

Jørgensen, C. B., and Larsen, L. O. (1963a). Neuro-adenohypophysial relationships. *Symp. Zool. Soc. London* **9**, 59–82.

Jørgensen, C. B., and Larsen, L. O. (1963b). Effect of corticotropin and growth hormone on survival in hypophysectomized toads. *Proc. Soc. Exptl. Biol. Med.* **113**, 94–96.

Jørgensen, C. B., and Larsen, L. O. (1963c). Nature of the nervous control of pars intermedia function in amphibians: Rate of functional recovery after denervation. *Gen. Comp. Endocrinol.* **3**, 468–472.

Jørgensen, C. B., and Larsen, L. O. (1964). Further observations on molting and its hormonal control in *Bufo bufo* (L.). *Gen. Comp. Endocrinol.* **4**, 389–400.

Kent, A. K. (1961). The influence of extraction in sodium hydroxide on the activity of the color change factors of the teleost pituitary. *Gen. Comp. Endocrinol.* **1**, 409–415.

Knowles, F. (1958). Electron microscopy of a crustacean neurosecretory organ. *Proc. 2nd Intern. Symp. Neurosecretion, Lund, 1957*, pp. 105–109. Springer, Berlin.

Knowles, F. (1963). The ultrastructure of the neurointermediate lobe of the pituitary of the dogfish *Scylliorhinus stellaris.* *Gen. Comp. Endocrinol.* **3**, 712 (Abstract).

Knowles, F. (1964). The inter-relation of secretory and nervous function in the central nervous system of lower animals. *In* "Comparative Neurochemistry" (D. Richter, ed.), pp. 3–20. Pergamon Press, Oxford.

Knowles, F. (1965). Neuroendocrine correlations at the level of ultrastructure. *Arch. Anat. Microscop. Morphol. Exptl.* **54**, 343–358.

Kobayashi, H., Ishii, S., and Gorbman, A. (1959). The hypothalamic neurosecretory apparatus and the pituitary gland of a teleost, *Lepidogobius lepidus.* *Gunma J. Med. Sci.* **8**, 303–321.

Lanzing, W. J. R. (1954). The occurrence of a waterbalance, a melanophore-expanding and an oxytocic principle in the pituitary gland of the river lamprey (*Lampetra fluviatilis* L.) *Acta Endocrinol.* **16**, 277–291.

Larsen, L. O. (1965). Effects of hypophysectomy in a cyclostome, *Lampetra fluviatilis* (L.) Gray. *Gen. Comp. Endocrinol.* **5**, 16–30.

Legait, H. (1957). La vascularisation du lobe distal de l'hypophyse des Téléostéens comparée à celle des autres Vertébrés. *Compt. Rend. Soc. Biol.* **151**, 1940–1943.

Legait, H., and Legait, E. (1962). Relationships between the hypothalamus and pars intermedia in some mammals and amphibians. *Mem. Soc. Endocrinol.* **12**, 165–173.

Leloup, J., and Fontaine, M. (1960). Iodine metabolism in lower vertebrates. *Ann. N.Y. Acad. Sci.* **86**, Art. 2, 316–353.

Lofts, B. (1963). Gonadotrophic function in autotransplanted pituitaries of *Bufo bufo.* *Gen. Comp. Endocrinol.* **3**, 717–718.

McCann, S. M., and Ramirez, V. D. (1964). The neuroendocrine regulation of hypophysial luteinizing hormone secretion. *Recent Progr. Hormone Res.* **20**, 131–181.

Maetz, J. (1963). Physiological aspects of neurohypophysial function in fishes with some reference to the Amphibia. *Symp. Zool. Soc. London* **9**, 107–140.

Maetz, J., and Morel, F. (1965). Mécanismes endocriniens communs de l'osmorégulation chez les vertébrés. *Arch. Anat. Microscop. Morphol. Exptl.* **54**, 515–530.

Maetz, J., Bourguet, J., Lahlouh, B., and Hourdry, J. (1964). Peptides neurohypophysaires et osmorégulation chez *Carassius auratus.* *Gen. Comp. Endocrinol.* **4**, 508–522.

Masur, S. K. (1962). Autotransplantation of the pituitary in the red eft. *Am. Zoologist* **2**, 538 (Abstract).

Matty, A. J. (1960). The pituitary of *Myxine glutinosa.* *Nature* **185**, 180–181.

Mazzi, V. (1954). Sulla presenza e sul possibile significato di fibre neurosecretorie ipotalamo-ipofisarie nel lobe intermedio dell' ipofisi del Tritone cristato. *Monitore Zool. Ital.* **62**, 1–8.

Mazzi, V., and Peyrot, A. (1962–1963). Osservazioni preliminari sulle attitudini funzionali di autotrapianti eterotopici ipofisari nel Tritone crestato. *Monitore Zool. Ital.* **70/71**, 124–130.

Mellinger, J. (1960a). Contribution à l'étude de la vascularisation et du développement de la région hypophysaire d'un sélacien, *Scyliorhinus caniculus* (L.). *Bull. Soc. Zool. France* **85**, 123–139.

Mellinger, J. (1960b). La circulation sanguine dans le complexe hypophysaire de la Roussette. *Bull. Soc. Zool. France* **85**, 395–399.

Mellinger, J. (1962). Existence de plusieurs systèmes neurosécrétoires hypothalamo-hypophysaires chez les poissons elasmobranches *Scyliorhinus caniculus* et *Sc. stellaris.* Microscopie ordinaire et microscopie électronique. *Compt. Rend.* **255**, 1789–1791.

Mellinger, J. (1963a). Étude histophysiologique du système hypothalamo-hypophysaire de *Scyliorhinus caniculus* (L.) en état de mélanodispersion permanente. *Gen. Comp. Endocrinol.* **3**, 26–45.

Mellinger, J. (1963b). Les rélations neuro-vasculo-glandulaires dans l'appareil hypophysaire de la Roussette, *Scyliorhinus caniculus* (L.). Thesis, Fac. Sci. University of Strasbourg (No. 238, Ser. E).

Meurling, P. (1960). Presence of a pituitary portal system in elasmobranchs. *Nature* **187**, 336–337.

Meurling, P. (1962). The relations between neural and intermediate lobes in the pituitary of *Squalus acanthias.* *Z. Zellforsch. Mikroskop. Anat.* **58**, 51–69.

Meurling, P. (1963). Nerves of the neuro-intermediate lobe of *Etmopterus spinax* (Elasmobranchi). *Z. Zellforsch. Mikroskop. Anat.* **61**, 183–201.

Motais, R., and Maetz, J. (1964). Action des hormones neurohypophysaires sur les échanges de sodium (Mesurés à l'aide du radio-sodium Na^{24}) chez un téléostéen euryhalin: *Platichthys flesus* L. *Gen. Comp. Endocrinol.* **4**, 210–224.

Nikolski, G. W. (1957). "Spezielle Fischkunde." Deut. Verlag Wiss., Berlin.

Öztan, N. (1963). The hypothalamic neurosecretory system of a poeciliid fish, *Platypoecilus maculatus* and its sterile hybrid backcross with *Xiphophorus helleri.* *Gen. Comp. Endocrinol.* **3**, 1–14.

Olivereau, M., and Ball, J. N. (1964). Contribution à l'histophysiologie de l'hypophyse des téléostéens, en particulier de celle de *Poecilia* species. *Gen. Comp. Endocrinol.* **4**, 523–532.

Olsson, R. (1959). The neurosecretory hypothalamus system and the adenohypophysis of *Myxine.* *Z. Zellforsch. Mikroskop. Anat.* **51**, 97–107.

Olsson, R. (1963). The evolution of neurosecretory cells and systems. *Proc. 16th Intern. Congr. Zool., Washington, D.C., 1963* Vol. 3, pp. 38–43.

Olsson, R., Fernholm, B., and Frenne, A. (1965). Cytology of *Myxine* adenohypophysis. *Naturwiss.* **52**, 92.

Pasteels, J. L., Jr. (1960). Étude éxpérimentale des différentes catégories d'éléments chromophiles de l'hypophyse adulte de *Pleurodeles Waltlii,* de leur fonction et de leur contrôle par l'hypothalamus. *Arch. Biol.* (*Liège*) **71**, 409–471.

Pehlemann, F.-W. (1962). Experimentelle Untersuchungen zur Determination und Differenzierung der Hypophyse bei Anuren (*Pelobates fuscus, Rana esculenta*). *Arch. Entwicklungsmech. Organ.* **153**, 551–602.

Pickford, G. E., and Atz, J. W. (1957). "The Physiology of the Pituitary Gland of Fishes." N.Y. Zool. Soc., New York.

Pickford, G. E., and Atz, J. W. (1964). The pituitary gland and its relation to the reproduction of fishes in nature and in captivity. An annotated bibliography for the years 1956–1963. *FAO Fisheries Biol. Tech. Paper* No. 37, 1–61.

Ramirez, V. D., Nallar, R., and McCann, S. M. (1964). Purification of luteinizing hormone-releasing factor from beef hypothalamus. *Proc. Soc. Exptl. Biol. Med.* **115**, 1072–1076.

Rosenkilde, P. (1963). Effect of transplantation of pars distalis of the hypophysis on the thyroid function in *Bufo bufo*. *Gen. Comp. Endocrinol.* **3**, 729 (Abstract).

Roth, W. D. (1956). Some evolutionary aspects of neurosecretion in the sea lamprey, *Petromyzon marinus*. *Anat. Record* **124**, 437 (Abstract).

Sachs, H. (1959). Vasopressin biosynthesis. *Biochim. Biophys. Acta* **34**, 572–573.

Sawyer, W. H. (1961). Neurohypophysial hormones. *Pharmacol. Rev.* **13**, 225–277.

Sawyer, W. H. (1965). Active neurohypophysial principles from a cyclostome (*Petromyzon marinus;* and two cartilaginous fishes (*Squalus acanthias* and *Hydrolagus collei*). *Gen. Comp. Endocrinol.* **5**, 427–439.

Sawyer, W. H., and Pickford, G. E. (1963). Neurohypophyseal principles of *Fundulus heteroclitus:* Characteristics and seasonal changes. *Gen. Comp. Endocrinol.* **3**, 439–445.

Schally, A. V., and Bowers, C. Y. (1964). Purification of luteinizing hormone-releasing factor from bovine hypothalamus. *Endocrinology* **75**, 608–614.

Schally, A. V., Bowers, C. Y., and Locke, W. (1964). Neurohumoral functions of the hypothalamus. *Am. J. Med. Sci.* **248**, 79–101.

Scharrer, E. (1954). Neurosecretion in the vertebrates: a survey. *Pubbl. Staz. Zool. Napoli* **24**, Suppl., 8–10.

Scharrer, E. (1959). General and phylogenetic interpretations of neuroendocrine interrelations. *In* "Comparative Endocrinology" (A. Gorbman, ed.), pp. 233–249. Wiley, New York.

Schiebler, T. H., and Hartmann, J. (1963). Experimentelle und histochemische Untersuchungen am neurosekretorischen System des Teleostierhypothalamus. *Anat. Anz.* **112**, Suppl., 84–92.

Schiebler, T. H., and von Brehm, H. (1958). Über jahreszyklische und altersbedingte Veränderungen in den neurosekretorischen Systemen von Teleostiern. *Naturwiss.* **45**, 450–451.

Schott, J. (1960). Études préliminaires du contrôle de l'activité gonadotrope par les centres hypothalamiques chez la grenouille mâle, *Rana temporaria* L. *Ann. Endocrinol.* (*Paris*) **21**, 203–216.

Schreiber, V. (1964). La régulation hypothalamique de l'hormone thyréotrope antéhypophysaire *Ann. Endocrinol.* (*Paris*) **25**, 385–400.

Schreibman, M. P., and Kallman, K. D. (1964). Functional pituitary grafts in fresh water teleosts. *Am. Zoologist* **4**, No. 176 (Abstract).

Stahl, A. (1953). La neurosécrétion chez les poissons téléostéens. Contribution à l'étude de la neurohypophyse chez les mugilidés. *Compt. Rend. Soc. Biol.* **147**, 841–844.

Stahl, A., and Leray, C. (1962). The relationship between diencephalic neurosecretion and the adenohypophysis in teleost fishes. *Mem. Soc. Endocrinol.* **12**, 149–164.

Sterba, G. (1955). Das Adrenal- und Interrenalsystem im Lebenslauf von *Petromyzon planeri* Bloch. *Zool. Anz.* **155**, 151–168.

Strahan, R. (1959). Pituitary hormones of *Myxine* and *Lampetra*. *Trans. 1st Asia and Oceania Reg. Congr. Endocrinol., 1959* No. 24. Kyoto, Japan.

Strahan, R. (1962). In Discussion. *Gen. Comp. Endocrinol.* Suppl. 1, 46.

Stutinsky, F., and Befort, J. J. (1964). Effets des stimulations électriques du diencéphale de *Rana esculenta* mâle. *Gen. Comp. Endocrinol.* **4**, 370–379.

Thomsen, E. (1954). Studies on the transport of neurosecretory material in *Calliphora erythrocephala* by means of ligaturing experiments. *J. Exptl. Biol.* **31**, 322–330.

Tuurala, O. (1959). Über den Einfluss von Natriumchlorid und Wasserbelastung auf das Blutbild des Frosches (*Rana temporaria* L.). *Ann. Acad. Sci. Fennicae, Ser. A,* **IV,** No. 46.

van Dongen, W. J., Jørgensen, C. B., Larsen, L. O., Lofts, B., van Oordt, P. G. W. J., and Rosenkilde, P. (1966). Function and cytology of the normal and autotransplanted pars distalis of the hypophysis in the toad *Bufo bufo* (L.). *Gen. Comp. Endocrinol.* **6,** 491–518.

Vivien, J. H. (1959). Contribution a l'étude des régulation hypothalamo-pituitaires chez *Rana temporaria* et *Triton cristatus.* Methode des autogreffes hypophysaires. *Proc. 15th Intern. Congr. Zool., London, 1958* pp. 561–564.

Voitkevich, A. A. (1961). The humoral effect of neurosecretion of preoptic nuclei on the metamorphosis of the larvae of Amphibia. *Dokl.–Biol. Sci. Sect.* (*Engl. Transl.*) **138,** 399–402.

Voitkevich, A. A. (1962). Neurosecretory control of the amphibian metamorphosis. *Gen. Comp. Endocrinol.* Suppl. 1, 133–147.

Voitkevich, A. A. (1963). On the relation of neurosecretion to growth and cell differentiation in the amphibian adenohypophysis. *Gen. Comp. Endocrinol.* **3,** 554–567.

Voitkevich, A. A. (1964). Changes in the thyrotrophic properties of the amphibian hypophysis in ontogenesis and after extirpation of the preoptic region of the diencephalon. *Dokl.–Biol. Sci. Sect.* (*Engl. Transl.*) **150,** 674–676.

Voitkevich, A. A., and Ovchinnikova, G. A. (1964). The nature of the regulatory influence exerted by the hypothalamus on the anterior lobe and pars intermedia of the hypophysis. *Bull. Exptl. Biol. Med.* (*USSR*) (*Engl. Transl.*) **55,** 207–210.

von Euler, U. S. (1963). Adrenergic neurohormones. *In* "Comparative Endocrinology" (U. S. von Euler and H. Heller, eds.), pp. 209–238. Academic Press, New York.

Walvig, F. (1963). The gonads and the formation of the sexual cells. *In* "The Biology of Myxine" (A. Brodal and R. Fänge, eds.), pp. 530–580. Universitetsforlaget, Oslo.

Waring, H. (1963). "Color Change Mechanisms of Cold-Blooded Vertebrates." Academic Press, New York.

Whitten, J. M. (1964). Connective tissue membranes and their apparent role in transporting neurosecretory and other secretory products in insects. *Gen. Comp. Endocrinol.* **4,** 176–192.

Wilson, L. D., Weinberg, J. A., and Bern, H. A. (1957). The hypothalamic neurosecretory system of the tree frog, *Hyla regilla.* *J. Comp. Neurol.* **107,** 253–268.

Wingstrand, K. G. (1959). Attempts at a comparison between the neurohypophysial region in fishes and tetrapods, with particular regard to amphibians. *In* "Comparative Endocrinology" (A. Gorbman, ed.), pp. 393–403. Wiley, New York.

Wingstrand, K. G. (1966). Comparative anatomy and evolution. *In* "The Pituitary Gland" (G. W. Harris and B. T. Donovan, eds.), Vol. 1, Chapter 3. Butterworth, London and Washington, D.C.

Young, J. Z. (1935). The photoreceptors of lampreys. II. The functions of the pineal complex. *J. Exptl. Biol.* **12,** 254–270.

Zaitsev, A. V. (1955). Voprosy neirosekretornoi deyatelnosti ganglioznykh kletok gipotalamicheskikh yader u shchuki i sazana u soyazi s sezonnym proyaoleniem gonadotropnoi funktsii gipofiza. [Neurosecretory activity of the ganglion cells of the subthalamic nuclei in the pike and carp in relation to the seasonal manifestation of the gonadotropic function of the hypophysis]. *Dokl. Akad. Nauk SSSR* **101,** 351–354. (English Abstract in *Biol. Abstr.* **31,** No. 7812.)

CHAPTER 30

Neuroendocrine Mechanisms in Birds

DONALD S. FARNER, FRED E. WILSON, and ANDREAS OKSCHE

I. Introduction

In general, much less is known about neuroendocrine mechanisms in birds than in mammals. Nevertheless, there is now sufficient information to indicate that the avian mechanisms conform, in principle, with the general vertebrate pattern of neuroendocrine mechanisms although there are some features that appear to be peculiarly avian.

In birds, as in higher vertebrates in general, the hypothalamic neuroendocrine mechanisms provide the means by which the central nervous system exerts continuous control over the endocrine system. Of particular importance is the infundibulum as the diencephalic structure that contains the final neural pathways that terminate in the two neurohemal

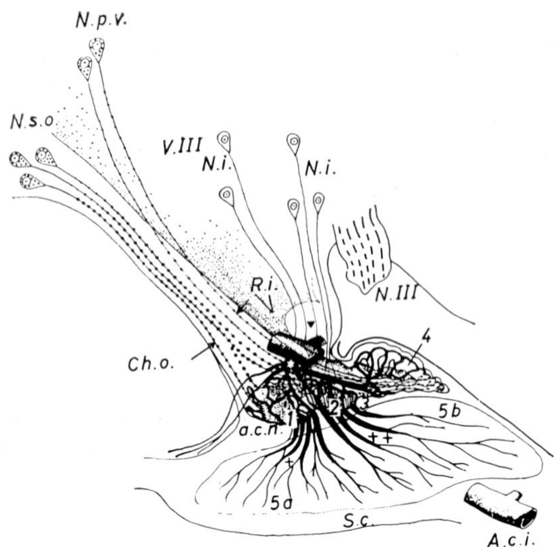

FIG. 1. Schematic parasagittal section through the infundibulum and the hypophysis of *Zonotrichia leucophrys gambelii.* Ch.o., optic chiasm; N. III, oculomotor nerve; V. III, third ventricle; R.i., infundibular recess; N.s.o., supraoptic nucleus; N.p.v., paraventricular nucleus; arrows, supraoptico-hypophyseal neurosecretory tract; N.i., infundibular nucleus; triangle (▼), tuberohypophyseal tract; 1, median eminence, anterior division; 2, median eminence, posterior division; 3, infundibular stem; 4, neural lobe; A.c.i., internal carotid artery; *, infundibular artery; a.c.n., anterior capillary network; +, portal vessels, anterior group; ++, portal vessels, posterior group; S.c., cavernous sinus; 5a, pars distalis, cephalic lobe; 5b, pars distalis, caudal lobe. (From Oksche, 1965; courtesy, Excerpta Medica Foundation.)

organs, the neural lobe and the median eminence (Figs. 1 and 2). Through the neural lobe are released the so-called posterior lobe hormones, oxytocin and arginine vasotocin; from the median eminence are released into the hypophyseal portal system the as yet unidentified neurohormones that control, to varying degrees, the secretory functions of the pars distalis of the anterior pituitary. The neurosecretory fibers of the external palisade layer of the median eminence constitute a major depot of Gomori-positive neurosecretory material, second quantitatively only to that of the neural lobe (Benoit and Assenmacher, 1953a,b, 1955; Oksche *et al.,* 1964a). Quantitatively, the median eminence is a more extensive neurosecretory storage organ in birds and reptiles than in mammals. Functionally, the neural lobe and median eminence appear to be mutually independent.

A characteristic feature of the avian hypothalamus is the occurrence of neurosecretory cells in diffuse clusters rather than in discrete nuclei (see below). Also characteristic of birds is the essentially superficial position of the primary capillaries of the hypophyseal portal system and the essentially external (to the median eminence) course of the "portal veins." These features of the vascular system and indeed the organization of the infundibulum, in general, offer attractive advantages to the experimentalist (Assenmacher, 1958). Further, the rather strict photoperiodic control of reproductive activity in certain temperate-zone species has made these birds attractive experimental subjects of investigations on the hypothalamic control of the gonadotropic functions of the pars distalis. (For reviews, see Benoit and Assenmacher, 1955; Assenmacher, 1958; Farner and Oksche, 1962; Farner, 1959, 1964a.)

The striking accumulations of neurosecretory material in the median eminence, correlations between the activity of the neurosecretory system and gonadal development, and the effects of sectioning the neurosecretory tract (see Assenmacher, 1958; Farner and Oksche, 1962) have caused most investigators to focus primary attention on the neurosecretory system in the control of the pars distalis. Much less attention has been directed to the infundibular nucleus and its fibers despite the fact that the latter are important components of the median eminence.

As in other classes of vertebrates, the medullary tissue of the adrenal and the fibers leading thereto constitute an important battery of neuroendocrine mechanisms. Since those in birds appear to be very similar to those in mammals, despite important structural differences, they will not be considered further (see Chapter 25).

Recent investigations on the domestic fowl (Axelrod *et al.*, 1964) raise the possibility that the pineal, by its production and release of melatonin, may be a component of some sort of neuroendocrine mechanism in birds.

II. General Features of the Avian Hypothalamo-Hypophyseal System

As noted above, this chapter is restricted to neuroendocrine mechanisms involving the hypothalamus and the anterior and posterior (neural) lobes of the pituitary gland. Two components, each involving a neurohemal organ, are to be recognized. (1) The neural-lobe component includes neurosecretory cells of the supraoptic and paraventricular nuclei, their axons that form the supraoptico-hypophyseal tract, and the neural lobe which is composed largely of neurosecretory terminals. Early ontogenic stages show that the neural lobe is a ventrocaudal extension of the diencephalon (Scharrer and Scharrer, 1954a,b; Bargmann, 1954; Diepen, 1962). (2) The eminential component includes neurosecretory cells of the supraoptic and paraventricular nuclei and their axons and collaterals that leave the supraoptico-hypophyseal tract to pass into the reticular and/or palisade layers of the median eminence; in addition, it includes the non-neurosecretory (i.e., Gomori-negative) cells of the infundibular nucleus and their axons which pass via the tuberohypophyseal tract to terminate in the median eminence. Both Gomori-positive and Gomori-negative fibers of the palisade layer of the median eminence are in juxtaposition with the capillaries of the hypophyseal portal system (Figs. 1 and 2).

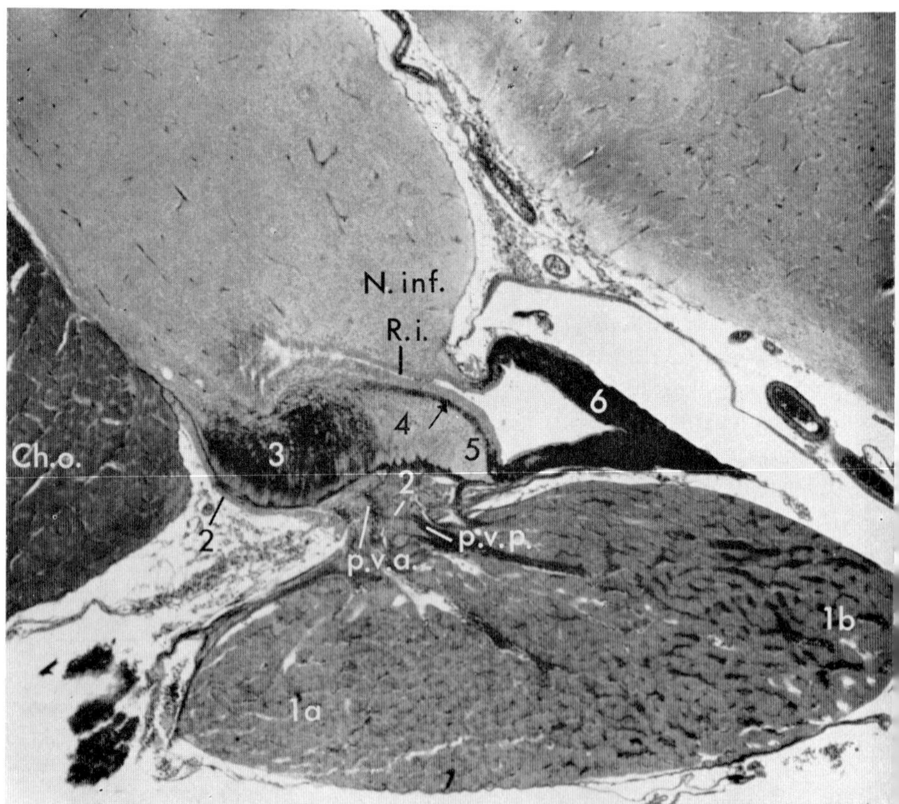

FIG. 2. Aldehyde-fuchsin preparation of a parasagittal section through the infundibulum and hypophysis of *Zonotrichia leucophrys gambelii.* Ch.o., optic chiasm; R.i., infundibular recess; arrow, supraoptico-hypophyseal neurosecretory tract; N.inf., infundibular nucleus; p.v.a., portal vessel, anterior group; p.v.p., portal vessel, posterior group; 1a, pars distalis, cephalic lobe; 1b, pars distalis, caudal lobe; 2, pars tuberalis; 3, median eminence, anterior division; 4, median eminence, posterior division; 5, infundibular stem; 6, neural lobe. Bouin. × 100. (From Farner, 1964a, courtesy of *American Scientist.*)

From a comparative aspect there are two adenoneurohypophyseal contact zones (Spatz, 1954, 1958; Diepen, 1962): (1) a proximal contact zone in the region of the infundibulum covered by the pars tuberalis; and (2) a distal contact zone in the intrasellar hypophysis which is obviously absent in birds (Wingstrand, 1951). Indeed, there are many species in which the pars distalis and the neural lobe are separated by a bony lamella; in all cases they are separated at least by dense connective tissue. It appears certain that in birds there is no direct vascular connection between the neural lobe and the pars distalis (Wingstrand, 1951; Assenmacher, 1952; Vitums *et al.*, 1964).

The proximal contact zone is well developed in birds; it is the eminential neurohemal organ. The neurohypophyseal element is represented by the ventral wall of the median eminence; the vascular element, by the primary portal capillaries. The report of Okamoto and Ihara (1960) that neurosecretory fibers penetrate the pars distalis in the domestic fowl requires confirmation, bearing in mind the occurrence of bundles of fine connective tissue fibers that may be stained by aldehyde fuchsin. Metuzals (1955, 1956) has reported that, in the mallard, there are hypothalamic nerve fibers in significant numbers that follow the strands of cells of the pars tuberalis and finally enter the pars distalis. This report also has not yet been confirmed. On the basis of exhaustive studies on many species of birds, Wingstrand (1951) could only reach the conclusion that those few nerve fibers that can be demonstrated are autonomic fibers associated with blood vessels and that they, therefore, are not involved in the control of the secretory activity of the cells of the pars distalis. Also, Stutinsky (1958) was only able to demonstrate some fibers from the infundibular wall that penetrate a short distance into the pars tuberalis. In summary, then, the available anatomical evidence indicates that there is no direct nervous control of the pars distalis by the hypothalamus. Of special significance in the function of the eminential component, then, are the vascular connections. The primary capillaries of the hypophyseal portal system, supplied by a special branch of the internal carotid artery, lie between the surface of the infundibulum (primarily the median eminence) and the cells of the pars tuberalis. Blood from these capillaries drains into large-caliber endothelial tubes, the "portal veins," from which it then passes into the sinus capillaries of the pars distalis. Detailed descriptions of the portal systems for a number of species are given by Green (1951), Wingstrand (1951), Assenmacher (1951, 1952), and Vitums *et al.* (1964). (See also Section III,B and Chapter 2, Volume I.)

With silver techniques the median eminence shows an abundance of neurovascular contacts. Glial processes are also involved in these contacts (Oksche *et al.*, 1959, 1963; Kobayashi *et al.*, 1961; Bern and Nishioka, 1965). The nerve fibers, as noted above, are derived from the supraoptico-hypophyseal tract and from the tuberohypophyseal tract which arises from the infundibular and ventromedial nuclei of the posterior hypothalamus (Spatz, 1954, 1958). Wingstrand (1951) placed emphasis on the endings of the tuberohypophyseal system in the zona externa and was of the impression that the neurosecretory elements were confined to the zona interna. On the other hand, Benoit and Assenmacher (1953a) demonstrated in the domestic mallard a dense palisade arrangement of neurosecretory endings in juxtaposition with primary portal capillaries and placed little emphasis on the tuberoinfundibular system. We (Oksche, 1960, 1962, 1965; Farner and Oksche, 1962) have emphasized that, in the zona externa of the avian infundibulum, these two fiber systems occur in such close association that, at the finest structural level, they cannot be separated with the light microscope. The high density of pericapillary hypothalamic nerve endings, primarily an intermingling of the two fiber systems, is characteristic of the structure of the median eminence of birds. It is also clear that fibers from the supraoptic nucleus and paraventricular nucleus pass into the median eminence and not only into the neural lobe as assumed by Spatz (1954) on the basis of studies on mammals.

III. The Morphology of the Avian Hypothalamo-Hypophyseal System

A. The Hypothalamic Elements

There have been only a few extensive studies of the avian hypothalamus. The older literature has been reviewed very adequately by Ariëns Kappers *et al.* (1936). Recently, the hypothalamus of the domestic fowl has been described in precise stereotaxic coordinates by van Tienhoven and Juhász (1962). The classical comparative treatise of the avian hypothalamo-hypophyseal system is that of Wingstrand (1951) whose investigations include sixty-nine species of thirty-four families.

According to Spatz (1954, 1958) and Diepen (1962), the vertebrate hypothalamus can be divided into rostral and caudal divisions (Figs. 1 and 2). The former contains the magnocellular nuclear regions, including the supraoptic nucleus and the paraventricular nucleus; the latter, the parvocellular tuberal nuclei among which are included the infundibular nucleus and the ventromedial nucleus. Because of the development of selective staining of neurosecretory material (Bargmann, 1949), the magnocellular nuclear regions of the avian hypothalamus have been studied extensively, whereas comparatively little attention has been given to the tuberal nuclei.

1. *The Hypothalamic Nuclei*

a. The "Gomori-Positive" Magnocellular Nuclei. The pioneer studies of Huber and Crosby (1929) recognized distinctive clusters of large ganglionic cells in the anterior hypothalamus. These observations were confirmed by Kurotsu (1935); Kuhlenbeck (1936) identified these groups of cells as the paraventricular and supraoptic nuclei. Unlike the situation in fish, amphibians, and mammals, neurosecretion was not demonstrated in these cells until the introduction of chrom-alum-hematoxylin staining (Bargmann *et al.*, 1950). At about the same time, Wingstrand (1951) demonstrated neurosecretory material in the paraventricular and supraoptic nuclei of the pigeon. Since then, the hypothalamic neurosecretory system has been investigated in a considerable number of species (Bargmann and Jacob, 1952; Stolze, 1952; Wingstrand, 1951, 1954; Benoit and

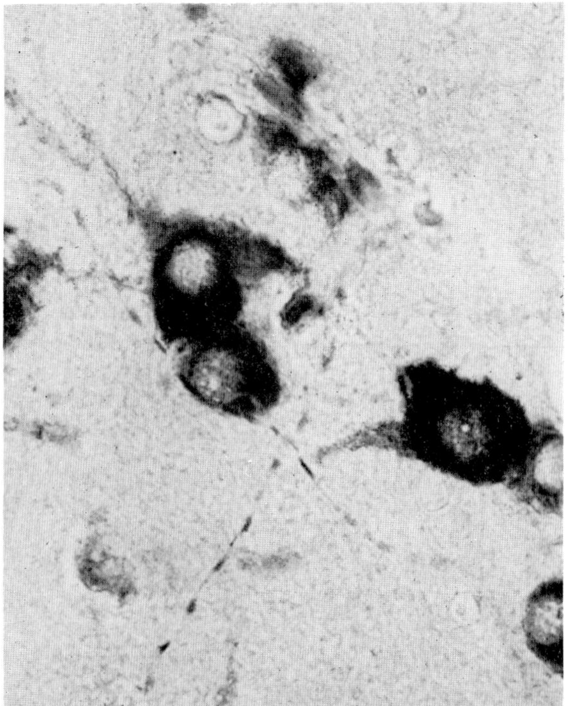

FIG. 3. Neurosecretory cells in the paraventricular nucleus of *Coturnix coturnix*. Note dense accumulation of aldehyde-fuchsin-positive material in the perikarya and axons beaded with aldehyde-fuchsin-positive granules. Bouin. Aldehyde-fuchsin stain. × 1250. (From Oksche *et al.*, 1964b, courtesy of Springer-Verlag.)

Assenmacher, 1953a,b; Barry, 1954; Yasuda, 1954; Mosier, 1955; Stutinsky, 1955, 1958; Fujita, 1956a,b; Oksche *et al.*, 1959, 1963, 1964b; Laws, 1961; Kobayashi *et al.*, 1961; Arai, 1963; Arai *et al.*, 1963; Wolfson and Kobayashi, 1962; Wolfson, 1963; Legait, 1959). An extensive series of investigations on domestic races of the mallard by Benoit and his colleagues (Benoit and Assenmacher, 1953a, 1955; Assenmacher, 1958) constitute the pioneer investigations on the role of the hypothalamic neurosecretory system in the control of the gonadotropic function of the pars distalis. The system has also been studied extensively in the domestic fowl by Legait (1959), Mikami (1960), and Graber and Nalbandov (1965). Among wild species, the system has been studied most extensively in the white-crowned sparrow, *Zonotrichia leucophrys gambelii* (Oksche *et al.*, 1959; Farner and Oksche, 1962; Laws, 1961; Oksche, 1962, 1965); the zebra finch, *Taeniopygia castanotis* (Oksche *et al.*, 1963); and the white-eye, *Zosterops palpebrosa japonica* (Arai, 1963; Arai *et al.*, 1963; Hirano *et al.*, 1962; Uemura and Kobayashi, 1963).

Compared with those of other vertebrates, the neurosecretory cells of the avian hypothalamus are diffusely distributed (Figs. 4 and 5). Both the supraoptic and the paraventricular nuclei consist of richly vascularized (Vitums *et al.*, 1964) clusters of neurosecretory cells (Fig. 4) that are interconnected by more isolated cells. This characteristically loose

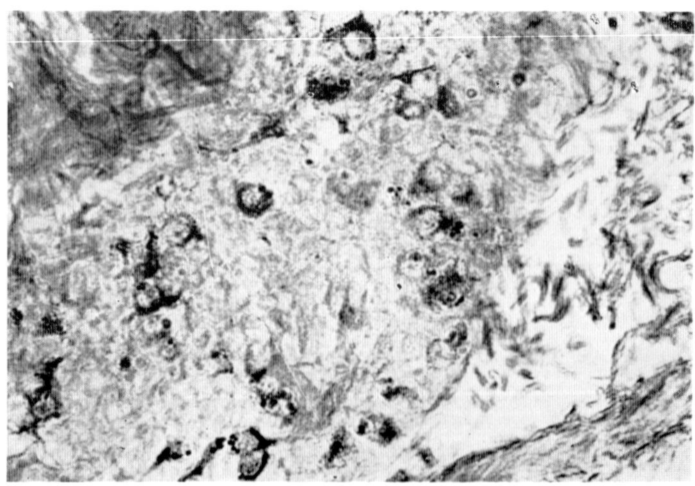

FIG. 4. Neurosecretory cells in the supraoptic nucleus (median division) of a male *Zonotrichia leucophrys gambelii*. October. Note globular form of neurosecretory material in the perikarya; also, the diffuse distribution of ganglionic cells. Bouin. Aldehyde-fuchsin. × 500.

arrangement of the neurosecretory nuclei has resulted in difficulties in nomenclature since it has been necessary, in the absence of information on homologies, to resort almost exclusively to topographical designations of clusters of cells and divisions of nuclear areas. The major morphological problem, however, is the lack of information on the terminal dispositions of fibers from the various clusters of neurosecretory cells. Asso-

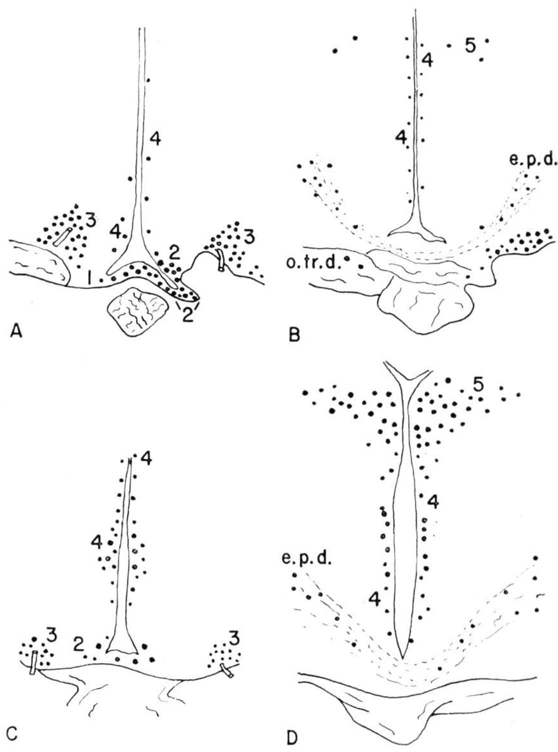

FIG. 5. Schematic illustration of the diffuse organization of the neurosecretory nuclei in birds; the neurosecretory cells are represented by black dots. Only a part of the hypothalamus that lies along the third ventricle is shown. The predominant nuclear divisions are emphasized. A and C are more rostral than B and D. A, B: *Zonotrichia leucophrys gambelii;* C, D: *Coturnix coturnix japonica.* Note the quantitative differences in the distribution of the neurosecretory elements in the two species. Supraoptic nucleus: 1, preoptic division; 2, median division; 3, lateral division. Paraventricular nucleus: 4, periventricular division; 5, dorsolateral division. Neurosecretory cells are also found in the entopeduncular tract (e.p.d.) and the optic tract (o.tr.d.); their origin and the divisions to which they belong are uncertain. (Based on Oksche *et al.*, 1959, 1964b.)

ciated therewith are the questions concerning functional specificity of individual clusters or groups of cells.

Worthy of note here are those neurosecretory cells that are scattered through the entopeduncular tract (Arai, 1963; Arai *et al.*, 1963; Uemura and Kobayashi, 1963); Laws (1961) has described conspicuous changes in these cells at the beginning of the photorefractory period in *Zonotrichia leucophrys gambelii.* Also of interest is the group of neurosecretory cells that is scattered through the optic tract (Fig. 5) of several species (Oksche *et al.*, 1963).

Relatively little attention has been given to the comparative morphology of the neurosecretory nuclei of birds. Our own investigations (Oksche *et al.*, 1959, 1963, 1964b; Farner and Oksche, 1962; also unpublished observations) indicate that the paraventricular nucleus (Figs. 3 and 5) in galliform species is much more extensively developed and has greater neurosecretory activity than in passerine species such as *Zonotrichia leucophrys gambelii* and *Taeniopygia castanotis.*

b. The Gomori-Negative Parvocellular Nuclei. The infundibular nucleus of *Zonotrichia leucophrys gambelii* (Figs. 1, 2, and 6) is extensive; our limited observations on a few other species suggest that this may be generally true in birds, a suggestion that appears to be consistent with the limited discussion of Wingstrand (1951). As a source of fibers of the tuberohypophyseal tract, this nucleus is of special significance (Fig. 6). Dorsally it becomes practically continuous with a large nuclear formation, probably homologous with the ventromedial nucleus of mammals, which also probably contributes fibers to the tuberohypophyseal tract. The neuroendocrine function of these nuclei in birds is still unknown, although it does appear certain that, at least in some species, the infundibular nucleus is functionally involved in the control of the gonadotropic function of the pars distalis (see Section IV,B).

Although there are both mammillary and suprachiasmatic nuclei in the avian hypothalamus, neither their functions nor their relationships to other parts of the hypothalamus are known. Since they appear not to send fibers to either of the neurohemal organs, and since they are not known to communicate synaptically with the supraoptic, paraventricular, or infundibular nuclei, they are not considered further here. (For a general discussion of these nuclei in higher vertebrates, see Diepen, 1962.)

A nucleus corresponding to the Gomori-negative, phloxinophilic lateral tuberal nucleus of teleost fishes (see Diepen, 1962) is absent in birds. Also, the neurosecretory dorsolateral tuberal nuclei, described in some species of mammals by Barry (1961), appear not to have a homolog in birds.

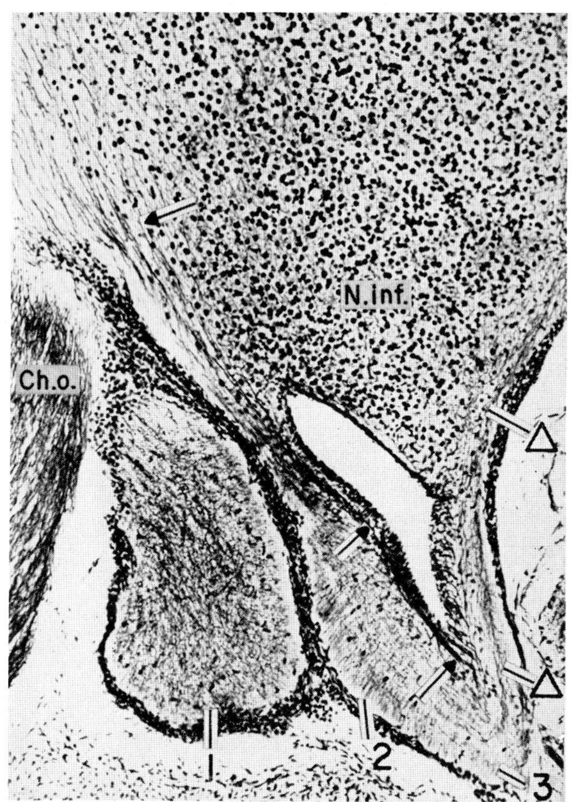

FIG. 6. Nervous structure of the (1) anterior and (2) posterior divisions of the median eminence of *Zonotrichia leucophrys gambelii.* Lateral sagittal section. The lateral protuberance of the anterior division is sectioned tangentially; its connection with the remainder of the infundibulum is thus obscured. 3, infundibular stem; Ch.o., optic chiasm; N.inf., infundibular nucleus; arrows, supraoptico-hypophyseal neurosecretory tract; triangles, tuberohypophyseal tract. Bodian silver. × 130.

2. *The Fiber Tracts*

Four efferent hypothalamic tracts have been recognized in birds by Wingstrand (1951): (1) A supraoptico-hypophyseal tract, now known to be generally Gomori-positive, (2) an anterior hypophyseal tract, (3) a tuberohypophyseal tract, and (4) a posterior hypophyseal tract. There is general agreement that the supraoptico-hypophyseal tract is formed by neurosecretory axons from the supraoptic and paraventricular nuclei. Its fibers pass, in part, into the neural lobe and, in part, into the median eminence (Figs. 1 and 2), especially into its anterior division. These latter fibers, at least in *Zonotrichia leucophrys gambelii,* may pass into the palisade layer, especially in the rostral part of the anterior division; more frequently they penetrate into the reticular layer, the organization and function of which is still not understood. The tuberohypophyseal tract is formed by fibers from the infundibular nucleus (Wingstrand, 1951; Oksche, 1962) and also possibly from the ventromedial nucleus. Since the infundibular nucleus extends quite far dorsally and cannot be separated definitely from the ventromedial nucleus, one must not exclude the possibility that the Gomori-negative posterior hypophyseal tract of Wingstrand is, in reality, a caudal bundle of the tuberohypophyseal tract. It is possible also that the anterior hypophyseal tract should be considered as a bundle in the supraoptico-hypophyseal tract, being derived from the most rostral, in part preoptic, neurosecretory cells.

3. *The Neurohemal Organs*

a. The Neural Lobe. The neural lobe is the enlarged and proliferated terminal portion of the infundibulum (Fig. 2). In form it varies extensively from species to species (Wingstrand, 1951; Farner and Oksche, 1962) as well as among individuals within a species. Morphologically it ranges from a simple thin-walled sac, through a diverticulated complex, to a compact form with the lumen very much reduced (Fig. 7). The electron-microscope studies of Duncan (1956) on the domestic fowl in-

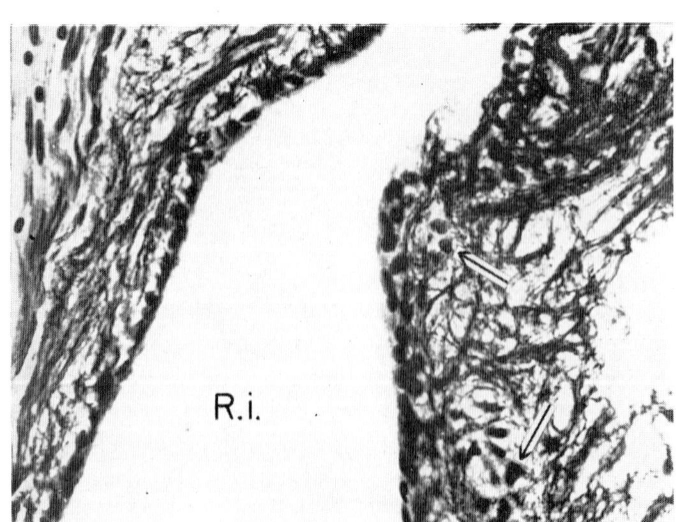

FIG. 7. Nervous structure of the neural lobe of *Zonotrichia leucophrys gambelii.* Arrows, pituicyte; R.i., infundibular recess. Bodian silver. × 350.

dicate that the mass of the tissue consists of endings of fibers from the neurosecretory supraoptico-hypophyseal tract. These endings contain elementary granules with diameters of 1000–2000 Å, and are surrounded by processes of glial pituicytes. In general, the diameters of the electron-dense elementary neurosecretory granules of the avian neural lobe (Fig. 8) appear to lie within this range (Kobayashi *et al.*, 1961; Oota and

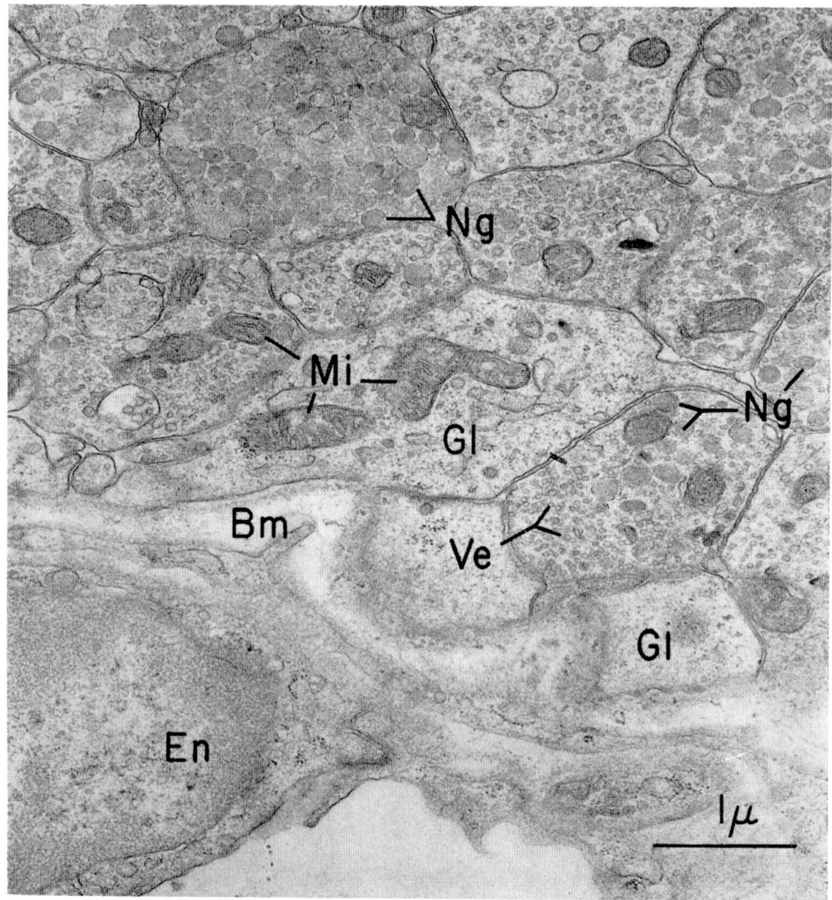

FIG. 8. Electron-microscope preparation of the neural lobe of an adult male *Zonotrichia leucophrys gambelii*. Axons bordering on capillary contain many neurosecretory granules (Ng) and small vesicles (Ve). A layer of glial processes (Gl) is usually interposed between the axons and the basement membrane region (Bm). En, endothelial cell nucleus; Mi, mitochondria. Dichromate-buffered osmium-fixed; Maraglas-embedded; stained with lead and uranium salts. (H. A. Bern, L. R. Mewaldt, R. S. Nishioka, and D. S. Farner, unpublished data.)

Kobayashi, 1962; Nishioka *et al.*, 1964; Bern and Nishioka, 1965; Kobayashi *et al.*, 1965). The processes of the pituicytes in those species that have been studied (see also Nishioka *et al.*, 1963, 1964) suggest that it is very possible that they may be involved somehow in the transfer of neurohormones from the neurosecretory axon to the capillaries.

The lumen of the neural lobe is lined with ependymal cells. The electron microscope studies of Nishioka *et al.* (1963, 1964) on *Zonotrichia leucophrys gambelii* show very fine diverticula of the infundibular recess that are lined with epithelial-like cells; these cells are, in reality, a modified form of ependymal cell. The existence of these diverticula raises the possibility of release of neurohormone into the cerebrospinal fluid. The secretory activity of ependymal cells suggested by Payne (1959), on the basis of light microscopy, remains to be confirmed by studies with the electron microscope.

Blood is supplied to the neural lobe via a branch of the infundibular artery (Fig. 1); this blood does not drain into the hypophyseal portal system (Wingstrand, 1951; Vitums *et al.*, 1964).

b. The Median Eminence. Immediately caudal to the optic chiasm, the ventral wall of the infundibulum enlarges to form the median eminence (Fig. 2). Rostrally, the median eminence has pronounced protuberances that diminish caudally, finally disappearing at the level of the bundle of hypophyseal portal vessels; beyond this it is possible to differentiate an infundibular stem (Wingstrand, 1951). This is, of course, an arbitrary separation since there is a gradual transition in structure between the median eminence and the infundibular stem.

Basically, the organization of the avian median eminence conforms to the general pattern characteristic of the classes of terrestrial vertebrates. The following layers can therefore be recognized (Fig. 9): (1) the zona interna with (a) an ependymal layer and (b) a fiber layer; and (2) the zona externa with (a) a reticular layer [the superficial eminential plexus of Wingstrand (1951)], and (b) a palisade layer [the stratum glandulare of Wingstrand (1951); the "couches des anses" of Benoit and Assenmacher (1955)]. The palisade-like appearance of the outermost layer is due to the radially arranged ependymal processes and nerve fibers. On the basal surface of the palisade layer lies the primary capillary network of the hypophyseal portal system. Most of the external surface of the median eminence, and also the primary capillary network, is covered by the pars tuberalis of the anterior pituitary.

Even under low magnification, it is possible to differentiate distinct anterior and posterior divisions of the median eminence (Fig. 2). Investigations with classical histological techniques, with *in toto* staining (Oksche *et al.*, 1964a), and with electron microscopy (Bern and Nishioka,

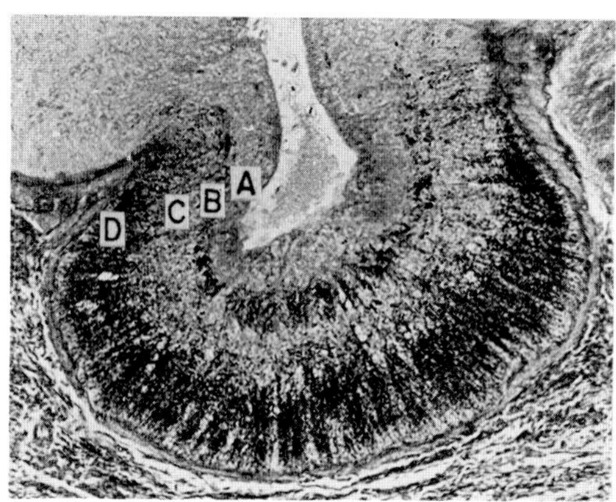

FIG. 9. Aldehyde-fuchsin preparation of a transverse section through the anterior division of the median eminence of a male *Zonotrichia leucophrys gambelii* sacrificed in October. A, ependymal layer; B, fiber layer; C, reticular layer; D, palisade layer (A and B, zona interna; C and D, zona externa). Bouin. × 170.

1965; Bern *et al.*, 1966; Nishioka *et al.*, 1964; Oota and Kobayashi, 1962; Kobayashi *et al.*, 1961) make it abundantly clear that there are very great interspecific differences in the fine structure of the avian median eminence.

The median eminence differs markedly from the neural lobe in fine structure. The median eminence, unlike the neural lobe, contains tuberoinfundibular (Gomori-negative) as well as neurosecretory (Gomori-positive) fibers. By means of a combination of silver impregnation and subsequent aldehyde-fuchsin staining (Oksche, 1962), it has been possible to differentiate the two fiber systems to a considerable extent. In *Zonotrichia leucophrys gambelii, Coturnix coturnix japonica, Melopsittacus undulatus,* and *Taeniopygia castanotis,* distinct bundles of neurosecretory axons, or their collaterals, pass into the median eminence. From the rostral to the caudal end of the median eminence there is a gradual decrease in the ratio of neurosecretory to Gomori-negative, tuberoinfundibular components (Oksche *et al.*, 1959, 1963, 1964b; Oksche, 1965; Kobayashi *et al.*, 1961; Oota and Kobayashi, 1962). The two types of fibers may be inseparably intertwined in the reticular layer in which the fine structure of the two systems and their interrelationships is still unknown. As noted above, nerve fibers throughout the palisade layer are interspersed by glial elements which frequently extend peripherally to the primary capillaries of the portal system (Wingstrand, 1951; Oksche *et al.*, 1959; Kobayashi *et al.*, 1961; Oksche, 1962). These relationships are particularly striking in electron-microscope preparations (Fig. 10).

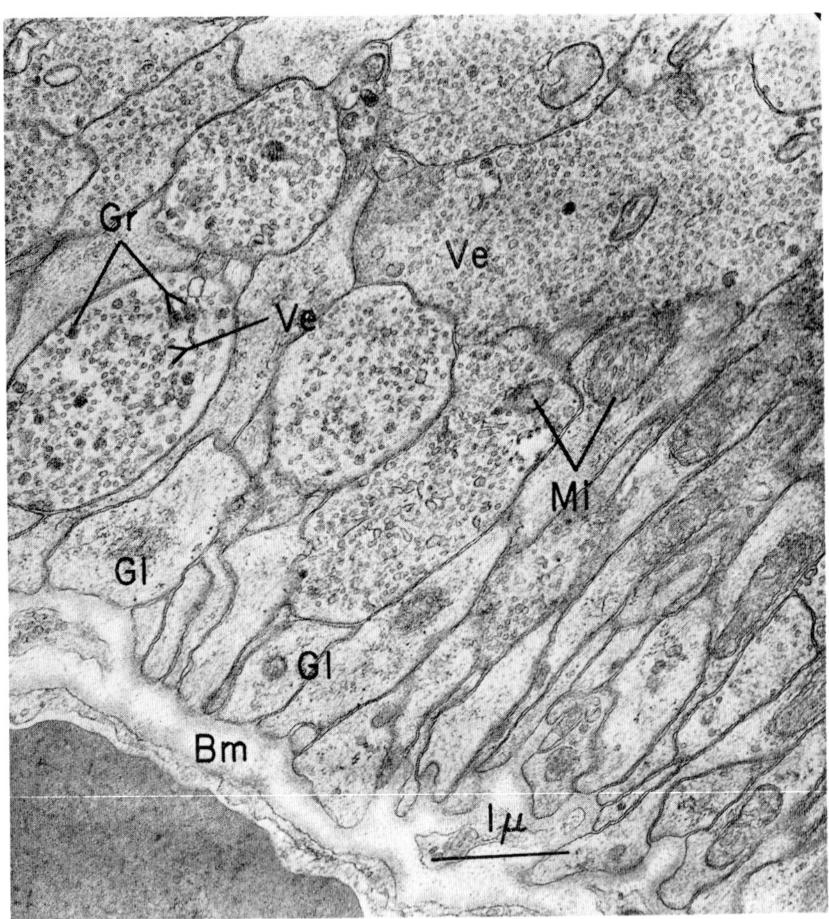

FIG. 10. Electron-microscope preparation of a ventral area of the posterior division of the median eminence of a refractory male *Zonotrichia leucophrys gambelii*. Axons contain many small vesicles (Ve) in addition to a few small dense granules (Gr). A layer of glial processes (Gl) is interposed between the axons and the basement membrane region (Bm) of the portal capillary. Note erythrocyte at lower left. Vesicles intermediate in size and density between granules and small vesicles are evident. Mi, mitochondria. Dichromate-buffered osmium-fixed; Maraglas-embedded; stained with lead and uranium salts. (H. A. Bern, L. R. Mewaldt, R. S. Nishioka and D. S. Farner, unpublished data.)

Some attention has been given to the ultrastructure of the outer palisade layer and the associated primary portal capillaries. On the basis of investigations on four passerine species (*Passer domesticus, Agelaius tricolor, Zonotrichia leucophrys gambelii,* and *Zonotrichia atricapilla*) and on earlier investigations on *Melopsittacus undulatus* (Kobayashi *et al.*,

1961; Oota and Kobayashi, 1962), Bern and Nishioka (1965) recognize three types of granules and vesicles in the avian median eminence: (1) typical elementary neurosecretory granules, about 1700 Å in diameter (average), and less electron-dense vesicles presumably derived therefrom; (2) smaller, electron-dense granules, measuring approximately 1000 Å in diameter, "conceivably adrenergic in type"; and (3) small vesicles forming the major constituent of the terminals of the axons, resembling "cholinergic" synaptic vesicles (Fig. 10). In the passerine species studied, all of these types of vesicles could be observed in single endings. Bodies of intermediate sizes were found with sufficient frequency to suggest the possibility of transformation among the types. Very substantial interspecific differences were observed in ultrastructure among these species. In all species studied thus far, it has been found that a glial layer is generally interposed between the terminals of the axons and the pericapillary basement membrane (Fig. 10).

A very important question is that of possible functional synaptic contacts between neurosecretory and Gomori-negative fibers either in the reticular layer or in the peripheral part of the palisade layer. The possibility of this type of functional relationship has been raised several times (Barry and Cotte, 1961; Kobayashi *et al.*, 1961; Oota and Kobayashi, 1962, 1963a,b; Bern, 1962; Farner, 1962b, 1964a). However, further investigations including observations with the electron-microscope as well as biochemical and pharmacological investigations are necessary in order to explore adequately the probable existence of such functions.

From observations with the light microscope, it is obvious that the anterior and posterior divisions of the median eminence, and also the infundibular stem, have a characteristic neural organization. In *Zonotrichia leucophrys gambelii*, the role of the median eminence is emphasized by the distinctive portal system by which blood from the anterior median eminence passes to the cephalic lobe of the pars distalis and blood from the posterior median eminence passes primarily to the caudal lobe (Vitums *et al.*, 1964). It seems likely that a similar arrangement exists in other species of birds. Details concerning this arrangement and its probable importance in hypothalamic control of the pars distalis are presented with the description of the pars distalis (see Section III,B). The microanatomy of the median eminence certainly suggests that it must be more complex functionally as a neurohemal organ than is the neural lobe.

B. The Adenohypophyseal Elements

In its gross aspects the adenohypophysis is relatively uniform among the orders of birds. Its general anatomy and ontogeny have been described very capably in the excellent monograph of Wingstrand (1951). As in the other classes of vertebrates, the adenohypophysis of birds is derived ontogenetically from Rathke's pouch; however, the avian adenohypophysis is peculiar in that it completely lacks a pars intermedia. The gland consists largely of a bilobed pars distalis that lies in a bony case surrounded almost completely by cavernous and intercavernous sinuses (Wingstrand, 1951; Assenmacher, 1952; Vitums *et al.*, 1964). The cephalic and caudal lobes are clearly distinguishable macroscopically in many species (Fig. 2). The second component of the adenohypophysis is the pars tuberalis, which, according to Wingstrand (1951), consists of three parts: (1) the pars tuberalis proper, a thin sheet of cells contiguous with the lateral and basal surfaces of the median eminence and the infundibular stem; (2) the portal zone connecting the pars tuberalis proper with the pars distalis and through which pass the hypophyseal portal vessels; and (3) the paired pars tuberalis interna which is continuous with the portal zone and is fused with the pars distalis. Our observations on *Zonotrichia leucophrys gambelii* (Fig. 2), *Coturnix coturnix japonica*, and *Taeniopygia castanotis*, as well as those of Assenmacher (1952, 1958) on the domestic mallard, are consistent with this description. The function of the pars tuberalis in birds is unknown.

It has been well established in studies on more than one hundred avian species in a wide variety of families (Rahn and Painter, 1941; Wingstrand, 1951, 1963; Mikami, 1958, 1960; Tixier-Vidal *et al.*, 1962; Tixier-Vidal, 1963) that there is a conspicuous differentiation of cell types between the caudal and cephalic lobes of the pars distalis, although there are still many uncertainties concerning the functions of the individual types of cells. Primarily on the basis of investigations on the tinctorial properties of cells in the domestic mallard, Tixier-Vidal (1963) has recognized seven types of adenohypophyseal cells, and on the basis of experiments and seasonal observations has with confidence assigned functions to five of them (Table I, see also Tixier-Vidal and Assenmacher, 1963). She has concluded that the same cells occur in the pars distalis of the house sparrow (*Passer domesticus*), the domestic guinea fowl, the weaver finch (*Euplectes pyromelana*), the pigeon, and the turtle dove (*Streptopelia turtur*).

Mikami (1958) has conducted similar investigations on the domestic fowl and has reached generally similar but not identical conclusions. After castration, the adenohypophysis hypertrophies as the result of an increase in both the number and size of basophiles ("castration" cells) in both the cephalic and caudal lobes. All basophiles in the caudal lobe differentiate into castration cells, but the basophiles of the cephalic lobe appear to be of two functional types; some become castration cells after

TABLE I

TYPES OF CELLS IN THE PARS DISTALIS OF THE MALLARD ACCORDING TO TIXIER-VIDAL[a]

Type	Lobe	Secretion
Alpha	Caudal	Growth hormone
Gamma	Caudal	LH
Delta	Caudal and cephalic	TSH
Beta	Cephalic	FSH
Eta	Cephalic	Prolactin
Epsilon	Cephalic	ACTH
Kappa	Cephalic	? MSH

[a] For tinctorial properties, observations on annual cycles, and responses to experimental manipulations, see Tixier-Vidal (1963).

gonadectomy whereas others become thyroidectomy cells after thyroidectomy. Both types of cells are observed in the hypertrophic cephalic lobe of castrated, thyroidectomized fowl. Differing with Tixier-Vidal (1963), Mikami (1958) has assigned a thyrotropin (TSH)-producing role to the type of basophile that is found only in the cephalic lobe. Since no substantial differences were observed between the cephalic and the caudal lobes with respect to gonadal function, he concluded that follicle-stimulating hormone (FSH)-producing basophiles were distributed throughout the entire gland. In agreement with the scheme of Tixier-Vidal (1963), "adrenalectomy" cells were observed only in the cephalic lobe.

From the aspect of neuroendocrine mechanisms, the differentiation of cells in the cephalic and caudal lobes, even though the functions of the individual types of cells may not yet be completely understood, is extremely important in light of the vascularization of the gland. Assenmacher (1952, 1953, 1958) has demonstrated that the adenohypophysis of the duck sometimes receives some blood from a hypophyseal artery, but in the vast majority of birds, blood reaches this gland only via the hypophyseal portal system (Wingstrand, 1951; Vitums *et al.*, 1964). A recent investigation of the vascularization of the pars distalis of *Zonotrichia leucophrys gambelii* (Figs. 1 and 2) shows clearly that the sinusoid system of the cephalic lobe receives blood solely from portal vessels that drain the primary capillary bed of the anterior median eminence, whereas the caudal lobe receives blood from the posterior median eminence (Vitums *et al.*, 1964).

It should be emphasized that there are no important interconnections between these vascular systems (Fig. 1) either at the level of the primary capillary beds or at the level of the sinusoid systems in the adenohypophysis. Therefore, in this species at least, there is the anatomic basis for individual neuroendocrine controls by the anterior and posterior divisions of the median eminence over the cephalic and caudal lobes of the pars distalis. Obviously, studies on other species are necessary in order to ascertain how general this pattern is among birds. The investigations of Assenmacher (1951, 1952, 1953) suggest that the same may be true in the domestic mallard. Physiological investigations of the significance of this division of portal function have not been reported, but it seems possible that the cells of the cephalic lobe are controlled primarily by neurohormones from the supraoptic and paraventricular nuclei, whereas those of the caudal lobe are controlled primarily by neurohormones from the infundibular nuclei.

IV. Functional Aspects

Knowledge of the mechanisms involved in hypothalamic control of the anterior pituitary in birds is fragmentary and as yet restricted to a small number of species. As noted above, primary emphasis has been placed on the aldehyde-fuchsin-positive neurosecretory system whereas little attention has been given to the Gomori-negative elements that may also be involved in the control of adenohypophyseal function.

A. Regulation of the Gonadotropic Activity of the Adenohypophysis

1. *Investigations on Ducks*

Much of our knowledge of hypothalamic control of the gonadotropic function of the adenohypophysis is based on the investigations of Benoit and his colleagues on the drakes of domestic varieties of the mallard (*Anas platyrhynchos*), in which the testicular cycle is photoperiodically controlled. (For summaries see Benoit and Assenmacher, 1953a,b, 1955, 1959; Benoit, 1957, 1961, 1962; Assenmacher and Benoit, 1958; Assenmacher, 1958, 1963.) Five types of experiments have been performed.

a. Transplantation of the Pars Distalis. (Assenmacher, 1958; Benoit and Assenmacher, 1959; Benoit, 1961.) Whereas hypophysectomized, ungrafted controls died about a month after operation, adult males with viable auto- or homografts of the pars distalis in the anterior chamber of the eye, the frontal lobes of the brain, or the cervical muscles were generally in good health up to the time of autopsy. The testes of the experimental animals were always atrophic, even after a prior period of photostimulation. Although the grafted pituitaries were well vascularized, the cells were small and degranulated and appeared to have undergone dedifferentiation. No basophiles were observed in the transplanted pituitaries. It appears, therefore, that in the absence of the normal portal blood supply the pars distalis of the drake is incapable of initiating or maintaining testicular activity. Because there is apparently no direct nervous connection between the hypothalamus and the pars distalis, it must be concluded that the control normally exerted by the hypothalamus via the hypophyseal portal system could not be exerted via the systemic circulation in the animals with transplanted adenohypophyses.

b. Tractotomy (Section of the Hypophyseal Portal Vessels). The hypophyseal portal system has been described above in conjunction with the anatomy of the anterior pituitary (Section III,B). The palisade layer of the anterior median eminence was especially rich in Gomori-positive neurosecretory material in tractotomized, photostimulated drakes sacrificed 6 months after tractotomy. The neural lobe was intact and normal in appearance. In all cases, the cephalic lobe of the pars distalis contained a central atrophic zone and generally was hypotrophic. In most cases, there was an indication of hypotrophy of the caudal lobe, but generally of much lesser extent than in the cephalic lobe. The testes were small with a virtual cessation of spermatogenic activity, inactive interstitial cells, and involuted epididymal canals. Ischemia and the resultant atrophy of the cephalic lobe were thought not to be responsible for the cessation of gonadotropic activity (Benoit and Assenmacher, 1953a, 1959; Assenmacher and Benoit, 1956; Assenmacher, 1958; Benoit, 1961). Therefore, the absence of any vascular connection between the aldehyde-fuchsin-positive zone of the median eminence and the pars distalis might best account for the abolition of the photoperiodic testicular response observed after complete tractotomy. The results of tractotomy, therefore, support the conclusions from the experiments with transplants of the pars distalis.

c. Eminentiotomy. (Benoit and Assenmacher, 1953a,b, 1955, 1959; Assenmacher, 1958; Benoit, 1961.) When the supraoptico-hypophyseal neurosecretory tract in the anterior median eminence was severed completely (eminentiotomy), fibers of the neurosecretory tract proximal to the lesion were found to contain Gomori-positive granules whereas those distal to the lesion had degenerated. Both the median eminence and the neural lobe were atrophic and contained no aldehyde-fuchsin-positive neurosecretory material. Although damage was sustained by the primary capillary plexus, especially in its rostral portion, its caudal part was relatively normal and the hypophyseal portal vessels were intact. Thus, a reasonably normal capillary plexus was spread along the basal surface of the median eminence which was atrophic and contained neither nerve fibers nor neurosecretory granules. In the cephalic lobe of the pars distalis, a small, central necrotic zone was commonly found; hypotrophy was less pronounced in the caudal lobe. Eminentiotomies were performed in drakes with maximally developed testes (Benoit and Assenmacher, 1953a). At autopsy, either 1 or 6 months after eminentiotomy, the testes had regressed and resembled those of hypophysectomized males. In other animals, however, subtotal interruption of the supraoptico-hypophyseal tract resulted in hypotrophy of the median eminence and neural lobe rather than atrophy, as in the case of completely eminentiotomized males. Although the testes were small at autopsy, there was histological evidence of spermatogenesis and the interstitial cells appeared active. The results cited above suggest that complete severance of the supraoptico-hypophyseal tract in the anterior median eminence precludes all possibility for the transmission of some neurosecretion-associated gonadotropin-releasing factor to the pars distalis via the hypophyseal portal system. The lesions may also have involved the anterior bundles of the tuberohypophyseal tract. The probable role of the infundibular (arcuate) nuclei is discussed subsequently (see Sections IV,A,2 and 3, and Section IV,B).

d. Mischotomy. (Benoit and Assenmacher, 1953a,b, 1955, 1959; Assenmacher, 1958; Benoit, 1961.) When the supraoptico-hypophyseal tract was sectioned at the level of the infundibular stem (mischotomy), neurosecretory material accumulated at the proximal boundary of the lesion; distally, the neural lobe atrophied and was almost totally depleted of neurosecretory material. The structure of the median eminence was unaltered. The hypophyseal portal system was essentially intact, and the pars distalis showed cytological signs of normal secretory activity. At autopsy, the testes were developed maximally. Thus, mischotomy had interfered in no demonstrable way with the hypothalamic mechanism regulating gonadotropic activity of the pars distalis.

e. Lesions of the Anterior Hypothalamus. (Assenmacher, 1957a,b,c, 1958.) In one series of experiments, drakes were subjected in the spring to surgical ablation of a part of the supraoptic region of the anterior hypothalamus. They were then sacrificed in the fall after having been photostimulated for a month. In all cases, only a small lesion was detected histologically in the region of the supraoptic nuclei. The uninjured cells of the supraoptic nuclei, as well as those of the paraventricular nuclei, were particularly rich in neurosecretory granules. Although the neural lobe was reduced in volume, both it and the zona externa of the median eminence were rich in aldehyde-fuchsin-positive material. Cytologically, the pars distalis appeared to be active; the testes were well developed. The surgical intervention, therefore, had no demonstrable effect on the photoperiodic testicular response. In another experimental series, larger lesions were effected surgically or by electrocautery in drakes that were sacrificed 15 days or 1 month later. Histological examination of the anterior hypothalami revealed large lesions extending rostrocaudally from the supraoptic nuclei to the anterior portion of the paraventricular nuclei and, dorsoventrally, from the angulation of the septomesencephalic tract to and including fibers of the dorsal supraoptic decussation. The neural lobe was somewhat reduced in volume, but rich in aldehyde-fuchsin-positive material. The cytology of the pars distalis suggested inactivity, an inference supported by the regressed state of the testes. Histologically, the testes resembled those of hypophysectomized or tractotomized males. These experiments suggest a positive correlation between the depletion of Gomori-positive material in the zona externa of the median eminence and testicular regression. Further, they would seem to indicate that the neurosecretion-bearing axons of the supraoptico-hypophyseal tract terminating in the median eminence are a component of the hypothalamic mechanism regulating gonadotropic activity of the pars distalis. However, caution in interpretation is necessary since the effective lesions were massive. Not only were aldehyde-fuchsin-positive neurosecretory nuclear areas destroyed, but Gomori-negative nuclear areas as well. Because of the diffuse distribution of ganglionic cells in the neurosecretory nuclei, undoubtedly only a fraction of the total number present were ablated. Subtotal ablation is verified by the observation that the neural lobe was rich in neurosecretory material. Although the results are suggestive, more detailed experiments are necessary before the effects of these lesions can be attributed exclusively to the destruction of neurosecretory cells.

The simplest hypothesis that can explain the results of these experiments is that the gonadotropic activity of the adenohypophysis is controlled by the hypothalamic neurosecretory system in which neurosecretory cells of the supraoptic and/or paraventricular nuclei produce stainable neurosecretory material that contains a regulatory component (a gonadotropin-releasing factor); this neurosecretory material passes via axons eventually into the zone of neurovascular contact in the median eminence where the gonadotropin-releasing factor is transferred into the primary capillaries of the hypophyseal portal system and is thence transported to the pars distalis. Therefore, photoperiodic control of testicular activity in the drake would appear to be dependent upon the functional integrity of both the hypothalamic neurosecretory system and the adenohypophyseal portal system. It should be emphasized that, in addition to the observations and precautions concerning this hypothesis that already have been discussed, the evidence for the association of a gonadotropin-releasing factor, as yet unidentified in birds, with the aldehyde-fuchsin-positive neurosecretory material is only correlative.

2. *Investigations on Galliform Species*

Relatively little is known about neurohormonal mechanisms in male domestic fowl. However, gonadotropic activity of the pars distalis is dependent upon the functional integrity of its vascular connections with the median eminence since autotransplantation of the pars distalis to the kidney capsule results in immediate and permanent testicular regression (Ma and Nalbandov, 1963). Following castration, Mikami (1960) observed changes indicative of secretory activity in the neurosecretory cells of the supraoptic nucleus; he regarded these observations as consistent with a hypothesis that assigns to this nucleus an important role in the control of the gonadotropic activity of the pars distalis. On the other hand, Graber and Nalbandov (1965), in an extensive series of experiments, found that castration has little effect on the neurosecretory cells, although aldehyde-fuchsin-positive material appears to accumulate in the cells; there was also a slight decrease in the amount of neurosecretory material in the median eminence. The unpublished observations of Yasuda (see Farner and Oksche, 1962), based on very large electrolytic lesions, indicate that testicular atrophy follows destruction of the infundibular nuclei; atrophy did not occur, however, in birds with lesions in the supraoptico-hypophyseal tract. Should fibers of the tuberohypophyseal tract be found to have a role in the release of neurohormones from the neurosecretory fibers, as suggested by several investigators (Kobayashi *et al.*, 1961; Bern, 1963; Farner, 1964a), these observations might be more easily reconciled with those of Benoit and Assenmacher on the drake. Although it seems unlikely, the possibility that very different mechanisms are involved in the two species should not be rejected at this time.

A variety of evidence suggests that the episodic release of ovulation-inducing hormone in the hen is controlled by a neural mechanism. Among the early evidence was the pharmacological demonstration that several barbiturates, including pentobarbital sodium (Nembutal), induce ovulation in a significant proportion of injected hens (Fraps, 1953). The same barbiturates enhance the ovulation-inducing potency of progesterone when the latter is administered at nearly subovulatory dosages. Phenobarbital sodium, on the other hand, fails to induce ovulation and, in addition, suppresses the effect of progesterone when administered at a normally effective dosage. Both adrenolytic (Zarrow and Bastian, 1953; van Tienhoven *et al.*, 1954) and parasympatholytic (Zarrow and Bastian,

1953) drugs may block spontaneous as well as progesterone-induced ovulation.

In inducing ovulation, progesterone undoubtedly activates a neural mechanism. Anterior hypothalamic lesions made within 2.5 hours after the subcutaneous injection of progesterone prevent ovulation (Ralph and Fraps, 1959b). On the other hand, intrahypothalamic injection of progesterone, unlike intrapituitary injection, results in ovulation (Ralph and Fraps, 1960).

In hens, the presence of an irritant in the magnum (Huston and Nalbandov, 1953) or in the isthmus (van Tienhoven, 1953) results in the suppression of ovulation for as long as 3 weeks. However, neither the combs, ovaries, nor oviducts of these anovulatory fowl regress or diminish in size. Ovarian follicles do not undergo atresia and are potentially ovulable, as indicated by their response to progesterone or mammalian luteinizing hormone. Since transection of the hypophyseal portal vessels leads rapidly to ovarian regression, follicular atresia, and reduction in size of the comb (Shirley and Nalbandov, 1956b), it appears that at least basal amounts of gonadotropin are released throughout the anovulatory period. Further, the maintenance of the comb and oviduct implies continued secretion of androgen and estrogen from the ovary, functions contingent upon a supply of gonadotropin. These results are probably best explained by assuming a neurogenic inhibition, originating at the level of the magnum or the isthmus, of the episodic release of ovulation-inducing hormone in amounts sufficient to ensure ovulation (Huston and Nalbandov, 1953; Nalbandov, 1959).

According to Ralph (1959), electrolytic lesions at the extreme rostral end of the hypothalamus within a ventromedian portion of the nucleus preopticus paraventricularis consistently result in an immediate cessation and prolonged interruption of ovulation in adult laying hens. Since some effectively lesioned hens did not resume ovulation during the 1-month experimental period and, at autopsy, most were observed to have atrophic ovaries and oviducts, this neural region, in addition to participating in the events culminating in ovulation, might also function in gonadal maintenance. Although the neural mechanisms involved in ovulation and maintenance of the ovary may be different (Huston and Nalbandov, 1953; Nalbandov, 1959), experimental attempts to permanently dissociate these two processes have generally been unsuccessful (Ralph and Fraps, 1959a).

Diencephalic sites other than the ventromedian (preoptic) paraventricular region have been implicated in the mechanism by which the gonadotropic function of the pars distalis is controlled (Ralph and Fraps, 1959a). Lesions scattered throughout an essentially dorsocaudal thalamic region are effective in the prevention of ovulation and the induction of ovarian and oviducal regression. Lesions scattered throughout a hypothalamic area that includes most of the preoptic division of the paraventricular nuclei, part of the magnocellular paraventricular and lateral hypothalamic nuclei, the anterior and supraoptico-hypophyseal tracts, the tuberal and mammillary regions and the median eminence are also effective. Although reproductive dysfunction cannot be correlated consistently with specific loci in either region, the failure to detect ovarian or oviducal recrudescence at autopsy, 6 weeks after lesioning, suggests that some specific nervous mechanism was interrupted permanently. Also, progesterone injected into the caudal neostriatum, the region of the anterior hypophyseal tract, or within the tuberomammillary region induces premature ovulation (Ralph and Fraps, 1960). The possibility that the last area is a component of a mechanism that controls adenohypophyseal gonadotropic function is of substantial interest and is emphasized by the additional observation that electrolytic destruction of the infundibular nuclei results in cessation of ovulation and atrophy of the ovary (M. Yasuda, personal communication). Following the electrolytic destruction of the paraventricular nuclei, the median eminence, or the pars tuberalis, Egge and Chiasson (1963) observed cessation of the egg-laying cycle and reduction in size of the comb; an exclusively mammillary lesion in one hen did not impair reproductive activity.

Delayed ovulation following stimulation of the anterior median eminence appears to be related to the peculiar effects of electrolytically deposited iron rather than to the effects of stimulation per se (Opel and Fraps, 1961). Electrical stimulation of the preoptic hypothalamus, however, can delay ovulation, as also can sham operation (Opel, 1963). In view of the results of experiments involving hypothalamic lesions (Ralph, 1959), the significance of the failure of electrical stimulation to induce ovulation is unclear.

It can thus be seen that a preoptic ventromedian portion of the paraventricular nucleus and fiber tracts associated therewith seem most likely to be involved in the control of ovulation and possibly of gonadal maintenance in female domestic fowl (see Fraps, 1961, for review). Unfortunately, because the conventional Gomori stains were not used in most of the experiments, the relationships of the effective lesions to neurosecretory nuclei and tracts is obscure. Ovulation and oviposition occur normally in polydipsic hens with electrolytic lesions in the supraoptic nuclei (Ralph, 1960) and in hens that are polydipsic because of neurohypophysectomy (Shirley and Nalbandov, 1956a). The supraoptic lesions were situated lateral to the part of the paraventricular region known to be involved in ovulation. However, it is difficult to assess the role of the supraoptic nuclei from these experiments since it is probable that the nuclei were only partially destroyed.

It has generally been assumed that the basic pattern of regulation of adenohypophyseal gonadotropic function in the domestic fowl is not substantially different from that in the domestic duck. However, the limited observations of Ralph and Fraps (1959a, 1960) discussed above and the unpublished studies of Yasuda (see Farner and Oksche, 1962; also personal communication) suggest the possibility that the infundibular nucleus and its fibers may have an important functional role. Moreover, an extensive recent investigation (Graber and Nalbandov, 1965) suggests no consistent relationship between the density of aldehyde-fuchsin-positive material and the functional state of the reproductive system.

In the Japanese quail (*Coturnix coturnix japonica*), the duration of the daily photoperiod affects the rate of testicular development (W. O. Wilson *et al.*, 1962; Follett and Farner, 1966a). Little is known regarding the role of the hypothalamic neurosecretory system in the control of gonadotropin secretion. On the basis of a total gonadotropin bioassay utilizing the uptake of P^{32} in 1-day-old chick testes, Bacon *et al.* (1964) reported that the pituitary of the male contains more gonadotropin than the gland of the female. This observation has been confirmed in our laboratory (Follett and Farner, 1966b). The anterior pituitaries of males and females maintained on a 20-hour daily photoperiod since hatching were also found to contain more gonadotropin when assayed at 28 or 30 days of age than the pituitaries of males and females maintained on a 6-hour daily photoperiod (Follett and Farner, 1966b). The gonadal weights were greater in the birds subjected to the 20-hour daily photoperiods, indicating that the plasma level of gonadotropin was elevated. It would appear, therefore, that photoperiodic stimulation increases the synthesis as well as the release of pituitary gonadotropins.

3. *Investigations on Passeriform Species*

The possible involvement of the hypothalamic neurosecretory system and other hypothalamic elements in the regulation of adenohypophyseal gonadotropic function in *Zonotrichia leucophrys gambelii*, a species which has a single annual reproductive period restricted to late spring and early summer, has been investigated extensively in our laboratories. The reproductive cycle is rigidly controlled by day length (Farner, 1958, 1959, 1961, 1962a, 1964a; Farner and A. C. Wilson, 1957; Oksche *et al.*, 1959). Conventional histological investigations of the hypothalamic neurosecretory system have been made at various times throughout the annual cycle. During the midwinter period of sexual quiescence, neurosecretory material tends to be coarsely granular and globular and accumulates in the perikarya of the ganglionic cells of both the supraoptic and paraventricular nuclei and in the radial fibers of the palisade layer of the anterior median eminence. These cytological observations may reflect a state of relative inactivity of the eminential component of the neurosecretory system (Oksche *et al.*, 1959; Farner *et al.*, 1962). Decreasing amounts of aldehyde-fuchsin-positive material and other changes in the cells of the neurosecretory nuclei suggest that the activity of the system increases gradually during the vernal and early summer period of sexual activity. The period of maximal testicular development in late spring and early summer is characterized by a reduction of neurosecretory material in the zona externa of the median eminence. The onset of testicular regression marks the beginning of the refractory period during which it is impossible to induce activity photoperiodically (Farner and Mewaldt, 1955; Laws, 1961); during this period, large amounts of neurosecretory material occur in both the neurosecretory nuclei and in the zona externa of the median eminence (Oksche *et al.*, 1959; Laws, 1961; Farner *et al.*, 1962). Termination of the refractory period is not abrupt (Farner, 1964a); rather, it appears that there is a gradual increase in sensitivity of the response mechanism beginning in late October and early November and continuing into early summer (Laws, 1961; Farner, 1962a; Farner *et al.*, 1962). In highly photosensitive, photostimulated experimental birds in which marked testicular growth and development occur, changes in neurosecretory activity are observed at the level of both the neurosecretory nuclei and the median eminence. These changes are similar to those that occur with natural photoperiodic stimulation (Oksche *et al.*, 1959; Farner, 1962a; Farner *et al.*, 1962). In less photosensitive birds subjected to long daily photoperiods during midwinter, when testicular growth is stimulated at a lower rate, alterations in neurosecretory material are much less conspicuous or absent (Oksche *et al.*, 1959; Laws, 1961). Although these correlations between the hypothalamic neurosecretory system and the state of the reproductive system are suggestive, they must be viewed with caution; aldehyde-fuchsin does not stain neurohormones but rather material presumed to be the carrier for the neurohormones, and mechanisms controlling other adenohypophyseal functions also operate through the median eminence. The need for cautious interpretation is emphasized by the fact that the behavior of the neurosecretory system of *Zonotrichia albicollis,* a very closely related species with similar photoperiodic controls, is similar in some respects but obviously different in others (Wolfson and Kobayashi, 1962; Wolfson, 1963).

Coincident with the changes already described, photosensitive birds subjected to long daily photoperiods show an increase in acid phosphatase activity at the level of both the supraoptic nuclei and the median eminence (Kobayashi and Farner, 1960; Farner *et al.*, 1964) and an increase in catheptic proteinase activity in the median eminence (Kobayashi *et al.*, 1962; Farner *et al.*, 1964). Similar increases in enzymic activities are not observed, however, at these same loci in refractory birds subjected to long daily photoperiods. In *Zonotrichia albicollis* subjected to daily photoperiods of stimulatory duration, increases in acid phosphatase activity in the region of the supraoptic nuclei and in the median eminence also have been demonstrated (Kobayashi *et al.*, 1960; Wolfson and Kobayashi, 1962; Wolfson, 1963). Although the functional roles of these enzymes are unknown, these results probably reflect increased activity of the eminential component of the neurosecretory system during photostimulation of photosensitive birds (Kobayashi and Farner, 1960; Kobayashi *et al.*, 1962; Kawashima *et al.*, 1964). It is possible that the increased proteinase and acid phosphatase activities of the median eminence are in some way associated with proteolysis of the neurosecretory material and transport of the presumed active principle thus liberated into the primary capillary plexus of the hypophyseal portal system. However, it must be emphasized that these enzymic activities could also be associated with the activity of the Gomori-negative neural component.

The photoperiodic effects are restricted almost exclusively to the eminential component of the neurosecretory system; the amount of neurosecretory material in the pars nervosa is only slightly affected, if indeed at all. In contrast, dehydration has little or no effect on the density of neurosecretory material in the palisade layer of the anterior median eminence, although with severe dehydration there may be a slight reduction in density in its most rostral region (Kawashima *et al.*, 1964). On the other hand, dehydration and osmotic stress result in a marked depletion of neurosecretory material in the pars nervosa and in the neurosecretory fiber tract leading thereto (Oksche *et al.*, 1959; Kawashima *et al.*, 1964).

If it is assumed that extensive accumulation of aldehyde-fuchsin-positive material in the eminential component represents an inactive storage state and that during photoperiodic stimulation of highly photosensitive birds this material becomes less stainable (Oksche *et al.*, 1959; Farner, 1962a; Farner *et al.*, 1962), the data on experimental manipulation of the daily photoperiod and the observations on the annual cycle of activity can be interpreted as supporting the hypothesis of Benoit and Assenmacher (see Section IV,A,1). However, certain additional considerations are pertinent. Since, in the palisade layer of the anterior median eminence, there is an intimate relationship between neurosecretory fibers of the supraoptico-hypophyseal tract and Gomori-negative fibers of the tuberohypophyseal tract, there is the possibility that, through ephapses, fibers of the tuberohypophyseal tract may control the release of the presumed neurohormone from neurosecretory fibers (Oksche, 1960, 1962; Farner and Oksche, 1962; Farner, 1964a). In order to test this possibility, and to attack the more general question of basic mechanisms involved in hypothalamic control of adenohypophyseal gonadotropic function, electrolytic lesions were created in the median eminence and the infundibular nuclear region in *Zonotrichia leucophrys gambelii.* Midline lesions that involve both the anterior and posterior divisions of the median eminence result in marked suppression or total abolition of the photoperiodic testicular response, or, in the case of naturally photostimulated birds, in gonadal regression (Wilson, 1965; Wilson and Farner, 1965). Moreover, essentially similar results were obtained when the damage was restricted essentially to the infundibular nuclei. By comparison, virtually total interruption of the supraoptico-hypophyseal tract in the anterior median eminence results in only partial suppression of the photoperiodic testicular response. Similar lesions when created in naturally photostimulated birds apparently have little, if any, inhibitory effect on gonadal maintenance. These observations would appear to deemphasize the role of the eminential component of the neurosecretory system and emphasize that of the infundibular nuclei and the tuberohypophyseal tract. The problem of the control mechanism cannot be completely resolved at present, but in *Zonotrichia leucophrys gambelii,* as in domestic fowl, the infundibular nuclei undoubtedly play a prominent role in the mechanism by which the hypothalamus governs the gonadotropic activity of the pars distalis. The infundibular nuclei may be the site of production of a Gomori-negative neurosecretory product which regulates an adenohypophyseal gonadotropic function independently of the Gomori-positive eminential component of the neurosecretory system.

Although it has not been possible to assign specific functions to the individual neurosecretory nuclei or to their divisions in *Zonotrichia leucophrys gambelii* (Farner and Oksche, 1962; Oksche *et al.*, 1959; Laws, 1961), activation of individual divisions in the Japanese white-eye (*Zosterops palpebrosa japonica*) has been reported (Uemura and Kobayashi, 1963). Correlated with photoinduction of gonadal growth in this species is the activation and increase in nuclear diameter of neurosecretory cells of the lateral divisions of the supraoptic nuclei and the anterior and periventricular divisions of the paraventricular nuclei. Similar changes are not observed in other divisions. Exogenous estradiol, which inhibits gonadal development, activates the median divisions of the supraoptic nuclei, but nullifies the effect of photostimulation on the lateral divisions.

Although no difference in the amount of neurosecretory material in the median eminence was noted between photostimulated and estrogen-treated photostimulated birds, both groups had more aldehyde-fuchsin-positive material in the median eminence than did controls subjected to short daily photoperiods. Similarly, in *Zonotrichia albicollis,* increasing amounts of neurosecretory material in the median eminence are observed following exposure to daily photoperiods of stimulatory duration (Kobayashi *et al.,* 1960; Wolfson and Kobayashi, 1962; Wolfson, 1963).

B. Comments on Comparative Aspects of Hypothalamic Control of the Gonadotropic Functions of the Adenohypophysis

Although the current state of our knowledge does not permit firm generalizations, some useful comments on comparative aspects of the control of gonadotropin secretion can be made. It is now clear that in both birds and mammals, one or more neurohormones that control gonadotropin secretion from the pars distalis are released into the hypophyseal portal system. An important question from the comparative aspect is that of the nuclei and tracts involved. As noted above, most investigators of the avian control mechanisms have placed primary or exclusive emphasis on the aldehyde-fuchsin-positive magnocellular (supraoptic and paraventricular) neurosecretory nuclei and the fibers that lead therefrom into the median eminence (Benoit and Assenmacher, 1955; Assenmacher, 1958; Farner, 1962a; Farner *et al.,* 1962). Less emphasis has been placed on the aldehyde-fuchsin-negative tuberal nuclei and the tuberohypophyseal tract that also terminates in the median eminence. It now seems clear from a series of experiments on domestic fowl (M. Yasuda, personal communication) and *Zonotrichia leucophrys gambelii* (Wilson, 1965; Wilson and Farner, 1965) that the infundibular nucleus is definitely involved in the control of the gonadotropic function of the pars distalis although its relative importance compared to that of the supraoptic and paraventricular nuclei is still unknown. With respect to mammals, a somewhat different emphasis has developed. Most investigators (for reviews, see Szentágothai *et al.,* 1962; Flerkó, 1963; Schreiber, 1963) have placed primary emphasis on the infundibular nucleus and the tuberohypophyseal tract as essential elements in the control of gonadotropin secretion from the pars distalis and have ascribed no role therein to the aldehyde-fuchsin-positive neurosecretory elements. Lesions in the anterior hypothalamus, which may or may not include the magnocellular nuclei, frequently result in precocious development. Consequently, it appears that there may exist among mammals an ill-defined anterior hypothalamic area that has an inhibitory role in the mechanism that controls gonadotropin secretion (see Chapter 15, Volume I). At present, there is no evidence that any elements of the anterior hypothalamus have such a function in birds.

Although evidence is limited, it appears that the hypothalamic inhibition of the release of prolactin which is well established in mammals (for reviews, see Meites *et al.*, 1963; Everett and Nikitovitch-Winer, 1963) may not exist in birds (Ma and Nalbandov, 1963; Assenmacher *et al.*, 1962; Assenmacher, 1963; Assenmacher and Baylé, 1964). Rather, there is now good evidence that the avian hypothalamus produces a prolactin-releasing neurohormone (Kragt and Meites, 1965).

A still greater paucity of knowledge makes even more difficult a comparison of the neuroendocrine control of gonadotropin secretion in birds and amphibians. Of special interest is the observation that extirpation of the aldehyde-fuchsin-positive preoptic nucleus (homologous with the supraoptic and paraventricular nuclei of higher vertebrates) in *Rana temporaria* interferes neither with seasonal development of the gonads nor with gametogenesis. However, this procedure does interfere with ovulation (Dierickx, 1963a,b). As noted above, the hypothalamic neurosecretory system is believed to be important in the photoperiodic testicular response in the domestic mallard (Benoit and Assenmacher, 1955; Assenmacher, 1958). In *Rana esculenta,* electrical stimulation of the preoptic nuclear region has been observed to cause spermiation (Befort and Stutinsky, 1961).

C. Regulation of Other Tropic Functions of the Avian Adenohypophysis

Although much less is known about the nongonadotropic functions of the avian adenohypophysis, it appears that these functions are less rigidly controlled by neuroendocrine mechanisms. The ovary, oviduct, and comb atrophy following transection of the hypophyseal stalk in domestic fowl, but the weight and histological appearance of the thyroids and adrenals are unaffected (Shirley and Nalbandov, 1956b). It seems probable that the adenohypophysis has an intrinsic adrenocorticotropic activity independent of hypothalamic control and possible negative feedback mechanisms associated therewith. This suggestion is supported by the observations of Assenmacher (1958) on the domestic drake. Despite the reduction in adrenal weights following tractotomy, eminentiotomy, pituitary transplantation, or adenohypophysectomy, the cytological changes following adenohypophysectomy are clearly distinguishable from those following interruption of the neurovascular connections between the hypothalamus and the pars distalis. Anterior hypothalamic lesions that abolish gonadotropin secretion by the pars distalis do not affect adrenal weights. Emphasizing further the existence of an intrinsic ACTH secretion by the pars distalis is the apparently normal adrenocorticotropic response to insulin after a variety of insults to the neurovascular connections between the hypothalamus and the pars distalis. Egge and Chiasson (1963) concluded that in domestic fowl there is no correlation between hypothalamic lesions in a variety of sites and corticoid titer. Thus it appears that, in some ways at least, the avian adrenal is able to function independently of the neurovascular connections between the hypothalamus and the pars distalis.

The avian adrenal gland apparently also enjoys a certain degree of functional autonomy. According to Ma and Nalbandov (1963), there is an immediate decrease in the adrenal weights of both adenohypophysectomized male domestic fowl and those in which adenohypophysectomy is followed by autotransplantation of the pituitary. However, the adrenals in both groups not only regain their original weight but eventually surpass it; there is also a return in ascorbic acid content to control levels. Apparently unlike the situation in domestic mallards, the adrenals of domestic fowl do not show permanent atrophic changes following adenohypophysectomy. There is an increase in the ratio of interrenal (cortical) to chromaffin (medullary) tissue following adenohypophysectomy, but there is no apparent difference in this ratio in adenohypophysectomized-autotransplanted males and in controls. However, adenohypophysectomized chickens are extremely sensitive to abrupt changes in the ambient temperature or nocturnal fasting whereas adenohypophysectomized-autotransplanted fowl are as stress-resistant as controls. It is possible that there is an extrahypophyseal source of an ACTH-like hormone in pigeons (Miller, 1961). Following either hypophysectomy or adenohypophysectomy, the adrenals atrophy; however, the interrenal tissue hypertrophies markedly following intramuscular injections of insulin, formaldehyde, or epinephrine. Following massive lesions of the median eminence and ventral hypothalamus plus hypophysectomy, the adrenals hypertrophy rather than atrophy. When hypophysectomized birds with lesions are injected with formaldehyde, the adrenal response is similar but more extensive than that in intact or hypophysectomized pigeons. The cytological changes induced in the interrenal tissue by a variety of stresses are indistinguishable from those induced by injections of corticotropin. Since hypertrophy and hyperplasia are also seen in denervated adrenals following injection of formaldehyde, it would appear that the interrenal tissue responds to a humoral agent; this agent is presumably not of hypophyseal origin, and is liberated in the absence of the median eminence or the ventral hypothalamus.

In dehydrated white-crowned sparrows, a decrease in the density of neurosecretory material in the most rostral regions of the anterior median eminence correlates positively with an increase in activity of the interrenal cells and a reduction in the amount of sudanophilic material contained therein (Kawashima *et al.*, 1964). However, adrenalectomy has no apparent effect on the density of neurosecretory material in either the median eminence or the pars nervosa in male domestic fowl (Mikami, 1960).

Regarding the thyrotropic function of the adenohypophysis, Assenmacher (1958) observed no changes in either weight or histological appearance of the thyroid glands in mallards following tractotomy. Reductions in weight and height of epithelium were noted, however, after eminentiotomy, pituitary autotransplantation, and anterior hypothalamic lesions, although these were less striking than those following adenohypophysectomy. There is no hyperplastic response to propylthiouracil after tractotomy; in addition, tractotomy reduces significantly the rate of release of I^{131}-labeled thyroid hormone (Assenmacher and Tixier-Vidal, 1959).

In male domestic fowl, thyroidectomy results in a reduction of neurosecretory material in the median eminence and in the neural lobe (Mikami, 1960). Adenohypophysectomy alone evokes a drastic and immediate reduction in thyroid weight and rate of I^{131} incorporation, but adenohypophysectomy followed by autotransplantation affects neither the weight of the thyroids nor I^{131} uptake significantly (Ma and Nalbandov, 1963). The weight and histological appearance of the thyroids are unaffected by transection of the hypophyseal stalk (Shirley and Nalbandov, 1956b). Lesions in the anterior hypothalamus apparently inhibit TSH secretion in domestic fowl (Egge and Chiasson, 1963).

Our present knowledge, therefore, suggests that the avian pars distalis has a residual low rate of thyrotropic activity and that any increase in activity must require the effect of neurohormone(s) from the hypothalamus (Assenmacher and Tixier-Vidal, 1963).

V. Neurohormones and Releasing Mechanisms

Morphological and experimental evidence suggest strongly that neurohormones are transferred into blood capillaries in both of the neurohemal organs of the avian hypothalamus (Benoit and Assenmacher, 1953a,b, 1955; Assenmacher, 1958, 1963; Assenmacher and Tixier-Vidal, 1964; Farner and Oksche, 1962; Bentley, 1963; Heller, 1963). There is now a considerable body of knowledge concerning the neurohormones of the neural lobe, but little is known about the neurohormones of the median eminence. Knowledge concerning the processes involved in the release of neurohormones in the neurohemal organs is sparse.

A. Neurohormones

1. *Neural Lobe*

Only in the neural lobe of the domestic fowl has there been unequivocal chemical demonstration of arginine vasotocin and oxytocin (Acher *et al.*, 1960; Chauvet *et al.*, 1960). However, pharmacological assays and, in some instances, chromatographic evidence, indicate that these octapeptides occur also in the neural lobe of the domestic turkey (Munsick, 1964); *Coturnix coturnix japonica* (Follett and Farner, 1966a; Farner and Follett, 1966); the domestic pigeon (Heller and Pickering, 1961; Pickering and Heller, 1959; Ishii *et al.*, 1962a,b); *Zonotrichia leucophrys gambelii* (W. H. Sawyer, S. Kawashima, and D. S. Farner, unpublished observations); *Melopsittacus undulatus* (Hirano, 1964; Kobayashi, 1965); and the domestic mallard (Hirano, 1964; Kobayashi, 1965). A third neurohypophyseal hormone, arginine vasopressin, has been reported from one laboratory for a single species, the domestic fowl (Acher *et al.*, 1960; Chauvet *et al.*, 1960; Acher, 1963). However, this observation lacks confirmation (Heller, 1963; Munsick, 1964), and it seems unlikely that arginine vasopressin is an avian neurohormone.

Although the identity of the neural lobe hormones of birds appears reasonably certain (Sawyer, 1961), their functions are, as yet, inadequately understood. It appears probable that arginine vasotocin functions as the antidiuretic hormone in birds (Munsick *et al.*, 1960; Bentley, 1963). In the domestic pigeon, dehydration causes a reduction in the content of arginine vasotocin and the aldehyde-fuchsin-positive material in the neural lobe (Oota, 1962; Ishii *et al.*, 1962a,b). This suggests that in birds, as in mammals, the antidiuretic hormone is associated with the aldehyde-fuchsin-positive carrier molecule. Histological observations in a number of species suggest that extensive release of antidiuretic hormone is accompanied by a decrease in the amount of Gomori-positive neurosecretory material in the neural lobe (Farner and Oksche, 1962; Oksche *et al.*, 1964b; Kawashima *et al.*, 1964, Weber and Bachmann, 1964). This decrease is less conspicuous in species adapted to desert conditions (Oksche *et al.*, 1963; Uemura, 1964a). Indeed, it appears that there is a degree of specific adaptation of the entire neural lobe component of the hypothalamic neurosecretory system to the relative availability of water in the environment (Oksche *et al.*, 1963; Péczely, 1963; Uemura, 1964a). Aldehyde-fuchsin presumably reacts with the molecules of carrier protein (the neurophysine of Acher; see Chapter 6, Volume I) rather than the neurohormone itself. This could explain the observation by Wingstrand (1953, 1954) that antidiuretic activity develops in the hypothalamus of the chick embryo before the appearance of aldehyde-fuchsin-positive material. However, although a neurophysine has been isolated from the neural lobe of the domestic fowl (Chauvet *et al.*, 1960), there is still only presumptive evidence that it is stained by aldehyde-fuchsin.

At the ultrastructural level, arginine vasotocin appears to be associated with large (1000–2000 Å) electron-dense neurosecretory granules. In pigeons, dehydration results in a disappearance of most of these granules from the neural lobe; "empty" granules with electron-lucent centers and electron-dense membranes persist, however, suggesting the release therefrom of antidiuretic hormone (Oota, 1962).

In addition to its function as an antidiuretic hormone, arginine vasotocin may have a role in the process of oviposition. In the domestic fowl there is a marked reduction in arginine vasotocin, but not in oxytocin in the neural lobe at the time of oviposition. It has been suggested (Munsick *et al.*, 1960; Tanaka and Nakajo, 1962a,b) that oviposition may be caused by a discharge of arginine vasotocin from the neural lobe. Posterior pituitary preparations (Tanaka and Nakajo, 1962b) and pure arginine vasotocin (Munsick *et al.*, 1960) are highly effective in the induction of oviposition. Shirley and Nalbandov (1956a) found that the removal of the neural lobe does not arrest oviposition permanently, but this observation does not necessarily disprove the hypothesis that arginine vasotocin plays a role in the process.

The function of oxytocin in birds is obscure. Except for the blood vessels, all responsive tissues are less sensitive to it than to arginine vasotocin (Munsick *et al.*, 1960), and the ratio of oxytocin to arginine vasotocin in the neural lobes of the species studied thus far is relatively low (Follett, 1963; Munsick, 1964). Because of this, Bentley (1963) has suggested that oxytocin in birds ". . . may represent the vestigial survival of a biochemical synthetic process that is not essential for the animal's physiological well-being." Although supporting evidence is lacking, Munsick *et al.* (1960) have suggested that oxytocin may function as an adenohypophyseal releasing factor. Oxytocin in relatively small doses increases the concentrations of glucose and free fatty acids in the blood of domestic fowl (Kook *et al.*, 1964). It also increases blood sugar levels in *Zonotrichia leucophrys gambelii* (B. K. Follett and J. R. King, unpublished observation). However, it is premature to speculate on the physiological significance of these observations at the present time.

2. *Median Eminence*

Experimental and morphological evidence from several species (Sections IV,A and C) indicates clearly that the gonadotropic, thyrotropic, and adrenocorticotropic functions of the pars distalis are at least in part controlled neurohormonally. Both arginine vasotocin and oxytocin occur in the median eminence of a variety of species (Hirano *et al.*, 1962; Ishii *et al.*, 1962a,b; Hirano, 1964; Kobayashi, 1965; W. H. Sawyer, S. Kawashima, and D. S. Farner, unpublished observation; Follett and Farner, 1966a; Farner and Follett, 1966). However, it is still uncertain if these are actually transferred into the portal blood since they must pass through the axons of the fiber layer en route to the neural lobe. For *Zosterops palpebrosa japonica* there is evidence that a neurohypophyseal hormone, presumably arginine vasotocin, has some role in the control of gonadotropic function of the pars distalis; there is an increase in arginine vasotocin-like activity in the median eminence during photostimulated testicular development (Ishii *et al.*, 1962a,b; Hirano *et al.*, 1962) without a change in activity in the neural lobe. In male *Anas platyrhynchos,* long daily photoperiods, which stimulate testicular growth, cause a decrease in vasotocin-like activity in the median eminence without a change in the neural lobe (Ishii *et al.*, 1962a). However, it has not been possible to demonstrate a significant change in arginine vasotocin or oxytocin in the median eminence of photostimulated *Zonotrichia leucophrys gambelii* (W. H. Sawyer, S. Kawashima, and D. S. Farner, unpublished observation). Observations on *Coturnix coturnix japonica* have yielded equivocal results; young of both sexes held on long daily photoperiods showed marked gonadal growth in comparison with controls held on short daily photoperiods; in the long-day females this gonadal growth was associated with an increase in arginine vasotocin in the median eminence whereas in the males it was not (B. K. Follett and D. S. Farner, unpublished observation).

The relationship between the aldehyde-fuchsin-positive material of the neurosecretory fibers of the zona externa and a possible gonadotropin-releasing factor or neurohormone remains uncertain at this time. Because observations on other photoperiodic species are only partially in agreement with our observations on *Zonotrichia leucophrys gambelii,* and because of the results of experiments involving hypothalamic lesions in this species (see Section IV,A,3), the relatively simple hypothesis that the gonadotropin-releasing factor is attached to an aldehyde-fuchsin-positive carrier substance (Farner, 1962a; Farner and Oksche, 1962; Farner *et al.*, 1962) in a manner analogous to the relationship between antidiuretic hormone and neurophysine in the neural lobe obviously requires modification. The possible relationship between neurosecretory granules and the aldehyde-fuchsin-positive material of the fibers of the zona externa has not been carefully investigated.

B. Releasing Mechanisms

The present state of knowledge does not permit the construction of a hypothesis concerning the processes involved in the release of neurohormones from either of the avian neurohemal organs; it is only possible to present an inventory of the information that appears to be pertinent to an understanding of the phenomena.

Increases in acid phosphatase activity have been demonstrated in the neural lobe of dehydrated pigeons (Kobayashi *et al.*, 1962) and *Zonotrichia leucophrys gambelii* (Farner *et al.*, 1964; Kawashima *et al.*, 1964) without corresponding increases in activity in the median eminence. Similarly, photostimulation of testicular growth in *Zonotrichia leucophrys gambelii* (Kobayashi and Farner, 1960; Farner *et al.*, 1964) and *Zonotrichia albicollis* (Wolfson and Kobayashi, 1962) has been shown to cause an increase in acid phosphatase activity in the median eminence without change in the activity in the neural lobe. These observations suggest that an acid phosphatase may be involved in some way in the release of neurohormones into the primary capillaries of the hypophyseal portal system.

In *Zonotrichia leucophrys gambelii* photoperiodic stimulation that causes gonadal growth is accompanied by an increase in catheptic proteinase activity in the median eminence with no change in such activity in the neural lobe (Kobayashi *et al.*, 1962). Dehydration, on the other hand, causes an increase in activity in both the neural lobe and median eminence. The former is possibly associated with increased release of antidiuretic hormone and the latter possibly with the transfer of corticotropin-releasing factor since dehydration causes a depletion of sudanophilic material from adrenocortical cells (Kawashima *et al.*, 1964).

Specific acetylcholinesterase activity has been demonstrated in the palisade layer of *Zonotrichia leucophrys gambelii* (Kobayashi and Farner, 1964), *Zosterops palpebrosa japonica* (Uemura, 1964b), and *Passer montanus* (Kobayashi, 1965). The activity appears to be associated with both aldehyde-fuchsin-positive and aldehyde-fuchsin-negative fibers, perhaps more so with the former. It is weaker in the neural lobe than in the median eminence. These observations, plus the finding of synaptic vesicle-like bodies in the terminals of the fibers of the median eminence (Kobayashi *et al.*, 1961; Oota and Kobayashi, 1962; Kobayashi and

Oota, 1964; Bern and Nishioka, 1965) and in the neural lobe (Kobayashi *et al.*, 1965), suggest that cholinergic mechanisms may be involved in the release of hormones in both neurohemal organs.

There is also some suggestion of the involvement of an adrenergic mechanism, especially in the median eminence (Kobayashi and Oota, 1964). Kobayashi (1965) has reported the occurrence of monoamine oxidase in the vicinity of the primary capillaries in the median eminence; activity in the neural lobe was much weaker. He suggests that the activity in the median eminence may be associated primarily with the aldehyde-fuchsin-negative fibers. He suggests further that the smaller electron-dense bodies of the fibers of the median eminence may contain catecholamines (see also Bern and Nishioka, 1965).

VI. Afferent Information for Hypothalamic Neuroendocrine Mechanisms

Hypothalamic neuroendocrine mechanisms must be stimulated, at least in part, by a neural or hormonal input of transformed information derived ultimately from remote external or internal sources. Although the input probably operates most extensively at the level of the nerve cell bodies of the pertinent hypothalamic nuclei, it is also necessary to entertain the possibility of ephaptic neuronal relationships and, further, of hormonal effects on axonal endings. At this stage in the development of knowledge concerning avian neuroendocrine mechanisms, there is no reason to assume that, in birds, there are significant differences from the better known mechanisms in mammals. This brief discussion is confined to a few well-documented investigations.

A. Neural Afferent Information

Neural afferent information may be introduced into the nervous system by transduction in extero- or interoceptors of changes in the external or internal environment. A further possible neural component, that imposed by circadian timers, is discussed in Section VI,C.

Among the most spectacular and extensively studied cases of the use of external information in the operation of a hypothalamic neuroendocrine mechanism is that of the photoperiodic control of reproductive cycles in many species living in mid and high latitudes (for reviews, see Farner, 1959, 1961, 1964a; Farner and Oksche, 1962; Assenmacher, 1963). Although many functional parameters have been described empirically, little is known about receptors and neural pathways. In the male domestic mallard, it seems clear that there are both ocular and encephalic receptors, the latter occurring on restricted surfaces of the diencephalon and rhinencephalon (Benoit, 1938, 1961; Benoit and Assenmacher, 1953b). There is now considerable evidence for the existence of a direct retinohypothalamic tract with at least some of the fibers terminating in the regions of the supraoptic and paraventricular nuclei (Sestini, 1936; Sestini and Donatelli, 1936; Brugi, 1937; Blümcke, 1961; Farner and Oksche, 1962); however, it is not clear if any of these fibers terminate in the infundibular nucleus, as has been demonstrated in some mammals (Knoche, 1956, 1957, 1958, 1960). Although this anatomical evidence makes it probable that there may be direct transmission from the retina to the hypothalamic nuclei in the photosexual responses, confirmatory experimental evidence is lacking.

It appears unlikely, however, that such a simple scheme of direct transmission of information can be involved in most cases in which external information is used to modify endocrine function. Of interest here is the observation that *Anas acuta* and *Anas platyrhynchos* taken from the wild do not show ovarian development because of a failure to produce adequate gonadotropin (Phillips and van Tienhoven, 1960). This inhibition of production of gonadotropin, at least in mallards, can be eliminated by lesions in the ventral medial archistriatum and in the occipitomesencephalic tract (Phillips, 1964). Such lesions also greatly reduce fear or escape behavior; stimulation of these areas in free-moving birds elicits mostly fear or escape responses (see also Rougeul *et al.*, 1959). Consistent with the results of these investigations are the observations that electrical stimulation of the archistriatum and paleostriatum primitivum in the domestic fowl causes delays in ovulation and oviposition (Juhász and van Tienhoven, 1964). These observations on ducks and chickens provide clear examples of the role of afferent impulses from other centers in the control of the activity of the hypothalamic nuclei involved in neuroendocrine mechanisms.

Another interesting case of the use of external information in the control of reproductive activity is that described by Immelmann (1962) for *Taeniopygia castanotis* in the arid regions of Australia. In this species, the beginning of the rainy season induces reproductive activity almost immediately. The specific stimulus involved is not known although there is evidence (D. S. Farner and D. L. Serventy, unpublished observations) that a change in osmotic state plays an important role. For extensive discussions of the use of environmental information in functions involving hypothalamic neuroendocrine mechanisms, the reader is referred to the reviews of van Tienhoven (1961) and Lehrman (1961).

B. Hormonal Afferent Information

The relatively scattered literature concerning the effects of hormones on the avian hypothalamus suggests that birds have evolved a pattern of negative feedbacks which is similar to that in mammals. Although definitive proof is lacking, there is a variety of evidence that indicates the possible existence of negative feedbacks involving gonadal hormones operating at the hypothalamic level in domestic fowl (Legait, 1959; Hohlweg and Daume, 1959), *Zosterops palpebrosa japonica* (Uemura and Kobayashi, 1963), *Zonotrichia leucophrys gambelii* (Kobayashi and Farner, 1966), and the domestic mallard (Benoit *et al.*, 1950a,b; Assenmacher, 1958). It has been suggested that feedback of testicular hormone may be involved in the development of photorefractoriness in mallards (Assenmacher, 1958) and *Zonotrichia leucophrys gambelii* (Farner, 1964a,b) although, at least in the latter, functions in addition to a simple gonadal feedback must be involved.

Injection of progesterone into the neostriatum, the paraventricular nuclear region, or the posterior hypothalamus can induce ovulation in the domestic fowl (Ralph and Fraps, 1959b, 1960); however, it is not yet clear that these observations reflect a natural mechanism.

The investigations of Assenmacher (1958) on ducks strongly suggest that hypertrophy of the thyroid accompanies administration of propylthiouracil because a reduced level of thyroid hormone results in increased hypothalamic stimulation of thyrotropin secretion. As noted above, it must be borne in mind that the pars distalis has a residual level of thyrotropic activity that does not require a functional connection with the hypothalamus.

C. Circadian Functions in Neuroendocrine Mechanisms

Although many physiological processes reflect underlying circadian functions, little attention has been given to neuroendocrine mechanisms from this aspect. Some attention has been given recently to the role of circadian "clocks" in time measurement in photoperiodic mechanisms in birds. In *Carpodacus mexicanus* (Hamner, 1963, 1964) and in *Zonotrichia leucophrys gambelii* (Farner, 1964b) it is now clear that a circadian element is involved in the "measurement" of the duration of the daily photoperiod in the photoperiodic testicular response. In *Zonotrichia leucophrys gambelii,* at least, this is empirically expressed as a cycle in photosensitivity; photosensitivity, in terms of testicular response, is zero from the beginning of the daily photoperiod until somewhat after the eighth hour when it increases gradually to a maximum at about the seventeenth hour, after which it again decreases. Although the site of this cycle in photosensitivity is unknown, this mechanism has an important role in the processing of external information before it is finally transmitted neurohormonally. It is quite possible that such circadian functions may be associated widely with neuroendocrine functions. Certainly the investigation of these relationships should prove to be a fascinating aspect of neuroendocrinology in the future.

VII. Summary

In the avian hypothalamus there are two neurohemal organs, the neural lobe and the median eminence. The former contains endings of fibers that originate from neurosecretory cells of the supraoptico-paraventricular nuclear complex in the anterior hypothalamus. The functions of this system include the synthesis, transport, and release of the "neural lobe" hormones, arginine vasotocin and oxytocin. Arginine vasotocin is the avian antidiuretic hormone and may also function in oviposition. The function of oxytocin is obscure. It appears certain that neurohormones released from the neural lobe do not regulate the release of tropic hormones from the pars distalis. There are no vascular or neural connections between the neural lobe and the pars distalis nor does blood from the neural lobe reach the pars distalis via the portal vessels.

The battery of neuroendocrine mechanisms that regulate in varying degrees the gonadotropic, adrenocorticotropic, and thyrotropic activities of the avian pars distalis operate through the median eminence. As yet, however, none of the neurohormones have been identified. The median eminence contains endings of fibers from both the supraoptico-hypophyseal tract and the tuberohypophyseal tract. The former originate from neurosecretory cells of the magnocellular nuclei and mostly pass to the palisade layer via the reticular layer; the latter originate from Gomori-negative cells of the parvocellular tuberal nuclei. Whereas the anterior division of the median eminence receives fiber endings primarily from the supraoptico-hypophyseal tract, the posterior division receives fiber endings primarily from the tuberohypophyseal tract. However, fiber endings from the latter tract also contribute importantly to the innervation of the anterior division. In juxtaposition with the fiber endings of both tracts are the primary capillaries of the portal system. Detailed anatomical studies indicate the existence, in one species at least, of distinct anterior and posterior capillary plexuses that drain the anterior and posterior divisions of the median eminence, respectively, via distinct anterior and posterior groups of portal vessels that provide the sole afferent blood supplies to the cephalic and caudal lobes of the pars distalis. Although the physiological significance of this regional distribution of vessels is presently obscure, the existence of noninterconnecting vascular systems provides the anatomical basis for control of the cephalic lobe of the pars distalis by the anterior division of the median eminence and of the caudal lobe of the pars distalis by the posterior division of the median eminence. Although this pattern may be general among birds, the necessarily detailed studies have not been done.

The avian neural lobe and median eminence receive neurosecretory fiber endings of apparently common origin. Despite this, these neurohemal organs function with a high degree of mutual independence.

The gonadotropic activity of the avian pars distalis is rigidly controlled by the central nervous system. Photoperiodic induction of testicular activity in the domestic mallard appears to be dependent upon the integrity of the fibers of the supraoptico-hypophyseal tract that terminate in the median eminence. The eminential component of the neurosecretory system thus represents the terminal component of the photoperiodic control mechanism in this species. Histological observations on the behavior of the eminential component of the neurosecretory system in birds exposed to photoperiodic conditions that induce testicular growth suggest that this component may also be an element of the photoperiodic control mechanism in at least three passerine species. However, in the white-crowned sparrow, interruption of the neurosecretory tract in the anterior division of the median eminence does not inhibit photoperiodically induced testicular growth. On the other hand, lesions in the region of the infundibular nuclei or of the two divisions of the median eminence abolish or markedly suppress the photoperiodic testicular response. Similarly, in the domestic fowl, lesions in the infundibular nuclear region restrict gonadal activity, although interruption of the neurosecretory tract in the median eminence does not induce testicular atrophy. These observations therefore suggest that, in two species at least, the tuberoinfundibular neuron system may represent the terminal component of the neuroendocrine mechanism that regulates the release from the pars distalis of a growth-stimulating gonadotropin. Since the integrity of the eminential component of the neurosecretory system appears not to be essential for gonadal activity in some species, generalizations regarding the neuroendocrine mechanisms that regulate adenohypophyseal gonadotropic activity in birds, at least at this time, are not possible.

Unlike the situation in mammals, a hypothalamic stimulatory mechanism appears to regulate the release of prolactin from the avian pars distalis. The neural elements of this mechanism have not yet been identified.

The thyrotropic and adrenocorticotropic activities of the avian pars distalis are only partially regulated by hypothalamic neuroendocrine mechanisms. The pars distalis appears to have a residual low rate of thyrotropic activity but elevated thyrotropic activity requires the effects of neurohormones from the hypothalamus. A somewhat similar situation appears to hold for the corticotropic function of the pars distalis. However, the adrenal cortex is also able to function semi-independently of the pars distalis. The elements of the hypothalamic neuroendocrine mechanisms that participate in the regulation of the thyrotropic and adrenocorticotropic activities of the avian pars distalis have not yet been clearly defined.

There is suggestive evidence that cholinergic mechanisms may be involved in the release of neurohormones from both the neural lobe and the median eminence. Adrenergic mechanisms may also be involved in their release from the median eminence.

Acknowledgments

The authors wish to acknowledge the kind interest of Professor Dr. W. Bargmann (Universität Kiel), in whose institute many of the neurohistological studies were completed and parts of the manuscript were prepared. Much of the previously unpublished material comes from investigations supported by the National Institutes of Health through a grant (B–1353) to D. S. Farner. For the use of unpublished material, the authors are grateful to Professors Howard Bern, James R. King, Hideshi Kobayashi, L. R. Mewaldt, Andrew V. Nalbandov, W. H. Sawyer, and M. Yasuda; and to Doctors Brian Follett, Jean Graber, and S. Kawashima. The manuscript was prepared while F. E. Wilson was the holder of the William T. Porter Fellowship of the American Physiological Society. Acknowledgment is also made to the Deutsche Forschungsgemeinschaft for support of the pertinent investigations of A. Oksche cited herein.

References

Acher, R. (1963). The comparative chemistry of neurohypophysial hormones. *In* "Comparative Aspects of Neurohypophysial Morphology and Function." *Symp. Zool. Soc.* (*London*) **9**, 83–92.

Acher, R., Chauvet, J., and Lenci, M. (1960). Isolement de l'ocytocine du poulet. *Biochim. Biophys. Acta* **38**, 344–345.

Arai, Y. (1963). Diencephalic neurosecretory centers of the passerine bird, *Zosterops palpebrosa japonica.* *J. Fac. Sci. Univ. Tokyo, Sect. IV* **10**, 249–268.

Arai, Y., Kambara, S., and Takahashi, K. (1963). The entopeduncular neurosecretory cell group in the diencephalon of the passerine bird, *Emberiza rustica latifascia.* *Zool. Mag.* (*Tokyo*) **72**, 84–88 (in Japanese).

Ariëns Kappers, C. U., Huber, G. C., and Crosby, E. C. (1936). "The Comparative Anatomy of the Nervous System of Vertebrates, Including Man," Vol. II. Macmillan, New York.

Assenmacher, I. (1951). Le développement embryologique du système porte hypophysaire chez le canard domestique. *Compt. Rend.* **234**, 563–565.

Assenmacher, I. (1952). La vascularisation du complexe hypophysaire chez le canard domestique. *Arch. Anat. Microscop. Morphol. Exptl.* **47**, 448–572.

Assenmacher, I. (1953). Étude anatomique du système arteriel cervicocephalique chez l'oiseau. *Arch. Anat. Histol. Embryol.* **35**, 181–202.

Assenmacher, I. (1957a). Répercussions de lésions hypothalamiques sur le conditionnement génital du canard domestique. *Compt. Rend.* **245**, 210–213.

Assenmacher, I. (1957b). Nouvelles données sur le rôle de l'hypothalamus dans les régulations hypophysaires gonadotropes chez le canard domestique. *Compt. Rend.* **245**, 2388–2390.

Assenmacher, I. (1957c). Le rôle de l'hypothalamus dans les régulations hypophysaires. *Presse Med.* **65**, 1612–1614.

Assenmacher, I. (1958). Recherches sur le contrôl hypothalamique de la fonction gonadotrope préhypophysaire chez le canard. *Arch. Anat. Microscop. Morphol. Exptl.* **47**, 447–572.

Assenmacher, I. (1963). Les régulations hypothalamiques de la fonction gonadotrope. *Acta Neuroveget.* (*Vienna*) **25**, 339–382.

Assenmacher, I., and Baylé, J. D. (1964). La sécrétion prolactinique du pigeon en réponse à différents traitements. *Compt. Rend. Soc. Biol.* **158**, 255–259.

Assenmacher, I., and Benoit, J. (1956). Nouvelles recherches sur les relations entre la neurosécrétion hypothalamique, le système porte hypophysaire et l'activité gonadotrope de la préhypophyse. *Compt. Rend.* **242**, 2986–2988.

Assenmacher, I., and Benoit, J. (1958). Quelques aspects du contrôle hypothalamique de la fonction gonadotrope de la préhypophyse. *In* "Pathophysiologia Diencephalica" (S. B. Curri and L. Martini, eds.), pp. 401–427. Springer, Vienna.

Assenmacher, I., and Tixier-Vidal, A. (1959). Action de la section des veines portes hypophysaires sur le fonctionnement thyroïdien, étudié à l'aide du radio-iode I^{131}, chez le canard Pékin. *J. Physiol.* (*Paris*) **51**, 391–392.

Assenmacher, I., and Tixier-Vidal, A. (1963). Étude physiologique de l'activité thyroïdienne du canard mâle après section des veines portes hypophysaires. *Ann. Endocrinol.* (*Paris*) **24**, 509–523.

Assenmacher, I., and Tixier-Vidal, A. (1964). Répercussions de la section des veines portes hypophysaires sur la préhypophyse du canard Pékin mâle, entier ou castré. *Arch. Anat. Microscop. Morphol. Exptl.* **53**, 6–108.

Assenmacher, I., Tixier-Vidal, A., and Boissin, J. (1962). Contenu en hormones gonadotropes et en prolactine de l'hypophyse du canard soumis à un traitement lumineux ou réserpinique. *Compt. Rend. Soc. Biol.* **156**, 1555–1559.

Axelrod, J., Wurtman, R. J., and Winget, C. M. (1964). Melatonin synthesis in the hen pineal gland and its control by light. *Nature* **201**, 1134.

Bacon, W., Cherms, F. L., and McShan, W. H. (1964). Gonadotropin assay of pituitaries from sexually mature male and laying female *Coturnix* quail. *Endocrinology* **74**, 498–500.

Bargmann, W. (1949). Über die neurosekretorische Verknüpfung von Hypothalamus and Neurohypophyse. *Z. Zellforsch. Mikroskop. Anat.* **34**, 610–634.

Bargmann, W. (1954). "Das Zwischenhirn-Hypophysensystem." Springer, Berlin.

Bargmann, W., and Jacob, K. (1952). Über Neurosekretion im Zwischenhirn der Vögel. *Z. Zellforsch. Mikroskop. Anat.* **36,** 556–562.

Bargmann, W., Hild, W., Ortmann, R., and Schiebler, T. H. (1950). Morphologische und experimentelle Untersuchungen über das hypothalamisch-hypophysäre System. *Acta Neuroveget.* (*Vienna*) **1,** 233–275.

Barry, J. (1954). Contribution à l'étude de la neurosécrétion. *Biol. Med.* (*Paris*) **13,** 1–15.

Barry, J. (1961). Recherches morphologiques et expérimentales sur la glande diencéphalique de l'appareil hypothalamo-hypophysaire. *Ann. Sci. Univ. Besançon, Zool. Physiol.* **15,** 3–133.

Barry, J., and Cotte, G. (1961). Étude préliminaire, au microscope électronique, de l'éminence médiane du cobaye. *Z. Zellforsch. Mikroskop. Anat.* **53,** 714–724.

Befort, J. J., and Stutinsky, F. (1961). Effet des stimulations électriques du noyau préoptique de *Rana esculenta* mâle. *J. Physiol.* (*Paris*) **53,** 270–272.

Benoit, J. (1938). Action de divers éclairements localisés dans la région orbitaire sur la gonadostimulation chez le canard mâle impubère. Croissance testiculaire provoquée par l'éclairement direct de la région hypophysaire. *Compt. Rend. Soc. Biol.* **127,** 909–914.

Benoit, J. (1957). Radiation lumineuses et activité sexuelle du canard. *Rev. Suisse Zool.* **64,** 577–587.

Benoit, J. (1961). Opto-sexual reflex in the duck: physiological and histological aspects. *Yale J. Biol. Med.* **34,** 97–116.

Benoit, J. (1962). Hypothalamo-hypophyseal control of the sexual activity in birds. *In* "Progress in Comparative Endocrinology." *Gen. Comp. Endocrinol.* Suppl. 1, 254–274.

Benoit, J., and Assenmacher, I. (1953a). Rapport entre la stimulation sexuelle préhypophysaire et la neurosécrétion chez l'oiseau. *Arch. Anat. Microscop. Morphol. Exptl.* **42,** 334–386.

Benoit, J., and Assenmacher, I. (1953b). Action des facteurs externes et plus particulièrement du facteur lumineux sur l'activité sexuelle des oiseaux. *IIe Réunion Endocrinologistes Langue Franc.* pp. 33–80.

Benoit, J., and Assenmacher, I. (1955). Le contrôle hypothalamique de l'activité préhypophysaire gonadotrope. *J. Physiol.* (*Paris*) **47,** 427–567.

Benoit, J., and Assenmacher, I. (1959). The control by visible radiations of the gonadotropic activity of the duck hypophysis. *Recent Progr. Hormone Res.* **15,** 143–164.

Benoit, J., Assenmacher, I., and Walter, F. X. (1950a). Réponses du mécanisme gonado-stimulant à l'éclairement artificiel et de la préhypophyse aux castrations bilatérale et unilatérale, chez le canard domestique mâle, au cours de la période de régression testiculaire saisonnière. *Compt. Rend. Soc. Biol.* **144,** 573–577.

Benoit, J., Assenmacher, I., and Walter, F. X. (1950b). Activité gonadotrope de l'hypophyse du canard domestique, au cours de la régression testiculaire saisonnière et de la prépubérté. *Compt. Rend. Soc. Biol.* **144,** 1403–1407.

Bentley, P. J. (1963). Neurohypophysial function in amphibians, reptiles and birds. *In* "Comparative Aspects of Neurohypophysial Morphology and Function." *Symp. Zool. Soc.* (*London*) **9,** 141–152.

Bern, H. A. (1962). The properties of neurosecretory cells. *In* "Progress in Comparative Endocrinology." *Gen. Comp. Endocrinol.* Suppl. 1, 117–132.

Bern, H. A. (1963). The secretory neuron as a doubly specialized cell. *In* "The General Physiology of Cell Specialization" (D. Mazia and A. Tyler, eds.), pp. 349–362. McGraw-Hill, New York.

Bern, H. A., and Nishioka, R. S. (1965). Fine structure of the median eminence of some passerine birds. *Proc. Zool. Soc. Calcutta* **18**, 107–119.

Bern, H. A., Nishioka, R. S., Mewaldt, L. R., and Farner, D. S. (1966). Photoperiodic and osmotic influences on the ultrastructure of the hypothalamic neurosecretory system of the White-crowned Sparrow, *Zonotrichia leucophrys gambelii*. *Z. Zellforsch. Mikroskop. Anat.* **69**, 198–227.

Blümcke, S. (1961). Vergleichend experimentell-morphologische Untersuchungen zur Frage einer retino-hypothalamischen Bahn bei Huhn, Meerschweinchen und Katze. *Z. Mikroskop.-Anat. Forsch.* **67**, 469–513.

Brugi, G. (1937). Reperti istologici sperimentale nel pollo a conferma del l'isestenza di dirette conessioni del tratto ottico con la zona anteriore dell'ipothalami. *Monitore Zool. Ital.* **48**, 264–268.

Chauvet, J., Lenci, M., and Acher, R. (1960). Présence de deux vasopressines dans la neurohypophyse du poulet. *Biochim. Biophys. Acta* **38**, 571–573.

Diepen, R. (1962). Der Hypothalamus. *In* "Handbuch der mikroskopischen Anatomie des Menschen" (W. Bargmann, ed.), Vol. IV, Part 7, pp. 1–525. Springer, Berlin.

Dierickx, K. (1963a). The total extirpation of the preoptic magnocellular nuclei of *Rana temporaria*. *Arch. Intern. Pharmacodyn.* **143**, 268–275.

Dierickx, K. (1963b). The extirpation of the neurosecretory preoptic nucleus and the reproduction of *Rana temporaria*. *Arch. Intern. Pharmacodyn.* **145**, 580–589.

Duncan, D. (1956). An electron microscope study of the neurohypophysis of a bird, *Gallus domesticus*. *Anat. Record* **125**, 457–471.

Egge, A. S., and Chiasson, R. B. (1963). Endocrine effects of diencephalic lesions in the white leghorn hen. *Gen. Comp. Endocrinol.* **3**, 346–361.

Everett, J. W., and Nikitovitch-Winer, M. (1963). Physiology of the pituitary gland as affected by transplantation or stalk transection. *In* "Advances in Neuroendocrinology" (A. V. Nalbandov, ed.), pp. 289–304. Univ. of Illinois Press, Urbana, Illinois.

Farner, D. S. (1958). Photoperiodism in animals with special reference to avian testicular cycles. *In* "Photobiology." *Proc. 19th Ann. Biol. Colloq., Oregon State Coll. 1958* pp. 17–29.

Farner, D. S. (1959). Photoperiodic control of annual gonadal cycles in birds. *In* "Photoperiodism and Related Phenomena in Plants and Animals," Publ. No. 55, pp. 717–750. Am. Assoc. Advance. Sci., Washington, D.C.

Farner, D. S. (1961). Comparative physiology: photoperiodicity. *Ann. Rev. Physiol.* **23**, 71–96.

Farner, D. S. (1962a). Hypothalamic neurosecretion and phosphatase activity in relation to the photoperiodic control of the testicular cycle of *Zonotrichia leucophrys gambelii*. *In* "Progress in Comparative Endocrinology." *Gen. Comp. Endocrinol.* Suppl. 1, 160–167.

Farner, D. S. (1962b). Comments on: Oksche, A., The fine nervous, neurosecretory, and glial structure of the median eminence in the White-crowned Sparrow. *Mem. Soc. Endocrinol.* **12**, 199–208.

Farner, D. S. (1964a). The photoperiodic control of reproductive cycles in birds. *Am. Scientist* **52**, 137–156.

Farner, D. S. (1964b). Time measurement in vertebrate photoperiodism. *Am. Naturalist* **98**, 375–386.

Farner, D. S., and Follett, B. K. (1966). Light and other factors affecting avian reproduction. *J. Animal Sci.* **25**, 90–118.

Farner, D. S., and Mewaldt, L. R. (1955). The natural termination of the refractory period in the White-crowned Sparrow. *Condor* **57**, 112–116.

Farner, D. S., and Oksche, A. (1962). Neurosecretion in birds. *Gen. Comp. Endocrinol.* **2**, 113–147.

Farner, D. S., and Wilson, A. C. (1957). A quantitative examination of testicular growth in the White-crowned Sparrow. *Biol. Bull.* **113**, 254–267.

Farner, D. S., Oksche, A., and Lorenzen, L. (1962). Hypothalamic neurosecretion and the photoperiodic testicular response in the White-crowned Sparrow, *Zonotrichia leucophrys gambelii. Mem. Soc. Endocrinol.* **12**, 187–197.

Farner, D. S., Kobayashi, H., Oksche, A., and Kawashima, S. (1964). Proteinase and acid-phosphatase activities in relation to the function of the hypothalamo-hypophysial neurosecretory systems of photostimulated and of dehydrated White-crowned Sparrows. *In* "Progress in Brain Research" (W. Bargmann and J. P. Schadé, eds.), Vol. V: Lectures on the Diencephalon, pp. 147–156. Elsevier, Amsterdam.

Flerkó, B. (1963). The central nervous system and the secretion and release of luteinizing hormone and follicle stimulating hormone. *In* "Advances in Neuroendocrinology" (A. V. Nalbandov, ed.), pp. 211–224. Univ. of Illinois Press, Urbana, Illinois.

Follett, B. K. (1963). Mole ratios of the neurohypophysial hormones in the vertebrate neural lobe. *Nature* **198**, 693–694.

Follett, B. K., and Farner, D. S. (1966a). The effect of daily photoperiod on gonadal growth, neurohypophysial hormone content, and neurosecretion in the hypothalamo-hypophysial system of the Japanese Quail (*Coturnix coturnix japonica*). *Gen. Comp. Endocrinol.* **7**, 111–124.

Follett, B. K., and Farner, D. S. (1966b). Pituitary gonadotropins in the Japanese Quail (*Coturnix coturnix japonica*). *Gen. Comp. Endocrinol.* **7**, 125–131.

Fraps, R. M. (1953). Neural control of the release of pituitary gonadotrophin for ovulation in the hen. *Poultry Sci.* **32**, 899.

Fraps, R. M. (1961). Ovulation in the domestic fowl. *In* "Control of Ovulation" (C. A. Villee, ed.), pp. 133–162. Pergamon Press, Oxford.

Fujita, H. (1956a). Die histologische Untersuchung des Hypothalamus-Hypophysensystems der Vögel. I. Das Neurosekretionsbild beim Haushuhn und der Hausente. *Arch. Histol. Japon.* **9**, 109–114 (in Japanese).

Fujita, H. (1956b). Die histologische Untersuchung des Hypothalamus-Hypophysensystems der Vögel. II. Ontogenetische Studien über den Bau und das Neurosekretions- und Nisslbild des Hypothalamus-Hypophysensystems des Haushuhnes. *Arch. Histol. Japon.* **9**, 213–224 (in Japanese).

Graber, J. W., and Nalbandov, A. V. (1965). Neurosecretion in the White Leghorn cockerel. *Gen. Comp. Endocrinol.* **5**, 485–492.

Green, J. D. (1951). The comparative anatomy of the hypophysis, with special reference to its blood supply and innervation. *Am. J. Anat.* **88**, 225–311.

Hamner, W. M. (1963). Diurnal rhythm and photoperiodism in testicular recrudescence of the House Finch. *Science* **142**, 1294–1295.

Hamner, W. M. (1964). Circadian control of photoperiodism in the House Finch demonstrated by interrupted-night experiments. *Nature* **203**, 1400–1401.

Heller, H. (1963). Pharmacology and distribution of neurohypophysial hormones. *In* "Comparative Aspects of Neurohypophysial Morphology and Function." *Symp. Zool. Soc. (London)* **9**, 93–106.

Heller, H., and Pickering, B. T. (1961). Neurohypophysial hormones of non-mammalian vertebrates. *J. Physiol.* (*London*) **155**, 98–114.

Hirano, T. (1964). Further studies on the neurohypophysial hormones in the avian median eminence. *Endocrinol. Japon.* **11**, 87–95.

Hirano, T., Ishii, S., and Kobayashi, H. (1962). Effects of prolongation of daily photoperiod on gonadal development and neurohypophyseal hormone activity in the median eminence and the pars nervosa of the passerine bird, *Zosterops palpebrosa japonica.* *Annotationes Zool. Japon.* **35**, 64–71.

Hohlweg, W., and Daume, E. (1959). Lokale hormonelle Beeinflussung des Hypophysen-Zwischenhirnsystems bei Hähnen. *Endokrinologie* **37**, 95–104.

Huber, G. C., and Crosby, E. C. (1929). The nuclei and fiber paths of the avian diencephalon with consideration of telencephalic and certain mesencephalic centers and connections. *J. Comp. Neurol.* **48**, 1–225.

Huston, T. M., and Nalbandov, A. V. (1953). Neurohumoral control of the pituitary in the fowl. *Endocrinology* **52**, 149–156.

Immelmann, K. (1962). Beiträge zu einer vergleichenden Biologie australischer Prachtfinken (Spermestidae). *Zool. Jahrb., Abt. System. Oekol. Geogr. Tiere* **90**, 1–196.

Ishii, S., Hirano, T., and Kobayashi, H. (1962a). Preliminary report on the neurohypophysial hormone activity in the avian median eminence. *Zool. Mag.* (*Tokyo*) **71**, 206–211 (in Japanese).

Ishii, S., Hirano, T., and Kobayashi, H. (1962b). Neurohypophyseal hormones in the avian median eminence and pars nervosa. *Gen. Comp. Endocrinol.* **2**, 433–440.

Juhász, L. P., and van Tienhoven, A. (1964). Effect of electrical stimulation of telencephalon on ovulation and oviposition in the hen. *Am. J. Physiol.* **207**, 286–290.

Kawashima, S., Farner, D. S., Kobayashi, H., Oksche, A., and Lorenzen, L. (1964). The effect of dehydration on acid-phosphatase activity, catheptic-proteinase activity, and neurosecretion in the hypothalamo-hypophysial system of the White-crowned Sparrow, *Zonotrichia leucophrys gambelii.* *Z. Zellforsch. Mikroskop. Anat.* **62**, 149–181.

Knoche, H. (1956). Morphologisch-experimentelle Untersuchungen über eine Faserverbindung der Retina mit den vegetativen Zentren des Zwischenhirnes und mit der Hypophyse. *Z. Zellforsch. Mikroskop. Anat.* **45**, 201–264.

Knoche, H. (1957). Über die Ausbreitung und Herkunft der nervösen Nodulusfasern in Hypothalamus und Retina. *Z. Zellforsch. Mikroskop. Anat.* **48**, 602–616.

Knoche, H. (1958). Die retino-hypothalamische Bahn von Mensch, Hund und Kaninchen. *Z. Mikroskop.-Anat. Forsch.* **63**, 461–486.

Knoche, H. (1960). Ursprung, Verlauf und Endigung der retino-hypothalamischen Bahn. *Z. Zellforsch. Mikroskop. Anat.* **51**, 658–704.

Kobayashi, H. (1965). Histochemical, electron microscopic and pharmacologic studies on the median eminence. Proc. 2nd Intern. Congr. of Endocrinol., London, 1964. *Excerpta Med., Intern. Congr. Ser.* **83**, 570–576.

Kobayashi, H., and Farner, D. S. (1960). The effect of photoperiodic stimulation on phosphatase activity in the hypothalamo-hypophysial system of the White-crowned Sparrow, *Zonotrichia leucophrys gambelii.* *Z. Zellforsch. Mikroskop. Anat.* **53**, 1–24.

Kobayashi, H., and Farner, D. S. (1964). Cholinesterases in the hypothalamo-hypophysial neurosecretory system of the White-crowned Sparrow, *Zonotrichia leucophrys gambelii.* *Z. Zellforsch. Mikroskop. Anat.* **63**, 965–973.

Kobayashi, H., and Farner, D. S. (1966). Evidence of a negative feedback on photoperiodically induced gonadal development in the White-crowned Sparrow, *Zonotrichia leucophrys gambelii*. *Gen. Comp. Endocrinol.* **6**, 443–452.

Kobayashi, H., and Oota, Y. (1964). Functional electron microscopy of the vertebrate neurosecretory storage-release organs. *Gunma Symp. Endocrinol.* **1**, 63–79.

Kobayashi, H., Wolfson, A., Wise, M. A., and Haubrich, D. R. (1960). Acid phosphatase activity of the hypothalamico-hypophyseal system in relation to gonadal growth induced by light and darkness in the White-throated Sparrow (*Zonotrichia albicollis*). *Anat. Record* **137**, 372.

Kobayashi, H., Bern, H. A., Nishioka, R. S., and Hyodo, Y. (1961). The hypothalamo-hypophyseal neurosecretory system of the parakeet, *Melopsittacus undulatus*. *Gen. Comp. Endocrinol.* **1**, 545–564.

Kobayashi, H., Kambara, S., Kawashima, S., and Farner, D. S. (1962). The effect of photoperiodic stimulation on proteinase activity in the hypothalamo-hypophysial system of the White-crowned Sparrow, *Zonotrichia leucophrys gambelii*. *Gen. Comp. Endocrinol.* **2**, 296–310.

Kobayashi, H., Hirano, T., and Oota, Y. (1965). Electron microscopic and pharmacological studies on the median eminence and pars nervosa. Les Travaux du IVe Symp. Intern. d'Endocrinologie comparée. *Arch. Anat. Microscop. Morphol. Exptl.* **54**, 277–293.

Kook, Y., Cho, K. B., and Yun, K. O. (1964). Metabolic effects of oxytocin in the chicken. *Nature* **204**, 385–386.

Kragt, C. L., and Meites, J. (1965). Stimulation of pigeon pituitary release by pigeon hypothalamic extract *in vitro*. *Endocrinology* **76**, 1169–1176.

Kuhlenbeck, H. (1936). Über die Grundbestandteile des Zwischenhirnbauplans der Vögel. *Gegenbaurs Morphol. Jahrb.* **77**, 61–109.

Kurotsu, T. (1935). Über den Nucleus magnocellularis periventricularis bei Reptilien und Vögeln. *Proc. Koninkl. Ned. Akad. Wetenschap., Sect. Sci.* **38**, 784–797.

Laws, D. F. (1961). Hypothalamic neurosecretion in the refractory and post-refractory periods and its relationship to the rate of photoperiodically induced testicular growth in *Zonotrichia leucophrys gambelii*. *Z. Zellforsch. Mikroskop. Anat.* **54**, 275–306.

Legait, H. (1959). Contribution à l'étude morphologique et expérimentale du système hypothalamo-neurohypophysaire de la Poule Rhode-Island. Thesis, University of Louvain-Nancy: Société d'Impressions typographiques.

Lehrman, D. S. (1961). Hormonal regulation of parental behavior in birds and infrahuman mammals. *In* "Sex and Internal Secretions" (W. C. Young, ed.), 3rd ed., Vol. 2, pp. 1268–1400. Williams & Wilkins, Baltimore, Maryland.

Ma, R. C. S., and Nalbandov, A. V. (1963). Physiology of the pituitary gland as affected by transplantation or stalk transection: Discussion. *In* "Advances in Neuroendocrinology" (A. V. Nalbandov, ed.), pp. 306–311. Univ. of Illinois Press, Urbana, Illinois.

Meites, J., Nicoll, C. S., and Talwalker, P. K. (1963). The central nervous system and the secretion and release of prolactin. *In* "Advances in Neuroendocrinology" (A. V. Nalbandov, ed.), pp. 238–277. Univ. of Illinois Press, Urbana, Illinois.

Metuzals, J. (1955). Die Innervation der Drüsenzellen der pars distalis der Hypophyse bei der Ente (mit Vergleich zwischen nervösem Endplexus und argyrophilem Bindegewebe). *Z. Zellforsch. Mikroskop. Anat.* **43**, 319–334.

Metuzals, J. (1956). The innervation of the adenohypophysis of the duck. *J. Endocrinol.* **14**, 87–95.

Mikami, S. (1958). The cytological significance of regional patterns in the adenohypophysis of the fowl. *J. Fac. Agr. Iwate Univ.* **3**, 473–545.

Mikami, S. (1960). The structure of the hypothalamo-hypophysial neurosecretory system in the fowl and its morphological changes following adrenalectomy, thyroidectomy and castration. *J. Fac. Agr. Iwate Univ.* **4**, 359–379.

Miller, R. A. (1961). Hypertrophic adrenals and their response to stress after lesions in the median eminence of totally hypophysectomized pigeons. *Acta Endocrinol.* **37**, 565–576.

Mosier, H. D. (1955). The development of the hypothalamo-neurohypophysial secretory system in the chick embryo. *Endocrinology* **57**, 661–669.

Munsick, R. A. (1964). Neurohypophysial hormones of chickens and turkeys. *Endocrinology* **75**, 104–112.

Munsick, R. A., Sawyer, W. H., and Van Dyke, H. B. (1960). Avian neurohypophyseal hormones: pharmacological properties and tentative identification. *Endocrinology* **66**, 860–871.

Nalbandov, A. V. (1959). Neuroendocrine reflex mechanisms: Bird ovulation. *In* "Comparative Endocrinology" (A. Gorbman, ed.), pp. 161–173. Wiley, New York.

Nishioka, R. S., Bern, H. A., and Mewaldt, L. R. (1963). Some ultrastructural aspects of the neurohypophysis of the White-crowned Sparrow. *Am. Zoologist* **3**, 136.

Nishioka, R. S., Bern, H. A., and Mewaldt, L. R. (1964). Ultrastructural aspects of the neurohypophysis of the White-crowned Sparrow, *Zonotrichia leucophrys gambelii,* with special reference to the relation of neurosecretory axons to ependyma in the pars nervosa. *Gen. Comp. Endocrinol.* **4**, 304–313.

Okamoto, S., and Ihara, Y. (1960). Neural and neurovascular connections between the hypothalamic neurosecretory center and the adenohypophysis. *Anat. Record* **137**, 485–499.

Oksche, A. (1960). Optico-vegetative regulatory mechanisms of the diencephalon. *Anat. Anz.* **108**, 320–329.

Oksche, A. (1962). The fine nervous, neurosecretory, and glial structure of the median eminence in the White-crowned Sparrow. *Mem. Soc. Endocrinol.* **12**, 199–206.

Oksche, A. (1965). The fine structure of the neurosecretory system of birds in relation to its functional aspects. Proc. 2nd Intern. Congr. of Endocrinol., London, 1964. *Excerpta Med., Intern. Congr. Ser.* **83**, 167–171.

Oksche, A., Laws, D. F., Kamemoto, F. I., and Farner, D. S. (1959). The hypothalamo-hypophysial neurosecretory system of the White-crowned Sparrow, *Zonotrichia leucophrys gambelii.* *Z. Zellforsch. Mikroskop. Anat.* **51**, 1–42.

Oksche, A., Farner, D. S., Serventy, D. L., Wolff, F., and Nicholls, C. A. (1963). The hypothalamo-hypophysial neurosecretory system of the Zebra Finch, *Taeniopygia castanotis.* *Z. Zellforsch. Mikroskop. Anat.* **58**, 846–914.

Oksche, A., Mautner, W., and Farner, D. S. (1964a). Das räumliche Bild des neurosekretorischen Systems der Vögel unter normalen und experimentellen Bedingungen. *Z. Zellforsch. Mikroskop. Anat.* **64**, 83–100.

Oksche, A., Wilson, W. O., and Farner, D. S. (1964b). The hypothalamic neurosecretory system of *Coturnix coturnix japonica.* *Z. Zellforsch. Mikroskop. Anat.* **61**, 688–709.

Oota, Y. (1962). Effect of dehydration on the fine structure of the pars nervosa of the pigeon. *Zool. Mag.* (*Tokyo*) **71**, 235–242 (in Japanese).

Oota, Y. (1963). On the synaptic vesicles in the neurosecretory organs of the carp, bullfrog, pigeon and mouse. *Annotationes Zool. Japon.* **36**, 167–172.

Oota, Y., and Kobayashi, H. (1962). Fine structure of the median eminence and pars nervosa of the pigeon. *Annotationes Zool. Japon.* **35**, 128–138.

Oota, Y., and Kobayashi, H. (1963a). Synapses between neurosecretory axons and the processes of non-neurosecretory neurons. *Zool. Mag.* (*Tokyo*) **72**, 35–39 (in Japanese).

Oota, Y., and Kobayashi, H. (1963b). Fine structure of the median eminence and the pars nervosa of the bullfrog, *Rana catesbeiana.* *Z. Zellforsch. Mikroskop. Anat.* **60**, 667–687.

Opel, H. (1963). Delay in ovulation in the hen following stimulation of the preoptic brain. *Proc. Soc. Exptl. Biol. Med.* **113**, 488–492.

Opel, H., and Fraps, R. M. (1961). Blockade of gonadotrophin release for ovulation in the hen following stimulation with stainless steel electrodes. *Proc. Soc. Exptl. Biol. Med.* **108**, 291–296.

Payne, F. (1959). Cytologic evidence of secretory activity in the neurohypophysis of the fowl. *Anat. Record* **134**, 433–453.

Péczely, P. (1963). Különböző ökotípusú madárfajok neurosecretiojának vizsgálata. *Biol. Kozlemen.* **11**, 45–49.

Phillips, R. E. (1964). "Wildness" in the Mallard duck: Effects of brain lesions and stimulation on "escape behavior" and reproduction. *J. Comp. Neurol.* **122**, 139–155.

Phillips, R. E., and van Tienhoven, A. (1960). Endocrine factors involved in the failure of pintail ducks *Anas acuta* to reproduce in captivity. *J. Endocrinol.* **21**, 253–261.

Pickering, B. T., and Heller, H. (1959). Chromatographic and biological characteristics of fish and frog neurohypophysial extracts. *Nature* **184**, 1463–1465.

Rahn, H., and Painter, B. T. (1941). The comparative histology of the bird pituitary. *Anat. Record* **79**, 297–310.

Ralph, C. L. (1959). Some effects of hypothalamic lesions on gonadotrophin release in the hen. *Anat. Record* **134**, 411–431.

Ralph, C. L. (1960). Polydipsia in the hen following lesions in the supraoptic hypothalamus. *Am. J. Physiol.* **198**, 528–530.

Ralph, C. L., and Fraps, R. M. (1959a). Long-term effects of diencephalic lesions on the ovary of the hen. *Am. J. Physiol.* **197**, 1279–1283.

Ralph, C. L., and Fraps, R. M. (1959b). Effect of hypothalamic lesions on progesterone-induced ovulation in the hen. *Endocrinology* **65**, 819–824.

Ralph, C. L., and Fraps, R. M. (1960). Induction of ovulation in the hen by injection of progesterone into the brain. *Endocrinology* **66**, 269–272.

Rougeul, A., Assenmacher, I., and Kordon, C. (1959). Étude oscillographique d'une activation non-specifique dans l'encéphale du canard eveillé. *J. Physiol.* (*Paris*) **51**, 560–561.

Sawyer, W. H. (1961). Comparative physiology and pharmacology of the neurohypophysis. *Recent Progr. Hormone Res.* **17**, 437–465.

Sawyer, W. H., Munsick, R. A., and Van Dyke, H. B. (1960). Antidiuretic hormones. *Circulation* **21**, 1027–1037.

Scharrer, E., and Scharrer, B. (1954a). Hormones produced by neurosecretory cells. *Recent Progr. Hormone Res.* **10**, 183–240.

Scharrer, E., and Scharrer, B. (1954b). Neurosekretion. *In* "Handbuch der mikroskopischen Anatomie des Menschen" (W. von Möllendorff, ed.), Vol. VI, Part 5, pp. 953–1066. Springer, Berlin.

Schreiber, V. (1963). "The Hypothalamo-Hypophysial System." Publ. House Czech. Acad. Sci., Prague.

Sestini, F. (1936). Sur di una radiazione frontale del chiasma dei nervi ottici negli ucelli. *Atti Reale Accad. Fisiocr. Siena* **6**, 33–34.

Sestini, F., and Donatelli, L. (1936). Sulla omologia, sulla origine, sulla terminazione e sulla propabile interpretazione funzionale del fascetto della lamina terminale negli ucelli. *Rass. Studi Psichiat.* **25**, 501–525.

Shirley, H. V., and Nalbandov, A. V. (1956a). Effects of neurohypophysectomy in domestic chickens. *Endocrinology* **58**, 477–483.

Shirley, H. V., and Nalbandov, A. V. (1956b). Effects of transecting hypophyseal stalks in laying hens. *Endocrinology* **58**, 694–700.

Spatz, H. (1954). Das Hypophysen-Hypothalamus-System in seiner Bedeutung für die Fortpflanzung. *Verhandl. Anat. Ges.* (*Mainz*) **14**, 46–85.

Spatz, H. (1958). Die Proximale (Suprasellära) Hypophyse, ihre Beziehungen zum Diencephalon und ihre Regenerationspotenz. *In* "Pathophysiologia Diencephalica" (S. B. Curri and L. Martini, eds.), pp. 54–77. Springer, Vienna.

Stolze, R. (1952). Über Neurosekretion im Vogelhirn. Dissertation, Med. Fac., University of Kiel.

Stutinsky, F. (1955). Contribution à l'étude du complexe hypothalamo-neurohypophysaire. Sci. Thesis, University of Paris.

Stutinsky, F. (1958). Rapports du neurosécrétat hypothalamique avec l'adénohypophyse dans conditions normales et expérimentales. *In* "Pathophysiologia Diencephalica" (S. B. Curri and L. Martini, eds.), pp. 78–103. Springer, Vienna.

Szentágothai, J., Flerkó, B., Mess, B., and Halász, B. (1962). "Hypothalamic Control of the Anterior Pituitary." Akad. Kiadó, Budapest.

Tanaka, K., and Nakajo, S. (1962a). Participation of neurohypophysial hormone in oviposition in the hen. *Endocrinology* **70**, 453–458.

Tanaka, K., and Nakajo, S. (1962b). Oviposition-inducing activities of the chicken posterior pituitary extract, synthetic oxytocin and mammalian vasopressin. *Proc. Section Papers 12th World's Poultry Congr., Sydney, 1962* pp. 123–125.

Tixier-Vidal, A. (1963). Histophysiologie de l'adénohypophyse des oiseaux. *In* "Cytologie de l'adénohypophyse" (J. Benoit and C. Da Lage, eds.). *Colloq. Intern. C.N.R.S.* (*Paris*) **128**, 255–273.

Tixier-Vidal, A., and Assenmacher, I. (1963). Action de la métopirone sur la préhypophyse du canard mâle: essai d'identification des cellules corticotropes. *Compt. Rend. Soc. Biol.* **157**, 1350–1354.

Tixier-Vidal, A., Herlant, M., and Benoit, J. (1962). La préhypophyse du canard Pékin mâle au cours du cycle annuel. *Arch. Biol.* (*Liège*) **73**, 318–368.

Uemura, H. (1964a). Effects of water deprivation on the hypothalamo-hypophysial neurosecretory system of the Grass Parakeet, *Melopsittacus undulatus. Gen. Comp. Endocrinol.* **4**, 193–198.

Uemura, H. (1964b). Cholinesterases in the hypothalamo-hypophysial neurosecretory system of the bird. *Zool. Mag.* (*Tokyo*) **73**, 118–126 (in Japanese).

Uemura, H., and Kobayashi, H. (1963). Effects of prolonged daily photoperiods and estrogen on the hypothalamic neurosecretory system of the passerine bird, *Zosterops palpebrosa japonica. Gen. Comp. Endocrinol.* **3**, 253–264.

van Tienhoven, A. (1953). Further study on the neurogenic blockage of LH release in the hen. *Anat. Record* **115**, 374–375.

van Tienhoven, A. (1961). Endocrinology of reproduction in birds. *In* "Sex and Internal Secretions" (W. C. Young, ed.), 3rd ed., Vol. 2, pp. 1088–1169. Williams & Wilkins, Baltimore, Maryland.

van Tienhoven, A., and Juhász, L. P. (1962). The chicken telencephalon, diencephalon and mesencephalon in stereotaxic coordinates. *J. Comp. Neurol.* **118,** 185–198.

van Tienhoven, A., Nalbandov, A. V., and Norton, H. W. (1954). Effect of dibenamine on progesterone-induced and "spontaneous" ovulation in the hen. *Endocrinology* **54,** 605–611.

Vitums, A., Mikami, S., Oksche, A., and Farner, D. S. (1964). Vascularization of the hypothalamo-hypophysial complex in the White-crowned Sparrow, *Zonotrichia leucophrys gambelii. Z. Zellforsch. Mikroskop. Anat.* **64,** 541–569.

Weber, W., and Bachmann, H. (1964). Zur Entwicklung und Funktion des Zwischenhirn-Hypophysensystems bei *Columba livia dom. Naturwiss.* **51,** 321.

Wilson, F. E. (1965). The effects of hypothalamic lesions on the photoperiodic testicular response in White-crowned Sparrows, *Zonotrichia leucophrys gambelii.* Doctoral Dissertation, Washington State University, Pullman, Washington.

Wilson, F. E., and Farner, D. S. (1965). Effects of hypothalamic lesions on testicular growth. *Federation Proc.* **24,** 129.

Wilson, W. O., Abplanalp, H., and Arrington, L. (1962). Sexual development of coturnix as affected by changes in photoperiods. *Poultry Sci.* **41,** 17–22.

Wingstrand, K. G. (1951). "The Structure and Development of the Avian Pituitary from a Comparative and Functional Viewpoint." Gleerup, Lund.

Wingstrand, K. G. (1953). Neurosecretion and antidiuretic activity in chick embryos with remarks on the subcommissural organ. *Arkiv Zool.* **6,** 41–67.

Wingstrand, K. G. (1954). The ontogeny of the neurosecretory system in chick embryos. *Pubbl. Staz. Zool. Napoli* **24,** Suppl., 27–31.

Wingstrand, K. G. (1963). Comparative histology of the adenohypophysis of birds. *In* "Cytologie de l'adénohypophyse" (J. Benoit and C. Da Lage, eds.). *Colloq. Intern. C.N.R.S.* (*Paris*) **128,** 243–253.

Wolfson, A. (1963). The role of light in the neuroendocrine system: Discussion. *In* "Advances in Neuroendocrinology" (A. V. Nalbandov, ed.), pp. 402–425. Univ. of Illinois Press, Urbana, Illinois.

Wolfson, A., and Kobayashi, H. (1962). Phosphatase activity and neurosecretion in the hypothalamo-hypophyseal system in relation to the photoperiodic gonadal response in *Zonotrichia albicollis. In* "Progress in Comparative Endocrinology." *Gen. Comp. Endocrinol.* Suppl. 1, 168–179.

Yasuda, M. (1954). Studies on the nucleus magnocellularis praeopticus et supraopticus and nucleus magnocellularis paraventricularis in fowls. *Japan. J. Zootech. Sci.* **25,** 41–48.

Zarrow, M. X., and Bastian, J. W. (1953). Blockade of ovulation in the hen with adrenolytic and parasympatholytic drugs. *Proc. Soc. Exptl. Biol. Med.* **84,** 457–459.

CHAPTER 31

Brain Neurohumors and Endocrine Function

WILLIAM F. GANONG and LEOLA LORENZEN

I. Introduction

A group of organic compounds are suspected of being chemical mediators at synaptic junctions in the central nervous system. These compounds, often referred to collectively as "neurohumors," include 5-hydroxytryptamine (serotonin, 5-HT), norepinephrine, dopamine, acetylcholine, histamine, substance P, and γ-aminobutyric acid (GABA). Small amounts of epinephrine, tyramine, and other amines are also found in the brain. Variations in the brain content of these substances have been studied intensively by psychopharmacologists because some of the drugs which affect mental function alter the brain content of some of the neurohumors. By contrast, relatively little attention has been paid to these compounds by neuroendocrinologists, even though most of the compounds are found in particularly high concentration in the hypothalamus. In this chapter, the distribution and metabolism of the neurohumors are described and the data suggesting that they are synaptic mediators are summarized. Their relation to endocrine function is then reviewed in detail.

II. Distribution of Neurohumors in the Brain

The distribution of acetylcholine, 5-hydroxytryptamine, substance P, norepinephrine, histamine, and GABA in the brains of experimental animals is summarized in Table I. The distribution of these substances in human brain is similar, with high concentrations in some parts and low concentrations in others (Bertler, 1961; Hornykiewicz, 1964). This uneven distribution is also illustrated in Table II which lists the concentrations of norepinephrine, dopamine, 5-hydroxytryptamine, histamine, and

TABLE I

Brain Content of a Number of Substances Suspected of Serving as Transmitters at Synapses in the Central Nervous System[a]

	Dog[b]					Rat[c]
	Acetyl-choline	Substance P	Sero-tonin	Norep-inephrine	Hista-mine	(γ-amino-butyric acid)
Cerebral cortex—somasthetic	2.8	—	—	0	0	210
Cerebral cortex—motor	4.5	19	0.02	0.18		
Caudate nucleus	2.7	46	0.10	0.06	0	—
Thalamus	3.0	13	0.02	0.16	0	—
Hypothalamus	1.8	70	0.25	1.03	30	380
Hippocampus	—	15	0.05	—	—	—
Medulla	1.6	25	0.03	—	—	200
Cerebellum	0.2	2	0.01	0.07	0	160
Spinal cord	1.6	29	0	—	0	—
Sympathetic ganglia	30	7	0	6.00	5	—
Area postrema	—	460	0.24	1.04	—	—

[a] From Ganong (1965a). All values in micrograms per gram, except data for substance P which are expressed in units per gram.

[b] Data on dog from various authors, compiled by Paton (1958).

[c] Data on rat γ-aminobutyric acid from Berl & Waelsch (1958).

TABLE II

AMINE AND SUBSTANCE P CONTENT OF SELECTED PORTIONS OF THE HUMAN BRAIN[a]

	Fresh tissue[b]				
	Norepinephrine	Dopamine	5-Hydroxytryptamine	Histamine	Substance P
Amygdala	0.21	0.6	0.26	—	—
Caudate nucleus	0.09	3.5	0.33	0.5	85
Putamen	0.12	3.7	0.32	0.7	—
Globus pallidus	0.15	0.5	0.23	0.6	—
Thalamus	0.13	0.3	0.26	0.4	12
Hypothalamus	1.25	0.8	0.29	2.5	102
Substantia nigra	0.21	0.9	0.55	—	699

[a] Data on histamine from P. L. McGeer (1964). Data on norepinephrine, dopamine, and 5-hydroxytryptamine from Hornykiewicz (1964). Data on substance P from Zetler and Schlusser (1955); see also Anton and Sayre (1964). From Ganong (1965a).

[b] All values in micrograms per gram except data for substance P which are expressed in units per gram.

substance P in selected portions of the central nervous system in man. Epinephrine is found in the brain in small amounts; its distribution is similar to that of norepinephrine. The metabolite of norepinephrine, normetanephrine (3-methoxynorepinephrine), has also been isolated from brain tissue (Häggendal, 1963). Systemically administered tryptamine is taken up by the brain (Pletscher *et al.*, 1963). Tyramine is found in the central nervous system, with the highest concentrations in the brain stem and spinal cord (S. Spector *et al.*, 1963).

The highest concentration of acetylcholine is in the motor cortex, while the highest concentrations of norepinephrine and 5-hydroxytryptamine are in the hypothalamus and parts of the limbic system. Halevy (1960) has presented evidence that there is more 5-hydroxytryptamine in the anterior than in the posterior hypothalamus. High concentrations of histamine are found in the anterior pituitary, posterior pituitary, and median eminence of the hypothalamus (Harris *et al.*, 1952; Quastel and Quastel, 1961; Green, 1964). Much of the histamine in the body is in mast cells, and there are mast cells in the pituitary gland and the hypothalamus. It appears that all the histamine in the posterior pituitary is in mast cells, while the histamine in the anterior pituitary and neighboring ventral hypothalamus is not (Green, 1964). This conclusion is based on experiments with compound 48/80, a substance which depletes mast cell histamine without affecting the histamine outside of these cells, and reserpine, which decreases the histamine outside of mast cells but does not deplete mast cell histamine. At least in the cat, reserpine is said to cause a marked depletion of brain histamine as well as brain norepinephrine and 5-hydroxytryptamine (Green, 1964; see, however, Ungar and Witten, 1963). Large amounts of 5-hydroxytryptamine, histamine, and norepinephrine are found in the area postrema (Table I; Adam, 1961), and there is a high content of 5-hydroxytryptamine in the pineal gland (Bertler *et al.*, 1963). About half of the 5-hydroxytryptamine in the pineal is in parenchymal cells and half is in sympathetic nerve endings. The latter component is markedly reduced by sympathectomy (De Iraldi *et al.*, 1963). The significance of the amine content of the pineal gland is discussed in Chapters 18 and 32.

The dopamine concentration of the caudate nucleus and putamen (but not the globus pallidus) is high, while the norepinephrine content of these nuclei is low (Table II). These parts of the basal ganglia apparently have biochemical machinery that is similar to that in the parts of the brain that are rich in norepinephrine, but they lack dopamine β-oxidase, the enzyme that catalyzes the conversion of dopamine to norepinephrine. Consequently, catecholamine biosynthesis stops at dopamine. There are moderate amounts of 5-hydroxytryptamine, norepinephrine, and dopamine in the spinal cord of rabbits, localized for the most part in the intermediate gray column (Carlsson *et al.*, 1964) and in the posterior horn (E. G. McGeer and McGeer, 1962). After cord section, the 5-hydroxytryptamine content of the cord below the section declines markedly (Carlsson *et al.*, 1963; Magnusson and Rosengren, 1963).

Substance P is a polypeptide found in high concentration in the hypothalamus and other parts of the brain stem in animals and humans (Zetler and Schlusser, 1955). The substantia nigra contains particularly large amounts (Lembeck and Starke, 1963), and relatively large quantities are also found in the dorsal roots of the spinal nerves (Gaddum, 1960; Stern, 1963).

γ-Aminobutyric acid is found in highest concentration in the diencephalon and corpora quadrigemina, and the concentration in the cerebral hemispheres, pons, and medulla is low (Berl and Waelsch, 1958; Roberts, 1962). In the cerebellar cortex and the cerebral cortex, it is most plentiful in the superficial gray layers (Hirsch and Robins, 1962).

It is worth noting that several of the substances suspected of serving as synaptic mediators in the central nervous system are also found in large quantities outside the central nervous system. In mammals, the highest concentrations of 5-hydroxytryptamine are found in the intestine, where the amine facilitates peristalsis, and in platelets. The 5-hydroxytryptamine liberated from platelets in traumatized tissue probably promotes the constriction of injured blood vessels (see Lewis, 1964; Ganong, 1965a). Substance P is also found in the intestine, where it appears to be associated with the neurons in Meissner's plexus (Gaddum, 1960; Haefely and Hürlimann, 1962; Häggendal and Malmfors, 1963). The retina contains substance P and dopamine (Haefely and Hürlimann, 1962; Häggendal and Malmfors, 1963). Histamine is found in many non-neural tissues. Acetylcholine is the chemical mediator liberated at the endings of the spinal motor neurons supplying skeletal muscles, and in the autonomic nervous system at the endings of all preganglionic neurons and all parasympathetic postganglionic neurons. Some postganglionic sympathetic neurons are also cholinergic, although norepinephrine is liberated at the endings of most postganglionic sympathetic neurons (Wolfe *et al.*, 1962). There is some evidence that even in the adrenergic neurons there is a cholinergic discharge which precedes and is responsible for the release of norepinephrine (Burn, 1963). Epinephrine is the main secretion of the adrenal medulla in many mammalian species (see Chapter 25), although norepinephrine is also secreted by this gland.

III. Metabolism of Neurohumors

A. 5-Hydroxytryptamine

5-Hydroxytryptamine is formed in the body by hydroxylation and decarboxylation of the essential amino acid, tryptophan (Fig. 1). It is

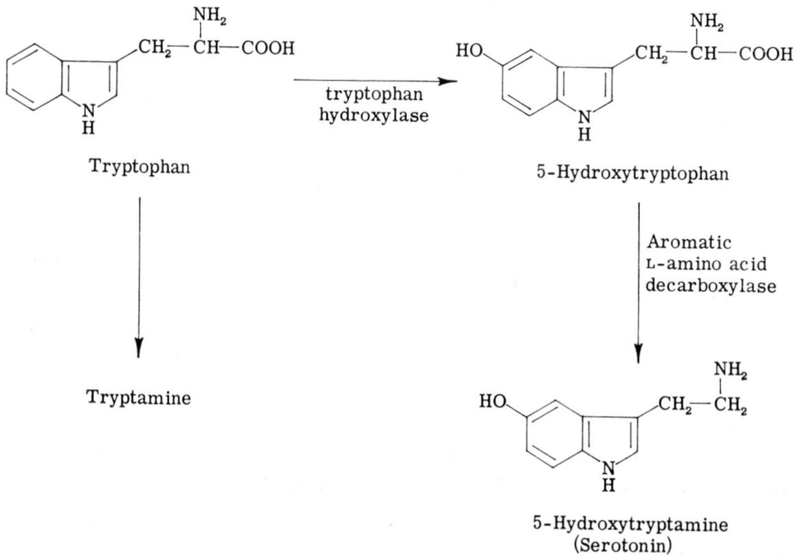

Tryptophan → (tryptophan hydroxylase) → 5-Hydroxytryptophan

5-Hydroxytryptophan → (Aromatic L-amino acid decarboxylase) → 5-Hydroxytryptamine (Serotonin)

Tryptophan → Tryptamine

FIG. 1. Biosynthesis of 5-hydroxytryptamine. The same enzyme catalyzes the decarboxylation of 5-hydroxytryptophan, dopa, histidine, and several other amino acids.

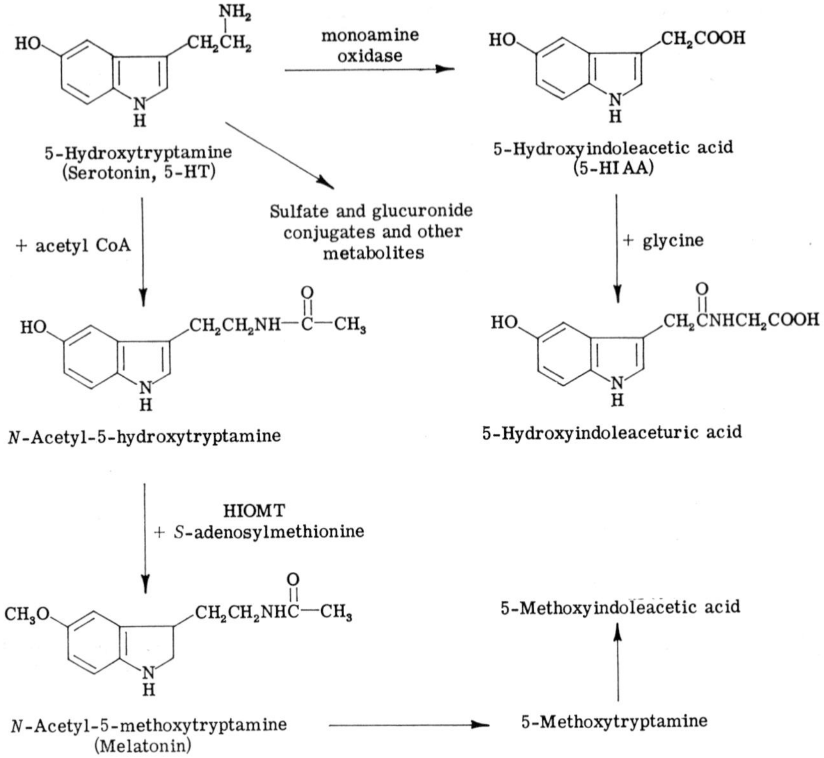

5-Hydroxytryptamine (Serotonin, 5-HT) — monoamine oxidase → 5-Hydroxyindoleacetic acid (5-HIAA)

5-Hydroxytryptamine → Sulfate and glucuronide conjugates and other metabolites

5-Hydroxytryptamine + acetyl CoA → N-Acetyl-5-hydroxytryptamine

5-HIAA + glycine → 5-Hydroxyindoleaceturic acid

N-Acetyl-5-hydroxytryptamine — HIOMT + S-adenosylmethionine → N-Acetyl-5-methoxytryptamine (Melatonin)

N-Acetyl-5-methoxytryptamine (Melatonin) → 5-Methoxytryptamine → 5-Methoxyindoleacetic acid

FIG. 2. Catabolism of 5-hydroxytryptamine and biosynthesis and catabolism of melatonin. In oxidative deaminations catalyzed by monoamine oxidase, an intermediate step is formation of the aldehyde derivative. The *O*-methyltransferase that catalyzes the methoxylation of *N*-acetyl-5-hydroxytryptamine is found only in the pineal gland. (From Wurtman *et al.,* 1963b.)

metabolized principally by conversion to 5-hydroxyindoleacetic acid (5-HIAA), which is the major urinary metabolite of 5-hydroxytryptamine (Fig. 2). This reaction is catalyzed by monoamine oxidase. Some of the 5-hydroxytryptamine is acetylated and then methoxylated to form melatonin. The enzyme catalyzing the methoxylation, hydroxyindole-*O*-methyltransferase, is found only in the pineal gland (Wurtman *et al.,* 1963b). The activity of this enzyme is apparently regulated in part by incident light, and the effect of light is mediated via the eyes and the sympathetic nerves to the pineal (see Chapter 18).

B. Catecholamines

Dopamine, norepinephrine, and epinephrine are synthesized from phenylalanine or tyrosine, for the most part via the pathway shown in

Phenylalanine → (phenylalanine hydroxylase) → *p*-Tyrosine → (tyrosine hydroxylase) → Dihydroxyphenylalanine (dopa)

↓ aromatic L-amino acid decarboxylase

Dihydroxyphenylethylamine (Dopamine) → (dopamine β-oxidase) → Norepinephrine → (phenylethanolamine-*N*-methyltransferase, *S*-adenosylmethionine) → Epinephrine

FIG. 3. Biosynthesis of catecholamines.

Fig. 3. The enzymes involved at each step have been intensively studied. Congenital absence of phenylalanine hydroxylase is the underlying defect in the form of mental retardation known as phenylpyruvic oligophrenia. The hydroxylation of tyrosine by tyrosine hydroxylase to form dihydroxyphenylalanine (dopa) is a key step in catecholamine biosynthesis from the biochemical point of view, but relatively little is known as yet about the properties of the enzyme. The aromatic L-amino acid decarboxylase that catalyzes the conversion of dopa to dopamine is a ubiquitous enzyme that is also responsible for the decarboxylation of 5-hydroxytryptophan to form 5-hydroxytryptamine and of histidine to form histamine. It can be inhibited by analogs of dopa (Sjoerdsma *et al.*, 1963). One of these analogs, α-methyl-dopa, is used clinically in the treatment of essential hypertension (Sjoerdsma, 1963). Formation of epinephrine from norepinephrine requires phenylethanolamine-*N*-methyltransferase, the enzyme that catalyzes the transfer of the methyl group from S-adenosylmethionine to norepinephrine. This enzyme has not been found in tissues other than the adrenal medulla, and there is considerable debate about whether the small amounts of epinephrine found in other tissues are synthesized in the tissues or represent epinephrine taken up from the blood stream (Holtz, 1959; Weiner, 1964).

Two enzymes, monoamine oxidase (MAO) and catechol-*O*-methyltransferase (COMT), play a major role in the metabolism of epineph-

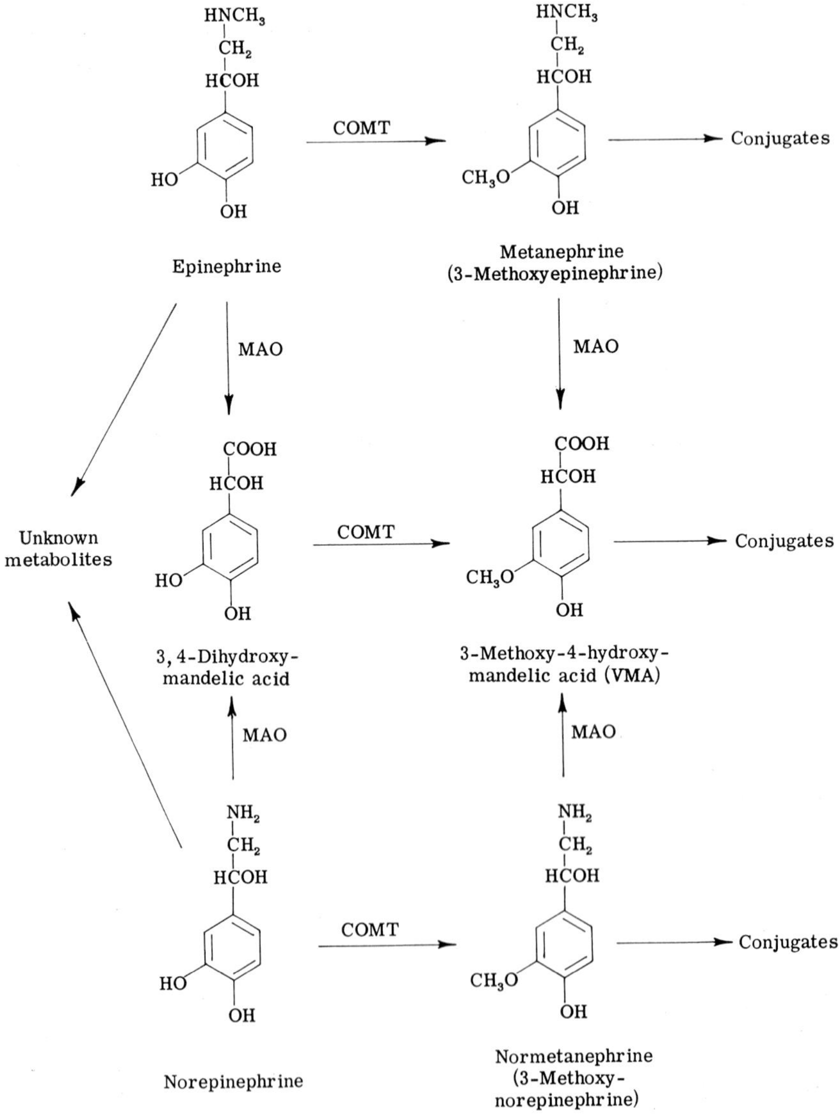

MAO = Monoamine oxidase
COMT = Catechol-*O*-methyltransferase

FIG. 4. Catabolism of epinephrine and norepinephrine. The conjugates are mostly glucuronides and sulfates. See legend for Fig. 2. (From Ganong, 1965a.)

rine and norepinephrine (Kopin, 1964). The location of monoamine oxidase in tissues can be demonstrated by a histochemical technique (Mustakallio *et al.*, 1961). The enzyme catalyzes the oxidative deamination of epinephrine and norepinephrine to form 3,4-dihydroxymandelic acid (Fig. 4), and catechol-*O*-methyltransferase catalyzes the conversion of this compound to 3-methoxy-4-hydroxymandelic acid (vanilmandelic acid, VMA). Alternately, epinephrine and norepinephrine are first converted to metanephrine and normetanephrine respectively (La Brosse *et al.*, 1958), and these compounds are deaminated to form 3-methoxy-

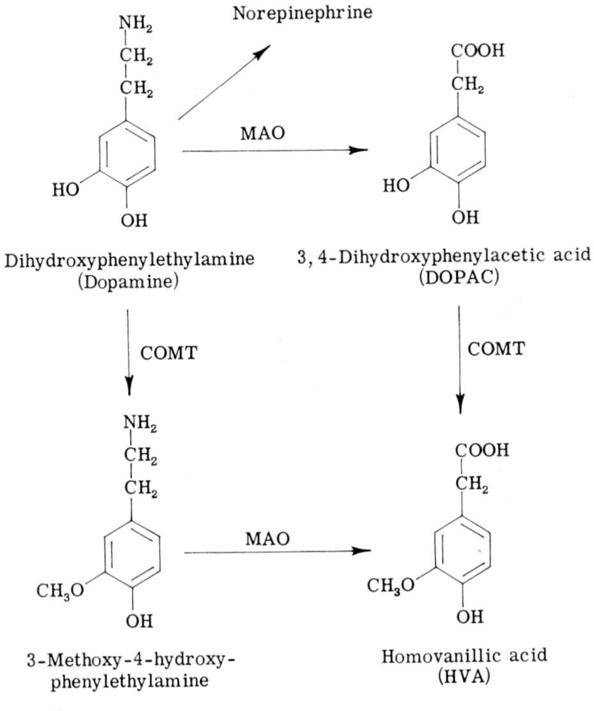

Norepinephrine

NH_2–CH_2–CH_2 (ring, HO, OH)

MAO →

COOH–CH_2 (ring, HO, OH)

Dihydroxyphenylethylamine (Dopamine)

3, 4-Dihydroxyphenylacetic acid (DOPAC)

COMT ↓

COMT ↓

NH_2–CH_2–CH_2 (ring, CH_3O, OH)

MAO →

COOH–CH_2 (ring, CH_3O, OH)

3-Methoxy-4-hydroxy-phenylethylamine

Homovanillic acid (HVA)

FIG. 5. Catabolism of dopamine. See legend for Fig. 2. (Data from Werdinius *et al.*, 1963.)

4-hydroxymandelic acid. Metanephrine, normetanephrine, and the mandelic acid derivatives are physiologically inert. In the circulation and the liver, most of the catecholamines are *O*-methylated before they are deaminated, while in the other tissues, the reverse is said to be true (Crout *et al.*, 1961). However, intrathecal administration of pyrogallol, a drug which selectively inhibits catechol-*O*-methyltransferase (Axelrod and Laroche, 1959), has been reported to increase brain catecholamine content (Masami *et al.*, 1962); therefore, *O*-methylation may be a more

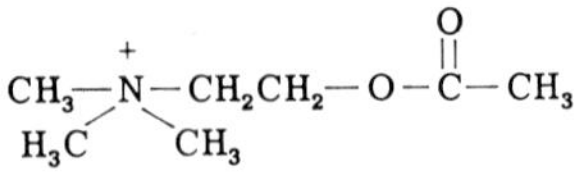

$$CH_3-\overset{+}{N}(CH_3)_2-CH_2CH_2-O-\overset{O}{\overset{\|}{C}}-CH_3$$

Acetylcholine

$$HS\text{-}CoA + ATP + \text{acetate} \xrightarrow{\text{acetylthiokinase}} \text{Acetyl CoA} + H_2O + ADP$$

$$\text{Acetyl CoA} + \text{choline} \xrightarrow{\text{choline acetylase}} \text{Acetylcholine} + HS\text{-}CoA$$

$$\text{Acetylcholine} + H_2O \xrightarrow{\text{cholinesterase}} \text{Choline} + \text{acetate}$$

FIG. 6. Summary of reactions involved in synthesis and breakdown of acetylcholine. HS-CoA, reduced coenzyme A; acetyl-CoA, acetyl coenzyme A.

important metabolic pathway in the brain than was previously thought.

Dopamine, like epinephrine and norepinephrine, can be deaminated and then *O*-methylated, or *O*-methylated and then deaminated. These reactions and the products formed are shown in Fig. 5; 3,4-dihydroxy phenylacetic acid (DOPAC) and homovanillic acid (HVA) have been isolated from brain and spinal fluid (Werdinius *et al.*, 1963).

C. Acetylcholine

Acetylcholine is formed by the reaction of active acetate (acetyl coenzyme A) with choline in the presence of the enzyme choline acetylase (Fig. 6). Adenosine triphosphate (ATP) provides the energy for the formation of active acetate. The acetylcholine is loosely bound to protein and stored in the endings of cholinergic neurons. By an unknown mechanism, nerve impulses arriving at the endings cause liberation of free acetylcholine into the space between the neuron and the next succeeding nerve or muscle cell. The liberated acetylcholine causes depolarization of the postsynaptic membrane and then is rapidly destroyed by hydrolysis. A variety of different esterases can catalyze this hydrolysis, but an esterase which is specific for acetylcholine (specific cholinesterase, acetylcholinesterase) is present in large quantities at cholinergic nerve endings. The general term for the esterases which hydrolyze other esters as well as acetylcholine is nonspecific cholinesterase.

D. Histamine

Histamine can be formed by brain tissue from the amino acid histidine

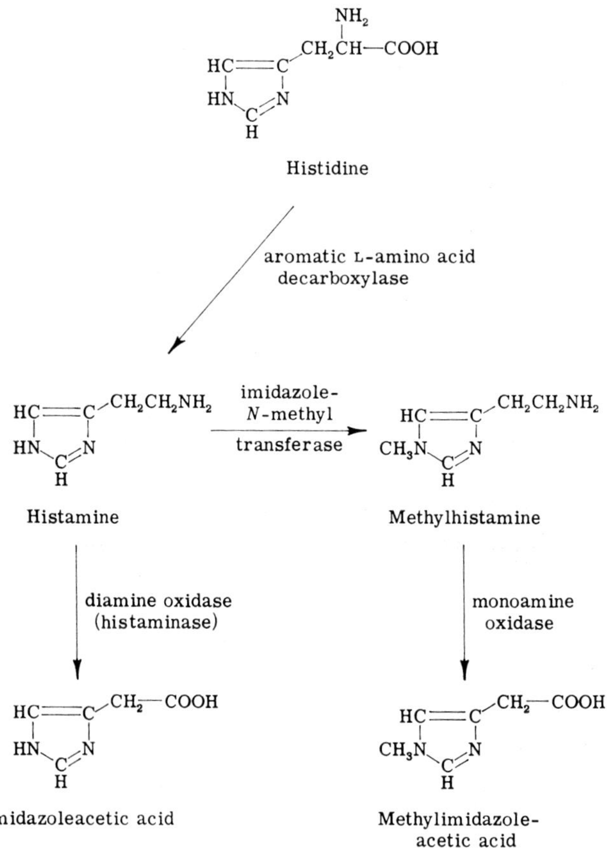

FIG. 7. Biosynthesis and catabolism of histamine. (From Ganong, 1965a.)

(Fig. 7). The decarboxylase is the same one that is involved in the synthesis of 5-hydroxytryptamine and the catecholamines. *In vitro*, hypothalamic tissue forms much more histamine than do other parts of the brain (White, 1964). The principal pathway for metabolism of histamine in the brain is ring-*N*-methylation (Green, 1964; White, 1964). Outside the brain, histamine is also oxidatively deaminated to form imidazoleacetic acid, and methylhistamine is deaminated to form methylimidazoleacetic acid. There is some uncertainty about whether deamination occurs in the brain (Crossland, 1962; Green, 1964; White, 1964). Monoamine oxidase catalyzes the oxidative deamination of methylhistamine, while diamine oxidase, an enzyme which is also called histaminase, catalyzes the oxidative deamination of histamine.

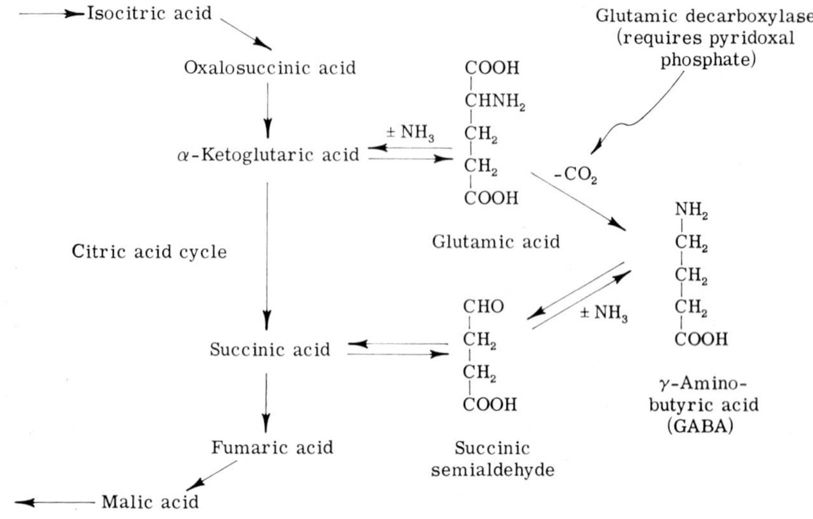

FIG. 8. Formation and metabolism of γ-aminobutyric acid (GABA).

E. Substance P

Substance P is a basic polypeptide with a molecular weight of 1600. It contains thirteen different amino acids, but its exact structure is as yet unknown (Haefely and Hürlimann, 1962). Little is known about its synthesis and destruction, although there is some evidence that the brain contains enzymes that catalyze these processes (Krivoy *et al.*, 1963).

F. γ-Aminobutyric Acid

γ-Aminobutyric acid is bound to protein in the nervous system (Sano and Roberts, 1963). It is formed from α-ketoglutaric acid, and metabolized by conversion to succinic acid via succinic semialdehyde (Fig. 8). Thus, the pathway for GABA synthesis and destruction is essentially an offshoot of the citric acid cycle. The first reaction in the breakdown of GABA is a transamination, α-ketoglutaric acid being aminated to form glutamic acid when GABA is converted to succinic semialdehyde; the enzyme involved is therefore called GABA-α-ketoglutaric transaminase.

IV. Neurohumors as Mediators at Synapses in the Brain

Much has been written about the "mediator function" of the substances discussed in the preceding sections of this chapter, and the impression has sometimes been created that such a function is an established fact.

Actually, much of the evidence supporting the concept that these substances are mediators at synapses in the brain is indirect, and the amount of evidence varies from one compound to another.

A. Experimental Approaches

Substances which are unevenly distributed in the nervous system have generally been considered candidates for a synaptic mediator function, especially if the distribution of the enzymes involved in their synthesis and breakdown parallels that of the substances. Because of the variation in the number of synapses from region to region in the brain, one would expect mediators to be distributed unevenly.

A change in behavior or some other neural function when the effective concentration of a suspected synaptic transmitter is changed is also evidence for a mediator function. There are numerous ways that changes in the concentration of mediators or their access to effectors can be brought about. Mediators must be synthesized, stored in nerve endings, and liberated from these endings; they must exert their effect on the postsynaptic neurons and then be inactivated. Facilitation or inhibition of any of these five processes alters the postsynaptic response.

Attempts to produce effects by systemic injection of a suspected mediator may be misleading because the degree to which many substances enter the nervous system from the blood ("cross the blood-brain barrier") is limited. A word of caution is in order in this regard; the exact anatomical limits of the blood-brain barrier may vary, depending on the substance tested. For example, Weil-Malherbe *et al.* (1959) have demonstrated that although epinephrine is excluded from the rest of the brain, it enters quite readily into the hypothalamus. The problem of the blood-brain barrier can be circumvented by employing intrathecal, intraventricular, or intracerebral injections, but these techniques in some ways introduce more problems than they solve.

Some investigators have argued that if a substance and the enzymes responsible for its synthesis and its breakdown are unevenly distributed in the central nervous system, and if changing the effective concentration of the substance in the brain produces a particular reproducible neural response, the synaptic mediator function of the substance is proved. Actually, all such evidence is indirect and far from conclusive. Indeed, it would be difficult to draw any conclusions about mediators in the brain if it had not been for the development of a number of new methods for studying suspected synaptic transmitters.

Among the most important of these methods are histochemical techniques for demonstrating suspected mediators in brain tissue. Before they were developed, it could not be determined whether the neurohumors were in neurons or glial cells, and whether or not they were concentrated at nerve endings. Another important advance has been isolation of the nerve ending fraction from brain homogenates by differential centrifugation. It is difficult to isolate a part of the brain containing only one type of synapse, but this has been approached in studies of the isolated lateral geniculate body. It has also been possible in some instances to show increased release of suspected mediators into the perfusing fluid when a perfused brain is stimulated.

Additional evidence on mediator function has come from studies of the application of minute amounts of chemicals to the cell membranes of single neurons in the central nervous system. The technique has been called microelectrophoresis or iontophoresis, and it has been described in detail by Curtis (1964). A micropipette with two barrels is used. One barrel is filled with a conducting solution and used to record the electrical responses of cells. A solution of the chemical under study is placed in the other barrel. The micropipette is lowered into the brain until it is close to a neuron. The electrical responses of the neuron are then studied as the chemical diffuses out of the other barrel onto the surface of the cell. Alternately, the pH of the solution of the chemical being studied is adjusted until most of the chemical is in the ionized form. The ions are then made to move out of the barrel and onto the cell membrane by passing a very weak cathodal or anodal current through the barrel. Micropipette assemblies made up of more than two pipettes have been constructed and some containing five barrels have been used successfully.

All of the compounds suspected of being synaptic mediators are distributed unevenly in the central nervous system. The other evidence for a synaptic mediator function is summarized below for each of the neurohumors.

B. 5-Hydroxytryptamine and Norepinephrine

The enzymes principally involved in the synthesis and the metabolism of 5-hydroxytryptamine and norepinephrine in tissue, aromatic L-amino acid decarboxylase and monoamine oxidase, are found in the various parts of the brain in concentrations that parallel the 5-hydroxytryptamine and norepinephrine content (Bogdanski *et al.*, 1957; Davison, 1958; Kuntzman *et al.*, 1961; Mustakallio *et al.*, 1961; Quastel and Quastel, 1961). A marked reduction in the brain concentration of catecholamines and 5-hydroxytryptamine is produced by the tranquilizer, reserpine, while increased activity and elevated mood occur when increased concentrations of both amines are produced by drugs that inhibit monoamine oxidase (Brodie *et al.*, 1961; Poschel and Ninteman, 1963). Injection of norepinephrine into the limbic system or hypothalamus has been reported to cause increased food intake in rats, while injection of derivatives of acetylcholine into the same areas causes drinking (Grossman, 1960, 1962; Fisher and Coury, 1962; Stein and Seiffer, 1962; Fisher, 1964; Wolf and Miller, 1964). On the basis of these observations, it has been postulated that there is an adrenergic circuit in the limbic-hypothalamic area that controls food intake, and a cholinergic circuit that controls water intake. Local injection experiments have also led to the postulate that 5-hydroxytryptamine is involved in the control of temperature regulation. Canal and Ornesi (1961) found that intraventricular injections of typhoid vaccine produced fever in animals, and this effect was prevented by a drug which blocks the effects of 5-hydroxytryptamine. Feldberg and Myers (1963) confirmed the observation that injecting pyrogens into the ventricle caused fever, and they also observed that intraventricular injections of 5-hydroxytryptamine had the same effect, while injections of norepinephrine decreased the febrile response to the pyrogens.

Recently, a histochemical technique has been developed which permits the visualization of the neurohumoral amines within cells (Carlsson *et al.*, 1962a; Falck, 1962). The method makes 5-hydroxytryptamine, norepinephrine, epinephrine, and dopamine fluoresce. By treating animals with various drugs which selectively increase or decrease the content of one or the other of these amines, it is possible to decide which amine is present at a particular locus (Carlsson *et al.*, 1962a,b).

Studies with this stain demonstrate that 5-hydroxytryptamine, norepinephrine, and dopamine are present primarily in nerve cells and not in glia, as some had speculated they might be (Utley, 1963). Furthermore, the stain shows that the amines are localized in granules which are particularly prominent in the synaptic endings of the neurons (Figs. 9 and 10). Of particular interest to neuroendocrinologists is the observation that there are large numbers of what appear to be dopamine-containing nerve terminals in close apposition to the portal vessels in the median eminence of the hypothalamus (Fuxe, 1963, 1964).

Another piece of evidence that the amines are synaptic mediators is the detection of 5-hydroxytryptamine and acetylcholine in a fraction of brain cell homogenate identifiable as pinched-off nerve endings (Michaelson and Whittaker, 1963; Zieher and DeRobertis, 1963). Norepinephrine is found in a similar granule fraction (Hagen, 1962).

Injection of 5-hydroxytryptamine or norepinephrine inhibits the response of single lateral geniculate neurons to orthodromically conducted

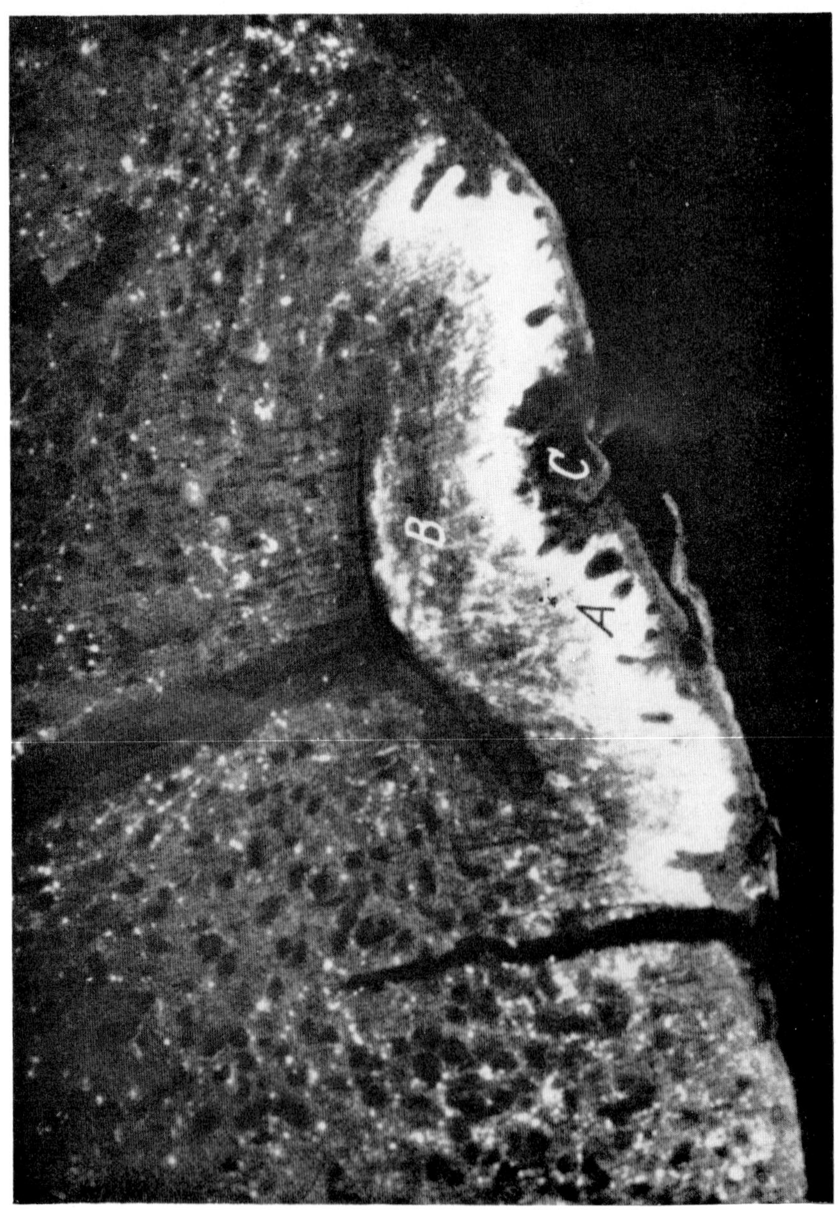

FIG. 9. For descriptive legend see p. 600.

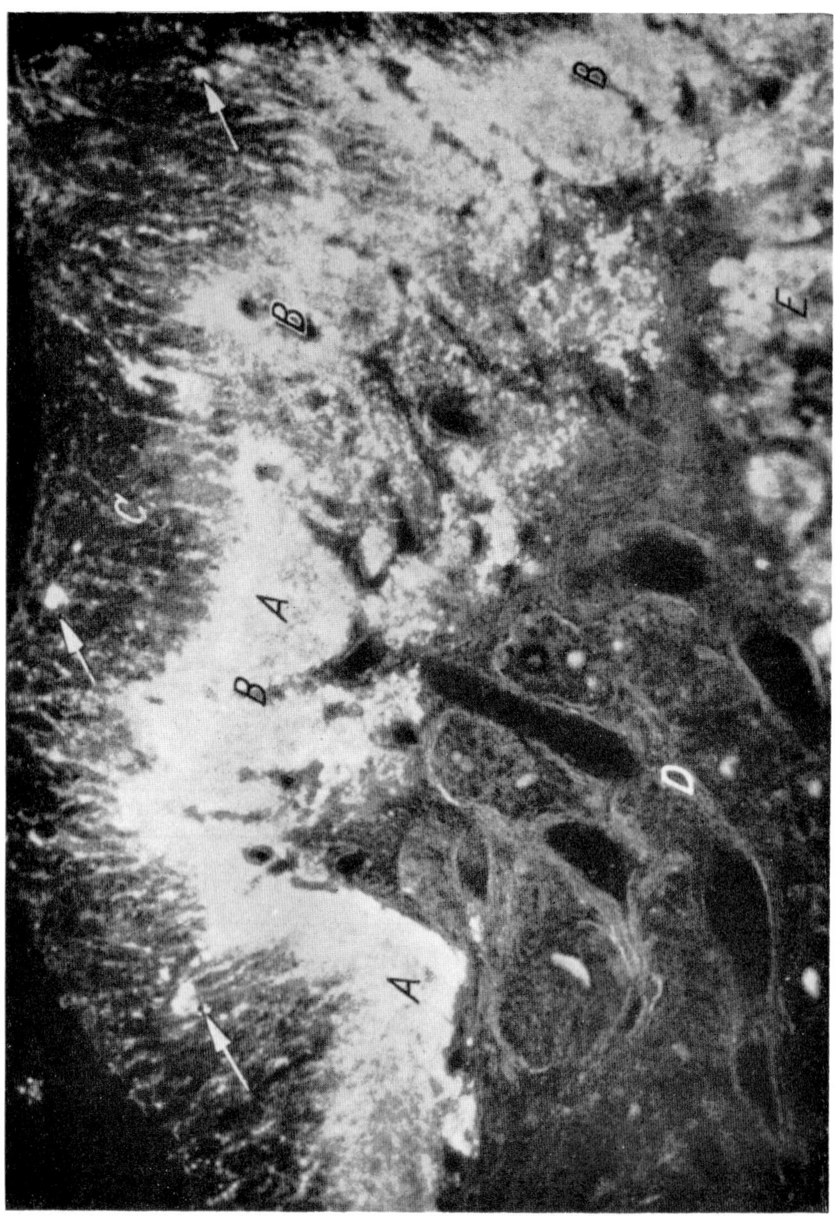

Fig. 10. For descriptive legend see p. 600.

impulses, but not to antidromic stimulation, indicating that these amines depress conduction at the synaptic junctions between the optic nerve fibers and the neurons that form the geniculocalcarine tract (Bishop *et al.*, 1958; Curtis and Davis, 1962).

C. Dopamine

As noted above, the principal characteristic of parts of the brain that have a high dopamine content is the absence of dopamine β-oxidase, the enzyme responsible for the conversion of dopamine to norepinephrine. The other enzymes necessary for the formation and metabolism of norepinephrine are present, and dopamine is metabolized by monoamine oxidase and/or catechol-*O*-methyltransferase to DOPAC and homovanillic acid (Fig. 5). Parkinson's disease is characterized by several abnormalities of motor function, and in this disease the dopamine content of the neostriatum is said to be less than one-half of normal (Barbeau *et al.*, 1961). Hypothalamic norepinephrine is also depressed, but not to as marked a degree. Reserpine increases brain DOPAC levels (Roos *et al.*, 1963). Administration of dopamine and dopa to animals treated with reserpine improves their performance of a conditioned avoidance response (Seiden and Carlsson, 1964; Seiden and Hanson, 1964). Thus, dopamine appears to be associated in some way with the function of the extrapyramidal system, and possibly plays a role in more complex forms of behavior. The best evidence that it does this by serving as a synaptic transmitter is the demonstration by Fuxe (1963, 1964) and by Carlsson *et al.* (1962a) of its presence in the terminal buttons of neurons. It has also been found in the nerve-ending fraction isolated from homogenized brain tissue, but there is more in the supernatant than there is in the nerve-ending fraction (Laverty *et al.*, 1963).

FIG. 9. Transverse section of ventral hypothalamus of the mouse, stained by a technique which makes monoamines fluoresce. Note large amounts of fluorescent material accumulated in middle zone of median eminence (A), which is indented by capillary loops from pars tuberalis (C). Internal zone of median eminence (B) contains less fluorescent material. × 165. (Reproduced, with permission, from Fuxe, 1964.)

FIG. 10. Section of median eminence and adjacent pituitary of the cat, stained by a technique which makes monoamines fluoresce. There is fluorescent material in the middle zone (A) around the capillary loops of the primary plexus of the portal-hypophyseal vessel system (B). There is very little fluorescent material in the pars tuberalis of the pituitary (D) and, except for a few fluorescent masses (arrows), in the internal zone of the median eminence (C). Some of the cells in the pars distalis fluoresce (E). × 165. (Reproduced, with permission, from Fuxe, 1964.)

D. Acetylcholine

There are histochemical techniques as well as chemical methods for demonstrating choline acetylase, true cholinesterase, and nonspecific cholinesterase in tissues (Abrahams *et al.*, 1957; Quastel and Quastel, 1961; Abrahams, 1963). The distribution of the first two enzymes in the nervous system parallels the distribution of acetylcholine (Feldberg, 1950; Burgen and Chipman, 1951; Bennett *et al.*, 1958; Quastel and Quastel, 1961; Gaddum, 1963). The enzymes are found in neurons, although Abrahams (1963) claims there is some true cholinesterase in glial cells as well. Alterations in brain acetylcholine and cholinesterase content can be correlated with changes in brain function. In blinded rats, for instance, Krech *et al.* (1963) found marked alterations in the cholinesterase activity of the superior colliculi and occipital cortex. Stark and Boyd (1963) found that drugs that inhibit cholinesterase decrease the rate of hypothalamic self-stimulation if they cross the blood-brain barrier, and have no effect if they do not. There is some evidence for the presence of cholinergic and adrenergic synapses in the reticular formation (Magoun, 1963).

The presence of acetylcholine in the nerve-ending fraction of brain homogenates is further evidence for a synaptic function (DeRobertis *et al.*, 1962; Ryall, 1963; Zieher and DeRobertis, 1963). The small synaptic vesicles seen in the terminal buttons of cholinergic neurons are believed to contain acetylcholine (Hagen, 1962). Neurons in the infundibular portion of the hypothalamus have been shown to contain these vesicles in addition to the larger granules of neurosecretory material (DeRobertis, 1961; see Chapter 5, in Volume I).

The observation that brain tissue can make acetylcholine *in vitro* was originally made by Stedman and Stedman in 1937, and release of this neurohumor from various parts of the brain has since been demonstrated (Mitchell, 1963). Additional evidence for the presence of cholinergic synapses in the brain is the demonstration that neurons in the medulla (Salmoiraghi and Steiner, 1963) and neurons in the cerebellum (Crawford *et al.*, 1963) discharge more rapidly when acetylcholine is placed on their cell membranes by microelectrophoresis. This technique is discussed above, and its theoretical and practical implications have been discussed in detail by Curtis (1964). In the case of the cerebellum, the microelectrophoretic evidence is supplemented by histochemical studies showing that the granule cell processes which end on the dendrites of the Purkinje cells contain large amounts of true cholinesterase. However, liberation of acetylcholine by the granule cell endings in response to physiological stimuli which activate these cells has not been demonstrated.

E. Histamine

Histamine has received much less attention as a possible synaptic mediator than the other neurohumors. This amine is unevenly distributed in the brain, and it can be synthesized and metabolized to *N*-methylhistamine by brain tissue. The distribution of histidine decarboxylase and of the histamine methylating enzyme in brain parallels the distribution of histamine (Crossland, 1962; Green, 1964; White, 1964). Injection of histamine into the third ventricle causes profound changes in the electrical activity of the adjacent structures, although there is some question about the physiological significance of these effects (Sawyer, 1955). The drug tremorine increases the histamine content of the brain, and so to a lesser extent do mescaline and chlorpromazine (Ungar and Witten, 1963). Lysergic acid diethylamide (LSD-25), Metrazol, strychnine, amphetamine, and reserpine had no effect in Ungar and Witten's experiments, although as noted above, others report that reserpine depletes brain histamine (see Green, 1964). The methylation of histamine is inhibited by chlorpromazine, 5-hydroxytryptamine, bufotenine, and estrogens (Green, 1964; White, 1964). Diamine oxidase, the enzyme that catalyzes the deamination of histamine, is inhibited by bulbocapnine (P. L. McGeer *et al.*, 1963). Histamine sediments with the microsomal fraction of brain homogenates according to Green (1964), and with the pinched-off nerve endings according to Michaelson and Dowe (1963). Further investigation of the possible synaptic mediator function of histamine would seem to be in order.

F. Substance P

The uneven distribution of substance P in the brain is the main reason for suspecting that it is a synaptic mediator. The brain appears to contain enzymic mechanisms for synthesizing and metabolizing the polypeptide, but the distribution of the enzymes has not been analyzed. There are relatively large amounts of substance P in the dorsal roots of the spinal nerves and in the fasciculus gracilis and fasciculus cuneatus. Systemic injection of substance P causes enhancement of the dorsal root potential, an electrical response presumably associated with conduction in the sensory pathways (Krivoy and Kroeger, 1963). Thus, the peptide may play some role in facilitating conduction in the sensory pathways, or it could be the synaptic mediator at the endings of the touch and pressure fibers in the posterior columns of the spinal cord (Krivoy *et al.*, 1963; Stern, 1963). Substance P activity has been found in subcellular particles obtained from peripheral nerves (U. S. von Euler, 1963) and in a nerve-ending fraction of brain cells that also contains 5-hydroxytryptamine, norepinephrine, and acetylcholine (Cleugh *et al.*, 1964).

G. γ-Aminobutyric Acid

Glutamic decarboxylase, the enzyme primarily responsible for GABA synthesis, is found only in the nervous system. γ-Aminobutyric acid-α-ketoglutaric transaminase, which is responsible for the metabolism of GABA to succinic semialdehyde, is found in other tissues as well. The amount of GABA decarboxylase in different parts of the brain parallels the GABA content, but the correlation between GABA content and the transaminase is not striking (Roberts, 1962). γ-Aminobutyric acid is closely linked in some way to brain excitability (Killam, 1958). Pyridoxine deficiency lowers the brain GABA content and causes convulsions. It was thought at one time that GABA was the "inhibitory mediator" liberated by the Golgi bottle neurons responsible for the production of direct inhibition in the spinal cord, but this view has been rendered unlikely because the effect of GABA on cell membranes does not appear to be specific (see Eccles, 1964). γ-Aminobutyric acid is found in the cytoplasmic fraction of brain homogenates, but it has not been proved that GABA occurs in neurons. Indeed, some is said to be present in glia (Himwich, 1963; Utley, 1963). These facts, plus the close relation of GABA to the citric acid cycle have led to the suggestion that GABA is an alternate substrate for oxidative metabolism in the brain (McKhann and Tower, 1959). This and related aspects of the physiology of GABA are discussed in detail in a review by Elliot and Jasper (1959).

H. Summary

It is apparent that there is considerable variation in the amount of evidence supporting the view that any one of the substances discussed above is a synaptic mediator in the central nervous system. In the case of acetylcholine, data from the experiments on microelectrophoresis, the histochemical and the brain perfusion studies, and many other investigations make it seem almost certain that acetylcholine is a synaptic mediator in the brain. The demonstration that 5-hydroxytryptamine, norepinephrine, and dopamine occur in the axon terminals of neurons in the brain makes the case for these three substances being synaptic mediators a strong one. The data on histamine are too incomplete to make a definite conclusion, and this amine and substance P require further study. It appears that in spite of its nonuniform distribution in the nervous system, GABA is not a chemical mediator of synaptic activity. This amino acid is concerned instead with neuronal excitability and probably with brain energy supplies.

V. Melatonin

Melatonin (*N*-acetyl-5-methoxytryptamine) is found in the pineal gland and in peripheral nerves (see Chapter 32). Since hydroxyindole-*O*-methyltransferase, the enzyme responsible for the formation of melatonin from *N*-acetyl-5-hydroxytryptamine (Fig. 2), is found only in the pineal gland, Barchas and Lerner (1964) argue that the melatonin must be secreted into the blood stream and carried in the circulation to the peripheral nerves. Apparently, melatonin is not present in any part of the brain except the pineal region (Barchas and Lerner, 1964), and it does not appear to be a synaptic transmitter. However, it has been claimed that melatonin can be converted to carbolines, compounds in which the side chain of the melatonin is cyclized to form a third ring, and these compounds have a close resemblance to certain of the hallucination-producing harmala plant alkaloids (McIsaac *et al.*, 1961). These carbolines were also claimed to be the factors controlling aldosterone secretion, but this view is probably no longer tenable (Farrell, 1964; see also Chapter 11, in Volume I). In rats, melatonin is said to have antithyroid activity and to depress ovarian function (Baschieri *et al.*, 1963; Wurtman *et al.*, 1963a).

VI. Relation of Neurohumors to Endocrine Function

Since the highest concentration of many of the neurohumors discussed above is in the hypothalamus and one of the major functions of the hypothalamus is the regulation of endocrine function, it is logical to investigate the relation of the neurohumors to the mechanisms controlling endocrine function. Perhaps the most direct evidence for such a relation is the production of multiple endocrine changes by reserpine. This drug, which causes a marked depletion of the 5-hydroxytryptamine and norepinephrine in the brain, produces adrenocorticotropic hormone (ACTH) hypersecretion, lactation, blockade of ovulation, and other endocrine changes (see Gaunt *et al.*, 1961, 1962). Conversely, certain monoamine oxidase inhibiting drugs which increase hypothalamic 5-hydroxytryptamine and norepinephrine levels block ACTH secretion (Tullner and Hertz, 1964; Ganong, 1965b; Ganong *et al.*, 1965). Central nervous system–active drugs also affect the secretion of the hormones of the intermediate lobe of the pituitary (Scott and Nading, 1961). The effects of these and other drugs on neuroendocrine processes are discussed in detail in Chapter 27. In this chapter, consideration is limited to the relation of brain neurohumors to endocrine function, and particularly to anterior and posterior pituitary function.

A. Relation to Anterior Pituitary Secretion

In the case of the anterior pituitary, there are data relating neurohumors to the secretion of all its hormones except growth hormone.

1. *Absence of Releasing Factor Activity*

The evidence that the hypothalamus controls anterior pituitary secretion by the selective secretion of humoral "releasing factors" into the portal circulation is reviewed in Chapter 8 (Volume I). There appear to be at least five releasing factors—corticotropin-releasing factor (CRF), thyrotropin-releasing factor (TRF), somatotropin-releasing factor (SRF), follicle-stimulating hormone-releasing factor (FSHRF), and luteinizing hormone-releasing factor (LRF), plus prolactin-inhibiting factor (PIF). The enticing possibility that the releasing factors might be the neurohumors found in the hypothalamus has been considered by several investigators. There is considerable evidence that the releasing factors and the PIF are small polypeptides (see Table IV, Chapter 8, in Volume I), but the possibility that the neurohumors could also have activity deserves consideration. In general, the results obtained have been negative.

a. Corticotropin-Releasing Factor. Epinephrine and norepinephrine liberate ACTH in the rat, but apparently they do not act directly on the pituitary because they fail to increase ACTH secretion after transection of the midbrain (Martini *et al.*, 1960). Doses of adrenergic-blocking agents which abolish the adrenocortical response to epinephrine do not block the response to other stresses (see Ganong, 1963, for references). Hypothalamic lesions block the adrenal ascorbic acid depleting activity of histamine, epinephrine, oxytocin, and substance P (see Chapter 8, in Volume I), indicating that these neurohumors do not act directly on the pituitary. The ACTH-releasing activity of hypothalamic tissue added to cultures of anterior pituitary cells could not be explained, according to Guillemin and Rosenberg (1955), by its content of histamine, acetylcholine, 5-hydroxytryptamine, oxytocin, norepinephrine, epinephrine, or vasopressin. Saffran and his associates (1955) found that norepinephrine had no CRF activity *in vitro,* although it did potentiate the action of CRF.

Guillemin *et al.* (1957) found CRF activity in a sample of substance P prepared from intestines, and Swingle *et al.* (1956) found CRF activity in another preparation of substance P. However, both groups of investigators felt that the activity was due to something in the samples that could be separated from substance P. In addition, they tested for CRF activity by incubating their samples with pituitaries *in vitro,* and it now appears that this system responds in a nonspecific way to a variety of substances. Briggs and Munson (1955) blocked the *in vivo* ACTH-releasing effects of histamine, epinephrine, and vasopressin by pretreating their rats with morphine and pentobarbital, drugs which presumably act on the nervous system rather than the pituitary. On the basis of similar experiments on the effects of pharmacological blockade of ACTH secretion in rats, Guillemin (1955) concluded that acetylcholine, epinephrine, norepinephrine, and histamine were not releasing factors for ACTH.

γ-Aminobutyric acid, dopamine, and 5-hydroxytryptamine apparently have not been tested for direct ACTH-releasing activity. In addition, most of the experiments on the other neurohumors were performed in rats using adrenal ascorbic acid levels rather than corticosteroid outputs as the end points. The problem of blocking ACTH secretion in rats is complex, and use of adrenal ascorbic acid as an end point may be misleading (see Ganong, 1963). However, it does seem unlikely that any overlooked activity would be revealed by repeating these studies with more reliable indicators of pituitary-adrenal function.

b. Thyrotropin-Releasing Factor. Relatively few data are available on the effects of various neurohumors on thyrotropin (TSH) secretion. Norepinephrine, epinephrine, 5-hydroxytryptamine, and acetylcholine in moderate doses do not stimulate TSH secretion in intact animals, although they do augment the effects of exogenous TSH (see D'Angelo, 1963, for references). There appears to be a direct stimulating effect of catecholamines on the thyroid gland in the dog, but large doses of catecholamines inhibit TSH secretion. Lysine and arginine vasopressin and α- and β-melanocyte-stimulating hormone (MSH) have a direct stimulating effect on the thyroid gland, but they lack TSH-releasing activity (Crosson *et al.*, 1960; D'Angelo, 1963; Guillemin and Schally, 1963; Reichlin, 1963; Bowers *et al.*, 1964). Bradykinin, substance P, and α- and β-MSH have no TRF activity *in vitro* (Guillemin *et al.*, 1963, 1965).

c. Somatotropin-Releasing Factor. The somatotropin-releasing factor recently isolated from hypothalamic tissue (Franz *et al.*, 1962; Deuben and Meites, 1964; Schally *et al.*, 1964b) is a polypeptide which is not vasopressin or oxytocin (see Chapters 8 and 13, in Volume I, and Reichlin, 1963), but data on whether or not any of the neurohumors found in the hypothalamus have somatotropin-releasing activity are not available.

d. Follicle-Stimulating Hormone-Releasing Factor. The follicle-stimulating hormone(FSH)-releasing activity of hypothalamic extracts is due at least in part to a polypeptide, and oxytocin and vasopressin do not have this activity (Chapter 8, in Volume I). Older indirect evidence that the suspected synaptic mediators are not gonadotropin-releasing factors has been summarized by Harris (1955) and by Reichlin (1963).

e. Luteinizing-Hormone Releasing Factor. Taubenhaus and Soskin (1941) showed that application of acetylcholine to the exposed pituitary of the rat caused pseudopregnancy, and Markee *et al.* (1948) produced ovulation in rabbits by microinjection of epinephrine into the pituitary. However, the nonspecificity of response in the first experiment leaves it open to question, and the effect of epinephrine may have been due to the acid pH of the injected solution (Donovan and Harris, 1956). The polypeptide factor regulating luteinizing hormone (LH) release has been isolated and studied more extensively than any of the other releasing factors except CRF (Chapter 8, in Volume I). In the course of their studies of LRF, McCann *et al.* (1960) and Courrier *et al.* (1961) have shown that 5-hydroxytryptamine, histamine, epinephrine, norepinephrine, acetylcholine, bradykinin, and substance P as well as Pitressin, Pitocin, lysine vasopressin, oxytocin, and α- and β-MSH do not have LRF activity.

f. Prolactin-Inhibiting Factor. The factor in hypothalamic extracts which inhibits prolactin secretion seems to be separate from LRF (Schally *et al.*, 1964a). This is of some physiological interest, because it had been suggested that a single factor might be responsible for stimulation of LH secretion and inhibition of prolactin secretion (see Chapter 15, in Volume I). The chemical nature of PIF is not yet known, but in the system in which Meites and his associates carried out their studies of PIF, acetylcholine, epinephrine, norepinephrine, 5-hydroxytryptamine, histamine, substance P, oxytocin, lysine vasopressin, and arginine vasopressin had no prolactin inhibitory activity (see Nicoll and Meites, 1962; Talwalker *et al.*, 1963).

2. *Effects of Neurohumors on the Portal Vessels*

Since most of the suspected synaptic mediators are substances which constrict or dilate blood vessels, it is possible that neurohumors liberated into the portal-hypophyseal blood could affect anterior pituitary secretion by altering the caliber of portal vessels, thus changing adenohypophyseal blood flow. There are two reported studies of the effects of neurohumors on portal blood flow in living animals. Worthington (1955) observed that locally applied epinephrine constricted and methacholine, a cholinergic agent, dilated the portal vessels in the mouse, while systemically administered epinephrine increased portal blood flow. Arimura and Long (1962) did not observe any direct effect of epinephrine, norepinephrine, Pitressin, or histamine on the vessels in the rat, although changes in systemic blood pressure did influence portal flow. It is unfortunate that in order to observe changes in the portal vessels *in vivo,* the pituitary region must be exposed by an extensive and severely stressful surgical procedure.

Another approach to this problem is the measurement of anterior pituitary blood flow by an isotope dilution technique (Goldman and Sapirstein, 1958). With this method flow can be measured in the unstressed state. In rats, ether stress causes a 40% increase in pituitary blood flow within 2.5 minutes after the onset of the stress (Goldman, 1963). It is not possible as yet to say whether this response is due to neurohumors or is simply an increased blood flow secondary to increased adenohypophyseal metabolism (metabolic hyperemia). Further studies of pituitary blood flow with this and other techniques would be of interest.

It is also possible that portal blood flow is controlled in part by vasomotor nerve fibers, but the supply of adrenergic fibers to the portal vessels is scanty (Fuxe, 1964).

3. *ACTH and Adrenocortical Function*

Although the suspected synaptic mediators apparently are not in themselves releasing factors, there is abundant evidence that they are involved in various ways in the control of releasing factor secretion. Studies of the relation between brain chemistry and adrenal cortical function provide data on the effects of adrenalectomy, hypophysectomy, and a wide variety of stresses on brain amine content. In addition, there have been experiments on the effect of 5-hydroxytryptamine, norepinephrine, and related compounds on ACTH secretion and on the adrenal cortex itself. The effects of adrenocortical hormones on brain excitability are discussed in Chapter 26.

The effects of a variety of stressful stimuli on brain content of suspected chemical mediators are summarized in Table III. An additional pertinent datum is the observation that stimulation of the amygdala, a nucleus concerned in a major way with emotional stresses, caused a decline in hypothalamic norepinephrine content (Gunne and Reis, 1963). In Table IV, the effects of a number of drugs on brain neurohumors are summarized. It should be emphasized that Table IV includes only those drugs known to have an effect on ACTH secretion and omits a large number of other drugs that affect neurohumor content. The tables show that stressful stimuli and drugs exert no consistent effect on brain 5-hydroxytryptamine, some stimuli causing an increase and some a decrease, but the majority producing no change. On the other hand, most of the stressful stimuli and drugs which increase ACTH secretion decrease brain norepinephrine. Conversely, the monoamine oxidase inhibitors increase norepinephrine content, and some of these drugs decrease ACTH secretion. However, it has been claimed that the stress-induced decrease in brain norepinephrine is due to a decline in norepinephrine that is outside of nerve endings (Levi and Maynert, 1964). In addition, changes in norepinephrine content do not always accompany changes in ACTH secretion. Rats exposed to cold and then given reserpine certainly secrete ACTH, but they fail to show an appreciable decline in brain norepinephrine (Brodie *et al.*, 1961).

Very little study has been devoted to the effects of stressful stimuli on brain content of substance P, GABA, and acetylcholine, but the experiments that have been reported generally indicate no change. The decline in GABA produced by hypoglycemia is of interest because hypoglycemia causes convulsions, and the decreased brain GABA content brought on by pyridoxine (vitamin B_6) deficiency is associated with convulsions (Roberts, 1962). It has been claimed that increased acetylcholinesterase activity in various hypothalamic nuclei is associated with increased anterior and posterior pituitary activity (Pepler and Pearse, 1957).

Since the stressful stimuli listed in Table III cause increased ACTH secretion and adrenalectomy has the same effect on ACTH secretion, one might expect that brain norepinephrine would be decreased by adrenalectomy. However, as shown in Table V, adrenalectomy has been reported to cause no change in brain norepinephrine levels. Reports of the effects of adrenalectomy and hypophysectomy on brain 5-hydroxytryptamine and GABA levels are conflicting. Other pertinent studies include the report by Hicks and West (1958) that adrenalectomy increases the 5-hydroxytryptamine and histamine content of the skin, ears, feet, liver, and lungs of adrenalectomized rats; however, these investigators did not measure the brain content of these amines. Friedman *et al.* (1963) have reported that adrenalectomy enhances the depleting effect of the drug tremorine on brain stem norepinephrine. Efron and Brodie (1962) observed that adrenalectomized animals were more sensitive to the toxic

TABLE III

EFFECT OF STRESSFUL STIMULI ON BRAIN NEUROHUMORS[a]

Stressful stimulus	Animal species	Effect on brain content of: 5-Hydroxy-tryptamine	Norepi-nephrine	Substance P	γ-Amino-butyric acid	Acetyl-choline	References
Electroshock with convulsions	Rat	NC					Bertaccini (1959)
	Rat	NC					See Bonnycastle *et al.* (1957)
	Rat, rabbit, cat	I					Breitner *et al.* (1961)
Electric shock	Rat	NC	NC				Toh (1960); Freedman *et al.* (1962)
	Guinea pig		D				Paulsen and Hess (1963)
	Rat	NC	D				Levi and Maynert (1964)
Electric shock, Cold	Rat	NC	D			NC	Maynert and Levi (1964)
Stimulate brain stem	Rat, rabbit, cat	NC					Breitner *et al.* (1961)
Cold, Heat	Rat	D					Toh (1960)
Cold, Cold swim, Warm swim, Exercise	Rat	I	D				Freedman (1963)
Surgery, Immobilization	Dog	I					Halevy (1960)
Immobilization	Rat		NC				Moore and Lariviere (1963)
Hemorrhage	Rabbit		D				Coleman and Glaviano (1963)

Morphine withdrawal syndrome	Rabbit, dog		D			Maynert and Klingman (1962)
	Dog, rabbit, rat	NC			NC	Maynert *et al.* (1962)
	Cat		NC			Maynert and Klingman (1962)
Hypoglycemia	Rat				D	Roberts and Simonsen (1960)
	Dog				D	Stone *et al.* (1962)
	Dog	NC		NC		Paasonen and Vogt (1956)
	Cat		D			Vogt (1954)
Diabetes	Rat				NC	Roberts (1962)
Anoxia, Thirst	Rat	NC	NC			Freedman *et al.* (1962)
Conditioned avoidance responses	Rat	NC	NC			Freedman *et al.* (1962)

[a] D, decrease; NC, no change; I, increase.

TABLE IV

EFFECT OF DRUGS THAT ALTER ACTH SECRETION ON BRAIN NEUROHUMOR CONTENT[a]

Drug	Effect on ACTH secretion	Effect on brain content of					References
		5-Hydroxy-tryptamine	Norepi-nephrine	Dopamine	Substance P	γ-Amino-butyric acid	
Chlorpromazine	I[b]				NC	NC	Roberts *et al.* (1958); Laszlo (1963)
Ether	I[b]	I, NC	D		NC		Vogt (1954); Paasonen and Vogt (1956); Bonnycastle *et al.* (1962); Laszlo (1963)
Ethyl alcohol	I[b]	I, D	D				Gursey and Olson (1960); Bonnycastle *et al.* (1962); Duritz and Truitt (1963)
Lysergic acid diethylamide (LSD-25)	I[c]				NC	NC	Roberts *et al.* (1958); Laszlo (1963)
Morphine	I[b]		D		NC	NC	Vogt (1954); Roberts *et al.* (1958); Laszlo (1963); Maynert and Levi (1964)
Reserpine	I[b]	D	D	D	NC	NC	Paasonen and Vogt (1956); Roberts *et al.* (1958); Laszlo (1963); P. L. McGeer *et al.* (1963)

α-Methyl-*m*-tyrosine	NC[d]	NC	D				Brodie *et al.* (1961)
Amphetamine	D[e]	D			NC		Paasonen and Vogt (1956)
Barbiturates	D[b]	I			NC		Bonnycastle *et al.* (1962); Laszlo (1963)
Diphenylhydantoin	D[b]	I, NC			NC	NC	Bonnycastle *et al.* (1957, 1962); Roberts *et al.* (1958); Woodbury and Vernadakis (1958); Laszlo (1963)
Monoamine oxidase inhibitors	D[e]	I	I	NC		NC	Roberts *et al.* (1958); Brodie *et al.* (1961)

[a] I, increase; NC, no change; D, decrease.

[b] For references, see Ganong (1963).

[c] For references, see Ganong *et al.* (1961).

[d] For references, see Brodie *et al.* (1961).

[e] Decreased by some inhibitors but not by others (Lorenzen and Ganong, unpublished observations).

TABLE V

EFFECT OF ADRENALECTOMY AND HYPOPHYSECTOMY ON BRAIN CONTENT OF 5-HYDROXYTRYPTAMINE, NOREPINEPHRINE, AND γ-AMINOBUTYRIC ACID IN THE RAT[a]

	Effect on brain content of			
Procedure	5-Hydroxy-tryptamine	Norepi-nephrine	γ-Amino-butyric acid	References
Adrenalectomy	I			De Maio (1959)
	NC			Resnick *et al.* (1961)
	I			Sofer and Gubler (1962)
	D[b]	NC		Pfeifer *et al.* (1963)
			NC	Roberts (1962)
			D	Woodbury and Vernadakis (1958)
Hypophysectomy	I			De Maio (1959)
	NC			Yeh *et al.* (1959)
	NC			Resnick *et al.* (1961)
			NC	Roberts (1962)

[a] I, increase; NC, no change; D, decrease.
[b] Effect reversed by prolonged glucocorticoid treatment.

effects of reserpine. Hypophysectomy did not have this effect, but cortisol treatment returned the sensitivity of adrenalectomized animals to normal. Finally, Enerbäck (1960) has reported that adrenalectomy increases 5-hydroxyindoleacetic acid excretion in rats. Since this is the major urinary metabolite of 5-hydroxytryptamine, the results suggest accelerated metabolism of this neurohumor in adrenalectomized animals.

The effects of brain amines and related compounds on ACTH secretion have also been investigated. 5-Hydroxytryptamine provokes ACTH secretion when administered to normal rats (Bertelli *et al.*, 1954; Mousatché and Pereira, 1957; Fiore-Donati *et al.*, 1959). Hypophysectomy blocks this response when the dose is small, but large doses of 5-hydroxytryptamine increase glucocorticoid and aldosterone secretion by a direct action on the adrenal gland (Hume, 1958; Verdesca *et al.*, 1961; Connors and Rosenkrantz, 1962). Histamine also stimulates ACTH secretion (Hume, 1958; Casentini *et al.*, 1959), and Hume claims that large doses of histamine can increase corticoid secretion by a direct action on the adrenal cortex in the dog. Large doses of epinephrine and norepinephrine increase ACTH secretion in rats, and at one time, it was claimed that the increase in ACTH secretion produced by stressful stimuli was due to a direct effect of the elevated levels of circulating adrenal medullary hormones on the pituitary (C. N. H. Long, 1951). Brodie *et al.* (1961) have reported results that seem to support this conclusion. They found that 18 hours after administration of the adrenergic blocking agent, Dibenamine, reserpine and cold had little stimulating effect on adrenocortical secretion in rats. Dibenamine itself did not increase adrenocortical secretion. However, the adrenocortical response to most stresses is unaffected by doses of adrenergic blocking agents which block the response to epinephrine (see above). In addition, stressful stimuli still cause increased ACTH secretion in the absence of the adrenal glands in rats, and catecholamines do not increase glucocorticoid secretion in dogs and humans (for discussion and references see Ganong, 1963). It has been claimed that epinephrine increases the circulating blood ACTH level in humans (Vernikos-Danellis and Marks, 1962), but this observation could not be confirmed when a more specific assay for blood ACTH was used (Vance and Shioda, 1964).

Acetylcholine and the acetylcholine derivative, Mecholyl, increase ACTH secretion (Hume, 1958; Casentini *et al.*, 1959), but so does the acetylcholine-blocking drug, atropine (Dordoni and Fortier, 1950). Therefore, it seems likely the ACTH-releasing activity of acetylcholine is secondary to the nonspecific stressing effects of the circulatory and other changes produced by the neurohumor.

Reports on the effects of substance P are conflicting. According to Casentini *et al.* (1959), this neurohumor does not increase ACTH secretion in rats. Other investigators claim that it does, and that this effect is blocked by lesions of the median eminence (see Chapter 8, in Volume I). Still others have reported that substance P preparations contain a factor which has CRF activity (Swingle *et al.*, 1956; Guillemin *et al.*, 1957; see above).

Krieger *et al.* (1964) have reported that injection of GABA or the acetylcholine derivative, carbachol, into the median eminence of unanesthetized cats caused an increase in their peripheral plasma 17-hydroxycorticoid levels. Injection of 5-hydroxytryptamine, tantalum, and luxol blue did not have this effect. However, the physiological significance of these observations is questionable; injections of any substance into the ventricles or into brain tissue must be very carefully controlled to rule out a wide variety of possible complicating factors (Olds and Olds, 1958).

Recently, a good deal of attention has been focused on the effects of stress on the response to reserpine. When administered to rats, this drug produces sedation, increased plasma corticosterone levels, and decreased brain content of 5-hydroxytryptamine and norepinephrine. The half-life of corticosterone is unaffected by the drug, so the increased plasma corticosterone levels are due to increased adrenal secretion (Maickel *et al.*, 1961). Garattini and Valzelli (1958) found that if rats were exposed to cold before receiving reserpine, they did not become sedated and brain 5-hydroxytryptamine did not decrease until they were brought back into warm surroundings. Sulser and Brodie (1960) confirmed these findings and added the observation that the depletion of brain norepinephrine was also inhibited, although not to as great a degree as the depletion of 5-hydroxytryptamine. These reports have not gone unchallenged; cold does not affect all the actions of reserpine (Knoll and Knoll, 1963), and apparently it does not inhibit the sedation produced by reserpine in mice (Airaksinen and Mattila, 1962). However, no reports have appeared which contradict the basic observation on the effect of cold in rats.

Further experiments on the effect of cold have been carried out by Brodie and his associates (Sulser and Brodie, 1960; Brodie *et al.*, 1961; Maickel *et al.*, 1961). They found that hypophysectomized or adrenalectomized rats placed in the cold showed prompt sedation and brain amine depletion when given reserpine. Cold alone increased ACTH secretion but did not produce brain amine depletion or sedation. However, not all investigators agree with Brodie and his associates that cold alone is without effect on brain amine levels in rats (see Table III).

The results of these and related experiments are summarized in Table VI. They indicate that inhibition by cold of the effects of reserpine on brain amines and behavior occurs only if the pituitary and adrenals are intact. The effect of cold does not appear to be due to increased circulating adrenocortical hormone levels per se, because reserpine itself increases adrenocortical secretion. However, it may be that inhibition occurs if adrenocortical hormone levels are high before the reserpine is given. Stresses that increase ACTH secretion are known to modify responses to other central nervous system–active drugs (Rupe *et al.*, 1963), and the field is a fertile one for further research.

Some other interesting relationships between reserpine-induced sedation, brain amine depletion, and increased ACTH secretion have also been reported. Brodie and his associates (1961) tested a number of isomers of reserpine and found that all those which produced brain amine depletion caused increased ACTH secretion. Martel *et al.* (1962) and Gaunt *et al.* (1962) observed that pretreatment with monoamine oxidase-inhibiting drugs blocked the increase in ACTH secretion produced by reserpine. In addition, Brodie *et al.* (1961) reported separation of brain norepinephrine depletion from ACTH secretion in rats by the administration of α-methyl-*m*-tyrosine. This compound depleted brain norepinephrine without producing increased ACTH secretion, 5-hydroxytryptamine depletion, or sedation. On the other hand, imipramine and demethylimipramine blocked the sedative effects of reser-

TABLE VI
SUMMARY OF EFFECTS OF RESERPINE IN RATS EXPOSED TO COLD AND RESULTS OF RELATED EXPERIMENTS CARRIED OUT BY BRODIE AND CO-WORKERS[a]

Procedure	Sedation[b]	Decreased brain content of 5-Hydroxy-tryptamine	Decreased brain content of Norepi-nephrine	Increased adrenocortical secretion
Reserpine	+	+	+	+
Cold	−	−	−	+
Cold and reserpine	−	−	−	+
Cold and reserpine in hypophysectomized or adrenalectomized animals	+	+	+	−
α-Methyl-*m*-tyrosine	−	−	+	−
Reserpine and imipramine or demethylimipramine	−	+	+	+
Monoamine oxidase inhibitor, then reserpine	−	−	−	−

[a] References: Sulser and Brodie (1960); Maickel *et al.* (1961); Brodie *et al.* (1961); Martel *et al.* (1962).
[b] +, present; −, absent.

pine without affecting the increase in ACTH secretion or the decline in brain amines (Brodie *et al.*, 1961; Martel *et al.*, 1962). Discussion of the effects on behavior of changes in brain amine content is outside the scope of this chapter, but it might be noted that the relation, if any, between sedation and brain amine levels is certainly a complex one (Costa *et al.*, 1962; Boullin, 1963; Comer *et al.*, 1963).

4. *Thyrotropin and Thyroid Function*

Injections of epinephrine or substance P into the mammillary bodies or substance P into the ventromedial nuclei of the hypothalamus have been reported to depress thyroid function (C. von Euler and Holmgren, 1956; Harrison, 1961). Injections of norepinephrine, GABA, 5-hydroxytryptamine, dopamine, and acetylcholine were without effect in these experiments. However, the results of all experiments on local injection into the central nervous system must be evaluated with care because there are numerous variables which can affect them (Olds and Olds, 1958; Curtis *et al.*, 1961). The significance of the decreased thyroid function produced by systemic injection of melatonin in rats is uncertain (Baschieri *et al.*, 1963). Large doses of reserpine have been reported to depress thyroid function in rats, but the depression appears to be secondary to decreased food intake (Premachandra and Turner, 1960).

Hyperthyroid animals have been reported to be more sensitive than normal animals to the vascular effects of epinephrine (Wurtman *et al.*, 1963c) and 5-hydroxytryptamine (Spencer and West, 1961). Put and Hogenhuis (1962) and Towne *et al.* (1959) found that in rats, thyroid hypofunction induced by the administration of propylthiouracil and hyperthyroidism produced by thyroxine treatment both increased brain 5-hydroxytryptamine. Thyroidectomy had no effect, a finding confirmed by Resnick and his associates (1961). However, Skillen *et al.* (1961) could find no effect of thyroxine or propylthiouracil on brain 5-hydroxytryptamine, 5-hydroxytryptophan decarboxylase, or monoamine oxidase in rats. Roberts *et al.* (1958) found that thyroidectomy had no effect on brain GABA content. Thus, thyroid hypofunction does not appear to alter the brain content of 5-hydroxytryptamine or GABA. However, it produces relatively prominent alterations in the electroencephalogram (Lansing and Trunnell, 1963) and definite alterations in brain function in humans and animals (Michael and Gibbons, 1963; Eayrs, 1964), so investigation of its effects on other amines would seem to be in order.

5. *Gonadotropins and Testicular Function*

There does not appear to be any direct relation between gonadal function and the content of 5-hydroxytryptamine in the brain in males; neither castration nor testosterone treatment alters the brain content of this amine (Kato, 1959; Resnick *et al.*, 1961). 5-Hydroxytryptamine does cause testicular atrophy when injected into male rats, but treatment with exogenous gonadotropins does not overcome the atrophy while administration of vasodilator drugs does (Boccabella *et al.*, 1962). Thus, the effect appears to be due to constriction of the blood vessels supplying the testes, rather than inhibition of gonadotropin secretion.

Interrelations between the testes and other substances suspected of being synaptic mediators do not appear to have been investigated. Testosterone does have the interesting effect in mice of increasing the amount of nerve growth factor extractable from the salivary glands (Reiss, 1961; Caramia *et al.*, 1962). The salivary glands of mature male mice normally contain more nerve growth factor than the glands of females. Castration lowers the level in males and testosterone treatment increases the level in females. The nerve growth factor was discussed in detail at a recent symposium (Whipple, 1964). Another interesting finding relating sex hormones to brain function is the observation (Westfall *et al.*, 1964) that male mice sleep longer than female mice when given pentobarbital. Estrogens shorten barbiturate sleeping time in males and testosterone lengthens barbiturate sleeping time in females.

There are some data suggesting the existence of a sex difference in brain 5-hydroxytryptamine content. Kato (1959) reported that the brains of sexually mature male rats contained less 5-hydroxytryptamine than the brains of females. There were no sex differences in prepubertal rats. Estrogen treatment increased the level in immature animals, while testosterone was without effect. Wurtman and Axelrod (1963) reported that the monoamine oxidase content of liver was greater in male rats than it was in females. Skillen *et al.* (1961) found less 5-hydroxytryptophan decarboxylase and monoamine oxidase in the brains of male rats, but they found no significant sex difference in 5-hydroxytryptamine content.

6. *Gonadotropins and Reproductive Function in the Female*

a. Puberty. It now seems quite certain that the hypothalamus and limbic system play a primary role in determining the time at which puberty occurs, but the details of the way the brain carries out this function are still uncertain. In humans, neural regulation is important in the male as well as the female (Jolly, 1955), but almost all the studies of neural regulation in experimental animals have been carried out in females. According to Corbin and Schottelius (1961), injections of 5-hydroxytryptamine into the third ventricle of female rats delay the onset of puberty, while injections of oxytocin accelerate it and injections of epinephrine and vasopressin have no effect. These observations are of questionable significance because of the multiple problems involved in injection experiments of this type. However, Robson and Botros (1961) have reported that systemic injections of 5-hydroxytryptamine or the monoamine oxidase inhibitor, iproniazid, delay the onset of puberty. Reserpine treatment is said to delay the onset of puberty in rats (Carraro *et al.*, 1965) and chickens (Hagen and Wallace, 1960).

b. Estrous Cycles. The complex neuroendocrine control of the estrous and menstrual cycles of mammals has been discussed in Chapter 15 (Volume I). Apparently none of the neurohumoral agents discussed in this chapter acts directly on the pituitary, but there is evidence for cholinergic, adrenergic, and 5-hydroxytryptamine–regulated links in the chains of neurons that regulate hypothalamic secretion of the gonadotropin-regulating releasing factors. Kobayashi *et al.* (1963) found that there were cyclic variations of the choline acetylase activity in the posterior hypothalamus of rats coincident with the estrous cycle. The highest activity was observed in diestrus and the lowest in estrus. Sawyer and associates (see Markee *et al.*, 1948; Sawyer *et al.*, 1949; Sawyer, 1963; Everett, 1964) found they could block ovulation in rats by properly timed injections of atropine or adrenergic blocking agents. They concluded that there is a cholinergic discharge followed by an adrenergic discharge in the sequence of neural events that lead to ovulation in the rat. They presented evidence that a similar sequence of neural events was required for ovulation in the rabbit, even though the rabbit, unlike the rat, ovulates only after copulation (Sawyer *et al.*, 1949, 1950). Atropine also blocks ovulation in the cow when given at certain times during the estrous cycle (Hansel *et al.*, 1957).

Robson and Botros (1961) have reported that 5-hydroxytryptamine causes ovarian atrophy in adult mice, and that the effect is not due to decreased ovarian responsiveness to gonadotropins. Some monoamine oxidase inhibitors had a similar effect. Others have reported that monoamine oxidase inhibitors exert an antifertility effect, and suggested that they act by inhibiting implantation of fertilized ova in the endometrium (W. G. Spector, 1960; Bovet-Nitti and Bignami, 1963). Kato (1959) found that estrogens increased brain 5-hydroxytryptamine content. Injection of histamine or norepinephrine into the third ventricle of anesthetized rabbits was found to cause ovulation (Sawyer, 1955; Donovan and Harris, 1956), but histamine did not cause ovulation in unanesthetized rabbits, and the effects of intraventricular norepinephrine may have been due to the low pH of the injected solution. It is of interest in this context that intraventricular injection of histamine causes prominent changes in the electroencephalogram recorded from the medial forebrain bundle, and lesions of this bundle in male rats lower the 5-hydroxytryptamine content of the brain (Harvey *et al.*, 1963).

Estrogens act directly on at least two neural centers in the hypothalamus; they act in the vicinity of the arcuate nuclei, where they bring about inhibition of FSH secretion, and they act in the suprachiasmatic region, where they initiate estrous behavior. Progesterone may also act on the hypothalamus. The effects of these hormones on gonadotropin secretion and sexual behavior are discussed in detail in Chapters 15 (Volume I) and 22. However, it is worth noting here that estrogens and progesterone cause changes in the excitability of neurons in many parts of the brain (see Chapter 26), and estrogens produce morphological alterations in hypothalamic neurons (Lisk and Newton, 1963). The Soulairacs have argued that there are important adrenergic and cholinergic components of sexual behavior in the male rat (see Soulairac, 1963). This may well be true, but it is difficult to accept disruption of sexual behavior by relatively huge systemically administered doses of catecholamines and cholinergic agents as good evidence for the conclusion. Reserpine does not inhibit the estrous behavior induced in ovariectomized female rats by estrogens and progesterone, while drugs which inhibit monoamine oxidase do, leading to the suggestion that heat is normally inhibited by an adrenergic or "serotoninergic" system (Meyerson, 1964). However, the doses of drugs used in this study were large, and this again raises the question of the specificity of the results.

There is some evidence for a direct effect of 5-hydroxytryptamine on the ovary. This amine causes enlargement of the preputial glands in rats, and its effect on these glands is reduced by ovariectomy (Fiore-Donati *et al.*, 1959). The antiovarian action of melatonin (Wurtman *et al.*, 1963a) may be due to a direct action of this pineal amine on the ovary.

c. *Pseudopregnancy and Pregnancy.* Considerable attention has been focused on the effects of 5-hydroxytryptamine on the condition of the uterus in pseudopregnant and pregnant animals. Poulson *et al.* (1960) found that 5-hydroxytryptamine produced abortion with placental hemorrhage in mice. It also caused toxic changes in deciduomas, and Lindsay *et al.* (1961) suggested that the changes might be secondary to diminished ovarian secretion, since treatment with progesterone prevented their occurrence. The problem in these experiments is the difficulty in determining the degree to which the observed changes are due to changes in endocrine function and the degree to which they are due to the action of 5-hydroxytryptamine on uterine blood vessels. It is also interesting that reserpine, a drug which depletes body stores of 5-hydroxytryptamine, causes a decrease in the size of deciduomas (De Feo, 1957). Furthermore, 5-hydroxytryptamine, along with a variety of other neurohumors, and many stresses were reported by Fraschini *et al.* (1963) to facilitate deciduoma formation.

Shelesnyak and his associates (see Carlsen *et al.*, 1961; Shelesnyak, 1962; Kraicer *et al.*, 1963) have studied the relation of histamine and of agents that block adrenergic function to the formation of deciduomas. They feel that local release of histamine in the uterus initiates the process of "decidualization," but they have also found that a single injection of ergocornine methanesulfonate, an antiadrenergic derivative of ergot, interrupts pregnancy by preventing decidual development (Carlsen *et al.*, 1961). They have presented evidence that the effect of the drug is due to a shift in the pattern of ovarian secretion. Since the drug exerted its antideciduoma effect in animals with pituitary transplants, they concluded that the hormonal changes were not secondary to changes in neural mechanisms controlling gonadotropin secretion. However, an effect of the drug on the brain has not been completely ruled out.

d. Lactation. One of the most striking effects of reserpine in experimental animals is mammary gland enlargement with secretion of milk (Meites *et al.*, 1959, 1963). A single injection of reserpine in rabbits lowers pituitary prolactin content, and this effect is prevented by lesions in the basal tuberal region of the hypothalamus (Kanematsu *et al.*, 1963). Direct injection into the cerebral ventricles of doses of reserpine much smaller than those effective systemically, or implantation of crystalline reserpine phosphate into the posterior tuberal portion of the hypothalamus also causes lactation (Sawyer, 1957; Kanematsu and Sawyer, 1963). The neurohumoral basis of this response is unsettled. Systemically administered 5-hydroxytryptamine increases prolactin secretion (Meites *et al.*, 1959), but so do several other neurohumors and many unrelated stresses (Fraschini *et al.*, 1963). In fact, the correlation between stimuli which increase ACTH secretion and those which increase prolactin secretion is quite striking, although its significance is not clear (see Chapter 16, in Volume I). Injections of 5-hydroxytryptamine into the ventricles or directly into the pituitary have no effect on the mammary glands (Sawyer, 1957). An additional effect of systemic injection of 5-hydroxytryptamine is inhibition of oxytocin secretion, with consequent interruption of the milk ejection reflex (see below).

B. Relation to Pituitary Intermediate Lobe Secretion

There is a moderate amount of indirect evidence linking the suspected mediators of synaptic conduction in the brain to the function of the intermediate lobe of the pituitary. The potent hallucinogenic drug lysergic acid diethylamide (LSD-25) inhibits the secretion of intermediate lobe hormone in the toad (Burgers *et al.*, 1958). Conversely, phenothiazine tranquilizer drugs stimulate MSH secretion in frogs (Scott and Nading, 1961). Lysergic acid diethylamide is a serotonin antagonist outside the central nervous system, but it apparently is not a serotonin antagonist in the brain (Rothlin, 1957). It is possible that the effects of the phenothiazines on intermediate lobe secretion are due to the antiadrenergic action of these compounds. Although the functions of α- and β-MSH in mammals remain a mystery, there are some interesting bits of evidence indicating that they affect synaptic transmission in the central nervous system (Krivoy and Guillemin, 1961; Krivoy and Kroeger, 1963; Krivoy *et al.*, 1963). A finding which supports this hypothesis is the observation that the brain contains an enzyme which inactivates β-MSH (J. M. Long *et al.*, 1961). It has also been reported that polypeptides with MSH activity increase the permeability of the blood-aqueous humor barrier in the rabbit's eye (Dyster-Aas and Krakau,

1964). The actions of α- and β-MSH and their secretion are discussed in more detail in Chapters 23 and 24.

C. Relation to Posterior Pituitary Secretion

1. *Vasopressin Secretion*

There appear to be adrenergic and cholinergic components in the mechanisms regulating vasopressin secretion. Evidence for this conclusion and data showing that adrenergic-blocking agents prevent the increase in vasopressin secretion normally produced by noxious stimuli are presented in Chapter 6 (Volume I).

The role of acetylcholine in the discharge of the neurons in the supraoptic and paraventricular nuclei appears to be an important one. These nuclei contain large amounts of true cholinesterase (Abrahams *et al.*, 1957; Holmes, 1961). There is some cholinesterase in the neurohypophysis as well, and endings of the supraoptic and paraventricular neurons in the posterior pituitary contain not only large secretory granules ("neurosecretion"), but small "synaptic vesicles" (DeRobertis, 1961). It has been suggested that these vesicles contain acetylcholine, and that release of vasopressin from the neurons requires the local release of acetylcholine (Koelle and Geesey, 1961). However, Holmes (1961) has presented evidence that in mammals, the material in the neurohypophysis is nonspecific cholinesterase, rather than true cholinesterase. In birds, there is some true cholinesterase in the neurohypophysis, but there is much more in the supraoptic and paraventricular nuclei (see Chapter 30). These findings suggest that the supraoptic and paraventricular neurons are not cholinergic, but that cholinergic fibers from other regions converge on them. Evidence supporting this hypothesis is provided by the experiments of Pickford (1947) and Abrahams and Pickford (1956). These investigators demonstrated that direct injections of cholinesterase-inhibiting drugs or acetylcholine into the supraoptic nuclei of dogs increased vasopressin secretion. More recently it has been demonstrated that single neurons in the supraoptic nucleus which increase their rate of firing when hypertonic solutions are injected also discharge at a more rapid rate when acetylcholine is administered (Koizumi *et al.*, 1964).

2. *Oxytocin Secretion*

Abrahams and Pickford (1956) have presented evidence that oxytocin as well as vasopressin is secreted when cholinergic agents are injected into the supraoptic nuclei. Although there is undoubtedly considerable overlap in the functions of the supraoptic and paraventricular nuclei, the former is now known to be concerned primarily with the control of vasopressin secretion (see Chapter 6, Volume I), while the latter is concerned mainly with the control of oxytocin secretion (see Chapter 7, Volume I).

The major function of oxytocin in mammals appears to be the ejection of milk from the ducts of the lactating breast. Oxytocin is liberated in response to sensory impulses originating in touch receptors in the nipple (milk ejection reflex). There is some evidence that there are both cholinergic and adrenergic neurons in the reflex arc. Grosvenor and Turner (1957) found that milk excretion was inhibited by atropine, a cholinergic-blocking agent, and Dibenamine, an adrenergic-blocking agent. Oxytocin overcame the block in both cases. More recently, Meites and his associates (see Meites *et al.*, 1963) have shown that 5-hydroxytryptamine and drugs which cause its release inhibit the milk ejection reflex. This may be due to the presence in the brain of a system inhibiting oxytocin secretion, although one hesitates to draw this conclusion because detectable amounts of systemically injected 5-hydroxytryptamine do not cross the normal blood-brain barrier (Erspamer, 1960; Gaddum, 1963).

Recently, it has been claimed that oxytocin brings about "hyperarousal" of the hippocampal electroencephalogram (Kawakami *et al.*, 1964), but the doses which produced this effect were very large.

VII. Conclusions

The neurohumors discussed in this chapter are a group of amines and other compounds suspected of being chemical mediators at synapses in the central nervous system. They include 5-hydroxytryptamine, norepinephrine, dopamine, acetylcholine, substance P, histamine, and GABA. Small amounts of epinephrine and tyramine are also found in the brain. Because some tranquilizer, psychic energizer, and hallucinogenic drugs alter the concentration of these substances in the brain, the substances have been studied intensively by psychopharmacologists and psychiatrists. Until recently, the hypothesis that they are synaptic mediators rested largely on indirect evidence: they are unevenly distributed in the nervous system, their distribution is paralleled by that of enzymes involved in their synthesis and catabolism, and they produce changes in neural functions when they are injected into various parts of the central nervous system or their local concentration is altered by treatment with various drugs. However, new experimental techniques are now providing a growing body of more direct evidence that some of the neurohumors are actually synaptic mediators. Norepinephrine, dopamine, and 5-hydroxytryptamine have been demonstrated histochemically in nerve endings in the brain, and these compounds plus acetylcholine have been found in relatively high concentration in the fraction of brain homogenates that contains nerve endings. Substance P and histamine are also found in nerve endings, but their function in the nervous system is still unsettled. γ-Aminobutyric acid is probably not a synaptic mediator, and instead appears to be concerned in some way with the regulation of brain excitability.

Norepinephrine, 5-hydroxytryptamine, histamine, substance P, and GABA are found in particularly high concentration in the hypothalamus. With the exception of GABA, these neurohumors could be mediators in the hypothalamic and limbic neural circuits that form the substrate for the generation and expression of emotion. It has been suggested that 5-hydroxytryptamine is a mediator in temperature-regulating centers in the hypothalamus. Norepinephrine is postulated to be a mediator in a hypothalamic-limbic circuit that controls appetite, and acetylcholine, a mediator in a similar circuit that controls thirst.

It also seems likely that some of the neurohumors play a role in regulating anterior and posterior pituitary function. The releasing factors isolated from hypothalamic extracts are probably polypeptides, and the neurohumors do not appear to have any direct action on the anterior pituitary. However, the neurohumors are in all probability synaptic mediators at some of the synapses in the afferent paths that converge on the median eminence and regulate the secretion from it of releasing factors. A list of the presently known relations between the neurohumors and endocrine function includes the following items:

1. The stressful stimuli which increase ACTH secretion often cause a decrease in hypothalamic norepinephrine content, although the significance of this decrease is unknown. There are no consistent effects of stress on other brain neurohumors.

2. Cold in some way prevents the sedation and depletion of brain amines in rats that is usually produced by reserpine. This inhibition of the response to reserpine is absent in hypophysectomized animals, but its cause is still unknown. The whole area of modification of drug effects by stressful stimuli is one which invites further research.

3. In some animal species, there are sex differences in barbiturate-induced sleeping time and in the salivary gland content of nerve growth factor which appear to depend on differences in the secretion of gonadal hormones.

4. There appear to be adrenergic and cholinergic neurons in the network of nerve cells that regulate gonadal secretion in the adult female. Delay of the preovulatory release of LH by adrenergic and cholinergic

agents in spontaneously ovulating species as well as those which ovulate only after copulation is possibly the most convincing evidence for this conclusion. 5-Hydroxytryptamine exerts deleterious effects on deciduomas; these effects deserve further study to see if they are secondary to a decrease in luteal function or mediated through the vascular effects of the amine. The inhibitory effects of ergot derivatives on deciduoma development are also an inviting subject for future research.

5. Reserpine initiates lactation in virgin rabbits by a local action on the ventral hypothalamus. The effect is associated with an increase in prolactin secretion, but prolactin secretion is also increased by a variety of stressful stimuli. Indeed, many stimuli which increase ACTH secretion also increase prolactin secretion.

6. The secretion of vasopressin is regulated in part by what seem to be excitatory cholinergic nerve fibers which end on the neurons in the supraoptic nuclei. The origin of these fibers is unknown. The increase in vasopressin secretion produced by noxious stimuli is blocked by adrenergic blocking agents.

7. There is some evidence that there are adrenergic and cholinergic neurons in the pathways mediating oxytocin release in response to stimulation of the nipple of the breast (the milk ejection reflex). This reflex is inhibited by 5-hydroxytryptamine and by drugs which cause the release of this neurohumor.

It is now clear that the nervous system plays a role in the regulation of endocrine function, and is in turn acted on by hormones in many diverse ways. The nature of the control exerted over the anterior pituitary by the hypothalamus has been defined, and work on the isolation, complete identification, and synthesis of the releasing factors that mediate pituitary control is progressing rapidly. The big field which is just opening up is the mapping of the neural pathways which control the hypothalamo-pituitary unit, pathways in which the neurohumors discussed in this chapter are almost certainly synaptic mediators. Drugs are rapidly becoming available which can stimulate or inhibit the synthesis, the storage in nerve endings, the release, the action on effector neurons, or the destruction of all these mediator agents. Study of the effects of these drugs in combination with related investigations of the endocrine actions of the neurohumors should provide some of the most exciting future chapters in neuroendocrine research.

References

Abrahams, V. C. (1963). Histochemical localization of cholinesterases in some brain stem regions of the cat. *J. Physiol.* (*London*) **165**, 55–56P (Abstract).

Abrahams, V. C., and Pickford, M. (1956). The effect of anticholinesterase injected into the supraoptic nuclei of chloralosed dogs on the release of the oxytocic factor of the posterior pituitary. *J. Physiol.* (*London*) **133**, 330–333.

Abrahams, V. C., Koelle, G. B., and Smart, P. (1957). Histochemical demonstration of cholinesterase in the hypothalamus of the dog. *J. Physiol.* (*London*) **139**, 137–144.

Adam, H. M. (1961). Histamine in the central nervous system and hypophysis of the dog. *In* "Regional Neurochemistry" (S. S. Kety and J. Elkes, eds.), pp. 293–306. Pergamon Press, Oxford.

Airaksinen, M. M., and Mattila, M. (1962). The sedative and lethal actions of reserpine in mice, as modified by 5-hydroxytryptamine, 3,4-dihydroxyphenylalanine, methylphenidate and nikethamide in cold and warm environments. *Acta Pharmacol. Toxicol.* **19**, 199–204.

Anton, A. H., and Sayre, D. F. (1964). The distribution of dopamine and DOPA in various animals and a method for their determination in diverse biological material. *J. Pharmacol. Exptl. Therap.* **145**, 326–333.

Arimura, A., and Long, C. N. H. (1962). Influence of various vasoactive materials upon the hypophyseal portal vessels of rats: observation *in situ*. *Japan. J. Physiol.* **12**, 429–432.

Axelrod, J., and Laroche, M. J. (1959). Inhibition of *O*-methylation of epinephrine and norepinephrine *in vitro* and *in vivo*. *Science* **130**, 800.

Barbeau, A., Murphy, G. F., and Sourkes, T. L. (1961). Excretion of dopamine in diseases of basal ganglia. *Science* **133**, 1706–1707.

Barchas, J. D., and Lerner, A. B. (1964). Localization of melatonin in the nervous system. *J. Neurochem.* **11**, 489–491.

Baschieri, L., DeLuca, F., Cramarossa, L., deMartino, C., Oliverio, A., and Negri, M. (1963). The modification of thyroid activity by melatonin. *Experientia* **19**, 15–17.

Bennett, E. L., Krech, D., Rosenzweig, M. R., Karlsson, H., Dye, N., and Ohlander, A. (1958). Cholinesterase and lactic dehydrogenase activity in the rat brain. *J. Neurochem.* **3**, 153–160.

Berl, S., and Waelsch, H. (1958). Determination of glutamic acid, glutamine, glutathione and γ-aminobutyric acid and their distribution in brain tissue. *J. Neurochem.* **3**, 161–169.

Bertaccini, G. (1959). Effect of convulsant treatment on the 5-hydroxytryptamine content of brain and other tissues of the rat. *J. Neurochem.* **4**, 217–222.

Bertelli, A., Cantone, G., and Martini, L. (1954). Azione della serotinina sull'asse ipotisi-surrene. *Atti Soc. Lombarda Sci. Med. Biol.* **9**, 10–12.

Bertler, A. (1961). Occurrence and localization of catecholamines in the human brain. *Acta Physiol. Scand.* **51**, 97–107.

Bertler, A., Falck, B., and Owman, C. (1963). Cellular localization of 5-hydroxytryptamine in the rat pineal gland. *Kgl. Fysiograf. Sallskap. Lund, Forh.* **33**, 13–16.

Bishop, P. O., Field, G., Hennesy, B. L., and Smith, J. R. (1958). Action of *d*-lysergic acid diethylamide on lateral geniculate synapses. *J. Neurophysiol.* **21**, 529–549.

Boccabella, A. V., Salgado, E. D., and Alger, E. A. (1962). Testicular function and histology following serotonin administration. *Endocrinology* **71**, 827–837.

Bogdanski, D. F., Weissbach, H., and Udenfriend, S. (1957). The distribution of serotonin, 5-hydroxytryptophan decarboxylase and monoamine oxidase in brain. *J. Neurochem.* **1**, 272–278.

Bonnycastle, D. D., Giarman, N. J., and Paasonen, M. K. (1957). Anticonvulsant compounds and 5-hydroxytryptamine in rat brain. *Brit. J. Pharmacol.* **12**, 228–231.

Bonnycastle, D. D., Bonnycastle, M. F., and Anderson, E. G. (1962). The effect of a number of central depressants upon brain 5-hydroxytryptamine levels in the rat. *J. Pharmacol. Exptl. Therap.* **135**, 17–20.

Boullin, D. J. (1963). Behavior of rats depleted of 5-hydroxytryptamine by feeding a diet free of tryptophan. *Psychopharmacologia* **5**, 28–38.

Bovet-Nitti, F., and Bignami, G. (1963). Action of certain derivatives of 2-amino-methyl-benzodioxane on the hormonal equilibrium of the reproduction cycle, pseudopregnancy and pregnancy in the rat. *Proc. 1st Intern. Pharmacol. Meeting, Stockholm, 1961* Vol. 10, p. 3. Pergamon Press, Oxford.

Bowers, C. Y., Redding, T. W., and Schally, A. V. (1964). Effects of certain peptides of neural origin on the pituitary-thyroid axis. *Clin. Res.* **12**, 39 (Abstract).

Breitner, C., Picchioni, A., Chin, L., and Burton, L. E. (1961). Effect of electrostimulation on brain 5-hydroxytryptamine concentration. *Diseases Nervous System* **22**, 93–96.

Briggs, F. N., and Munson, P. L. (1955). Studies on the mechanism of stimulation of ACTH secretion with the aid of morphine as a blocking agent. *Endocrinology* **57**, 205–219.

Brodie, B. B., Maickel, R. P., and Westermann, E. G. (1961). Action of reserpine on pituitary-adrenocortical system through possible action on hypothalamus. *In* "Regional Neurochemistry" (S. S. Kety and J. Elkes, eds.), pp. 351–361. Pergamon Press, Oxford.

Burgen, A. S. V., and Chipman, L. M. (1951). Cholinesterase and succinic dehydrogenase in the central nervous system of the dog. *J. Physiol.* (*London*) **114**, 296–305.

Burgers, A. C. J., Leemreis, W., Dominiczak, T., and Van Oordt, G. J. (1958). Inhibition of the secretion of intermedine by *d*-lysergic acid diethylamide (LSD-25) in the toad, *Xenopus laevis.* *Acta Endocrinol.* **29**, 191–200.

Burn, J. H. (1963). The liberation of norepinephrine. *Physiol. Physicians* **1**, No. 10, 1–3.

Canal, N., and Ornesi, A. (1961). Serotonin encitalica eipertermia da vaccino. *Atti Accad. Med. Lombarda* **6**, 69–73.

Caramia, F., Angeletti, P. U., and Levi-Montalcini, R. (1962). Experimental analysis of the mouse submaxillary gland in relationship to its nerve-growth factor content. *Endocrinology* **70**, 915–922.

Carlsen, R. A., Zielmaker, G. H., and Shelesnyak, M. C. (1961). Termination of early (pre-nidation) pregnancy in the mouse by single injection of ergocornine methanesulphonate. *J. Reprod. Fertility* **2**, 369–373.

Carlsson, A., Falck, B., and Hillarp, N.-Å. (1962a). Cellular localization of brain monoamines. *Acta Physiol. Scand.* **56**, Suppl. 196.

Carlsson, A., Falck, B., Hillarp, N.-Å., and Torp, A. (1962b). Histochemical localization at the cellular level of hypothalamic noradrenaline. *Acta Physiol. Scand.* **54**, 385–386.

Carlsson, A., Magnusson, T., and Rosengren, E. (1963). Five-hydroxytryptamine of the spinal cord normally and after transection. *Experientia* **19**, 359.

Carlsson, A., Falck, B., Fuxe, K., and Hillarp, N.-Å. (1964). Cellular localization of monoamines in the spinal cord. *Acta Physiol. Scand.* **60**, 112–119.

Carraro, A., Corbin, A., Fraschini, F., and Martini, L. (1965). Effect of prepuberal reserpine treatment on puberty, pituitary LH and the estrous cycle of the rat. *J. Endocrinol.* **32**, 387–393.

Casentini, S., De Poli, A., Hukovic, S., and Martini, L. (1959). Studies on the control of corticotrophin release. *Endocrinology* **64**, 483–493.

Cleugh, J., Gaddum, J. H., Mitchell, R. R., Smith, M. W., and Whittaker, V. P. (1964). Substance P in brain extracts. *J. Physiol.* (*London*) **170**, 69–85.

Coleman, B., and Glaviano, V. V. (1963). Tissue levels of norepinephrine and epinephrine in hemorrhagic shock. *Science* **139**, 54.

Comer, M. S., Costa, E., and Brodie, B. B. (1963). The relationship between the reserpine syndrome and the blockade of the storage process for serotonin. *Pharmacologist* **5**, 245 (Abstract).

Connors, M., and Rosenkrantz, H. (1962). Serotonin uptake and action on the adrenal cortex. *Endocrinology* **71**, 407–413.

Corbin, A., and Schottelius, B. A. (1961). Hypothalamic neurohumoral agents and sexual maturation of immature female rats. *Am. J. Physiol.* **201**, 1176–1180.

Costa, E., Gessa, G. L., Hirsch, C., Kuntzman, R., and Brodie, B. B. (1962). On current status of serotonin as a brain neurohormone and in action of reserpinelike drugs. *Ann. N.Y. Acad. Sci.* **96**, 118–133.

Courrier, R., Guillemin, R., Justiz, M., Sakiz, E., and Aschheim, P. (1961). Presénce dans un extrait d-hypothalamus d'une substance qui stimule la sécrétion de l'hormone antéhypophysaire de lutéinisation (LH). *Compt. Rend.* **253**, 922–927.

Crawford, J. M., Curtis, D. R., Voorhoeve, P. E., and Wilson, W. J. (1963). Excitation of cerebellar neurons by acetylcholine. *Nature* **200**, 579–580.

Crossland, J. (1962). Some possible mediators of noncholinergic central transmission. *In* "Neurochemistry" (K. A. C. Elliott *et al.*, eds.), pp. 657–672. Thomas, Springfield, Illinois.

Crosson, J., Falch, J., and Reichlin, S. (1960). Failure to demonstrate TSH-releasing activity of pitressin and oxytocin. *Endocrinology* **66**, 777–779.

Crout, J. R., Creveling, C. A., and Udenfriend, S. (1961). Norepinephrine metabolism in rat brain and heart. *J. Pharmacol. Exptl. Therap.* **132**, 269–277.

Curtis, D. R. (1964). Microelectrophoresis. *In* "Physical Techniques in Biological Research" (W. L. Nastuk, ed.), Vol. 5, Part A, pp. 144–190. Academic Press, New York.

Curtis, D. R., and Davis, R. (1962). Pharmacological studies upon neurons of the lateral geniculate nucleus of the cat. *Brit. J. Pharmacol.* **18**, 217–246.

Curtis, D. R., Perri, D. D., and Watkins, J. C. (1961). The excitation of spinal neurons by the iontophoretic application of agents which chelate calcium. *J. Neurochem.* **6**, 1–20.

D'Angelo, S. A. (1963). The central nervous regulation of the secretion and release of thyroid stimulating hormone. *In* "Advances in Neuroendocrinology" (A. V. Nalbandov, ed.), pp. 158–204. Univ. of Illinois Press, Urbana, Illinois.

Davison, A. N. (1958). Physiological role of monoamine oxidase. *Physiol. Rev.* **38**, 729–747.

De Feo, J. (1957). Effect of large doses of reserpine on the deciduoma response. *Anat. Record* **127**, 409 (Abstract).

De Iraldi, A. P., Zieher, L. M., and DeRobertis, E. D. P. (1963). The 5-hydroxytryptamine content and synthesis of normal and denervated pineal gland. *Life Sciences* **9**, 691–696.

De Maio, D. (1959). Influence of adrenalectomy and hypophysectomy on cerebral serotonin. *Science* **129**, 1678–1679.

DeRobertis, E. D. P. (1961). Morphological bases of synaptic processes and neurosecretion. *In* "Regional Neurochemistry" (S. S. Kety and J. Elkes, eds.), pp. 248–258. Pergamon Press, Oxford.

DeRobertis, E. D. P., De Iraldi, A. P., Delores, G. A., Salganicoff, A., and Salganicoff, L. (1962). Cholinergic and non-cholinergic nerve endings in rat brain. *J. Neurochem.* **9,** 23–35.

Deuben, R. R., and Meites, J. (1964). Stimulation of pituitary growth hormone release by a hypothalamic extract *in vitro.* *Endocrinology* **74,** 408–414.

Donovan, B. T., and Harris, G. W. (1956). Adrenergic agents and the release of gonadotropic hormones in the rabbit. *J. Physiol.* (*London*) **132,** 577–585.

Dordoni, F., and Fortier, C. (1950). Effect of eserine and atropine on ACTH release. *Proc. Soc. Exptl. Biol. Med.* **75,** 815–816.

Duritz, G., and Truitt, Jr., E. B. (1963). The role of acetaldehyde in the action of alcohol on brain norepinephrine and serotonin. *Federation Proc.* **22,** 272 (Abstract).

Dyster-Aas, K., and Krakau, C. E. T. (1964). Increased permeability of the blood-aqueous humor barrier in the rabbit's eye provoked by melanocyte stimulating peptides. *Endocrinology* **74,** 255–265.

Eayrs, J. T. (1964). Effect of thyroid hormones on brain differentiation. *In* "Brain-thyroid Relationships" (M. P. Cameron and M. O'Connor, eds.), pp. 60–71. Little, Brown, Boston, Massachusetts.

Eccles, J. C. (1964). "The Physiology of Synapses." Springer, Berlin.

Efron, D. H., and Brodie, B. B. (1962). Role of the pituitary-adrenal system in activity and toxicity of reserpine in rats. *Pharmacologist* **4,** No. 2, 173 (Abstract).

Elliot, K. A. C., and Jasper, H. H. (1959). Gamma-aminobutyric acid. *Physiol. Rev.* **39,** 383–406.

Enerbäck, L. (1960). Influence of alcohol on urinary excretion of 5-hydroxyindole acetic acid in the rat. *Endocrinology* **67,** 717–719.

Erspamer, V. (1960). Recent researches in the field of 5-hydroxytryptamine and related indolealkyl amines. *Progr. Drug Res.* **3,** 151–367.

Everett, J. W. (1964). Central neural control of reproductive functions. *Physiol. Rev.* **44,** 373–431.

Falck, B. (1962). Observations on the possibilities of the cellular localization of monoamine by a fluorescence method. *Acta Physiol. Scand.* **56,** Suppl. 197.

Farrell, G. (1964). Recent contributions to the study of the role of the central nervous system in aldosterone secretion. *In* "Aldosterone" (E. E. Baulieu and P. Robel, eds.), pp. 247–261. Blackwell, Oxford.

Feldberg, W. (1950). The role of acetylcholine in the central nervous system. *Brit. Med. Bull.* **6,** 312–321.

Feldberg, W., and Myers, R. D. (1963). A new concept of temperature regulation by amines in the hypothalamus. *Nature* **200,** 1325.

Fiore-Donati, L., Pollice, L., and Chieco-Bianchi, L. (1959). Response of adrenal and preputial glands of rats to administration of 5-hydroxytryptamine. *Experientia* **15,** 193–195.

Fisher, A. E. (1964). Chemical stimulation of the brain. *Sci. American* **210,** 60–68.

Fisher, A. E., and Coury, J. N. (1962). Cholinergic tracing of a central neural circuit underlying the thirst drive. *Science* **138,** 691–693.

Franz, J., Haselbach, C. H., and Libert, O. (1962). Studies on the effect of hypothalamic extracts on somatotrophic pituitary function. *Acta Endocrinol.* **41,** 336–350.

Fraschini, R., Martini, L., Motta, M., and Pecile, A. (1963). Studies on mechanisms controlling luteotrophic hormone release. *Proc. 1st Intern. Pharmacol. Meeting, Stockholm, 1961* Vol. 10, p. 103. Pergamon Press, Oxford.

Freedman, D. X. (1963). Psychotomimetic drugs and brain biogenic amines. *Am. J. Psychiat.* **119,** 843–850.

Freedman, D. X., Barchas, J. D., and Schoenbrun, R. L. (1962). Response of brain amines to exhaustion-stress and LSD-25. *Federation Proc.* **21,** 337 (Abstract).

Friedman, A. H., Aylesworth, R. J., and Friedman, G. (1963). Tremorine: its effect on amines of the central nervous system. *Science* **141,** 1189–1190.

Fuxe, K. (1963). Cellular localization of monoamines in the median eminence and in the infundibular stem of some mammals. *Acta Physiol. Scand.* **58,** 383–384.

Fuxe, K. (1964). Cellular localization of monoamines in the median eminence and the infundibular stem of some mammals. *Z. Zellforsch. Mikroskop. Anat.* **61,** 710–724.

Gaddum, J. H. (1960). Substance P distribution. *In* "Polypeptides which Affect Smooth Muscles and Blood Vessels" (M. Schachter, ed.), pp. 163–170. Pergamon Press, Oxford.

Gaddum, J. H. (1963). Chemical transmission in the central nervous system. *Nature* **197,** 741–743.

Ganong, W. F. (1963). The central nervous system and the synthesis and release of adrenocorticotropic hormone. *In* "Advances in Neuroendocrinology" (A. V. Nalbandov, ed.), pp. 92–149. Univ. of Illinois Press, Urbana, Illinois.

Ganong, W. F. (1965a). "Review of Medical Physiology," 2nd ed. Lange Med. Publ., Los Altos, California.

Ganong, W. F. (1965b). The effect of chlorpromazine and related drugs on ACTH release. Proc. 2nd Intern. Endocrine Congr. *Excerpta Med., Intern. Congr. Ser.* **83,** 624–628.

Ganong, W. F., Goldfien, A., Halevy, A., Davidson, J. M., and Boryczka, A. T. (1961). Effect of lysergic acid diethylamide on adrenocortical and adrenal medullary function in the dog. *Acta Endocrinol.* **37,** 583–588.

Ganong, W. F., Wise, B. L., Shackleford, R., Boryczka, A. T., and Zipf, B. (1965). The site at which α-ethyltryptamine acts to inhibit the secretion of ACTH. *Endocrinology* **76,** 526–530.

Garattini, S., and Valzelli, L. (1958). Researches on the mechanism of reserpine sedative action. *Science* **128,** 1278–1279.

Gaunt, R., Chart, J. J., and Renzi, A. A. (1961). Endocrine pharmacology. *Science* **133,** 613–621.

Gaunt, R., Renzi, A. A., and Chart, J. J. (1962). Endocrine pharmacology of reserpine. *Endocrinology* **71,** 527–535.

Goldman, H. (1963). Effect on the pituitary gland: endocrine gland blood flow. *Endocrinology* **72,** 588–591.

Goldman, H., and Sapirstein, L. A. (1958). Determination of blood flow to the anterior pituitary gland. *Am. J. Physiol.* **194,** 433–435.

Green, J. P. (1964). Histamine and the nervous system. *Federation Proc.* **23,** 1095–1102.

Grossman, S. P. (1960). Eating and drinking elicited by direct adrenergic or cholinergic stimulation of the hypothalamus. *Science* **132,** 301–302.

Grossman, S. P. (1962). Effects of adrenergic and cholinergic blocking agents on hypothalamic mechanisms. *Am. J. Physiol.* **202,** 1230–1236.

Grosvenor, C. C., and Turner, C. W. (1957). Evidence for adrenergic and cholinergic components in milk let-down reflex in lactating rat. *Proc. Soc. Exptl. Biol. Med.* **95,** 719–722.

Guillemin, R. (1955). A re-evaluation of acetylcholine, adrenaline, noradrenaline and histamine as possible mediators of the pituitary adrenocorticotrophic activation by stress. *Endocrinology* **56,** 248–255.

Guillemin, R., and Rosenberg, B. (1955). Humoral hypothalamic control of anterior pituitary: a study with combined tissue cultures. *Endocrinology* **57,** 599–607.

Guillemin, R., and Schally, A. V. (1963). Recent advances in the chemistry of neuroendocrine mediators originating in the central nervous system. *In* "Advances in Neuroendocrinology" (A. V. Nalbandov, ed.), pp. 314–328. Univ. of Illinois Press, Urbana, Illinois.

Guillemin, R., Hearn, W. R., Check, W. R., and Householder, D. E. (1957). Control of corticotrophin release: further studies with *in vitro* methods. *Endocrinology* **60,** 488–506.

Guillemin, R., Yamazaki, E., Gard, D. A., Justiz, M., and Sakiz, E. (1963). *In vitro* secretion of thyrotropin (TSH): stimulation by a hypothalamic peptide. *Endocrinology* **73,** 564–572.

Guillemin, R., Sakiz, E., and Ward, D. M. (1965). Further purification of TSH-releasing factor (TRF) from sheep hypothalamic tissues, with observations on the amino acid composition. *Proc. Soc. Exptl. Biol. Med.* **118,** 1132–1137.

Gunne, L. M., and Reis, D. J. (1963). Changes in brain catecholamines associated with electrical stimulation of the amygdaloid nucleus. *Life Sciences* **11,** 804–809.

Gursey, D., and Olson, R. E. (1960). Depression of serotonin and norepinephrine levels in brain stem of rabbit by ethanol. *Proc. Soc. Exptl. Biol. Med.* **104,** 280–281.

Haefely, W., and Hürlimann, A. (1962). Substance P, a highly active naturally occurring polypeptide. *Experientia* **18,** 297–303.

Häggendal, J. (1963). The presence of 3-*O*-methylated noradrenaline (normetanephrine) in normal brain tissue. *Acta Physiol. Scand.* **59,** 261–268.

Häggendal, J., and Malmfors, T. (1963). Evidence of dopamine-containing neurons in the retina of rabbits. *Acta Physiol. Scand.* **59,** 295–296.

Hagen, P. B. (1962). Some current ideas on the biosynthesis and storage of simple amines and some considerations of their relationship to central nervous system function. *J. Neuropsychiatry* **4,** 107–112.

Hagen, P. B., and Wallace, A. C. (1960). An effect of reserpine on growth and sexual maturation. *Federation Proc.* **19,** 168 (Abstract).

Halevy, A. (1960). The effects of physiological stimuli on the 5-hydroxytryptamine (serotonin) content of the blood and brain. Ph.D. Thesis, University of California (San Francisco).

Hansel, W., Armstrong, D. T., and McEntee, K. (1957). Recent studies on the mechanism of ovulation in the cow. *In* "Symposium on Reproductive and Infertility" (F. X. Gassener, ed.), pp. 63–74. Pergamon Press, Oxford.

Harris, G. W. (1955). "Neural Control of the Pituitary Gland," p. 298. Edward Arnold, London.

Harris, G. W., Jacobsohn, D., and Kahlson, G. (1952). The occurrence of histamine in cerebral regions related to the hypophysis. *Ciba Colloq. Endocrinol.* **4,** 186–194.

Harrison, T. S. (1961). Some factors influencing thyrotropin release in the rabbit. *Endocrinology* **68,** 466–478.

Harvey, J. A., Heller, A., and Moore, R. Y. (1963). The effect of unilateral and bilateral medial forebrain bundle lesions on brain serotonin. *J. Pharmacol. Exptl. Therap.* **140,** 103–110.

Hicks, R., and West, G. B. (1958). Adrenalectomy and tissue amines. *Nature* **182,** 401–402.

Himwich, W. H. (1963). General neurophysiology (biochemical aspects). *Progr. Neurol. Psychiat.* **18,** 20–45.

Hirsch, H. E., and Robins, E. (1962). Distribution of γ-aminobutyric acid in the layers of the cerebral cortex. Implications for its physiological role. *J. Neurochem.* **9,** 63–70.

Holmes, R. L. (1961). Phosphatase and cholinesterase in the hypothalamo-hypophysial system of the monkey. *J. Endocrinol.* **23,** 63–67.

Holtz, P. (1959). Role of L-dopa decarboxylase in the biosynthesis of catecholamines in nervous tissue and the adrenal medulla. *Pharmacol. Rev.* **11,** 317–329.

Hornykiewicz, O. (1964). The distribution and metabolism of catecholamines and 5-hydroxytryptamine in human brain. *In* "Comparative Neurochemistry" (D. Richter, ed.), pp. 379–386. Pergamon Press, Oxford.

Hume, D. M. (1958). The method of hypothalamic regulation of pituitary and adrenal secretion in response to trauma. *In* "Pathophysiologica Diencephalica" (S. B. Curri *et al.*, eds.), pp. 217–228. Springer, Vienna.

Jolly, H. (1955). "Sexual Precocity," p. 276. Thomas, Springfield, Illinois.

Kanematsu, S., and Sawyer, C. H. (1963). Effects of intrahypothalamic implants of reserpine on lactation and pituitary prolactin content in the rabbit. *Proc. Soc. Exptl. Biol. Med.* **113,** 967–969.

Kanematsu, S., Hilliard, J., and Sawyer, C. H. (1963). The effect of reserpine on pituitary prolactin content and its hypothalamic site of action in the rabbit. *Acta Endocrinol.* **44,** 467–474.

Kato, R. (1959). Serotonin content of the rat brain in relation to sex and age. *J. Neurochem.* **5,** 202.

Kawakami, M., Teresawa, E., and Kawachi, J. (1964). Studies on the oxytocin-sensitive component in the reticular activating system. *Japan. J. Physiol.* **14,** 104–121.

Killam, K. F. (1958). Possible role of gamma-aminobutryric acid as an inhibitor transmitter. *Federation Proc.* **17,** 1018–1024.

Knoll, J., and Knoll, B. (1963). Reserpine: modifications of its tranquilizer effect and analysis of its central mode of action. *Proc. 1st Intern. Pharmacol. Meeting, Stockholm, 1961* Vol. 10, p. 34. Pergamon Press, Oxford.

Kobayashi, T., Kobayashi, T., Kato, J., and Minaguchi, H. (1963). Fluctuation in choline acetylase activity in hypothalamus of rat during estrous cycle and after castration. *Endocrinol. Japon.* **10,** 175–182.

Koelle, G. B., and Geesey, C. N. (1961). Localization of acetylcholinesterase in the neurohypophysis and its functional implications. *Proc. Soc. Exptl. Biol. Med.* **106,** 625–628.

Koizumi, K., Ishikawa, T., and Brooks, C.McC. (1964). Control of activity of neurons in the supraoptic nucleus. *J. Neurophysiol.* **27,** 878–892.

Kopin, I. J. (1964). Storage and metabolism of catecholamines: the role of monoamine oxidase. *Pharmacol. Rev.* **16,** 179–191.

Kraicer, P. F., Marcus, G. J., and Shelesnyak, M. C. (1963). Studies on the mechanism of decidualization. III. Decidualization in the histamine-depleted rat. *J. Reprod. Fertility* **5,** 417–421.

Krech, D., Rosenzweig, N. R., and Bennett, E. L. (1963). Effects of complex environments and blindness on rat brain. *Arch. Neurol.* **8,** 403–412.

Krieger, H. P., Kolodny, H., and Krieger, D. T. (1964). Alterations of plasma 17-hydroxycorticoids by chemical stimulation of median eminence. *Federation Proc.* **23**, 205 (Abstract).

Krivoy, W. A., and Guillemin, R. (1961). On a possible role of β-melanocyte-stimulating hormone (βMSH) in the central nervous system of the mammalia: an effect of βMSH in the spinal cord of the cat. *Endocrinology* **69**, 170–175.

Krivoy, W. A., and Kroeger, D. (1963). The neurogenic effect of high potency substance P. *Experientia* **19**, 366–367.

Krivoy, W. A., Lane, M., and Kroeger, D. C. (1963). The actions of certain polypeptides on synaptic transmission. *Ann. N.Y. Acad. Sci.* **104**, 312–329.

Kuntzman, R., Shore, P. A., Bogdanski, D., and Brodie, B. B. (1961). Microanalytical procedures for fluorometric assay of brain DOPA-5HTP decarboxylase, norepinephrine and serotonin and a detailed mapping of decarboxylase activity in brain. *J. Neurochem.* **6**, 226–232.

La Brosse, E. H., Axelrod, J., and Kety, S. S. (1958). *O*-methylation, the principal route of metabolism of epinephrine in man. *Science* **128**, 593–594.

Lansing, R. W., and Trunnell, J. B. (1963). Electroencephalographic changes accompanying thyroid deficiency in man. *J. Clin. Endocrinol. Metab.* **23**, 470–480.

Laszlo, I. (1963). Removal of interfering nucleotides from brain extracts containing substance P. Effects of drugs on brain concentrations of substance P. *Brit. J. Pharmacol.* **21**, 113–126.

Laverty, R., Michaelson, I. A., Sharman, D. F., and Whittaker, V. P. (1963). The subcellular localization of dopamine and acetylcholine in the dog caudate nucleus. *Brit. J. Pharmacol.* **21**, 482–490.

Lembeck, F., and Starke, K. (1963). Substance P content and effect on capillary permeability of extracts of various parts of human brain. *Nature* **199**, 1295–1296.

Levi, R., and Maynert, E. W. (1964). The subcellular localization of brain stem norepinephrine and 5-hydroxytryptamine in stressed rats. *Biochem. Pharmacol.* **3**, 615–621.

Lewis, G. P. (1964). Five-hydroxytryptamine (serotonin, enteramine, 5HT). *In* "The Hormones" (G. Pincus *et al.*, eds.), Vol. 4, pp. 387–402. Academic Press, New York.

Lindsay, D., Poulson, D. E., and Robson, J. M. (1961). The effect of 5-hydroxytryptamine and of amine oxidase inhibitors on experimental deciduomata in mice. *J. Endocrinol.* **23**, 209–215.

Lisk, R. D., and Newton, M. (1963). Estradiol: evidence for its direct effect on hypothalamic neurons. *Science* **139**, 223–224.

Long, C. N. H. (1951). Regulation of ACTH secretion. *Recent Progr. Hormone Res.* **7**, 75–97.

Long, J. M., Krivoy, W. A., and Guillemin, R. (1961). On the possible role of β-melanocyte stimulating hormone (β-MSH) in the central nervous system of the mammal: enzymatic inactivation *in vitro* of β-MSH by brain tissue. *Endocrinology* **69**, 176–181.

McCann, S. M., Talesnik, S. M., and Friedman, H. M. (1960). LH-releasing activity in hypothalamic extracts. *Proc. Soc. Exptl. Biol. Med.* **104**, 432–434.

McGeer, E. G., and McGeer, P. L. (1962). Catecholamine content of spinal cord. *Can. J. Biochem. Physiol.* **40**, 1141–1151.

McGeer, P. L. (1964). The distribution of histamine in cat and human brain. *In* "Comparative Neurochemistry" (D. Richter, ed.), pp. 387–391. Pergamon Press, Oxford.

McGeer, P. L., McGeer, E. G., and Wada, J. A. (1963). Central aromatic amine levels and behavior. II. Serotonin and catecholamine levels in various cat brain areas following administration of psychoactive drugs or amine precursors. *Arch. Neurol.* **9**, 81–89.

McIsaac, W. M., Khairallah, P. A., and Page, I. H. (1961). 10-Methoxyharmalan, a potent serotonin antagonist which affects conditioned behavior. *Science* **134**, 674–675.

McKhann, G. M., and Tower, D. B. (1959). Gamma-aminobutyric acid: a substrate for oxidative metabolism of cerebral cortex. *Am. J. Physiol.* **196**, 36–38.

Magnusson, T., and Rosengren, E. (1963). Catecholamines of the spinal cord normally and after transection. *Experientia* **19**, 229–230.

Magoun, H. W. (1963). "The Waking Brain," 2nd ed. Thomas, Springfield, Illinois.

Maickel, R. P., Westermann, E. O., and Brodie, B. B. (1961). Effects of reserpine and cold exposure on pituitary adrenocortical function in rats. *J. Pharmacol. Exptl. Therap.* **134**, 167–175.

Markee, J. E., Sawyer, C. H., and Hollingshead, W. H. (1948). Adrenergic release of luteinizing hormone from the hypophysis of the rabbit. *Recent Progr. Hormone Res.* **2**, 117–131.

Martel, R. R., Westermann, E. O., and Maickel, R. P. (1962). Dissociation of reserpine-induced sedation and ACTH hypersecretion. *Life Sciences* **4**, 151–155.

Martini, L., Pecile, A., Saito, S., and Tani, F. (1960). The effect of midbrain transection on ACTH release. *Endocrinology* **66**, 501–507.

Masami, M., Hiroshi, Y., and Reiji, I. (1962). Effect of pyrogallol on the catecholamine content of the rabbit brain. *Biochem. Pharmacol.* **11**, 1109–1110.

Maynert, E. W., and Klingman, G. I. (1962). Tolerance to morphine. I. Effects on catecholamines in the brain and adrenal glands. *J. Pharmacol. Exptl. Therap.* **135**, 285–295.

Maynert, E. W., and Levi, R. (1964). Stress-induced release of brain norepinephrine and its inhibition by drugs. *J. Pharmacol. Exptl. Therap.* **143**, 90–95.

Maynert, E. W., Klingman, G. I., and Kaji, H. K. (1962). Tolerance to morphine. II. Lack of effects on brain 5-hydroxytryptamine and γ-aminobutyric acid. *J. Pharmacol. Exptl. Therap.* **135**, 296–299.

Meites, J., Nicoll, C. S., and Talwalker, P. K. (1959). Effects of reserpine and serotonin on milk secretion and mammary growth in the rat. *Proc. Soc. Exptl. Biol. Med.* **101**, 563–565.

Meites, J., Nicoll, C. S., and Talwalker, P. K. (1963). The central nervous system and the secretion and release of prolactin. *In* "Advances in Neuroendocrinology" (A. V. Nalbandov, ed.), pp. 238–277. Univ. of Illinois Press, Urbana, Illinois.

Meyerson, B. J. (1964). The effect of neuropharmacological agents on hormone-activated estrus behavior in ovariectomized rats. *Arch. Intern. Pharmacodyn.* **150**, 4–33.

Michael, R. P., and Gibbons, J. L. (1963). Interrelations between the endocrine system and neuropsychiatry. *Intern. Rev. Neurobiol.* **5**, 243–302.

Michaelson, I. A., and Dowe, G. (1963). The subcellular distribution of histamine in brain tissue. *Biochem. Pharmacol.* **12**, 949–956.

Michaelson, I. A., and Whittaker, V. P. (1963). The subcellular localization of 5-hydroxytryptamine in guinea pig brain. *Biochem. Pharmacol.* **12**, 203–211.

Mitchell, J. F. (1963). The spontaneous and evoked release of acetylcholine from the cerebral cortex. *J. Physiol.* (*London*) **165**, 98–116.

Moore, K. E., and Lariviere, E. W. (1963). Effects of D-amphetamine and restraint on the control of norepinephrine and dopamine in rat brain. *Biochem. Pharmacol.* **12**, 1283–1288.

Moussatché, H., and Pereira, N. A. (1957). Release of adrenocorticotrophin by 5-hydroxytryptamine. *Acta Physiol. Latinoamer.* **7**, 71–75.

Mustakallio, K. K., Levonen, E., and Raekallio, J. (1961). Histochemical demonstration in rat of monoamine oxidase inhibition by β-phenyl-isopropyl hydrazine. *Science* **134**, 344.

Nicoll, C. S., and Meites, J. (1962). Failure of neurohypophyseal hormones to influence prolactin secretion *in vitro*. *Endocrinology* **70**, 927–929.

Olds, J., and Olds, M. F. (1958). Positive reinforcement by stimulating hypothalamus with iproniazid and other compounds. *Science* **127**, 1175–1176.

Paasonen, M. K., and Vogt, M. (1956). The effect of drugs on the amounts of substance P and 5-hydroxytryptamine in mammalian brain. *J. Physiol.* (*London*) **131**, 617–626.

Paton, W. D. M. (1958). Central and synaptic transmission in the nervous system (pharmacological aspects). *Ann. Rev. Physiol.* **20**, 431–470.

Paulsen, E. C., and Hess, S. M. (1963). The rate of synthesis of catecholamines following depletion in guinea pig brain and heart. *J. Neurochem.* **10**, 453–459.

Pepler, W. J., and Pearse, A. G. E. (1957). The histochemistry of the esterases of rat brain, with special reference to those of the hypothalamic nuclei. *J. Neurochem.* **1**, 193–202.

Pfeifer, A. K., Vizi, E., Satory, E., and Galambos, E. (1963). The effect of adrenalectomy on the norepinephrine and serotonin content of the brain and on reserpine action in rats. *Experientia* **19**, 482–483.

Pickford, M. (1947). The action of acetylcholine in the supraoptic nucleus of the chloralosed dog. *J. Physiol.* (*London*) **106**, 264–270.

Pletscher, A., Kunz, E., Staebler, H., and Gey, K. F. (1963). The uptake of tryptamine by brain *in vivo* and its alteration by drugs. *Biochem. Pharmacol.* **21**, 1065–1070.

Poschel, B. P. H., and Ninteman, F. W. (1963). Norepinephrine, a possible excitatory neurohumor of the reward system. *Life Sciences* **10**, 782–788.

Poulson, E., Botros, M., and Robson, J. M. (1960). Effect of 5-hydroxytryptamine and iproniazid on pregnancy. *Science* **131**, 1101–1102.

Premachandra, B. N., and Turner, C. W. (1960). Reserpine and thyroid activity in the pigeon. *Federation Proc.* **19**, 171 (Abstract).

Put, T. R., and Hogenhuis, L. A. H. (1962). Brain serotonin and thyroid function. *Acta Physiol. Pharmacol. Neerl.* **10**, 343–352.

Quastel, J. H., and Quastel, D. M. J. (1961). "The Chemistry of Brain Metabolism in Health and Disease." Thomas, Springfield, Illinois.

Reichlin, S. (1963). Neuroendocrinology. *New Engl. J. Med.* **269**, 1182–1191, 1246–1250, 1296–1303.

Reiss, S. (1961). Growth control of neurons in the superior cervical ganglion of the mouse. *Am. Zoologist* **1**, 382 (Abstract).

Resnick, R. H., Smith, G. T., and Gray, S. J. (1961). Endocrine influences on tissue serotonin content of the rat. *Am. J. Physiol.* **201**, 571–573.

Roberts, E. (1962). Gamma-aminobutyric acid. *In* "Neurochemistry" (K. A. C. Elliott *et al.*, eds.), pp. 636–656. Thomas, Springfield, Illinois.

Roberts, E., and Simonsen, D. G. (1960). Free amino acids and related substances in normal and neoplastic tissues. *In* "Amino Acids, Proteins, and Cancer Biochemistry," J. P. Greenstein Memorial Symp. (J. T. Edsall, ed.), pp. 121–195. Academic Press, New York.

Roberts, E., Lowe, I. P., Guth, L., and Jelinek, B. (1958). Distribution of γ-aminobutyric acid and other amino acids in nervous tissue of various species. *J. Exptl. Zool.* **138**, 313–325.

Robson, J. M., and Botros, M. (1961). The effect of 5-hydroxytryptamine and of monoamine oxidase inhibitors on sexual maturity. *J. Endocrinol.* **22**, 165–175.

Roos, B.-E., Anden, N.-E., and Werdinius, B. (1963). Effect of drugs on the level of indole and phenolic acids in the central nervous system. *Acta Physiol. Scand.* **59**, Suppl. 213, 132 (Abstract).

Rothlin, E. (1957). Pharmacology of lysergic acid diethylamide and some related compounds. *J. Pharm. Pharmacol.* **9**, 569–587.

Rupe, B. D., Bousquet, W. F., and Miya, T. S. (1963). Stress modification of drug responses. *Science* **141**, 1186–1187.

Ryall, R. W. (1963). The identification of acetylcholine in presynaptic terminals isolated from brain. *Biochem. Pharmacol.* **12**, 1055–1056.

Saffran, M., Schally, A. V., and Benfey, B. F. (1955). Stimulation of the release of corticotropin from adenohypophysis by a neurohypophysial factor. *Endocrinology* **57**, 439–444.

Salmoiraghi, G. C., and Steiner, F. A. (1963). Acetylcholine sensitivity of cat's medullary neurons. *J. Neurophysiol.* **26**, 581–597.

Sano, K., and Roberts, E. (1963). Binding of γ-aminobutyric acid by mouse brain preparations. *Biochem. Pharmacol.* **12**, 489–502.

Sawyer, C. H. (1955). Rhinencephalic involvement in pituitary activation by intraventricular histamine in the rabbit under Nembutal anesthesia. *Am. J. Physiol.* **180**, 37–46.

Sawyer, C. H. (1957). Induction of lactation in the rabbit with reserpine. *Anat. Record* **127**, 362–363 (Abstract).

Sawyer, C. H. (1963). Mechanisms by which drugs and hormones activate and block release of pituitary gonadotropins. *Proc. 1st Intern. Pharmacol. Meeting, Stockholm, 1961* Vol. I, pp. 27–46. Pergamon Press, Oxford.

Sawyer, C. H., Markee, J. E., and Townsend, B. F. (1949). Cholinergic and adrenergic components in the neurohumoral control of the release of LH in the rabbit. *Endocrinology* **44**, 18–37.

Sawyer, C. H., Markee, J. E., and Everett, J. W. (1950). Activation of the adenohypophysis by intravenous injection of epinephrine in the atropinized rabbit. *Endocrinology* **46**, 536–543.

Schally, A. V., Meites, J., Bowers, C. Y., and Ratner, A. (1964a). Identity of prolactin inhibiting factor (PIF) and luteinizing hormone releasing factor (LRF). *Proc. Soc. Exptl. Biol. Med.* **117**, 252–254.

Schally, A. V., Steelman, S. L., and Bowers, C. Y. (1964b). Stimulation and release of growth hormone *in vitro* by a hypothalamic factor. *Program 46th Meeting Endocrine Soc., San Francisco,* p. 143 (Abstract).

Scott, G. T., and Nading, L. K. (1961). Relative effectiveness of phenothiazine tranquilizing drugs causing release of MSH. *Proc. Soc. Exptl. Biol. Med.* **106**, 88–90.

Seiden, L. S., and Carlsson, A. (1964). Brain and heart catecholamine levels after L-dopa administration and reserpine treated mice: correlation with a conditioned avoidance response. *Psychopharmacologia* **5**, 178–181.

Seiden, L. S., and Hanson, L. C. F. (1964). Reversal of the reserpine-induced suppression of the conditioned avoidance response in the cat by L-DOPA. *Psychopharmacologia* **6**, 239–244.

Shelesnyak, M. C. (1962). Decidualization: the decidua and the deciduoma. *Perspectives Biol. Med.* **5**, 503–518.

Sjoerdsma, A. (1963). Chemotherapy of hypertension: yesterday—today—tomorrow. *Circulation* **28**, 161–164.

Sjoerdsma, A., Vendsalu, A., and Engelman, K. (1963). Studies on the metabolism and mechanism of action of methyldopa. *Circulation* **28**, 492–502.

Skillen, R. G., Thienes, C. H., and Strain, L. (1961). Brain 5-hydroxytryptamine, 5-hydroxytryptophan decarboxylase and monoamine oxidase in normal, thyroid-fed and propylthiouracil-fed male and female rats. *Endocrinology* **69**, 1099–1102.

Sofer, S., and Gubler, C. J. (1962). Studies on the effects of various procedures on the 5HT levels in the brain of rats. *Federation Proc.* **21**, 340 (Abstract).

Soulairac, M.-L. (1963). Étude expérimentale des régulations hormono-nerveuses du comportment sexuel du Rat mâle. *Ann. Endocrinol.* (*Paris*) **24**, Suppl. 3, 1–94.

Spector, S., Melman, K., Lovenberg, W., and Sjoerdsma, A. (1963). The presence and distribution of tyramine in mammalian tissues. *J. Pharmacol. Exptl. Therap.* **140**, 229–239.

Spector, W. G. (1960). Anti-fertility action of a monoamine oxidase inhibitor. *Nature* **187**, 514–515.

Spencer, P. S. J., and West, G. B. (1961). Sensitivity of the hyperthyroid and hypothyroid mouse to histamine and 5-hydroxytryptamine. *Brit. J. Pharmacol.* **17**, 137–143.

Stark, P., and Boyd, E. S. (1963). Effects of cholinergic drugs on hypothalamic self-stimulation response rates of dogs. *Am. J. Physiol.* **205**, 745–748.

Stedman, E., and Stedman, E. (1937). The mechanism of the biological synthesis of acetylcholine. I. The isolation of acetylcholine produced by brain tissue *in vitro*. *Biochem. J.* **31**, 817–827.

Stein, L., and Seiffer, J. (1962). Muscarinic synapses in the hypothalamus. *Am. J. Physiol.* **202**, 751–756.

Stern, P. (1963). Substance P as a sensory transmitter and its other central effects. *Ann. N.Y. Acad. Sci.* **104**, 403–415.

Stone, W. E., Tews, J. K., and Carter, S. H. (1962). Chemical changes in the brain during insulin hypoglycemia and recovery. *Physiologist* **5**, 218 (Abstract).

Sulser, F., and Brodie, B. B. (1960). Is reserpine tranquillization linked to change in brain serotonin or brain norepinephrine? *Science* **131**, 1440–1441.

Swingle, W. W., Parlow, A. F., Brannick, L. J., and Barrett, W. (1956). A component of substance P active in releasing ACTH. *Proc. Soc. Exptl. Biol. Med.* **92**, 594–597.

Talwalker, P. K., Ratner, A., and Meites, J. (1963). *In vitro* inhibition of pituitary prolactin synthesis and release by hypothalamic extract. *Am. J. Physiol.* **205**, 213–218.

Taubenhaus, M., and Soskin, S. (1941). Release of luteinizing hormone from the anterior hypothalamus by an acetylcholine-like substance from the hypothalamic region. *Endocrinology* **29**, 958–964.

Toh, C. C. (1960). Effects of temperature on the 5HT content of tissues. *J. Physiol. (London)* **151**, 410–415.

Towne, J., Put, T., and Schwartz, N. (1959). Brain serotonin and thyroid function. *Federation Proc.* **18**, 452 (Abstract).

Tullner, W. W., and Hertz, R. (1964). Suppression of corticosteroid production in the dog by Monase. *Proc. Soc. Exptl. Biol. Med.* **116**, 837–840.

Ungar, G., and Witten, J. W. (1963). Increase in brain histamine caused by tremorine. *Federation Proc.* **22**, 273 (Abstract).

Utley, J. D. (1963). Gamma-aminobutyric acid and 5-hydroxytryptamine concentrations in neurons and glial cells in the medial geniculate body of the cat. *Biochem. Pharmacol.* **12**, 1288–1230.

Vance, V. K., and Shioda, Y. (1964). Effect of intravenous epinephrine on blood ACTH concentration as measured by steroidogenesis in the hypophysectomized rat. *Endocrinology* **74**, 807–808.

Verdesca, A. S., Westermann, C. D., Crampton, R. S., Black, W. C., Nedeljkovic, R. I., and Hilton, J. G. (1961). Direct adrenocortical stimulatory effect of serotonin. *Am. J. Physiol.* **201**, 1065–1067.

Vernikos-Danellis, J., and Marks, B. H. (1962). Epinephrine-induced release of ACTH in normal human subjects: a test of pituitary function. *Endocrinology* **70**, 525–531.

Vogt, M. (1954). The concentration of sympathin in different parts of the central nervous system under normal conditions and after the administration of drugs. *J. Physiol. (London)* **131**, 125–136.

von Euler, C., and Holmgren, B. (1956). The thyroxin "receptor" of the thyroid-pituitary system. *J. Physiol. (London)* **131**, 125–136.

von Euler, U. S. (1963). Substance P in subcellular particles in peripheral nerves. *Ann. N.Y. Acad. Sci.* **104**, 449–463.

Weil-Malherbe, H., Axelrod, J., and Tomchick, R. (1959). Blood-brain barrier for adrenaline. *Science* **129**, 1226–1227.

Weiner, N. (1964). Catecholamines. *In* "The Hormones" (G. Pincus *et al.*, eds.), pp. 403–479. Academic Press, New York.

Werdinius, B., Antén, N. E., and Roos, B.-E. (1963). On the occurrence of phenolic acids in brain and cerebral spinal fluid. *Acta Physiol. Scand.* **59**, Suppl. 213, 161 (Abstract).

Westfall, B. A., Boulos, B. M., Shields, J. L., and Gard, S. (1964). Sex differences in pentobarbital sensitivity in mice. *Proc. Soc. Exptl. Biol. Med.* **115**, 509–510.

Whipple, H. E., ed. (1964). Symposium on nerve growth factor. *Ann. N.Y. Acad. Sci.* **118**, 149–232.

White, T. (1964). Biosynthesis, metabolism and function of histamine in the nervous system. *Federation Proc.* **23**, 1103–1106.

Wolf, G., and Miller, N. E. (1964). Lateral hypothalamic lesions: effects on drinking elicited by carbachol in preoptic area and posterior hypothalamus. *Science* **143**, 585–587.

Wolfe, D. E., Potter, L. T., Richardson, K. C., and Axelrod, J. (1962). Localizing tritiated norepinephrine in sympathetic axons by electron microscopic autoradiography. *Science* **138**, 440–441.

Woodbury, D. M., and Vernadakis, A. (1958). Relation of brain excitability to brain γ-aminobutyric acid concentration. *Federation Proc.* **17**, 420 (Abstract).

Worthington, W. C., Jr. (1955). Some observations on the hypophyseal portal system in the living mouse. *Bull. Johns Hopkins Hosp.* **97**, 343–357.

Wurtman, R. J., and Axelrod, J. (1963). Sex steroids, cardiac H^3 norepinephrine and tissue monoamine oxidase levels in the rat. *Biochem. Pharmacol.* **12,** 1417–1419.

Wurtman, R. J., Axelrod, J., and Chu, E. W. (1963a). Melatonin, a pineal substance: effect on the rat ovaries. *Science* **141,** 277–278.

Wurtman, R. J., Axelrod, J., and Phillips, L. S. (1963b). Melatonin synthesis in the pineal gland: control of light. *Science* **142,** 1071–1073.

Wurtman, R. J., Kopin, I. J., and Axelrod, J. (1963c). Thyroid function and the cardiac disposition of catecholamines. *Endocrinology* **73,** 63–74.

Yeh, S. D. J., Solomon, J. D., and Chow, B. F. (1959). Influence of vitamin B_6 on tissue serotonin levels in the rat. *Federation Proc.* **18,** 357 (Abstract).

Zetler, G., and Schlusser, L. (1955). Über die Verteilung von substanz P und cholinacetylase in Gehirn. *Arch. Exptl. Pathol. Pharmakol.* **224,** 159–175.

Zieher, L. M., and DeRobertis, E. D. P. (1963). Subcellular localization of 5-hydroxytryptamine in rat brain. *Biochem. Pharmacol.* **12,** 596–598.

CHAPTER 32

Possible Functions of the Pineal Gland

JULIAN I. KITAY

I. Introduction

A review of the evidence concerning the pineal gland, completed in 1954 (Kitay and Altschule), included 480 publications in the physiological literature of the preceding 50 years. Since that time, a renewal of interest in pineal function has resulted in the appearance of almost as many papers again. Two recent international meetings[1,2] have been devoted solely to consideration of the pineal gland. Since a comprehensive review of all the findings of the past 10 years would require a monograph, data limited primarily to the functions of the mammalian pineal gland are considered here. Additional information may be found in an excellent review of the anatomy and photoreceptive functions of the pineal organ in lower vertebrates by Kelly (1962). Pineal innervation is surveyed by Ariëns Kappers (1964) and an extensive discussion of anatomical developments is available (Ariëns Kappers and Schadé, 1965).

Experiments involving pinealectomy have always been complicated by the problem of trauma to neighboring tissues (Kitay and Altschule, 1954, Chapter 2). A technique of pineal ablation has been described which utilizes local implantation of yttrium spheres in the rat (Holmgren and Notter, 1961), but no reports are available concerning its experimental application. Owman (1963a) devised a method of pinealectomy in the fetal rat *in utero* and has described prenatal changes in the intestinal epithelium resulting therefrom (Owman 1963b).

The literature on pineal function has been filled with contradictory reports of the effects of pineal extracts (Kitay and Altschule, 1954, loc. cit.). Some of the variation associated with extract administration would seem to result from the diversity of metabolites in pineal tissue (see Section II) and the lack of a standardized method of bioassay. Other factors are considered by Reiss *et al.* (1963a). The advent of melatonin and other pure preparations of pineal origin should help to minimize confusion in the future. Emphasis in this review is placed upon such compounds, and references to studies involving extracts have been limited arbitrarily, for the most part, to those in which a reasonable pattern seems to have been established.

II. Pineal Contents and Metabolic Activity

A. Background

Earlier studies (Kitay and Altschule, 1954, Chapter 1) demonstrated the presence of ribo- and deoxyribonucleoprotein, glycogen, acid and

[1] Colloque sur la Glande Pineale. Clermont Ferrand, May 1962. *Ann. Endocrinol. (Paris)* **24**, 197–390 (1963).

[2] Proceedings of the International Conference on the Pineal Organ. Amsterdam, July 1963. See Ariëns Kappers and Schadé (1965).

alkaline phosphatase, and succinic dehydrogenase in mammalian pineal parenchymal cells. Pineal P^{32} uptake was observed to be high and considerable evidence indicated that the gland was outside the blood-brain barrier. Recent studies have greatly enhanced the scope of our knowledge concerning metabolic activity in the pineal gland.

B. Biogenic Amines

An observation of major significance in pineal physiology was made by Lerner *et al.* (1958), who isolated a factor from bovine pineal glands that lightened frog skin. This factor, melatonin, was also found in human pineal tissue and identified as *N*-acetyl-5-methoxytryptamine (Lerner *et al.*, 1958, 1959a,b,c, 1960). Metabolites of 5-hydroxytryptamine (serotonin), 5-methoxyindoleacetic acid, and 5-hydroxyindoleacetic acid, were identified also. These observations aroused considerable interest in investigating related constituents in pineal tissue. Giarman and Day (1958) reported that bovine glands contain 0.4 μg per gram of serotonin. Higher levels to 22.8 μg per gram were observed in human and simian pineals (Giarman *et al.*, 1960). These concentrations are notably higher than those found in brain tissue. The bovine gland was shown to have significant concentrations of histamine and catecholamines as well (Giarman and Day, 1958). The presence of melatonin (0.4 μg per gram), serotonin, and histamine was demonstrated in the rat pineal gland by Prop and Ariëns Kappers (1961). Quay and Halevy (1962) also measured serotonin in the rat together with related indoleamines such as 5-methoxytryptamine (80–128 μg per gram). Acidic substances that may interact with amines, such as neuraminic acid, taurine, and cysteic acid have been found in the bovine gland (Green *et al.*, 1962).

C. Enzymes

Giarman and Day (1958), in addition to demonstrating the presence of histamine and serotonin in the bovine pineal, also found 5-hydroxytryptophan decarboxylase (5-HTD), an enzyme involved with the synthesis of serotonin, and monoamine oxidase (MAO), which is concerned with the metabolism of a variety of amines. A histamine-metabolizing enzyme, histamine-*N*-methyl transferase (HNMT), was also found in the monkey pineal gland (Axelrod *et al.*, 1961).

The beef pineal has been shown to contain an *N*-acetylating enzyme which converts serotonin to *N*-acetylserotonin (Weissbach *et al.*, 1960). This enzyme is also present in brain and liver tissue.

Axelrod *et al.* (1961) demonstrated that hydroxyindole-*O*-methyl transferase (HIOMT), the enzyme responsible for *O*-methylation of *N*-

acetylserotonin, is uniquely present in the pineal gland of the monkey, cat, and cow. No HIOMT activity could be found in a wide variety of other organs and tissues.

Human pineal glands also contain HIOMT, HNMT, and MAO (Wurtman *et al.*, 1964a). The activities of these enzymes do not vary significantly with age. The rat pineal gland contains 5-HTD (De Iraldi and De Lores Arnaiz, 1964), MAO (Smith, 1963; Wurtman *et al.*, 1963b), and HIOMT (Wurtman *et al.*, 1963b). Other enzymes demonstrated in the rat include aminopeptidase (Niemi and Ikonen, 1960) and succinic dehydrogenase (Quay, 1959). The activity of the latter doubles during the first 6 weeks of life. Striking levels of HIOMT activity as well as MAO have also been found in a nonmammalian species, the hen, by Axelrod and Wurtman (1964).

D. Other Substances

Fajer *et al.* (1962) have studied the electrophoretic pattern of soluble proteins in the bovine pineal gland. A polypeptide has been isolated from this organ with biological and chromatographic characteristics similar to those of arginine vasotocin (Milcu *et al.*, 1963a). Another preparation, a polypeptide unrelated to insulin, has been reported to have hypoglycemic effects *in vivo* and *in vitro* (Milcu *et al.*, 1963b).

Fat is readily demonstrable in rat pineal parenchyma (Quay, 1957; Prop and Ariëns Kappers, 1961). This observation has led to a number of studies concerned with experimental variations in pineal lipid content.

Fractionation of bovine pineal glands suggested the presence of a carboline, 1-methyl-6-methoxy-1,2,3,4-tetrahydro-2-carboline (Farrell and McIsaac, 1961). Although this compound may be synthesized *in vitro* under physiological conditions of temperature and pH, and *in vivo* from 5-methoxytryptamine (McIsaac, 1961), it has not been positively identified in pineal tissue, owing to its low concentration (Taylor and Farrell, 1963).

Preliminary reports have been made of the demonstration in the pineal gland of ubiquinone and tocopherylquinone (Farrell *et al.*, 1964) and of 5-hydroxytryptophol and 5-methoxytryptophol (McIsaac *et al.*, 1964).

E. Anatomical Data

Utilizing the hematoxylin and phloxine staining technique of Gomori, Quay (1956a) demonstrated a secretory cycle in pineal parenchymal cells. Owman (1961) reported that histological evidence of secretory activity was greater in the fetal pineal organ than in the adult. The rat pineal contains autonomic nerve fibers which are supplied by two bilateral nervi conarii (Ariëns Kappers, 1960). Bilateral superior cervical ganglionectomy results in degeneration of these conary nerve fibers and ultimately of the neural network within the pineal gland. Functional changes associated with this observation are considered in a number of experiments discussed below. Electron microscopy has revealed several types of vesicles in the parenchymal cells and numerous bulbous nerve endings located chiefly near capillaries (Milofsky, 1957).

Dense osmium-staining granules have been described in pineal tissue enclosed in vesicles within both the parenchymal cells and sympathetic nerve endings (De Robertis and De Iraldi, 1961; Gusek and Santoro, 1961; deMartino *et al.*, 1963). Administration of reserpine results in a marked diminution in the number of granules, with recovery following cessation of treatment (De Iraldi and De Robertis, 1961). The composition of this osmiophilic material remains to be established.

F. Biochemical Data

Not only does the pineal contain significant quantities of biogenic amines, but their concentrations also vary significantly in response to a number of experimental manipulations.

Total pineal serotonin content was increased significantly following injection of 5-hydroxytryptophan without (De Iraldi *et al.*, 1963) or with a MAO inhibitor (Quay and Halevy, 1962; Bertler *et al.*, 1963). A similar effect was obtained upon feeding a diet fortified with L-tryptophan (Quay 1963c). Injection of serotonin alone did not alter total pineal serotonin (De Iraldi *et al.*, 1963) but a selective increase was observed in pineal neural tissue (with no change in parenchymal cells) following administration of serotonin with a MAO inhibitor (Owman, 1964). Injection of reserpine resulted in an over-all decrease of 50% in pineal serotonin, limited almost entirely to a loss from neural tissue (Bertler *et al.*, 1963). Bilateral superior cervical ganglionectomy produced a similar fall in pineal serotonin (De Iraldi *et al.*, 1963) which was also limited to neural tissue in the gland (Bertler *et al.*, 1963; Owman, 1964). No changes in serotonin content were obtained after unilateral ganglionectomy or after preganglionic cervical sympathectomy (Owman, 1964). Bilateral transection of the nervi conarii was as effective as bilateral ganglionectomy. Following the latter procedure, the increase in pineal serotonin content noted after injection of 5-hydroxytryptophan was markedly diminished (De Iraldi *et al.*, 1963), but 5-hydroxytryptophan decarboxylase activity was increased (De Iraldi and De Lores Arnaiz, 1964).

Tritiated norepinephrine administered intravenously was observed radioautographically to localize in the pineal gland in nonmyelinated axons containing granulated vesicles (Wolfe *et al.*, 1962). No uptake was noted in parenchymal cells. The catecholamine content (probably norepinephrine) of pineal neural tissue was observed to increase following injection of either norepinephrine (Bertler *et al.*, 1963) or dopamine (Owman, 1964).

Pineal succinic dehydrogenase activity was increased significantly by administration of norepinephrine and other sympathomimetic amines (Quay, 1959). Similar treatment resulted in a significant increase in the number of pineal cells stainable with acid hematin (Quay, 1962).

Rat pineal blood content, estimated by counting erythrocytes on stained sections, is lower than that of other endocrine organs (Quay, 1958). On the other hand, Goldman and Wurtman (1964), using an isotope indicator method, have demonstrated pineal blood flow to be considerably greater than the anatomical evidence would suggest.

Quay (1963a) has studied the respiration of rat pineal tissue under a variety of conditions *in vitro* and has demonstrated significant differences between pineal and ependymal tissue. The goat pineal organ metabolizes glucose to amino acids at a high rate *in vitro* (Hellman and Larsson, 1961). Oxygen consumption and glucose utilization was greatest in glands from young animals and decreased with age.

III. Melatonin

A. General

As noted previously (Section II,B), melatonin or *N*-acetyl-5-methoxytryptamine was discovered by Lerner and co-workers in 1958. Since then, at least two methods for the synthesis of the compound have been published (Szymuszkovicz *et al.*, 1960; Supniewski *et al.*, 1961). Techniques have been described for the chromatographic isolation of melatonin from the rat pineal gland (Prop and Ariëns Kappers, 1961), and for its determination by fluorimetry (Axelrod and Weissbach, 1961) or by bioassay (Mori and Lerner, 1960).

B. Relation to Skin Pigmentation

Melatonin was originally isolated with the purpose of obtaining the pigment-active substance observed to be present in pineal extracts (Kitay and Altschule, 1954, Chapter 9). This compound is the most potent skin-lightening agent known (Lerner and Case, 1959). Its effectiveness is 10^5 times greater than that of norepinephrine, and concentrations of 10^{-10} *M* are capable of contracting melanophores in amphibian skin *in vitro* (Burgers and Van Oordt, 1962; Novales, 1963). Thus far, melatonin has been found only in mammalian pineal organs but is without effect on mammalian melanocytes, including those of man. A physiological role for melatonin in amphibians has been proposed by Bagnara (1961, 1963, 1964) who studied the response of tadpole melanocytes to light, hypophysectomy, pinealectomy, and melatonin administration. His studies suggest that melatonin or a melatoninlike substance is secreted by the pineal gland in response to darkness and participates with pituitary melanocyte-stimulating hormone (MSH) in adaptive responses to changes in environmental illumination.

C. Synthesis

The steps involved in the synthesis of melatonin *in vivo* are summarized in the following paragraphs (Fig. 1).

1. *N-Acetylation of Serotonin*

Serotonin is the major precursor of melatonin and is present in pineal tissue in significant quantities (see Section II,B). *N*-Acetylserotonin is one of the metabolites formed *in vivo* following administration of serotonin (McIsaac and Page, 1959). Weissbach *et al.* (1960) have demonstrated the enzymic *N*-acetylation of serotonin *in vitro* by soluble supernatant fractions of rat liver and brain, and beef pineal. The presence of acetyl coenzyme A is required.

2. *O-Methylation of N-Acetylserotonin*

Although the acetylating enzyme is present in several tissues, the enzyme responsible for *O*-methylation of *N*-acetylserotonin, HIOMT, has been found only in the pineal gland (Axelrod and Weissbach, 1960, 1961). S-Adenosylmethionine is an essential cofactor. The enzyme has a high substrate specificity for *N*-acetylserotonin. It can *O*-methylate other compounds such as serotonin and 5-hydroxyindoleacetic acid, but at a markedly slower rate, suggesting that *N*-acetylation normally precedes the *O*-methylation step.

D. Distribution

Apart from its presence in the pineal gland, significant quantities of melatonin have been found in peripheral nerve (Lerner *et al.*, 1959c). Since HIOMT does not occur in neural tissue (Axelrod *et al.*, 1961),

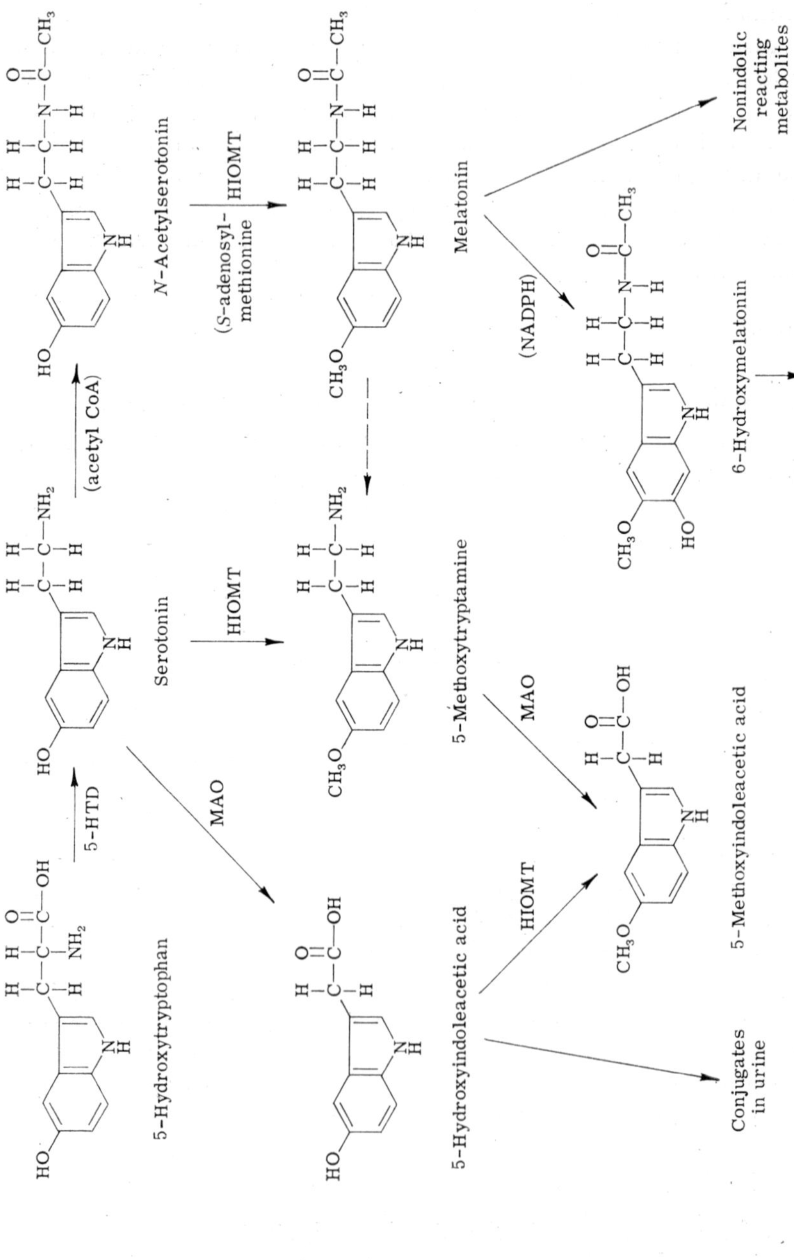

5-Hydroxytryptophan

5-HTD

Serotonin

(acetyl CoA)

N-Acetylserotonin

MAO

HIOMT

(*S*-adenosyl-methionine) HIOMT

5-Hydroxyindoleacetic acid

5-Methoxytryptamine

Melatonin

HIOMT

MAO

(NADPH)

Conjugates in urine

5-Methoxyindoleacetic acid

6-Hydroxymelatonin

Conjugates in urine

Nonindolic reacting metabolites

this represents a site of storage of melatonin probably derived from the circulation (Wurtman *et al.*, 1964d).

Tritiated melatonin, injected in rats, has a multiphasic disappearance curve with a rapid decrease in circulating levels during the first 10 minutes ($T_{1/2} = 2$ minutes) and a progressively slower rate of disappearance thereafter (Kopin *et al.*, 1961). Melatonin is widely dispersed among all tissues examined, including in particular, the pineal gland and ovary (Wurtman *et al.*, 1963a, 1964d). Other tissues that concentrate melatonin include the iris-choroid of the eye, and the thyroid and pituitary glands.

E. Metabolism

The major metabolic product (Fig. 1) of melatonin is *N*-acetyl-5-methoxy-6-hydroxytryptamine, which is formed in the liver and excreted in conjugated form, mainly as the sulfate but also as the glucuronide (Kopin *et al.*, 1960, 1961; Kveder and McIsaac, 1961). Only small amounts are metabolized to 5-methoxyindoleacetic acid and to non-indolic reacting compounds. About 70% of an administered dose of melatonin appears in the urine within 24 hours (Kveder and McIsaac, 1961). No melatonin can be detected in urine in unchanged form.

IV. Relation to the Brain

A. General

Pinealectomized rats showed increased spontaneous motor activity and pineal extract administration depressed such activity (Reiss *et al.*, 1963b). No disturbance of behavior was observed in rats treated with melatonin (Gessner *et al.*, 1961). Lerner and Case (1960) described a mildly sedative effect of melatonin in one human subject without accompanying metabolic changes. Melatonin administration depressed the electroencephalogram (EEG) in rabbits (Supniewski *et al.*, 1961). Local instillation of melatonin in the preoptic regions of the cat resulted in increased amplitude and slowing of electrical activity in the EEG, followed by sleep (Marczynski *et al.*, 1964). Similar but less obvious effects were obtained after injection into the nucleus centralis medialis and no effect following injection into the brain stem reticular formation.

FIG. 1. Steps involved in the synthesis and metabolism of melatonin and related indoleamines. MAO, monoamine oxidase; 5-HTD, 5-hydroxytryptamine decarboxylase; HIOMT, hydroxyindole-*O*-methyl transferase; acetyl CoA, acetyl coenzyme A; NADPH, dihydronicotinamide-adenine dinucleotide phosphate (TPNH). (Adapted from Kveder and McIsaac, 1961.)

B. Hypothalamus

No change in hypothalamic uptake of P^{32} was found in pinealectomized rats (Malm *et al.*, 1959). After pinealectomy, mean nuclear diameters were increased in cells of the supraoptic, paraventricular, ventral, and dorsal premammillary nuclei (Carnicelli *et al.*, 1963). Decreased neurosecretory activity in the paraventricular nuclei was described in the pinealectomized rat (Miline, 1963) and the opposite after pineal extract administration (Aron *et al.*, 1961; Miline, 1963). On the other hand, pinealectomy was followed by stimulatory changes in the paraventricular nuclei of the turtle (Combescot and Demaret, 1963).

C. Pineal Changes

Chronic stress produced regressive changes in the pineal gland and habenular ganglion of the hare (Miline and Stern, 1960). These effects were prevented by the administration of reserpine. Total body irradiation of rats resulted, 1 week later, in stimulatory changes in the habenulopineal complex associated with histological evidence of depressed thyroid activity (Miline *et al.*, 1960, 1963b). Opposite changes were observed 2 months postirradiation. Rats subjected to prolonged olfactory stimulation demonstrated pineal involution and atrophy (Miline *et al.*, 1963a).

V. Effects of Light on the Pineal Gland

A. Pineal Weight and Structure

Fiske *et al.* (1960) reported that pineal weight decreased in rats subjected to constant light for prolonged periods (see also Section III,B; VI,F; and Chapter 18). Under these conditions, female animals enter a state of continuous estrus. This observation has been confirmed by Quay (1961), Wurtman *et al.* (1961), and Moszkowska (1963). The pineal weight response to constant light was unaffected by gonadectomy, administration of thiouracil, adrenalectomy, or hypophysectomy (Fiske *et al.*, 1962). Phloxine-staining granules in mouse pineal parenchymal cells were decreased by light and increased by darkness (Quay, 1956b). Constant light resulted in decreases in the size of rat pineal parenchymal cells, the number of nucleoli, and the intensity of cytoplasmic basophilia (Roth *et al.*, 1962). Quay (1963d) also noted a decrease in nucleolar size.

B. Pineal Constituents and Metabolism

Pineal lipid content was decreased by light stimulation in the rat and hamster, an effect which was blocked by prior blinding (Quay, 1961). Comparable changes occurred in pineal serotonin content (Quay and Halevy, 1962). Pineal O_2 consumption, succinic dehydrogenase activity, and glycogen content were all decreased by constant light (Quay, 1963d). No changes were observed in adenosine triphosphate (ATP) content, P^{32} uptake, or 5-hydroxyindoleacetic acid content. Pineal HIOMT activity was inhibited by constant light in intact adult rats of both sexes and in immature, oophorectomized or hypophysectomized female animals (Wurtman *et al.,* 1964c). No effect of light was seen in animals pretreated with bilateral orbital enucleation or superior cervical ganglionectomy. In contrast to the rat, the hen pineal gland responded to light with an increase in HIOMT activity (Axelrod and Wurtman, 1964). Another stimulatory effect of constant light was described by Snyder *et al.* (1964), who found an increase in rat pineal 5-hydroxytryptophan decarboxylase activity. Again, the response was blocked by blinding or cervical sympathectomy and, in addition, by administration of sympathetic nerve blocking agents. Light had no effect on pineal MAO activity in any of these studies. The uptake of tritiated melatonin by the rat pineal (and ovary) was diminished by constant light exposure (Wurtman *et al.,* 1963a, 1964d).

The foregoing effects of light were observed in experiments based on chronic light stimulation for intervals measured in days or weeks. Recently, Roth (1964) reported that exposure to as little as 4 hours of light significantly reduced pineal uptake of P^{32} in the rat compared to animals kept in constant darkness.

C. Circadian Rhythms

Quay has studied the diurnal variation of several pineal constituents in the rat. Serotonin content (1963b) is lowest at night and reaches a peak at midday. A similar, associated response occurs in 5-hydroxyindoleacetic acid (1964). Melatonin content is low during the day and peaks with the onset of darkness. No significant fluctuation was observed in 5-methoxyindoleacetic acid.

VI. Relation to the Gonads

A. Background

Ten years ago, a pineal-gonadal relationship seemed to be the one most clearly suggested by the evidence available (Kitay and Altschule,

1954, Chapter 5). Pinealectomy had been observed to stimulate the genital system; responses included gonadal hypertrophy, acceleration of vaginal opening, and prolongation of estrus. Pineal extract administration produced opposite effects. No information was available concerning the mechanisms responsible for these changes. Subsequent studies have both confirmed and extended the earlier observations.

B. Effects of Pinealectomy

In confirmation of earlier observations, Wurtman *et al.* (1959) found ovarian hypertrophy in pinealectomized rats. This effect was reversed by administration of a pineal extract. Carnicelli *et al.* (1963) described testicular hypertrophy in male rats whereas Roth (1964) observed no effect on testicular weight but did find increases in the weights of the seminal vesicles and ventral prostate gland.

C. Effects of Pineal Extracts and Melatonin

A bovine pineal extract was found to inhibit spontaneous persistent estrus in "middle-aged" rats (Meyer *et al.*, 1961). Ariëns Kappers (1962) reported that administration of melatonin to rats at a dose of 100 μg daily for 14 days exerted no effect on the ovaries or testes. A dose of 500 μg per day did inhibit the development of the spermatic vesicles. In contrast, Wurtman *et al.* (1963a) found that injection of considerably smaller doses of melatonin for 28 days delayed vaginal opening and decreased ovarian weight in female rats. Further studies from the same laboratory (Chu *et al.*, 1964) demonstrated that melatonin administered intraperitoneally (20 μg daily for 28 days) or subcutaneously (2 μg daily for 6 weeks) inhibited the frequency of estrus. Estrus induced by prior pinealectomy was likewise inhibited. No effect was obtained upon injection of *N*-acetylserotonin, 6-hydroxymelatonin, or serotonin. Estrus was also inhibited in mice.

A preliminary report by McIsaac *et al.* (1964) indicates that 5-methoxytryptophol, formed by *O*-methylation of 5-hydroxytryptophol by HIOMT, is considerably more potent than melatonin in decreasing ovarian weight and inhibiting estrus.

D. Effects on Pituitary Gonadotropins

Pinealectomy in the rat increased pituitary content of gonadotropins, determined by the mouse-uterine weight assay (Barbarossa *et al.*, 1959). Thieblot and Blaise (1963) found that pineal extract reduced both pituitary gonadotropin content and the circulating level of gonadotropins in castrated male rats. In a series of studies (Moszkowska, 1963), pineal implants inhibited the gonadotropic activity of simultaneous pituitary implants in chick embryo preparations and in rat preparations both *in vivo* and *in vitro*.

E. Gonadectomy and Sex Hormone Administration

Fiske *et al.* (1962) found an increase in pineal weight in gonadectomized rats. Pineal phospholipid content increased after oophorectomy and seemed to vary in relation to the estrus cycle (Zweens, 1963). Hungerford and Panagiotis (1962) observed no change in pineal lipid after castration or after testosterone administration. No change in pineal mitotic activity was seen in rats given testosterone or estradiol (Quay and Levine, 1957).

Brewer and Quay (1958) observed no alteration in pineal P^{32} uptake after oophorectomy or after administration of female sex hormones. Quay (1963b, 1964) found evidence of variations in pineal serotonin, 5-hydroxyindoleacetic acid, and melatonin in relation to the estrus cycle.

F. Pineal–Gonads–Light

The relations of the pineal gland with the gonads and with light stimulation (see Section V) suggested by Fiske *et al.* (1960, 1962) have been explored further in a number of studies. Ovarian weight in pinealectomized rats subjected to constant light did not increase further beyond the increment produced by light stimulation alone (Wurtman *et al.*, 1961), indicating that the effects of these two variables are not additive. Similar data were obtained using estrus as the end point (Ifft, 1962). On the other hand, administration of pineal extracts inhibited light-induced ovarian hypertrophy (Wurtman *et al.*, 1961) and estrus (Jöchle, 1956; Ifft, 1962; Moszkowska, 1963).

Wurtman *et al.*, (1963a, 1964d) observed a decrease in ovarian uptake of tritiated melatonin in rats exposed to constant light and found that a single injection of melatonin inhibited estrus under such conditions. Rats in continuous darkness had a decreased incidence of estrus associated with an increase in pineal weight and HIOMT activity (Wurtman *et al.*, 1963b). Opposite effects were observed with constant light. Estrus was stimulated in association with ovarian hypertrophy, whereas pineal weight and HIOMT activity were diminished (Wurtman *et al.*, 1964b). Bilateral blinding or superior cervical ganglionectomy blocked all the changes of light noted, whereas unilateral ganglionectomy was without effect.

VII. Relation to the Adrenal Glands

A. General

Earlier evidence (Kitay and Altschule, 1954, Chapter 6) relating the pineal gland to the adrenal glands was confusing and contradictory. The data continue to be inconsistent. (See also Chapter 11).

Wurtman *et al.* (1959) reported an increase in adrenal weight in pinealectomized rats which was reversed by administration of pineal extract. In contrast, Dill (1961) found pinealectomy to be without effect and treatment with pineal extract to result in adrenal hypertrophy and increased corticosterone secretion. Steroid production by rat adrenal slices *in vitro* from pinealectomized donors was diminished (Jouan *et al.*, 1963). Pinealectomy did not affect adrenal P^{32} uptake in the rat (Malm *et al.*, 1959), but adrenalectomy was associated with an increase in pineal P^{32} uptake (Lingjaerde *et al.*, 1958b). No change in adrenal histology was observed in pinealectomized hamsters (Girod *et al.*, 1963).

B. Aldosterone Secretion

Farrell (1959a,b, 1960a,b) reported in a series of experiments that extracts of bovine pineal glands stimulated aldosterone secretion in decerebrate dogs. The active factor was termed "adrenoglomerulotropin." Another pineal fraction was found to inhibit aldosterone secretion. Pinealectomy resulted in a transient decline in aldosterone output. Blood in the vein of Galen draining the pineal area was observed to contain a material which stimulated aldosterone secretion. Painstaking studies (Farrell and McIsaac, 1961) to define the active substance in adrenoglomerulotropin suggested the presence of a carboline (see Section II,D). This compound was observed to stimulate aldosterone secretion when administered to decerebrated dogs in submicrogram doses, but it has not been positively identified in pineal tissue.

Davis (1961) observed no change in aldosterone secretion in pinealectomized dogs. Lucis *et al.* (1961) demonstrated that fresh extracts of diencephalon which included the pineal gland were capable of stimulating aldosterone production by rat adrenal slices *in vitro*. Pineal preparations alone had no effect. Mulrow *et al.* (1963) were unable to confirm that the carboline exerted a stimulatory effect on aldosterone secretion in hypophysectomized dogs with intact brains. The question of the physiological significance of the carboline and related compounds is discussed further in Chapter 11.

Ubiquinone and tocopherylquinone, compounds found in bovine pineal extract, were observed to depress aldosterone output in dogs (Farrell *et al.*, 1964).

C. Electrolyte Balance

No change in sodium/potassium ratio in saliva could be demonstrated in pinealectomized sheep (Coghlan *et al.*, 1960). Sodium retention has been recorded in rats after either pinealectomy (Tanner and Hungerford, 1962) or pineal extract administration (Machado and Da Silva, 1963). Other investigators (Wurtman *et al.*, 1960; Yamada, 1961) found no changes in electrolyte balance.

D. Zona Glomerulosa

Giacomelli (1962) observed decreased nuclear size in glomerulosa cells of pinealectomized rats. Others (Wurtman *et al.*, 1960; Rennels and Dill, 1961; Bugnon *et al.*, 1963) found no changes. Stimulatory effects of pineal extracts on the glomerulosa have been described (Romani *et al.*, 1960) but, again, others failed to confirm this finding (Wurtman *et al.*, 1960; Bugnon *et al.*, 1963; Palkovits and Földvari, 1963).

E. Miscellaneous

Pinealectomy did not alter renal renin content in rats (Bruinvels *et al.*, 1964). Sodium restriction, adrenalectomy, or angiotensin administration in rats each decreased pineal lipid content (Panagiotis and Hungerford, 1961). The reverse effect was obtained after injection of deoxycorticosterone acetate.

VIII. Relation to the Thyroid Gland

Pinealectomy in rats did not alter thyroidal uptake of P^{32} (Malm *et al.*, 1959). However, histological evidence of thyroid hyperactivity has been described in rats (Miline, 1963; Scepovic, 1963) and in turtles (Combescot and Demaret, 1963). Propylthiouracil administration in rats decreased pineal lipid content (Hungerford and Panagiotis, 1962). Melatonin administered to male rats at a dose of 150 μg per day for 10 days was observed to prevent the increase in thyroid weight produced by thiouracil and to decrease thyroidal I^{131} uptake (Baschieri *et al.*, 1963).

IX. Relation to the Pituitary Gland

Pinealectomy in the rat produced no changes in pituitary cytology (Holmes, 1956) or uptake of P^{32} (Malm *et al.*, 1959). Hypophysectomy decreased pineal lipid content (Hungerford and Panagiotis, 1962). Reiss *et al.* (1963c) found an increase in pineal P^{32} uptake in hypophysectomized rats whereas Skaug *et al.* (1958) observed no change. However, the latter group also reported that either thymectomy (Skaug *et al.*, 1959) or chlorpromazine administration (Lingjaerde *et al.*, 1958a) increased pineal P^{32} uptake in hypophysectomized rats compared to hypophysectomy alone.

X. Comment

The mammalian pineal gland contains significant quantities of a variety of biogenic amines, including melatonin, serotonin, histamine, and catechols, as well as a number of enzymes concerned with amine synthesis and metabolism. The parenchymal cells and sympathetic nerve endings in the gland both appear to be rich in amine content. However, pineal neural tissue concentrates and releases amines more rapidly than does the parenchyma. The functional significance of this difference is unclear.

A distinguishing characteristic of the pineal gland in mammals is its ability to synthesize melatonin. Melatonin is also found in peripheral nerve, but the enzyme responsible for the final step in its biosynthesis, HIOMT, is found only in the pineal gland. Although considerable information has been accumulated concerning its synthesis and metabolism, the physiological role of melatonin remains to be established. It clearly contracts amphibian melanophores but has not been demonstrated in the amphibian pineal organ. Studies in mammals are still relatively few. Injected melatonin is concentrated by the rat ovary and inhibition of gonadal function results from its prolonged administration in small doses. Additional effects of melatonin include inhibitory changes in rat brain and thyroid gland. The possibility has been raised that other substances of pineal origin may also have significant biological activity.

A firm association appears to have been established between the pineal gland and environmental illumination. Variations in light exposure influence a number of metabolic processes within the gland, as indicated by changes in weight, cytology, oxygen consumption, serotonin content, and HIOMT activity, among others. Pineal concentrations of serotonin, 5-hydroxyindoleacetic acid, and melatonin all vary according to a diurnal rhythm. The superior cervical ganglia also seem to be concerned with pineal metabolic activity and to be involved in the pathway through which changes in light affect the gland. Prior ganglionectomy prevents the pineal changes induced by exposure to constant light.

In general, earlier experiments demonstrating an inhibitory relationship of the pineal to the gonads have been confirmed. This association has been broadened by the observation that the gland may participate in the gonadal response to environmental light. Although several studies suggest that gonadal inhibition is exerted via the pituitary gland, the capacity of the ovary to take up melatonin prompts consideration of a direct effect also.

Reference has been made to recent studies relating the pineal gland to the brain, and to the adrenal and thyroid glands. Owing either to the relative paucity or inconsistency of the data currently available, evaluation of these relations is difficult.

The title of this chapter provides considerable freedom in its invitation to discuss "possible" functions of the pineal gland. The variety and scope of the observations presented here offer ample stimulation for such discussion. However, a persistent feature of the pineal literature has been an extraordinarily high ratio of hypotheses to data. All too often, the quantity of the former has been inversely correlated to that of the latter. Publications in recent years have reversed this association and the era of speculation has been supplanted by one of data accumulation. This is as it should be. Although comments affirming the nonvestigiality of the mammalian pineal gland no longer seem necessary, firm conclusions concerning its functions would be premature.

References

Ariëns Kappers, J. (1960). The development, topographical relations and innervation of the epiphysis cerebri in the albino rat. *Z. Zellforsch. Mikroskop. Anat.* **52,** 163–215.

Ariëns Kappers, J. (1962). Melatonin, a pineal compound. Preliminary investigations on its function in the rat. *Gen. Comp. Endocrinol.* **2,** 610–611.

Ariëns Kappers, J. (1964). Survey of the innervation of the pineal organ in vertebrates. *Am. Zoologist* **4,** 47–51.

Ariëns Kappers, J., and Schadé, J. P. (1965). Structure and function of the epiphysis cerebri. *Progr. Brain Res.* **10,** Elsevier, Amsterdam.

Aron, E., Combescot, C., Demaret, J., Guyon, L., and Mauvernay, R. Y. (1961). Modifications de la neurosécrétion observées dans l'encéphale du Rat après injection d'un extrait epiphysaire. *Compt. Rend. Soc. Biol.* **155,** 593–595.

Axelrod, J., and Weissbach, H. (1960). Enzymatic *O*-methylation of *N*-acetylserotonin to melatonin. *Science* **131,** 1312.

Axelrod, J., and Weissbach, H. (1961). Purification and properties of hydroxyindole-*O*-methyl transferase. *J. Biol. Chem.* **236,** 211–213.

Axelrod, J., and Wurtman, R. J. (1964). Melatonin synthesis in the hen pineal gland and its control by light. *Nature* **201,** 1134.

Axelrod, J., MacLean, P. D., Albers, R. W., and Weissbach, H. (1961). Regional distribution of methyl transferase enzymes in the nervous system and glandular tissues. *In* "Regional Neurochemistry" (S. S. Kety and J. Elkes, eds.), pp. 307–311. Pergamon Press, Oxford.

Bagnara, J. T. (1961). Pineal regulation of the body lightening reaction in amphibian larvae. *Science* **132,** 1481–1483.

Bagnara, J. T. (1963). The pineal and the body lightening reaction of larval amphibians, *Gen. Comp. Endocrinol.* **3,** 86–100.

Bagnara, J. T. (1964). Independent actions of pineal and hypophysis in the regulation of chromatophores of anuran larvae. *Gen. Comp. Endocrinol.* **4,** 299–303.

Barbarossa, C., deMartino, C., Peruzy, A. D., and Torlonia, G. (1959). Attivita gonadotropa ipofisaria nel ratto privato di pineale. *Folia Endocrinol.* (*Pisa*) **12,** 535–541.

Baschieri, L., deLuca, F., Cramarossa, L., deMartino, C., Oliverio, A., and Negri, M. (1963). Modification of thyroid activity by melatonin. *Experientia* **19,** 15–17.

Bertler, A., Falck, B., and Owman, C. (1963). Cellular localization of 5-hydroxytryptamine in the rat pineal gland. *Kgl. Fysiograf. Sallskap. Lund, Forh.* **33,** 13–16.

Brewer, G. F., and Quay, W. B. (1958). Pineal and hypophyseal phosphate uptake after castration and administration of sex hormones. *Proc. Soc. Exptl. Biol. Med.* **98,** 361–364.

Bruinvels, J., van Houten, J. C., and van Noordwijk, J. (1964). Influence of pinealectomy and hypophysectomy on the renin content of rat kidneys. *Quart. J. Exptl. Physiol.* **49,** 95–102.

Bugnon, C., Moreau, N., and Lenys, R. (1963). Recherches histophysiologiques sur les relations entre l'epiphyse et la zone glomérulaire du cortex surrénalien chez le Rat blanc. *Ann. Endocrinol.* (Paris) **24,** 348–355.

Burgers, A. C. J., and Van Oordt, G. J. (1962). Regulation of pigment migration in the amphibian melanophore. *Gen. Comp. Endocrinol.* Suppl. 1, 99–109.

Carnicelli, A., Saba, P., Cella, P. L., and Marescotti, V. (1963). Effects of epiphysectomy on karyometry of hypothalamic nuclei in rats. *Folia Endocrinol.* (*Pisa*) **16,** 229–234.

Chu, E. W., Wurtman, R. J., and Axelrod, J. (1964). An inhibitory effect of melatonin on the estrous phase of the estrous cycle of the rodent. *Endocrinology* **75,** 238–242.

Coghlan, J. P., Denton, D. A., Goding, J. R., and Wright, R. D. (1960). The control of aldosterone secretion. *Postgrad. Med. J.* **36,** 76–102.

Combescot, C., and Demaret, J. (1963). Histophysiologie de l'epiphyse chez la Tortue d'eau. *Ann. Endocrinol.* (*Paris*) **24,** 204–214.

Davis, J. O. (1961). Mechanisms regulating the secretion and metabolism of aldosterone in experimental secondary hyperaldosteronism. *Recent Progr. Hormone Res.* **17,** 293–331.

De Iraldi, A. P., and De Robertis, E. D. P. (1961). Action of reserpine on the submicroscopic morphology of the pineal gland. *Experientia* **17,** 122–124.

De Iraldi, A. P., Zieher, L. M., and De Robertis, E. D. P. (1963). The 5-hydroxytryptamine content and synthesis of normal and denervated pineal gland. *Life Sciences* **9,** 691–696.

De Iraldi, A. P., and De Lores Arnaiz, G. R. (1964). 5-Hydroxytryptophan-decarboxylase activity in normal and denervated pineal gland of rats. *Life Sciences* **3**, 589–593.

deMartino, C., deLuca, F., Paluello, F. M., Tonietti, G., and Orci, L. (1963). The osmiophilic granules of the pineal body in rats. *Experientia* **19**, 639–641.

De Robertis, E. D. P., and De Iraldi, A. P. (1961). Plurivesicular secretory processes and nerve endings in the pineal gland of the rat. *J. Biophys. Biochem. Cytol.* **10**, 361–372.

Dill, R. E. (1961). The effects of pinealectomy or pineal extracts on corticosterone secretion in the rat. *Anat. Record* **139**, 222.

Fajer, A., Hoxter, G., and Fraga, E. (1962). Electrophoretic pattern of the soluble proteins of a pineal body extract. *Nature* **196**, 274.

Farrell, G. (1959a). Steroidogenic properties of extracts of beef diencephalon. *Endocrinology* **65**, 29–33.

Farrell, G. (1959b). Glomerulotropic activity of an acetone extract of pineal tissue. *Endocrinology* **65**, 239–241.

Farrell, G. (1960a). Adrenoglomerulotropin. *Circulation* **21**, 1009–1015.

Farrell, G. (1960b). Epiphysis cerebri in the control of steroid secretion. *Federation Proc.* **19**, 601–604.

Farrell, G., and McIsaac, W. M. (1961). Adrenoglomerulotropin. *Arch. Biochem. Biophys.* **94**, 543–544.

Farrell, G., Fabre, L. F., and McIsaac, W. M. (1964). Effect of quinones on aldosterone secretion. *Program 46th Meeting Endocrine Soc., San Francisco*, p. 63 (Abstract).

Fiske, V. M., Bryant, G. K., and Putnam, J. (1960). Effect of light on the weight of the pineal in the rat. *Endocrinology* **66**, 489–491.

Fiske, V. M., Pound, J., and Putnam, J. (1962). Effect of light on the weight of the pineal organ in hypophysectomized, gonadectomized, adrenalectomized or thiouracil-fed rats. *Endocrinology* **71**, 130–133.

Gessner, P. K., McIsaac, W. M., and Page, I. H. (1961). Pharmacological actions of some methoxyindolealkylamines. *Nature* **190**, 179–180.

Giacomelli, F. (1962). Über Veränderungen der Nebennierenrinde nach Pinealektomie. *Endokrinologie* **42**, 144–150.

Giarman, N. J., and Day, M. (1958). Presence of biogenic amines in the bovine pineal body. *Biochem. Pharmacol.* **1**, 235.

Giarman, N. J., Freedman, D. X., and Picard, L. (1960). Serotonin content of the pineal glands of man and monkey. *Nature* **186**, 480–481.

Girod, C., Czyba, J. C., and Durand, N. (1963). Influence de l'epiphysectomie sur le cortex surrénal du Hamster dore. *Compt. Rend. Soc. Biol.* **157**, 1008–1009.

Goldman, H., and Wurtman, R. J. (1964). Flow of blood to the pineal body of the rat. *Nature* **203**, 87–88.

Green, J. P., Day, M., and Robinson, J. D. (1962). Some acidic substances in neoplatic mast cells and in the pineal body. *Biochem. Pharmacol.* **11**, 957–960.

Gusek, W., and Santoro, A. (1961). Zur Ultrastruktur der Epiphysis cerebri der Ratte. *Endokrinologie* **41**, 105–129.

Hellman, B., and Larsson, S. (1961). Utilization of uniformly labeled ^{14}C-glucose in the pineal body of goats. *Acta Endocrinol.* **38**, 353–360.

Holmes, R. L. (1956). Effect of pinealectomy on the rat pituitary. *Nature* **177**, 791.

Holmgren, U., and Notter, G. (1961). A technique for destruction of the pineal body using yttrium-90 spheres. *Nature* **189**, 773–774.

Hungerford, G. F., and Panagiotis, N. M. (1962). Response of pineal lipid to hormone imbalances. *Endocrinology* **71**, 936–942.

Ifft, J. D. (1962). Effects of pinealectomy, a pineal extract and pineal grafts on light-induced prolonged estrus in rats. *Endocrinology* **71**, 181–182.

Jöchle, W. (1956). Über die Wirkung eines Epiphysenextraktes (Glanepin) auf Sexualentwicklung und Sexualzyklus junger weiblicher Ratten unter normalen Haltungsbedingungen und bei Dauerbeleuchtung. *Endokrinologie* **33**, 287–295.

Jouan, P., Patay, R., and Patay, M. (1963). Étude de la sécrétion *in vitro* du cortex surrénal chez le rat epiphysectomise. *Compt. Rend. Soc. Biol.* **157**, 711–714.

Kelly, D. E. (1962). Pineal organs: photoreception secretion, and development. *Am. Scientist* **50**, 597–625.

Kitay, J. I., and Altschule, M. D. (1954). "The Pineal Gland." Harvard Univ. Press, Cambridge, Massachusetts.

Kopin, I. J., Pare, C. M. B., Axelrod, J., and Weissbach, H. (1960). 6-Hydroxylation, the major metabolic pathway for melatonin. *Biochim. Biophys. Acta* **40**, 377–378.

Kopin, I. J., Pare, C. M. B., Axelrod, J., and Weissbach, H. (1961). The fate of melatonin in animals. *J. Biol. Chem.* **236**, 3072–3075.

Kveder, S., and McIsaac, W. M. (1961). The metabolism of melatonin (*N*-acetyl-5-methoxytryptamine) and 5-methoxytryptamine. *J. Biol. Chem.* **236**, 3214–3220.

Lerner, A. B., and Case, J. D. (1959). Pigment cell regulatory factors. *J. Invest. Dermatol.* **32**, 211–221.

Lerner, A. B., and Case, J. D. (1960). Melatonin. *Federation Proc.* **19**, 590–592.

Lerner, A. B., Case, J. D., Takahashi, Y., Lee, T. H., and Mori, W. (1958). Isolation of melatonin, the pineal gland factor that lightens melanocytes. *J. Am. Chem. Soc.* **80**, 2587.

Lerner, A. B., Case, J. D., Biemann, K., Heinzelman, R. V., Szymuszkovicz, J., Anthony, W. C.., and Krivis, A. (1959a). Isolation of 5-methoxyindole-3-acetic acid from bovine pineal glands. *J. Am. Chem. Soc.* **81**, 5264.

Lerner, A. B., Case, J. D., and Heinzelman, R. V. (1959b). Structure of melatonin. *J. Am. Chem. Soc.* **81**, 6084-6085.

Lerner, A. B., Case, J. D., Mori, W., and Wright, M. R. (1959c). Melatonin in peripheral nerve. *Nature* **183**, 1821.

Lerner, A. B., Case, J. D., and Takahashi, Y. (1960). Isolation of melatonin and 5-methoxyindole-3-acetic acid from bovine pineal glands. *J. Biol. Chem.* **235**, 1992–1997.

Lingjaerde, P., Malm, O. J., and Skaug, O. E. (1958a). Some biochemical aspects of the effect of chlorpromazine in the rat. *Conf. Neurol.* **18**, 125–137.

Lingjaerde, P., Malm, O. J., Natvig, R. A., and Skaug, O. E. (1958b). The effect of adrenalectomy on the uptake of radioactive phosphorus in the rat. *Acta Endocrinol.* **28**, 558–565.

Lucis, O. J., Dyrenfurth, I., and Venning, E. H. (1961). Effect of various preparations of pituitary and diencephalon on the *in vitro* secretion of aldosterone and corticosterone by the rat adrenal gland. *Can. J. Biochem. Physiol.* **39**, 901–913.

Machado, A. B., and Da Silva, C. R. (1963). Pineal body and urinary sodium excretion in the rat, *Experientia* **19**, 264–265.

McIsaac, W. M. (1961). Formation of 1-methyl-6-methoxy-1,2,3,4-tetrahydro-2-carboline under physiological conditions. *Biochim. Biophys. Acta* **52**, 607–609.

McIsaac, W. M., and Page, I. H. (1959). The metabolism of serotonin (5-hydroxytryptamine). *J. Biol. Chem.* **234**, 858–864.

McIsaac, W. M., Taborsky, R. G., and Farrell, G. (1964). 5-Methoxytryptophol: Effect on estrus and ovarian weight. *Science* **145**, 63–64.

Malm, O. J., Skaug, O. E., and Lingjaerde, P. (1959). The effect of pinealectomy on bodily growth, survival rate and P^{32} uptake in the rat. *Acta Endocrinol.* **30**, 22–28.

Marczynski, T. J., Yamaguchi, N., Ling, G. M., and Grodzinska, L. (1964). Sleep induced by the administration of melatonin (5-methoxy-*n*-acetyltryptamine) to the hypothalamus in unrestrained cats. *Experientia* **20**, 435–437.

Meyer, C. J., Wurtman, R. J., Altschule, M. D., and Lazo-Wasem, E. A. (1961). The arrest of prolonged estrus in "middle-aged" rats by pineal gland extract. *Endocrinology* **68**, 795–800.

Milcu, S. M., Milcu, I., and Nanu, L. (1963a). Le rôle de la glande pinéale dans le métabolisme des glucides. *Ann. Endocrinol* (*Paris*) **24**, 233–254.

Milcu, S. M., Pavel, S., and Neacsu, C. (1963b). Biological and chromatographic characterization of a polypeptide with pressor and oxytocic activities isolated from bovine pineal gland. *Endocrinology* **72**, 563–566.

Miline, R. (1963). La part du noyau paraventriculaire dans l'histophysiologie corrélative de la glande thyroïde et de la glande pinéale. *Ann. Endocrinol.* (*Paris*) **24**, 255–269.

Miline, R., and Stern, P. (1960). Effect of reserpine on the stressogenic reactivity of habenular-pineal complex. *Anat. Record* **136**, 243–244.

Miline, R., Werner, R., Ciglar, M., Petrusevska, M., Zoric, V., and Scepovic, M. (1960). Sur la réactivité stressogène du complexe habénulo-épiphysaire. *Acta Anat.* **42**, 270.

Miline, R., Deceverski, V., and Krstic, R. (1963a). Influence d'excitations olfactives sur le systeme habenulo-epiphysaire. *Ann. Endocrinol.* (*Paris*) **24**, 377–379.

Miline, R., Werner, R., Scepovic, M., Deceverski, V., and Krstic, R. (1963b). Contribution a l'étude de l'influence de l'irradiation sur le ganglion de l'habenula et la glande pinéale. *Ann. Endocrinol.* (*Paris*) **24**, 380–384.

Milofsky, A. (1957). The fine structure of the pineal in the rat, with special reference to the parenchyma. *Anat. Record* **127**, 435–436.

Mori, W., and Lerner, A. B. (1960). A microscopic bioassay for melatonin. *Endocrinology* **67**, 443–450.

Moszkowska, A. (1963). L'antagonisme epiphysohypophysaire. *Ann. endocrinol.* (*Paris*) **24**, 215–226.

Mulrow, P. J., Ganong, W. F., and Boryczka, A. (1963). Further evidence for a role of the renin-angiotensin system in regulation of aldosterone secretion. *Proc. Soc. Exptl. Biol. Med.* **112**, 7–10.

Niemi, M., and Ikonen, M. (1960). Histochemical evidence of aminopeptidase activity in rat pineal gland. *Nature* **185**, 928.

Novales, R. R. (1963). Responses of cultured melanophores to the synthetic hormones α-MSH, melatonin and epinephrine. *Ann. N.Y. Acad. Sci.* **100**, 1035–1047.

Owman, C. (1961). Secretory activity of the fetal pineal gland of the rat. *Acta Morphol. Neerl. Scand.* **3**, 367–394.

Owman, C. (1963a). Pinealectomy of the rat foetus *in utero.* A method for producing localized intracerebral lesions during the last third of gestation. *Quart. J. Exptl. Physiol.* **48**, 402–407.

Owman, C. (1963b). Prenatal changes in epithelium of small intestine of rat foetus pinealectomized *in utero. Quart. J. Exptl. Physiol.* **48**, 408–422.

Owman, C. (1964). Sympathetic nerves probably storing two types of monoamines in the rat pineal gland. *Intern. J. Neuropharmacol.* **2,** 105–112.

Palkovits, M., and Földvari, P. I. (1963). Effect of the subcommissural organ and the pineal body on the adrenal cortex. *Endocrinology* **72,** 28–32.

Panagiotis, N. M., and Hungerford, G. F. (1961). Response of the pineal and adrenal glands to sodium restriction. *Endocrinology* **69,** 217–224.

Prop, N., and Ariëns Kappers, J. (1961). Demonstration of some compounds present in the pineal organ of the albino rat by histochemical methods and paper chromatography. *Acta Anat.* **45,** 90–109.

Quay, W. B. (1956a). The demonstration of a secretory material and cycle in the parenchymal cells of the mammalian pineal organ. *Exptl. Cell Res.* **10,** 541–544.

Quay, W. B. (1956b). Volumetric and cytologic variation in the pineal body of peromyscus leucopus (*Rodentia*) with respect to sex, captivity and day-length. *J. Morphol.* **98,** 471–491.

Quay, W. B. (1957). Cytochemistry of pineal lipids in rat and man. *J. Histochem Cytochem.* **5,** 145–153.

Quay, W. B. (1958). Pineal blood content and its experimental modification. *Am. J. Physiol.* **195,** 391–395.

Quay, W. B. (1959). Experimental modifications and changes with age in pineal succinic dehydrogenase activity. *Am. J. Physiol.* **196,** 951–955.

Quay, W. B. (1961). Reduction of mammalian pineal weight and lipid during continuous light. *Gen. Comp. Endocrinol.* **1,** 211–217.

Quay, W. B. (1962). Experimental and cytological studies of pineal cells staining with acid hematein in the rat. *Acta Morphol. Neerl. Scand.* **5,** 87–100.

Quay, W. B. (1963a). Pineal and ependymal respiration with diverse substrates and inorganic ions. *Am. J. Physiol.* **204,** 245–250.

Quay, W. B. (1963b). Circadian rhythm in rat pineal serotonin and its modifications by estrous cycle and photoperiod. *Gen. Comp. Endocrinol.* **3,** 473–479.

Quay, W. B. (1963c). Effect of dietary phenylalanine and tryptophan on pineal and hypothalamic serotonin levels. *Proc. Soc. Exptl. Biol. Med.* **114,** 718–721.

Quay, W. B. (1963d). Cytologic and metabolic parameters of pineal inhibition by continuous light in the rat. *Z. Zellforsch. Mikroskop. Anat.* **60,** 479–490.

Quay, W. B. (1964). Circadian and estrous rhythms in pineal melatonin and 5-hydroxyindole-3-acetic acid. *Proc. Soc. Exptl. Biol. Med.* **115,** 710–713.

Quay, W. B., and Halevy, A. (1962). Experimental modification of the rat pineal's content of serotonin and related indole amines. *Physiol. Zool.* **35,** 1–7.

Quay, W. B., and Levine, B. E. (1957). Pineal growth and mitotic activity in the rat and the effects of colchicine and sex hormones. *Anat. Record* **129,** 65–77.

Reiss, M., Davis, R. H., Sideman, M. B., Mauer, I., and Plichta, E. S. (1963a). Action of pineal extract on the gonads and their function. *J. Endocrinol.* **27,** 107.

Reiss, M., Davis, R. H., Sideman, M. D., and Plichta, E. S. (1963b). Pineal gland and spontaneous activity of rats. *J. Endocrinol.* **28,** 127–128.

Reiss, M., Mauer, I., Sideman, M. D., Davis, R. H., and Plichta, E. S. (1963c). Pituitary-pineal-brain interrelationships. *J. Neurochem.* **10,** 851–857.

Rennels, E. G., and Dill, R. E. (1961). Effect of pinealectomy on the histology and lipid content of the rat adrenal gland. *Texas Rept. Biol. Med.* **19,** 843–850.

Romani, J. D., Keller, A., and Piotti, L. E. (1960). Action d'un extrait epiphysaire sur la distribution des lipids et des phosphatases alcalines du cortex surrénal. *Ann. Endocrinol.* (*Paris*) **21,** 79–85.

Roth, W. D. (1964). Comments on J. Ariëns Kappers' review and observations on pineal activity. *Am. Zoologist* **4,** 53–57.

Roth, W. D., Wurtman, R. J., and Altschule, M. D. (1962). Morphologic changes in the pineal parenchyma cells of rats exposed to continuous light or darkness. *Endocrinology* **71,** 888–892.

Scepovic, M. (1963). Contribution a l'étude histophysiologique de la glande thyroïde chez les rats epiphysectomises. *Ann. Endocrinol.* (*Paris*) **24,** 371–376.

Skaug, O. E., Lingjaerde, P., and Malm, O. J. (1958). P^{32} uptake in hypophysectomized rats. *Acta Endocrinol.* **29,** 315–320.

Skaug, O. E., Lingjaerde, P., and Malm, O. J. (1959). P^{32} uptake in thymectomized hypophysectomized rats. *Acta Endocrinol.* **31,** 309–313.

Smith, B. (1963). Monoamine oxidase in the pineal gland, neurohypophysis and brain of the albino rat. *J. Anat.* (*London*) **97,** 81–86.

Snyder, S. H., Axelrod, J., Fischer, J. E., and Wurtman, R. J. (1964). Neural and photic regulation of 5-hydroxytryptophan decarboxylase in the rat pineal gland. *Nature* **203,** 981–982.

Supniewski, J., Misztal, S., and Marczynski, T. J. (1961). The synthesis and biological properties of melatonin. *Dissertationes Pharm.* (*Warsaw*) **13,** 205–217.

Szymuszkovicz, J., Anthony, W. C., and Heinzelman, R. V. (1960). *N*-acetyl 5-methoxytryptamine. *J. Org. Chem.* **25,** 857–859.

Tanner, W. D., and Hungerford, G. F. (1962). Sodium and potassium excretion in pinealectomized and adrenalectomized rats. *Proc. Soc. Exptl. Biol. Med.* **109,** 388–390.

Taylor, A. N., and Farrell, G. (1963). Facteur glomerulotrope. *Ann. Endocrinol.* (*Paris*) **24,** 228–232.

Thieblot, L., and Blaise, S. (1963). Influence de la glande pinéale sur les gonades. *Ann. Endocrinol.* (*Paris*) **24,** 270–286.

Weissbach, H., Redfield, B. G., and Axelrod, J. (1960). Biosynthesis of melatonin: enzymic conversion of serotonin to *N*-acetylserotonin. *Biochim. Biophys. Acta* **43,** 352–353.

Wolfe, D. E., Potter, L. T., Richardson, K. C., and Axelrod, J. (1962). Localizing tritiated norepinephrine in sympathetic axons by electron microscopic autoradiography. *Science* **138,** 440–442.

Wurtman, R. J., Altschule, M. D., and Holmgren, U. (1959). Effects of pinealectomy and of a bovine pineal extract in rats. *Am. J. Physiol.* **197,** 108–110.

Wurtman, R. J., Altschule, M. D., Greep, R. O., Falk, J. L., and Grave, G. (1960). The pineal gland and aldosterone. *Am. J. Physiol.* **199,** 1109–1111.

Wurtman, R. J., Roth, W., Altschule, M. D., and Wurtman, J. J. (1961). Interactions of the pineal and exposure to continuous light on organ weights of female rats. *Acta Endocrinol.* **36,** 617–624.

Wurtman, R. J., Axelrod, J., and Chu, E. W. (1963a). Melatonin, a pineal substance: Effect on the rat ovary. *Science* **141,** 277–278.

Wurtman, R. J., Axelrod, J., and Phillips, L. S. (1963b). Melatonin synthesis in the pineal gland: Control by light. *Science* **142,** 1071–1073.

Wurtman, R. J., Axelrod, J., and Barchas, J. D. (1964a). Age and enzyme activity in the human pineal. *J. Clin. Endocrinol. Metab.* **24,** 299–301.

Wurtman, R. J., Axelrod, J., Chu, E. W., and Fisher, J. E. (1964b). Mediation of some effects of illumination on the rat estrous cycle by the sympathetic nervous system. *Endocrinology* **75,** 266–272.

Wurtman, R. J., Axelrod, J., and Fisher, J. E. (1964c). Melatonin synthesis in the pineal gland: Effect of light mediated by the sympathetic nervous system. *Science* **143,** 1328–1329.

Wurtman, R. J., Axelrod, J., and Potter, L. T. (1964d). The uptake of H^3-melatonin in endocrine and nervous tissues and effects of constant light exposure. *J. Pharmacol. Exptl. Therap.* **143**, 314–318.

Yamada, T. (1961). The effect of electrical ablation of the nuclei habenulae, pineal body and subcommissural organ on endocrine function, with special reference to thyroid function. *Endocrinology* **69**, 706–711.

Zweens, J. (1963). Influence of the estrous cycle and ovariectomy on the phospholipid content of the pineal gland in the rat. *Nature* **197**, 1114–1115.

CHAPTER 33

Abnormalities of Neuroendocrine Functions in Man

JACK H. OPPENHEIMER

Previous chapters in this book have documented the control exerted by the central nervous system (CNS) over endocrine function in experimental animals. Sufficient clinical data have now been accumulated to indicate that man is no phylogenetic exception in this regard. Disturbance in the operation of higher nervous centers may result in profound alterations in adenohypophyseal function as well as in abnormalities in electrolyte balance. Evidence favoring the operation of neuroendocrine mechanisms in man is reviewed in this chapter.

Although there is general agreement regarding the participation of the central nervous system in the regulation of endocrine function in man, detailed information about precise neuroendocrine pathways and mechanisms is almost entirely lacking. The clinical investigator in this area is beset by a host of problems which are only partially shared by his colleagues working with experimental animals. Therefore, this chapter begins with a brief discussion of the limitations and difficulties encountered in the study of human neuroendocrinology. Future studies will undoubtedly lead to the development of techniques which will obviate many of these problems.

I. Limitations in the Study of Neuroendocrine Functions in Man

A. Indirect Nature of Measurements

Of the anterior pituitary hormones, only gonadotropins can be measured directly with techniques that are now generally available to the clinician. Even in the case of urinary gonadotropins, the bioassay techniques commonly employed for clinical purposes do not distinguish between follicle-stimulating hormone (FSH) and luteinizing hormone (LH). Thus, activity of the various tropic hormones of the adenohypophysis is usually inferred by the concentration of secretory products of the target gland in blood or urine or, even more indirectly, by the response of specific tissues to target gland secretion. The problem is even more complicated when attempts are made to assess CNS influences on the pituitary. For example, the clinician is forced to base conclusions regarding the liberation of corticotropin-releasing factor (CRF) not on a direct measurement of its concentration in the portal blood, nor on an assay of adrenocorticotropic hormone (ACTH) found in the systemic circulation, but by a determination of the concentration of unconjugated cortisol in blood or degradative products of cortisol in urine. Knowledge of CNS influences over endocrine function in man is thus largely based on observations twice removed from the variable under study. Hopefully, newly developed methods for assessing tropic hormones in blood (Yalow *et al.*, 1964) will find general clinical applicability and will allow more direct analyses of neuroendocrine mechanisms. The ultimate desideratum, that of measuring neurohumors in the living patient, is predicated not only on the development of appropriate assay procedures but on the finding of suitable and accessible sampling fluids as well.

In the case of the antidiuretic hormone (ADH) of the posterior pituitary, the problem of the multiple relay system is no longer applicable since ADH originates in the hypothalamus and acts directly on the target tissue. However, present methods for measuring this hormone in urine and blood (Sawyer, 1961) are not very sensitive and are generally unavailable to the clinician. Reliance is therefore placed on measurements of renal concentrating mechanisms as a guide to the activity of circulating ADH.

An additional problem, one certainly not confined to neuroendocrinology, is the significance of the relationship between the concentration of a given hormone in blood, its secretory rate from the gland of origin, and the excretion of its metabolites in urine. Moreover, the multiple effects of protein binding on the circulating concentration of hormones have further complicated the analysis of these already tangled theoretic considerations. Some of these problems have been considered in detail with respect to adrenal steroid hormones by Yates and Urquhart (1962).

B. Complications Introduced by the Interplay of Hormones and Other Metabolic Factors

Lesions in the central nervous system frequently may affect the secretion of a variety of tropic hormones from the adenohypophysis. Therefore, consideration must be given to the known interaction of the hormones of target glands. Hypothyroidism may in itself be responsible for diminished secretion and excretion of steroid hormones (Peterson, 1959). The interrelationship between the hormones of the anterior pituitary and ADH has received considerable attention (Kleeman *et al.*, 1958; Dingman and Despointes, 1960). Not only is it necessary to consider the effect of other hormonal disturbances, but the effect of concomitant nonhormonal metabolic derangements must be evaluated. For example, a poor nutritional state may lead to diminished gonadotropin excretion and the cessation of menstrual cycles in women (Waife, 1954; Zubrian and Gomez-Mont, 1953; Perloff *et al.*, 1954). Thus, the association of amenorrhea and absent urinary gonadotropins in a patient with CNS disease may be due to nutritional factors rather than to a direct effect of the lesion on CNS gonadotropin centers. Many similar examples of pitfalls in the interpretation of endocrine data could be cited.

C. Uncertainty Regarding the State of Pituitary Function

In order to ascribe a particular endocrine deficit to a known hypothalamic lesion, it is necessary to exclude the possibility of concomitant intrinsic disease of the pituitary and the target glands in question. Whereas it is relatively easy to rule out limited thyroidal and adrenal capacity by observing the effect of exogenously administered ACTH and thyrotropin (TSH), the possibility of pituitary failure cannot be evaluated as readily. If "releasing factors" of hypothalamic origin were available, this problem could be approached directly. In the absence of such diagnostic tools, the clinician must rely on indirect and more or less unsatisfactory evidence to assure himself that the pituitary is capable of normal response. A commonly used criterion for absence of the pituitary involvement is the demonstration of a radiologically intact sella turcica. Not all pathological processes within the pituitary, however, lead to radiographic changes in the bony casing of the gland.

D. Limitations in the Localization of Cerebral Lesions

The experimental neuroendocrinologist may place lesions in test animals wherever he chooses, and he can test the accuracy of his manipulations at the completion of the experiment. The clinical investigator must confine his observations to the results of spontaneous intracerebral disease or to operative intervention designed to palliate disease. Unfortunately, even with the best modern diagnostic techniques, the ability to pinpoint neurological lesions is frequently inadequate. Even when a mass is localized, the possibility remains that a particular endocrine deficit is related to associated edema of noncontiguous cerebral structures or to a generalized increase in intracranial pressure. Thus, the opportunity to study the effects of well-defined therapeutic neurosurgical measures such as stalk section is particularly valuable.

II. Gross Deficits of Endocrine Function in Cerebral Disease

A. Previous Observations

One of the major lines of evidence which indicates that adenohypophyseal function in man is at least under partial control of higher cerebral centers is the association of gross endocrine deficits with certain disorders of the CNS. Bauer (1954, 1959) has reviewed the findings in sixty autopsied cases of hypothalamic disease reported in the literature. In this series, the author demonstrated that the most frequently encountered clinical manifestation was an alteration of sexual function and development. Such abnormalities were demonstrable in forty-three of the 60 patients. Precocious puberty occurred in twenty-four cases, nineteen males and five females. Hypogonadism was present in nineteen cases, twelve males and seven females. A wide variety of pathological processes involved the hypothalamus. These included neoplasms of various histological types, inflammatory lesions such as tuberculous meningoencephalitis, congenital malformations, and degenerative lesions like tuberous sclerosis. The location of these lesions correlated to some extent with the type of abnormality encountered. Gonadal depression was associated predominantly with lesions in the inferior and more anterior region of the hypothalamus, whereas precocious puberty was frequently associated with disease in the posterior hypothalamus and often in the mammillary bodies. In this series, twenty-one cases of diabetes insipidus were reported. This was considered to be a relatively late development in the clinical course. Other "vegetative" abnormalities included somnolence, psychic disturbances, obesity and emaciation, and disturbance of temperature control. Since very few objective tests of endocrine function were carried out, it was difficult to be certain about thyroid and adrenal activity in these patients.

Selenkow and associates (1959) were the first to document diminished thyrotropic and adrenocorticotropic function as a consequence of CNS disease. These authors described a 27-year-old female with adrenal, thyroidal, and gonadal insufficiency as well as diabetes insipidus due to sarcoidosis of the hypothalamus. The patient expired; autopsy revealed widespread replacement of the hypothalamus by granulomata, but the pituitary was only minimally involved and the target glands were entirely spared. Sarcoidosis can also produce endocrine abnormalities by direct involvement of pituitary, thyroid, or adrenal tissue.

Kahana *et al.* (1962) further emphasized the widespread endocrine repercussions possible with intracerebral disease. These authors described the clinical and laboratory findings on fourteen illustrative patients. Since no postmortem studies were available, the evidence favoring a hypothalamic origin of the observed endocrine abnormalities must be considered only presumptive. Adrenocorticotropic and thyrotropic failure were observed in a patient with a glioma of the optic chiasm as well as in patients with third ventricle tumors. Of particular interest in this series were four patients with internal hydrocephalus which had developed in childhood. These patients exhibited profound alterations in the pattern of sexual development. In three, pubescence was delayed; one of the patients did not menstruate until age 18½, another not until age 23. The third patient died at age 18½ without having menstruated at all. A fourth patient developed pubic hair and enlargement of the breasts at age 5 but, despite evidence of normal genital development, the patient had not menstruated at age 15, 10 years after the beginning of pubertal changes. This patient also had normal uninary gonadotropin excretion. The authors postulated that she was an example of constant gonadotropin secretion resulting in persistent estrogen secretion. Other cases of precocious puberty in association with internal hydrocephalus have been reported (Wilkins, 1957).

Another observation of interest in the series by Kahana and colleagues was the development of gonadotropin deficiency in a patient with a meningioma of the floor of the anterior fossa. The deficiency was manifested both by amenorrhea and the absence of detectable urinary gonadotropin excretion. After resection of the tumor, normal menstrual cycles resumed and the patient succeeded in becoming pregnant.

In discussing the usefulness of various laboratory tests Kahana *et al.* suggested that the serum protein-bound iodine (PBI) and the 24-hour thyroidal accumulation of radioiodine may not adequately measure thyroid function in the neuroendocrine patient. On the other hand, they emphasized the diagnostic value of elevated serum cholesterol concentrations, especially if such elevated levels returned to normal after replacement therapy with thyroid hormone. Failure of the PBI and radioiodine accumulation tests to correlate with the clinical impression of thyroid deficiency raises the possibility of a qualitatively altered thyroid metabolism in these patients. A normal level of serum PBI in the presence of clinical hypothyroidism raises the possibility of the presence of a noncalorigenic iodinated compound in serum or an abnormality in thyroxine binding by plasma proteins.

B. Illustrative Case Reports

The development of panhypopituitarism in association with intracerebral disease is illustrated by the four previously unpublished case histories which follow.

Patient M.D. (Montefiore Hospital and Medical Center No. 124–7–40): *Sarcoidosis of the central nervous system with panhypopituitarism and galactorrhea.*

A 25-year-old Negro female was admitted on June 29, 1961, for evaluation of her endocrine and neurological status. The patient gave birth to a normal child in December 1958 after her only pregnancy. Delivery was uneventful. Menstrual cycles, however, did not resume, and galactorrhea persisted after she had ceased nursing. The patient noted slight dryness of the skin and began to complain of polydipsia and polyuria. Eight months after her delivery she experienced the first in a series of generalized seizures. Endocrine studies elsewhere revealed an atrophic endometrial biopsy and a low serum PBI concentration. Polyuria did not respond to infusion of hypertonic saline. Maximal urine specific gravity after overnight dehydration was 1.012. Physical examination at the time of her first admission revealed a blood pressure of 75/45. Hair distribution was normal, but pelvic examination showed evidence of atrophic changes. Milky fluid could be expressed from her breasts. Her skin was only moderately dry. There were no other physical findings suggestive of hypothyroidism. Endocrine studies revealed a serum PBI of 3.2 and 2.0 μg/100 ml, a 24-hour thyroidal I^{131} accumulation of 22%, a serum cholesterol of 263 mg/100 ml, and a basal metabolic rate of −12%. Baseline urinary 17-ketosteroid excretion on two occasions was 3.8 and 3.0 mg/24 hours (normal 5–15 mg/24 hours); urinary 17-ketogenic steroids, 4.7 and 2.6 mg/24 hours (normal 6–18 mg/24 hours). After infusion of 25 units ACTH over an 8-hour period, excretion of 17-ketosteroids rose to 4.7 mg/24 hours and 17-ketogenic steroids to 9.7 mg/24 hours. The concentration of cerebrospinal fluid protein was persistently elevated (190–290 mg/100 ml), and the cerebrospinal fluid glucose concentration was depressed (35–46 mg/100 ml). Five to sixteen white cells per mm^3, mostly lymphocytes, were observed in the cerebrospinal fluid. Cultures and direct examination for cryptococcus organisms were negative. X-Rays of the chest and skull were normal. A tuberculin skin test was negative. A Kveim test was read as negative. Serum albumin and globulin concentrations as well as serum calcium and phosphorous levels were normal.

Because of the laboratory and clinical evidence suggestive of hypopituitarism, the patient was started on endocrine replacement therapy including 10 mg of hydrocortisone twice a day and 2 grains of dessicated thyroid a day. The patient experienced marked symptomatic improvement on this regimen. Although the urinary specific gravity remained persistently below 1.012, the patient's symptoms did not require posterior pituitary replacement.

In May 1962, the patient was readmitted because of increasing weakness and right-sided paresis. A positive Babinski sign could be elicited on the right side. The patient became increasingly stuporous after admission, and despite large doses of steroid replacement therapy she died in respiratory failure on July 25, 1963.

Autopsy revealed a diffuse granulomatous meningoencephalitis as well as granulomatous infiltration of lungs, spleen, and liver consistent with sarcoidosis. The hypothalamic nuclei were largely replaced, and the hypophyseal stalk was completely destroyed. Although the sarcoid process also involved the adenohypophysis, the bulk of glandular tissue appeared intact. No sarcoid nodules were evident in the target glands. The adrenals appeared atrophic, each gland weighing 2.5 gm. The vaginal mucosa was also found to be atrophic. Evidence of active breast secretion was obtained in microscopic sections of mammary tissue.

Comment: Although the diagnosis of hypothalamic sarcoidosis was considered during the patient's life, her attending physicians minimized this diagnostic possibility because of the apparently negative Kveim test, the normal serum protein distribution, and the unremarkable chest X-ray. A subsequent review of the histological sections through the Kveim nodule has suggested that the skin reaction should have been considered positive for sarcoidosis. Had the diagnosis of sarcoidosis been made during the patient's life, large therapeutic doses rather than small replacement doses of corticosteroids would have been indicated in view of the beneficial results with steroids reported by Shealy and associates (1961) in CNS sarcoidosis. The ultimate outcome, however, might have been the same despite such treatment.

Although this patient probably did have some residual thyroidal and adrenal activity, laboratory evidence of diminished anterior pituitary function was reminiscent in many ways of the earlier case reported by Selenkow *et al.* (1959). Since the bulk of the pituitary was histologically intact, it is likely that diminished ACTH and TSH secretion by the pituitary can be attributed to the widespread hypothalamic lesions. Van Buren and Bergenstal (1960) have indicated that normal TSH and ACTH function can be retained in partially hypophysectomized man with as little as 29% of anterior pituitary tissue remaining.

The occurrence of galactorrhea in this patient deserves comment. In experiments in rats with transplanted pituitaries, lactation is continued or even increased in spite of diminished release of FSH and LH (Everett and Nikitovitch-Winer, 1963). This finding has suggested that the secretion of prolactin (luteotropin) may be under tonic inhibitory control of the CNS (see Chapter 16). A number of clinical situations in which galactorrhea is associated with diminished gonadotropin production may be cited. In the Chiari-Frommel syndrome persistent breast secretion occurs after recent pregnancy, accompanied by amenorrhea and uterine involution. In the cases studied by Argonz and DelCastillo (1953) and by Forbes *et al.* (1954) amenorrhea and decreased urinary gonadotropin excretion was associated with galactorrhea. No relation to recent pregnancy was noted. Forbes *et al.* (1954) found that seven of the fifteen patients studied had pituitary tumors. Eckles *et al.* (1958) reported galactorrhea after stalk section in women with breast cancer. In patient M. D., it is very likely that galactorrhea resulted from the release of the pituitary from inhibitory hypothalamic stimuli.

Patient W.W. (Montefiore Hospital and Medical Center No. 122–0–72): *Pinealoma with panhypopituitarism.*

A 37-year-old electronics salesman presented himself for admission on March 10, 1961, with a 4-month history of impotence, loss of libido, polydipsia and polyuria, cold intolerance, nausea, general malaise, and diplopia. The patient also complained of dizziness on assuming an erect position. Physical examination revealed a blood pressure of 110/80, a pulse of 80, and a rectal temperature of 100°F (37.8°C). Skin texture and hair distribution were normal. The genitalia were normal. Neurological examination revealed paralysis of upward gaze on command (Parinaud's sign), with weakness of the superior rectus muscle on the left and probably on the right as well. Visual fields were normal. Laboratory studies included a serum PBI of 3.9 μg/100 ml and two separate 24-hour thyroidal accumulations of I^{131} amounting to 12 and 13% of the administered dose. Injection of 10 units of TSH on 3 successive days increased the thyroidal uptake of iodine to 86% of the administered dose. The red cell uptake of I^{131}-labeled triiodothyronine was 7% (normal, 13–21%). Serum cholesterol concentration was 304 mg/100 ml. Urinary excretion of 17-ketosteroids was 5.8 mg/24 hours (normal, 10–20 mg/24 hours); excretion of 17-ketogenic steroids was 6.0 mg/24 hours, (normal, 7–20 mg/24 hours). Urinary gonadotropin excretion was between 16 and 80 mouse uterine units per 24 hours. A 4-hour infusion of ACTH (Christy *et al.*, 1957b) resulted in a rise in plasma unconjugated cortisol concentration from 8.6 to 23.8 μg/100 ml. This response is less than normal and compatible with hypopituitarism. The patient's polyuria could not be modified either with the intravenous infusion of hypertonic saline or the injection of nicotine, but was easily terminated by the subcutaneous administration of 20 units of aqueous Pitressin (vasopressin). The blood glucose levels (milligrams per 100 ml) during a glucose tolerance test were as follows: fasting, 64; 30 minutes 141; 1 hour, 160; 2 hours, 141; 3 hours, 107; 4 hours, 46. Serum sodium, potassium, chloride, calcium, and phosphorus were within normal limits. X-Rays of the skull (Fig. 1) revealed a robust type of calcification in the region of the pineal. The sella turcica was normal. Pneumoencephalography revealed a mass about 1.5 cm in diameter encroaching upon the posterior-superior portion of the third ventricle, with narrowing but no obstruction of the aqueduct of Sylvius.

The patient was given 1 ml of Pitressin tannate in oil intramuscularly. Urine volume decreased from 5 liters to approximately 1 liter per day. He was discharged on a regimen of dessicated thyroid, 2 grains a day; cortisone, 12.5 mg twice a day; depot-testosterone, 400 mg intramuscularly every 3 weeks; and Pitressin tannate, 1 ml every 2–3 days, as required. The patient received X-ray therapy at the region of the pineal (5000 r, tumor dose). He experienced marked improvement in response to the radiation therapy and endocrine replacement. He has returned to work and remains fully active 4 years after the onset of symptoms, complaining at present only of minimal residual diplopia.

Comment: The association of panhypopituitarism, diabetes insipidus, and pinealoma are here clearly documented. The gratifying response to endocrine replacement and radiation therapy is illustrated. Of interest is the finding of normal excretion of urinary gonadotropins in the presence of diminished libido and impotence. It appears possible that the patient's symptoms were due to an imbalance between FSH and LH excretion rather than a simple "across-the-board" fall in pituitary gonadotropin secretion.

Patient A.M. (Duke Medical Center No. D-98127): *Suprasellar craniopharyngioma with panhypopituitarism and diabetes inspidus.*

The patient was first admitted to Duke Hospital on October 7, 1954, at age 15 years, 11 months. She complained of headaches, nausea, and vomiting of 1 year's duration and blurred vision for the previous 3 months. Pubarche and thelarche had occurred, but not menarche. Physical examination revealed bilateral papilledema. There was no evidence of endocrine deficiency. Laboratory studies showed a thyroidal accumulation of 45% of the administered dose of I^{131}, a serum cholesterol of 216 mg/100 ml, urinary excretion of 17-ketosteroids of 3.9 mg/24 hours, maximal specific gravity of 1.025 on random urine specimens, and a urinary gonadotropin excretion of 3 rat uterine units (normal for menstruating females, 2–10 units).

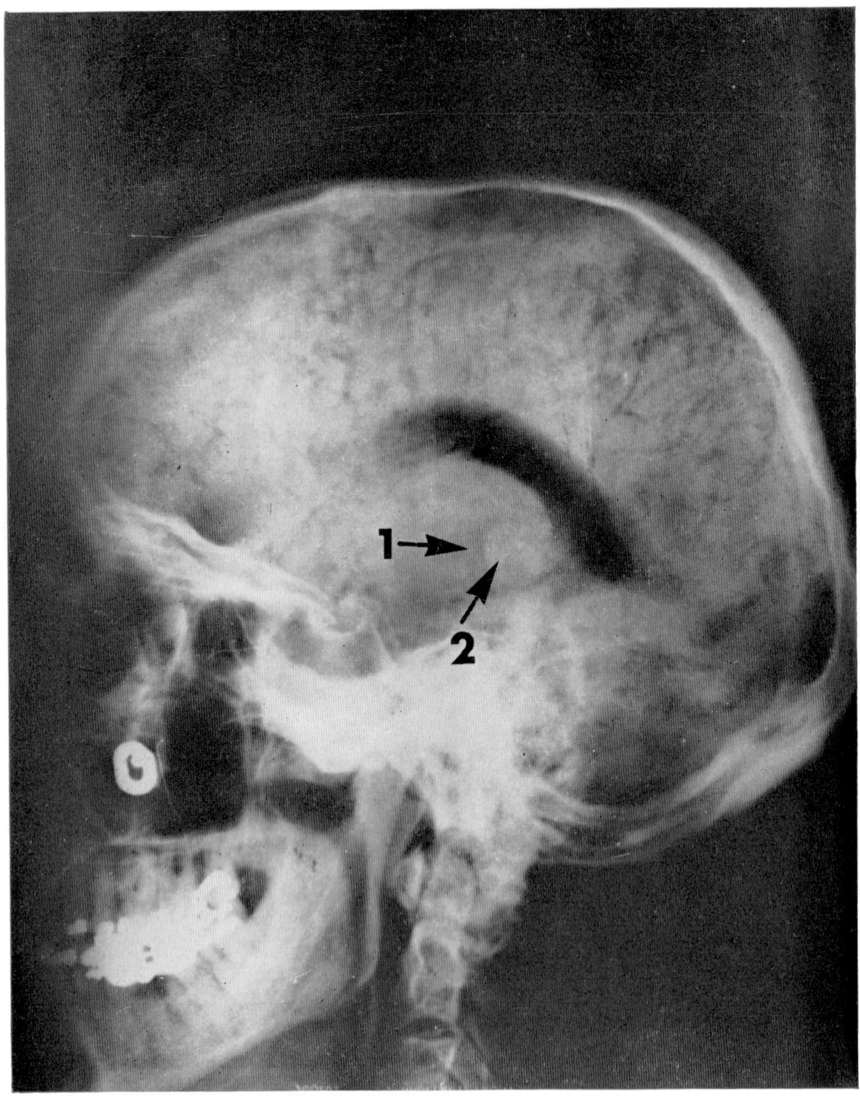

Fɪɢ. 1. Patient W.W. Pneumoencephalogram showing encroachment of pinealoma on posterior portion of third ventricle. Arrow No. 1: third ventricle. Arrow No. 2: pinealoma with calcification.

X-Rays of the skull showed amorphous suprasellar calcification; the sella itself was not enlarged. A craniotomy was performed, and a large suprasellar cyst was aspirated and partially resected. Histological examination identified the cyst as a craniopharyngioma.

Postoperatively, the patient gained 45 lb (19.5 kg) in the subsequent 7 months.

Menarche did not occur and vision did not improve. In March 1956 urinary 17-hydroxycorticosteroid excretion was noted to be low, 1.7 mg/24 hours (normal urinary Porter-Silber chromogens, 2–12 mg/24 hours); urinary 17-ketosteroid excretion was 3.4 mg/24 hours. Her serum PBI was 5.2 μg/100 ml, and her serum cholesterol had risen to 298 mg/100 ml. In April 1957, the patient was started on cyclic estrogen therapy. In April 1958, urinary 17-hydroxycorticosteroid excretion was 0.8 mg/24 hours and 17-ketosteroid excretion, 1.3 mg/24 hours.

In March 1959, the patient was brought to the Emergency Room because of marked polydipsia and polyuria. Blood pressure was 160/110. Physical examination showed no change except for the presence of questionably prolonged relaxation time of the deep tendon reflexes. Urinary specific gravity was 1.001. The patient was started on posterior pituitary snuff for presumptive diabetes insipidus. A striking decrease in urinary volume was noted. Admission to the hospital was arranged. When the patient presented herself again for admission she was apprehensive but rational and oriented. The patient had discontinued the use of posterior pituitary snuff and was complaining of excessive thirst. Urine specific gravity was 1.001. The serum sodium concentration was 124 mEq per liter; potassium, 4.4 mEq per liter; chloride, 78 mEq per liter. The blood urea nitrogen concentration was 4 mg/100 ml. The patient became increasingly agitated and irrational after admission. She suddenly expired 4 days after admission.

Postmortem examination showed that the craniopharyngioma had replaced almost the entire hypothalamus. There was also extension of tumor into the posterior fossa with encroachment on the midbrain and pons. The optic chiasm was thin and distorted. No remnant of the hypophyseal stalk was seen connecting hypothalamus to pituitary. The tumor did not extend into the sella turcica, and the pituitary was grossly intact. Combined adrenal weight was 8 gm, and each adrenal cortex measured approximately 1 mm in thickness; the normal weight of both adrenals is 10–12 gm, and the cortex is normally 1.3–1.4 mm thick. The uterus and ovaries were small. Histologically, the pituitary appeared to be entirely intact. The ovaries showed Graafian follicles in all stages of development but none with a theca cone. Theca lutein cells were also present. The endometrium showed good estrogenic stimulation in spite of the fact that the patient had not taken any estrogen for at least 3 months prior to death.

Comment: The delay in the appearance of menarche in spite of evidence of estrogenic activity suggests the possibility of a disturbance in the cyclical release of gonadotropic hormones, reminiscent of the patterns observed by Kahana and associates (1962) in patients with internal hydrocephalus. Adrenocorticotropic failure is suggested both by the low urinary steroid excretion and the diminished adrenal mass. The possible role of adrenal insufficiency in the development of the hyponatremia and in the patient's death remains unclear. At autopsy there appeared to be complete section of the pituitary stalk. The pathological findings, together with the clinical data, suggest that craniopharyngiomas may produce anterior pituitary insufficiency as a result of hypothalamic as well as direct pituitary involvement.

Patient M.B. (Montefiore Hospital and Medical Center No. 102–4–14): *Meningioma of the optic chiasm with panhypopituitarism.*

The patient, a 44-year-old married female, presented herself on December 1, 1958, because of increasing visual difficulty for the previous 1½ years. Four years previously, at the age of 40, her menstrual cycles had suddenly stopped. Shortly before admission she had begun to complain of increasing cold intolerance, loss of body hair, and dryness of the skin. On admission, her blood pressure in a reclining position was 120/70 with a fall to 90/60 on standing. Her skin was sallow and

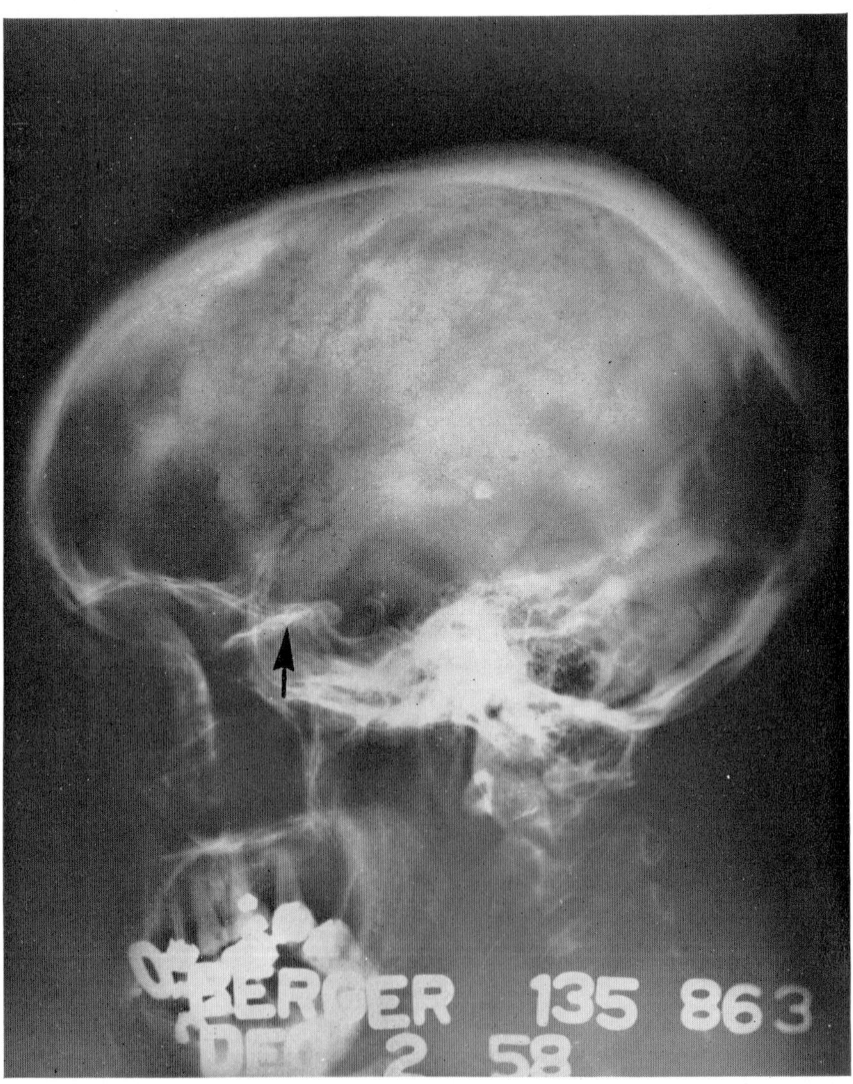

Fig. 2. Patient M.B. Lateral skull X-Rays demonstrating increased bone density (arrow) from the anterior clinoid process to the olfactory groove, due to a meningioma in this region.

had a parchmentlike consistency. Pubic and axillary hair were diminished. Bilateral optic atrophy was present. Examination of the visual fields revealed bitemporal hemianopia. X-Rays of the skull (Fig. 2) with lateral laminograms showed increased bone density in the left anterior clinoid process extending anteriorly to the tuberculum sellae and the olfactory groove region. These findings were considered to be compatible with a meningioma arising from the tuberculum sellae.

Endocrine laboratory studies revealed low baseline urinary steroid excretion (17-ketosteroids, 2.7 mg/24 hours 17-ketogenic steroids, 4.0 mg/24 hours). After infusion of 40 units of ACTH over an 8-hour period, urinary 17-ketosteroids excretion rose to 4.0 mg/24 hours and 17-ketogenic steroids to 13.7 mg/24 hours. The serum PBI concentration was 3.3 μg/100 ml. Fasting blood sugar was 65 mg/100 ml. Serum electrolytes showed persistently low serum sodium concentrations (125–130 mEq per liter). The serum potassium concentration ranged between 4.2 and 4.8 mEq per liter. The FSH excretion was less than 6 mouse uterine units per 24 hours. Maximal urinary specific gravity of random urine specimens was 1.028.

After appropriate steroid treatment, a craniotomy was performed and revealed the presence of a meningioma arising from the tuberculum sellae. The tumor, which had compressed the optic chiasm, was partially resected. Postoperatively, the patient received a dose of 6000 r to the tumor area. She has required endocrine replacement therapy including 3 grains of dessicated thyroid a day and 10 mg of cortisol twice a day.

Comment: The striking degree of adenohypophyseal deficiency exhibited by this patient in association with a meningioma of the tuberculum sellae is reminiscent of the pattern described by Kahana *et al.* (1962) in a similar case (B.W., No. 11). The two patients, however, differed insofar as patient M.B. did not have any evidence of diabetes insipidus. In both cases conclusive proof that the adenohypophyseal insufficiency resulted from hypothalamic involvement is lacking, and, it is at least theoretically possible that the meningioma may have invaded the pituitary proper or produced necrosis of pituitary tissue by interruption of its vascular supply. However, the sella turcica was not enlarged or eroded in either instance.

Table I is a summary of the incidence of tropic hormone failure and diabetes insipidus in nineteen neuroendocrine patients studied by modern laboratory techniques. Abnormalities of gonadal function are encountered most frequently followed, in order of decreasing frequency, by thyrotropic and adrenocorticotropic failure. This relative incidence of tropic hormone failure is similar to that found in patients with intrinsic pituitary disease (Peters *et al.*, 1954). Almost all clinical observers have noted that loss of gonadal function precedes the development of other endocrine abnormalities in patients with chromophobe adenomas. It is possible that the loss of gonadotropic function is due not only to destruction of pituitary elements by the tumor, but to suprasellar extension of the mass with disruption of the normal connections to the hypothalamus as well. The experience of Van Buren and Bergenstal

TABLE I

Endocrine Manifestations of Central Nervous System Disease in 19 Patients

Diagnosis	Number of cases	Tropic harmone deficiency: Gonado-tropin	TSH	ACTH	Precocious puberty	Diabetes insipidus	Autopsies performed
Sarcoidosis	2[a,b]	2	2	2	0	2	2
Tumor impinging on third ventricle	6[c,d,e]	6	4	1	0	4	0
Hydrocephalus	5[c,f]	3	2	1	1	1	0
Meningioma of floor of anterior fossa	1[c]	1	0	0	0	0	0
Arteriovenous aneurysm of cerebrum	1[c]	1	0	0	0	0	0
Schüller-Christian disease	1[g]	0	1	1	0	1	1
Glioma of optic chiasm	2[c,h]	2	2	2	0	1	0
Extrasellar craniopharyngioma	1[i]	1	1	1	0	1	0
Total	19	16	12	8	1	10	4

[a] From Selenkow *et al.* (1959).
[b] From Patient M.B., this report.
[c] From Kahana *et al.* (1962).
[d] From Oppenheimer *et al.* (1961).
[e] From Patient W.W., this report.
[f] From Hays *et al.* (1963).
[g] From Avioli *et al.* (1962).
[h] From Patient M.B., this report.
[i] From Patient A.M., this report.

(1960) with patients partially hypophysectomized for breast cancer is of interest in this connection. These authors compared the extent of endocrine deficiency after hypophysectomy to the completeness of pituitary ablation as judged by detailed examination of the sellar contents at autopsy. Immediately after operation, their patients showed panhypopituitarism, regardless of the completeness of pituitary removal. Conceivably, this state of hypopituitarism could have resulted from the interruption of normal anatomical connections between hypothalamus and the pituitary. Gonadotropic deficiency persisted in these patients, but, if sufficient adenohypophyseal tissue remained behind, thyrotropic function tended to return to normal. The restoration of thyroidal and adrenal function may indicate that TSH and ACTH-producing cells possess a greater degree of independence from neural influence than the adenohypophyseal cells responsible for the manufacture of gonadotropins. Ten of the nineteen neuroendocrine patients listed in Table I had diabetes insipidus, a clinical abnormality to be anticipated from the location of the primary lesions.

The increasingly frequent use of hypophyseal stalk section in the treatment of diabetic retinopathy (Field *et al.*, 1961, 1962) presents an unusual opportunity for careful study of the nature of the pituitary-hypothalamic interrelationship in man. Evidence already at hand suggests that functional hypopituitarism, including diminished ACTH production, results from stalk section (Van Wyk *et al.*, 1960a,b). Careful postmortem examination of the pituitaries from such patients should be helpful in assessing the importance of vascular damage to the pituitary in the production of the hypopituitary state.

C. General Therapeutic Implications

The evidence presented above documents the fact that adenohypophyseal failure may occur in disease of the CNS. From a therapeutic point of view, it is exceedingly important that this possibility be taken into consideration when patients with lesions in or about the hypothalamus are subjected to surgery or relatively traumatic diagnostic procedures such as pneumoencephalography. Such patients, like patients with primary pituitary disease, deserve pretreatment with glucocorticoids. The intramuscular injection of 200 mg cortisone acetate 24 hours before the contemplated procedure will adequately protect the patient, since intramuscular cortisone will act as a repository preparation. The intravenous administration of a soluble glucocorticoid during surgery (100–200 mg hydrocortisone sodium succinate) will afford additional protection. Unless there are postoperative complications, steroids can be rapidly withdrawn to maintenance levels. After the clinical condition of the patient has sufficiently stabilized, the necessity of continued replacement can be reassessed. Similar therapy with supplemental steroids is indicated for intercurrent infections and accidental trauma. Restoration of euthyroidal status in these patients is also desirable before they are subjected to surgery, but, since the degree of thyroidal insufficiency is generally mild, hypothyroidism does not pose as grave a clinical problem as does acute adrenal insufficiency.

III. Asymptomatic Disturbances in Endocrine Control Mechanisms

In addition to the gross deficits of endocrine function detailed in the previous section, considerable evidence has been accumulated in the past 5 years to indicate that patients with CNS disease may also have asymptomatic disturbances in endocrine control mechanisms which are apparent only after detailed laboratory studies. Although the clinical significance of these abnormalities is not clear at this time, investigation of such derangements may lead to a better understanding of the operation of normal physiological control processes.

A. Disturbance in Diurnal Variation of Plasma Cortisol Levels

The concentration of unconjugated plasma cortisol undergoes a well-defined circadian variation with levels highest in the early morning hours and lowest in the evening (Bliss *et al.*, 1953). There is evidence that this variation is due to rhythmic release of ACTH rather than alterations in the metabolism of cortisol (Ney *et al.*, 1963). Mason (1958) has indicated that in the monkey the limbic system may play a role in determining the circadian variation in plasma cortisol.

Diffuse disease of the CNS associated with disturbances in consciousness may cause deviations in the normal diurnal fluctuation of plasma steroid levels (Perkoff *et al.*, 1959). Krieger (1961) has shown abnormalities in diurnal variation in patients with temporal lobe epilepsy and pretectal disease in whom consciousness was not disturbed. Suprasellar tumors (Hökfelt and Luft, 1959) and other hypothalamic lesions (Krieger and Krieger, 1964b) may also cause a variety of abnormal patterns. Krieger (1961) has reported exceedingly high peak plasma 17-hydroxycorticoid values (50–125 μg/100 ml) in some of her patients. None of these patients developed stigmata of Cushing's disease, and the urinary excretion of 17-hydroxycorticosteroids was normal. This raises the possibility that these patients may metabolize steroids in an abnormal fashion. It would certainly appear important to determine the chemical nature of the material causing the high plasma Porter-Silber chromogen level in order to rule out possible chemical artifacts.

No specific correlation has been established so far between the location of the neurological lesion and any particular abnormality in the diurnal cortisol pattern. Occasionally the abnormal curve will revert to a normal pattern following radiotherapy or spontaneous clearing of symptoms (Krieger and Krieger, 1964b). Frequently, abnormalities in plasma cortisol variation are not associated with any other detectable endocrine abnormalities.

B. Disturbance of Pituitary-Adrenal Interrelationship

The nature of the factors regulating the interplay between hormonal secretions of the pituitary and adrenal glands, including the operation of the negative feedback mechanism, have been critically examined in the past decade (Yates and Urquhart, 1962; Estep *et al.*, 1963). Still unresolved is the question of whether the receptor site sensitive to the concentration of circulating cortisol and responsible for modulating the secretion of ACTH by the pituitary is located within the CNS, within the adenohypophysis itself, or possibly in both places (see Chapter 9). Efforts to resolve this question in man have been undertaken by studying the operation of the negative feedback mechanism in patients with CNS disease.

Oppenheimer *et al.* (1961) studied fourteen patients with disorders of the hypothalamus and temporal lobes. Each of these patients was tested with methopyrapone (Metapirone), a drug which, in the dosage administered, selectively inhibits 11β-hydroxylation in the adrenal (Liddle *et al.*, 1959). Since this is the final step in the biosynthesis of cortisol, the concentration of circulating cortisol falls. This fall causes increased release of ACTH from the pituitary, and large quantities of compound S (11-deoxycortisol), the immediate precursor of cortisol enter the circulation. The metabolites of compound S are measured as 17-ketogenic steroids in the urine. A normal response to methopyrapone in the presence of an intact target gland, pituitary, and negative feedback system is at least a twofold increase in 17-ketogenic steroid excretion.

Of the fourteen patients with CNS disease studied with methopyrapone, three failed to exhibit a significant increase in urinary 17-ketogenic steroid excretion (Fig. 3): P.T. an 18-year-old male with a third ventricular tumor and hypogonadism; D.O., a 9-year-old girl with precocious puberty, general ventricular dilatation, and mental retardation; and W.N., a 43-year-old man with posttraumatic temporal lobe epilepsy. The three patients showed no radiological evidence of pituitary disease.

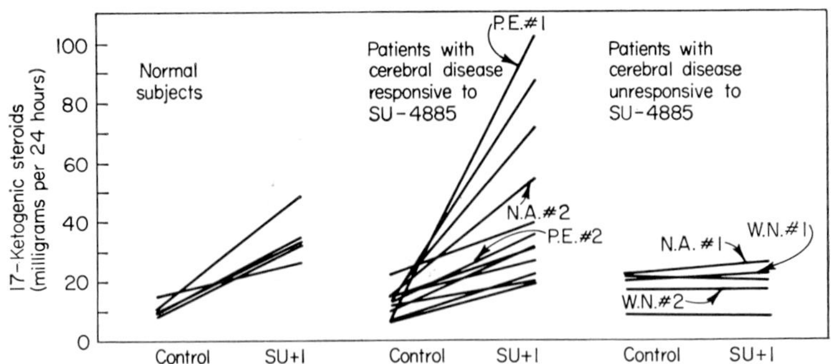

FIG. 3. Methopyrapone (SU-4885) tests in normal subjects and in patients with cerebral disease. "Control": 17-ketogenic steroid excretion on the day before administration of SU-4885. "SU + 1": 17-ketogenic steroid excretion on the day following administration of SU-4885. (From Oppenheimer *et al.*, 1961.)

They had normal baseline urinary excretions of steroids and no clinical evidence of diminished adrenal function. Infusion of ACTH induced a normal rise in plasma 17-hydroxycorticosteroids.

Not only were these patients unable to respond normally to lowered levels of circulating cortisol, but two of them (D.O. and W.N.) failed to demonstrate a decrease in urinary steroid excretion when tested with what are usually suppressive doses of dexamethasone (Fig. 4). However, W.N. showed a brisk adrenal response to the infusion of corticotropin-releasing factor (Fraction D of Guillemin) and to the administration of a bacterial pyrogen (Fig. 5). Clearly, this patient had a pituitary capable of secreting large amounts of ACTH.

On the basis of the observations made in these three patients, it was postulated that in man CNS centers exist which are responsive both to lowered and to elevated levels of circulating glucocorticoids. The functions of such centers could be disrupted by CNS disease. Bacterial pyrogen increased ACTH secretion in patient W.N. This suggests the possibility that the response to stressful stimuli is mediated by pathways different from those involved in the operation of the negative feedback mechanism regulating the concentration of cortisol. However, the alternative explanation that the stimulus to ACTH secretion of reduced circulating cortisol levels is simply less strong than the stimulus of pyrogen administration must also be considered.

Two of the patients unresponsive to methopyrapone (W.N. and D.O.) were taking the anticonvulsant diphenylhydantoin (Dilantin) at the time of the tests. The possibility that diphenylhydantoin by itself could blunt the methopyrapone response was not fully appreciated until the later studies of Krieger (1962). On the other hand, no evidence that diphenyl-

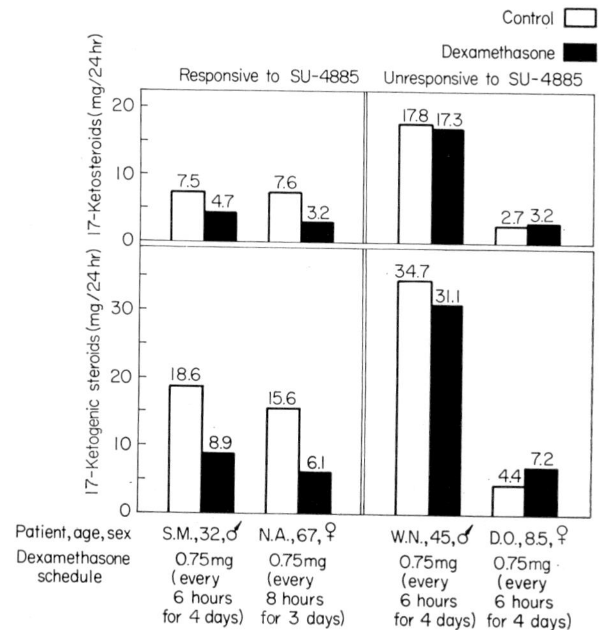

FIG. 4. Dexamethasone suppression tests in two patients responsive to methopyrapone (SU-4885) and in two patients unresponsive to SU-4885. The white columns represent the control steroid excretion on the day preceding administration of dexamethasone. The black columns represent steroid excretion on the fourth day of dexamethasone administration. (From Oppenheimer *et al.*, 1961.)

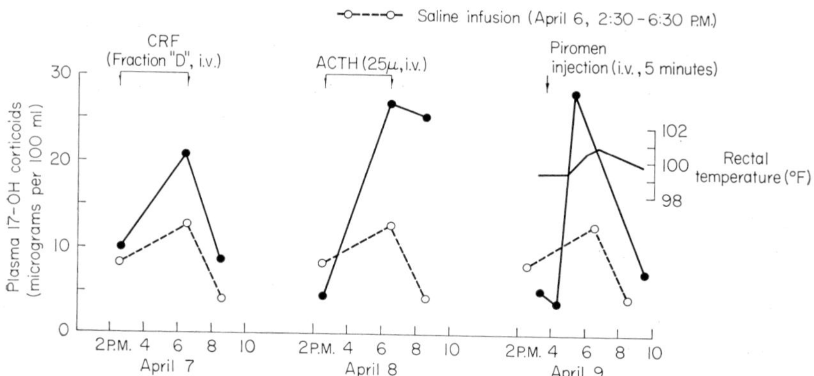

FIG. 5. Plasma 17-hydroxy corticosteroid responses to intravenous infusion of saline, CRF (Fraction D of Guillemin), ACTH, and bacterial lipopolysaccharide (Piromen) in patient W.N. Observations during the infusion of saline on April 6 were considered to be appropriate control values, and are indicated by the broken line. (From Oppenheimer *et al.*, 1961.)

hydantoin can also block the pituitary suppressibility by dexamethasone has been presented. Moreover, one of the patients (P.vT) was not taking any medication. Krieger *et al.* (1964) have subsequently reported two patients with hypothalamic disease who were unresponsive to methopyrapone and who were not taking any medication at the time of testing. Gold *et al.* (1961) also reported methopyrapone unresponsiveness in patients with hypothalamic tumors, but no specific mention is made of concomitant drug administration.

McCarthy *et al.* (1964) have recently reported that head trauma may result in resistance both to methopyrapone stimulation and dexamethasone suppression. Their patients were not receiving any drugs. One patient who was insensitive to methopyrapone and dexamethasone showed a normal rise in plasma corticosteroid levels following the injection of a bacterial pyrogen; he thus resembled patient W.N. in the earlier series. Unresponsiveness to methopyrapone with normal responsiveness to the stimuli of hypoglycemia and pyrogens was also noted by Van Wyk *et al.* (1960b) in patients who had undergone pituitary stalk section.

There thus appears to be reasonably good clinical evidence that CNS disease can result in a major disturbance of the servomechanism regulating the concentration of circulating cortisol under baseline environmental conditions. Patients exhibiting such a disturbance may still be capable of responding in a normal fashion to stressful stimuli. This may be due to the existence of separate pathways for the two types of responses or, alternately, the stimulus of reduced circulating cortisol may be quantitatively less potent than the stimuli of pyrogen, hypoglycemia, or surgery. It is not possible at present to decide between these two possibilities.

IV. Effect of Drugs on Neuroendocrine Function in Man

The possible effect of diphenylhydantoin on the methopyrapone test has already been mentioned in the previous section. In her original studies, Krieger (1962) evaluated the methopyrapone test both before and during the administration of diphenylhydantoin in eight patients. Three patients showed no rise in steroid excretion in response to methopyrapone while taking the anticonvulsant; four patients exhibited a diminished response, and one patient exhibited an increased response when compared to the results of the test done in the control period. The drug was found to have no effect on the baseline excretion of urinary steroids, nor on the response to exogenously administered ACTH. The possibility that diphenylhydantoin has a central site of action which is responsible for inhibiting the adrenal pituitary feedback control is an attractive hypothesis in view of the anticonvulsant actions of the drug, the evidence of its metabolic action and localization in the central nervous tissue (Woodbury, 1955; Roth and Barlow, 1961). On the other hand, a number of investigators have demonstrated varying effects of diphenylhydantoin on adrenal histology and function in the rat, and recent studies have suggested that this drug may have a profound effect on the extra-adrenal metabolism of cortisol (Werk *et al.*, 1964).

Other drugs which have been reported to block the normal response to methopyrapone include chlorpromazine (Gold *et al.*, 1960; Feldschuh *et al.*, 1961) as well as carisoprodol, meprobamate, and nialamide (Gold *et al.*, 1960). Again, it was found that patients taking these "psychotropic" drugs did not exhibit any diminution of baseline urinary steroid excretion, manifested no clinical indications of hypoadrenalism, and responded with increased urinary steroid excretion after surgery and other stressful stimuli (Gold *et al.*, 1960). On the other hand, Christy and associates (1957a) found that chlorpromazine inhibited the adrenal cortical response to insulin hypoglycemia without interfering with the adrenal response to exogenously administered ACTH. These authors suggested that chlorpromazine acted at a hypothalamic site.

Chlorpromazine may also induce nonpuerperal lactaction (Marshall and Leiberman, 1956; Sulman and Winnik, 1956; Winnik and Tannenbaum, 1955). This again may reflect the hypothalamic site of action of this drug (Dundee, 1954). Chlorpromazine may suppress normally inhibitory pathways which prevent release of prolactin under ordinary circumstances.

V. Possible Relationship between the Central Nervous System and Certain Clinical States

A. Graves' Disease

A history of a psychologically traumatic precipitating event is often elicited in patients with Graves' disease. The thesis that the CNS may play a causal role in the development of the hyperthyroid state has been proposed (Ham *et al.*, 1951). Robbins and Vinson (1960), however, did not find any significant abnormalities on objective psychological testing in patients with treated hyperthyroidism. It appears possible that the psychological problems presented by the hyperthyroid patient may simply be a reflection of the metabolic effect of the thyroid hormones on the CNS. Furthermore, the role of the pituitary in the pathogenesis of Graves' disease is uncertain. Hyperthyroidism in the virtual absence of any pituitary tissues has been reported (Becker, 1959, Fajans, 1958; Werner and Stewart, 1958; Albeux-Fernet *et al.*, 1955; McCullagh *et al.*, 1957). On the other hand, remission of hyperthyroidism associated with a pituitary adenoma after radiation therapy was observed by Jailer and Holub (1960). The possible role and source of the long-acting thyroid stimulator is still obscure (McKenzie, 1961) as is its relationship to TSH (Meek *et al.*, 1964).

B. Cushing's Syndrome

It now appears very probable that Cushing's syndrome associated with bilateral adrenal hyperplasia is due to a net increase in pituitary ACTH secretion. The earlier evidence favoring this view was summarized by Jailer *et al.* (1956). More recently, the demonstration that pituitary tumors are frequently observed after bilateral adrenalectomy for Cushing's syndrome (Nelson *et al.*, 1958, 1960; Salassa *et al.*, 1959) has added additional weight to the thesis that pituitary function is abnormal in this disease. Furthermore, elevated plasma (Ney *et al.*, 1963) and urinary (Fujital *et al.*, 1963) levels of ACTH have been reported in patients with Cushing's syndrome due to bilateral adrenal hyperplasia.

Whether the hypothalamus or higher nervous centers are in turn responsible for increased pituitary ACTH secretion is unknown. Heinbecker and Pfeiffenberger (1950), on the basis of histological observations in central nervous tissue, suggested that the hypothalamus might be primarily responsible for pituitary and adrenal hypersecretion. It is unclear, however, whether these alterations were the consequence or the cause of the elevated circulating steroid levels.

Of particular interest with respect to the possible hypothalamic etiology of Cushing's syndrome is the recent case report of Wolff *et al.* (1964). A 14-year-old boy had cyclical attacks of nausea, emotional disturbances, and weight change. During the attacks, there was a striking increase in urinary excretion of cortisol metabolites, and elevated plasma ACTH levels were demonstrated. Although his baseline glucose tolerance curve was normal, during the attack a diabetic pattern was observed. In addition, the patient became hypertensive during the crises and was described as developing facial plethora. Roentgenographic findings as well as abnormalities in thermoregulatory mechanisms suggested that the patient's symptoms were due to a hypothalamic lesion. The attacks could be abolished by the administration of dexamethasone.

C. Relationship of Psychic Factors to Menstrual Disturbances, Hirsutism, and the Polycystic Ovary Syndrome

The relationship between psychic disturbances and menstrual irregularities has been clinically recognized for many years. There is a high incidence of such abnormalities in patients with psychotic and psychoneurotic disorders (Ripley and Papanicolaou, 1942; Rakoff, 1963). After appropriate psychotherapy or spontaneous improvement, normal menstrual cycles will frequently resume in such patients.

Klinefelter *et al.* (1943) first coined the term "hypothalamic amenorrhea" to designate the syndrome of amenorrhea associated with normal FSH excretion and evidence of estrogenic deficiency. These authors postulated that in such patients the psychogenic stimuli served to block the normal release of LH, which together with FSH appears to be necessary for ovarian estrogen production. Rakoff (1963) has suggested that the problem of psychogenic amenorrhea is more complex and has proposed a new classification (Table II) based on (1) the urinary excretion of FSH, (2) estrogen production as gauged by vaginal smear and bioassay techniques, (3) the urinary excretion of pregnandiol, (4) the urinary excretion of 17-ketosteroids, and (5) the level of the serum PBI. The author distinguishes a number of hormonal patterns in psychogenic amenorrhea including low, normal, and high FSH excretion together with variable expressions of estrogenic deficiency. It should be emphasized that the techniques for measuring urinary gonadotropins heretofore have been imprecise and have not served adequately to distinguish between FSH and LH. One would hope that the newer methods such as those used by McCann (1963) as well as those that are exploiting the specificity of the immunological reaction will serve to clarify some of the outstanding problems in this area. In addition, the gonadotropins of human origin (Gemzell *et al.*, 1958; Rosenberg *et al.*, 1963) should be very useful investigative tools to delineate the pathogenic mechanism in psychogenic amenorrhea.

Psychological factors have also been implicated in the development of "idiopathic" hirsutism in women (Lloyd, 1963). In such women, an increased excretion of the adrenal androgens, androsterone and etiocholanolone, has been noted (Kappas *et al.*, 1956). The influence of psychological stress on the adrenal production of glucocorticoids in man is, of course, well recognized (Bliss *et al.*, 1956) and by itself constitutes important evidence of the control exerted by the CNS over adenohypophyseal function. Suggestions have also been made that the syndrome of polycystic ovaries (Stein-Leventhal syndrome) is related

TABLE II

Hormonal Patterns in Psychogenic Amenorrhea[a,b]

Pattern	Excretion of harmones			Serum PBI	Estrogen production	Remarks
	FSH	Pregnanediol	17-Keto-steroids			
1	↓	↓	—	—	↓	Hypogonadotropism
2	↓	↓	—	↓	↓	Hypogonadotropism and hypothyroidism
3	↓	↓	↓	—	↓	Anorexia nervosa
4*	↓	↓	—	—	↓	Galactorrhea; prolactin ↑?
5	—	↓	—	—	↓	Hypothalamic amenorrhea of Klinefeter *et al.* (1943); LH ↓?
6	—	↓	—	—	— or ↑	Persistent estrus
7	↑	↓	—	—	↓	"Menopausal" symptoms
8*	— or ↓	↓	↑	—	↓	Adrenogenital syndrome
9*	↓ or —	↑	—	—	— or ↑	Pseudocyesis

[a] From Rakoff (1963).

[b] Key: ↓, below normal range; ↑, above normal range; —, within normal range; *, occurred in chronic cases only. Other patterns observed in both acute and chronic cases.

to disturbed cyclical release of gonadotropins (McArthur *et al.*, 1958). The role of psychological factors in the development of hirsutism and polycystic ovaries appears to be much less firmly established than the relationship between menstrual irregularity and emotional stimuli.

VI. Role of the Central Nervous System in the Regulation of Salt and Water Metabolism in Man

A. Deficiency of Antidiuretic Hormone: Diabetes Insipidus

Vasopressin (ADH) can be considered a neuroendocrine hormone par excellence. It may be manufactured in the supraoptic and paraventricular nuclei of the hypothalamus and conveyed to the posterior pituitary by way of the axons of the neurohypophyseal tract (see Chapter 6). From the posterior pituitary it is released in response to a variety of stimuli including increased plasma osmolality, hemorrhage, pharmacologic agents such as nicotine, and nonspecific stresses. The most important function of ADH clearly is the renal conservation of water (for review see Leaf, 1960). Other properties of ADH, including the release of ACTH from the adenohypophysis (McCann and Fruit, 1957) and thyroxine from the thyroid gland (Werner *et al.*, 1964), probably are not physiologically important.

In man, the antidiuretic principle has been shown to be arginine vasopressin, a polypeptide which was synthesized by du Vigneaud (1956). Histological evidence for the hypothalamic origin of ADH in man has been presented (Müller, 1955; Sloper and Adams, 1955). Clinical evidence lends additional support for the belief that ADH is secreted in the hypothalamus. Thus, diabetes insipidus results only after high pituitary stalk section and retrograde axonal degeneration; low stalk section with pituitary removal does not result in permanent abnormalities in the release of ADH (Lipsett and Pearson, 1957). Similarly, diabetes insipidus rarely occurs with purely intrasellar tumors but quite frequently accompanies lesions of the hypothalamus and stalk.

The manner in which diabetes insipidus develops after neurosurgical procedures in the region of the pituitary-hypothalamic area deserves special comment. Characteristically, a triphasic response is encountered (Lipsett *et al.*, 1956). A period of temporary polyuria commences 2 or 3 days after surgery and lasts 1–5 days. This is followed by an interphase lasting between 1 and 5 days and is characterized by the appearance of normal urine volumes. Lastly, permanent polyuria develops. However, other patterns are frequently observed following neurosurgical procedures (Randall *et al.*, 1960). A transient period of polyuria may be followed by a permanent restoration of urine volumes to normal. On the other hand, a permanent increase in urine volume may be observed within the first several days after surgery without an interphase.

The explanations for the variable patterns of polyuria following neurosurgical operations are probably complex. The interphase period may be due to the release of preformed ADH from the posterior lobe of the pituitary. The initial increase in urine volume observed in the triphasic response may be due to injury to hypothalamic centers. In addition, some of the patients undergoing surgery in the region of the third ventricle may have had latent diabetes insipidus preoperatively. Large doses of glucocorticoids given before and during surgery may uncover this latent ADH deficiency.

Appropriate management of diabetes insipidus in the postoperative patient is of critical importance, especially when the patient is unconscious and cannot voluntarily compensate for undue water loss. For this reason, 4-hour urine collections should be performed after any surgical procedure in the hypothalamic-pituitary region. Any sudden increase in urine volume can then be offset by appropriate intravenous infusion of fluids. If increased urinary volume persists after 12–24 hours, a trial of antidiuretic therapy is indicated. Since the course of postoperative diabetes insipidus is variable, therapy should be started with the short-acting aqueous Pitressin. Treatment can be started in normal adults with 5 pressor units (0.25 ml) or in children with 2 pressor units (0.1 ml) injected subcutaneously. The effect of the aqueous Pitressin is generally dissipated by the end of 4–6 hours. If polyuria is not controlled with the initial dose, the dose is successively doubled until urine volume is reduced to normal levels. With the larger doses the aqueous Pitressin may be effective for as long as 12 hours. Intake and output are carefully balanced, both by adjusting the dose of Pitressin and by regulating the volume of infused fluids. Daily hematocrit and electrolyte determinations are obtained as additional indices of the state of hydration and the need for sodium and potassium replacement. Overhydration is to be avoided at all costs, since this can lead to dangerous intracerebral edema in the postoperative patient. If the patient is known to have diabetes insipidus prior to surgery, his daily maintenance of Pitressin tannate in oil is reduced to one-half or one-third during the operative and immediate postoperative period. When the postoperative patient regains full consciousness and can express and satisfy a normal sensation of thirst, diabetes insipidus can be treated quite satisfactorily with Pitressin tannate in oil in the usual doses. Posterior pituitary powder administered as snuff is to be avoided during the postoperative period because of its tendency to induce sneezing and thereby to raise intracranial pressure.

As previously pointed out, the recognition of diabetes insipidus may be hampered by the excretion of normal urinary volumes if the patient has associated deficiency of adenohypophyseal function. A diminished osmolal load for urinary excretion may be partially responsible for the low urine volume in such patients. Furthermore, in the presence of dehydration, patients with diabetes insipidus may excrete urine with osmolal concentrations as high as 300 mOsm per kilogram of water and specific gravities as high as 1.010. In experimental animals, Berliner and Davidson (1957) have produced urine hypertonic to serum in the absence of ADH by greatly reducing the glomerular filtration rate. The clinical importance of recognizing unapparent diabetes insipidus as well as the possible importance of the thyroid hormones in determining urine volume under such circumstances is illustrated by the following case.

Patient S.R. (Montefiore Hospital and Medical Center No. 140–18–3).

A 9½-year-old boy was admitted to the Montefiore Hospital and Medical Center on April 6, 1963, in apparent adrenal insufficiency. A large craniopharyngioma had been resected on March 14, 1963. Prior to operation, baseline urinary steroids indicated diminished adrenal function (17-ketogenic steroids, 1.5 mg/24 hours 17-ketosteroids, 0.5 mg/24 hours). The patient had been placed on appropriate steroid replacement therapy preoperatively and postoperatively. The patient was discharged on March 31, but steroids were discontinued at home. The boy began complaining of increasing nausea and vomiting and on the morning of admission was found unconscious and without detectable blood pressure by his personal physician. Cortisol was administered intravenously with prompt restoration of blood pressure. Although serum electrolytes at the time of his admission were not typical of adrenal insufficiency (concentrations in mEq per liter: Na, 135; K, 3.3; CO_2, 34; and Cl, 91), the patient was treated as though he were in Addisonian crisis with the intravenous infusion of approximately 2.3 liters isotonic saline and a total of 200 mg cortisol as the sodium succinate ester during the first 24 hours of his hospital stay.

Some 36 hours after admission the patient began to have generalized seizures, which became increasingly frequent and terminated in status epilepticus. During this time, the concentration of serum sodium was found to be 170 mEq per liter. Repeated determinations verified the existence of severe hypernatremia. Serum potassium was 3.7 CO_2, 24; and Cl, 142 mEq per liter. Infusions of saline were immediately stopped, and steroid administration was reduced to 10 mg cortisol twice a day. The serum sodium promptly fell, and the seizures abated.

In an effort to explain the hypernatremia with its accompanying neurological consequences, note was taken of a number of clinical and laboratory findings. Urine volumes during the first several days did not exceed 1.6 liters, and random urine specimens did not have specific gravities in excess of 1.010 despite the severe hypernatremia. At the same time it was noted that the patient's skin showed some dryness and that there was definite delay in the relaxation phase of his deep tendon reflexes; these findings suggested hypothyroidism. A 24-hour thyroidal accumulation of radio-iodine of 4.3%, a serum PBI of 1.2 μg/100 ml, and a serum cholesterol of 362 mg/100 ml confirmed the clinical suspicion of diminished thyroid function. It was accordingly suggested that hypothyroidism prevented the appropriate expression of an underlying deficiency of ADH. It was postulated that, with a restricted total urine volume and an inability to form an appropriately concentrated urine, the infusion of saline had resulted in the observed hypernatremia.

The patient was treated with 100 μg of triiodothyronine per day. Within 7 days he became increasingly alert and showed general clinical improvement. At the same time, the urine volume increased. When the rate of urine formation exceeded 320 ml per hour, Pitressin tannate was administered with good control of urine flow. The patient was discharged on replacement therapy of dessicated thyroid, cortisol, and vasopressin. Growth hormone was later added with an excellent clinical response. The requirement for continued vasopressin therapy was demonstrated on a subsequent hospital admission when it was shown that after 8 hours of dehydration the maximal urinary concentration achieved was 183 mOsm per kilogram with a simultaneous plasma osmolality of 325 mOsm per kilogram. The child has continued to do well up to the present, some 19 months after the initial surgery.

B. Hyponatremia and the Inappropriate Secretion of Antidiuretic Hormone

In 1957 Schwartz and associates described two patients with bronchogenic carcinoma who in the absence of renal or adrenal disease displayed pronounced hyponatremia with increased urinary excretion of sodium. Restriction of water intake served to correct the hyponatremia. The authors pointed out the similarity of the pattern displayed by these patients to the known effects of Pitressin administered to normal subjects (Leaf *et al.*, 1953) and suggested that the naturally occurring syndrome was due to an inappropriate secretion of the ADH. Since the original report, similar disturbances in sodium and water balance have been noted in a number of patients suffering from a variety of diseases including bronchogenic carcinoma, cerebral disease, myxedema, and acute intermittent porphyria (Goldberg, 1963).

Since primary central nervous diseases including tumors, vascular lesions, and head trauma can give rise to this syndrome, the postulated inappropriate secretion of ADH in patients with bronchogenic carcinoma may be due to cerebral metastases. However, Amatruda *et al.* (1963) have reported the finding of ADH-like activity in extracts of tumor tissue obtained at autopsy from a patient with this syndrome. It may well be that a variety of pathogenic mechanisms may lead to the same clinical pattern. It would also appear likely that many reported cases with so-called cerebral salt wasting (Peters *et al.*, 1950) were examples of inappropriate secretion of ADH. It should be emphasized, however, that more sensitive and specific tests of circulating hormone concentrations must be developed before the currently postulated pathogenic mechanism can be considered proved.

C. Disturbance of Normal Thirst Mechanisms

Patients with CNS disease are frequently dehydrated and have elevated concentrations of serum sodium either because motor limitations prevent them from satisfying a normal sensation of thirst or because a clouded sensorium blunts normal appreciation of thirst (Welt *et al.,* 1952). Since it has been shown experimentally that specific hypothalamic centers are intimately concerned with the thirst mechanism (Anderson and McCann, 1953), one would anticipate that some patients with hypothalamic disease might show abnormalities in the appreciation of thirst without at the same time exhibiting an obtunded consciousness. Recently, two case reports have been published which would appear to confirm the existence of such abnormalities in association with hypothalamic disease. Avioli *et al.* (1962) described a patient with Schüller-Christian disease of the hypothalamus who exhibited persistent hypernatremia without increased awareness of thirst. His general consciousness was not otherwise disturbed. Other abnormalities attributed to the hypothalamic lesion included deficiency of pituitary ACTH production and a partial deficiency in the production or release of ADH. The partial diabetes insipidus was apparently reversed after a course of prednisone therapy, but the hypernatremia and impaired thirst sensation persisted. Hays *et al.* (1963) investigated a patient with occult hydrocephalus who presented on two separate occasions severe dehydration and impaired perception of thirst. Again, this patient gave evidence of associated diminished anterior pituitary function.

D. Possible Regulation of Aldosterone by the Central Nervous System

The precise role of the CNS in the regulation of aldosterone production by the zona glomerulosa of the adrenal cortex is still obscure (see Chapter 11). Earlier evidence favoring the thesis that the diencephalon was directly responsible for the secretion of a tropic hormone (Farrell, 1958, 1959) has largely been superseded by the demonstration of the importance of the renin-angiotensin system in the stimulation of aldosterone secretion (Davis *et al.,* 1959, 1961; Mulrow *et al.,* 1962; Slater *et al.,* 1963).

In man, two studies have indicated that certain patients with CNS disease may exhibit an inability to increase the urinary excretion of aldosterone after dietary sodium restriction. Hökfelt and Luft (1959) reported that six of nine patients with suprasellar disease did not respond in the anticipated manner to low sodium diets. Similarly, Krieger and Krieger (1964a) indicated that six out of seven patients with pretectal disease failed to increase aldosterone excretion after a similar stimulus. Baseline urinary aldosterone excretion was normal. Despite the apparent absence of aldosterone response to sodium deprivation, these patients showed no clinical or laboratory evidence of sodium wastage. The mechanism of the renal conservation of sodium under such conditions is not clear. Final evaluation of the role of the CNS in the regulation of aldosterone production is predicated on measurements of actual aldosterone secretory rates by the newer isotopic techniques.

VII. Summary

There are many difficulties in the study of human neuroendocrine relationships. Despite such obstacles, sufficient clinical data have been accumulated to indicate that the CNS of man does have a profound influence over anterior pituitary function. This evidence is largely based on the correlation of gross endocrine deficiencies and asymptomatic alterations in endocrine control mechanisms with lesions in the CNS. The use of drugs affecting the nervous system may prove useful in the experimental study of neuroendocrine relationships in man. The role of the CNS in the pathogenesis of certain endocrine disorders such as Cushing's syndrome, Graves' disease, and idiopathic hirsutism remains speculative. The syndrome of diabetes insipidus results from a deficiency in the production or secretion of ADH which is a well-recognized neuroendocrine hormone. Other disturbances in salt and water metabolism may occur in association with CNS disease because of disturbances in the perception of thirst and, very likely, because of an inappropriate production of ADH. The secretion of aldosterone, however, does not appear to be under the primary control of the CNS of man.

Acknowledgments

The author thanks Drs. Leo Davidoff, Emanuel Feiring, Bernard Sachs, and Arthur Gaynor for permission to cite case histories of patients hospitalized on their services. Dr. Harold Jacobson granted permission to reproduce the roentgenograms in Figs. 1 and 2. Dr. James Wyngaarden kindly allowed the publication of a case (A.M.) from the files of the Duke Medical Center. Miss Joan Tomes rendered invaluable secretarial assistance. Studies were partially supported by Grant NBO3000 from the United States Public Health Service as well as by Contract U-1238 and Career Scientist Award 1–222 from the Health Research Council of New York City.

References

Albeux-Fernet, G. J., Braun, S., and Romani, J. D. (1955). Results of surgical hypophysectomy in a case of malignant edematous exophthalmos. *J. Clin. Endocrinol.* **15,** 1239–1246.

Amatruda, T. T., Mulrow, P. J., Gallagher, J. C., and Sawyer, W. H. (1963). Carcinoma of the lung with inappropriate antidiuresis. Demonstration of antidiuretic-hormone-like activity in tumor extract. *New Engl. J. Med.* **269,** 533–549.

Anderson, B., and McCann, S. M. (1953). Drinking, antidiuresis and milk ejection from electrical stimulation with hypothalamus of goat. *Acta Physiol. Scand.* **35,** 191–201.

Argonz, J., and DelCastillo, E. B. (1953). A syndrome characterized by estrogenic insufficiency, galactorrhea and decreased urinary gonadotrophin. *J. Clin. Endocrinol.* **13,** 79–87.

Avioli, L. V., Earley, L. E., and Kashima, H. K. (1962). Chronic and sustained hypernatremia, absence of thirst, diabetes insipidus, and adrenocorticotrophic insufficiency resulting from widespread destruction if the hypothalamus. *Ann. Internal Med.* **56,** 131–140.

Bauer, H. G. (1954). Endocrine and other clinical manifestations of hypothalamic disease. *J. Clin. Endocrinol.* **14,** 13–31.

Bauer, H. G. (1959). Endocrine and metabolic conditions related to pathology in the hypothalamus. A review. *J. Nervous Mental Disease* **128,** 323–338.

Becker, D. (1959). The effects of hypophysectomy on certain parameters of thyroid function in two patients with Grave's disease. *J. Clin. Endocrinol.* **19,** 840–844.

Berliner, R. W., and Davidson, D. G. (1957). Production of hypertonic urine in the absence of pituitary antidiuretic hormone. *J. Clin. Invest.* **36,** 1416–1427.

Bliss, E. L., Sandberg, A. A., Nelson, D. H., and Eik-Nes, K. (1953). The normal levels of 17-hydroxycorticosteroids in the peripheral blood of man. *J. Clin. Invest.* **32,** 818–823.

Bliss, E. L., Migeon, C. J., Branch, C. H. H., and Samuels, L. T. (1956). Reaction of the adrenal cortex to emotional stress. *Psychosomat. Med.* **18,** 56–76.

Christy, N. P., Longson, D., Horwitz, W. A., and Knight, M. M. (1957a). Inhibitory effect of chlorpromazine upon the adrenal cortical response to insulin hypoglycemia in man. *J. Clin. Invest.* **36,** 543–549.

Christy, N. P., Longson, D., and Jailer, J. W. (1957b). Studies in Cushing's syndrome. I. Observations on the response of plasma 17-hydroxycorticosteroids to corticotrophin. *Am. J. Med.* **23,** 910–916.

Davis, J. O., Bahn, R. C., Yankopoulos, W. A., Kliman, B., and Peterson, R. E. (1959). Acute effects of hypophysectomy and diencephalic lesions on aldosterone secretion. *Am. J. Physiol.* **197,** 380–386.

Davis, J. O., Carpenter, C. C. J., Ayers, C. R., Holman, J. E., and Bahn, R. C. (1961). Evidence for secretion of an aldosterone-stimulating hormone by the kidney. *J. Clin. Invest.* **40,** 684–695.

Dingman, J. F., and Despointes, R. H. (1960). Adrenal steroid inhibition of vasopressin release from the neurohypophysis of normal subjects and patients with Addison's disease. *J. Clin. Invest.* **39,** 1851–1863.

Dundee, J. W. (1954). A review of chlorpromazine hydrochloride. *Brit. J. Anaesthesia* **26,** 357–379.

du Vigneaud, V. (1956). Hormones of the posterior pituitary gland: oxytocin and vasopressin. *Harvey Lectures* **50,** 1–26.

Eckles, N. E., Ehni, G., and Tannenbaum, L. (1958). Induction of lactation in the human female by pituitary stalk section. *Anat. Record* **130,** 295 (Abstract).

Estep, H. L., Island, D. P., Ney, R. L., and Liddle, G. W. (1963). Pituitary-adrenal dynamics during surgical stress. *J. Clin. Endocrinol.* **23,** 419–425.

Everett, J. W., and Nikitovitch-Winer, M. (1963). Physiology of the pituitary gland as affected by transplantation or stalk transection. *In* "Advances in Neuroendocrinology" (A. V. Nalbandov, ed.), pp. 289–304. Univ. of Illinois Press, Urbana, Illinois.

Fajans, S. S. (1958). Hyperthyroidism in a patient with postpartum necrosis of the pituitary: case report and implications. *J. Clin. Endocrinol. Metab.* **18,** 271–277.

Farrell, G. (1958). Regulation of aldosterone secretion. *Physiol. Rev.* **38,** 709–728.

Farrell, G. (1959). Steroidogenic properties of extracts of beef diencephalon. *Endocrinology* **65,** 29–33.

Feldschuh, J., Musacchio, I., and Kupperman, H. S. (1961). Chlorpromazine effect on ACTH function—evaluated by SU-4885 technique. *Program 43rd Meeting Endocrine Soc., New York,* p. 57 (Abstract).

Field, R. A., Hall, W. A., Contreras, J. S., and Sweet, W. H. (1961). Hypophyseal-stalk section in the treatment of advancing diabetic retinopathy. Report of three cases. *New Engl. J. Med.* **264,** 689–698.

Field, R. A., Schepas, C. L., Sweet, W. H., and Appels, A. (1962). The effect of hypophyseal stalk section on advancing diabetic retinopathy. Report of thirteen cases. *Diabetes* **11,** 465–469.

Forbes, A. P., Henneman, P. H., Griswold, G. C., and Albright, F. (1954). Syndrome characterized by galactorrhea, amenorrhea, and low urinary FSH: comparison with acromegaly and normal lactation. *J. Clin. Endocrinol.* **14,** 265–271.

Fujita, R., Ibayashi, H., Motohashi, K., Uchikawa, T., and Okinaka, S. (1963). Clinical applications of urinary ACTH assay. *J. Clin. Endocrinol. Metab.* **23,** 143–148.

Gemzell, C. A., Diczfalusy, E., and Tillinger, G. (1958). Clinical effect of human pituitary follicle-stimulating hormone (FSH). *J. Clin. Endocrinol. Metab.* **18,** 1333–1348.

Gold, E. M., Kent, J. R., and Forsham, P. H. (1960). Modification of pituitary-adrenal response to SU-4885 by psychotrophic drugs. *Program 42nd Meeting Endocrine Soc., Miami Beach, Florida,* p. 29 (Abstract).

Gold, E. M., Kent, J. R., and Forsham, P. H. (1961). Clinical use of a new diagnostic agent, Methopyrapone (SU-4885), in pituitary and adrenocortical disorders. *Ann. Internal Med.* **54,** 175–188.

Goldberg, M. (1963). Hyponatremia and the inappropriate secretion of antidiuretic hormone (editorial). *Am. J. Med.* **35,** 293–298.

Ham, G. C., Alexander, F., and Carmichael, H. T., (1951). A psychosomatic theory of thyrotoxicosis. *Psychosomat. Med.* **13,** 18–35.

Hays, R. M., McHugh, P. R., and Williams, H. E. (1963). Absence of thirst in association with hydrocephalus. *New Engl. J. Med.* **269,** 227–231.

Heinbecker, P., and Pfeiffenberger, M. (1950). Further clinical and experimental studies on the pathogenesis if Cushing's syndrome. *Am. J. Med.* **9,** 3–23.

Hökfelt, B., and Luft, R. (1959). The effect of suprasellar tumors on the regulation of adrenocortical function. *Acta Endocrinol.* **32,** 177–186.

Jailer, J. W., and Holub, D. A. (1960). Remission of Grave's disease following radiotherapy of a pituitary neoplasm. *Am. J. Med.* **28,** 497–500.

Jailer, J. W., Longson, D., Christy, N. P. (1956). Cushing's syndrome—an adrenal or pituitary disease? *J. Clin. Endocrinol. Metab.* **16,** 1276–1279.

Kahana, L., Lebovitz, H., Lusk, W., McPherson, H. T., Davidson, E. T., Oppenheimer, J. H., Engel, F. L. Woodhall, B., and Odom, G. (1962). Endocrine manifestations of intracranial extrasellar lesions. *J. Clin. Endocrinol. Metab.* **22,** 304–324.

Kappas, A., Pearson, O. H., West, D. D., and Gallagher, T. F. (1956). A study of "idiopathic" hirsutism: A transitional adrenal abnormality. *J. Clin. Endocrinol. Metab.* **16,** 517–528.

Kleeman, C. R., Maxwell, M. H., and Rockney, R. E. (1958). Mechanism of impaired water excretion in adrenal and pituitary insufficiency: The role of altered glomerular filtration rate and solute excretion. *J. Clin. Invest.* **37**, 1799–1807.

Klinefelter, H. F., Jr., Albright, F., and Griswold, G. C. (1943). Experience with a quantitative test for normal or decreased amounts of follicle-stimulating hormone in the urine in endocrinological diagnosis. *J. Clin. Endocrinol. Metab.* **3**, 529–544.

Krieger, D. T. (1961). Diurnal pattern of plasma 17-hydroxycorticosteroids in pretectal and temporal Lobe Disease. *J. Clin. Endocrinol. Metab.* **21**, 695–698.

Krieger, D. T. (1962). Effect of diphenylhydantoin on pituitary-adrenal interrelations. *J. Clin. Endocrinol. Metab.* **22**, 490–493.

Krieger, D. T., and Krieger, H. P. (1964a). Aldosterone excretion in pretectal disease. *J. Clin. Endocrinol. Metab.* **24**, 1055–1066.

Krieger, D. T., and Krieger, H. P. (1964b). Adrenal function in central nervous system disease. *Proc. Assoc. Res. Nervous Mental Disease* (in press).

Krieger, D. T., Kolodny, H., and Krieger, H. P. (1964). Metopirone test in hypothalamic-pituitary disease. *J. Clin. Endocrinol. Metab.* **11**, 1169–1177.

Leaf, A. (1960). Diabetes insipidus. *In* "Clinical Endocrinology" (E. B. Astwood, ed.), pp. 73–90. Grune & Stratton, New York.

Leaf, A., Bartter, F. C., Santos, R. F., and Wrong, O. (1953). Evidence in man that urinary electrolytes loss induced by pitressin is a function of water retention. *J. Clin. Invest.* **32**, 868–878.

Liddle, G. W., Estep, H. L., Kendall, J. W., Jr., Williams, W. C., Jr., and Townes, A. W. (1959). Clinical application of a new test of pituitary reserve *J. Clin. Endocrinol. Metab.* **19**, 875–894.

Lipsett, M. B., and Pearson, O. H. (1957). Further studies of the polyuria induced by hypophysectomy. *J. Lab. Clin. Med.* **49**, 190–199.

Lipsett, M. B, MacLean, J. P., West, C. D., Li, M. C., and Pearson, O. H. (1956). An analysis of the polyuria induced by hypophysectomy in man. *J. Clin. Endocrinol. Metab.* **16**, 183–195.

Lloyd, C. W. (1963). Central nervous system regulation of endocrine function in the human. *In* "Advances in Neuroendocrinology" (A. V. Nalbandov, ed.), pp. 460–500. Univ. of Illinois Press, Urbana, Illinois.

McArthur, J. W., Ingersoll, F. M., and Worcester, J. (1958). The urinary excretion of interstitial cell and follicle-stimulating hormone activity by women with diseases of the reproductive system. *J. Clin. Endocrinol. Metab.* **18**, 1202–1215.

McCann, S. M. (1963). Recent studies on the regulation of hypophysial luteinizing hormone secretion. *Am. J. Med.* **34**, 379–393.

McCann, S. M., and Fruit, A. (1957). Effect of synthetic vasopressin on release of adrenocorticotrophin in rats with hypothalamic lesions. *Proc. Soc. Exptl. Biol. Med.* **96**, 566–567.

McCarthy, C. F., Willis, M. R., Keane, P. M., Gough, K. R., and Read, A. E. (1964). The SU-4885 (Methyrapone) response after head injury. *J Clin. Endocrinol. Metab.* **24**, 121–124.

McCullagh, E. P., Clamen, M., and Gardner, W. J. (1957). Clinical progress in the treatment of exophthalmos of Grave's disease, with particular reference to the effect of pituitary surgery. *J. Clin. Endocrinol. Metab.* **17**, 1277–1291.

McKenzie, J. M. (1961). Studies on the thyroid activator of hyperthyroidism. *J. Clin. Endocrinol. Metab.* **21**, 635–647.

Marshall, W. K., and Leiberman, D. M. (1956). A rare complication of chlorpromazine treatment. *Lancet* **I**, 162.

Mason, J. W. (1958). The central nervous system regulation of ACTH secretion. *In* "Reticular Formation of the Brain" (H. H. Jasper, L. D. Proctor, R. S. Knighton, W. C. Noshay, and R. T. Costello, eds.), pp. 645–670. Little, Brown, Boston, Massachusetts.

Meek, J. C., Jones, A. E., Lewis, U. J., VanderLaan, W. P. (1964). Isolation and characterization of the long-acting thyroid stimulator of Grave's disease. *J. Clin. Invest.* **43,** 1258 (Abstract).

Müller, W. (1955). Neurosekretstauung im Tractus Supraopticohypophyseus des Menschen durch einen raumbeegenden Prozess. *Z. Zellforsch. Mikroskop. Anat.* **42,** 439–442.

Mulrow, P. J., Ganong, W. F., Cera, G., and Kuljian, A. (1962). The nature of the aldosterone-stimulating factor in dog kidneys. *J. Clin. Invest.* **41,** 505–516.

Nelson, D. H., Meakin, J. W., Dealy, J. B., Matson, D. D., Emerson, K., and Thorn, G. W. (1958). ACTH-producing tumor of the pituitary gland. *New Engl. J. Med.* **259,** 161–164.

Nelson, D. H., Meakin, J. W., and Thorn, G. W. (1960). ACTH-producing pituitary tumors following adrenalectomy for Cushing's syndrome *Ann. Internal Med.* **52,** 560–569.

Ney, R. L., Shimizu, N., Nicholson, W. E., Island, D. P., and Liddle, G. W. (1963). Correlation of plasma ACTH concentration with adrenocortical response in normal human subjects, surgical patients, and patients with Cushing's disease. *J. Clin. Invest.* **42,** 1669–1677.

Oppenheimer, J. H., Fisher, L. V., and Jailer, J. W. (1961). Disturbance of the pituitary-adrenal interrelationship in diseases of the central nervous system. *J. Clin. Endocrinol. Metab.* **21,** 1023–1036.

Perkoff, G. T., Eik-Nes, K., Nugent, C. A., Fred, H. L., Nimer, R. A., Rush, L., Samuels, L. T., and Tylee, F. H. (1959). Studies of the diurnal variation of plasma 17-OHCS in man. *J. Clin. Endocrinol. Metab.* **19,** 432–443.

Perloff, W. H., Lasche, E. M., Nodine, J. H., Schneeberg, N. G., and Viellard, C. B. (1954). The starvation state and functional hypopituitarism. *J. Am. Med. Assoc.* **155,** 1307–1313.

Peters, J. P., Welt, L. G., Sims, E. A. H., Orloff, J., and Needham, J. (1950). A salt-wasting syndrome associated with cerebral disease. *Trans. Assoc. Am. Physicians* **63,** 57–64.

Peters, J. P., German, W. J., Man, E. B., and Welt, L. G. (1954). Function of gonads, thyroid and adrenals in hypopituitarism. *Metab. Clin. Exptl.* **3,** 118–137.

Peterson, R. E. (1959). The miscible pool and turnover rate of adrenocortical steroids in man. *Recent Progr. Hormone Res.* **15,** 231–274.

Rakoff, A. E. (1963). Hypothalamic amenorrhea. *In* "Advances in Neuroendocrinology" (A. V. Nalbandov, ed.), pp 500–510. Univ. of Illinois Press, Urbana, Illinois.

Randall, R. V., Clark, E. C., Dodge, H. W., Jr., and Glove, J. G. (1960). Polyuria after operation for tumors in the region of the hypophysis and hypothalamus. *J. Clin. Endocrinol. Metab.* **20,** 1614–1621.

Ripley, H. S., and Papanicolaou, G. N. (1942). The menstrual cycle with vaginal smear studies in schizophrenia, depression and elation. *Am. J. Psychiat.* **98,** 567–573.

Robbins, L. R., and Vinson, D. B. (1960). Objective psychologic assessment of the thyrotoxic patient and the response to treatment: preliminary report. *J. Clin. Endocrinol. Metab.* **20,** 120–129.

Rosenberg, E., Coleman, J., Demany, M., and Garcia, C. (1963). Clinical effect of human postmenopausal gonadotrophin. *J. Clin. Endocrinol. Metab.* **23,** 181–190.

Roth, L. J., and Barlow, C. F. (1961). Drugs in the brain. *Science* **134,** 22–31.

Salassa, R. M., Kearns, T. P., Kernohan, J. W., Sprague, R. G., and MacCarty, C. S. (1959). Pituitary tumors in patients with Cushing's syndrome. *J. Clin. Endocrinol. Metab.* **19,** 1523–1539.

Sawyer, W. H. (1961). Biologic assays for oxytocin and vasopressin. *Methods Med. Res.* **9,** 210–219.

Schwartz, W. B., Bennett, W., Curelop, S., and Bartter, F. C. (1957). Syndrome of renal sodium loss and hyponatremia probably resulting from inappropriate secretion of antidiuretic hormone. *Am. J. Med.* **23,** 529–542.

Selenkow, H. A., Tyler, H. A., Matson, D. D., and Nelson, D. H. (1959). Hypopituitarism due to hypothalamic sarcoidosis. *Am. J. Med. Sci.* **238,** 456–63.

Shealy, C. N., Kahana, L., Engel, F. L., and McPherson, H. T. (1961). Hypothalamic-pituitary sarcoidosis. A report on four patients, one with prolonged remission of diabetes insipidus following steroid therapy. *Am. J. Med.* **30,** 46–55.

Slater, J. D. H., Barbour, B. H., Henderson, H. H., Casper, A. G. T., and Bartter, F. C. (1963). Influence of the pituitary and the renin-angiotensin system on the secretion of aldosterone, cortisol, and corticosterone. *J. Clin. Invest.* **42,** 1504–1520.

Sloper, J. C., and Adams, C. W. M. (1955). Effect of hypophysectomy on hypothalamic neurosecretion in the human hypothalamus. *Exerpta Med., Sect. III* **8,** 898–879.

Sulman, F. G., and Winnik, H. Z. (1956). Hormonal effects of chlorpromaxine. *Lancet* **1,** 161–162.

Van Buren, J. M., and Bergenstal, M. D. (1960). An evaluation of graded hypophysectomy in man. A quantitative functional and anatomical study. *Cancer* **13,** 155–171.

Van Wyk, J. J., Drugger, G. S., and Newsome, J. F. (1960a). The effect of pituitary stalk-section on the adrenal function of women with cancer of the breast. *Clin. Res.* **8,** 87.

Van Wyk, J. J., Drugger, G. S., Newsome, J. F., and Thomas, P. Z. (1960b). The effect of pituitary stalk section on the adrenal function of women with cancer of the breast. *J. Clin. Endocrinol. Metab.* **20,** 157–170.

Waife, S. O. (1954). The endocrine glands and nutrition. *Am. J. Clin. Nutr.* **2,** 422–423.

Welt, L. G., Seldin, D. W., Nelson, W. P., German, W. J., and Peters, J. P. (1952). Role of the central nervous system in metabolism of electrolytes and water. *Arch. Internal Med.* **90,** 355–378.

Werk, E. E., McGee, J., and Sholiton, L. J. (1964). Effect of diphenylhydantoin on cortisol metabolism in man. *J. Clin. Invest.* **43,** 1824–1835.

Werner, S. C., and Stewart, W. B. (1958). Hyperthyroidism in a patient with a pituitary chromophobe adenoma and a fragment of normal pituitary. *J. Clin. Endocrinol. Metab.* **18,** 266–270.

Werner, S. C., Tierney, J., and Talleberg, T. (1964). Thyrotrophic and "long-acting thyroid stimulator" effects from certain polypeptides. *J. Clin. Endocrinol. Metab.* **24,** 339–346.

Wilkins, L. (1957). "The Diagnosis and Treatment of Endocrine Disorders in Childhood and Adolescence," p. 200. Williams & Wilkins, Baltimore, Maryland.

Winnik, H. Z., and Tannenbaum, L. (1955). Apparition de galactorrhea au cours du traitment de largactil. *Presse Med.* **63,** 1092.

Wolff, S. M., Adler, R. C., Buskirk, E. R., and Thompson, R. H. (1964). A syndrome of periodic hypothalamic discharge. *Am. J. Med.* **36,** 956–967.

Woodbury, D. M. (1955). Effect of diphenylhydantoin on electrolytes and radiosodium turnover in brain and other tissues of normal, hyponatremic and pretectal rate. *J. Pharmacol. Exptl. Therap.* **115,** 74–95.

Yalow, R. S., Glick, M. D., Roth, J., and Berson, S. A. (1964). Radioimmunoassay of human plasma ACTH. *J. Clin. Endocrinol.* **24,** 1219–1225.

Yates, F. E., and Urquhart, J. (1962). Control of plasma concentrations of adrenocortical hormones. *Physiol. Rev.* **42,** 359–443.

Zubrian, S., and Gomez-Mont, F. (1953). Endocrine disturbances in chronic human malnutrition. *Vitamins Hormones* **11,** 97–132.

Author Index

Numbers in italic show the page on which the complete reference is listed.

D

E

F

I

J

K

P

S

Subject Index

D

H

I

Q

R

S

U

W

X

Y

Z